# ANNUAL REVIEW OF PHYSIOLOGY

# EDITORIAL COMMITTEE (1988)

Responsible for the organization of Volume 50
(Editorial Committee, 1986)

# ANNUAL REVIEW OF PHYSIOLOGY

## VOLUME 50, 1988

ROBERT M. BERNE, *Editor*

University of Virginia Medical School

JOSEPH F. HOFFMAN, *Associate Editor*

Yale University School of Medicine

ANNUAL REVIEWS INC.   4139 EL CAMINO WAY,   P.O. BOX 10139   PALO ALTO, CALIFORNIA 94303-0897

*International Standard Serial Number: 0066–4278*
*International Standard Book Number: 0–8243–0350-4*
*Library of Congress Catalog Card Number: 39–15404*

Typesetting by Kachina Typesetting Inc., Tempe, Arizona; John Olson, President
Typesetting coordinator, Janis Hoffman

PRINTED AND BOUND IN THE UNITED STATES OF AMERICA

# PREFACE

The symbol on the cover and title page of this volume highlights its special significance as the 50th Anniversary Volume of the *Annual Review of Physiology (ARP)*.

J. Murray Luck, the founder of Annual Reviews Inc. and the editor of the first eight volumes of *ARP,* provided an account of its founding in "Confessions of a Biochemist," his illuminating and entertaining prefatory chapter to Volume 50 of the *Annual Review of Biochemistry* (1).

> There have been many corporate adventures, the first in 1938 when Annual Reviews and the American Physiological Society (APS) agreed to share in the parentage of an *Annual Review of Physiology (ARP)*. The numerous discussions with officers of the Society and their Board of Publications Trustees are minutely documented in the files of Annual Reviews. From the first it was perfectly clear to both parties that, ideally, they should initiate the new *Review* under a plan of joint participation. But it soon emerged that the obstacles to be overcome were numerous and the initial resistance within the Society was formidable. The details need not be recited. The names of those who were singularly helpful deserve to be mentioned. Their wisdom, good sense, integrity, and simple honesty had earned for them the deepest respect of their fellow physiologists: A. J. Carlson, Walter J. Meek, Wallace Fenn, Frank C. Mann, Carl J. Wiggers, and Ralph W. Gerard. Participation of the Society in publication of the *Review* was formally approved and a Joint Board of Management (JBM) was agreed to: Walter Meek and Chauncey Leake as representatives of the APS and Carl Schmidt and Murray Luck on behalf of Annual Reviews. Volume I appeared in 1939. After a few years of JBM direction, and a subsequent series of gradual transitions, the *ARP* became a full-fledged member of the Annual Reviews family with its own Editorial Committee responsible to the Directors of Annual Reviews.
>
> It was just as well. Quite innocently, the two parties had fashioned a working arrangement that seemed to make sense: Annual Reviews would be the business partner, the APS would elect the Editorial Committee of the new *Review,* and the two parties, year by year, would share equally in any profits or any losses. But it was quite illegal: Annual Reviews Inc., in charge of operations, was thereby enabled to jeopardize the assets of its partner and might indeed run the APS into bankruptcy! So said the attorneys. A new agreement provided that the two parties would divide equally any profits, but any losses would have to be borne by Annual Reviews. Finally, at the request of the Society, the annual operating surplus, if any, ceased to be divided.

Initially, the goal of this new publication was to provide readers with "a comprehensive survey of the year's research in physiology." Authors of reviews were invited to write "a critical appraisal of the contemporary field— an analysis and interpretation of the most significant contributions." Howev-

v

er, as the number of research publications grew year by year, the format of the reviews changed, and sometimes the articles were quite different, even within a single volume. It became increasingly difficult to cover the literature. Some reviews were little more than compilations of the year's literature, whereas others were indeed critical analyses of the most important current papers in physiology. Such differences reflected the points of view of some authors rather than those of the editors, who favored a carefully selected menu of thoughtful summaries and critiques of the most important literature.

In 1947 Victor E. Hall, who had been an associate editor for the first eight volumes of *ARP,* assumed the editorship and continued as editor until his retirement in 1971. Just before his death in 1981, he collaborated with Ralph Sonnenschein, a longtime associate editor, on a chapter of reminiscences and reflections about *ARP,* and Volume 44 was dedicated to his memory (2, 3). Under Dr. Hall's able leadership *ARP* continued to flourish throughout the publications of Volumes 9–33 and introduced a new feature: the prefatory chapters. Eugene F. DuBois, author of the first prefatory chapter, "Fifty Years of Physiology in America," recorded the circumstances of this innovation (4).

To the Editor of the Annual Review of Physiology:

In your letter of June 15, 1949 you extend to me the tempting invitation to write a prefatory chapter for Volume XII which will appear in 1950. In your letter you say: "This is an invitation, the motive behind which is our desire to make the Review something more than a consideration in detail of the current advances in our science. Physiology is a form of human activity as well as an accumulation of knowledge. As such it has a history of hopes, ambitions, enthusiasms, fashions and phobias. Older members of the profession are retiring, newer ones rising to prominence. New institutions are being founded, older ones changing their form and function. New patterns of financial support, of teaching and research are emerging with various influences on their conduct. The economic position of the members of the professions relative to that of other callings alters, creating problems of adequate staffing of laboratories. Interest in the philosophic basis of science is increasing as we attempt to approach our ultimate task, the revealing of the nature of man."

Your request is a serious challenge, and I would not dare to attempt a chapter in the short time available were it not for the implication that in subsequent years other physiologists would be called upon to fill the many gaps.

This new feature proved to be an immediate success, and the *Annual Review of Biochemistry* adopted it immediately. Eventually, the majority of the more than two dozen Annual Review series' editorial committees did likewise.

These prefatory chapters took many forms. In some, senior physiologists reviewed the development of a particular area of physiology, whereas in others the authors reminisced about their experiences during their scientific careers. Still other prefatory chapters expounded aspects of the philosophy of the physiological sciences or combined a personal history with a general view of the impact of physiology in a rapidly growing scientific environment.

Meanwhile, the growing burden of maintaining adequate coverage of the entire field of physiology in the face of a commitment to in-depth criticism was somewhat eased by the startup of additional Annual Reviews series, some of which dealt with subjects previously embraced by physiology: for example, Annual Reviews of Microbiology (1947), Plant Physiology (1950), and Medicine (1950). By the time Victor Hall retired in 1971, a total of ten new series had been added to the growing family of Annual Reviews.

Julius H. Comroe, Jr. was appointed editor of *ARP* in 1972 and served for four years. Dr. Comroe emphasized his belief that a review should not be "an all-inclusive annotated organized bibliography" and that the role of author should change "from that of an observer, recorder, and commentator to that of a statesman in physiological science." He also called attention to the increasing difficulty the editorial committees of *ARP* faced in making their annual selections of authors and topics because of the "number and complexity of scientific papers." As a result of his experiences as editor, he proposed some changes in format that were subsequently implemented.

Ernst Knobil succeeded Julius Comroe as editor in 1976. He served as the editor of *ARP* for Volumes 38–40. He also found it necessary to wrestle with the problems of breadth versus depth, and in an attempt to resolve this problem he appointed Gerhard Giebisch as a section editor, who divided renal physiology into four relatively short chapters, each dealing with a specific aspect of renal physiology from the special perspectives of different researchers. It was Dr. Knobil's hope that "this prototype or a variant thereof may become a standard editorial instrument." As is often the case with novel ideas, it took a little time before this format was adopted by *ARP*.

In 1979 I. S. Edelman, who had been associate editor for Volume 35 and Volumes 37–40, was appointed editor, and he and his editorial committee made the decision to sectionalize *ARP* completely, starting with Volume 41. Initially there were seven sections (later eight) each with its own editor: renal, gastrointestinal, endocrine, cardiovascular, respiratory, comparative, cell and membrane physiology, plus a special topic section. It was Dr. Edelman's intention that "each section editor will formulate themes to be covered by a series of complementary articles emphasizing his sector's most timely and important developments" (5).

After serving as a member of the editorial committee since 1978, it was my privilege to accept appointment as editor of *ARP* in 1983. Sectionalization of *ARP* has been continued, and a second special topic section has been added to cover the increased number of important physiological topics, such as cell and molecular physiology, that have fallen outside of the realm of the earlier organ system format. In keeping with current advances in physiology and the application of molecular biology to physiological problems, the reviews have become more molecular in focus, and the title of cell and membrane physiology has been changed to cell and molecular physiology. Interorgan system reviews with common denominators have also been planned; such a review on the subject of smooth muscle will appear in Volume 51. In addition, the decision was made to reorient the prefatory chapter. Instead of the personal reminiscences and historical vignettes that have appeared in the past, prefatory chapters will focus on perspectives and current trends in physiology and will be written by acknowledged experts. The first of these new prefatory chapters, "Muscle Contraction," by Sir Andrew Huxley, appears in this volume.

Now my time has come to retire as editor. I want to express my warmest appreciation to all the people who have unselfishly helped me for the past five years. I am most grateful to the current section editors: Joe Hoffman, Bob Forster, Carl Gottschalk, Jack Kostyo, Harvey Sparks, Fred White, and George Sachs, as well as the special topic editors and previous section editors who served during my tour of duty. They each willingly and expertly initiated, organized, and edited their respective sections. I also want to welcome the new section editors, Howard Morgan, who will edit the cardiovascular section, and Paul De Weer, who will edit the cell and molecular section and also will serve as associate editor. I also thank the many authors of the reviews and the staff at Annual Reviews Inc. who have helped put it all together, in particular our production editors, Ike Burke, Dave DeRoche, Mary Lee MacKichan, and Jennifer Berenson.

My ten year association with *ARP* has been an interesting and rewarding experience, and although I will miss the stimulating association with my scientific colleagues on the editorial committee, I am pleased to turn over the reins to the new editor, Joseph F. Hoffman, a distinguished scholar and a true connoisseur of food and wine as well as of science.

ROBERT M. BERNE<br>
EDITOR

## Literature Cited

1. Luck, J. M. 1981. Confessions of a biochemist. *Ann. Rev. Biochem.* 50:1–22
2. Hall, V. E., Sonnenschein, R. R. 1981. The *Annual Review of Physiology*: past and present. *Ann. Rev. Physiol.* 43:1–5
3. Edelman, I. S. 1982. Dedication. *Ann. Rev. Physiol.* 44:xiii
4. DuBois, E. F. 1950. Fifty years of physiology in America. A letter to the editor. *Ann. Rev. Physiol.* 12:1–6
5. Edelman, I. S. 1979. Preface. *Ann. Rev. Physiol.* 41:v

*Annual Review of Physiology*
*Volume 50, 1988*

# CONTENTS

# OTHER REVIEWS OF INTEREST TO PHYSIOLOGISTS

From the *Annual Review of Biochemistry,* Volume 57 (1988):

*Glycobiology,* T. W. Rademacher, R. B. Parekh, and R. A. Dwek

*Hormonal Regulation of Hepatic Gluconeogenesis and Glycolysis,* S. J. Pilkis, M. R. El-Maghrabi, and T. H. Claus

*Molecular and Cellular Biology of Intermediate Filaments,* P. M. Steinert and D. R. Roop

*Lens Crystallins: The Evolution and Expression of Proteins for a Highly Specialized Tissue,* G. J. Wistow and J. Piatigorsky

*Regulation and Expression of the Adaptive Response to Alkylating Agents,* T. Lindahl, B. Sedgwick, M. Sekiguchi, and Y. Nakabeppu

*DNA Repair Enzymes,* A. Sancar and G. B. Sancar

*Biological Aspects of Inorganic Polyphosphates,* H. G. Wood and J. E. Clark

*Interactions Between Deoxyribonucleotide and DNA Synthesis,* P. Reichard

*Cell-Surface Anchoring of Proteins Via Glycosyl-Phosphatidylinositol Structures,* M. A. J. Ferguson and A. F. Williams

*Fibronectin and its Receptors,* E. Ruoslahti


From the *Annual Review of Medicine,* Volume 39 (1988):

*The Supraventricular Tachycardias,* K. Robinson and D. Krikler

*The Erythroid Membrane Skeleton: Expression and Assembly During Erythropoiesis,* C. M. Woods and E. Lazarides

*Selective Manipulation of the Immune Response in vivo by Monoclonal Antibodies,* W. E. Seaman and D. Wofsy

*Serum Creatinine and Renal Function,* A. S. Levey, R. D. Perrone, and N. E. Madias

*Mediators of Ischemic Renal Injury,* J. V. Bonventre

*Dyspnea: Physiological and Pathophysiological Mechanisms,* K. Wasserman and R. Casaburi


From the *Annual Review of Neuroscience,* Volume 11 (1988):

*Tachykinins,* J. E. Maggio

*Modulation of Ion Channels in Neurons and Other Cells,* I. B. Levitan

*Adenosine 5'-Triphosphate-Sensitive Potassium Channels,* F. M. Ashcroft

*5-Hydroxytyptamine Receptor Subtypes,* S. J. Peroutka

*Excitatory Amino Acid Neurotransmission: NMDA Receptors and Hebb-Type Synaptic Plasticity,* C. W. Cotman, D. T. Monaghan, and A. H. Ganong

*Mutations and Molecules Influencing Biological Rhythms,* J. C. Hall and M. Rosbash

*Neuroethology of Electric Communication,* C. D. Hopkins
*Transgenic Mice: Applications to the Study of the Nervous System,* M. G. Rosenfeld, E. B. Crenshaw III, S. A. Lira, L. Swanson, E. Borrelli, R. Heyman, and R. M. Evans
*The Control of Neuron Number,* R. W. Williams and K. Herrup
*Probing the Molecular Structure of the Voltage-Dependent Sodium Channel,* R. L. Barchi
*Animal Solutions to Problems of Movement Control: The Role of Proprioceptors,* Z. Hasan and D. G. Stuart

From the *Annual Review of Pharmacology and Toxicology,* Volume 28 (1988):

*The Opioid System and Temperature Regulation,* M. W. Adler and E. B. Geller
*In Vivo Assessment of Neurotransmitter Biochemistry in Humans,* J. R. Barrio, S.-C. Huang, and M. E. Phelps
*Regulation of the Release of Coexisting Neurotransmitters,* T. Bartfai, K. Iverfeldt, G. Fisone, and P. Serfözö
*Arterial Wall Changes in Chronic Cerebrovasospasm,* J. A. Bevan and R. D. Bevan
*Vascular Smooth Muscle Membrane in Hypertension,* D. F. Bohr and R. C. Webb
*Advances in Cardiac Cellular Electrophysiology: Implications for Automaticity and Therapeutics,* G. A. Gintant and I. S. Cohen
*Neuroleptics and Neuroendocrine Function,* J. W. Gunnet and K. E. Moore
*Serotonin and Vascular Responses,* N. K. Hollenberg
*Endogenous Anorectic Agents—Satietins,* J. Knoll
*Neuromodulatory Actions of Peptides,* I.-M. Kow and D. W. Pfaff
*Recent Advances in Blood-Brain Barrier Transport,* W. M. Pardridge
*Mechanism of Action of Novel Marine Neurotoxins on Ion Channels,* C. H. Wu and T. Narahashi

Andrew Huxley

*Ann. Rev. Physiol. 1988. 50:1–16*

# PREFATORY CHAPTER: MUSCULAR CONTRACTION

*Sir Andrew Huxley*

The Master's Lodge, Trinity College, Cambridge CB2 1TQ, England

## MUSCULAR CONTRACTION

Since 1950 each issue of the *Annual Review of Physiology* has opened with an article by a well-known physiologist reviewing aspects of the history of the subject or of his own life and work. The Editor invited me to write this year's prefatory chapter but proposed that this, the fiftieth issue, should be the first in which there should be a different emphasis. He proposed that the new format "would present perspectives on topics by experts in the field . . . We would hope that the author would summarize the key background material, provide a state-of-the-art view of the subject, pose the important unanswered questions (as well as the approaches to possible solutions), and speculate a bit about future developments." He asked me to write on skeletal muscle, adding in a parenthesis "you could include cardiac and smooth muscle too, if you so desire." I do not so desire, for two good reasons: First, I am not familiar enough with either of those rapidly expanding fields, and second, to do so would expand the topic far beyond what could be dealt with in the space I was offered. For the same two reasons, I shall not aim to cover the whole field of "skeletal muscle" but shall restrict myself to an aspect on which I have myself been engaged, namely, the actual mechanism by which force and shortening are brought about. I shall not touch on the metabolism, excitation, excitation-contraction coupling, structure, development, or disease of muscle. Again, for the same two reasons I shall not aim to be comprehensive but will take this as an opportunity to present a personal viewpoint, concentrating on experimental work on the intact contractile system rather than biochemical or structural studies or in vitro experiments on separated filaments or other reconstituted systems. There will inevitably be huge omissions (not least because posts I have held in the last few years have prevented me from

1

keeping up to date with the literature in the way that I could have wished), and no one must be offended because his or her work has chanced to be among these omissions.

## Revolutions in Muscle Theory: ATP, Actin, and Myosin

During the last sixty years, theories of muscle contraction have undergone a series of revolutions. It was A. V. Hill (29) who first used the word "revolution" in this context, in his article of 1932 in *Physiological Reviews*, describing the overthrow of the lactic acid theory by Lundsgaard's (52) experiment of 1930 in which a muscle poisoned with iodoacetic acid was found to be capable of performing many contractions without producing any lactic acid. The breakdown of "phosphagen" (phosphoryl creatine) had already been demonstrated in 1927 both by the Eggletons (12) and Fiske & Subbarow (16) and was therefore ready to replace lactic acid formation as the "primary energy-producing reaction." A second revolution which replaced phosphoryl creatine by adenosine triphosphate (ATP) took place a few years later, though it was not finally clinched until 1962 when Cain et al (8) found a poison (fluorodinitrobenzene) that relegated the splitting of phosphoryl creatine (PC) to the recovery processes, just as iodoacetate had relegated lactic acid formation. The key role of ATP is now universally accepted. The next two breakthroughs do not in my view rank as "revolutions" since they did not overthrow views previously accepted, but they were of major importance: the discovery by Engelhardt & Ljubimowa (13) (1939) in Moscow that myosin is itself an ATPase, and the discovery by Straub (60) in Hungary that "myosin" was a complex of two proteins, actin and what is now known as myosin, together with the recognition by Albert Szent-Györgyi (61) that the dissociation of these two proteins was brought about by ATP.

## Sliding Filaments

The next real revolution—and the last up to the present—was the discovery that shortening of a muscle fiber takes place by relative sliding motion of two sets of filaments in each half-sarcomere rather than by shortening of continuous protein filaments as had previously been universally supposed. The key pieces of evidence were, first, that the myosin and actin were differently localized in relation to the striation pattern with myosin in the A band (26, 28), second that transverse sections under the electron microscope showed a double array of overlapping filaments (42), and third, that the width of the A band did not change during shortening [interference microscopy of intact living muscle fibers, A. F. Huxley & Niedergerke (38, 39); phase microscopy of separated myofibrils, H. E. Huxley & Hanson (44), Harman (27)]. The original observations in each case were made in 1953 and were made entirely independently by the different groups; the first published suggestion of shortening by sliding was made by H. E. Huxley (42).

For the purposes of this article, I shall assume that changes of length of striated muscle take place entirely by sliding, without any shortening or lengthening of the individual filaments. There may of course be yet another revolution in store for us, in which perhaps it might be shown that small cyclical length changes in one of the filaments are converted into continuous motion by some ratchet mechanism. Such a process is indeed to be found among the many proposals for specific mechanisms that have been made during the last thirty years [see my review of 1974 (36)], but I do not know of any evidence for it. There are strong hints that in striated muscle of the horseshoe crab (*Limulus,* an arachnid) the thick filaments shorten when a whole fiber shortens. This finding needs to be pursued, but there is at present no comparable evidence for vertebrate or other striated muscles. Some kind of shortening—perhaps crumpling of the ends—must take place in thick filaments during extreme shortening when contraction bands are formed at the level of the Z line. This again calls for further investigation but is outside my scope in this article.

## *Independent Force Generators*

As regards the mechanism that generates the sliding motion, a rather general proposition that is widely, though not universally, accepted is that a relative force between adjacent filaments of the two types is generated more or less independently at each of a number of sites uniformly distributed along that part of their lengths where they overlap each other. This was proposed in our 1954 article (38) on sliding filaments on the basis of evidence that was already more than a decade old, namely the observation by Ramsey & Street (58) that active tension declines linearly as an isolated muscle fiber is stretched (prior to stimulation) beyond an optimum near its slack length and reaches zero at about double that optimum length. According to the independent-force-generator version of the sliding-filament theory, this decline in force would be a direct consequence of the reduced amount of overlap of thick and thin filaments and hence the smaller number of sites within each overlap zone contributing to the total force.

However, those measurements of force at different muscle lengths were complicated by the variation of sarcomere length (and hence amount of overlap) along the fiber found by A. F. Huxley & Peachey (40). Most importantly, in a stretched fiber the sarcomere length was often substantially less in the few tenths of a millimeter at each end of the fiber than in the middle, and when the fiber was stimulated these regions would undergo extreme shortening with consequent stretching of the middle parts and an upward "creep" of tension. To avoid this complication, my colleagues and I devised a servo control system which, during a contraction, holds constant the length of a selected segment of the fiber. With this equipment we found (25) that the developed force was closely proportional to filament overlap, estimated from sarcomere length within the segment and electron microscopic measurements of filament length. More particularly, force was proportional to the amount of overlap of each thin filament with that part of the thick filament that carried the projections known as cross-bridges, demonstrated in 1957 in the elegant electron micrographs of longitudinal sections by H. E. Huxley (43), greatly strengthening his suggestion that these projections were themselves the force generators.

This interpretation of the length-tension relation was strongly challenged about ten years ago by Pollack and his collaborators (56, 63, 64), who found much less decline of force with increasing length than in our results. However, they always recorded tension in fibers held by stationary hooks in the tendons at the two ends and never used servo control of segment length, a precaution that I regard as essential in experiments of this kind. Indeed, we did not attempt such experiments until we had developed our "spot follower" and servo system. In tetanic contractions at a length above the optimum, with the fiber ends held stationary, the rise of tension during the creep is often very substantial, and it is this raised value that was taken by Pollack. The creep was much reduced in our experiments using servo control of segment length, and since we attributed the residual creep to progressive increase of nonuniformity of striation spacing, we took the tension value that was reached during the initial quick rise (25). This explanation of the creep has since been confirmed by several groups who have used servo control of length in shorter and more uniform segments and obtained flat-topped tetani, with no detectable creep (4, 11, 47).

Pollack claimed that his measurements (by light diffraction) of sarcomere length along his fibers did not show a large enough increase of variability during a contraction to account for the creep. However, this evidence was not satisfactory because the ends of frog fibers, where sarcomeres are shortest and great shortening occurs during a tetanus, are commonly obscured by overlying tendon, which would defeat sarcomere length measurement by light diffraction; I have never seen a fiber free at *both* ends from such obscuration. In a more recent paper (2), however, Altringham & Pollack used straightforward photomicrography to record the local shortening of the ends of fibers that Peachey and I had reported twenty years before (40). They concluded that the creep is indeed explained by this local shortening, and they withdrew the objection that Pollack had previously raised against our interpretation (25) of the length-tension relation. More detail is presented in the paper of Altringham & Bottinelli (1), who also introduced a new and ingenious way of avoiding the complications due to local length changes. They recorded continuously by light diffraction the striation spacing at a position within the central region of a fiber. At the onset of stimulation the spacing first falls (the fiber shortens as it stretches the tendon attachments) and later begins to rise as the fiber ends, which have shorter striations, generate more force and shorten and stretch the middle of the fiber. Tension was recorded at the time when striation spacing was stationary at its minimum and was plotted against this minimum value. The resulting length-tension relation agreed closely with that found by Gordon et al (25). Good agreement was also found in measurements on skinned fibers when force was plotted against the shortest, rather than the average, sarcomere length within the segment (48).

The following points emerge from more recent determinations of length-tension curves. Akster et al (68) compared the curves from two muscles of a fish and found a shift agreeing with a difference in thin-filament length determined by electron microscopy. Bagni et al (4) found a similar but smaller shift between fibers from tibialis anterior and semitendinosus of the frog. Edman & Reggiani (11) found a more rounded relationship than other observers, suggesting greater variability of overlap. The latter two points need to be explored with the electron microscope.

If all cross-bridges are identical and act independently, the speed of shortening under zero load ought not to be affected by the amount of overlap, since even a very small number of cross-bridges would be able to cause sliding motion at a speed limited by their own intrinsic properties, and having a larger number of cross-bridges working in parallel would not increase this speed. This result was found by us experimentally (25) in isotonic contractions without after-load. A more thorough investigation of speed of shortening of completely unloaded fibers was made by Edman (10), who found a constant speed of shortening at lengths from substantially below that at which overlap is just complete up to that at which appreciable resting tension appears. At still greater lengths the speed was actually increased (up to well over double that at full overlap), and he attributed this to shortening being aided by the passive tension. It is not known whether in this situation the myofibrils remain straight or whether they are thrown into waves by the longitudinal compressive force, as occurs in fibers passively shortened below their slack length (7, 24).

For these reasons I believe—and I shall assume throughout this article—that the force generators are the cross-bridges between thick and thin filaments seen with the electron microscope (43) and that they act more or less independently of each other to produce more or less equal contributions to the total force.

## Energy Utilization and Cyclic Action of Cross-Bridges

An essential piece of background to all thinking about the mechanism of contraction is the 1938 paper of A. V. Hill (30), which established relationships between load, speed of shortening, and rate of energy liberation (heat plus work) during contraction. These relationships, expressed by simple equations, made quantitative the discovery by Fenn (14, 15) [made in Hill's laboratory soon after World War I and foreshadowed by experiments of Heidenhain and Fick half a century earlier (cited in 31)] that the total energy liberated is greater if a stimulated muscle is allowed to shorten, thus doing mechanical work, than if it is held at constant length. This clearly implies that the rates of the important chemical reactions are governed by the mechanical conditions, a fact not sufficiently recognized by many biochemists even now.

A very perceptive point made by Dorothy Needham (54) in 1950 (well before any idea of sliding filaments) was that A. V. Hill's relation between rate of energy liberation and speed of shortening had analogies with the Michaelis-Menten relation between rate of reaction and substrate concentration in enzyme-catalyzed reactions. This led her to propose that the contractile elements act cyclically, as enzymes do. This idea did not catch on at the time because it is difficult to imagine *cyclic* action of elements in a continuous contractile filament: Creation of new folds would have a *cumulative* effect in reducing the length of the filament. This difficulty disappears if one thinks in terms of sliding filaments. Indeed, if one accepts the idea of myosin molecules acting as independent force generators, it is necessary to suppose that they act cyclically since the total length of each molecule is only a fraction of the range over which sliding of adjacent filaments can occur in a single contraction. Several noncyclic mechanisms for generation of the sliding movement have been proposed (see 36), but they have not been satisfactorily reconciled with the length-tension relation or with the relation between shortening speed and energy liberation, so I shall not consider them further here.

The almost universally accepted idea at present, which I shall assume to be true for the rest of this article, is that during shortening each cross-bridge, consisting of the head(s) of a myosin molecule, attaches to actin molecule(s) of the adjacent thin filament, exerts force until it detaches after a certain amount of sliding has occurred, and begins the cycle afresh by reattaching further along the thin filament. The proposition that actual attachment occurs is not universally accepted, but I regard it as being sufficiently strongly supported by (*a*) the great increase in stiffness that occurs when a muscle is activated and (*b*) the observation of Sheetz & Spudich (59) that a myosin-coated polystyrene bead ceases to undergo Brownian movement when it comes in contact with, and begins to move along, an actin bundle.

## The Cross-Bridge Cycle

The first mathematical theory of contraction based on sliding filaments with cyclic action of cross-bridges was worked out by me in the couple of years after the discovery of sliding filaments and published in 1957 (34). It made admittedly primitive assumptions about the rate constants for attachment and detachment (by utilization of a "high-energy phosphate" molecule) of cross-bridges as functions of the relative positions of the thick and thin filament sites, which necessarily move relative to one another as the filaments slide. I was able to get an adequate fit to A. V. Hill's 1938 relations between load, shortening speed, and rate of energy liberation during shortening. As regards lengthening, the discontinuity in the force-velocity curve between shortening and lengthening (50) was immediately explained, and the very low rate of energy liberation (33, 46) was explained by the additional postulate that overstretched cross-bridges can break without utilization of energy from chemical reactions. Fresh experiments by A. V. Hill (32) a few years later showed that the rate of energy liberation did not (as in his 1938 equations) increase indefinitely with shortening speed but passed through a maximum. I was able to accommodate this new evidence (35) by postulating that attachment takes place in two stages and that the first, but not the second, is easily reversible without utilization of chemical energy.

Even with the last-mentioned addition, it is now clear that the theory is incomplete. It cannot explain the length transients seen in response to a sudden change of load, reported in 1960 by Podolsky (55), or the tension transients following a sudden change of length, which my colleagues and I have studied since the late 1960s (17–20), without postulation of additional steps that occur on the millisecond time scale while the cross-bridge is attached. Also, the functions chosen to represent the rate constants for attachment and detachment were only first guesses and cannot be expected to be better than rough approximations to the truth even if, as I believe, the general outline is correct, i.e. that the cross-bridge is elastic, that its rate constant for attachment is moderate if the relative positions of the thick and thin sites are such that positive force would be exerted if attachment occurs, but that its rate constant for detachment is low until shortening by sliding brings the cross-bridge to the position where it exerts zero force and becomes high at positions where the force exerted is negative. I will assume this much for the purposes of this article. It is a skeleton theory: Plenty of questions remain, not least because the theory contains no specific statements about the nature of the actin-myosin bond, the nature or location of the elastic element, or the mechanism for breaking the bond at the right time.

In my 1957 article I denoted the "high-energy phosphate" molecule by XP and avoided committing myself to the assumption that it actually was ATP. Also, I assumed that it caused dissociation by becoming bound to actin, not to myosin. What was in my mind was that myosin was the enzyme and that XP bound to actin was the substrate. A related possibility that I was thinking of, but did not incorporate in the theory, was that adenosine might be permanently bound to actin as a prosthetic group and be rephosphorylated from the diphosphate to the triphosphate by reaction with PC in solution in the sarcoplasm; in that case, XP would have been PC, not ATP. These possibilities evaporated when, five years later, Cain et al (8) showed that muscle (appropriately poisoned) can contract more or less normally with utilization of ATP but not of PC, and many in vitro studies showed that ATP could both bind to, and be split by, myosin without any involvement of actin. My theory therefore needed to be modified by (a) specifying that XP was in fact ATP and (b) that it caused dissociation by binding to the myosin side of the cross-bridge, not the actin side. The kinetics, which are the interesting part of the theory, are not altered by this change in postulates.

The general outline of the 1957 theory has recently been supported, as regards overall events in steady shortening, by the experiments of Brenner & Eisenberg on skinned muscle fibers contracting under conditions of altered ATP concentration (6).

## Transient Responses

I have already mentioned that the initial changes of length when load on stimulated muscle is changed (isotonic transient) and the initial changes of force when length is suddenly changed (isometric transient) require additions to my 1957 theory. The two types of transient are clearly alternative expressions of the same underlying properties of the muscle. If one assumes linearity for small changes of load or length, it is easy to calculate the expected time course of the isotonic transient given the time course of the isometric transient. This was done by C. M. Armstrong, F. J. Julian and myself in 1966; we obtained agreement as good as could be expected in view of the nonlinearities of the phenomena, but in our published note (3) we only stated the conclusion and did not present the results. I shall assume that the underlying phenomena are the same in both cases. Since the isotonic transient is a damped oscillation while the isometric transient has only a finite number of phases (three components decaying approximately exponentially after the initial tension change), it is probable that the directly relevant independent variable is length change rather than force. For this reason we have concentrated on the isometric transient (force response to step change of length) both in our experiments and in our attempts to explain the results.

Measurements of the isometric transients at different muscle lengths (18) led to the conclusion that the phenomenon is a property of the cross-bridges alone; the filaments are so stiff that their compliance contributed only a small fraction to that which was measured. It has to be admitted, however, that it was assumed tacitly that cross-bridge stiffness was not affected by change of lateral spacing between filaments; if this turns out to be an important factor (23), the conclusion about filament compliance may have to be reconsidered. It is most unlikely that the conclusion that each cross-bridge contains an elastic element almost free from damping and obeying Hooke's law closely could be upset. According to our present estimates, the compliance of this elastic element is such that force is reduced to zero from the isometric value by ~4 nm of relative sliding movement of the filaments.

In 1971 R. M. Simmons and I (41) gave a tentative explanation of the isometric transient. We postulated a sequence of attached states with progressively increasing affinity and with progressively increasing stretch of the elastic component of the cross-bridge. This provided a semiquantitative explanation of two striking nonlinearities in the phenomenon. My present view of that theory is that it is still at least a valuable working hypothesis with a substantial chance of turning out to be correct in essentials, but I do not claim that it would be justifiable at present to place much reliance on its correctness. A testable prediction from the theory is that even during isometric contraction each cross-bridge should be in an equilibrium, switching between adjacent attached states on a time scale related to the time constant of the early tension recovery phase of the isometric transient (a few tenths of a millisecond in frog muscle at 0°C). This time scale is too long for investigation with most of the probes of cross-bridge orientation that have so far been extensively used [fluorescence and electron paramagnetic resonance (epr)], but there is hope for solution of the problem with probes using phosphorescence or saturation transfer epr.

## Stepwise Shortening

Reports that length changes in muscle often take place in a stepwise or oscillatory manner have given rise to a good deal of controversy in the last few years. The situation was presented recently in a pair of articles (37, 57). My own view, presented in one of those articles (37), is that some of the phenomena are instrumental artifacts and that those which are genuine are expressions of properties that are more effectively studied as "isotonic transients" (55) or better still as "isometric transients" (17–20).

## UNANSWERED QUESTIONS

In my 1974 review (36) I finished by listing seven unknowns, as follows:

1. which structure is the elastic element in the cross-bridge;
2. what is the nature of this elasticity;
3. what structure undergoes the stepwise change;
4. whether the attachment of the myosin head is to a single actin monomer or to two (or more) monomers within the thin filament;
5. what kind of bonds hold the myosin head to the thin filament;
6. how binding of ATP causes myosin to dissociate from actin; and
7. what is the significance of the fact that each myosin molecule has two heads.

None of these questions has yet been answered, and I still regard them as among the most important. Question 3 was formulated on the provisional assumption that the essentials of our 1971 theory (41) are correct, i.e. that each attached cross-bridge has more than one possible state and that it is in fairly rapid equilibrium between two or more of these states.

Since these questions are not yet answered, it might be supposed that little progress has been made in recent years. This is not the case because several fresh approaches have been made to the problem in the last few years and have begun to yield a new crop of information bearing not only on the questions I have listed but on other aspects of the problem. It is still too early to expect decisive answers to have emerged.

## NEW APPROACHES

Up-to-date reviews of several aspects of the molecular mechanism of muscle contraction were published in the 1987 issue of *Annual Review of Physiology* (Volume 49) as a Special Topic section. Those articles cover most of what I might have said in this section in much greater detail than would be possible in the space allotted to me. The following paragraphs therefore concentrate for the most part on a few aspects not covered in that group of reviews.

### Molecular Genetics and Myosin Structure

Watson & Crick proposed the double helix structure of DNA in 1953 and it was soon a commonplace to say that it was revolutionizing every branch of biology. However, it was some 30 years before it even began to make an impact on our understanding of muscle. In 1983 Karn et al (49) sequenced a myosin gene from the nematode *Caenorhabditis elegans,* and since then many sequences, partial or complete, either from DNA or from the protein itself, have been obtained for myosins from other organisms, including *Drosophila.* Several highly conserved regions have been recognized, but their respective functions have not yet been identified. High-quality crystals of the head (S-1 fraction) of myosin were obtained a few years ago (66), and great progress is to be expected when the tertiary structure has been worked out from these crystals by x-ray diffraction and has been correlated with the sequence. It is to be hoped that this will lead to identification of the site(s) for attachment to actin and to elucidation of the allosteric process by which binding of ATP to myosin reduces its affinity for actin.

### Time-Resolved X-Ray Diffraction

Low-angle x-ray diffraction has been the principal method for obtaining ultrastructural information from living muscle, but until recently the exposures required were so long that variations with time could not be studied except by stroboscopic methods on the oscillatory activity of asynchronous insect flight muscles. The advent of the synchrotron as an x-ray source of much higher intensity than that of normal x-ray tubes, together with digital recording to allow averaging of results from several contractions, has made a time resolution of the order of 1 ms possible; several groups are exploiting this technique.

The most interesting results refer to two situations, the onset of contraction (51) and the isometric transient (response to small stepwise shortening) (45). As regards the former, changes in the relative intensities of the equatorial reflections indicate a shift of material from the surface of the thick filaments towards the thin filaments. It is debated whether this directly indicates actual attachment of cross-bridges or merely outward movement of cross-bridges to permit subsequent attachment. Since the change is substantially earlier than the rise of tension, the former interpretation if correct is usually taken to imply that there is a lag (several milliseconds in frog muscle at low temperature) within the cross-bridge cycle between attachment and contribution to force. An alternative explanation could be that during the rise of activation there is a phase when cross-bridges attach but do not exert force, or exert less force than during full activation.

The other very striking result I wish to draw attention to is the large drop in intensity of the meridional reflection at 14.3 nm observed by H. E. Huxley and his collaborators when the muscle is suddenly shortened by say 10 nm per half sarcomere (45). This change appears to lag behind the length change itself by about 0.5 ms (frog muscle at 5°C) and is therefore likely to be related to Phase 2 of the tension transient (early tension recovery) rather than Phase 1 (tension drop simultaneous with the shortening). It may seen ungrateful to respond to such a technical triumph by asking for more, but I would dearly like to see this experiment repeated with a quicker step and with finer time resolution in the recording, to see whether the time course of the drop of intensity is similar to that of the early tension recovery in the tension transient. Several explanations for the drop of intensity are possible. H. E. Huxley et al (45) suggest either unequal longitudinal displacements of the ends of myosin heads closest to the thick filament shaft or an increased obliquity of the myosin heads, which might be nearly perpendicular to the fiber axis during isometric contraction. Another possibility is that only one of the two heads of each myosin molecule is attached and generating force during isometric contraction and that the other head is able to attach rapidly after the shortening step at a position roughly midway between the positions of the already-attached bridges. This mechanism would require a much higher rate constant for attachment of the second head than for a head whose twin was unattached. This supposition is not unreasonable since the attached first head might hold the second head in a favorable position. Another difficulty for this idea is that no increase in stiffness accompanies the early rise of tension; this could be explained if the two heads share a single elastic element (e.g. in S-2).

This method clearly has great promise for the future. It would be exciting to see the results of applying it to muscle of teleost fishes, in which Luther & Squire (53) have shown that all the thick filaments in a sarcomere are similarly oriented (in contrast to the situation in other vertebrates), so that the diffraction pattern is much more informative.

## "Caged" ATP and Other Substances

The phrase "caged X" refers to a substance that is decomposed by a flash of light into X plus another (preferably inert) substance; the original caged X does not share in the characteristic actions of X. Thus a skinned muscle fiber loaded with caged ATP will undergo a sudden increase in the ATP concentration when exposed to an appropriate flash. The most thorough development of this technique in its application to muscle has been made by Goldman and colleagues (21, 22). From rigor (zero ATP) in the absence of calcium, the liberated ATP is expected to dissociate the cross-bridges and produce a relaxed condition. This was indeed found to happen, but only after a short-lived rise of tension attributable to active contraction, i.e. the system was turned on by the presence of rigor bridges (5) despite the absence of calcium. A refinement of this experiment involved comparison of the tension time courses observed with different amounts of initial tension in the rigor fiber. This made it possible to separate the component due to preexisting cross-bridges from that due to cross-bridges formed after the release of ATP.

This method is also being used with caged calcium to produce sudden activation of a skinned fiber. This approach promises to greatly increase the value of the skinned fiber preparation since the chief drawback of the latter has lain in the slowness of activation by inward diffusion of added calcium, which causes nonuniform contraction and consequent disorganization of the fiber structure.

## Birefringence

Muscle has been studied with polarized light for a century and a half [e.g. in 1858 von Brücke (65) deduced correctly that the birefringence was due to rodlets that were not individually stretched when a muscle fiber as a whole was stretched], and records of the fall of birefringence on stimulation were made in several laboratories before World War II. Nevertheless this technique was little used except in the elegant study by Eberstein & Rosenfalck (9) on living isolated fibers, until the mid-1970s. Two investigations (62, 67) then showed that the strength of birefringence is reduced in rigor as well as during contraction and that the amount of the reduction is proportional to filament overlap. These results imply that the change occurs only in the overlap zone.

The birefringence technique, like x-ray diffraction, has the advantage of providing ultrastructural information on living tissue, at rest or in contraction. It is less specific than x-ray diffraction but is capable of much better time resolution. The major changes observed are presumably due chiefly to changes in the orientation of parts of the myosin molecules, though some of the small changes soon after stimulation are probably due to membrane events and are thus outside the scope of this article. This technique deserves to be more widely used. Observations by Dr. Malcolm Irving on changes in birefringence in response to quick changes in length are due to be published soon.

## CONCLUSION

In this article I have restricted myself almost entirely to aspects of the mechanism of force development and shortening that can be elucidated by experiments on intact, working muscle. Recent experiments of this and other kinds have tended to confirm the version of the sliding-filament theory that came to be widely accepted within a dozen years after the first proposal of sliding filaments in 1953: Force is generated by cross-bridges that consist of the heads of myosin molecules projecting from each thick filament and that act cyclically and more or less independently of one another. They attach to an adjacent thin filament, generate force, and detach as a consequence of binding of ATP. The rate constants for attachment and detachment are functions of the displacement of the myosin site relative to the actin site that occurs as the filaments slide past each other. It is this last feature that makes experiments on the intact contractile structure a continuing necessity: In vitro it is impossible to apply a load or to control the sliding motion, even if the contractile proteins are in their filamentary form. Although experiments on intact muscle can give no more than hints about the intimate details of the contraction process, understanding at this deeper level is advancing fast not only through in vitro biochemical investigations and structural studies but especially through techniques that are partly physiological and partly biochemical in nature. These include methods that depend on removing the surface membrane of muscle fibers so as either to change the concentrations of key solutes or to attach probes to the working protein molecules and include methods that follow movements of separated thick or thin filaments sliding over stationary actin or myosin, respectively. Molecular genetics too has begun to make an impact. It is nowadays necessary for those interested in muscle contraction, whether their own work is physiological, biochemical, structural, or genetical, to try to keep abreast with the advances made by the other disciplines: New observations can be interpreted only within the complex framework provided by the many different approaches now being used.

## Literature Cited

1. Altringham, J. D., Bottinelli, R. 1985. The descending limb of the sarcomere length-force relation in single muscle fibres of the frog. *J. Muscle Res. Cell Motil.* 6:585–600
2. Altringham, J. D., Pollack, G. H. 1984. Sarcomere length changes in single frog muscle fibres during tetani at long sarcomere lengths. In *Contractile Mechanisms in Muscle,* ed. G. H. Pollack, H. Sugi, pp. 473–93. New York/London: Plenum
3. Armstrong, C. M., Huxley, A. F., Julian, F. J. 1966. Oscillatory responses in frog skeletal muscle fibres. *J. Physiol. London* 186:26–7P
4. Bagni, M. A., Cecchi, G., Colomo, F., Tesi, C. 1986. The sarcomere length-tension relation in short length-clamped segments of frog single muscle fibres. *J. Physiol. London* 377:91P
5. Bremel, R. D., Weber, A. 1972. Cooperation within actin filament in vertebrate skeletal muscle. *Nature New Biol.* 238:97–101
6. Brenner, B., Eisenberg, E. 1986. Rate of force generation in muscle: Correlation with actomyosin ATPase activity in solution. *Proc. Natl. Acad. Sci. USA* 83:3542–46
7. Brown, L. M., González-Serratos, H., Huxley, A. F. 1984. Structural studies of the waves in striated muscle fibres shortened passively below their slack length. *J. Muscle Res. Cell Motil.* 5:273–92
8. Cain, D. F., Infante, A. A., Davies, R. E. 1962. Chemistry of muscle contraction. Adenosine triphosphate and phosphorylcreatine as energy supplies for single contractions of working muscle. *Nature* 196:214–17
9. Eberstein, A., Rosenfalck, A. 1963. Birefringence of isolated muscle fibres in twitch and tetanus. *Acta Physiol. Scand.* 57:144–66
10. Edman, K. A. P. 1979. The velocity of unloaded shortening and its relation to sarcomere length and isometric force in vertebrate muscle fibres. *J. Physiol. London* 291:143–59
11. Edman, K. A. P., Reggiani, C. 1987. The sarcomere length-tension relation determined in short segments of intact muscle fibres of the frog. *J. Physiol. London* 385:709–32
12. Eggleton, P., Eggleton, G. P. 1927. The inorganic phosphate and a labile form of organic phosphate in the gastrocnemius of the frog. *Biochem. J.* 21:190–95

13. Engelhardt, W. A., Ljubimowa, M. N. 1939. Myosine and adenosine-triphosphatase. *Nature* 144:668–9
14. Fenn, W. O. 1923. A quantitative comparison between the energy liberated and the work performed by the isolated sartorius muscle of the frog. *J. Physiol. London* 58:175–203
15. Fenn, W. O. 1924. The relation between the work performed and the energy liberated in muscular contraction. *J. Physiol. London* 58:373–95
16. Fiske, C. H., Subbarow, Y. 1927. The nature of the "inorganic phosphate" in voluntary muscle. *Science* 65:401–3
17. Ford, L. E., Huxley, A. F., Simmons, R. M. 1977. Tension responses to sudden length change in stimulated frog muscle fibres near slack length. *J. Physiol. London* 269:441–515
18. Ford, L. E., Huxley, A. F., Simmons, R. M. 1981. The relation between stiffness and filament overlap in stimulated frog muscle fibres. *J. Physiol. London* 311:219–49
19. Ford, L. E., Huxley, A. F., Simmons, R. M. 1985. Tension transients during steady shortening of frog muscle fibres. *J. Physiol. London* 361:131–50
20. Ford, L. E., Huxley, A. F., Simmons, R. M. 1986. Tension transients during the rise of tetanic tension in frog muscle fibres. *J. Physiol. London* 372:595–609
21. Goldman, Y. E., Hibberd, M. G., Trentham, D. R. 1984. Relaxation of rabbit psoas muscle fibres from rigor by photochemical generation of adenosine-5'-triphosphate. *J. Physiol. London* 354:577–604
22. Goldman, Y. E., Hibberd, M. G., Trentham, D. R. 1984. Initiation of active contraction by photogeneration of adenosine-5'-triphosphate in rabbit psoas muscle fibres. *J. Physiol. London* 354:605–24
23. Goldman, Y. E., Simmons, R. M. 1986. The stiffness of frog skinned muscle fibres at altered lateral filament spacing. *J. Physiol. London* 378:175–94
24. González-Serratos, H. 1971. Inward spread of activation in vertebrate muscle fibres. *J. Physiol. London* 212:777–99
25. Gordon, A. M., Huxley, A. F., Julian, F. J. 1966. The variation in isometric tension with sarcomere length in vertebrate muscle fibres. *J. Physiol. London* 184:170–92
26. Hanson, J., Huxley, H. E. 1953. Structural basis of the cross-striations in muscle. *Nature* 172:530–32

27. Harman, J. W. 1954. Contractions of skeletal muscle myofibrils by phase microscopy (motion picture). *Fed. Proc.* 13:430

28. Hasselbach, W. 1953. Elektronenmikroskopische Untersuchungen an Muskelfibrillen bei totaler und partieller Extraktion des L-Myosins. *Z. Naturforsch.* 8b:449–54

29. Hill, A. V. 1932. The revolution in muscle physiology. *Physiol. Rev.* 12:56–67

30. Hill, A. V. 1938. The heat of shortening and the dynamic constants of muscle. *Proc. R. Soc. London Ser. B* 126:136–95

31. Hill, A. V. 1959. The heat production of muscle and nerve, 1848–1914. *Ann. Rev. Physiol.* 21:1–18

32. Hill, A. V. 1964. The effect of load on the heat of shortening of muscle. *Proc. R. Soc. London Ser. B* 159:297–318

33. Hill, A. V., Howarth, J. V. 1959. The reversal of chemical reactions in contracting muscle during an applied stretch. *Proc. R. Soc. London Ser. B* 151:169–93

34. Huxley, A. F. 1957. Muscle structure and theories of contraction. *Prog. Biophys. Biophys. Chem.* 7:255–318

35. Huxley, A. F. 1973. A note suggesting that the cross-bridge attachment during muscle contraction may take place in two stages. *Proc. R. Soc. London Ser. B* 183:83–86

36. Huxley, A. F. 1974. Muscular contraction. Review lecture given at the meeting of the Physiological Society at Leeds University on 14–15 December, 1973. *J. Physiol. London* 243:1–43

37. Huxley, A. F. 1986. Comments on "Quantal mechanisms in cardiac contraction." *Circ. Res.* 59:9–14

38. Huxley, A. F., Niedergerke, R. 1954. Interference microscopy of living muscle fibres. *Nature* 173:971–73

39. Huxley, A. F., Niedergerke, R. 1958. Measurement of the striations of isolated muscle fibres with the interference microscope. *J. Physiol. London* 144:403–25

40. Huxley, A. F., Peachey, L. D. 1961. The maximum length for contraction in vertebrate striated muscle. *J. Physiol. London* 156:150–65

41. Huxley, A. F., Simmons, R. M. 1971. Proposed mechanism of force generation in striated muscle. *Nature* 233:533–38

42. Huxley, H. E. 1953. Electron microscope studies of the organisation of the filaments in striated muscle. *Biochim. Biophys. Acta* 12:387–94

43. Huxley, H. E. 1957. The double array of filaments in cross-striated muscle. *J. Biophys. Biochem. Cytol.* 3:631–48

44. Huxley, H. E., Hanson, J. 1954. Changes in the cross-striations of muscle during contraction and stretch and their structural interpretation. *Nature* 173:973–76

45. Huxley, H. E., Simmons, R. M., Faruqi, A. R., Kress, M., Bordas, J., Koch, M. H. J. 1983. Changes in the x-ray reflections from contracting muscle during rapid mechanical transients and structural implications. *J. Mol. Biol.* 169:469–506

46. Infante, A. A., Klaupiks, D., Davies, R. E. 1964. Adenosine triphosphate: Changes in muscles doing negative work. *Science* 144:1577–78

47. Julian, F. J., Moss, R. L. 1980. Sarcomere length-tension relations of frog skinned muscle fibres at lengths above the optimum. *J. Physiol. London* 304: 529–39

48. Julian, F. J., Sollins, M. R., Moss, R. L. 1978. Sarcomere length non-uniformity in relation to tetanic responses of stretched skeletal muscle fibres. *Proc. R. Soc. London Ser. B* 200:109–16

49. Karn, J., Brenner, S., Barnett, L. 1983. Protein structural domains in the *Caenorhabditis elegans unc-54* myosin heavy chain gene are not separated by introns. *Proc. Natl. Acad. Sci. USA* 80:4253–57

50. Katz, B. 1939. The relation between force and speed in muscular contraction. *J. Physiol. London* 96:45–64

51. Kress, M., Huxley, H. E., Faruqi, A. R., Hendrix, J. 1986. Structural changes during activation of frog muscle studied by time-resolved x-ray diffraction. *J. Mol. Biol.* 188:325–42

52. Lundsgaard, E. 1930. Untersuchungen über Muskelkontraktionen ohne Milchsäurebildung. *Biochem. Z.* 217:162–77

53. Luther, P. K., Squire, J. M. 1980. Three-dimensional structure of the vertebrate muscle A-band. II. The myosin filament superlattice. *J. Mol. Biol.* 141:409–39

54. Needham, D. M. 1950. Myosin and adenosinetriphosphate in relation to muscle contraction. *Biochim. Biophys. Acta* 4: 42–49

55. Podolsky, R. J. 1960. Kinetics of muscular contraction: The approach to the steady state. *Nature* 188:666–68

56. Pollack, G. H. 1983. The cross-bridge theory. *Physiol. Rev.* 63:1049–1113

57. Pollack, G. H. 1986. Quantal mechanisms in cardiac contraction. *Circ. Res.* 59:1–8

58. Ramsey, R. W., Street, S. F. 1940. The

isometric length-tension diagram of isolated skeletal muscle fibers of the frog. *J. Cell. Comp. Physiol.* 15:11–34

59. Sheetz, M. P., Spudich, J. A. 1983. Movement of myosin-coated fluorescent beads on actin cables in vitro. *Nature* 303:31–35

60. Straub, F. B. 1943. Actin. *Stud. Inst. Med. Chem. Univ. Szeged* (1942) 2:3–15

61. Szent-Györgyi, A. 1942. Discussion. *Stud. Inst. Med. Chem. Univ. Szeged* (1941–42) 1:67–71

62. Taylor, D. L. 1976. Quantitative studies on the polarization optical properties of striated muscle. I. Birefringence changes of rabbit psoas muscle in the transition from rigor to relaxed state. *J. Cell Biol.* 68:497–511

63. ter Keurs, H. E. D. J., Iwazumi, T., Pollack, G. H. 1978. The sarcomere length-tension relation in skeletal muscle. *J. Gen. Physiol.* 72:565–92

64. ter Keurs, H. E. D. J., Iwazumi, T., Pollack, G. H. 1979. The length-tension relation in skeletal muscle: Revisited. In *Cross-Bridge Mechanism in Muscle Contraction,* ed. H. Sugi, G. H. Pollack, pp. 277–95. Tokyo: Univ. Tokyo Press

65. von Brücke, E. 1858. Untersuchungen über den Bau der Muskelfasern mit Hülfe des polarisirten Lichtes. *Denkschr. Akad. Wiss. Wien Math.-Naturwiss. Kl.* 15:69–84

66. Winkelmann, D. A., Mekeel, H., Rayment, I. 1985. Packing analysis of crystalline myosin subfragment-1: Implications for the size and shape of the myosin head. *J. Mol. Biol.* 181:487–501

67. Yanagida, T. 1976. Birefringence of glycerinated crab muscle fiber under various conditions. *Biochim. Biophys. Acta* 420:225–35

ADDED IN PROOF:

68. Akster, H. A., Granzier, H. L. M., ter Keurs, H. E. D. J. 1984. Force - sarcomere length relations vary with thin filament length in muscle fibres of the perch (Perca fluviatilis L.). *J. Physiol. London* 353:61P

# GASTROINTESTINAL PHYSIOLOGY

## *PEPTIDE REGULATION OF ACID SECRETION*

*Introduction,* George Sachs, *Section Editor*

The understanding of the regulation of events in the gastrointestinal tract has changed enormously since the elucidation of the structure of gastrin in 1963 by R. A. Gregory and coworkers. The articles in this section focus largely on the peptides that are now thought to affect gastric function, many of which were not known even a decade ago. It seemed logical to divide this frontier into three areas. The role of peptides in the central nervous system that affect gastric acid secretion is discussed by Taché. The action of peptides as regulators of acid secretion is reviewed by Walsh, and the structural and chemical organization of the peripheral myenteric plexus by Sternini. Since there is rather little known about the direct cellular effects of mediators on the parietal cell, although this is being corrected rapidly, the cellular action of various agonists on the pancreatic acinar cell are described by Petersen.

The regulation of acid secretion some years ago appeared deceptively simple. Three physiological regulators were known, namely acetyl choline release from vagal efferents, gastrin released from G cells as a function of meal stimulation, and histamine, which was shown to be a potent stimulant of secretion. No mechanism of inhibition of parietal cell function had been described. It was also very difficult to demonstrate a physiological role for histamine, since no measurable changes occurred during stimulation of acid secretion. In the early seventies, James Black and coworkers developed a class of compounds based on the structure of histamine that were potent inhibitors of acid secretion. They became known as H2 receptor antagonists. A surprising finding, given the climate of the era, was that these antagonists were good inhibitors of acid secretion induced by gastrin or cholinergic stimulants. This led to the concept that histamine was the common mediator of acid secretory stimulation. Further work showed however that independent receptors exist for muscarinic agents of the M2 type and for gastrin on the parietal cell, and that the latter two agents affected $[Ca]_i$ rather than cAMP. In the case of histamine, both cAMP and $[Ca]_1$ levels are apparently elevated. The duality of the second messenger systems thus allowed for the potentiation described by workers such as Morton Grossman in the dog. The source of histamine with stimulation by vagal or gastrin pathways remains mysterious. Additional evidence that a major fraction of gastrin or vagally mediated acid secretion depends on histamine release is the inhibition of gastrin-mediated secretion in rabbit gastric glands by agents that prevent histamine release, such as chromoglycate analogs. These agents also simultaneously prevent histamine release in the preparation.

One means of inhibiting acid secretion would be to remove the stimulus. Thus switching off vagal efferents, removing of the food stimulus, activating gastrin release, and blocking histamine liberation would all be expected to reduce acid secretion. However it appears that this simple mechanism is not the only means whereby the body regulates this important gastric function, and only now are we developing some understanding of down regulation of acid secretion. For example the parietal cell has both epidermal growth factor and somatostatin receptors that inhibit acid secretion; presumably there are other inhibitory receptors yet undiscovered. Furthermore, somatostatin inhibits G cell gastrin release. The complex innervation, partly sensory, partly efferent, with a bewildering number of peptides must also function in regulation of acid secretion. Particularly intriguing is the differential effect of some peptides when injected into the CNS and when given peripherally.

Therefore, these chapters on regulation of acid secretion, centrally, peripherally, and directly should give some insight into current thinking in the area. On the other hand, modern electrophysiological studies of the parietal cell are few, and only recently has patch clamp technology been applied to this cell. One of the pioneers of the application of patch clamp to epithelial cells has written an overview of current information on the pancreatic acinar cell. In this cell type there is a multiplicity of channels, many of them regulated by $[Ca]_i$; in turn most hormones interact with the Ca system, thus altering channel and transport function in this enzyme secretory cell that must bear considerable resemblance to the peptic cell. This review should therefore be thought of as much more generally applicable to epithelia than just the model cell discussed.

*Ann. Rev. Physiol. 1988. 50:19–39*
*Copyright © 1988 by Annual Reviews Inc. All rights reserved*

# CNS PEPTIDES AND REGULATION OF GASTRIC ACID SECRETION

## Y. Taché

Center for Ulcer Research and Education, Veterans' Administration Medical Center and Department of Medicine and Brain Research Institute, University of California, Los Angeles, California 90073

## INTRODUCTION

The influence of the central nervous system (CNS) on gastric secretory and motor function has been recognized for one and a half centuries, ever since William Beaumont's studies of his fistulous subject. In 1833 he reported that "fear, anger, whatever depresses or disturbs the nervous system" was accompanied by suppression of gastric secretion and by a marked delay in gastric digestion and emptying (4). A landmark in the establishment of a physiological role for the brain in the regulation of gastric secretion was Pavlov's work at the beginning of this century. He discovered that sham feeding, anticipation of eating, and the sight or smell of food were powerful stimulants of both gastric acid and pepsin secretion in the dog (78). These studies were extended to humans in 1907 (40) and since then have been amply confirmed (17). Brain pathways influencing gastric secretion were subsequently investigated via electrical stimulation or lesions of specific nuclei in various experimental animals (5, 25). More recently, advances in neurophysiological techniques, the development of sensitive anterograde and retrograde transport techniques and the discovery of a large number of peptides and their receptors in brain structures influencing gastric function have provided new tools and impetus to the investigation of the anatomical and chemical substrates mediating brain-gut interactions.

19

0066-4278/88/0315-0019$02.00

This review emphasizes recent advances in the elucidation of brain sites, mechanisms of action, and possible physiological roles of neuropeptides in the regulation of gastric secretion.

## NEUROANATOMIC BASIS OF CNS PEPTIDERGIC CONTROL OF GASTRIC ACID SECRETION

Several brain sites have been identified as involved in the control of gastric acid secretion on the basis of experiments using electrical stimulation or lesion of these areas, namely the hypothalamus (lateral, ventromedial, and paraventricular nucleus), the locus coeruleus, the amygdala (centromedial), and the dorsal vagal complex (medial dorsal motor nucleus of the vagus) (5, 45, 103). Subsequently, the introduction of sensitive anterograde and retrograde transport techniques and electrophysiological approaches has allowed the delineation of the central organization of gastric afferent and efferent pathways, particularly in the medulla, and their connections with forebrain nuclei (84, 94, 103). The bulk of sensory and motor innervation of the stomach is carried within the vagus nerve (94). Gastric vagal afferent fibers terminate predominantly within the nucleus of the solitary tract and to a lesser extent in the ventral part of the area postrema and the dorsal motor nucleus (94). Gastric efferent fibers arise mostly from cells located in the medial subnucleus of the dorsal motor nucleus of the vagus and the nucleus ambiguus (45, 94). Gastric neurons in the dorsal motor nucleus of the vagus possess an extensive plexus of dendrites that penetrates the nucleus tractus solitarius. This interconnection provides an anatomical basis for monosynaptic vagovagal interactions and telencephalic influence on gastric secretion (94). In particular, gastric neurons in the nucleus tractus solitarius and the dorsal nucleus of the vagus are activated by electrical microstimulation of the paraventricular nucleus and lateral hypothalamus (84, 95). The gastric sympathetic efferent pathways are organized hierarchically between spinal and supraspinal levels (103).

Since 1970, over 60 biologically active peptides have been characterized in the brain and/or the spinal cord by bioassay, immunohistochemical, chemical, and more recently, molecular biological methods (42). These peptides and their receptors are densely localized in brain structures known to influence visceral function, such as the hypothalamus and the dorsal motor nucleus (15, 99). Neuropharmacological studies have established that neuropeptides exert multiple CNS-mediated actions on behavior, pain perception, glucoregulation, thermoregulation, and cardiovascular and respiratory function (129). Recently, growing evidence indicates also that several peptides act within the brain to alter gastric function (12, 103).

# PEPTIDES ACTING IN THE BRAIN TO STIMULATE GASTRIC ACID SECRETION

## Thyrotropin Releasing Hormone

CHARACTERISTICS OF THE SECRETORY RESPONSE    Data consistently indicate that thyrotropin releasing hormone (TRH) injected into the cerebrospinal fluid (CSF) stimulates gastric acid secretion by increasing both the volume and the concentration of acid in conscious and anesthetized rats (116, 120). The gastric secretory response to a single intracisternal injection of TRH has a rapid onset, reaches its peak value within 30 min, and returns to basal levels after 90–120 min (109). Gastric acid secretion is also enhanced by injection of a number of TRH analogues into the CSF, including the stable analogues   RX77368   [$p$-Glu-His-(3,3'-dimethyl)-Pro-NH$_2$],   MK771   (L-$p$-2-aminoadipyl-His-thiazolidine-4-carboxamide),   DN-1417   ($\tau$-butyrolactone-$\tau$-carbonyl-His-Pro-NH$_2$), and (3methyl-His$^2$)-TRH, and analogues devoid of in vitro or in vivo thyrotropin releasing activity, such as A45474   [$p$-Glu-His-(1,3'-dicarboxymethyl)-Pro-NH$_2$]   and   ($N$-Val$^2$)-TRH (56, 101, 108, 109, 115, 120). The specificity of TRH action was further demonstrated by the inactivity of TRH-OH, cyclo(His-Pro), and (1methyl-His$^2$)-TRH (66, 120). The sensitivity to TRH is not altered after three consecutive intracerebroventricular injections (61). However, the sensitivity is decreased in aged rats (39–62 weeks), whereas the bethanechol secretory response is unchanged (60). In the rabbit, cerebroventricular injection of RX77368 stimulated basal gastric secretion (Y. Taché & S. J. Mulvihill, unpublished observation). By contrast, in the dog the injection of TRH into the third ventricle did not modify basal or pentagastrin-stimulated gastric secretion (49).

BRAIN SITES AND MECHANISMS OF ACTION    The stimulatory effect of CSF injection of TRH is mediated by the CNS, since intravenous administration of up to 50-fold higher doses produces either no change or a slight increase in gastric acid secretion (59, 109, 120). TRH microinjected into the lateral hypothalamus in doses ranging from 2–5 nmol stimulated gastric acid secretion, whereas TRH microinjection into the caudate putamem was ineffective (57). Further studies demonstrated that the site most responsive to TRH is located in the dorsal vagal complex. Microinjection of 5–500 pmol of TRH or RX77368 into the dorsal vagal nucleus and the nucleus tractus solitarius dose dependently stimulated gastric acid secretion in anesthetized rats. Microinjection of similar doses of TRH or RX77368 into other medullary nuclei, e.g. the area postrema, lateral, dorsal, and parvocellular reticular nuclei, the medial longitudinal fasciculus, or the cuneate nucleus, or various hypothalamic sites, e.g. the anterior, lateral, ventromedial, or dorsomedial hypothalamus or the paraventricular nucleus, did not modify gastric acid secretion (72, 83, 98). Electrophysiological studies demonstrated that TRH induced rhythmic bursts of activity in neurons in the respiratory division of the nucleus tractus solitarius (14). To what extent TRH also acts by modulating the membrane excitability of gastric neurons in the dorsal vagal complex has not been explored.

Some of the pharmacological effects of TRH appear to be mediated by interacting with other neuronal systems in the CNS, including the cholinergic pathways (128). The activation of cholinergic muscarinic receptors in the dorsal motor nucleus stimulates gastric acid secretion (71). However, the CNS action of TRH is not mediated by an interaction with cholinergic muscarinic and dopaminergic receptors in the brain since central injection of atropine or haloperidol does not alter the stimulatory effect on gastric secretion of TRH injected intracisternally or into the dorsal vagal nucleus (72, 115). The stimulatory effect of CSF injection of TRH is exerted by the tripeptide itself rather than formation of active TRH metabolites in the brain (66, 98, 109). All the centrally acting peptidergic inhibitors of gastric secretion and the $\alpha_2$-adrenergic agonist clonidine prevent the stimulatory effect of central TRH (51, 57, 59, 107, 117). The mechanisms of this interaction are unknown.

PERIPHERAL PATHWAYS    Pharmacological, surgical, electrophysiological, and endocrinological approaches have established the underlying peripheral mechanisms mediating the stimulatory effect of centrally injected TRH. Its action is not hormonally mediated through changes in hypophysiotropic hormones or gastrin release (108, 109, 115). The secretory response to CSF or dorsal motor nucleus injection of TRH is abolished by vagotomy and peripheral injection of atropine. Neither spinal cord transection nor adrenalectomy alone or with chemical sympathectomy by guanethidine affected the gastric response to TRH (58, 115, 120). CSF injection of TRH increases vagal efferent discharges to the stomach and sympathetic outflow to the adrenal gland and reduces gastric sympathetic activity (97, 108). Moreover, the fact that the most responsive site is located in the dorsal vagal complex further indicates that TRH action is conveyed from the brain to the stomach by activation of vagal efferent pathways and peripheral cholinergic receptors (72, 98).

PHYSIOLOGICAL ROLE    Growing structural and functional evidence supports the hypothesis that medullary TRH plays a physiological role in the regulation of gastric acid secretion in the rat. The highest concentrations of TRH immunoreactivity and receptors in the medulla have been measured in the dorsal vagal complex (43, 63). The immunoreactivity is localized in nerve fibers and terminals, whereas TRH cell bodies are contained in the raphe nuclei (43, 74). The endogenous release of brain TRH in response to cold exposure (1) mimics the stimulatory effect induced by central injection of TRH (72, 82, 126). Recent studies demonstrated that intracerebroventricular injection of TRH antiserum significantly inhibited gastric acid secretion stimulated by pylorus ligation in rats (32). Taken together these findings support the view that TRH in the dorsal vagal complex may be an important neuroactive peptide involved in the vagal stimulation of gastric secretion in the rat. An important issue yet to be established is whether dorsal motor nucleus injection of TRH in the dog induces a secretory response and whether it is involved in the cephalic phase of gastric secretion.

## Oxytocin

Rogers & Hermann (83) demonstrated that microinjection of low doses of oxytocin into the dorsal motor nucleus of the vagus stimulated gastric acid secretion in the rat. The dorsal motor nucleus of the vagus appears the most sensitive site tested so far, as microinjection of oxytocin into the area postrema or the cisterna magna did not stimulate gastric secretion (83, Y. Taché, unpublished observation). Peptide action is receptor specific, since vasopressin tested under similar conditions is inactive and the oxytocin/vasopressin antagonist [1-($\beta$-mercapto-$\beta$,$\beta$-diethylpropionic acid)-$O$-ethyltyrosine-Orn$^8$]-vasotocin injected into the dorsal motor nucleus of the vagus blocked the stimulatory effect of oxytocin (83). Oxytocin action is inhibited by peripheral injection of atropine, which suggests a cholinergically mediated mechanism of action (83). In the dog, injection of oxytocin into the third brain ventricle did not alter the gastric secretory response to pentagastrin (49).

The existence of oxyntinergic neurons projecting from the paraventricular nucleus to preganglionic cell groups in the dorsal vagal complex and the spinal cord provides an anatomical basis for a role of oxytocin in the regulation of autonomic function (44, 99). The fact that oxytocin antagonist prevented gastric acid secretion elicited by electrical stimulation of the paraventricular nucleus (83, 86) suggests a possible role of medullary oxytocin in the paraventricular-dorsomotor nucleus descending pathways to the stomach.

## Cholecystokinin and Gastrin

Gastrin and pentagastrin elicited a short-lasting stimulation of gastric secretion in rats only when injected into the lateral hypothalamus (124). CSF injection of the peptides was found ineffective in rats and dogs (37, 49, 62, 117, 124). Sulfated cholecystokinin-8 (CCK-8) injected into the lateral ventricle in rats and into the left cerebral cortex in guinea pig increased gastric secretion (37, 91). Tachyphylaxis developed after the first central injection of CCK both in the rat and guinea pig (37, 91).

The stimulatory effect of pentagastrin and CCK-8 is mediated by the CNS. Centrally effective doses of CCK-8 and pentagastrin given intravenously did not modify gastric secretion and CCK-like immunoreactivity was not detected in the circulation following central injection (37, 91, 124). CCK and gastrin secretory effects were blocked by vagotomy and atropine, which suggests a vagal, cholinergically mediated pathway (37, 91, 124).

CCK-8 shares with gastrin a complete homology of the C-terminal fragment and appears to account for the so-called gastrinlike immunoreactivity previously reported in the brain (16). This suggests that the endogenous peptide likely to exert an effect is CCK-8 and not gastrin. However, the fact that the stimulatory effect of CSF injection of CCK-8 on gastric secretion has not been reproduced by other investigators in rats and dogs (49, Y. Taché, unpublished observation), casts doubt on the significance of these observations. Further work using central injection of recently developed CCK antagonists may help to assess the role of the peptide in the central regulation of gastric secretion.

## Somatostatin

The reported gastric response to CSF injection of somatostatin has varied depending upon the peptide and species used. In the rat, intracisternal injection of somatostatin-14 or -28 did not modify gastric secretion (119). In contrast, intracisternal injection of oligosomatostatin analogues, such as [D-Trp$^8$]-somatostatin with deletions (Des) of amino acids (AA) in positions 1, 2, 4, 5, 12, and 13 (ODT8-SS) and Des-AA$^{1,2,4,5,12,13}$-[D-Trp$^8$,D-Cys$^{14}$]-somatostatin, had a stimulatory effect, mostly by increasing the volume of gastric secretion (77, 119). In the dog, injection into the third or lateral brain ventricle of somatostatin-14, somatostatin-28, or ODT8-SS did not modify basal gastric secretion but enhanced gastric secretion in response to a meal or to a low dose but not in response to a submaximal dose of pentagastrin (49, 77). The analogue was 20 times more potent than somatostatin-14, in agreement with results of previous studies (9, 77).

The effects of CSF injection of oligosomatostatin analogue are mediated by the CNS since intravenous administration of ODT8-SS did not influence gastric secretion in rats or dogs (77, 119) and somatostatin is a well-established peripheral inhibitor of gastric secretion (77). The brain site and mechanism of action of somatostatin and its analogue are unknown. In rats, the stimulatory effect of ODT8-SS is reversed by vagotomy and atropine but not adrenalectomy, which suggests a vagal, cholinergically mediated action (119). By contrast, in dogs the stimulatory effect is neither vagal nor gastrin related but may involve the inhibition of sympathetic nerve activity (6, 77).

The fact that in dogs CSF injection of somatostatin enhances gastric secretion induced by a threshold dose of stimulant but does not alter basal secretion rules out its involvement in the cephalic phase of gastric secretion. Since ODT8-SS has less than 6% of the potency of somatostatin in the cortical binding assay (80), the subpopulation of receptors on which these oligosomatostatin analogues act is unknown (80).

## PEPTIDES ACTING IN THE BRAIN TO INHIBIT GASTRIC ACID SECRETION

### Bombesinlike Peptides

CHARACTERISTICS OF THE INHIBITORY RESPONSE    Bombesin was the first peptide reported to completely inhibit gastric acid secretion by reducing both the volume and the concentration of acid in pylorus-ligated rats when injected into the cisterna magna (121). Since then, these observations have been expanded to other animal species, including the rabbit, cat, and dog (2, 69, 76). In dogs bombesin injected into the third brain ventricle was a more effective inhibitor of gastric acid secretion than 30 other peptides tested under similar conditions (49). In rats the intracisternal $ED_{50}$ to inhibit gastric secretion is ~6 pmol (121). Other naturally occurring bombesinlike peptides, including gastrin releasing peptide (GRP), alytesin, ranatensin, and litorin, also suppressed gastric secretion when injected into the cerebrospinal fluid of rats, although their activity was less than that of bombesin (26, 49, 117). The acetylated C-terminal octapeptide but not heptapeptide fragment of GRP has full biological activity (117). The inhibitory effect of bombesin or GRP injected into the CSF is long acting and extends to all types of gastric stimulants including a meal, pentagastrin, histamine, insulin, 2-deoxy-D-glucose, central TRH, cysteamine, and the GABA agonists, muscimol and baclofen (110).

BRAIN SITES AND MECHANISMS OF ACTION    Bombesin inhibits gastric secretion when injected into the cerebrospinal fluid either at the level of the lateral, third, or fourth brain ventricle, or the cisterna magna in the rat, cat, or dog (28, 110). The existence of both forebrain and hindbrain sites of action was demonstrated by the fact that bombesin was equally effective when injected into the lateral or fourth ventricle in the presence or the absence of an aqueductal plug blocking the passage of the infusate from the lateral to the fourth ventricle (28). Moreover, the inhibitory effect of intracisternal bombesin was not altered by coronal transection of the brain at the superior colliculus (28). Bombesin microinjected into various hypothalamic sites inhibited gastric secretion only when applied into the paraventricular nucleus, whereas injection into the lateral or ventromedial hypothalamus or the caudate putamen was ineffective (27). The paraventricular nucleus is the only hypothalamic nucleus that sends direct, monosynaptic projections to preganglionic cell groups of both the parasympathetic and sympathetic divisions of the autonomic nervous system in the brain stem and spinal cord (99) and has been shown to alter the activity of gastric afferent and efferent neurons in the dorsal vagal complex (84, 85). Preliminary evidence suggests other sites responsive to microinjection of bombesin are localized in the dorsal vagal complex, nucleus ambiguus, and spinal cord (30, 38). The centrally mediated action of bombesin is independent from interaction with brain dopamine, catecholamine, serotonin, and opioid pathways (102, 105).

PERIPHERAL PATHWAYS    Bombesin's action does not require the integrity of prostaglandin pathways (102) and is not related to changes in pituitary hormone nor gastrin secretion (49, 76, 105, 117, 121). Pharmacological, surgical, and electrophysiological approaches and experiments in cross-circulated rats suggest that the inhibitory effect of bombesin is mediated by changes in the autonomic nervous system activity, along with other mechanisms that remain to be elucidated (114). Bombesin injected into the CSF suppresses the nerve activity of the gastric ramus of the vagus (97). Vagally induced acid secretion is inhibited by microinjection of bombesin into the dorsal motor nucleus at a threshold dose lower than required with injection into the cisterna magna (38). These results indicates that the inhibitory effect of bombesin against vagal stimulants may be mediated by decreasing the parasympathetic outflow to the stomach. The existence of a non-vagal-dependent inhibitory pathway was demonstrated by the fact that the gastric secretory response to pentagastrin was unaltered in dogs with vagally denervated pouches (76) and in rats with subdiaphragmatic vagotomy (114, 121). In addition, bombesin injected into the dorsal vagal nucleus yields only 25% inhibition of the pentagastrin response, whereas the same dose (6 pmol) given intracisternally induced 50–75% inhibition (38). The possibility that this inhibition may be mediated through the sympathetic nervous system is suggested by the decreases in nerve activity of the gastric splanchnic nerve and the stimulation of adrenal epinephrine secretion induced by CSF injection of bombesin (10, 97). Moreover, acute adrenalectomy, transection of the spinal cord up to the seventh cervical level, or blockade of $\alpha_2$-adrenergic receptors but not $\alpha_1$- or $\beta$-adrenergic receptors partly prevented the rise in gastric pH induced by intracisternal injection of bombesin in pylorus-ligated rats (110, 114, 121). By contrast, in dogs ganglionic blockade with chlorisondamine, a peripherally acting blocker of sympathetic and parasympathetic ganglia, did not prevent CSF bombesin–induced inhibition of pentagastrin-stimulated gastric secretion (49). From these studies, it appears the pathways through which bombesin expresses its inhibitory effect are still unknown in the dog, whereas in rats it may be partly related to alteration of autonomic nervous system activity.

PHYSIOLOGICAL ROLE    The assessment of the physiological role of neuronal bombesin has been hampered by the lack of specific bombesin antagonists biologically active in vivo. Spantide inhibited the binding of bombesinlike peptides and substance P to brain receptors in vitro (127), but when injected into the CSF it proved to be toxic and did not block the effects of central injection of bombesin (13, 110). The possible role of brain bombesinlike peptides in the regulation of gastric function is, however, substantiated by anatomical and pharmacological studies. Brain sites responsive to bombesin, such as the paraventricular nucleus and the dorsal nucleus, show a high density of bombesinlike immunoreactivity and receptors (65, 75, 130). Moreover, bombesin appears to be the most potent centrally acting peptide inhibiting gastric acid secretion in rats and dogs (47, 49, 110).

## Calcitonin

Injection of salmon calcitonin into the CSF of rats inhibits gastric secretion stimulated by pentagastrin (11) and vagus-dependent stimuli, such as pylorus ligation (51, 53, 67, 90), insulin (11, 67), central TRH (57, 67), and the GABA agonists, baclofen and muscimol (24, 55), but does not prevent the gastric response to histamine or bethanechol (24). Salmon calcitonin was more potent than rat CGRP in anesthetized rats (35, 70) or equipotent in conscious rats (51). Porcine, rat, human, and [Asu$^{1,7}$]-eel calcitonin injected intracerebroventricularly inhibited gastric secretion in the rat (53, 57, 70), whereas the linear peptide was inactive (53). In the dog, rat, and human, calcitonin injected into the third ventricle also inhibited pentagastrin and meal-stimulated gastric acid secretion (49).

Although [$^{125}$I]calcitonin appears rapidly in the peripheral circulation after intracerebroventricular injection into the rat, the highest amounts of intact calcitonin and breakdown products were retained by the brain, predominantly by the hypothalamus and the medulla, and to some extent by the kidneys, but not the stomach (90). In the dog, injection into the third ventricle was not associated with the appearance of immunoreactive calcitonin in the plasma (49). A central site of action for salmon calcitonin was further demonstrated by the marked difference in the potency of CSF as compared with peripheral administration (67, 90). The lateral and the paraventricular nuclei are responsive sites, whereas the ventromedial hypothalamus, globus pallidus, and corpus striatum are inactive sites (34, 39, 57).

The brain mechanisms involved in the response to calcitonin appear unrelated to alteration of neuronal calcium fluxes (11) but require the integrity of the central serotoninergic but not catecholaminergic pathways (54). The peripheral mechanisms underlying the inhibitory effect of calcitonin are not mediated by alteration of gastric mucosal blood flow (3), prostaglandin generation in the gastric mucosa (34, 113), or changes in plasma levels of calcium or gastrin (49, 53). Ganglionic blockade prevents the expression of the inhibitory effect, whereas vagotomy does not (34, 46, 49). Further studies are required to elucidate the role of the sympathetic nervous system in the inhibitory effect of calcitonin.

Specific receptors for salmon calcitonin have been characterized in the brain and found predominantly in the hypothalamus and the brain stem (19, 23). An important unresolved issue concerns the presence in the rat brain of salmon calcitonin, which differs by 14 out of 32 residues from rat calcitonin. Although salmon calcitonin has been detected in the human brain by immunohistochemical method (20), observations related to the processing of the calcitonin gene in the rat brain do not indicate the presence of calcitonin in neural tissue (87). Further studies are required to elucidate the existence of an endogenous ligand for salmon calcitonin receptors in the brain and the physiologic significance of the potent CNS-mediated inhibitory effect of the peptide in rats and dogs.

## Calcitonin Gene–Related Peptide

Injection of rat CGRP into the cisterna magna or the lateral ventricle inhibits gastric acid secretion stimulated by pylorus ligation, CSF injection of TRH, pentagastrin, histamine, and bethanechol in conscious and anesthetized rats (35, 51, 112). The intracisternal $ED_{50}$ is 13 pmol (51, 112). In conscious dogs, third ventricle injection of rat CGRP also suppressed the gastric secretory response to pentagastrin, 2-deoxy-D-glucose, or a meal but not to a submaximal dose of histamine (49, 50). The biological activity of rat CGRP seems to require the intact molecule since the N-terminal fragment, CGRP1-14, the C-terminal residue, [Tyr23]-CGRP23-27, and the linear peptide molecule devoid of the disulfur bridge, [acetaminomethyl-$Cys^{2,7}$]-CGRP, were inactive (50, 53). Human CGRP, which differs by four residues from rat CGRP, had less potent inhibitory activity than rat CGRP (49).

Intravenous and CSF injections of rat CGRP were equipotent inhibitors of gastric acid secretion in the rat and dog (112, 118). However, several pieces of evidence demonstrate that the effect of CSF injection is via a CNS action and not due to leakage of the peptide into the circulation. CGRP antiserum injected intravenously prevented the inhibitory effect of intravenous but not of intracerebroventricular injection of CGRP in rats (52). CGRP-like immunoreactivity was not detected in dog plasma following injection of peptide into the third ventricle at an antisecretory dose (49). Microinjection of the peptide into specific brain nuclei mimicked the effects of CSF injection (112). CGRP-responsive sites have been localized in the lateral hypothalamus, although further studies are required to further establish their precise distribution in the forebrain and the hindbrain (112).

In the rat, the inhibitory effect of central injection of CGRP is not expressed by alteration of gastrin release (112) or changes in gastric mucosal blood flow (3, 51). CSF injection of CGRP selectively stimulated the noradrenergic sympathetic outflow (22). However, blockade of noradrenergic pathways with guanethidine or bretylium tozylate alone or in combination with adrenalectomy did not alter the inhibitory effect of CGRP (51, 112). Vagotomy reversed CGRP action, which suggests an inhibitory effect mediated by vagus-dependent mechanisms (51, 112). The mechanisms underlying the inhibitory effect of CSF injection in dogs are unknown. Chlorisondamine, vagotomy, naloxone, and vasopressin antagonist do not alter the inhibition of gastric acid secretion (49, 50) induced by CGRP injected into the CSF. Moreover, the gastrin response to a meal was not altered despite the suppression of the gastric acid secretory response (49, 50).

CGRP-like immunoreactivity and receptors have been localized in specific brain nuclei regulating visceral function (87, 93, 96). The role of CGRP in the central regulation of gastric secretion is yet to be established.

## Corticotropin Releasing Factor

Injection of corticotropin releasing factor (CRF) into the CSF inhibited gastric acid secretion stimulated by pylorus ligation, pentagastrin, intracisternal TRH, 2-deoxy-D-glucose, or a meal but not by histamine in rats and dogs (48, 49, 107, 111). Rat and ovine CRF were found to be equipotent but less potent that bombesin, CGRP, or calcitonin (47, 49, 111). CSF injection of non-mammalian CRF-like peptides, such as sauvagine or urotensin I, also inhibited gastric acid secretion stimulated by pentagastrin in the dog and were twice as effective as rat or human CRF.

Although intravenous injection of CRF also inhibited gastric secretion (106), the effect observed upon CSF injection is mediated through the CNS. This was demonstrated by the lack of CRF-immunoreactivity in the circulation following CRF injection into the third ventricle in the dog (49) and by mapping studies of the site of action in the hypothalamus (29, 107). Responsive sites were found in the lateral and ventromedial hypothalamus and the paraventricular nucleus (29, 107). Interestingly, the inhibition of gastric acid output induced by hypothalamic microinjection of CRF is associated with a decrease in the concentration of acid but an increase in the secretory volume (29). No other centrally acting inhibitory peptide enhanced the volume of gastric acid secretion. Extrahypothalamic responsive sites have not been investigated, except the dorsomedial frontal cortex and the caudate putamen, which were found to be inactive (29, 107).

CRF acts centrally to stimulate adrenergic and noradrenergic sympathetic outflow (7). Its effect on the parasympathetic nervous system has not been directly assessed, although a decrease in cardiac parasympathetic outflow has been suggested (21). Adrenalectomy, vagotomy, and cervical cord transection in the rat and ganglionic blockade in the dog prevented the inhibition of gastric secretion induced by injection of CRF into the CSF (49, 107, 111). In the rat, CRF action has also been shown to be independent of prostaglandin synthetic pathways, changes in gastrin release and pituitary hormone secretion, and opioid receptor interaction (107, 111). By contrast, in the dog vagotomy had no effect, and blockade of opioid receptors by naloxone or the vasopressin antagonist [1- ($\beta$-mercapto, $\beta,\beta$-dimethylpropionic acid)-2-($O$-methyltyrosin)]-Arg[8]-vasopressin partly prevented the inhibitory effect of central CRF (48). Taken together these data indicate that in the rat, CRF acts mostly by altering the activity of both the sympathetic and parasympathetic nervous system. In the dog, CRF action is not vagus dependent and may involve the activation of the sympathetic outflow and opioid and vasopressin dependent mechanisms.

A physiological role for central CRF has been substantiated by the finding that the CRF antagonist, $\alpha$-helical CRF 9-41 blocks part of the endocrine, behavioral, and autonomic responses to stress and by the topographical distribution of CRF-stained pathways in the forebrain, medulla, and pons (8, 41, 81, 100). Recent studies also demonstrated that central CRF may mediate alterations of gastrointestinal transit time induced by stress (125). CSF injection of CRF mimicked the inhibitory effect of stress on gastric acid secretion in experimental animals (31, 64, 92, 123), and CRF antagonist prevented stress-induced alteration of gastric acid secretion (R. Stephens & Y. Taché, unpublished observations). These results suggest a possible role of brain CRF in regulating acid secretion under stress conditions.

## Opioid Peptides

$\beta$-ENDORPHIN    Intracerebroventricular or intracisternal injection of $\beta$-endorphin inhibited basal and TRH- or pylorus ligation–stimulated gastric secretion in conscious or anesthetized rats (49, 66, 89, 121). Peptide action is dose dependent with an $ED_{50}$ of 600 pmol (89). In conscious dogs, injection of $\beta$-endorphin into the 3rd ventricle suppressed pentagastrin, 2-deoxy-D-glucose and meal-stimulated gastric acid secretion but did not alter the gastric response to histamine (49). $\beta$-Endorphin was found less effective than bombesin, CRF, calcitonin or CGRP (49). Peptide inhibitory action is centrally mediated by an interaction with opiate receptors at brain sites which remain to be established (89). The fact that ganglionic blockade by chlorisondamine and vagotomy abolished the inhibitory effect of $\beta$-endorphin in rats and dogs suggest that peptide action is expressed by vagal-dependent mechanisms (49, 88).

ENKEPHALINS    Stable enkephalin analogues, such as (D-Ala$^2$)-Met-enkephalinamide, D-Ala-Met-enkephalin, and [D-Ala$^2$,$N$-Me-Phe$^4$,Met(O)$^5$-ol]-enkephalin, injected into the lateral cerebroventricle of rats also suppressed gastric acid secretion stimulated by vagal stimulants such as pylorus ligation, TRH, muscimol, or insulin (18, 55, 66, 68). Enkephalins injected into the CSF appear to be less potent than other classes of opioid peptides (103). The naturally occurring peptide, met-enkephalin, did not alter the gastric acid secretory response to pentagastrin when injected into the third brain ventricle in the dog (49). The inactivity of met-enkephalin may be related to its rapid degradation before reaching the site of action. Upon peripheral injection of the analogues, there is little or no inhibition of gastric acid secretion, which suggests that the effect observed after CSF injection is centrally mediated (18, 68). The brain sites and pathways involved in enkephalin action are still unknown but involve interaction with opioid receptors (18, 66, 68).

DYNORPHIN AND DERMORPHIN    The naturally occurring opioid peptide dynorphin A (1–13), injected intracisternally or intracerebroventricularly significantly reduced gastric acid secretion stimulated by pylorus ligation or TRH administration in rats (66, 122). Other related opioid peptides, such as the heptapeptide dermorphin, isolated from an amphibian skin extract, when injected into the CSF suppressed gastric acid secretion elicited by vagal stimulants, such as pylorus ligation, gastric distention, or insulin, but failed to antagonize histamine-induced secretion (36). Dermorphin action was very potent: 1 pmol injected into the lateral ventricle inhibited acid secretion induced by gastric distention by 50%, whereas the equiactive dose given subcutaneously is ten-thousand times greater (36). Naloxone reversed the inhibitory effect of dermorphin (36).

ROLE OF OPIOID PEPTIDES    Taken together these studies indicate that the activation of various types of brain opioid receptors inhibits vagal but not histamine stimulation of gastric acid secretion through vagus-dependent pathways. Opioid peptides do not appear to exert a central tonic inhibitory effect on gastric acid secretion, since blockade of brain opioid receptors by intracerebroventricular injection of naloxone did not modify gastric acid secretion in pylorus-ligated rats (66, 79). However, the role of opioid peptides in the regulation of gastric acid secretion needs to be further assessed using highly selective agonists and antagonists of $\mu$, $\delta$, and k opiate receptors microinjected into brain nuclei known to influence gastric secretion.

*Neurotensin*

Neurotensin was the first peptide reported by Osumi et al (73) to inhibit basal gastric secretion upon injection into the lateral ventricle in rats. However, these results were not confirmed by various investigators who injected the peptide into the CSF at similar or up to 30 times higher doses (33, 121). A recent study demonstrated that a 35-nmol dose of neurotensin injected into the lateral ventricle inhibited pentagastrin-stimulated gastric acid secretion in the rat (131). In the dog, CSF injection of neurotensin was found to be a weak inhibitor as compared with other peptides (49). The high concentrations of the peptide required to observe an inhibitory effect and the absence of a control study to evaluate a possible peripheral site of action after leakage of the peptide from the CSF preclude any conclusions based on the available data.

## CONCLUSIONS

Convergent information has clearly established that TRH and TRH analogues act in the dorsal motor nucleus of the vagus to stimulate parasympathetic outflow to the stomach and gastric acid secretion in the rat and rabbit (116). Less information and/or reproducible data have been reported regarding the stimulatory effect of central injection of cholecystokinin, gastrin, somatostatin, and oxytocin. None of the peptides tested so far have been able to stimulate basal gastric secretion in the dog after intracerebroventricular injection (49). To what extent the discrepancy is related to species differences or inactivation of the peptide before reaching the site of action in the dog brain needs to be further investigated. The role of medullary TRH or oxytocin in the cephalic phase of gastric acid secretion also needs to be established.

Bombesin and bombesinlike peptides, calcitonin, CGRP, CRF, and opioid peptides act in the brain to inhibit gastric acid secretion in both rats and dogs. Bombesin and CGRP act in the brain to inhibit gastric acid secretion elicited by vagal stimulants, pentagastrin, histamine, and bethanechol, whereas the central inhibitory effect of calcitonin, CRF, and opioid peptides is selective for vagal stimulants and pentagastrin (24, 36, 48, 51, 107, 110, 112).

The demonstrated central stimulation or inhibition of gastric acid secretion by specific neuropeptides has several implications. It raises the possibility that these peptides and their receptors localized in the brain nucleus regulating gastric function may play a role in mediating the gastric response to centrally acting stimuli, such as the thought, sight, smell, taste, conditioned anticipation of food, gastric distention, hypoglycemia, or stress (103). So far, the assessment of the physiological significance of the central action of these peptides has been hampered by the lack of specific antagonists for bombesin, calcitonin, CGRP, TRH, and somatostatin. However, preliminary evidence using central injection of TRH antibody and oxytocin or CRF antagonist suggests that endogenous medullary TRH may play a role in the vagovagal stimulation of gastric acid secretion, that oxytocin may be involved in the descending communication from the paraventricular nucleus to neurons in the dorsal motor nucleus that regulate gastric secretion, and that central CRF may contribute to the gastric response to stress (32, 86).

The peptides acting in the brain to influence gastric acid secretion provide an alternative chemical approach to study brain-stomach interactions that is more sensitive, selective, and consistent than electrical ablation or stimulation of brain nuclei (103). Through their use, information can be derived on central sites, pathways, and peripheral neurohumoral mechanisms involved in gastric secretory regulation. For instance, the direction of the gastric secretory response elicited by microinjection of active peptides into a specific brain nuclei is not related to the site of injection but to the type of receptors activated in the nucleus. In rats, microinjection into the lateral hypothalamus of TRH (57) or pentagastrin (124) stimulates gastric acid secretion, whereas that of CRF (107), CGRP (112), or calcitonin (57) inhibits gastric acid secretion. Dorsal motor nucleus injection of TRH (72, 83) or oxytocin (83) stimulates secretion, whereas that of bombesin (38) inhibits secretion. The stimulation or inhibition of gastric secretion mediated by the CNS is not secondary to changes in gastrin secretion. All the stimulatory peptides act by activation of vagal efferent pathways, whereas the mechanisms of action of the inhibitors appears more complex and is well less understood.

Further research on the role of brain peptides in gastric acid secretion should provide new insights in the understanding of underlying pathways and mechanisms involved in brain-stomach interactions and the etiology of gastric ulcers, since the same peptides exert potent effects mediated by the CNS to prevent or stimulate experimental ulcer formation (104).

ACKNOWLEDGMENTS

The author's work cited here was supported by the National Institute of Arthritis, Metabolism and Digestive Disease, Grants AM30110, AM33061, and AM17238. The author thanks Dr. H. Raybould for valuable comments on the manuscript.

## Literature Cited

1. Arancibia, S., Tapia-Arancibia, L., Assenmacher, I., Astier, H. 1983. Direct evidence of short-term cold-induced TRH release in the median eminence of unanesthetized rats. *Neuroendocrinology* 37:225–28
2. Aronchick, C., Feng, H.-S., Brooks, F. P., Chey, W. Y. 1983. Bombesin in the 4th ventricle of cats inhibits vagally stimulated antral contractions and acid secretion. *Gastroenteroloy* 84:1093 (Abstr.)
3. Bauerfeind, P., Cucala, M., Hof, R. P., Emde, C., Hof, A., et al. 1987. Calcitonin gene–related peptide mediates CNS regulation of gastric secretion and blood flow. *Gastroenterology* 92:1311 (Abstr.)
4. Beaumont, W. 1833. *Experiments and Observations on the Gastric Juice and the Physiology of Digestion*, ed. W. Osler, pp. 1–280. New York: Dover
5. Brooks, F. P. 1967. Central neural control of acid secretion. In *Handbook of*

*Physiology*, Sect. 6: *The Alimentary Canal*, ed. C. F. Code, pp. 805–26. Washington, DC: Am. Physiol. Soc.

6. Brown, M. R. 1983. Central nervous system sites of action of bombesin and somatostatin to influence plasma epinephrine levels. *Brain Res.* 276:253–57

7. Brown, M. R., Fisher, L. A., Webb, V., Vale, W. W., Rivier, J. E. 1985. Corticotropin-releasing factor: A physiologic regulator of adrenal epinephrine secretion. *Brain Res.* 328:355–57

8. Brown, M. R., Gray, T. S., Fisher, L. A. 1986. Corticotropin-releasing factor receptor antagonist: Effects on the autonomic nervous system and cardiovascular function. *Regul. Peptides* 16:321–29

9. Brown, M., Rivier, J., Vale, W. 1977. Somatostatin: Central nervous system (CNS) action on glucoregulation. *Metabolism* 27 (Suppl. 1):1253–56

10. Brown, M., Taché, Y., Fisher, D. 1979. Central nervous system action of bombesin: Mechanism to induce hyperglycemia. *Endocrinology* 105:660–65

11. Bueno, L., Fioramonti, J., Ferre, J. P. 1983. Calcitonin-CNS action to control the pattern of intestinal motility in rats. *Peptides* 4:63–66

12. Burks, T. F., Galligan, J. J., Porreca, F., Barber, W. D. 1985. Regulation of gastric emptying. *Fed. Proc.* 44:2897–2901

13. Cowan, A., Khunamwat, P., Zu Zhu, X., Gmerek, D. E. 1985. Effects of bombesin on behavior. *Life Sci.* 37:135–45

14. Dekin, M. S., Richerson, G. B., Getting, P. A. 1985. Thyrotropin-releasing hormone induces rhythmic bursting in neurons of the nucleus tractus solitarius. *Science* 229:67–69

15. Diz, D. I., Barnes, K. L., Ferrario, C. M. 1987. Functional characteristics of neuropeptides in the dorsal medulla oblongata and vagus nerve. *Fed. Proc.* 46:30–35

16. Dockray, G. J., Gregory, R. A., Hutchison, J. B., Harris, J. I., Runswick, M. J. 1978. Isolation, structure and biological activity of two cholecystokinin octapeptides from sheep brain. *Nature* 274:711–13

17. Feldman, M., Richardson, C. T. 1986. Role of thought, sight, smell and taste of food in the cephalic phase of gastric acid secretion in humans. *Gastroenterology* 90:426–33

18. Ferri, S., Arrigo-Reina, R., Candeletti, S., Costa, G., Murari, G., et al. 1983. Central and peripheral sites of action for the protective effect of opioids of the rat stomach. *Pharmacol. Res. Commun.* 15:409–18

19. Fischer, J. A., Sagar, S. M., Martin, J. B. 1981. Characterization and regional distribution of calcitonin binding sites in the rat brain. *Life Sci.* 29:663–71

20. Fischer, J. A., Tobler, P. H., Henke, H., Tschopp, F. A. 1983. Salmon and human calcitonin-like peptides coexist in the human thyroid and brain. *J. Clin. Endocrinol. Metab.* 57:1314–16

21. Fisher, L. A., Brown, M. R. 1984. Corticotropin-releasing factor and angiotensin II: Comparison of CNS actions to influence neuroendocrine and cardiovascular function. *Brain Res.* 296:41–47

22. Fisher, L. A., Kikkawa, D. O., Rivier, J. E., Amara, S. G., Evans, R. M., et al. 1983. Stimulation of noradrenergic sympathetic outflow by calcitonin gene-related peptide. *Nature* 305:534–36

23. Goltzman, D., Mitchell, J. 1985. Interaction of calcitonin and calcitonin gene-related peptide at receptor sites in target tissues. *Science* 227:1343–46

24. Goto, Y., Hagiwara, H., Taché, Y. 1986. Calcitonin as a selective inhibitor of vagal-mediated gastric acid secretion in the rats. *Gastroenterology* 90:1343 (Abstr.)

25. Grijalva, C. V., Lindholm, E., Novin, D. 1980. Physiological and morphological changes in the gastrointestinal tract induced by hypothalamic intervention: An overview. *Brain Res. Bull.* 5:19–31

26. Guglietta, A., Strunk, C. L., Irons, B. J., Lazarus, L. H. 1985. Central neuromodulation of gastric acid secretion by bombesin-like peptides. *Peptides* 6 (Suppl. 3):75–81

27. Gunion, M. W., Taché, Y. 1987. Bombesin microinfusion into the paraventricular nucleus suppresses gastric acid secretion in the rat. *Brain. Res.* In press

28. Gunion, M. W., Taché, Y. 1987. Fore- and hindbrain mediation of gastric hypoacidity after intracerebral bombesin. *Am. J. Physiol.* 15:G675–84

29. Gunion, M. W., Taché, Y. 1987. Intrahypothalamic microinfusion of corticotropin-releasing factor inhibits gastric acid secretion but increases secretion volume in rats. 1987. *Brain Res.* 411:151–61

30. Hamel, D., Taché, Y. 1984. Intrathecal injection of bombesin and rat CRF inhibits gastric secretion in rats. *Soc. Neurosci.* 10:812 (Abstr.)

31. Hayase, M., Takeuchi, K. 1986. Gastric acid secretion and lesion formation in

rats under water-immersion stress. *Dig. Dis. Sci.* 31:166–71

32. Hernandez, D. E., Jennes, L., Emerick, S. G. 1987. Inhibition of gastric acid secretion by immunoneutralization of endogenous brain thyrotropin-releasing hormone. *Brain Res.* 401:381–84

33. Hernandez, D. E., Mason, G. A., Adcock, J. W., Orlando, R. C., Prange, A. J. Jr. 1987. Effect of hypophysectomy, adrenalectomy, pituitary hormone secretion and gastric acid secretion on neurotensin induced protection against stress gastric lesions. *Life Sci.* 40:973–82

34. Hughes, J. J., Gosnell, B. A., Morley, J. E., Levine, A. S., Krahn, D. D., Silvis, S. E. 1985. The localization and mechanism of the effect of calcitonin on gastric acid secretion in rats. *Gastroenterology* 88:1424 (Abstr.)

35. Hughes, J. J., Levine, A. S., Morley, J. E., Gosnell, B. A., Silvis, S. E. 1984. Intraventricular calcitonin gene–related peptide inhibits gastric acid secretion. *Peptides* 5:665–67

36. Improta, G., Broccardo, M., Lisi, A., Melchiorri, P., Munari, C. 1982. Neural regulation of gastric acid secretion in rats: Influence of dermorphin. *Regul. Peptides* 3:251–56

37. Ishikawa, T., Osumi, Y., Nakagawa, T. 1985. Cholecystokinin intracerebroventricularly applied stimulates gastric acid secretion. *Brain Res.* 333:197–99

38. Ishikawa, T., Taché, Y. 1987. Inhibition of TRH stimulated gastric secretion by bombesin microinjected into the dorsal vagal complex. *Soc. Neurosci.* 13:1281

39. Ishikawa, T., Taché, Y. 1987. Intrahypothalamic injection of salmon calcitonin prevents stress-induced ulceration in rats. *Gastroenterology* 92:1448 (Abstr.)

40. Kaznelson, H. 1907. Scheinfutterungsversuche am Erwachsenen Menschen. *Pflüg. Arch. Gesamte Physiol. Menschen Tiere* 118:327–52

41. Krahn, D. D., Gosnell, B. A., Grace, M., Levine, A. S. 1986. CRF antagonist partially reverses CRF- and stress-induced effects on feeding. *Brain Res. Bull.* 17:285–89

42. Krieger, D. T. 1983. Brain peptides: What, where, and why. *Science* 222:975–85

43. Kubek, M. J., Rea, M. A., Hodes, Z. I., Aprison, M. H. 1983. Quantitation and characterization of thyrotropin-releasing hormone in vagal nuclei and other regions of the medulla oblongata of the rat. *J. Neurochem.* 40:1307–13

44. Lang, R. E., Heil, J., Ganten, D., Hermann, K., Rascher, W., Unger, Th. 1983. Effects of lesions in the paraventricular nucleus of the hypothalamus on vasopressin and oxytocin contents in brainstem and spinal cord of rat. *Brain Res.* 260:326–29

45. Laughton, W. B., Powley, T. L. 1987. Localization of efferent function in the dorsal motor nucleus of the vagus. *Am. J. Physiol.* 252:R13–R25

46. Lenz, H. J., Brown, M. R. 1987. Intracerebroventricular administration of human calcitonin, an human calcitonin gene–related peptide, inhibits meal-stimulated gastric acid secretion in the dog. *Dig. Dis. Sci.* 32:409–16

47. Lenz, H. J., Forquignon, I., Druge, G., Friemel, E., Rivier, J. E., et al. 1987. Central nervous system effects of hypothalamic peptides on gastric acid and proximal duodenal bicarbonate secretion in rats. *Gastroenterology* 92:1501 (Abstr.)

48. Lenz, H. J., Hester, S. E., Brown, M. R. 1985. Corticotropin-releasing factor. Mechanisms to inhibit gastric acid secretion in conscious dogs. *J. Clin. Invest.* 75:889–95

49. Lenz, H. J., Hester, S. E., Klapdor, R., Hestor, S. E., Webb, V. J., et al. 1986. Inhibition of gastric acid secretion by brain peptides in the dog: Role of the autonomic nervous system and gastrin. *Gastroenterology* 91:905–12

50. Lenz, H. J., Hester, S. E., Saik, R. P., Brown, M. R. 1986. CNS actions of calcitonin gene-related peptide on gastric acid secretion in conscious dogs. *Am. J. Physiol.* 250:G742–48

51. Lenz, H. J., Mortrud, M. T., Rivier, J. E., Brown, M. R. 1985. Central nervous system actions of calcitonin gene-related peptide on gastric acid secretion in the rat. *Gastroenterology* 88:539–44

52. Lenz, H. J., Mortrud, M. T., Vale, W. W., Rivier, J. E., Brown, M. R. 1984. Calcitonin gene–related peptide acts within the central nervous system to inhibit gastric acid secretion. *Regul. Peptides* 9:271–77

53. Lenz, H. J., Rivier, J. E., Brown, M. R. 1985. Biological actions of human and rat calcitonin and calcitonin gene-related peptide. *Regul. Peptides* 12:81–89

54. Levine, A. S., Hughes, J. J., Morley, J. E., Gosnell, B. A., Silvis, S. E. 1984. Calcitonin as a regulator of gastric acid secretion. *Psychopharmacol. Bull.* 20:459–62

55. Levine, A. S., Morley, J. E., Kneip, J., Grace, M., Silvis, S. E. 1981. Musci-

mol induces gastric acid secretion after central administration. *Brain Res.* 229:270–74

56. Maeda-Hagiwara, M., Watanabe, H. 1985. Intracerebroventricular injection of a TRH analogue, γ-butyrolactone-γ-carbonyl-L-histidyl-prolinamide, induces gastric lesions and gastric acid stimulation in rats. *Naunyn-Schmiedeberg's Arch. Pharmacol.* 330:142–46

57. Maeda-Hagiwara, M., Watanabe, H. 1985. Inhibitory effects of intrahypothalamic injection of calcitonin on TRH-stimulated gastric acid secretion in rats. *Jpn. J. Pharmacol.* 39:173–78

58. Maeda-Hagiwara, M., Watanabe, H., Watanabe, K. 1983. Enhancement by intracerebroventricular thyrotropin-releasing hormone of indomethacin-induced gastric lesions in the rat. *Br. J. Pharmacol.* 80:735–39

59. Maeda-Hagiwara, M., Watanabe, H., Watanabe, K. 1984. Inhibition by central alpha-2 adrenergic mechanism of thyrotropin-releasing hormone-induced gastric acid secretion in the rat. *Jpn. J. Pharmacol.* 36:131–36

60. Maeda-Hagiwara, M., Watanabe, H., Watanabe, K. 1984. Thyrotropin-releasing hormone (TRH)-induced gastric acid secretion in aging rats. *Jpn. J. Pharmacol.* 36:425–26

61. Maeda-Hagiwara, M., Watanabe, K. 1983. Influence of dopamine receptor agonists on gastric acid secretion induced by intraventricular administration of thyrotropin-releasing hormone in the perfused stomach of anaesthetized rats. *Br. J. Pharmacol.* 79:297–303

62. Manaker, S., Ackerman, S. H., Weiner, H. 1979. Intracerebroventricular pentagastrin fails to affect feeding and acid secretion in the rat. *Physiol. Behav.* 23:395–96

63. Manaker, S., Winokur, A., Rostene, W. H., Rainbow, T. C. 1985. Autoradiographic localization of thyrotropin-releasing hormone receptors in the rat central nervous system. *J. Neurosci.* 5:167–74

64. Menguy, R. 1960. Effects of restraint stress on gastric secretion in the rat. *Dig. Dis.* 5:911–16

65. Moody, T. W., O'Donohue, T. L., Jacobowitz, D. M. 1981. Biochemical localization and characterization of bombesin-like peptides in discrete regions of rat brain. *Peptides* 2:75–79

66. Morley, J. E., Levine, A. S., Silvis, S. E. 1981. Endogenous opiates inhibit gastric acid secretion induced by central administration of thyrotropin-releasing hormone (TRH). *Life Sci.* 29:293–97

67. Morley, J. E., Levine, A. S., Silvis, S. E. 1981. Intraventricular calcitonin inhibits gastric acid secretion. *Science* 214:671–73

68. Morley, J. E., Levine, A. S., Silvis, S. E. 1982. Endogenous opiates and stress ulceration. *Life Sci.* 31:693–99

69. Mulvihill, S. J., Pappas, T. N., Debas, H. T. 1985. The effect of intracerebroventricular pressure on brain peptide action. *Gastroenterology* 88:1511 (Abstr.)

70. Okimura, Y., Chihara, K., Abe, H., Kaji, H., Kita, T., et al. 1986. Effect of intracerebroventricular administration of rat calcitonin gene-related peptide (CGRP), human calcitonin and [Asul,7]-eel calcitonin on gastric acid secretion in rats. *Endocrinol. Jpn.* 33:273–77

71. Okuma, Y., Osumi, Y. 1986. Central cholinergic descending pathway to the dorsal motor nucleus of the vagus in regulation of gastric functions. *Jpn. J. Pharmacol.* 41:373–79

72. Okuma, Y., Osumi, Y., Ishigawa, T., Mitsuma T. 1987. Enhancement of gastric acid output and mucosal blood flow by tripeptide thyrotropin releasing hormone microinjected into the dorsal motor nucleus of the vagus in rats. *Jpn. J. Pharmacol.* 43:173–78

73. Osumi, Y., Nagasaka, Y., Fu, W. L. H., Fujiwara, M. 1978. Inhibition of gastric acid secretion and mucosal blood flow induced by intraventricularly applied neurotensin in rats. *Life Sci.* 23:2275–80

74. Palkovits, M., Mezey, E., Eskay, R. L., Brownstein, M. J. 1986. Innervation of the nucleus of the solitary tract and the dorsal vagal nucleus by thyrotropin-releasing hormone-containing raphe neurons. *Brain Res.* 373:246–51

75. Panula, P., Yang, H.-Y., Costa, E. 1984. Comparative distribution of bombesin/GRP- and substance-P-like immunoreactivities in rat hypothalamus. *J. Comp. Neurol.* 224:606–17

76. Pappas, T., Hamel, D., Debas, H., Walsh, J. H., Taché, Y. 1985. Cerebroventricular bombesin inhibits gastric acid secretion in dogs. *Gastroenterology* 89:43–48

77. Pappas, T., Taché, Y., Debas, H. 1985. Cerebro-ventricular somatostatin stimulates gastric acid secretion in the dog. In *Regulatory Peptides in Digestive, Nervous and Endocrine Systems. INSERM Symp. 25*, ed. M. J. M. Lewin, S. Bonfils, pp. 323–27. Amsterdam: Elsevier Science.

78. Pavlov, I. 1910. *The Work of the Digestive Glands.* Transl. W. H. Thompson. London: Griffin From Russian

79. Puurunen, J. 1985. Role of putative neurotransmitters in the central gastric antisecretory effect of prostaglandin $E_2$ in rats. *Br. J. Pharmacol.* 85:213–21
80. Reubi, J. C., Perrin, M. H., Rivier, J. E., Vale, W. 1981. High affinity binding sites for a somatostatin-28 analog in rat brain. *Life Sci.* 28:2191–98
81. Rivier, J., Rivier, C., Vale, W. 1984. Synthetic competitive antagonists of corticotropin-releasing factor: Effect on ACTH secretion in the rat. *Science* 224:889–91
82. Robert, A., Lancaster, C., Kolbasa, K. P., Olafsson, A., Lunn, J. 1986. Cold sensitizes to ulcer formation by aspirin, but not to gastric injury by ethanol and taurocholate. *Gastroenterology* 90:1605 (Abstr.)
83. Rogers, R. C., Hermann, G. E. 1985. Dorsal medullary oxytocin, vasopressin, oxytocin antagonist, and TRH effects on gastric acid secretion and heart rate. *Peptides* 6:1143–48
84. Rogers, R. C., Hermann, G. E. 1985. Gastric-vagal solitary neurons excited by paraventricular nucleus microstimulation. *J. Auton. Nerv. Syst.* 14:351–62
85. Rogers, R. C., Hermann, G. E. 1985. Vagal afferent stimulation-evoked gastric secretion suppressed by paraventricular nucleus lesion. *J. Auton. Nerv. Syst.* 13:191–99
86. Rogers, R. C., Hermann, G. E. 1986. Hypothalamic paraventricular nucleus stimulation-induced gastric acid secretion and bradycardia suppressed by oxytocin antagonist. *Peptides* 7:695–700
87. Rosenfeld, M. G., Mermod, J.-J., Amara, S. G., Swanson, L. W., Sawchenko, P. E., et al. 1983. Production of a novel neuropeptide encoded by the calcitonin gene via tissue-specific RNA processing. *Nature* 304:129–35
88. Rozé, C., Dubrasquet, M., Chariot, J., Souchard, M., Vaille, C. 1980. Mécanismes de l'action centrale de la béta-endorphine sur les secretions gastrique et pancréatique chez le rat: Effet de la vagotomie. *Gastroenterol. Clin. Biol.* 4:1A (Abstr.)
89. Rozé, C., Dubrasquet, M., Chariot, J., Vaille, C. 1980. Central inhibition of basal pancreatic and gastric secretions by β-endorphin in rats. *Gastroenterology* 79:659–64
90. Sabbatini, F., Fimmel, C. J., Pace, F., Tobler, P. H., Hinder, R. A., et al. 1985. Distribution of intraventricular salmon calcitonin and suppression of gastric secretion. *Digestion* 32:273–81
91. Sanders, D. J., Perry, K. W., Zahedi-Asl, S., Marr, A. P. 1984. Cortical in-

jections of CCK8 stimulate gastric acid and pepsin secretions in the guinea pig possibly via the vagus. *Dig. Dis. Sci.* 29:73S (Abstr.)
92. Schwille, P. O., Engelhardt, W., Wolf, U., Hanisch, E. 1981. Infusion of somatostatin antiserum in the rat—failure to raise stress induced low gastric acid secretion. *Horm. Metab. Res.* 13:710–11
93. Seifert, H., Chesnut, J., De Souza, E., Rivier, J., Vale, W. 1985. Binding sites for calcitonin gene–related peptide in distinct areas of rat brain. *Brain Res.* 346:195–98
94. Shapiro, R. E., Miselis, R. R. 1985. The central organization of the vagus nerve innervating the stomach of the rat. *J. Comp. Neurol.* 238:473–88
95. Shiraishi, T. 1980. Effects of lateral hypothalamic stimulation on medulla oblongata and gastric vagal neural responses. *Brain Res. Bull.* 5:245–50
96. Skofitsch, G., Jacobowitz, D. M. 1985. Calcitonin gene-related peptide: Detailed immunohistochemical distribution in the central nervous system. *Peptides* 6:721–45
97. Somiya, H., Tonoue, T. 1984. Neuropeptides as central integrators of autonomic nerve activity: Effects of TRH, SRIF, VIP and bombesin on gastric and adrenal nerves. *Regul. Peptides* 9:47–52
98. Stephens, R. L., Ishikawa, T., Weiner, H., Novin, D., Taché, Y. 1987. TRH and TRH analog microinjected into the dorsal vagal complex stimulated gastric acid secretion in the rat. *Am. J. Physiol.* In press
99. Swanson, L. W., Sawchenko, P. E. 1983. Hypothalamic integration: Organization of the paraventricular and supraoptic nuclei. *Ann. Rev. Neurosci.* 6:269–324
100. Swanson, L. W., Sawchenko, P. E., Rivier, J., Vale, W. W. 1983. Organization of ovine corticotropin-releasing factor immunoreactive cells and fibers in the rat brain: An immunohistochemical study. *Neuroendocrinology* 36:165–86
101. Szirtes, T., Kisfaludy, L., Palosi, E., Szporny, L. 1984. Synthesis of thyrotropin-releasing hormone analogues. 1. Complete dissociation of central nervous system effect from thyrotropin-releasing activity. *J. Med. Chem.* 27:741–45
102. Taché, Y. 1985. Intracisternal bombesin induced inhibition of gastric secretion is not mediated through prostaglandin or opioid pathways. *Peptides* 6 (Suppl. 3):69–73

103. Taché, Y. 1987. Central regulation of gastric acid secretion. In *Physiology of the Gastrointestinal Tract*, ed. L. R. Johnson, J. Christensen, M. Jackson, E. D. Jacobson, J. H. Walsh, Ch. 30, pp. 911–30. New York: Raven. 2nd ed.

104. Taché, Y. 1987. The peptidergic brain-gut axis: Influence on gastric ulcer formation. *Chronobiol. Int.* 4:11–19

105. Taché, Y., Collu, R. 1982. CNS mediated inhibition of gastric secretion by bombesin: Independence from interaction with brain catecholaminergic, and serotoninergic pathways and pituitary hormones. *Regul. Peptides* 3:51–59

106. Taché, Y., Goto, Y., Gunion, M., Rivier, J., Debas, H. 1984. Inhibition of gastric acid secretion in rats and in dogs by corticotropin-releasing factor. *Gastroenterology* 86:281–86

107. Taché, Y., Goto, Y., Gunion, M. W., Vale, W., Rivier, J., Brown, M. 1983. Inhibition of gastric acid secretion in rats by intracerebral injection of corticotropin-releasing factor. *Science* 222:935–37

108. Taché, Y., Goto, Y., Hamel, D., Pekary, A., Novin, D. 1985. Mechanisms underlying intracisternal TRH-induced stimulation of gastric acid secretion in rats. *Regul. Peptides* 13:21–30

109. Taché, Y., Goto, Y., Lauffenburger, M., Lesiege, D. 1984. Potent central nervous system action of $p$-Glu-His-(3,3'-dimethyl)-Pro NH$_2$, a stabilized analog of TRH, to stimulate gastric secretion in rats. *Regul. Peptides* 8:71–78

110. Taché, Y., Gunion, M. 1985. Central nervous system action of bombesin to inhibit gastric acid secretion. *Life Sci.* 37:115–23

111. Taché, Y., Gunion, M. 1985. Corticotropin-releasing factor: Central action to influence gastric secretion. *Fed. Proc.* 44:255–58

112. Taché, Y., Gunion, M., Lauffenburger, M., Goto, Y. 1984. Inhibition of gastric acid secretion by intracerebral injection of calcitonin gene related peptide in rats. *Life Sci.* 35:871–78

113. Taché, Y., Kolve, E., Maeda-Hagiwara, M., Kauffman, G. 1987. CNS action of calcitonin to alter experimental gastric ulcers in rats. *Gastroenterology* 93

114. Taché, Y., Lesiege, D., Goto, Y. 1986. Neural pathways involved in intracisternal bombesin-induced inhibition of gastric secretion in rats. *Dig. Dis. Sci.* 31:412–17

115. Taché, Y., Lesiege, D., Vale, W., Collu, R. 1985. Gastric hypersecretion by intracisternal TRH: Dissociation from hypophysiotropic activity and role of central catecholamine. *Eur. J. Pharmacol.* 107:149–55

116. Taché, Y., Maeda-Hagiwara, M., Goto, Y., Garrick, T. 1987. Central nervous system action of TRH to stimulate gastric function and ulceration. *Peptides* 8:Suppl. 1

117. Taché, Y., Marki, W., Rivier, J., Vale, W., Brown, M. 1981. Central nervous system inhibition of gastric secretion in the rat by gastrin-releasing peptide, a mammalian bombesin. *Gastroenterology* 81:298–302

118. Taché, Y., Pappas, T., Lauffenburger, M., Goto, Y., Walsh, J. H., Debas, H. 1984. Calcitonin gene-related peptide: Potent peripheral inhibitor of gastric acid secretion in rats and dogs. *Gastroenterology* 87:344–49

119. Taché, Y., Rivier, J., Vale, W., Brown, M. 1981. Is somatostatin or a somatostatin-like peptide involved in central nervous system control of gastric secretion? *Regul. Peptides* 1:307–15

120. Taché, Y., Vale, W., Brown, M. 1980. Thyrotropin-releasing hormone-CNS action to stimulate gastric acid secretion. *Nature* 287:149–51

121. Taché, Y., Vale, W., Rivier, J., Brown, M. 1980. Brain regulation of gastric secretion: Influence of neuropeptides. *Proc. Natl. Acad. Sci. USA* 77:5515–59

122. Taché, Y., Vale, W., Rivier, J., Brown, M. 1981. Brain regulation of gastric acid secretion in rats by neurogastrointestinal peptides. *Peptides* 2 (Suppl. 2):51–55

123. Takeuchi, K., Furukawa, O., Okabe, S. 1986. Induction of duodenal ulcers in rats under water-immersion stress conditions. Influence of stress on gastric acid and duodenal alkaline secretion. *Gastroenterology* 91:554–63

124. Tepperman, B. L., Evered, M. D. 1980. Gastrin injected into the lateral hypothalamus stimulates secretion of gastric acid in rats. *Science* 209:1142–43

125. Williams, C. L., Peterson, J. M., Villar, R. G., Burks, T. F. 1987. Corticotropin-releasing factor (CRF) directly mediates colonic responses to stress. *Am. J. Physiol.* In press

126. Witty, R. T., Long, J. F. 1970. Effect of ambient temperature on gastric secretion and food intake in the rat. *Am. J. Physiol.* 219:1359–62

127. Yachnis, A. T., Crawley, J. N., Jensen, R. T., McGrane, M. M., Moody, T. W. 1984. The antagonism of bombesin in the CNS by substance P analogues. *Life Sci.* 35:1963–69

128. Yarbrough, G. G. 1979. On the neuro-pharmacology of thyrotropin releasing hormone (TRH). *Prog. Neurobiol.* 12:291–312

129. Zadina, J. E., Banks, W. A., Kastin, A. J. 1986. Central nervous system effects of peptides, 1980–1985: A cross-listing of peptides and their central actions from the first six years of the journal peptides. *Peptides* 7:497–537

130. Zarbin, M. A., Kuhar, M. J., O'Dono-hue, T. L., Wolf, S. S., Moody, T. W. 1985. Autoradiographic localization of ($^{125}$I-Tyr$^4$) bombesin-binding sites in rat brain. *J. Neurosci.* 5:429–37

131. Zhang, L., Washington, J., Kauffman, G. 1987. Central neurotensin (NT) in-hibit carbachol (CARB), 2deoxy-D-glucose (2DG), and pentagastrin (G5), but not histamine (HIST) stimulated acid secretion in rat. *Gastroenterology* 92: 1709 (Abstr.)

*Ann. Rev. Physiol. 1988. 50:41–63*

# PEPTIDES AS REGULATORS OF GASTRIC ACID SECRETION[1]

## John H. Walsh

Center for Ulcer Research and Education, Veterans Administration Wadsworth Medical Center, University of California, Los Angeles, California 90073

## Introduction

Many factors lead to stimulation or inhibition of gastric acid secretion. This review emphasizes peptide mediators that act outside the central nervous system to influence gastric secretion. The principal mediators include a hormone, gastrin, a potential paracrine peptide, somatostatin, and several neuropeptides. Several other peptides are considered to be potential acid-inhibiting hormones, or enterogastrones. These mediators interact extensively with local neurotransmitters, especially acetylcholine and norepinephrine. Another nonpeptide produced in the gastric mucosa and essential for normal acid secretory function is histamine. Neuropeptides and transmitters that act on the central nervous system also regulate gastric secretion. This review focuses on the role of gastrin as a stimulatory hormone, regulation of gastrin synthesis and release, and inhibitory effects of somatostatin and other peptides on acid secretion and gastrin release.

Physiological conditions that lead to stimulation of acid secretion are classically divided into cephalic, gastric, and intestinal phases.

## Cephalic Phase

POTENTIAL MEDIATORS    Central nervous system mediators of the cephalic phase of gastric acid secretion are unknown. Peripheral mediation appears to be largely by vagal, muscarinic cholinergic nerves (27, 168). The stimulus to cephalic activation of gastric secretion can be as subtle as discussion of appetizing food, which is a stronger stimulant than the sight and smell of food but is weaker than sham feeding (esophageal fistula) (42). Modified sham feeding in man produces acid responses equal to those achieved with true

---

sham feeding, but the maximal response is ~50% of the maximal response to pentagastrin (168). Potential central activators of vagal outflow include thyrotropin releasing hormone (56), somatostatin (134), and GABA (55).

ROLE OF GASTRIN    Sham feeding causes release of small amounts of gastrin in man and dogs; these amounts are much smaller than those released in response to protein meals (119). The increase in gastrin in response to sham feeding does not seem to be responsible for a major part of the acid response. However, gastric acid responses to sham feeding in man were decreased after resection of the antrum and duodenal bulb had abolished the gastrin response to sham feeding (87). The gastrin responses can be inhibited by antral denervation (17) or by acidification of the gastric lumen (27, 86) without much effect on the acid response to sham feeding. Very large doses of atropine also prevent the gastrin response to sham feeding in dogs (129).

ROLE OF MUSCARINIC CHOLINERGIC NERVES    The effects of atropine upon gastrin release produced by sham feeding in man are unexpected. A small dose of atropine, 2.3 $\mu$g/kg of body weight (BW), enhanced the gastrin response to sham feeding and prevented the expected inhibition by antral acidification (47). The same dose of atropine prevents release of pancreatic polypeptide by sham feeding (44). Increased doses of atropine cause progressively decreased acid responses, and there are no further changes in hormone responses. Plasma somatostatin is not measurably altered by atrophine (46). Benzilonium, an anticholinergic with minimal central nervous system effects, produces similar enhancement of gastrin responses to sham feeding (170). The gastrin rise can be inhibited by pretreatment with a nonsedative neuroleptic agent, sulpiride (97).

CONTRIBUTION TO TOTAL ACID RESPONSE TO A MEAL    Sham feeding also enhances the acid secretory response to food in the stomach. Cephalic and gastric phase stimulation contribute equally to acid secretion during the first half hour after a meal in man; subsequently, the cephalic component decreases to about one third of the total (145). Pepsin responses to a liquid protein meal are similarly enhanced by sham feeding (52). Thus it appears that cephalic stimulation is an important component of the combined gastric acid secretory response to a meal. Release of acetylcholine appears to be the major stimulatory mechanism, although the small amounts of gastrin released may also contribute.

HYPOGLYCEMIC AND ADRENERGIC STIMULATION OF GASTRIN RELEASE    Insulin-induced hypoglycemia is an established, although nonphysiological, method for inducing "cephalic" stimulation of acid secretion and gastrin release (27). As with sham feeding, simple cholinergic stimulation cannot explain both responses. Atropine increases the gastrin response to insulin hypoglycemia in man, while inhibiting acid secretion (40, 153). Hypoglycemia leads to increased plasma epinephrine concentrations that are sufficient to account for a major portion of the gastrin response (15, 62, 143). Propranolol markedly inhibits the gastrin response to hypoglycemia and partially prevents the acid response (23, 79, 96). Propranolol has little effect on gastric responses to sham feeding (57), but it inhibits gastrin responses to extreme exercise (15) and antagonizes the hypergastrinemia associated with hyperthyroidism (159).

EFFECTS OF VAGOTOMY    Vagotomy leads to increased basal plasma gastrin concentrations, but markedly decreases the cephalic phase release of gastrin that is mediated largely through vagal pathways. Vagotomy either does not affect or enhances food-stimulated gastrin response. Vagotomy combined with antrectomy leads to decreased basal and stimulated plasma gastrin concentrations (179). Truncal vagotomy decreases gastrin responses to cephalic stimulation and to insulin hypoglycemia. Proximal gastric vagotomy enhances gastrin responses to vagal stimulation (63, 64). Antral vagotomy abolishes the plasma gastrin response to insulin, while proximal gastric vagotomy increases basal and food-stimulated gastrin release in dogs (29). These findings suggest that vagal stimulation of gastrin release is mediated by direct activation of antral vagal fibers and that vagal inhibition is mediated by a mechanism located in the acid-secreting portion of the stomach.

More than one mechanism appears to be involved in production of post-vagotomy hypergastrinemia. Gastrin cell hyperplasia is a late effect (53). Prolonged reduction of acid secretion may be partially explain the response. Reduced peak acid output in man after vagotomy is associated with decreased parietal cell sensitivity to gastrin, so hypergastrinemia could be a compensatory phenomenon (13). The onset of hypergastrinemia in dogs occurs within 24 hr and is too rapid to be explained by an increase in gastrin cells (68).

## Gastric Phase

EFFECTS OF GASTRIC DISTENTION    Gastric distention generally increases acid secretion and gastrin release. Under some circumstances distention inhibits stimulated acid secretion. In humans with intact stomachs, distention of the proximal stomach with a balloon increases acid secretion (58). In contrast, balloon distention of the antrum inhibits pentagastrin-stimulated acid secretion in man (152). Distention with liquid stimulates acid secretion without causing much change in serum gastrin (163). The effects of distention may be mediated by reflexes rather than by hormone release. In dogs there is evidence for the existence of a stimulatory pyloro-oxyntic reflex that is independent of gastrin release (30).

Prior administration of atropine in humans markedly increases the gastrin response to gastric distention with liquids. This increased response is not inhibited by low pH in the gastric lumen (150). The gastrin response that is enhanced by atropine is markedly inhibited by $\beta$-adrenergic inhibition caused by propranolol (137). In dogs there is evidence for a pH-sensitive reflex from the acid-secreting part of the stomach to the antrum causing gastrin release, known as the oxyntopyloric reflex (31).

GASTRIC PHASE STIMULATION BY NUTRIENTS    Intragastric titration makes possible the measurement of gastric acid secretion when liquid or semisolid food is present in the stomach (51). This method also permits simultaneous measurement of gastric emptying rates. An alternative method for measurement of gastric acid secretion and emptying is the serial dilution indicator method. The two methods produce similar results (67). Intragastric titration involves distention of the stomach with a test meal. The effects of distention alone can be studied by use of a liquid nonnutrient test meal such as isotonic sodium chloride or mannitol. Satisfactory stimulation of distention reflexes can be achieved by use of a 5% glucose meal (115). This concentration of glucose does not inhibit gastric secretion but delays gastric emptying. In addition, the glucose is completely absorbed in the intestine and does not cause diarrhea.

Distention alone increases gastric acid secretion two- to threefold over basal rates. Amino acids and digested protein, but not intact albumin, stimulate acid secretion up to about two thirds of the maximal rate achieved with pentagastrin stimulation (115, 146). The higher response to these nutrients than to distention alone represents chemical stimulation. Glucose and saline distention produce similar rates of acid secretion. Fat inhibits acid secretion. Amino acids and digested protein cause release of gastrin. Lowering the intragastric pH from 5.5 to 2.5 decreases markedly both the gastrin and the acid response to amino acids (178). Lowering of the intragastric pH when whole protein is present leads to generation of new buffer by pepsin digestion and could artifactually lead to underestimation of acid secretion rates. The most likely mediator of the chemical gastric phase of gastric acid secretion is the hormone gastrin.

STIMULANTS OF GASTRIN RELEASE    Potent intragastric stimulants of acid secretion act largely by stimulating release of gastrin. In dogs, cysteine, phenylalanine, and tryptophan were the most potent individual amino acids for stimulation of gastrin release (172). In man, tryptophan and phenylalanine were the best stimulants of gastrin release and acid secretion, but cysteine was ineffective (176). Milk is a good stimulant of gastrin and acid secretion in man (74). Other commonly ingested beverages such as cola drinks, beer, coffee, and tea are good stimulants of acid secretion independent of their amino acid, caffeine, or calcium content (120). Decaffeinated coffee is a strong stimulant of acid secretion and gastrin release (41). Caffeine itself is a weaker stimulant and does not cause gastrin release (192). Wine is a strong stimulant of gastrin release and acid secretion, while whiskey and pure alcohol do not stimulate gastrin release in man and have only minor effects on acid secretion (103, 139). Oral calcium carbonate also stimulates gastrin release and acid secretion in man (106).

pH DEPENDENCE OF GASTRIN RELEASE    Gastrin release stimulated by amino acids is progressively diminished as intraluminal pH falls below 4 and is markedly reduced when the pH reaches 2.5 (178). At pH 1.5 or 1.0, gastrin release by peptone is completely abolished (66, 89). Alkalinization of the gastric contents permits gastrin release by other agents. Short-term neutralization or alkalinization does not cause gastrin release in man, but prolonged neutralization for 5 hr or more does lead to gastrin release (136). It is not known whether changes in luminal pH are mediated by direct action on the antral gastrin cell or indirectly by altering the activity of other cells such as somatostatin cells or mucosal neurons.

CHOLINERGIC MODULATION OF FOOD-STIMULATED GASTRIN RELEASE
The release of gastrin stimulated by food is not mediated by muscarinic nerves and is not inhibited by most anticholinergic agents. Atropine enhances the total gastrin response to a meal in man if intragastric pH is not controlled (186). The mechanism probably involves increased intragastric pH and delayed gastric emptying of the meal. When intragastric pH is maintained at pH 5, atropine inhibits acid secretion without affecting gastrin release (88). Atropine has no effect on basal serum gastrin secretion in normal man but may cause a modest increase in patients with duodenal ulcer (153). Very low doses of atropine partially inhibit the gastrin secretion in response to amino acids in man, but moderately higher doses have no effect (151). Low doses of atropine may enhance gastrin secretion in response to food in dogs (71). Other ordinary anticholinergic agents have little effect on this response in man if intragastric pH is maintained constant (11, 43). However, the $M_1$ muscarinic antagonist pirenzipine may decrease the amount of gastrin released in response to a meal (175). The results obtained with anticholinergic agents suggest that the actions of cholinergic nerves on food-stimulated gastrin release are complex and indirect.

EFFECTS OF OTHER ANTISECRETORY AGENTS ON GASTRIN RELEASE    Prolonged and complete inhibition of gastric acid secretion leads to hypergastrinemia associated with antral gastrin cell hyperplasia. This effect has been demonstrated most clearly during prolonged administration of long-acting, highly potent inhibitors of the gastric H,K-ATPase, such as omeprazole or RP 40749 (50, 128). The effects of antisecretory drugs on gastrin production probably depend on the degree and duration of hypochlorhydria. Doses of omeprazole that produce marked but incomplete inhibition of acid secretion have lesser effects on serum gastrin levels (127). Basal serum gastrin concentrations can be elevated by large repeated doses of histamine $H_2$ receptor blockers, but hypergastrinemia is minimized by the shorter biological half-life of these agents. These agents also increase postprandial gastrin secretion if intragastric pH is uncontrolled (30).

When intragastric pH is controlled, neither cimetidine nor histamine alters gastrin secretion in response to amino acids (144). Cimetidine prevents stimulation of gastrin release by aluminum and magnesium antacids, possibly be preventing generation of ionic magnesium and aluminum (140). In dogs cimetidine also prevents the inhibition of bombesin-stimulated gastrin release caused by histamine (84).

One class of compounds that inhibit both acid secretion and gastrin release is the prostaglandin $E_2$ substituted analogs. The 16,16-dimethyl and 15(R),15-dimethyl prostaglandin analogs inhibit food-stimulated gastrin release (73), but no effect is found on gastrin released from tumors (72). A newly synthesized prostaglandin, enprostil, also is an effective inhibitor of gastrin release (164). Prostaglandin $E_1$ compounds have little or no effect on gastrin release (8).

STRUCTURE OF THE GASTRIN PRECURSOR    The structure of the gastrin precursor has been established precisely by analysis of the full length cDNA that codes for the porcine preprogastrin molecule (193). The human precursor structure is similar (14, 80). Human preprogastrin contains 101 amino acid residues. The porcine precursor contains 104 residues. The 34–amino acid sequence that comprises the most abundant form of gastrin (G34) found in the blood (25) is located near the carboxyl terminus of preprogastrin. Typical dibasic residues are located at the amino-terminal processing site, and the sequence Gly-Arg-Arg indicates the carboxyl-terminal amidation site. Beyond these residues are another nine amino acids in the porcine and six amino acids in the human precursor. Gastrin 17 (G17) is formed from the same precursor by processing at another dibasic amino acid region. The human gastrin gene contains three exons and two introns (75, 187). One of the introns is short and interrupts the gastrin sequence near the site at which gastrin 17 begins. The other is much longer and precedes the peptide initiation site. The entire gastrin gene contains about 4100 base pairs, while the cDNA contains about 600 base pairs.

POTENCY OF DIFFERENT GASTRINS FOR ACID STIMULATION    All naturally occurring amidated gastrins that are present in the circulation have similar biological activity, although their clearance rates and degradation pathways vary. Other gastrin gene products have no known biological activity. G34 and G17 appear to have similar potency for stimulation of acid secretion (39). Methionine oxidation markedly reduces the biological activity of these peptides (111). Methionine oxidation routinely occurs when gastrin is radioiodinated by ordinary oxidative methods, but biologically active nonoxidized labeled gastrin can be prepared (34).

Desamido-gastrin, in which the C-terminal phenylalanine amide is replaced by phenylalanine free acid, is virtually devoid of acid secretion–stimulating activity (122). The glycine-extended precursor of amidated gastrin also has almost no acid secretion–stimulating activity (4). The amino-terminal portions of G17 and G34 probably have no effects on acid secretion (135), although inhibitory activity of the N-terminal tridecapeptide of G17 was reported earlier (138).

HORMONAL ROLE OF GASTRIN IN FOOD-STIMULATED ACID SECRETION    Several criteria must be satisfied before a peptide can be classified as a circulating hormone. Gastrin now has met most of the requirements and can be considered a hormonal stimulant of postprandial acid secretion.

The two most important requirements for identification of a substance as a hormone are that its concentration and molecular forms in blood are sufficient to account for the observed biological response and that specific inhibitors prevent the biological response. It is known that two forms of gastrin, G17 and G34, are present in the blood after a meal (142). Although there was early evidence that the two forms differed in biological activity (183, 184), recent evidence suggests that the large and small forms have equivalent acid secretion–stimulating activity (39). The concentration of total biologically active gastrin in blood after an amino acid or protein meal is similar to the concentration required to cause the observed rate of acid stimulation (39, 49). Similar observations have been made for gastric acid secretion stimulated by bombesin that is associated with gastrin release in dogs (65) and in man (185).

Individual responsiveness to gastrin varies greatly. Decreased parietal cell sensitivity to gastrin is a common finding in women and occurs regularly after vagotomy (13, 45). Increased sensitivity to gastrin occurs after portacaval shunting (104). Inhibitory factors released by fat probably decrease parietal cell responsiveness to gastrin. The variable interplay of these factors may explain the wide variation in gastric acid responses to circulating gastrin after infusion of a mixed protein and fat meal in man (13).

Inhibition of gastrin to prove its hormonal role has been hampered by lack of specific and potent antagonists. A high dose of the gastrin/cholecystokinin antagonist proglumide partially antagonized exogenous pentagastrin but was not tested against endogenously released gastrin (112). Preliminary results with an anti-gastrin monoclonal antibody indicate that neutralization of circulating gastrin markedly inhibits the gastric acid secretion in response to a peptone meal or to gastric distention in dogs (95). If these results are confirmed, they will support the idea that gastrin is an important circulating stimulant of gastric acid secretion.

CIRCULATING SOMATOSTATIN AS AN INHIBITOR OF ACID SECRETION     Somatostatin is a potent inhibitor of in vivo acid secretion stimulated by gastrin but is less effective as an inhibitor of secretion stimulated by histamine (7). Acid secretion is also effectively inhibited by doses of somatostatin that do not inhibit gastrin release (181). The two forms of somatostatin present in gastrointestinal endocrine cells and nerves are the 28– and 14–amino acid forms, SS28 and SS14 (182). Somatostatin 14 is the predominant form in the stomach and is 5–10 times more potent than somatostatin 28 as an inhibitor of acid secretion and gastrin release (90, 158). The clearance rate of SS28 is proportionately slower than that of SS14, so that equimolar exogenous doses of the two peptides produce equivalent inhibition of acid secretion. Evidence suggesting that this inhibitory effect was mediated by local release of gastric prostaglandins (110) was not confirmed (2, 124). There is loss of effectiveness of intravenous somatostatin as an inhibiter of acid secretion after prolonged infusion (38). The mechanism for this "escape" phenomenon is undefined. There is no evidence that somatostatin inhibits acid secretion by inhibiting gastric mucosal blood flow (105).

Studies in man indicated that the maximal amount of somatostatin released after feeding may be sufficient to cause some inhibition of acid secretion but would not influence gastrin response to a meal (26). These results were based on comparisons with the effects of infused SS14. The role of circulating somatostatin in man may be minimal if a major proportion is SS28 and if SS28 has a much lower acid-inhibiting activity in man than in dog. One study has shown that somatostatin antibodies block the acid inhibition produced by intestinal fat in the rat, but it was not shown whether neutralization of circulating or of locally released somatostatin was the mechanism (157).

LOCALLY RELEASED SOMATOSTATIN AS AN INHIBITOR OF GASTRIN RELEASE     The concept that somatostatin might act as a local, paracrine regulator in the stomach was popularized by Larsson and coworkers. They showed that somatostatin cells in the stomach often possess cytoplasmic extensions that resemble short axonal processes, contain somatostatin granules, and terminate in the vicinity of cells known to be inhibited by somatostatin, including gastrin cells and parietal cells (100).

Cholinergic stimulation of gastrin release from isolated, perfused rat stomach is accompanied by reciprocal decreases in somatostatin release (113, 148). Atropine blocks both these effects. The muscarinic $M_1$ receptor antagonist pirenzepine also antagonizes both effects, but with lower affinity (173). Somatostatin inhibits carbachol-induced gastrin release from rat antral organ culture (61), and stimulation of gastrin release is associated with decreased release of somatostatin into the medium (189).

Several peptides that are known to inhibit gastrin release may act by causing local release of somatostatin. Glucagon, secretin, and vasoactive intestinal peptide all caused dose-dependent release of somatostatin from the isolated, perfused rat stomach (21). Secretin had similar action in the rat antral mucosa (191). Secretin inhibition of carbachol-induced gastrin release was abolished by antibodies to secretin in the latter preparation. Gastric inhibitory polypeptide also produced inhibition of gastrin release in this preparation that could be reversed by somatostatin antiserum (190). Intraluminal hydrochloric acid and arterial GIP perfusion both caused reciprocal increases in venous somatostatin and decreases in gastrin in the isolated, perfused pig antrum (69).

Mixed results have been obtained in efforts to enhance gastrin release from isolated perfused rat stomach by perfusion with somatostatin antibodies (20, 160), perhaps because of varying tissue penetration rates of the antibodies used.

There is considerable evidence that local somatostatin inhibits gastrin release under conditions that probably are physiological. Additional evidence indicates that local somatostatin modulates bombesin-stimulated gastrin release. However, at least one additional mechanism must mediate inhibition of gastrin release by intraluminal acid. In neonatal rats, up to 15 days after birth, acid inhibits basal gastrin release but exogenous somatostatin has no effect (76). In older rats somatostatin does inhibit gastrin release. Therefore, before gastrin-inhibiting receptors for somatostatin have developed, some other mechanism enables acid to inhibit gastrin release.

BOMBESIN ACTIONS ON THE STOMACH     One of the first actions described for the amphibian peptide bombesin was stimulation of gastric acid secretion in the dog but not in the rat (9). The mechanism for stimulation of acid secretion was found to be release of antral gastrin (10, 70). The mammalian form of bombesin was isolated from pig intestine by McDonald and coworkers in 1979 (121). This 27–amino acid peptide was called gastrin releasing peptide (GRP). Two major forms of GRP, containing either 27 or 10 amino acids (GRP27 and GRP10) were isolated from canine intestine (141). The structure of the human peptide also has been determined by amino acid sequencing (132) and by cDNA cloning (167).

The smallest bombesinlike peptide with significant gastrin-releasing activity is the C-terminal octapeptide amide (166); the nonapeptide is considerably more potent. GRP27, GRP10, and bombesin have similar acid-stimulating and gastrin-releasing activities in dogs, although GRP10 requires larger doses due to its more rapid clearance from the circulation (18). Other studies also have shown similar potency for GRP27 and bombesin in dogs (98). GRP27 and GRP10 have equal intrinsic activity to cause contraction of canine antral smooth muscle in vitro (118). Bombesin has especially high potency for stimulation of gastrin release and acid secretion in humans (180).

BOMBESIN/GRP AS A NEUROMODULATOR OF GASTRIN RELEASE    Gastrin release in vitro and in vivo generally is regulated by noncholinergic and nonadrenergic mechanisms, although both acetylcholine and epinephrine cause gastrin release. In isolated rat stomach there are atropine-resistant neuronal pathways that can be activated by electrical stimulation to cause gastrin release (154). Bombesin, or its mammalian counterparts GRP27 and GRP10, is present in nerve fibers in the antral mucosa (33). Bombesin produces atropine-resistant stimulation of gastrin release from isolated rat stomach (36, 113). This stimulation of gastrin release is not accompanied by a reciprocal decrease in somatostatin release and therefore clearly differs from the pattern produced by cholinergic stimulation (154). Electrical stimulation of the vagus nerves causes release of immunoreactive gastrin-releasing peptide from the stomach of the anesthetized pig (85) or sheep (12). Endogenous GRP also appears to mediate gastrin release caused by $\beta$-adrenergic stimulation in the rat stomach. This stimulation is prevented when antibodies to GRP are included in the gastric arterial perfusate (161).

Bombesin antiserum inhibited gastrin release caused either by electrical field stimulation or by chemical ganglionic stimulation in perfused rat stomachs (156). These results implied that GRP is involved in mediation of these responses but did not identify the gastrin cell as the target of GRP action. Two recent papers have shown that isolated canine gastrin cells in culture respond to stimulation with bombesin or GRP, which implies that the bombesin receptor is located on the gastrin cell (54, 174). Stimulation of isolated gastrin cells by bombesin is inhibited by somatostatin.

Bombesin causes antral gastrin cell proliferation as well as gastrin release. Daily treatment of rats with bombesin for a week increased gastrin cell proliferation and increased the total antral gastrin cell population (102).

In vivo studies also suggest that bombesinlike peptides could mediate noncholinergic neural release of gastrin but are unlikely to play any role in food-stimulated gastrin release. Atropine has no effect on bombesin-stimulated gastrin release, while cholinergic agonists have an inhibitory effect (177). The cholinergic agonist bethanecol did not inhibit food-stimulated gastrin release, which implies that bombesin peptides were not the primary mediators (123). Similarities in patterns of modification of gastrin responses to food and to bombesin have been found for several other pharmacological agents (66). Strong evidence against bombesin as a mediator of food-stimulated gastrin release was provided by the finding that intravenous desensitization to bombesin in dogs led to exaggerated rather than diminished gastrin responses to a meal (99). However, bombesin desensitization may diminish the gastrin response to sham feeding in dogs (T. O. G. Kovacs & J. H. Walsh, unpublished observations). Bombesin antiserum also inhibited the gastrin response to stomach distention in dogs (94). These results are consistent with a role of GRP in neural stimulation of gastrin release.

OTHER LOCAL MEDIATORS OF GASTRIN AND SOMATOSTATIN RELEASE
Gamma amino butyric acid can stimulate gastrin release and inhibit somatostatin release from rat antral mucosa (59). These effects are mediated by cholinergic neurons (60). Serotonin also causes gastrin release and inhibits somatostatin release from isolated rat stomach (93). These effects are mediated both by specific serotonin and by cholinergic receptors. Beta-adrenergic agonists stimulate somatostatin release from isolated perfused rat stomach (93). Evidence has been obtained that all luminal stimulants of gastrin release act by local reflexes that are inhibited by tetrodotoxin (147).

Isolated rat gastrin cells have been used to study hormonal responses to dietary components (107). Dietary amines, especially decarboxylated amino acids, were found to be potent gastrin-releasing agents (108). The stimulating effect of amino acids appeared to be directly related to their hydrophobicity (109). Monoamine oxidase has been suggested as an important intracellular mediator of stimulation of gastrin release by amino acids (32).

OPIOID PEPTIDE ACTIONS ON THE STOMACH    Met-enkephalin and a stable met-enkephalin analog stimulate gastric acid secretion in the dog (92). Peptides of the met-enkephalin series also enhance histamine-stimulated acid production by isolated rat parietal cells (149). There are numerous opioid receptors in the gastric muscle layers and some in the mucosa (130). Naloxone and another opiate receptor antagonist, nalmefene, inhibit acid secretory responses to food in man (41, 48). Large doses of naloxone also inhibited sham feeding–induced acid secretion in man (91), but smaller doses had no effect (169). These results imply that endogenous opioid peptides have some physiological stimulatory role in the regulation of acid secretion in the stomach. However, morphine and some opioid peptides, including D-Ala-2-enkephalin, inhibit acid secretion. Both stimulatory and inhibitory opiate receptors must exist in the stomach.

POTENTIAL ROLE OF OTHER GASTRIC NEUROPEPTIDES    The gastric mucosa and submucosa are supplied with nerve fibers containing gastrin-releasing peptide, vasoactive intestinal peptide, peptide histidine isoleucine, neuropeptide Y, enkephalins, calcitonin gene–related peptide, and substance P (37, 81). There are no somatostatin nerves in the gastric mucosa. Some of the nerve fibers originate in the submucosal plexus, which is relatively less dense in the stomach than in the intestine (22). Some of the nerve fibers are small sensory fibers of the type depleted by the selective neurotoxin capsaicin (114). Pretreatment with capsaicin reduces acid secretion stimulated by histamine but not by gastrin or cholinergic agents (3). Other fibers may be the peptidergic mediators of reflexes that inhibit gastric secretion, but the pathways have not yet been defined. It is likely that some of the peptide-containing nerves in the stomach act by releasing another neural mediator, such as serotonin, norepinephrine, or dopamine (6, 171), or by local release of somatostatin.

## Endogenous Inhibitors of Acid Secretion

Acid secretion is inhibited when the intestine is perfused with fat or hydrochloric acid (78). Cholecystokinin and secretin are released by fat and by acid, respectively, and have long been considered prime candidates for the hormones that mediate these inhibitory activities. These assumptions have been disputed on physiological grounds (77). Several other hormones have been considered as possible mediators of fat-induced acid inhibition. This "enterogastrone" could be enteroglucagon, neurotensin, peptide YY, gastric inhibitory polypeptide, or vasoactive intestinal peptide. All of these peptides, as well as cholecystokinin, are known to be released in response to fat in the intestine (24).

ACID-INDUCED INHIBITION    Acid in the lumen of the stomach may interfere with gastrin release directly or indirectly through the local antral release of somatostatin or prostaglandins. Acid in the duodenum causes release of secretin, which in turn may inhibit both acid secretion and gastrin release.
    Acidification of the gastric lumen below pH 3 causes decreased gastrin and acid secretion in response to amino acids in the lumen. The decreased acid secretory response to a peptone meal acidified to pH 2.5 can be explained entirely by the decreased gastrin responses (83). Although some secretin is released from the duodenum under these conditions, not enough is released in

man to account for inhibition of gastric acid secretion (83). Larger doses of secretin cause profound inhibition of acid secretion in man associated with decreased gastrin release and delayed gastric emptying (28). In dogs secretin may play a physiological role in acid inhibition produced by acidification of meals because intravenous administration of secretin antibody reverses much of the acid inhibition found under these conditions (19).

Luminal acidification of the stomach causes dose-dependent release of gastric somatostatin (155). This local release of somatostatin could account for acid inhibition. However, there is little evidence that parietal cells possess receptors for somatostatin. Thus somatostatin may stimulate the release of some as yet unidentified final inhibitory mediator. Prostaglandins do not appear to play a crucial role because cyclo-oxygenase inhibition does not interfere with the inhibitory response (125). The possibility that an intestinal inhibitor distinct from secretin is released by acid from the duodenal bulb has been entertained. This putative substance was named "bulbogastrone" but has never been isolated. The possibility of nervous reflex inhibition of acid secretion by intestinal acid also remains.

FAT-INDUCED INHIBITION    Fat in the intestine causes more profound and prolonged inhibition of gastric acid secretion than does intestinal acidification. This inhibition is associated with markedly delayed gastric emptying and with inconsistent changes in gastrin release. None of the hormones released in response to fat in the intestine has been shown to produce the same degree of acid inhibition when infused intravenously at similar blood concentrations. Gastric inhibitory polypeptide was an important candidate enterogastrone (16), but careful studies have shown that physiological concentrations of this peptide produce little if any inhibition of acid secretion in man (116). Much of the acid secretion–inhibiting activity present in crude GIP preparations appears to be due to cholecystokinin contamination (117). The only evidence in favor of the idea that GIP is an enterogastrone is positive immunoneutralization data obtained in one study in dogs (188). The inhibitory effect of GIP is seen best in the vagally denervated dog stomach and is reversed by cholinomimetic agents (165). In man, however, vagotomy does not markedly enhance the inhibitory action of GIP (162).

Cholecystokinin has not been adequately tested as a potential enterogastrone. Preliminary evidence indicates that circulating concentrations of this hormone after fat ingestion are not adequate to account for the major portion of the acid inhibition caused by fat (1).

Three hormones located in the distal small intestine are released in response to fat in the intestine. Neurotensin is an inhibitor of acid that requires vagal integrity for full activity (82). Because vagotomy markedly decreases the inhibitory effect of fat in the intestine on acid secretion in dogs and man, this peptide was suggested as the vagally dependent enterogastrone (131). Preliminary studies suggested that circulating neurotensin concentrations were sufficient to cause physiological inhibition. It is now recognized that neurotensin is degraded in blood into a slowly cleared molecular form that is measured by many radioimmunoassays that employ antisera specific for the amino terminus of the molecule (101). Concentrations of biologically active whole molecule, measured with antibody specific for the biologically active carboxyl terminus, are insufficient to account for acid inhibition caused by fat ingestion (126).

Enteroglucagon, or oxyntomodulin, is an elongated form of glucagon produced by intestinal glucagon cells. This peptide appears to be more active than glucagon as an inhibitor of acid secretion and cAMP production in the stomach and less active than glucagon in the liver (5). It has been suggested that it is an important enterogastrone (35). Peptide YY is also released in response to fat in the intestine. Circulating concentrations released after fat ingestion are nearly sufficient to account for the acid inhibition (133). It is possible that no single peptide accounts for the enterogastrone effects of fat in the intestine and that combinations of these peptides produce a cumulative inhibitory effect. However, inhibitory reflexes have not been excluded in any way.

## Summary

Several peptides are important regulators of gastric acid secretion. The best characterized is gastrin. This circulating hormone is produced in the gastric antrum and mediates the gastric phase of acid secretion. Somatostatin is important as an inhibitory regulator of acid secretion, but the relative importance of paracrine versus endocrine delivery to its targets remains to be determined. The mammalian bombesin peptides, GRP27 and GRP10, probably are mediators of neural release of gastrin. Opioid peptides in the gastric wall appear to act as endogenous neurostimulants of gastric acid secretion under some conditions. Other neuropeptides in the gastric mucosa and submucosa, including sensory neuropeptides, may be important regulators of acid secretion. Hormones or nerves activated by fat and other substances in the lumen of the small intestine cause inhibition of acid secretion, but the specific peptides responsible for this effect have not yet been identified from a long list of candidates. The effects of peptides on the parietal cell and the gastrin and somatostatin cells are functionally linked with those of cholinergic and adrenergic nerves and with locally released histamine.

ACKNOWLEDGMENTS

The author's work is supported by National Institutes of Health grants DK17294, DK17328, by the David H. Murdock Foundation, and by the Veterans Administration. The editorial assistance of David Claus is gratefully acknowledged.

## Literature Cited

1. Abrahm, D., Mogard, M., Maxwell, V., Sankaran, H., Deveny, C., Walsh, J. H. 1985. Cholecystokinin inhibition of meal-stimulated gastric acid secretion in man. *Gastroenterology* 88:1300 (Abstr.)

2. Albinus, M., Gomez-Pan, A., Hirst, B. H., Shaw, B. 1985. Evidence against prostaglandin-mediation of somatostatin inhibition of gastric secretions. *Regul. Peptides* 10:259–66

3. Alfoldi, P., Obal, F. Jr., Toth, E., Hideg, J. 1986. Capsaicin pretreatment reduces the gastric acid secretion elicited by histamine but does not affect the responses to carbachol and pentagastrin. *Eur. J. Pharmacol.* 123:321–27

4. Azuma, T., Yanagisawa, K., Kawai, K., Walsh, J. H. 1987. COOH-terminal glycine extended progastrin (gastrin-G) and peptidyl-glycine alpha-amidating monoxigenase (PAM) activity in rats serum. *Gastroenterology* 92:1302 (Abstr.)

5. Bataille, D., Gespach, C., Coudray, A. M., Rosselein, G. 1981. "Enteroglucagon": A specific effect on gastric glands isolated from the rat fundus. Evidence for an "oxyntomodulin" action. *Biosci. Rep.* 1:151–55

6. Bech, K. 1986. Effect of serotonin on bethanechol-stimulated gastric acid secretion and gastric antral motility in dogs. *Scand. J. Gastroenterol.* 21:655–61

7. Bech, K. 1986. Effect of somatostatin on histamine-stimulated gastric acid and pepsin secretion in dogs. *Scand. J. Gastroenterol.* 21:662–68

8. Becker, H. D., Reeder, D. D., Thompson, J. C. 1973. The effect of prostaglandin E1 on the release of gastrin and gastric secretion on dogs. *Endocrinology* 93:1148–51

9. Bertaccini, G., Erspamer, V., Impicciatore, M. 1973. The actions of bombesin on gastric secretion of the dog and the rat. *Br. J. Pharmacol.* 49:437–44

10. Bertaccini, G., Erspamer, V., Melchiorri, P., Sopranzi, N. 1974. Gastrin release by bombesin in the dog. *Br. J. Pharmacol.* 52:219–25

11. Bieberdorf, F. A., Walsh, J. H., Fordtran, J. S. 1975. Effect of optimum therapeutic dose of poldine on acid secretion, gastric acidity, gastric emptying, and serum gastrin concentration after a protein meal. *Gastroenterology* 68:50–57

12. Bladin, P. H., Shulkes, A., Fletcher, D. R., Hardy, K. J. 1983. Elevation of plasma gastrin and pancreatic polypeptide by electrical vagal stimulation in sheep: Effects of sequential stimulation. *Regul. Peptides* 6:89–97

13. Blair, A. J., Richardson, C. T., Walsh, J. H., Chew, P., Feldman, M. 1986. Effect of parietal cell vagotomy on acid secretory responsiveness to circulating gastrin in humans. Relationship to postprandial serum gastrin concentration. *Gastroenterology* 90:1001–7

14. Boel, E., Vuust, J., Norris, F., Norris, K., Wind, A., et al. 1983. Molecular cloning of human gastrin cDNA: Evidence for evolution of gastrin by gene duplication. *Proc. Natl. Acad. Sci. USA* 80:2866–69

15. Brandsborg, O., Brandsborg, M., Christensen, N. J. 1975. Plasma adrenaline and serum gastrin: Studies in insulin-induced hypoglycemia and after adrenaline infusions. *Gastroenterology* 68:455–60

16. Brown, J. C., Mutt, V., Pederson, R. A. 1970. Further purification of a polypeptide demonstrating enterogastrone activity. *J. Physiol. London* 209:57–64

17. Brown, M., Allen, R., Villarreal, J., Rivier, J., Vale, W. 1978. Bombesin-like activity: Radioimmunologic assessment in biological tissues. *Life. Sci.* 23:2721–28

18. Bunnett, N. W., Clark, B., Debas, H. T., DelMilton, R. C., Kovacs, T. O. G., et al. 1985. Canine bombesin-like gastrin releasing peptides stimulate gastrin release and acid secretion in the dog. *J. Physiol. London* 365:121–30

19. Chey, W. Y., Kim, M. S., Lee, K. Y., Chang, T.-M. 1979. Effect of rabbit antisecretin serum on postprandal pancreatic secretion in dogs. *Gastroenterology* 77:1268–75

20. Chiba, T., Kadowaki, S., Taminato, T., Chihara, K., Seino, Y., et al. 1981. Effect of antisomatostatin gamma-globulin on gastrin release in rats. *Gastroenterology* 81:321–26

21. Chiba, T., Taminato, T., Kadowaki, S., Abe, H., Chihara, K., et al. 1980. Effects of glucagon, secretin and vasoactive intestinal polypeptide on gastric somatostatin and gastrin release from isolated perfused rat stomach. *Gastroenterology* 79:67–71

22. Christensen, J., Rick, G. A. 1985. Nerve cell density in submucous plexus throughout the gut of cat and opossum. *Gastroenterology* 89:1064–69

23. Christensen, K. C. 1984. Specific beta-adrenergic mechanisms in the hypoglycaemic activation of gastrin and gastric

acid secretion. *Scand. J. Gastroenterol.*
19:339–42

24. Christiansen, J., Bech, A., Fahrenkrug,
J., Holst, J. J., Lauritsen, K., et al.
1979. Fat-induced jejunal inhibition of
gastric acid secretion and release of pancreatic glucagon, enteroglucagon, gastric inhibitory polypeptide, and vasoactive intestinal polypeptide in man.
*Scand. J. Gastroenterol.* 14:161–66

25. Collins, S. M., Gardner, J. D. 1982.
Cholecystokinin-induced contraction of
dispersed smooth muscle cells. *Am. J.
Physiol.* 243:G497–G504

26. Colturi, T. J., Unger, R. H., Feldman,
M. 1984. Role of circulating somatostatin in regulation of gastric acid secretion,
gastrin release, and islet cell function.
Studies in healthy subjects and duodenal
ulcer patients. *J. Clin. Invest.* 74:417–
23

27. Csendes, A., Walsh, J. H., Grossman,
M. I. 1972. Effects of atropine and of
antral acidification of gastrin release and
acid secretion in response to insulin and
feeding in dogs. *Gastroenterology*
63:257–63

28. Dalton, M. D., Eisenstein, A. M.,
Walsh, J. H., Fordtran, J. S. 1976.
Effect of secretin on gastric function in
normal subjects and in patients with
duodenal ulcer. *Gastroenterology* 71:
24–29

29. Debas, H. T., Hollinshead, J., Seal, A.,
Soon-Shiong, P., Walsh, J. H. 1984.
Vagal control of gastrin release in the
dog: Pathways for stimulation and inhibition. *Surgery* 95:34–37

30. Debas, H. T., Konturek, S. J., Walsh,
J. H., Grossman, M. I. 1974. Proof of a
pyloro-oxyntic reflex for stimulation of
acid secretion. *Gastroenterology* 66:
526–32

31. Debas, H. T., Walsh, J. H., Grossman,
M. I. 1975. Evidence of oxyntopyloric
reflex for release of antral gastrin.
*Gastroenterology* 68:687–90

32. Dial, E. J., Huang, J., Delansorne, R.,
Lichtenberger, L. M. 1986. Monoamine
oxidase: An important intracellular regulator of gastrin release in the rat.
*Gastroenterology* 90:1018–23

33. Dockray, G. J., Vaillant, C., Walsh, J.
H. 1979. The neuronal origin of bombesin-like immunoreactivity in the rat gastrointestinal tract. *Neuroscience* 4:1561–
68.

34. Dockray, G. J., Walsh, J. H., Grossman, M. I. 1976. Biological activity of
iodinated gastrins. *Biochem. Biophys.
Res. Commun.* 69:339–45

35. Dubrasquet, M., Bataille, D., Gespach,
C. 1982. Oxyntomodulin (glucagon-37

or bioactive enterolgucagon): A potent
inhibitor of pentagastrin-stimulated acid
secretion in rats. *Biosci. Rep.* 2:391–
95

36. DuVal, J. W., Saffouri, B., Weir, G.
C., Walsh, J. H., Arimura, A., Makhlouf, G. M. 1981. Stimulation of gastrin
and somatostatin secretion from the isolated rat stomach by bombesin. *Am. J.
Physiol.* 241:G242–47

37. Ekblad, E., Ekelund, M., Graffner, H.,
Hakanson, R., Sundler, F. 1985.
Peptide-containing nerve fibers in the
stomach wall of rat and mouse.
*Gastroenterology* 89:73–85

38. Ekelund, M., Ekman, R., Hakanson,
R., Sundler, F. 1984. Continuous infusion of somatostain evokes escape of
gastric acid inhibition in the rat.
*Gastroenterology* 86:861–65

39. Eysselein, V. E., Maxwell, V. E.,
Reedy, T., Wunsch, E., Walsh, J. H.
1984. Similar acid stimulatory potencies
of synthetic human big and little gastrins
in man. *J. Clin. Invest.* 73:1284–90

40. Farooq, O., Walsh, J. H. 1975. Atropine enhances serum gastrin response to
insulin in man. *Gastroenterology* 68:
662–66

41. Feldman, M., Moore, L., Walsh, J. H.
1985. Effect of oral nalmefene, an opi-
ate-receptor antagonist, on meal-
stimulated gastric acid secretion and
serum gastrin concentration in man.
*Regul. Peptides* 11:245–50

42. Feldman, M., Richardson, C. T. 1986.
Role of thought, sight, smell, and taste
of food in the cephalic phase of gastric
acid secretion in humans. *Gastroenterology* 90:428–33

43. Feldman, M., Richardson, C. T., Peterson, W. L., Walsh, J. H., Fordtran, J.
S. 1977. Effect of low-dose pro-
pantheline on food-stimulated gastric
acid secretion. Comparison with an "optimal effective dose" and interaction
with cimetidine. *N. Engl. J. Med.* 297:
1427–30

44. Feldman, M., Richardson, C. T.,
Taylor, I. L., Walsh, J. H. 1979. Effect
of atropine on vagal release of gastrin
and pancreatic polypeptide. *J. Clin. Invest.* 63:294–98

45. Feldman, M., Richardson, C. T.,
Walsh, J. H. 1983. Sex-related differences in gastrin release and parietal cell
sensitivity to gastrin in healthy human
beings. *J. Clin. Invest.* 71:715–20

46. Feldman, M., Unger, R. H., Walsh, J.
H. 1985. Effect of atropine on plasma
gastrin and somatostatin concentrations
during sham feeding in man. *Regul.
Peptides* 12:345–52

47. Feldman, M., Walsh, J. H. 1980. Acid inhibition of sham feeding–stimulated gastrin release and gastric acid secretion: Effect of atropine. *Gastroenterology* 78:722–76
48. Feldman, M., Walsh, J. H., Taylor, I. 1980. Effect of naloxone and morphine on gastric acid secretion and on serum gastrin and pancreatic polypeptide concentrations in man. *Gastroenterology* 79:294–98
49. Feldman, M., Walsh, J. H., Wong, H. C. 1978. Role of gastrin heptadecapeptide in the acid secretory response to amino acids in man. *J. Clin. Invest.* 61:308–13
50. Festen, H. P., Tuynman, H. A., Defize, J., Pals, G., Frants, R. R., et al. 1986. Effect of single and repeated doses of oral omeprazole on gastric acid and pepsin secretion and fasting serum gastrin and serum pepsinogen I levels. *Dig. Dis. Sci.* 31:561–66
51. Fordtran, J. S., Walsh, J. H. 1973. Gastric acid secretion rate and buffer content of the stomach after eating. Results in normal subjects and in patients with duodenal ulcer. *J. Clin. Invest.* 52:645–57
52. Frislid, K., Berstad, A., Guldvog, I. 1985. Simulated meal test. A new method for estimation of parietal and non-parietal secretion in response to food. *Scand. J. Gastroenterol.* 20:115–22
53. Gehling, N., Lawson, M. J., Alp, M. H., Rofe, S. B., Butler, R. N. 1986. Antral gastrin concentrations in duodenal ulcer patients after cimetidine and highly selective vagotomy. *Aust. NZ J. Surg.* 56:793–96
54. Giraud, A. S., Soll, A. H., Cuttita, F., Walsh, J. H. 1987. Bombesin stimulation of gastrin release from canine gastrin cells in primary culture. *Am. J. Physiol.* 252:G413–20
55. Goto, Y., Debas, H. T. 1983. GABA-mimetic effect on gastric acid secretion. Possible significance in central mechanisms. *Dig. Dis. Sci.* 28:56–59
56. Goto, Y., Taché, Y. 1985. Gastric erosions induced by intracisternal thyrotropin-releasing hormone (TRH) in rats. *Peptides* 6:153–56
57. Graffner, H., Jarhult, J. 1984. The effect of beta-blockade on gastric acid secretion, gastrin release, and plasma catecholamine concentrations during modified sham feeding in duodenal ulcer patients. *Scand. J. Gastroenterol.* 19:937–40
58. Grotzinger, U., Bergegardh, S., Olbe, L. 1977. Effect of fundic distension on gastric acid secretion in man. *Gut* 18:105–10
59. Harty, R. F., Franklin, P. A. 1983. GABA affects the release of gastrin and somatostatin from rat antral mucosa. *Nature* 303:623–24
60. Harty, R. F., Franklin, P. A. 1986. Cholinergic mediation of gamma-aminobutyric acid-induced gastrin and somatostatin release from rat antrum. *Gastroenterology* 91:1221–26
61. Harty, R. F., Maico, D. G., McGuigan, J. E. 1981. Somatostatin inhibition of basal and carbachol-stimulated gastrin release in rat antral organ culture. *Gastroenterology* 81:707–12
62. Hayes, J. R., Kennedy, T. L., Ardill, J., Shanks, R. G., Buchanan, K. D. 1972. Stimulation of gastrin release by catecholamines. *Lancet* 1:819–21
63. Hirschowitz, B. I., Gibson, R. G. 1978. Cholinergic stimulation and suppression of gastrin release in gastric fistula dogs. *Am. J. Physiol.* 235:E720–25
64. Hirschowitz, B. I., Gibson, R. G. 1979. Augmented vagal release of antral gastrin by 2-deoxyglucose after fundic vagotomy in dogs. *Am. J. Physiol.* 236:E173–79
65. Hirschowitz, B. I., Molina, E. 1983. Relation of gastric acid and pepsin secretion to serum gastrin levels in dogs given bombesin and gastrin-17. *Am. J. Physiol.* 244:G546–51
66. Hirschowitz, B. I., Molina, E. 1984. Analysis of food stimulation of gastrin release in dogs by a panel of inhibitors. *Peptides* 5:35–40
67. Hogan, D. L., Turken, D., Stern, A. I., Isenberg, J. I. 1983. Comparison of the serial dilution indicator and intragastric titration methods for measurement of meal-stimulated gastric acid secretion in man. *Dig. Dis. Sci.* 28:1001–4
68. Hollinshead, J. W., Debas, H. T., Yamada, T., Elashoff, J., Osadchey, B., Walsh, J. H. 1985. Hypergastrinemia develops within 24 hours of truncal vagotomy in dogs. *Gastroenterology* 88:35–40
69. Holst, J. J., Jensen, S. L., Knuhtsen, S., Nielsen, O. V., Rehfeld, J. F. 1983. Effect of vagus, gastric inhibitory polypeptide, and HCl on gastrin and somatostatin release from perfused pig antrum. *Am. J. Physiol.* 244:G515–22
70. Impicciatore, M., Debas, H., Walsh, J. H., Grossman, M. I., Bertaccini, G. 1974. Release of gastrin and stimulation of acid secretion by bombesin in dog. *Rend. Gastroenterol.* 6:99–101
71. Impicciatore, M., Walsh, J. H., Grossman, M. I. 1977. Low doses of atropine

enhance serum gastrin response to food in dogs. *Gastroenterology* 72:995–96

72. Ippoliti, A. F., Isenberg, J. I., Hagie, L. 1981. Effect of oral and intravenous 16,16-dimethyl prostaglandin E2 in duodenal ulcer and Zollinger-Ellison syndrome patients. *Gastroenterology* 80:55–59

73. Ippoliti, A. F., Isenberg, J. I., Maxwell, V., Walsh, J. H. 1976. The effect of 16,16-dimethyl prostaglandin E2 on meal-stimulated gastric acid secretion and serum gastrin in duodenal ulcer patients. *Gastroenterology* 70:488–91

74. Ippoliti, A. F., Maxwell, V., Isenberg, J. I. 1976. The effect of various forms of milk on gastric-acid secretion. Studies in patients with duodenal ulcer and normal subjects. *Ann. Intern. Med.* 84:286–89

75. Ito, R., Sato, K., Helmer, T., Jay, G., Agarwal, K. 1984. Structural analysis of the gene encoding human gastrin: The large intron contains an Alu sequence. *Proc. Natl. Acad. Sci. USA* 81:4662–66

76. Johnson, L. R. 1984. Effects of somatostatin and acid on inhibition of gastrin release in newborn rats. *Endocrinology* 114:743–46

77. Johnson, L. R., Grossman, M. I. 1969. Effects of fat, secretin, and cholecystokinin on histamine-stimulated gastric secretion. *Am. J. Physiol.* 216:1176–79

78. Johnson, L. R., Grossman, M. I. 1971. Intestinal hormones as inhibitors of gastric secretion. *Gastroenterology* 60:120–44

79. Kaess, H., Kuntzen, O., Teckentrupp, U., Dorner, M. 1975. The influences of propranolol on serum gastrin concentration and hydrochloric acid secretion in response to hypoglycemia in normal subjects. *Digestion* 13:193–200

80. Kato, K., Himeno, S., Takahashi, Y., Wakabayashi, T., Tarui, S., Matsubara, K. 1983. Molecular cloning of human gastrin precursor cDNA. *Gene* 26:53–57

81. Keast, J. R., Furness, J. B., Costa, M. 1985. Distribution of certain peptide-containing nerve fibres and endocrine cells in the gastrointestinal mucosa in five mammalian species. *J. Comp. Neurol.* 236:403–22

82. Kihl, B., Rokaeus, A., Rosell, S., Olbe, L. 1981. Fat inhibition of gastric acid secretion in man and plasma concentrations of neurotensin-like immunoreactivity. *Gastroenterology* 16:513–26

83. Kleibeuker, J. H., Eysselein, V. E., Maxwell, V. E., Walsh, J. H. 1984. Role of endogenous secretin in acid-induced inhibition of human gastric function. *J. Clin. Invest.* 73:526–32

84. Kleibeuker, J. H., Kauffman, G. L. Jr.,

Walsh, J. H. 1985. Intravenous histamine reduces bombesin-stimulated gastrin release in dogs. *Regul. Peptides* 11:209–15

85. Knuhtsen, S., Holst, J. J., Knigge, U., Olesen, M., Nielsen, O. V. 1984. Radioimmunoassay, pharmacokinetics, and neuronal release of gastrin-releasing peptide in anesthetized pigs. *Gastroenterology* 87:372–78

86. Knutson, U., Bergegardh, S., Olbe, L. 1974. The effect of intragastric pH variations on the gastric acid response to sham feeding in duodenal ulcer patients. *Scand. J. Gastroenterol.* 9:357–65

87. Knutson, U., Olbe, L., Ganguli, P. C. 1974. Gastric acid and plasma gastrin responses to sham feeding in duodenal ulcer patients before and after resection of antrum and duodenal bulb. *Scand. J. Gastroenterol.* 9:351–56

88. Konturek, S. J., Biernat, J., Oleksy, J., Rehfeld, J. F., Stadil, F. 1974. The effect of beta-adrenergic blockade upon gastric acid secertion and gastrin secretion during hypoglycaemia before and after vagotomy. *Scand. J. Gastroenterol.* 9:173–76

89. Konturek, S. J., Biernat, J., Oleksy, J., Rehfeld, J. F., Stadil, F. 1974. Effect of atropine on gastrin and gastric acid response to peptone meal. *J. Clin. Invest.* 54:593–97

90. Konturek, S. J., Kwiecien, N., Obtulowicz, W., Bielanski, W., Oleksy, J., Schally, A. V. 1985. Effects of somatostatin-14 and somatostatin-28 on plasma hormonal and gastric secretory responses to cephalic and gastrointestinal stimulation in man. *Scand. J. Gastroenterol.* 20:31–38

91. Konturek, S. J., Kwiecien, N., Obtulowicz, W., Swierczek, J., Bielanski, W., et al. 1983. Effect of enkephalin and naloxone on gastric acid and serum gastrin and pancreatic polypeptide concentrations in humans. *Gut* 24:740–45

92. Konturek, S. J., Tasler, J., Cieszkowski, M., Mikos, E., Coy, D. H., Schally, A. V. 1980. Comparison of methionine-enkephalin and morphine in the stimulation of gastric acid secretion in the dog. *Gastroenterology* 78:294–300

93. Koop, H., Behrens, I., Bothe, E., Koschwitz, H., McIntosh, C. H., et al. 1983. Adrenergic control of rat gastric somatostatin and gastrin release. *Scand. J. Gastroenterol.* 18:65–71

94. Kovacs, T. O. G., Cuttitta, F., Walsh, J. H. 1987. The effect of monoclonal antibody to bombesin on distention induced gastrin and acid secretion in dogs. *Gastroenterology* 92:1480 (Abstr.)

95. Kovacs, T. O. G., Maxwell, V. E., Walsh, J. H. 1987. The effect of immunoneutralization with antigastrin monoclonal antibody on gastric acid secretion in dogs. *Gastroenterology* 92:1480 (Abstr.)

96. Kronborg, O., Pedersen, T., Stadil, F., Rehfeld, J. F. 1974. The effect of betaadrenergic blockade upon gastric acid secretion and gastrin secretion during hypoglycaemia before and after vagotomy. *Scand. J. Gastroenterol.* 9:173–76

97. Lam, S. K., Lam, K. C., Lai, C. L., Yeung, C. K., Yam, L. Y., Wong, W. S. 1979. Treatment of duodenal ulcer with antacid and sulpiride. A doubleblind controlled study. *Gastroenterology* 76:315–22

98. Lambert, J. R., Hansky, J., Soveny, C., Hunt, P. 1984. Comparative effects of bombesin and porcine gastrin-releasing peptide in the dog. *Dig. Dis. Sci.* 29:1036–40

99. Larson, T., Sanchez, J., Taylor, I. L. 1983. Bombesin-induced tachyphylaxis markedly enhances gastrin response to a meal. *Am. J. Physiol.* 244:G652–55

100. Larsson, L.-I., Goltermann, N., DeMagistris, L., Rehfeld, J., Schwartz, T. W. 1979. Somatostatin cell processes as pathways for paracrine secretion. *Science* 205:1393–95

101. Lee, Y. C., Allen, J. M., Utterthal, L. O., Walker, M. C., Shemilt, J., et al. 1984. The metabolism of intravenously infused neurotensin in man and its chromatographic characterization in human plasma. *J. Clin. Endocrinol. Metab.* 59:45–50

102. Lehy, T., Accary, J. P., Labeille, D., Dubrasquet, M. 1983. Chronic administration of bombesin stimulates antral gastrin cell proliferation in the rat. *Gastroenterology* 84:914–19

103. Lenz, H. J., Ferrari-Taylor, J., Isenberg, J. I. 1983. Wine and five percent ethanol are potent stimulants of gastric secretion in humans. *Gastroenterology* 85:1082–87

104. Lenz, H. J., Struck, T., Greten, H., Koss, M. A., Eysselein, V. E. et al. 1987. Increased sensitivity of gastric acid secretion to gastrin in cirrhotic patients with portacaval shunt. *J. Clin. Invest.* 794:1120–24

105. Leung, F. W., Guth, P. H. 1985. Dissociated effects of somatostatin on gastric acid secretion and mucosal blood flow. *Am. J. Physiol.* 248:G337–41

106. Levant, J. A., Walsh, J. H., Isenberg, J. I. 1973. Stimulation of gastric secretion and gastrin release by single oral doses of calcium carbonate in man. *N. Engl. J. Med.* 289:555–58

107. Lichtenberger, L. M., Forssmann, W. G., Ito, S. 1980. Functional responsiveness of an isolated and enriched fraction of rodent G cells. *Gastroenterology* 79:447–59

108. Lichtenberger, L. M., Graziani, L. A., Dubinsky, W. P. 1982. Importance of dietary amines in meal-induced gastrin release. *Am. J. Physiol.* 243:G341–47

109. Lichtenberger, L. M., Nelson, A. A., Graziani, L. A. 1986. Amine trapping: Physical explanation for the inhibitory effect of gastric acidity on the postprandial release of gastrin. Studies on rats and dogs. *Am. J. Physiol.* 90:1223–31

110. Ligumsky, M., Goto, Y., Debas, H., Yamada, T. 1983. Prostaglandins mediate inhibition of gastric acid secretion by somatostatin in the rat. *Science* 219:301–3

111. Lin, T. M., Southyard, G. L., Spray, G. F. 1976. Stimulation of gastric acid secretion in the dog by the C-terminal penta-, tetra-, and tripeptides of gastrin and their O-methyl esters. *Gastroenterology* 70:733–36

112. Loewe, C. J., Grider, J. R., Gardiner, J., Vlahcevic, Z. R. 1985. Selective inhibition of pentagastrin- and cholecystokinin-stimulated exocrine secretion by proglumide. *Gastroenterology* 89:746–51

113. Martindale, R., Kauffman, G. L. Jr., Levin, S., Walsh, J. H., Yamada, T. 1982. Differential regulation of gastrin and somatostatin secretion from isolated perfused rat stomachs. *Gastroenterology* 83:240–44

114. Matthews, M. R., Cuello, A. C. 1982. Substance P–immunoreactive peripheral branches of sensory neurons innervate guinea pig sympathetic neurons. *Proc. Natl. Acad. Sci. USA* 79:1668–72

115. Maxwell, V., Eysselein, V. E., Kleibeuker, J., Reedy, T., Walsh, J. H. 1984. Glucose perfusion intragastric titration. *Dig. Dis. Sci.* 29:321–26

116. Maxwell, V., Shulkes, A., Brown, J. C., Solomon, T. E., Walsh, J. H., Grossman, M. I. 1980. Effect of gastric inhibitory polypeptide on pentagastrinstimulated acid secretion on man. *Dig. Dis. Sci.* 25:113–16

117. Mayer, E. A., Elashoff, J., Mutt, V., Walsh, J. H. 1982. Reassessment of gastric acid inhibition by cholecystokinin and gastric inhibitory polypeptide in dogs. *Gastroenterology* 83:1047–50

118. Mayer, E. A., Reeve, J. R. Jr., Khawaja, S., Chew, P., Elashoff, J., et al. 1986. Potency of natural and synthetic

canine gastrin-releasing decapeptide on canine antral muscle. *Am. J. Physiol.* 250:G581–87

119. Mayer, G., Arnold, R., Feurle, G., Fuchs, K., Ketterer, H., et al. 1974. Influence of feeding and sham feeding upon serum gastrin and gastric acid secretion in control subjects and duodenal ulcer patients. *Scand. J. Gastroenterol.* 9:703–10

120. McArthur, K., Hogan, D., Isenberg, J. I. 1982. Relative stimulatory effects of commonly ingested beverages on gastric acid secretion in humans. *Gastroenterology* 83:199–203

121. McDonald, T. J., Jornvall, H., Nilsson, G., Vagne, M., Ghatei, M., et al. 1979. Characterization of gastrin releasing peptide from porcine non-antral gastric tissue. *Biochem. Biophys. Res. Commun.* 90:227–33

122. McGuigan, J. E., Thomas, H. F. 1972. Physiological and immunological studies with desamidogastrin. *Gastroenterology* 62:553–57

123. Modlin, I. M., Lamers, C., Walsh, J. H. 1980. Mechanisms of gastrin release by bombesin and food. *J. Surg. Res.* 28:539–46

124. Mogard, M. H., Kauffman, G. L. Jr., Pehlevanian, M., Golanska, E. 1985. Prostaglandins may not mediate inhibition of gastric acid secretion by somatostatin in the rat. *Regul. Peptides* 10:231–36

125. Mogard, M. H., Maxwell, V. E., Kovacs, T. O. G., Van Deventer, G., Elashoff, J. D., et al. 1985. Somatostatin inhibits gastric acid secretion after gastric mucosal prostaglandin synthesis inhibition by indomethacin in man. *Gut* 26:1189–91

126. Mogard, M. H., Maxwell, V. E., Sytnik, B., Walsh, J. H. 1987. Regulation of gastric acid secretion by neurotensin in man: Evidence against a hormonal role. *J. Clin. Invest.* 80:1064–67

127. Naesdal, J., Bankel, M., Bodemar, G., Gotthard, R., Lundquist, G., Walan, A. 1987. The effect of 20 mg omeprazole daily on serum gastrin, 24-H intragastric acidity, and bile acid concentration in duodenal ulcer patients. *Scand. J. Gastroenterol.* 22:5–12

128. Nelis, G. F., Lamers, C. B., Pals, G. 1985. Influence of RP 40749 on basal and meal-stimulated serum-gastrin, serum-pepsinogen I, and gastrin content of the antral mucosa in duodenal ulcer patients. *Dig. Dis. Sci.* 30:617–23

129. Nilsson, G., Simon, J., Yalow, R. S., Berson, S. A. 1972. Plasma gastrin and gastric acid responses to sham feeding and feeding in dogs. *Gastroenterology* 63:51–59

130. Nishimura, E., Buchan, A. M., McIntosh, C. H. 1986. Autoradiographic localization of mu- and delta-type opioid receptors in the gastrointestinal tract of the rat and guinea pig. *Gastroenterology* 91:1084–94

131. Olsen, P. S., Pederson, J. H., Kirkegaard, P., Been, H., Stadil, F., et al. 1984. Neurotensin induced inhibition of gastric acid secretion in duodenal ulcer patients before and after parietal cell vagotomy. *Gut* 25:481–84

132. Orloff, M. S., Reeve, J. R. Jr., Ben-Avram, C. M., Shively, J. E., Walsh, J. H. 1984. Isolation and sequence analysis of human bombesin-like peptides. *Peptides* 5:865–70

133. Pappas, T. N., Debas, H. T., Taylor, I. L. 1986. Enterogastrone-like effect of peptide YY is vagally mediated in the dog. *J. Clin. Invest.* 77:49–53

134. Pappas, T. N., Taché, Y., Debas, H. T. 1985. Cerebro-ventricular somatostatin stimulates gastric acid secretion in the dog. In *Regulatory Peptides in Digestive, Nervous and Endocrine Systems. INSERM Symp. 25*, pp. 323–27, ed. M. J. M. Lewin, S. Bonfils, Amsterdam: Elsevier Science

135. Pauwels, S., Dockray, G. J., Walker, R., Marcus, S. 1984. N-terminal tryptic fragment of big gastrin. *Gastroenterology* 86:86–92

136. Peters, M. N., Feldman, M., Walsh, J. H., Richardson, C. T. 1983. Effect of gastric alkalinization on serum gastrin concentrations in humans. *Gastroenterology* 85:35–39

137. Peters, M. N., Walsh, J. H., Ferrari, J., Feldman, M. 1982. Adrenergic regulation of distention-induced gastrin release in humans. *Gastroenterology* 82:659–63

138. Petersen, B., Christiansen, J., Rehfeld, J. F. 1983. The N-terminal tridecapeptide fragment of gastrin-17 inhibits gastric acid secretion. *Regul. Peptides* 7:323–34

139. Peterson, W. L., Barnett, C., Walsh, J. H. 1986. Effect of intragastric infusions of ethanol and wine on serum gastrin concentration and gastric acid secretion. *Gastroenterology* 91:1390–95

140. Peterson, W. L., Walsh, J. H., Richardson, C. T. 1986. Cimetidine blocks antacid-induced hypergastrinemia. *Gastroenterology* 90:48–52

141. Reeve, J. R. Jr., Walsh, J. H., Chew, P., Clark, B., Hawke, D., Shively, J. E.

1983. Amino acid sequences of three bombesin-like peptides from canine intestine extracts. *J. Biol. Chem.* 258: 5582–88
142. Rehfeld, J. F. 1973. Gastrins in serum. A review of gastrin radioimmunoanalysis and the discovery of gastrin heterogeneity in serum. *Scand. J. Gastroenterol.* 8:577–83
143. Rehfeld, J. F., Stadil, F. 1973. The effect of gatrin on basal and glucose-stimulated insulin secretion in man. *J. Clin. Invest.* 52:1415–26
144. Richardson, C. T., Feldman, M. 1985. Effect of histamine and cimetidine on amino acid meal-stimulated gastrin release at a controlled intragastric pH in healthy human beings. *Regul. Peptides* 10:339–44
145. Richardson, C. T., Walsh, J. H., Cooper, K. A., Feldman, M., Fordtran, J. S. 1977. Studies on the role of cephalic-vagal stimulation in the acid secretory response to eating in normal human subjects. *J. Clin. Invest.* 60:435–41
146. Richardson, C. T., Walsh, J. H., Hicks, M. I., Fordtran, J. S. 1976. Studies on the mechanisms of food stimulated gastric acid secretion in normal human subjects. *J. Clin. Invest.* 58:623–31
147. Saffouri, B., DuVal, J. W., Makhlouf, G. M. 1984. Stimulation of gastrin secretion in vitro by intraluminal chemicals: Regulation by intramural cholinergic and noncholinergic neurons. *Gastroenterology* 87:557–61
148. Saffouri, B., Weir, G. C., Bitar, K. N., Makhlouf, G. M. 1980. Gastrin and somatostatin secretion by perfused rat stomach: Functional linkage of antral peptides. *Am. J. Physiol.* 238:G495–G501
149. Schepp, W., Schneider, J., Schusdziarra, V., Classen, M. 1986. Naturally occurring opioid peptides modulate H+-production by isolated rat parietal cells. *Peptides* 7:885–90
150. Schiller, L. R., Walsh, J. H., Feldman, M. 1980. Distention-induced gastrin release: Effects of luminal acidification and intravenous atropine. *Gastroenterology* 78:912–17
151. Schiller, L. R., Walsh, J. H., Feldman, M. 1982. Effect of atropine on gastrin release stimulated by an amino acid meal in humans. *Gastroenterology* 83:267–72
152. Schoon, I. M. 1980. The effects of antral distension on gastric acid secretion and on gastrointestinal hormones in man. *Acta Physiol. Scand. (Suppl.)* 482:1–33

153. Schrumpf, E., Vatn, M. H., Semb, L. S. 1974. Effect of atropine on insulin-stimulated gastrin release and gastric secretion of acid, pepsin, and intrinsic factor (IF). *Scand. J. Gastroenterol.* 9:665–69
154. Schubert, M. L., Bitar, K. N., Makhlouf, G. M. 1982. Regulation of gastrin and somatostatin secretion by cholinergic and noncholinergic intramural neurons. *Am. J. Physiol.* 243: G442–47
155. Schubert, M. L., Edwards, N. F., Makhlouf, G. M. 1986. Regulation of gastric somatostatin (SS) secretion by luminal acid: A feedback control mechanism. *Gastroenterology* 90:1621
156. Schubert, M. L., Saffouri, B., Walsh, J. H., Makhlouf, G. M. 1985. Inhibition of neurally mediated gastrin secretion by bombesin antiserum. *Am. J. Physiol.* 248:G456–62
157. Seal, A. M., Meloche, R. M., Liu, Y. Q. E., Buchan, A. M. J., Brown, J. C. 1987. Effects of monoclonal antibodies to somatostatin on somatostatin-induced and intestinal fat-induced inhibition of gastric acid secretion in the rat. *Gastroenterology* 92:1187–92
158. Seal, A. M., Yamada, T., Debas, H. T., Hollinshead, J. W., Osadchey, B., et al. 1982. Somatostatin-14 and -28 clearance and potency on gastric function in dogs. *Am. J. Physiol.* 243:G97–G102
159. Seino, Y., Miyamoto, Y., Moridera, K., Taminato, T., Matsukura, S., Imura, H. 1980. The role of the beta-adrenergic mechanism in the hypergastrinemia of hyperthyroidism. *J. Clin. Endocrinol. Metab.* 50:368–70
160. Short, G. M., Doyle, J. W., Wolfe, M. M. 1985. Effect of antibodies to somatostatin on acid secretion and gastrin release by the isolated perfused rat stomach. *Gastroenterology* 88:984–88
161. Short, G. M., Reel, G. M., Doyle, J. W., Wolfe, M. M. 1985. Effect of GRP on beta-adrenergic-stimulated gastrin and somatostatin release in the isolated rat stomach. *Am. J. Physiol.* 249:G197–G202
162. Simmons, T. C., Taylor, I. L., Maxwell, V. E., Brown, J. C., Grossman, M. I. 1981. Failure of gastric inhibitory polypeptide to inhibit pentagastrin-stimulated acid secretion in vagotomized human subjects. *Dig. Dis. Sci.* 26:902–4
163. Soares, E. C., Zaterka, S., Walsh, J. H. 1977. Acid secretion and serum gastrin at graded intragastric pressures in man. *Gastroenterology* 72:676–79
164. Soll, A. H., Walsh, J. H. 1979. Regula-

tion of gastric acid secretion. *Ann. Rev. Physiol.* 41:35–53

165. Soon-Shiong, P., Debas, H. T., Brown, J. C. 1984. Bethanechol prevents inhibition of gastric acid secretion by gastric inhibitory polypeptide. *Am. J. Physiol.* 247:G171–75

166. Sopranzi, N., Melchiorri, P. 1974. Natural and synthetic bombesin-like peptides as gastrin releasers. *J. Pharmacol.* 5:125

167. Spindel, E. R., Chin, W. W., Price, J., Rees, L. H., Besser, G. M., Habener, J. F. 1984. Cloning and characterization of cDNAs encoding human gastrin-releasing peptide. *Proc. Natl. Acad. Sci. USA* 81:5699–5703

168. Stenquist, B. 1979. Studies on vagal activation of gastric acid secretion in man. *Acta Physiol. Scand (Suppl.)* 465:1–31

169. Stenquist, B., Lind, T., Haglund, U., Holst, J. J., Rehfeld, J. F., Olbe, L. 1987. Do enkephalins participate in vagal activation of gastric acid secretion in man? *Regul. Peptides* 17:1–7

170. Stenquist, B., Rehfeld, J. F., Olbe, L. 1979. Effect of proximal gastric vagotomy and anticholinergics on the acid and gastrin responses to sham feeding in duodenal ulcer patients. *Gut* 20:1020–27

171. Stevens, M. H., Thirlby, R. C., Richardson, C. T., Fredrickson, M. A., Unger, R. H., Feldman, M. 1986. Inhibitory effects of beta-adrenergic agonists on gastric acid secretion in dogs. *Am. J. Physiol.* 251:G453–59

172. Strunz, U. T., Walsh, J. H., Grossman, M. I. 1978. Stimulation of gastrin release in dogs by individual amino acids. *Proc. Soc. Exp. Biol. Med.* 157:440–41

173. Sue, R., Toomey, M. L., Todisco, A., Soll, A. H., Yamada, T. 1985. Pirenzepine-sensitive muscarinic receptors regulate gastric somatostatin and gastrin. *Am. J. Physiol.* 248:G184–87

174. Sugano, K., Park, J., Soll, A. H., Yamada, T. 1987. Stimulation of gastrin release by bombesin and canine gastrin-releasing peptides. Studies with isolated canine G cells in primary culture. *J. Clin. Invest.* 79:935–42

175. Tatsuta, M., Itoh, T., Okuda, S., Tamura, H., Baba, M., Yamamura, H. 1981. Inhibition of gastrin secretion by pirenzepine (LS 519) in treatment of gastric ulcer. *Scand. J. Gastroenterol.* 16:269–71

176. Taylor, I. L., Byrne, W. J., Christie, D. L., Ament, M. E., Walsh, J. H. 1982. Effect of individual L-amino acids on gastric acid secretion and serum gastrin and pancreatic polypeptide release in humans. *Gastroenterology* 83:272–78

177. Taylor, I. L., Walsh, J. H., Carter, D., Wood, J., Grossman, M. I. 1979. Effects of atropine and bethanechol on bombesin-stimulated release of pancreatic polypeptide and gastrin in dog. *Gastroenterology* 77:714–18

178. Thomas, F. J., Koss, M. A., Hogan, D. L., Isenberg, J. I. 1986. Enprostil, a synthetic prostaglandin E2 analogue, inhibits meal-stimulated gastric acid secretion and gastrin release in patients with duodenal ulcer. *Am. J. Med.* 81:44–49

179. Thompson, J. C., Fender, H. R., Watson, L. C., Villar, H. V. 1976. The effects on gastrin and gastric secretion of five current operations for duodenal ulcer. *Ann. Surg.* 183:599–608

180. Varner, A. A., Modlin, I. M., Walsh, J. H. 1981. High potency of bombesin for stimulation of human gastrin release and gastric acid secretion. *Regul. Peptides* 1:289–96

181. Vatn, M. H., Schrumpf, E., Hanssen, K. F., Myren, J. 1977. The effect of somatostatin on pentagastrin-stimulated gastric secretion and on plasma gastrin in man. *Scand. J. Gastroenterol.* 12:833–39

182. Walsh, J. H. 1987. Gastrointestinal hormones. In *Physiology of the Gastrointestinal Tract*, ed. L. R. Johnson, Ch. 7, pp. 181–253. New York: Raven 2nd. ed.

183. Walsh, J. H., Debas, H. T., Grossman, M. I. 1974. Pure human big gastrin. Immunochemical properties, disappearance half time, and acid-stimulating action in dogs. *J. Clin. Invest.* 54:477–85

184. Walsh, J. H., Isenberg, J. I., Ansfield, J., Maxwell, V. E. 1976. Clearance and acid-stimulating action of human big and little gastrins in duodenal ulcer subjects. *J. Clin. Invest.* 57:1125–31

185. Walsh, J. H., Maxwell, V. E., Ferrari, J., Varner, A. A. 1981. Bombesin stimulates human gastric function by gastrin-dependent and independent mechanisms. *Peptides* 2:193–98

186. Walsh, J. H., Yalow, R. S., Berson, S. A. 1971. The effect of atropine on plasma gastrin response to feeding. *Gastroenterology* 60:16–21

187. Wilborg, O., Berglund, L., Boel, E., Norris, F., Norris, K., et al. 1984. Structure of a human gastrin gene. *Proc. Natl. Acad. Sci. USA* 81:1067–69

188. Wolfe, M. M., Hocking, M. P., Maico, D. G., McGuigan, J. E. 1983. Effects of antibodies to gastric inhibitory peptide on gastric acid secretion and gastrin release in the dog. *Gastroenterology* 84:941–48

189. Wolfe, M. M., Jain, D. K., Reel, G. M., McGuigan, J. E. 1984. Effects of carbachol on gastrin and somatostatin release in rat antral tissue culture. *Gastroenterology* 87:86–93

190. Wolfe, M. M., Reel, G. M. 1986. Inhibition of gastrin release by gastric inhibitory peptide mediated by somatostatin. *Am. J. Physiol.* 250:G331–35

191. Wolfe, M. M., Reel, G. M., McGuigan, J. E. 1983. Inhibition of gastrin release by secretin is mediated by somatostatin in cultured rat antral mucosa. *J. Clin. Invest.* 72:1586–93

192. Wright, L. F., Gibson, R. G., Hirschowitz, R. I. 1977. Lack of caffeine stimulation of gastrin release in man. *Proc. Soc. Exp. Biol. Med.* 154:538–39

193. Yoo, O. J., Powell, C. T., Agarwal, K. L. 1982. Molecular cloning and nucleotide sequence of full-length cDNA coding for porcine gastrin. *Proc. Natl. Acad. Sci. USA* 79:1049–53

*Ann. Rev. Physiol. 1988. 50:65–80*

# ELECTROPHYSIOLOGY OF PANCREATIC AND SALIVARY ACINAR CELLS

## *Ole H. Petersen and David V. Gallacher*

MRC Secretory Control Research Group, The Physiological Laboratory, University of Liverpool, Post Office Box 147, Liverpool, L69 3BX, England

## INTRODUCTION

The first intracellular microelectrode recordings of membrane potential and resistance in exocrine gland cells were reported more than thirty years ago (32, 33). The acetylcholine (ACh)-evoked membrane hyperpolarization was (wrongly) thought to be due to active chloride ion ($Cl^-$) uptake into the acinar cells, and arguments were presented in favor of the hypothesis that the $Cl^-$ pump was the central energy-requiring mechanism in the primary NaCl-rich fluid secretion (32, 33). At the same time Burgen (6) showed that salivary gland cells lose $K^+$ to their surroundings when they are stimulated to secrete, and in 1963 Douglas & Poisner (8) showed that ACh-evoked salivary secretion is calcium ion ($Ca^{2+}$)-dependent. These three important findings were not linked or properly explained until patch-clamp single-channel current recording studies (60) demonstrated the presence of $Ca^{2+}$-activated $K^+$ channels in the basolateral acinar cell membrane (34, 54).

The salivary and pancreatic acinar cells possess a number of different receptors capable of interacting specifically with a number of neurotransmitters and hormones. Two classes of receptors can be distinguished, those coupled to adenylate cyclase and those coupled to phospholipase C. The first group is of comparatively little interest here as activation of receptors linked to generation of cyclic AMP has little influence on acinar electrophysiological properties (50). Activation of receptors linked to phospholipase C generates diacylglycerol and inositol trisphosphate ($IP_3$). These receptors are very

65

0066-4278/88/0315-0065$02.00

important in the context of this review as $IP_3$ releases $Ca^{2+}$ from the endoplasmic reticulum (66), and this evokes opening of the $Ca^{2+}$-activated $K^+$ channels. The receptors belonging to this class are those for ACh, norepinephrine ($\alpha$-receptors), substance P, and adenosine triphosphate (ATP) in the salivary glands and for ACh, cholecystokinin, and bombesin on the pancreatic acinar cells (52). These receptors couple stimulation to an increase in membrane permeability as well as to secretion, hence the terms stimulus-permeability and stimulus-secretion coupling (56).

In this article we review recently obtained data concerning the characteristics of the $Ca^{2+}$-activated $K^+$ channel in both salivary and pancreatic acinar cells, and we consider the roles of the $K^+$ and $Cl^-$ channels (51), the $Na^+$-$K^+$-$Cl^-$ cotransporter (13, 69), and of the $Na^+$-$K^+$ pump (4, 5) in acinar primary secretion.

The patch-clamp technique of whole-cell current recording with perfusion of the cell interior has also recently made it possible to investigate electrogenic cotransport events. Much detailed information, reviewed here, is now available about the characteristics of the $Na^+$-alanine cotransporter in pancreatic acinar cells (28).

In this review we try to integrate the recently obtained patch-clamp data on ion channels and pumps in the exocrine acinar cells with current knowledge of epithelial transport and receptor transduction mechanisms, in an attempt to provide a plausible working model for secretion by these cells.

## ION CHANNELS IN THE PLASMA MEMBRANE

So far single-channel and whole-cell current recording studies on pancreatic and salivary acinar cells have revealed the existence of three different types of $Ca^{2+}$-activated ion channels, which are permeable to $K^+$, monovalent cations, and $Cl^-$, respectively.

### Calcium-Activated Potassium Channels

$Ca^{2+}$-activated $K^+$ channels were among the first ion channels studied directly by the patch-clamp technique (60). The first direct demonstration of $Ca^{2+}$-activated $K^+$-selective channels in epithelial cells was made by Maruyama et al (34) in studies on mouse and rat salivary glands and was soon followed by similar findings in the pig pancreatic acinar cells (40).

There are several types of $Ca^{2+}$-dependent pores, but the best-characterized is the high-conductance $Ca^{2+}$- and voltage-activated $K^+$ channel (200–300 pS in symmetrical $K^+$-rich solutions) (17, 34, 40). The basic characteristics of this channel have already been reviewed several times recently (51, 52, 54). Recent studies have shown that another divalent cation, $Mg^{2+}$, also plays a role in controlling the high-conductance channel. In excised inside-out patches from mouse parotid acinar cells the effects of changes in internal $Mg^{2+}$ concentration on single-channel currents at $[Ca^{2+}]_i = 10^{-8}$ M have been investigated. When $[Mg^{2+}]_i$ is increased from about $10^{-6}$ to $10^{-3}$ M, a marked increase is evoked in channel open-state probability in the voltage range –40 to +40 mV. Smaller, but nevertheless clear effects can be seen by varying $[Mg^{2+}]_i$ between 0.25, 0.75, and 1.13 mM at a constant $[Ca^{2+}]_i$ of $10^{-8}$ M (65). This finding raises the possibility that internal $Mg^{2+}$ may contribute to modulation of channel activity. The effects of $Mg^{2+}$ are, however, minor compared to those of $Ca^{2+}$.

The biophysics of the high-conductance $K^+$ channel is interesting because it is extremely selective, as shown most clearly by its ability to discriminate between $Rb^+$ and $K^+$. This was first shown by single-channel current recordings obtained from excised membrane patches of salivary and pancreatic acini (16). These results suggested that the high-conductance $K^+$ channel is a multisite channel that both $Rb^+$ and $K^+$ can enter; however, $Rb^+$ binds much more strongly than $K^+$ to sites within the channel. This model, proposed by us in 1984 (16), has since been confirmed by others working on reconstituted but similar $Ca^{2+}$-activated high-conductance $K^+$ channels from muscle (10).

In isolated intact cells single-channel currents due to opening of the high-conductance $K^+$ channels can be observed at the spontaneous resting potential. However, in acinar cells from pig pancreas (67) or mouse submandibular gland (17) the open-state probability is very low ($\sim$0.002). Depolarization of the plasma membrane evokes a marked increase in the fractional open time of the channels (17, 67). The electrical resistance of the plasma membrane, which is largely determined by the high-conductance $K^+$ channels, is therefore highly voltage dependent. In order to quantify the total membrane $K^+$ conductance, information is needed on channel density, as well as on single-channel conductance and average open-state probability. Density information can only be obtained by comparison of single-channel current data with whole-cell current recordings (60).

In resting pig pancreatic acinar cells, where this approach to channel quantification was first used, the total number of operational channels appears to be quite small, only about 50 per cell (40). In ensemble fluctuation analysis of whole-cell currents it is possible to estimate the number of channels per cell *(N)*, the single channel current amplitude, and the open-state probability *(p)* from measurements of current variance and mean current as a function of membrane potential. Such an analysis has been carried out on parotid acinar cells (35). The single-channel current-voltage relationship obtained from this analysis is virtually identical to that obtained directly from single-channel current recording. The estimate of *p* as a function of membrane potential from the ensemble fluctuation analysis also agrees closely with the direct single-channel current measurements. The estimate, from the ensemble noise analysis, of $N$ was scattered between 30 and 108 with a mean value of 76 channels per cell (35). Since the open-state probability ($p$) in the resting intact cells is only about 0.002 (17, 67), on average only 0.15 channel will be open in a single acinar cell. However, in the intact salivary glands and pancreas the acinar cells are extremely well coupled within units of 100–500 cells (50, 52).

Based on the conservative estimate of 100 cells per acinar unit, there would be 7500 functioning channels in the resting state; with $p = 0.002$ the average number of open channels would be 15 per acinar unit. Since the resting value of $p$ is so low, the membrane has an enormous reserve $K^+$ conductance that can be mobilized either by depolarizing influences or by hormones and neurotransmitters evoking intracellular $Ca^{2+}$ release (see section on activation of ion channels in acinar cells by neurotransmitters and hormones).

Although the high-conductance $Ca^{2+}$- and voltage-activated $K^+$ channels dominate the electrical characteristics of acinar cells from the pig pancreas and the rat parotid (35, 40), there are also smaller $Ca^{2+}$- and voltage-activated $K^+$ channels (20–50 pS) (34, 53), which seem to be dominant in the guinea pig pancreas (55).

## Calcium-Activated Nonselective Cation Channels

Acinar cells in mouse and rat pancreas do not have $Ca^{2+}$-activated $K^+$-selective channels (54). They do, however, possess $Ca^{2+}$-activated and voltage-insensitive nonselective channels with a unit conductance of about 30–35 pS under quasiphysiological ion gradients. These channels do not discriminate between $Na^+$, $K^+$, $Li^+$, and $Rb^+$, are impermeable to anions and have at most a very low $Ca^{2+}$ permeability (36, 37, 52). The $Ca^{2+}$-sensitivity of the channel decreases with time after excision, making its physiological importance difficult to assess (39). Recent experiments in our laboratory show that ATP acting on the membrane inside inhibits opening of the channels. At a concentration of 1 mM, ATP evokes almost complete channel closure. This channel type has also been reported to exist in salivary acinar cells along with to the $K^+$-selective pores (34).

## Calcium-Activated Chloride Channels

Intracellular microelectrode studies carried out many years ago clearly indicated that acinar cell membranes are permeable to $Cl^-$ (50). However, in the salivary glands and the pancreas there is still no direct information about single-channel properties of these important conductance pathways, although such data are available for many other secretory epithelia (15). The existence of $Ca^{2+}$-activated $Cl^-$ channels has been clearly established in a patch-clamp whole-cell current study on mouse and rat parotid acinar cells in which the $Ca^{2+}$ ionophore A23187 was shown to evoke a marked increase in $Cl^-$ conductance (25).

# Na$^+$–AMINO ACID COTRANSPORT

The resting membrane potential in acinar cells is due to the large transmembrane K$^+$ gradient and the existence of resting K$^+$ channels. The transmembrane K$^+$ gradient is established and maintained by the ATP-driven Na$^+$-K$^+$ pump (50, 52). The transmembrane Na$^+$ gradient that results from the operation of the Na$^+$-K$^+$ pump, together with the membrane potential, is the driving force for the uptake of a number of amino acids. Na$^+$ gradient–driven amino acid transport is generally regarded as an important mechanism of amino acid uptake, and such a process has been directly demonstrated for L-alanine in membrane vesicles isolated from the cat pancreas (70). Neutral amino acids, such as L-alanine and L-valine, when added to the bathing fluid of isolated pancreatic segments evoke marked Na$^+$-dependent and stereospecific membrane depolarization as well as a small increase in membrane conductance (26, 52).

The alanine-evoked Na$^+$-dependent acinar membrane depolarization or inward current observed in microelectrode experiments (26, 52), as well as the depolarization seen in experiments using the potential-sensitive dye diethyloxocarbocyanine (DOCC) (62), could in principle be explained either by (a) real cotransport of the neutral amino acid molecule and the sodium ion or (b) by an amino acid–receptor interaction that opens up a Na$^+$ conductance pathway (channel). In order to distinguish between these two possibilities, whole-cell current experiments have been carried out in the absence of any electrochemical driving force for Na$^+$ (28). An isolated pancreatic acinar cell or cell cluster is dialyzed with a 100-mM Na$_2$SO$_4$ solution, and the same solution is used in the bath. The membrane potential is clamped at 0 mV. Under these conditions there is of course no net transmembrane current flow. When L-alanine is added to the outside (bath) solution in a concentration of, for example, 5 mM, a substantial inward current is observed, which rises rapidly to a peak and then gradually declines to near zero within 5–10 min. Subsequent removal of the extracellular L-alanine evokes a transient outward current with a magnitude and time course similar to those of the initial inward current. A likely explanation for this result is that in the first part of the experiment alanine moves inward until internal and external alanine concentrations have become nearly equal. In the second part of the experiment the gradient is reversed and alanine moves outward, which leads to the outward-directed Na$^+$ current. This type of experiment has also been carried out using internal perfusion of the patch pipette and therefore the cell interior to ensure direct control of the internal alanine concentration. Such studies show clearly that the alanine effect is not due to opening of a Na$^+$-selective ion channel and constitute strong evidence for Na$^+$-alanine cotransport. These experiments have also shown that the transport system is at least qualitatively symmetrical with regard to inward and outward movement. The alanine-evoked current is stereospecific: D-alanine evokes very much smaller current signals than does L-alanine, and no currents can be elicited when all $Na^+$ is replaced by either $K^+$ or $Tris^+$ (28). L-alanine and 2-(methylamino)-isobutyric acid (MeAIB) have almost the same affinity for the cotransporter, and in the presence of a high concentration of MeAIB (20 mM) 1-mM L-alanine does not further increase the $Na^+$ current, which suggests that the two amino acids compete for the same site. The alanine-evoked current has also been shown to depend on external pH, with a maximum current at pH $\approx$ 7 and a current of $\sim$ 50% of the maximum at pH values of 6 or 8. All these findings indicate that the "A" system of amino acid transport (48) is responsible for the alanine-driven currents (28).

In the patch-clamp whole-cell current recording experiments the current under "zero-trans" conditions (i.e. with varying finite concentrations of $Na^+$ and alanine on the outside and zero concentrations on the inside) exhibited Michaelis-Menten behavior. The half-saturation concentration of alanine at the external site decreased from 18 mM at $[Na^+]_o$ = 5 mM to 2.9 mM at $[Na^+]_o$ = 150 mM. The half-saturation concentration of $Na^+$ was found to decrease from 63 mM at $[L\text{-ala}]_o$ = 1 mM to 14 mM at $[L\text{-ala}]_o$ = 10 mM. From reversal potential measurements in the presence of various alanine and $Na^+$ concentration gradients, a $Na^+$/alanine stoichiometric ratio of 1:1 could be inferred (28). The precise measurements obtained under voltage-clamp and well-defined ionic conditions have been used to discriminate between different mechanistic models, and these considerations favor a simultaneous transport model (27).

A wide variety of amino acids (acid, neutral, and basic) can induce membrane depolarization in pancreatic acinar cells (52); however, only the mechanism by which neutral amino acids evoke this effect has been studied in detail. No such studies have yet been carried out in salivary acinar cells, in which, in contrast with pancreatic cells (48), there may be no specific alanine uptake system (71).

# ACTIVATION OF ION CHANNELS IN ACINAR CELLS BY NEUROTRANSMITTERS AND HORMONES

In freshly dissociated salivary and pancreatic acinar cells the basolateral membrane is accessible to patch clamping. The cation channels reported in the preceding sections can all be localized to the basolateral membranes of the acinar cells. Thus in the acinar cells of all species investigated to date the single-channel events in the basolateral membranes are dominated by calcium-activated cation conductances. In every cell type investigated, save rodent pancreatic acinar cells, a highly selective, calcium- and voltage-activated $K^+$ channel has been identified. These calcium-activated cation channels are thought to be responsible for the permeability changes associated with secretagogue stimulation. This proposal can be directly tested by investigation of the effects of stimulus-permeability coupled neurotransmitters and hormones on the activity of ion channels in situ. This can be achieved either by whole-cell current recording or by single-channel current recording from cell-attached patches.

## Whole-Cell Current Recording

The first direct demonstration of a role for neurotransmitters in the regulation of ion channel currents in exocrine acinar cells was provided by Maruyama & Petersen (38), who reported the effect of the stimulus-permeability coupled agonist cholecystokinin (CCK) in pig pancreatic acinar cells. Almost identical effects have been described for the agonist acetylcholine (ACh) in rodent salivary (25) and lacrimal (12, 68) acinar cells. Stimulation of acinar cells with a stimulus-permeability coupled agonist results in a marked increase in the amplitude of the voltage-activated outward $K^+$ currents. The effects of hormonal stimulation in both pancreatic and salivary acinar cells are clearly calcium dependent (see 51). Secretagogue activation is thus associated with a calcium-dependent increase in outward $K^+$ currents. In pig pancreatic acinar cells the voltage and calcium sensitivity of the outward currents is consistent with activity in the high-conductance $K^+$ channel. Further, the agonist-induced outward currents are susceptable to blockade by low concentrations of TEA in the extracellular fluid (51). In the only study to date of ACh activation in parotid acinar cells (25) it was reported that the ACh-induced whole-cell $K^+$ currents are not diminished by external application of 5-mM TEA. This is surprising, since the voltage-activated outward currents in the unstimulated parotid acinar cells were totally abolished by 1-mM TEA in the extracellular solution (35). This apparent failure of external TEA to block ACh-evoked currents in the parotid acinar cells raises the possibility that ACh stimulation of salivary acinar cells may also activate $K^+$ pores other than the high-conductance $K^+$ channel.

Two other important features are apparent in the whole-cell recordings of agonist-induced currents in both the pancreatic and salivary acinar cells: (a) The total outward currents evoked in the cells by the agonists (or elevated intracellular calcium) are too large to be due solely to an increase in the open-state probability of the 50–100 high-conductance $K^+$ channels estimated to be present in unstimulated cells (25, 38). If the increased currents are due exclusively to activity in high-conductance $K^+$ channels, then it appears that agonist activation increases the number of functional channels per cell. (b) Whole-cell current recordings in pig pancreatic (67) and more markedly in rodent salivary acinar cells (25) and lacrimal gland (12, 14, 68) reveal that agonist activation (or elevation in intracellular calcium) results not only in increased outward current but also in activation of an inward current. This inward current in salivary acinar cells (25) and in lacrimal acinar cells (12, 14, 41) is shown to be due to activation of a calcium-dependent $Cl^-$ conductance pathway, yet no $Cl^-$ channels have been reported in the single-channel studies of excised basolateral membrane patches from either salivary or pancreatic acinar cells. The whole-cell $Cl^-$ current has been most extensively investigated in lacrimal acinar cells (12, 41). Ensemble noise analysis of whole-cell currents in this tissue suggest that the unitary conductance of the calcium-activated $Cl^-$ channels is 1–2 pS. These small channels may have been missed in the single-channel recordings of salivary and pancreatic membranes. Another explanation is that the $Cl^-$ channels are localized specifically to the luminal membrane of the acinar cells. This is not an unreasonable proposal since patch-clamp studies in other secretory epithelia have identified $Cl^-$ channels specifically in the luminal membranes (15). The significance of this hypothesis is discussed below.

## Single-Channel Current Recording in Cell-Attached Patches

The most direct demonstration of the messenger-mediated effects of neurotransmitters and hormones on the activity of ion channels is obtained in the cell-attached recording mode. The cells are intact, there is no disturbance of cell function, and ion channels are characterized in their most natural environment, i.e. while bathed on their intracellular aspect by cytosolic fluid. Any effect of agonists on intracellular electrolyte (including pH) composition (9, 31) will also be manifest. In this approach the agonists are applied to the solution bathing the acinar cells. The neurotransmitters or hormones thus have no direct access to the isolated patch membrane area and any effect of the stimulus-permeability coupled agonist must therefore be mediated by the generation of some intracellular mediator(s).

The ability of stimulus-permeability coupled agonists to activate currents in intact cells has now been demonstrated in human and rodent salivary acinar cells (17, 18, 44) and in pig and rodent pancreatic (37, 67) and lacrimal (41) acinar cells. In each of these tissues, except rodent pancreas, patch-clamp recordings from excised patches of basolateral membrane are dominated by currents due to the voltage- and calcium-activated high-conductance $K^+$ channel, and in each case this is the channel activated in situ by stimulus-permeability coupled agonists. The effects of the agonists are mimicked by the calcium ionophore A23187.

In salivary acinar cells the calcium-dependent effects of neurotransmitters on ion channels have been extensively investigated (17, 18). Acetylcholine stimulation results in a dramatic increase in the frequency and duration of opening of the high-conductance $K^+$ channels in the cell-attached patches. At the onset of activation, and during inactivation induced by application of atropine, currents are seen in the lower-conductance $K^+$ channel (which may actually be a substate of the "high-conductance" $K^+$ channel). In all of these experiments the solution in the recording pipette was calcium-free, and the only source of calcium to activate channels in the patch was the cytosol. In the absence of extracellular calcium, ACh stimulation results in an increase in the single-channel current amplitude but a fall in the open-state probability of the channels in the patch. These effects in $Ca^{2+}$-free solutions are thought to be due to the release of intracellular calcium, sufficient only for activation of $K^+$ channels in the membrane area outside the patch, and consequent acinar cell hyperpolarization (18, 43). The cell-attached recording configuration has been used to demonstrate that there is no voltage-dependent calcium influx pathway and that the calcium influx pathway is not activated by ACh if acinar cells are bathed in $Na^+$-free media (18, 43). The implications of this $Na^+$-dependent calcium influx pathway are discussed in the following sections.

In the pig pancreatic acinar cells the CCK activation of channels in situ was dependent on the presence of calcium in the recording pipette itself. In this tissue sustained activation of the high-conductance $K^+$ channel in the cell-attached patches only occurs when hormonal stimulation promotes entry of calcium across the area of membrane covered by the patch pipette. Therefore CCK stimulation must be associated with the generation of some intracellular regulator of calcium influx (67).

## RECEPTOR TRANSDUCTION MECHANISMS REGULATING ION CHANNEL ACTIVITY

The stimulus-permeability coupled secretagogues exert their effects on ion channels by releasing calcium from intracellular stores and by promoting influx of calcium from the extracellular to intracellular fluid. The receptor-mediated transduction mechanisms that regulate these effects are now the subject of much interest. In particular, the role of the inositol polyphosphates (see introduction) is being extensively investigated, and there are several recent reviews on this subject (see 1, 2, 57). The evidence that $Ins(1,4,5)P_3$ ($IP_3$) mobilizes intracellular calcium stores is now unequivocal. $IP_3$ apparently activates a calcium release pathway in the endoplasmic reticulum (ER) (45). Calcium-mobilizing ability has also been reported for cyclic $IP_3$ [$Ins(1:2,4,5)P_3$] and $Ins(1,4)P_2$. $Ins(1,3,4)P_3$ is much less effective in mobilizing intracellular calcium, and $IP_4$ is apparently ineffective in this role (see 24). In salivary acinar cells there is rapid production of the calcium-mobilizing form of $IP_3$ [$Ins(1,4,5)P_3$], which is consistent with its role in the rapid release of calcium stores. During sustained stimulation, which is dependent on calcium influx rather than release (see 18, 43), $Ins(1,3,4)P_3$

(product of $IP_4$ hydrolysis) dominates (23). Recent studies have also presented evidence of a different, $IP_3$-independent, pathway for regulating calcium release from ER (19, 22), specifically, one involving a guanine nucleotide regulatory mechanism.

In exocrine acinar cells the response to neurotransmitters is only sustained in the presence of external calcium. The receptor-mediated transduction mechanisms regulating calcium influx are poorly understood in these tissues. Putney (58) has suggested that the intracellular stores, ER, and the calcium influx pathway are functionally coupled, such that $IP_3$ promotes release of calcium from the ER, which in turn activates calcium influx. Based on whole-cell current recordings of lacrimal acinar cells, the effects of intracellular $IP_3$ are reported to be independent of extracellular calcium (11). Slack et al (64) have reported that injection of $IP_3$ into sea urchin eggs resulted in an activation that was dependent on extracellular calcium, i.e. calcium influx. Irvine & Moor (24) now report that this effect of $IP_3$ on calcium influx is unlikely to be a direct one but is probably due to conversion of $IP_3$ to $IP_4$ within the cells. They have also demonstrated an apparent effect of $IP_4$ on calcium influx (24). However, it was recently reported that $IP_3$ can activate calcium channels in excised patches of membrane from T lymphocytes (30, see also 47). Important new findings are still being reported, but studies to date seem to indicate that $Ins(1,4,5)P_3$ promotes calcium release from the ER and that $IP_4$, acting in concert with the calcium-mobilizing agent, then regulates calcium influx.

Gallacher & Morris have shown that the calcium influx pathway in salivary acinar cells cannot be activated by ACh if cells are bathed in $Na^+$-free solutions (18, 43). Since phosphatidylinositol (PI) turnover is independent of external $[Na^+]$ (29), this lack of sustained response cannot be due to blockade of phosphatidyl inositol bisphosphate ($PIP_2$) hydrolysis. In rat thymocytes calcium influx is similarly abolished if cells are bathed in $Na^+$-free media (20). In thymocytes the absence of calcium influx has been attributed to blockade of $Na^+$-$H^+$ exchange. In human platelets Siffert & Akkerman report (63) that $Na^+$-$H^+$ exchange is a prerequisite for calcium mobilization. In many tissues the stimulus promoting $Na^+$-$H^+$ exchange is activation of protein kinase C by diacylglycerol. In pancreatic acinar cells the stimulus-permeability and stimulus-phosphoinositide coupled agonist caerulein promotes intracellular alkalinization by stimulating $Na^+$-$H^+$ exchange (9). It is not clear how intracellular $[H^+]$ could influence calcium homeostasis. The calcium influx pathway itself could be pH sensitive, or the effects of $IP_3$ and/or $IP_4$ could be pH dependent. Brass & Joseph have reported an effect of pH on the apparent $K_m$ of $IP_3$ for calcium stores in permeabilized platelets (3). The $K_m$ of $IP_3$ was reduced by 40% for an increase in pH of 0.3 (pH 7.1 to 7.4). Studies on salivary acinar cells that employed phorbol esters to activate protein kinase C in the absence of any concomitant $PIP_2$ hydrolysis have shown that this pathway cannot in itself promote any permeability changes (59). It appears then that any effects of protein kinase C activation on calcium mobilization or calcium influx are most probably of a permissive or synergistic nature; for example, protein kinase C might activate $Na^+$-$H^+$ exchange and thus alter pH in a manner that augments the activity of $IP_3$ and or $IP_4$.

## ROLE OF ION CHANNELS AND PUMPS IN SECRETION

The main electrolytes in the isotonic primary acinar fluid in both salivary glands and pancreas are $Na^+$ and $Cl^-$, although $HCO_3^-$ and $K^+$ are also present (61, 71). In the salivary glands the primary secretion is the only source of the fluid in the final secretion (71), whereas in the pancreas a bicarbonate-rich fluid is added in the duct system (61). The proteins secreted are mainly derived from the acinar cells, and the mechanism underlying the release is exocytosis (42).

Figure 1 summarizes some of the most important electrolyte transport events in acinar cells. For the sake of clarity, different aspects are each shown in a separate cell. In cell a, neurotransmitters or hormones act by releasing intracellular $Ca^{2+}$ and increasing $[Ca^{2+}]_i$ (43, 49). The released $Ca^{2+}$ activates $K^+$ channels in the basolateral plasma membrane. The $Ca^{2+}$-activated $Cl^-$ channels are not well characterized. They may be present in the luminal cell membrane, because after stimulation the lumen becomes more negative with respect to the interstitial fluid (33). The $Cl^-$ channels may be derived in part from the secretory granules and inserted into the luminal membrane during exocytosis (7).

Cell b shows the ion transport events underlying NaCl secretion. The basolateral plasma membrane contains three transport proteins: the $Ca^{2+}$- and voltage-activated $K^+$ channel (blocked by tetraethylammonium or $Ba^{2+}$) (51), the $Na^+$-$K^+$-$Cl^-$ cotransporter (blocked by loop diuretics such as bumetanide, piretanide, and furosemide) (13, 69), and the energy-requiring $Na^+$-$K^+$ pump (blocked by ouabain) (4, 5, 46). In the steady secreting state $K^+$ recirculates via pump and cotransporter. The only net transport is $Cl^-$ uptake, and $Cl^-$ leaves the cell via the luminal $Cl^-$ channels. The lumen negativity allows $Na^+$ to move between the cells into the narrow intercellular spaces and through the tight junctions at their luminal ends. The net result of all these transport events is transcellular NaCl transport, with water following.

Cell c in Figure 1 presents the overall electrical circuit due to the transport events shown in cell b. The outward current across the basolateral membrane is mostly due to $K^+$ exit through the $Ca^{2+}$-activated channels, but it is also partly due to the imbalance of ion movements through the $Na^+$-$K^+$ pump. This outward current is matched by the inward current through the luminal

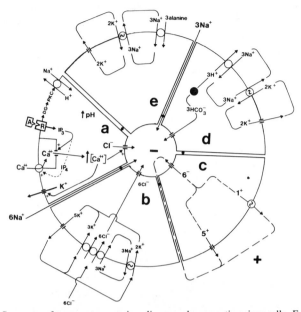

*Figure 1*   Summary of transport events in salivary and pancreatic acinar cells. For the sake of clarity different aspects are shown in separate cells labelled a–e for discussion in the text. The plasma membrane is divided into two parts by the tight junctions placed close to the lumen. All the transport events shown to take place across the basal membranes undoubtedly also occur in the lateral membranes. The stoichiometry of the $Na^+$-$K^+$ pump is $3:2$, as shown in cells b, d, and e. The stoichiometries shown for $Na^+$-$K^+$-$Cl^-$, $Na^+$-$H^+$, and $Na^+$-alanine co-(counter) transport do not indicate the number of ions moved for each turnover of the transporter, but rather indicate the total number of ions moved relative to each cycle of the $Na^+$-$K^+$ pump. If, for example, there were a $1:1$ ratio of the densities of $Na^+$-$K^+$ pumps and $Na^+$-$K^+$-$Cl^-$ cotransporters, the numbers shown in cell b would indicate that the $Na^+$-$K^+$-$Cl^-$ cotransporter turns over twice for each cycle of the $Na^+$-$K^+$ pump. The density of $K^+$ channels is no doubt far lower than that of the pumps. Abbreviations: A, agonist; R, receptor; $IP_3$, inositol(1,4,5)trisphosphate; DG, diacylglycerol; PKC, protein kinase C; $IP_4$, inositol (1,3,4,5)tetrakisphosphate.

$Cl^-$ channels. To complete the circuit, current has to pass between the cells and through the so-called tight junctions. This "paracellular" current is carried mainly by $Na^+$ moving from the interstitial fluid into the acinar lumen. The low transcellular specific resistance (which is much lower than the specific transmembrane resistance), described for many epithelia, was first demonstrated in salivary acini (33) and is explained by the leakiness of the so-called tight junctions (50). The initial $K^+$ release to the blood side (6) is due to $Ca^{2+}$ activation of $K^+$ channels, but $K^+$ has to be accompanied by something else, namely $Cl^-$ (46). In the initial period following stimulation, a large part of the paracellular cation flow is made up of $K^+$, which explains the "$K^+$ transient" in the secreted juice (6). The release of cellular KCl creates a more favorable overall electrochemical gradient for $Na^+$-$K^+$-$Cl^-$ uptake via the cotransporter, and the $Na^+$ inflow raises the intracellular $Na^+$ concentration, which stimulates the $Na^+$-$K^+$ pump (46). Both transport proteins help to reaccumulate $K^+$, and in the secreting steady state this exactly balances the $K^+$ lost via the channels. When stimulation is discontinued, $[Ca^{2+}]_i$ sharply decreases (43), and both $K^+$ and $Cl^-$ channels close. There is now net KCl reuptake through the $Na^+$-$K^+$ pump and $Na^+$-$K^+$-$Cl^-$ cotransporter. Thereafter the overall electrochemical gradient for $Na^+$-$K^+$-$Cl^-$ cotransport gradually becomes less favorable for uptake. When $Na^+$ inflow is reduced, the activity of the $Na^+$-$K^+$ pump is also brought back to the prestimulation level, and the gland is again in a true resting state.

Cell d illustrates the transport apparatus needed for the secretion of $NaHCO_3$. The $Na^+$-$H^+$ exchanger (21) is activated by stimulation (9) via diacylglycerol (see cell a). The only transport protein that has not been identified here is the postulated $HCO_3^-$ channel in the plasma membrane. This could be the $Cl^-$ channel already depicted in cells b and c with some $HCO_3^-$ permeability, or a combination of this $Cl^-$ channel with a $Cl^-$-$HCO_3^-$ exchanger, or a $Na^+$-dependent bicarbonate transporter with a stoichiometry of 3 $HCO_3^-$ per $Na^+$, such as the one found in the rat renal proximal tubule (72). In order to save space the electrical circuit of the bicarbonate transport apparatus is not shown, but the network could be similar to that involved in NaCl secretion in cell c.

Cell e shows the transporters involved in amino acid uptake. Only the sodium-alanine cotransporter is shown here because it is the only amino acid transporter that has been characterized in detail in electrophysiological experiments (26, 28).

One transporter that has been clearly identified, but is nevertheless not included in Figure 1, is the $Ca^{2+}$-activated nonselective cation channel. The possible role of this channel in fluid secretion is unclear, but various very hypothetical models incorporating this element have recently been discussed (51, 52).

## CONCLUSION

One of the best-characterized transport proteins in salivary and pancreatic acinar cells is the $Ca^{2+}$- and voltage-activated $K^+$ channel. This channel has a central role in many important aspects of secretion from acinar cells, since it is essential not only for chloride and bicarbonate secretion, but also for amino acid uptake and therefore protein synthesis and secretion. The $Ca^{2+}$-activated $K^+$ channel is the key to the understanding of the $Ca^{2+}$-dependence of fluid secretion as well as the stimulant-evoked $K^+$ release and membrane hyperpolarization described many years ago.

ACKNOWLEDGMENTS

This work was supported by grants from the Medical Research Council (United Kingdom) and The Wellcome Trust.

## Literature Cited

1. Abdel-Latif, A. A. 1986. Calcium-mobilizing receptors, polyphosphoinositides and the generation of second messengers. *Pharmacol. Rev.* 38:227–72

2. Berridge, M. J. 1986. Regulation of ion channels by inositol trisphosphate and diacylglycerol. *J. Exp. Biol.* 124:323–35

3. Brass, L. F., Joseph, S. K. 1985. A role for inositol trisphosphate in intracellular $Ca^{2+}$ mobilization and granule secretion in platelets. *J. Biol. Chem.* 260:15172–79

4. Bundgaard, M., Moller, M., Poulsen, J. H. 1977. Localization of sodium pump sites in cat salivary glands. *J. Physiol. London* 273:339–53

5. Bundgaard, M., Moller, M., Poulsen, J. H. 1981. Localization of sodium pump sites in cat pancreas. *J. Physiol. London* 313:405–14

6. Burgen, A. S. V. 1956. The secretion of potassium in saliva. *J. Physiol. London* 132:20–39

7. DeLisle, R. C., Hopfer, U. 1986. Electrolyte permeabilities of pancreatic zymogen granules: Implications for pancreatic secretion. *Am. J. Physiol.* 250:G489–96

8. Douglas, W. W., Poisner, A. M. 1963. The influence of calcium on the secretory response of the submaxillary gland to acetylcholine or to noradrenaline. *J. Physiol. London* 165:528–41

9. Dufresne, M., Bastie, M. J., Vaysse, N., Creach, Y., Hollande, E., Ribet, A. 1985. The amiloride sensitive $Na^+/H^+$ antiport in guinea pig pancreatic acini. *FEBS Lett.* 187:126–30

10. Eisenman, G., Latorre, R., Miller, C. 1986. Multi-ion conduction and selectivity in the high-conductance $Ca^{2+}$-activated $K^+$ channel from skeletal muscle. *Biophys. J.* 50:1025–34

11. Evans, M. G., Marty, A. 1986. Potentiation of muscarinic and α-adrenergic responses by an analogue of guanosine-5'-triphosphate. *Proc. Natl. Acad. Sci. USA* 83:4099–4103

12. Evans, M. G., Marty, A. 1986. Calcium-dependent chloride currents in isolated cells from rat lacrimal glands. *J. Physiol. London* 378:437–60

13. Exley, P. M., Fuller, C. M., Gallacher, D. V. 1986. Potassium uptake in the mouse submandibular gland is dependent on chloride and sodium and abolished by piretanide. *J. Physiol. London* 378:97–108

14. Findlay, I., Petersen, O. H. 1985. Acetylcholine stimulates a $Ca^{2+}$-dependent $Cl^-$ conductance in mouse lacrimal acinar cells. *Pflüg. Arch.* 403:328–30

15. Frizzel, R. A., Halm, D. R., Rechkemmer, G., Shoemaker, R. L. 1986. Chloride channel regulation in secretory epithelia. *Fed. Proc.* 45:2727–31

16. Gallacher, D. V., Maruyama, Y., Petersen, O. H. 1984. Patch-clamp study of rubidium and potassium conductances in single cation channels from mammalian exocrine acini. *Pflüg. Arch.* 401:361–67

17. Gallacher, D. V., Morris, A. P. 1986. A patch-clamp study of potassium currents in resting and acetylcholine-stimulated mouse submandibular acinar cells. *J. Physiol. London* 373:379–95

18. Gallacher, D. V., Morris, A. P. 1987. The receptor-regulated calcium influx in mouse submandibular acinar cells is sodium dependent: A patch-clamp study. *J. Physiol. London* 384:119–30

19. Gill, D. O., Ueda, T., Chueh, S.-H., Noel, M. W. 1986. $Ca^{2+}$ release from endoplasmic reticulum is mediated by a guanine nucleotide regulatory mechanism. *Nature* 320:461–64

20. Grinstein, S., Goetz, J. D. 1985. Control of free cytoplasmic calcium by intracellular pH in rat lymphocytes. *Biochim. Biophys. Acta* 819:267–70

21. Hellmessen, W., Christian, A. L., Fasold, H., Schulz, I. 1985. Coupled $Na^+-H^+$ exchange in isolated acinar cells from rat exocrine pancreas. *Am. J. Physiol.* 249:G125–36

22. Henne, V., Soling, H.-D. 1986. Guanosine 5'-triphosphate releases calcium from rat liver and guinea pig parotid gland. *FEBS Lett.* 202:267–73

23. Irvine, R. F., Anggard, E. A., Letcher, A. J., Downes, C. P. 1985. Metabolism of inositol (1,4,5) trisphosphate and inositol (1,3,4) trisphosphate in rat parotid glands. *Biochem. J.* 229:505–11

24. Irvine, R. F., Moor, R. M. 1986. Micro-injection of inositol (1,3,4,5) tetrakisphosphate activates sea urchin eggs by promoting $Ca^{2+}$ entry. *Biochem. J.* 240:917–20

25. Iwatsuki, N., Maruyama, Y., Matsumoto, O., Nishiyama, A. 1985. Activation of $Ca^{2+}$-dependent $Cl^-$ and $K^+$ conductances in rat and mouse parotid acinar cells. *Jpn. J. Physiol.* 35:933–44

26. Iwatsuki, N., Petersen, O. H. 1980. Amino acids evoke short-latency membrane conductance increase in pancreatic acinar cells. *Nature* 283:492–94

27. Jauch, P., Läuger, P. 1986. Electrogenic properties of the sodium-alanine cotransporter in pancreatic acinar cells. II. Comparison with transport models. *J. Membr. Biol.* 94:117–27

28. Jauch, P., Petersen, O. H., Läuger, P. 1986. Electrogenic properties of the sodium-alanine cotransporter in pancreatic acinar cells: I. Tight-seal whole-cell recordings. *J. Membr. Biol.* 94:99–115

29. Jones, L. M., Michell, R. H. 1976. Cholinergically stimulated phosphatidylinositol breakdown in parotid gland fragments is independent of the ionic environment. *Biochem. J.* 158:505–7

30. Kuno, M., Gardner, P. 1987. Ion channels activated by inositol 1,4,5-trisphosphate in plasma membrane of human T-lymphocytes. *Nature* 326:301–4

31. Landis, C. A., Putney, J. W. Jr. 1979. Calcium and receptor regulation of radiosodium uptake by dispersed rat parotid acinar cells. *J. Physiol. London* 297:369–77

32. Lundberg, A. 1956. Secretory potential and secretion in the sublingual gland of the cat. *Nature* 177:1080–81

33. Lundberg, A. 1958. Electrophysiology of salivary glands. *Physiol. Rev.* 38:21–40

34. Maruyama, Y., Gallacher, D. V., Petersen, O. H. 1983. Voltage and $Ca^{2+}$-activated $K^+$ channel in basolateral acinar cell membranes of mammalian salivary glands. *Nature* 302:827–29

35. Maruyama, Y., Nishiyama, A., Izumi, T., Hoshimiya, N., Petersen, O. H. 1986. Ensemble noise and current relaxation analysis of $K^+$ current in single isolated salivary acinar cells from rat. *Pflüg. Arch.* 406:69–72

36. Maruyama, Y., Petersen, O. H. 1982. Single-channel currents in isolated patches of plasma membrane from basal surface of pancreatic acini. *Nature* 299:159–61

37. Maruyama, Y., Petersen, O. H. 1982. Cholecystokinin activation of single-channel currents is mediated by internal messenger in pancreatic acinar cells. *Nature* 300:61–63

38. Maruyama, Y., Petersen, O. H. 1984. Control of $K^+$ conductance by cholecystokinin and $Ca^{2+}$ in single pancreatic acinar cells studied by the patch-clamp technique. *J. Membr. Biol.* 79:293–300

39. Maruyama, Y., Petersen, O. H. 1984. Single calcium-dependent cation channels in mouse pancreatic acinar cells. *J. Membr. Biol.* 81:83–87

40. Maruyama, Y., Petersen, O. H., Flanagan, P., Pearson, G. T. 1983. Quantification of $Ca^{2+}$-activated $K^+$ channels under hormonal control in pig pancreas acinar cells. *Nature* 305:228–32

41. Marty, A., Tan, Y. P., Trautmann, A. 1984. Three types of calcium-dependent channel in rat lacrimal glands. *J. Physiol. London* 357:293–325

42. Meldolesi, J., Ceccarelli, B. 1981. Exocytosis and membrane recycling. *Philos. Trans. R. Soc. London Ser. B* 296:55–65

43. Morris, A. P., Fuller, C. M., Gallacher, D. V. 1987. Cholinergic receptors regulate a voltage-insensitive but $Na^+$-dependent calcium influx pathway in salivary acinar cells. *FEBS Lett.* 211:195–99

44. Morris, A. P., Gallacher, D. V., Fuller, C. M., Scott, J. 1987. Cholinergic receptor-regulation of potassium channels and potassium transport in human submandibular acinar cells. *J. Dent. Res.* 66:541–46

45. Muallem, S., Schoeffield, M., Pandol, S., Sachs, G. 1985. Inositol trisphosphate modification of ion transport in rough endoplasmic reticulum. *Proc. Natl. Acad. Sci. USA* 82:4433–37

46. Nauntofte, B., Poulsen, J. H. 1986. Effects of $Ca^{2+}$ and furosemide on $Cl^-$ transport and $O_2$ uptake in rat parotid acini. *Am. J. Physiol.* 251:C175–85

47. Neher, E. 1987. Receptor-operated $Ca^{2+}$ channels. *Nature* 326:242

48. Norman, P. S. R., Mann, G. E. 1986. Transport characteristics of system A in the rat exocrine pancreatic epithelium analyzed using the specific nonmetabolized amino acid analogue α-methylaminoisobutyric acid. *Biochim. Biophys. Acta* 861:389–94

49. Pandol, S., Schoeffield, M. S., Sachs, G., Muallem, S. 1985. Role of free cytosolic calcium in secretagogue-stimulated amylase release from dispersed acini from guinea pig pancreas. *J. Biol. Chem.* 260:81–86

50. Petersen, O. H. 1980. *The Electrophysiology of Gland Cells.* New York: Academic. 253 pp.
51. Petersen, O. H. 1986. Calcium-activated potassium channels and fluid secretion by exocrine glands. *Am. J. Physiol.* 251:G1–G13
52. Petersen, O. H. 1987. Electrophysiology of exocrine gland cells. In *Physiology of the Gastrointestinal Tract,* ed. L. R. Johnson, pp. 745–71. New York: Raven. 2nd. ed.
53. Petersen, O. H., Findlay, I., Iwatsuki, N., Singh, J., Gallacher, D. V., et al. 1985. Human pancreatic acinar cells: Studies of stimulus-secretion coupling. *Gastroenterology* 89:109–17
54. Petersen, O. H., Maruyama, Y. 1984. Calcium-activated potassium channels and their role in secretion. *Nature* 307:693–96
55. Petersen, O. H., Suzuki, K. 1986. Patch-clamp studies of $K^+$ channels in guinea pig pancreatic acinar cells. *J. Physiol. London* 378:62P
56. Putney, J. W. 1979. Stimulus-permeability coupling: Role of calcium in the receptor regulation of membrane permeability. *Pharmacol. Rev.* 30:209–45
57. Putney, J. W. Jr. 1986. Identification of cellular activation mechanisms associated with salivary secretion. *Ann. Rev. Physiol.* 48:75–88
58. Putney, J. W. Jr. 1986. A model for receptor-regulated calcium entry. *Cell Calcium* 7:1–12
59. Putney, J. W. Jr., McKinney, J. S., Aub, D. L., Leslie, B. A. 1984. Phorbol ester–induced protein secretion in rat parotid gland. Relationship to the role of inositol lipid breakdown and protein kinase C activation in stimulus-secretion coupling. *Mol. Pharmacol.* 26:261–66
60. Sakmann, B., Neher, E. 1984. Patch-clamp techniques for studying ionic channels in excitable membranes. *Ann. Rev. Physiol.* 46:455–72
61. Schulz, I. 1987. Electrolyte and fluid secretion in the exocrine pancreas. See Ref. 52, pp. 1147–71
62. Schulz, I., Heil, K., Kribben, A., Sachs, G., Haase, W. 1980. Isolation and functional characterization of cells from exocrine pancreas. In *Biology of Normal and Cancerous Exocrine Pancreatic Cells,* INSERM Symp. No. 15, ed. A. Ribet, pp. 3–18. Amsterdam: Elsevier
63. Siffert, W., Akkerman, J. W. N. 1987. Activation of sodium-proton exchange is a prerequisite for $Ca^{2+}$ mobilization in human platelets. *Nature* 325:456–58
64. Slack, B. E., Bell, J. E., Benos, D. J. 1986. Inositol-1,4,5-trisphosphate injection mimics fertilization potentials in sea urchin eggs. *Am. J. Physiol.* 250:C340–44
65. Squire, L., Petersen, O. H. 1987. Modulation of $Ca^{2+}$ and voltage-activated $K^+$ channels by internal $Mg^{2+}$ in salivary acinar cells. *Biochim. Biophys. Acta.* 899:171–75
66. Streb, H., Bayerdorffer, E., Haase, W., Irvine, R. F., Schulz, I. 1984. Effect of inositol-1,4,5-trisphosphate on isolated subcellular fractions of rat pancreas. *J. Membr. Biol.* 81:241–53
67. Suzuki, K., Petersen, C. C. H., Petersen, O. H. 1985. Hormonal activation of single $K^+$ channels via internal messenger in isolated pancreatic acinar cells. *FEBS Lett.* 192:307–12
68. Trautmann, A., Marty, A. 1984. Activation of Ca-dependent $K^+$ channels by carbamoylcholine in rat lacrimal glands. *Proc. Natl. Acad. Sci. USA* 81:611–15
69. Turner, R. J., George, N. J., Baum, B. J. 1986. Evidence for a $Na^+/K^+/Cl^-$ cotransport system in basolateral membrane vesicles from the rabbit parotid. *J. Membr. Biol.* 94:143–52
70. Tyrakowski, T., Milutinovic, S., Schulz, I. 1978. Studies on isolated subcellular components of cat pancreas: III. Alanine-sodium cotransport in isolated plasma membrane vesicles. *J. Membr. Biol.* 38:333–46
71. Young, J. A., Cook, D. I., Van Lennep, E. W., Roberts, M. 1987. Secretion by the major salivary glands. See Ref. 52, pp. 773–815
72. Yoshitomi, K., Burckhardt, B.-Ch., Frömter, E. 1985. Rheogenic sodium-bicarbonate cotransport in the peritubular cell membrane of rat renal proximal tubule. *Pflüg. Arch.* 405:360–66

Ann. Rev. Physiol. 1988. 50:81–93

# STRUCTURAL AND CHEMICAL ORGANIZATION OF THE MYENTERIC PLEXUS

*Catia Sternini*

Department of Medicine, School of Medicine, University of California, Los Angeles; Center for Ulcer Research and Education, Veterans' Administration Wadsworth Medical Center, Los Angeles, California 90073

## INTRODUCTION

A major feature of the innervation of the alimentary canal is its highly developed intramural system, which consists of a large number of neurons (of the same order of magnitude as the number of neurons in the spinal cord; 22) and their axons. Enteric neurons are organized into two major plexuses (the Auerbach's or myenteric plexus and the Meissner's or submucosal plexus). Cell bodies occur only infrequently in the minor plexuses (the subserosal, deep muscle, and mucosal plexuses), which mainly contain nerve fiber bundles (38). Although the majority of enteric axons are of intrinsic origin, the enteric nervous system (ENS) also includes processes from extrinsic (parasympathetic and sympathetic) neurons and afferent fibers (mainly originating from cranio-spinal sensory ganglia), which make connections with the intramural ganglion cells and contribute to the fiber network. The ENS functions relatively independently from the central nervous system (CNS) and subserves complex functions, such as motility, secretion, and blood flow. Its neuronal organization, which represents the structural basis of these functions, is equally complex. This complexity has been recognized since the earliest studies, based on conventional staining methods, which identified heterogeneous populations of neurons within the ENS (see below). The diversity of enteric neurons has also been established from pharmacological and electrophysiological studies, which have demonstrated the existence of intrinsic inhibitory and excitatory motor neurons and interneurons, and secre-

81

0066-4278/88/0315-0081$02.00

tomotor, vasomotor, and sensory neurons and have identified four types of neurons on the basis of their electrophysiological properties (9, 22, 60). This heterogeneity has become even more evident with ultrastructural and immunohistochemical studies, which have led to the identification of subpopulations of neurons that differ in their morphology and chemistry (4, 22). Extensive reviews have been published on the structure, connectivity, and biochemistry of enteric neurons (10, 22, 24, 32, 33, 35). This review focuses on a detailed analysis of the myenteric plexus from an anatomical point of view and emphasizes the distribution and co-occurrence of neuropeptides.

## THE MYENTERIC PLEXUS

### Morphological Aspects and Fine Structure

The myenteric plexus consists of prominent ganglia and strands of nerve bundles, which form meshworks (Figure 1) between the longitudinal and circular muscle layers of the muscularis externa. The plexus extends without discontinuity from the esophagus to the anal canal along the various portions of the gastrointestinal tract, including the hepatobiliary tract (31, 32, 42). The meshes of the myenteric plexus differ in size and shape from those found in the submucosal plexus and vary in the different regions of the gastrointestinal tract; those of some species display specific architectural features (31, 32). The myenteric ganglia contain the majority of nerve cell bodies of the ENS (ranging in number from a few to more than 100 per ganglion; 22), which are usually grouped in a ganglion but can also be observed within a connecting strand. The number and neuron density of the myenteric ganglia vary along the gut. They are particularly high at the lesser curvature of the stomach and near the mesenteric attachment in the large intestine. The colon has a higher neuronal density than the small intestine, and the duodenum a higher density than the ileum. The majority of ganglion cells project within the plexus and to the gut wall (22), and some neurons also send axons to the prevertebral ganglia (12, 13, 58).

Dogiel reported the first morphological evidence for the existence of a heterogeneous population of neurons within the ENS (15). He described three types of neurons on the basis of cell body shape and the branching characteristics of their processes using methylene blue staining. Type I neurons are characterized by a flattened cell body, a long irregular axon, and numerous short, broad-based dendrites stemming from the perikaryon and the proximal axon. Type II neurons have a smooth, oval cell body and long processes only. Type III neurons are characterized by an oval or rectangular cell body, one long axon, and numerous, relatively short and irregular dendrites. Dogiel also showed that different types of neurons have different targets: Type I cells project to the muscle and type II to other ganglion cells. These observations

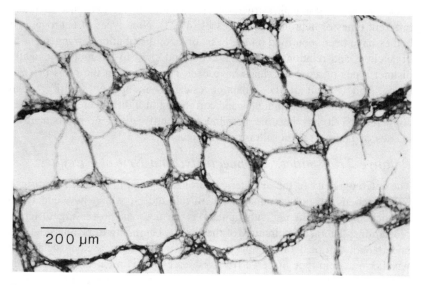

*Figure 1*    Meshworks of ganglia and interconnecting nerve strands of the myenteric plexus of the guinea pig duodenum. Whole-mount preparation processed for immunohistochemistry using the avidin-biotin peroxidase antiperoxidase method (as in the following figures) and antisera directed against rat CGRP.

suggested that morphological differences correspond to differences in function and led Dogiel to postulate that type I cells were motor neurons and type II cells were sensory neurons (15). Other investigators have not fully accepted this distinction, and modifications to this scheme have been proposed (39, 52); however, Dogiel's classification is the best to date and is still in use (9, 10). These types of cells have been identified using specific immunohistochemical techniques, which have also enabled researchers to demonstrate that type III neurons project, at least in part, to the mucosa (28).

At the ultrastructural level, the myenteric ganglia are compact structures that resemble the CNS in their general architecture. They consist exclusively of tightly packed neurons surrounded by a continuous basal lamina and separated from each other and from the connective tissue that borders the plexus by glial cells, which resemble the astroglia of the CNS, and their branching processes, without penetration of connective tissue or blood vessels (4, 30–35). The interior of the myenteric plexus is avascular. The capillaries are located outside the ganglia and differ from other enteric capillaries in the thickness of their walls, the absence of fenestrations, and the relative impermeability of their tight junctions. These characteristics are similar to those of the cerebral capillaries, which suggests the existence of a blood-myenteric barrier analogous to the blood-brain barrier (34).

One of the striking ultrastructural observations is the existence of many different types of neurons and processes (4, 22). Nine types of neuronal cell bodies have been identified on the basis of size, distribution, arrangement of organelles, and relationship to glial cells, and eight to ten morphologically distinct types of axon terminals have been recognized on the basis of size, shape, and content of the synaptic vesicles seen in their profiles. With immunocytochemical techniques and correlation of light and electron microscopy results, it has become possible to identify different neurochemical classes of neurons at the ultrastructural level.

## Putative Transmitters, Connectivity, and Neural Circuitry

The heterogeneity of the myenteric neuronal population has been confirmed by histochemical and immunohistochemical studies, which have identified neurochemically different subpopulations of neurons possessing different projections. The neural circuitry of the ENS is beginning to be analyzed and understood. Surgical or chemical denervation has been used to determine whether a certain type of nerve fiber originates from an extrinsic or intrinsic source. A variety of lesions in the gut wall and nerve tracing techniques have been used to determine the direction and destination of processes originating from different types of neurons (10, 59). The existence of several classes of enteric neurons has provided evidence for a multiplicity of putative enteric transmitters, including the classical transmitters acetylcholine (ACh) and norepinephrine (NE) as well as other substances, such as serotonin (5-HT), amino acids, and biologically active peptides (9, 10, 24, 53).

The presence of cholinergic neurons in the ENS, which has been established by a number of biochemical and pharmacological studies (22, 24), has recently been confirmed using antisera directed to choline acetyltransferase (ChAT), the enzyme that catalyzes the synthesis of ACh (25, 29). In the myenteric plexus, ChAT immunoreactivity is localized in a substantial proportion of nerve cell bodies (probably 20% or more of the entire population in the guinea pig small intestine) and varicose fibers. These fibers are numerous in the intestine, where they surround all the neurons and often obscure them, and are somewhat less dense in the stomach. These observations have begun to provide a morphological basis for determining the circuitry of enteric cholinergic neurons and for an understanding their organization.

Considerably more information is available on the distribution of noradrenergic neurons, which were initially studied by histofluorescence techniques and subsequently by immunohistochemistry with antisera directed to catecholamine-synthesizing enzymes, such as tyrosine hydroxylase and dopamine $\beta$-hydroxylase (10, 20, 21, 27, 35, 53). In the myenteric plexus, the majority of noradrenergic axons are distributed at the periphery near the junction with the connective tissue, and only a few fibers are present in the

interior of the plexus (10, 33, 35). Catecholamine fluorescence or immunoreactivity is usually not present in ganglion cells, except in some of
those of the guinea pig proximal colon. The disappearance of noradrenergic
fibers within the gut after experimental interruption of mesenteric nerves or
treatment with the sympathetic neurotoxin 6-hydroxydopamine (6-OHDA)
provides clear evidence that these fibers are extrinsic and probably originate
in the prevertebral ganglia (20, 26, 27). In the gut wall, noradrenergic fibers
are distributed to the mucosa, blood vessels, and muscle coat and are particularly numerous in the sphincter areas. At the ultrastructural level,
noradrenergic varicosities in the ENS differ from other sympathetic axons in
the periphery in that they contain many flattened vesicles (30–40 nm wide and
of varying lengths). Noradrenergic axo-axonic synapses have also been found
in the human myenteric plexus (10). The arrangement of the catecholamine-
containing fibers within the myenteric plexus suggests they have a direct
effect on smooth muscle and are involved in terminal axo-axonic interactions
(22, 35).

Evidence from pharmacological, autoradiographic, histochemical, and immunohistochemical investigations (8, 10, 24, 33, 35) suggests that serotonin
is a neurotransmitter of a population of intrinsic enteric neurons. Within the
ENS, serotonergic neurons are restricted to the myenteric plexus, where they
represent about 2% of the entire population. They have the appearance of
Dogiel's type I cells with numerous short processes that project in an anal
direction within and outside the myenteric plexus (8, 10, 23). Serotonergic
myenteric axons contain small agranular and large granular vesicles and
form synapses preferentially with those myenteric neurons classified electrophysiologically as type 2 or AH (10), i.e. those in which the action potential is followed by a prolonged after-hyperpolarization (60). However, there
is still debate as to whether or not serotonin is a genuine enteric transmitter,
and its proposed role in the mediation of peristaltic activity remains to be
defined.

Another candidate transmitter is $\gamma$-aminobutyric acid (GABA), a major
inhibitory transmitter in the brain, which has been identified within the ENS
on the basis of high-affinity uptake of [$^3$H]GABA and subsequently by
immunohistochemistry using antisera raised against GABA (1, 40, 41, 44).
GABAergic neurons seem to be restricted to the myenteric ganglia, although
extensive studies on the submucosal plexus have not been reported (1, 40).
These neurons are scattered within the ganglia, and their processes form dense
networks within the plexus that project to neighboring neurons and to the
circular muscle, where they run parallel to the muscle bundles. The majority
of the GABAergic innervation of the gut probably originates from intrinsic
ganglion cells, since there is no evidence for the presence of a GABAergic
component in the extrinsic innervation of the gut (40). The functional role of

GABAergic neurons in the complex neuronal circuitry that controls gut functions is unknown.

A large number (14 to date) of biologically active peptides have recently been discovered in nerve cell bodies and fibers of the ENS. This finding has opened a new frontier in the study of the organization of enteric innervation. The list of such peptides will certainly continue to grow, since new ones continue to be discovered. The distribution of peptide-containing neurons in the alimentary canal of several mammalian species has been extensively reviewed (10); therefore, this article is limited to a general description of several representative peptide immunoreactive patterns and a more detailed analysis of the distribution of the recently discovered calcitonin gene–related peptide.

VASOACTIVE INTESTINAL PEPTIDE    In the myenteric plexus, along the entire length of the gut, vasoactive intestinal peptide (VIP) immunoreactivity is present in a population of neurons having the appearance of Dogiel's type III cells; these cells are located in the core of the ganglia and are usually grouped in clusters of two or three. A second population of cells resembling type I neurons also shows VIP immunoreactivity; these are preferentially distributed as single cells at the periphery of the ganglia near the circular muscle surface (7, 9, 10). VIP neurons constitute 39% of the myenteric cells (this percent of cells, as those quoted below, refers to counts performed in the guinea pig small intestine following treatment with colchicine) (7) and project within the gut wall to the circular muscle layer and submucosa ganglia in an oral-to-anal direction. Some VIP neurons also send projections outside the gut to the inferior mesenteric ganglion (6, 10, 13, 22). VIP axons have a varicose appearance, often wrapping around individual cell bodies (7, 10), and are characterized by large granular and small agranular vesicles (46). Synapses between VIP immunoreactive varicosities and neurons have also been identified. VIP is released from the gut following vagal stimulation; this response may involve a cholinergic synapse (14, 22). VIP has been shown to relax gut muscle, which suggests this peptide may also be involved in the descending inhibition of the peristaltic reflex (14, 22, 51). The distribution and projections of VIP myenteric neurons appear to be consistent with such a functional role. The biological action of VIP on intestinal secretion and its vasodilator effect, together with the presence of VIP fibers in the mucosa and around blood vessels, also suggest a role for this peptide in regulating fluid secretion and blood flow (14, 51).

SUBSTANCE P OR RELATED TACHYKININS    Substance P (SP) is the most widely known member of the tachykinin peptide family, which includes several other bioactive peptides (e.g. substance K and neuromedin K) that share the same carboxyl-terminal sequence (48). In the myenteric plexus, SP or a related tachykinin peptide immunoreactivity is present in cell bodies with the appearance of Dogiel's type I and II neurons (37% of the total population), which are scattered throughout the ganglia and in varicose nerve fibers, which form dense baskets around most cells (5, 10). SP myenteric neurons have short projections and, like VIP-immunoreactive neurons, project outside the plexus to the circular muscle and submucosal plexus (10, 11). The bulk of enteric SP axons originate from intrinsic neurons, which are found in all regions of the gut. However, a small portion of SP fibers, namely those associated with blood vessels and some of the submucosal processes, seem to be derived from extrinsic, sensory sources, since they are depleted by treatment with the sensory neurotoxin capsaicin or by extrinsic denervation (36). SP varicosities contain large granular and small agranular vesicles and form synapses on myenteric neurons (47). SP originating from intrinsic neurons is likely to be responsible for slow depolarization of myenteric neurons (type 2 or AH) and muscle contraction (2, 14, 19, 43). These observations suggest a possible role for SP as an excitatory neurotransmitter in the gut, perhaps acting both on enteric neurons and directly on the muscle.

NEUROPEPTIDE Y    Neuropeptide Y (NPY), the neuronal component of the pancreatic polypeptide family (18), is expressed in ganglion cells and nerve fibers in both the enteric plexuses and in processes innervating the gut wall and small arteries and arterioles (26, 28, 57). Most of the myenteric NPY ganglion cells have a type III morphology (Figure 2; 28) and are located in the core of the plexus. Some of the cells with a type I morphology are preferentially distributed at the surface of the ganglia, near the circular muscle layer (28). NPY-containing cells represent ~28% of the myenteric neuronal population, are present along the entire length of the gut, and project to the circular muscle layer. Type III NPY cell axons also project to the submucosa and the mucosa with no preferential direction (oral, anal, or circumferential), sometimes running short distances within the plexus and reaching other ganglion cells before leaving the ganglia (28). The enteric NPY innervation also includes an extrinsic component (mainly associated with blood vessels), which appears to originate from sympathetic sources. This component is eliminated after mesenteric nerve interruption or treatment with the sympathetic neurotoxin 6-OHDA (26, 57). NPY function in the ENS is not yet established. NPY potentiates the vasoconstrictor effects of NE on many blood vessels, including splanchnic ones (16). Since NPY immunoreactivity is present in perivascular noradrenergic nerves within the gut (26), it is tempting to speculate that NPY regulates enteric blood flow, perhaps by acting in concert with NE.

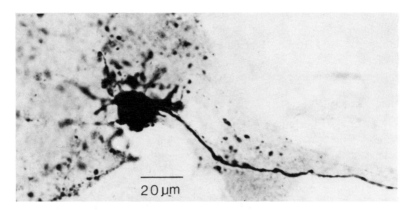

20 µm

*Figure 2*   NPY-immunoreactive neurons with the appearance of Dogiel's type III morphology, with an oval, relatively smooth cell body, a long axon, and numerous short, irregular dendrities. NPY antiserum was kindly provided by Dr. K. MacDonald.

CALCITONIN GENE–RELATED PEPTIDE    Calcitonin gene–related peptide (CGRP) is a 37–amino acid peptide, encoded by the calcitonin gene and generated by alternative RNA processing (50), that possesses potent biological activities (37), such as inhibition of gastric acid secretion and vasodilation. It is the most powerful vasoactive substance described to date. In the alimentary canal, CGRP immunoreactivity is present in neuronal structures in the gut (3, 28, 54, 56), with a similar distribution in several mammalian species, including primates (C. Sternini, unpublished) and in the hepatobiliary tract of rats and guinea pigs (C. Sternini, unpublished), as well as in nerve fibers and endocrine-like cells within the rat endocrine pancreas (55). In the myenteric plexus, CGRP immunoreactivity has a different distribution depending on the region of the gut. It is restricted to varicose nerve fibers that form loose networks around unstained cell bodies in the esophagus and stomach and is present in both ganglion cells and axons in the small and large intestine. CGRP-containing cells are distributed throughout the ganglia, with the highest density in the duodenum and colon. Most of these cells have the appearance of Dogiel's type III morphology, but some resemble type II neurons (Figure 3). CGRP myenteric axons form dense networks, wrapping around the cell bodies and often obscuring them (Figure 1). Within the gut wall, CGRP fibers project to the muscle coat, submucosa, and mucosa. In the latter layer CGRP-positive axons are particularly numerous around the intestinal glands, but they are also relatively abundant in the gastric mucosa, where they run parallel to the parietal cells and some approach the lumen.

An interesting feature of the enteric CGRP innervation is the great abundance of fibers associated with the vasculature, which suggests a possible role of this peptide in blood flow regulation. Unlike other peptides shown to be

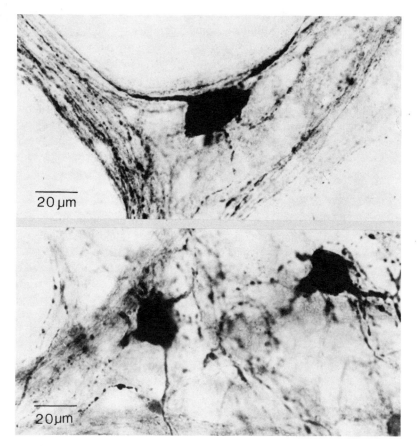

*Figure 3*    CGRP type II *(top)* and III *(bottom)* neurons in the myenteric plexus of the guinea pig duodenum. Note the smooth cell body and the long axons of the type II cell.

mostly intrinsic to the ENS, an important component of the CGRP innervation of the alimentary canal is extrinsic and presumably sensory. Evidence for this extrinsic, sensory origin derives from the disappearance of CGRP-immunoreactive axons innervating the esophagus, stomach, and pancreas, as well as those associated with enteric and pancreatic vasculature, following neonatal treatment with capsaicin or extrinsic denervation (36, 55, 56). In the intestine, however, capsaicin treatment caused depletion of CGRP peri-vascular fibers but only a partial reduction of the nonvascular CGRP axons. These results demonstrate that different subsets of neurons (intrinsic and extrinsic) give rise to the CGRP innervation of different regions of the alimentary canal (56). In contrast, 6-OHDA treatment did not modify the CGRP staining pattern, which demonstrates that these fibers are separated from catecholaminergic fibers (C. Sternini, unpublished). Most of the extrinsic CGRP fibers probably originate from spinal sensory ganglia. Using tract tracing techniques, in which a retrogradely transported fluorescent dye was injected in the pancreas or stomach wall, coupled with the immunohistochemical localization of CGRP, we found that the majority of fluorescently labeled cell bodies within the spinal ganglia also contained CGRP immunoreactivity (C. Sternini, unpublished). The CGRP distribution in the alimentary canal suggests that this peptide may affect the digestive system both directly, by acting on target tissues, and indirectly, by altering enteric blood flow. In addition, its presence in sensory fibers may represent a morphological basis for involvement of CGRP in sensory transmission.

## Putative Neurotransmitter Colocalization

It is apparent from the number of putative transmitters present in the ENS and from the partial overlap of their distributions that some enteric neuronal populations may express more than one transmitter substance. In the myenteric plexus of the guinea pig small intestine, type III neurons immunoreactive for NPY that project to the submucosa and mucosa also contain CGRP, somatostatin, cholecystokinin (CCK), and ChAT (28). NPY type I neurons that project to the muscle layer express enkephalin (ENK), dynorphin (DYN), and VIP (28). VIP type I cells that project to the prevertebral ganglia are also positive for gastrin releasing peptide, CCK, ENK, and DYN (10). In other species, VIP immunoreactivity colocalizes with peptide histide-isoleucine (PHI) (rat and pig intestine; 61), with PHI and NPY (rat gut; 17), and with the newly described peptide, galanin (pig duodenum and guinea pig colon; 49). In the guinea pig colon, co-occurrence of SP and 5-HT has been reported in myenteric ganglia (45). Finally, in both rats and guinea pigs, CGRP-containing axons projecting to the blood vessels and submucosa, and presumably originating from sensory spinal ganglia, also usually contain SP or related tachykinin immunoreactivity (36, 54). The presence of more than one putative transmitter within the same neuronal population suggests the possibility of complex interactions; however, the functional significance of this coexistence is still not known.

## SUMMARY AND CONCLUSIONS

The most striking characteristics of the myenteric plexus are the heterogeneity of its neuronal populations and the complexity of its organization. Myenteric neurons greatly differ in their morphological characteristics, projection patterns, and topographical arrangement within the ganglia. The discovery of histochemically distinct types of neurons together with the development of nerve-tracing techniques and specific lesions have allowed a better understanding of the relationships of enteric neurons to specific target tissues. Consequently, these techniques have contributed significantly to our knowledge of the highly ordered organization of the ENS, which represents the anatomical substrate for the neural coordination and integration of the complex functions it subserves. The existence of different types of neurons that probably use different substances as transmitters may reflect on the existence of defined functional roles for each type of neurons. To date, only ACh, NE, and probably 5-HT seem to satisfy all the criteria necessary for establishing a neurotransmitter (24, 35), although there is increasing evidence that some of the other substances, such as GABA, SP, and VIP, are enteric transmitters or modulators. The functional roles of the different types of neurons in the neural circuitry that regulates gastrointestinal functions remain to be elucidated.

ACKNOWLEDGMENTS

Original work cited here was partially supported by NIH grant AM 17328 and an SKB Fellowship. The author is very grateful to Drs. N. Brecha and L. Kruger for helpful comments on the manuscript and to Mr. K. Anderson for expert technical assistance.

*Literature Cited*

1. Baetge, G., Gershon, M. D. 1986. GABA in PNS: Demonstration in enteric neurons. *Brain Res. Bull.* 16:421–24
2. Bertaccini, G. 1982. Peptides: Candidate hormones, substance P. *Handbook Exp. Pharmacol.* 59/1:85–105
3. Clague, J. R., Sternini, C., Brecha, N. 1985. Localization of calcitonin gene-related peptide-like immunoreactivity in neurons of the rat gastrointestinal tract. *Neurosci. Lett.* 56:63–68
4. Cook, R. D., Burnstock, G. 1976. The ultrastructure of Auerbach's plexus in the guinea-pig. I. Neuronal elements. *J. Neurocytol.* 5:171–94
5. Costa, M., Cuello, A. C., Furness, J. B., Franco, R. 1980. Distribution of enteric neurons showing immunoreactivity for substance P in the guinea pig ileum. *Neuroscience* 5:323–31
6. Costa, M., Furness, J. B. 1983. The origins, pathways and terminations of neurons with VIP-like immunoreactivity in the guinea-pig small intestine. *Neuroscience* 8:665–76
7. Costa, M., Furness, J. B., Buffa, R., Said, S. I. 1980. Distribution of enteric nerve cell bodies and axons showing immunoreactivity for vasoactive intestinal peptide (VIP) in the guinea pig intestine. *Neuroscience* 5:587–96

8. Costa, M., Furness, J. B., Cuello, A. C., Verhofstad, A. A. J., Steinbusch, H. W. J., et al. 1982. Neurons with 5-hydroxytryptamine-like immunoreactivity in the enteric nervous system: Their visualization and reaction to drug treatment. *Neuroscience* 7:351–63
9. Costa, M., Furness, J. B., Gibbins, I. L. 1986. Chemical coding of enteric neurons. In *Coexistence of Neuronal Messengers: A New Principle in Chemical Transmission*, ed. T. Hökfelt, K. Fuxe, B. Pernow. 68:217–40. New York: Elsevier. 411 pp.
10. Costa, M., Furness, J. B., Llewellyn-Smith, I. J. 1987. Histochemistry of the enteric nervous system. See Ref. 42, pp. 1–40
11. Costa, M., Furness, J. B., Llewellyn-Smith, I. J., Cuello, A. C. 1981. Projections of substance P neurons within the guinea pig small intestine. *Neuroscience* 6:411–24
12. Crowcroft, P. J., Holman, M. E., Szurszewski, J. H. 1971. Excitatory input from the distal colon to the inferior mesenteric ganglion in the guinea-pig. *J. Physiol. London* 219:443–61
13. Dalsgaard, C. J., Hökfelt, T., Schultzberg, M., Lundberg, J. M., Terenius, L., et al. 1983. Origin of peptide-containing fibers in the inferior

mesenteric ganglion of the guinea pig: Immunohistochemical studies with antisera to substance P, enkephalin, vasoactive intestinal polypeptide, cholecystokinin and bombesin. *Neuroscience* 9:191–211

14. Dockray, G. J. 1987. Physiology of enteric neuropeptides. See Ref. 42, pp. 41–66

15. Dogiel, A. S. 1899. Über den Bau der Ganglien in den Geflechten des Darmes und der Gallenblase des Menschen und der Saügetiere. *Arch. Anat. Physiol. Leipzig, Anat. Abt.,* ed. Van Wilheim His pp. 130–58 Leipzig: Verlag

16. Edvinson, L., Eklab, E., Håkanson, R., Wahlastedt, C. 1984. Neuropeptide Y potentiates the effects of various vasoconstrictor agents on rabbit blood flow. *Br. J. Pharmacol.* 83:519–25

17. Eklab, E., Håkanson, R., Sundler, F. 1984. VIP and PHI coexist with an NPY-like peptide in intramural neurons of the small intestine. *Regul. Peptides* 10:47–55

18. Emson, P. C., DeQuidt, M. E. 1984. NPY—A new member of the pancreatic polypeptide family. *Trends Neurosci.* 7:31–35

19. Franco, R., Costa, M., Furness, J. B. 1979. Evidence for the release of endogenous substance P from intestinal nerves. *Naunyn-Schmiedebergs Arch. Pharmakol.* 306:185–201

20. Furness, J. B., Costa, M. 1974. The adrenergic innervation of the gastrointestinal tract. *Ergeb. Physiol. Biol. Chem. Exp. Pharmakol.* 69:1–54

21. Furness, J. B., Costa, M. 1975. The use of glyoxylic acid for the fluorescence histochemical demonstration of peripheral stores of noradrenaline and 5-hydroxytryptamine in whole mounts. *Histochemistry* 41:335–52

22. Furness, J. B., Costa, M. 1980. Types of nerves in the enteric nervous system. *Neuroscience* 5:1–20

23. Furness, J. B., Costa, M. 1982. Neurons with 5-hydroxytryptamine-like immunoreactivity in the enteric nervous system: Their projections in the guinea pig small intestine. *Neuroscience* 7:341–9

24. Furness, J. B., Costa, M. 1982. Identification of gastrointestinal neurotransmitters. In *Mediators and Drugs in Gastrointestinal Motility I,* ed. G. Bertaccini, pp. 383–461. Berlin: Spring-Verlag

25. Furness, J. B., Costa, M., Eckenstein, F. 1983. Neurones localized with antibodies against choline acetyltransferase in the enteric nervous system. *Neurosci. Lett.* 40:105–9

26. Furness, J. B., Costa, M., Emson, P. C., Håkanson, R., Moghimzadeh, E., et al. 1983. Distribution, pathways and reactions to drug treatment of nerves with neuropeptide Y- and pancreatic polypeptide-like immunoreactivity in the guinea-pig digestive tract. *Cell Tissue Res.* 234:71–92

27. Furness, J. B., Costa, M., Freeman, C. G. 1979. Absence of tyrosine hydroxylase activity and dopamine beta-hydroxylase immunoreactivity in intrinsic nerves of the guinea pig ileum. *Neuroscience* 4:305–10

28. Furness, J. B., Costa, M., Gibbins, I. L., Llewellyn-Smith, I. J., Oliver, J. R. 1985. Neurochemically similar myenteric and submucous neurons directly traced to the mucosa of the small intestine. *Cell Tissue Res.* 241:155–63

29. Furness, J. B., Costa, M., Keast, J. R. 1984. Choline acetyltransferase- and peptide immunoreactivity of submucous neurons in the small intestine of the guinea-pig. *Cell Tissue Res.* 237:329–36

30. Gabella, G. 1972. Fine structure of the myenteric plexus in the guinea pig ileum. *J. Anat. London* 11:69–97

31. Gabella, G. 1979. Innervation of the gastrointestinal tract. *Int. Rev. Cytol.* 59:129–93

32. Gabella, G. 1987. Structure of muscles and nerves in the gastrointestinal tract. See Ref. 42, pp. 335–82

33. Gershon, M. D. 1981. The enteric nervous system. *Ann. Rev. Neurosci.* 4:227–72

34. Gershon, M. D., Bursztajn, S. 1978. Properties of the enteric nervous system: Limitation of access of intravascular macromolecules to the myenteric plexus and muscularis externa. *J. Comp. Neurol.* 180:467–88

35. Gershon, M. D., Erde, S. M. 1981. The nervous system of the gut. *Gastroenterology* 80:1571–94

36. Gibbins, I. L., Furness, J. B., Costa, M., MacIntyre, I., Hillyard, C. J., et al. 1985. Co-localization of calcitonin gene-related peptide-like immunoreactivity with substance P in cutaneous, vascular and visceral neurons of guinea pigs. 1985. *Neurosci. Lett.* 57:125–30

37. Goodman, E. C., Iversen, L. L. 1986. Calcitonin gene-related peptide: Novel neuropeptide. *Life Sci.* 38:2169–78

38. Goyal, R. K. 1983. Neurology of the gut. In *Gastrointestinal Disease,* ed. M. H. Sleisenger, J. S. Fordtran, pp. 97–115. Philadelphia: Saunders. 3rd. ed.

39. Hill, J. C. 1927. A contribution to our knowledge of the enteric plexuses. *Phi-*

los. Trans. R. Soc. London Ser. B 215:355–87
40. Jessen, K. R., Hills, J. M., Saffrey, M. J. 1986. Immunohistochemical demonstration of GABAergic neurons in the enteric nervous system. J. Neurosci. 6:1628–34
41. Jessen, K. R., Mirsky, R., Dennison, M. E., Burnstock, G. 1979. GABA may be a neurotransmitter in the vertebrate peripheral nervous system. Nature 281:71–74
42. Johnson, L. R. 1987. Physiology of the Gastrointestinal Tract. New York: Raven. 1780 pp.
43. Katayama, Y., North, R. A. 1978. Does substance P mediate slow synaptic excitation within the myenteric plexus? Nature 274:387–88
44. Krantis, A., Kerr, D. I. B. 1981. Autoradiographic localization of ³H-gamma-aminobutyric acid in the myenteric plexus of the guinea-pig small intestine. Neurosci. Lett. 23:263–68
45. Legay, C., Saffrey, M. J., Burnstock, G. 1984. Coexistence of immunoreactive substance P and serotonin in neurons of the gut. Brain Res. 302:379–82
46. Llewellyn-Smith, I. J., Costa, M., Furness, J. B. 1985. Light and electron microscopic immunocytochemistry of the same nerves from whole mount preparations. J. Histochem. Cytochem. 33:857–66
47. Llewellyn-Smith, I. J., Furness, J. B., Murphy, R., O'Brien, P. E., Costa, M. 1984. Substance P containing nerves in the human small intestine. Distribution, ultrastructure and characterization of the immunoreactive peptide. Gastroenterology 86:421–35
48. Maggio, J. E. 1985. "Kassinin" in mammals: The newest tachykinins. Peptides 6 (Suppl. 3):237–43
49. Melander, T., Hökfelt, T., Rokaeus, A., Fahrenkrug, J., Tatemoto, K., et al. 1985. Distribution of galanin-like immunoreactivity in the gastro-intestinal tract of several mammalian species. Cell Tissue Res. 239:253–70
50. Rosenfeld, M. G., Mermod, J. J., Amara, S. G., Swanson, L. W., Sawchenko, P. E., et al. 1983. Production of a novel neuropeptide encoded by the calcitonin gene via tissue-specific RNA processing. Nature 304:129–35
51. Said, S. I. 1982. Vasoactive Intestinal Peptide. New York: Raven. 512 pp.
52. Schofield, G. C. 1968. Anatomy of

muscular and neural tissues in the alimentary canal. In Handbook of Physiology: Alimentary Canal, pp. 1579–627. ed. C. F. Code. Washington, D.C.: Am. Physiol. Soc.
53. Schultzberg, M., Hökfelt, T., Nilsson, G., Terenius, L., Rehfeld, J., et al. 1980. Distribution of peptide- and catecholamine-containing neurons in the gastrointestinal tract of rat and guinea pig: Immunohistochemical studies with antisera to substance P, vasoactive intestinal peptide, enkephalin, somatostatin, gastrin/cholecystokinin, neurotensin and dopamine B-hydroxylase. Neuroscience 5:689–744
54. Sternini, C., Anderson, K., Brecha, N. 1986. Colocalization of calcitonin gene-related peptide immunoreactivity with SP in the enteric nervous system. Gastroenterology 89:1648 (Abstr.)
55. Sternini, C., Brecha, N. 1986. Immunocytochemical identification of islet cells and nerve fibers containing calcitonin gene-related peptide-like immunoreactivity in the rat pancreas. Gastroenterology 90:1155–63
56. Sternini, C., Reeve, J. R. Jr., Brecha, N. 1987. Distribution and characterization of calcitonin gene-related peptide immunoreactivity in the digestive system of normal and capsaicin-treated rats. Gastroenterology 93:852–62
57. Sundler, F., Moghimzadeh, E., Håkanson, R., Ekelund, M., Emson, P. 1983. Nerve fibers in the gut and pancreas displaying neuropeptide-Y immunoreactivity. Intrinsic and extrinsic origin. Cell Tissue Res. 230:487–93
58. Szurszewski, J. H., Weems, M. A. 1975. A study of peripheral input to and its control by post-ganglionic neurons of the inferior mesenteric ganglion. J. Physiol. London 256:541–56
59. Takaki, M., Wood, J. D., Gershon, M. D. 1985. Heterogeneity of ganglia of the guinea pig myenteric plexus: An in vitro study of the origin and terminals within single ganglia using a covalently bound fluorescent retrograde tracer. J. Comp. Neurol. 235:488–502
60. Wood, J. D. 1987. Physiology of the enteric nervous system. See Ref. 42, pp. 67–109
61. Yanaihara, N., Nokihara, K., Yanaihara, C., Iwanaga, T., Fujita, T. 1983. Immunocytochemical demonstration of PHI and its coexistence with VIP in intestinal nerves of the rat and pig. Arch. Histol. Jpn. 46:575–81

# RENAL AND ELECTROLYTE PHYSIOLOGY

## *CHLORIDE TRANSPORT*

*Introduction,* Carl W. Gottschalk, *Section Editor*

Chloride ions constitute approximately two-thirds of the anions in plasma and other extracellular fluids, including the gomerular filtrate. Thus, chloride is the major anion filtered and reabsorbed in the renal tubules. The reabsorption of chloride ions by the renal tubular epithelium has traditionally been assumed to be passive and to be secondary to concentration and electrical gradients established, predominantly, by sodium and hydrogen ion transport. It has also been assumed that chloride reabsorption is not regulated. Recent evidence indicates that this simplistic view is erroneous; four reviews of the evidence are presented in this minisymposium on chloride transport.

Drs. Schild, Giebisch, and Green discuss chloride transport in the proximal renal tubule. They review recent studies indicating that a new model of chloride transport that includes active transcellular and passive intercellular pathways is necessary.

Dr. Greger discusses chloride transport in more distal parts of the tubule, including the thick ascending limb, distal convolution, and collecting ducts. He stresses the different mechanisms of transport in the various sections of the tubule and heterogeneity of transport in different nephrons and cell types.

Drs. de Rouffignac and Elalouf discuss hormonal regulation of chloride transport in the proximal and distal nephron. Recent advances in techniques for study of individual nephron segments now permit a much more detailed analysis of the numerous factors that influence transport than previously possible.

Drs. Galla and Luke discuss chloride transport and disorders of acid-base balance in view of the recently described transport processes considered in the three earlier chapters. They advance the hypothesis that the state of chloride depletion per se is responsible for the maintenance phase of chronic renal metabolic alkalosis whereas plasma volume depletion is a commonly associated epiphenomenon.

Ann. Rev. Physiol. 1988. 50:97–110

# CHLORIDE TRANSPORT IN THE PROXIMAL RENAL TUBULE

*L. Schild and G. Giebisch*

Department of Physiology, Yale University School of Medicine, New Haven, CT 06510,

*R. Green*

Department of Physiological Sciences, University of Manchester, Manchester, England

## INTRODUCTION

Until recently, the movement of chloride ions in the renal proximal tubule has been assumed to be predominantly passive and to follow sodium reabsorption (5, 28, 55, 57, 61). Evidence has begun to emerge, however, that in this tubule segment chloride reabsorption occurs even in the absence of appropriate electrochemical driving forces, which suggests the participation of an active transport component of total chloride reabsorption (4, 9, 22, 43). It is therefore opportune to reconsider the active and passive transepithelial transport mechanisms by which chloride ions are reabsorbed in the renal proximal tubule.

## MAGNITUDE OF CHLORIDE REABSORPTION

In the rat proximal tubule about half the filtered sodium and water is reabsorbed by the end of the proximal convoluted tubule, and a further 10–20% is reabsorbed in the proximal straight tubule. Several constituents of glomerular filtrate are avidly reabsorbed in the first part of the mammalian proximal tubule (S1 segment), and there is a rapid fall in the concentrations of glucose, amino acids, lactate, and bicarbonate. There is little chloride reabsorption in the early convoluted proximal tubule and consequently, there is a rapid rise in

97

tubular chloride concentration, which over the last two thirds of the proximal tubule then remains fairly constant (30, 56, 73, 75). This establishes a chemical gradient for chloride ion movement from the lumen to the peritubular interstitial fluid (73, 75). Of the chloride filtered, about 50–60% is reabsorbed by the proximal convoluted and straight tubules.

In the early part of the proximal convoluted tubule the transepithelial potential difference is lumen negative and depends on the electrogenic cotransport of glucose and sodium (8, 26, 27, 51). In superficial proximal tubules, which have a high chloride permeability, the movement of chloride ions down the chemical gradient, generated as described above, results in a chloride diffusion potential that renders the lumen positive by about 1–2 mV (26, 27). In deeper juxtamedullary nephrons the much lower chloride permeability reduces chloride diffusion potential, and the lumen remains electrically negative (45, 49).

In contrast to mammalian proximal tubules, *Necturus* proximal tubules reabsorb bicarbonate without a consequent change in luminal chloride concentration. As a result, no chloride diffusion potential is generated, and the transepithelial potential remains negative (29). Because of the differences in the chloride electrochemical gradient in proximal tubules of *Necturus* and rat, there are likely to be quantitative, if not qualitative, differences in the mechanisms of chloride transport.

## Routes of Chloride Reabsorption

In a leaky epithelium such as the renal proximal convoluted tubule, chloride ions can move through a paracellular or transcellular pathway. Movement through the paracellular pathway is purely passive: It occurs either down an electrochemical gradient or by solvent drag. However, movement through the cells requires expenditure of energy, although metabolism may not necessarily be directly coupled to chloride transport, i.e. it would be secondary as opposed to primary active transport (6). Chloride movement across cell membranes may occur via secondary active transport, whereby chloride flux against an electrochemical gradient is coupled to the flow of a second solute for which a favorable electrochemical potential difference exists. Transcellular movement requires transport across two cell membranes in series. Because of the vectorial nature of transport across proximal tubule cells, the mechanisms in the basolateral and apical cell membranes are likely to differ.

## EVIDENCE FOR BOTH PASSIVE AND ACTIVE MECHANISMS

The existence of a *passive* chloride flux in the proximal tubule is supported by several lines of evidence. Several studies indicate that the proximal convoluted and straight tubules have a high chloride conductance and that most of this conductance can be accounted for by the paracellular shunt pathway (5, 15, 27, 28, 35, 61, 62). Secondly, the amount of chloride and fluid reabsorption in the superficial proximal tubule is subject to modification by transepithelial chloride gradients (23, 33, 38, 55, 71). Thirdly, chloride transport was recently shown to be linearly related to the transepithelial electrochemical driving forces (4). Thus there is good evidence for passive chloride movement, and some would argue that it accounts for more than 90% of total chloride reabsorption (28, 61).

However, other studies have reported that a significant fraction of chloride reabsorption is dependent on active transport mechanisms. These include the demonstration of substantial transepithelial chloride transport in the absence of electrochemical driving forces (4, 9,) and inhibition of a component of chloride transport by metabolic inhibition (33, 35, 38), by removal of potassium (22) or by cooling (61). This fraction of chloride absorption was also inhibited by agents known to interfere with transport proteins, such as disulphonic stilbenes (SITS or DIDS) and furosemide (11, 37, 39, 53) or bumetanide (S. L. Greenwood, S. J. White, R. Green, unpublished observations).

The relative magnitudes of the chloride transport through the passive paracellular and by the active transcellular transport systems are controversial. Using stationary microperfusion (split drop) techniques in the rat proximal tubule, Frömter et al (28), by relating transepithelial net chloride fluxes to the electrochemical driving forces across the tubular epithelium, concluded that chloride absorption in this tubule segment is almost entirely passive. The "active" transport rate in these experiments, including secondary active transport modes such as cotransport and countertransport, represented only 1.5–12% of net chloride reabsorption. This conclusion was supported subsequently by results of Cassola et al (21), who calculated the transcellular flux of chloride on the basis of the initial rate of fall of intracellular chloride concentration when chloride was removed from the tubule lumen. They concluded that active, transcellular movement of chloride represents approximately 7% of the net chloride reabsorption. These results supported the older data of Neumann & Rector, who showed that removal of the chloride gradient across the epithelium prevented fluid and chloride movement (55).

However, other studies using luminal microperfusion methods in vivo demonstrated that 60–70% of chloride reabsorptive flux in the rat proximal tubule is inhibitable by cyanide, which suggests that active transport mechanisms participate in chloride reabsorption (33–35, 38). Furthermore, when transepithelial chloride fluxes were measured as a function of the electrochemical driving force for chloride, Alpern et al (4) demonstrated the presence of an active, cyanide-sensitive transcellular chloride flux of some 100–160 peq·min$^{-1}$·mm$^{-1}$.

The reasons for the discrepancy between the results referred to above and those in which an active transport component was deduced is not yet clear. Resolution of this problem will depend on the accurate measurement of the driving forces across the individual chloride transport barriers, i.e. the apical and the basolateral cell membranes, and the paracellular shunt.

# MECHANISM OF CHLORIDE REABSORPTION

## Passive Movement

In this section we consider passive movement of chloride through the paracellular pathway in response to a favorable electrochemical potential difference across the tubule epithelium. Because of preferential bicarbonate reabsorption in the early S1 segment of the proximal tubule, a concentration gradient for chloride develops between the tubule lumen and plasma. Although this is partly offset in the superficial proximal convoluted tubule by the simultaneous development of a small positive intraluminal potential of 1–2 mV (26), the calculated equilibrium potential would be about +6 mV, so there is still a favorable electrochemical gradient for chloride reabsorption. Similarly, Schafer et al (63) observed that the transepithelial voltage recorded in the proximal straight tubule perfused with solutions lacking bicarbonate and organic substrates was less positive than the Donnan equilibrium voltage calculated for the chloride distribution across the epithelium. They demonstrated that the displacement of the transepithelial voltage from the Donnan equilibrium voltage was caused by rheogenic Na$^+$ transport, which therefore represents a major driving force for passive chloride reabsorption. However, the amount of chloride transport driven by the transepithelial electrochemical gradient depends critically on the permeability of the proximal tubule to chloride ions.

ION PERMEABILITIES    A number of studies have documented the electrical "leakiness" of the proximal tubule (14, 40, 66). The electrical resistances of the apical and basolateral membranes are relatively high compared to that of the whole epithelium (10, 14), which implies that the low transepithelial resistance is due to ion shunting through the paracellular pathway. Accordingly, the major determinant of ion permeability and ion selectivity of the whole epithelium is the permeability and selectivity of the paracellular pathway. Whether permeability is measured by tracer flux, by transepithelial potential changes after single ion substitution, or after bionic salt dilution in the lumen, there is general agreement that the proximal tubule is highly permeable to chloride ions (15, 27, 45, 62).

Differences in chloride permeability occur both along the proximal tubule and in different populations of tubules. For instance, juxtamedullary proximal convoluted tubules are more permeable to sodium than to chloride, whereas in superficial convoluted tubules the relation is reversed. In addition, the first mm of the superficial convoluted tubule is more permeable to sodium than to chloride, whereas in all later segments the chloride permeability is greater than that to sodium. In the juxtamedullary nephrons, the relative permeabilities to chloride and sodium do not differ along the proximal tubule (45, 49).

SOLVENT DRAG    In addition to diffusion of chloride along an electrochemical gradient, passive reabsorption of chloride ions can result from solvent drag. Using the in vitro perfused rabbit proximal tubule, Corman & DiStefano (24) and Jacobson et al (46) attempted to demonstrate solvent drag for sodium and chloride by imposing osmotic gradients across the epithelium in the absence of active transport. However, they were unable to show any enhancement of solute transport that could account for solvent drag. In contrast, in the rat proximal tubule the data reported by Frömter et al indicated that solvent drag comprises a significant fraction (approximately 50%) of net chloride reabsorption (28). Whether these differences are attributable to species differences or technical reasons is not yet known.

The component of solute (chloride) movement due to solvent drag is defined by the first right-hand term of the following equation:

$$J_s = \bar{c}J_v (1 - \sigma) + P\left(\Delta c + \frac{zF}{RT} \psi \bar{c}\right) + J_{act}.$$

Here $J_s$ is net solute flux; $\bar{c}$ and $\Delta c$ are the mean concentration of solute and its gradient, respectively; $P$ is the permeability; $\psi$ is the potential across the tubule; $J_{act}$ is the active transport; and $J_v$ is the volume flux. $F$, $R$, $T$, and $z$ have their usual meaning; $\sigma$ is the reflection coefficient; and $\bar{c}J_v(1 - \sigma)$ is the term that delineates solvent drag.

It should be pointed out that given a chloride reflection coefficient in the rabbit proximal tubule of 0.7–0.8 (61), and according to the low rate of volume reabsorption observed in vitro in this tubule segment, the increased chloride flux due to solvent drag may not be detectable (60). Experiments in rats, where larger reabsorptive flows are measured and given a reflection coefficient for chloride similar to that found in the rabbit proximal tubule (36), the amount of net chloride flux due to solvent drag represents a significant fraction of total chloride flux across the proximal tubule of the rat (30a).

## Active Movement

Evidence for participation of some active Cl transport has been reported by many authors. This active component may include cotransport and countertransport mechanisms, and indeed, there is evidence to suggest that NaCl is transported across the epithelium in an electrically neutral fashion (4, 9, 43, 50). This active component of chloride transport represents the transcellular pathway for chloride reabsorption. Recent experiments demonstrate that the intracellular chloride activity is in excess of calculated equilibrium values (21), which indicates the presence of uphill transport across the luminal and/or basolateral membrane.

We shall look at the transport steps across luminal and basolateral membranes separately, but there are three types of mechanisms that act across each membrane: (*a*) ion movement through chloride channels, which is driven passively by electrochemical gradients; (*b*) transport of chloride ion coupled with a cation, either sodium, potassium, or both; (*c*) transport of chloride ion in exchange with another unknown anion, for which a variety of candidates have been suggested. At present there is no evidence for a specific chloride pump directly linked to the catabolism of ATP.

MECHANISMS OPERATING AT THE LUMINAL MEMBRANE

*Chloride conductive movement*    Studies on microvillus membrane vesicles have reported significant chloride conductive movement, which suggests the existence of specific chloride channels (44, 67, 68). Electrophysiological studies on intact epithelia, however, failed to demonstrate a chloride conductance across the luminal membrane (40, 50). The latter evidence is supported by the observation that the chloride conductance inhibitor anthracene-9-carboxylic acid did not significantly affect isotonic volume absorption when applied to the luminal surface in split drop experiments (39). However, anthracene-9-carboxylic acid reduced fluid reabsorption by about 25% in tubules perfused at 25 nl·min$^{-1}$ (R. Green, S. L. Greenwood & S. J. White, unpublished observations). The question whether chloride channels exist in the luminal membrane of proximal tubules is thus unresolved. Given the fact that the intracellular chloride activity is above the equilibrium value, if chloride channels are present in the apical membrane, they could be involved in chloride secretion rather than reabsorption.

*Cotransport with sodium*    In *Necturus* proximal tubule, Kimura & Spring (50) have demonstrated a significant fall in intracellular chloride activity following sudden removal of chloride or sodium from the luminal fluid. It was also shown that intracellular chloride activity is insensitive to changes in luminal membrane potential (50). The logical explanation for these observations is that a neutral, $Na^+$-coupled chloride transport system is responsible for these changes. However, Nakhoul & Boulpaep did not observe any changes in intracellular sodium activity when luminal chloride in another amphibian, *Ambystoma* was removed (54). Studies on brush border membrane vesicles isolated from *Necturus* kidney also failed to demonstrate a directly coupled $Na^+$-$Cl^-$ cotransport, which suggests that sodium transport across luminal membrane does not occur via a $Na^+$-$Cl^-$ symport (67).

In mammalian tubules there is also little evidence of neutral $Na^+$-$Cl^-$ cotransport. Studies of microvillus membranes from mammalian kidney have failed to demonstrate either direct $Na^+$-$Cl^-$ cotransport or $Na^+$-$2Cl^-$-$K^+$ symport (68). However, recent evidence suggests that such a symport may be present in cultured $LLCPK_1$ cells (17). These results are surprising since specific inhibitors of $Na^+$-$Cl^-$ and $Na^+$-$2Cl^-$-$K^+$ cotransport, such as furosemide, bumetanide, and piretanide, can reduce fluid reabsorption from the proximal tubule by as much as 40–50% (53; S. L. Greenwood, S. J. White, R. Green, unpublished observations). However, all these inhibitors, particularly at higher concentrations, have been shown to effect the $Cl^-$-$HCO_3^-$ exchange as well as carbonic anhydrase (16, 52, 74).

*Anion exchangers*    If electroneutral NaCl transport is to be explained in the absence of directly coupled $Na^+$-$Cl^-$ cotransport, then it seems likely that there are two exchanges operating in parallel: one that exchanges sodium for hydrogen and another that exchanges chloride for another anion. In this respect there is recent evidence both in *Necturus* and mammalian tubules that sodium reabsorption proceeds via a $Na^+$-$H^+$ exchange system (7). A number of separate anion exchangers have been proposed for electroneutral NaCl transport.

The first proposals (37, 53) postulated the existence of a $Cl^-$-$HCO_3^-$ or a $Cl^-$-$OH^-$ exchanger similar to that described in red blood cells (19). Data obtained with supposedly specific disulphonic stilbene inhibitors, SITS and DIDS, seemed to confirm the presence of such an exchanger at the luminal membrane (37, 39, 53). However, it is now known that SITS in particular attaches to $NH_2$ groups on proteins and may therefore interfere with a number of membrane proteins concerned with transport. Studies on microvillus membrane vesicles isolated from *Necturus* kidney identified the presence of $Na^+$-$H^+$ and $Cl^-$-$HCO_3^-$ exchangers (67), but the evidence from mammalian kidney cortex is confusing, some workers have found a $Cl^-$-$HCO_3^-$ exchanger (70, 76), but others deny its presence (65, 68).

One transport system that was uncovered, however, was a $Cl^-$-$Cl^-$ self-exchanger in the apical membrane from mammalian proximal tubule cells (47). While such exchange would not of itself cause net chloride reabsorption, other anions are likely to share this exchanger. Karniski & Aronson (47) tested a number of different substrates and observed a marked effect with formate. A formate gradient greatly accelerated $Cl^-$ influx into vesicles and caused the chloride ion concentration to overshoot its equilibrium level. Interestingly, this system was inhibited by DIDS and could not transport acetate, proprionate, butyrate, bicarbonate, or para-aminohippurate. If exchange of luminal chloride for intracellular formate accounts for a significant fraction of net chloride absorption, some mechanism for formate recycling must exist. Formate is a very permeable weak acid in its nonionized form, and experiments have shown that a pH gradient across the luminal membrane can serve to maintain a transmembrane formate gradient (47). This pH gradient would result mainly from $Na^+$-$H^+$ exchange, which would link the two parallel exchangers. Figure 1 provides an overview of the parallel arrangement of $Na^+$-$H^+$ and $Cl^-$-formate exchange in the apical cell membrane. In support of this model, formate added to luminal and peritubular fluid at physiological concentrations stimulates electroneutral NaCl reabsorption in the mammalian proximal tubule (64). In addition, studies with pH sensitive dyes show that a major fraction of $Cl^-$-base exchange at the luminal membrane of the rat proximal tubule is formate dependent and parallels $Na^+$-$H^+$ exchange (2).

More recently oxalate has also been found to induce uphill chloride uptake in rabbit microvillus membrane vesicles (48). The physiological significance of this latter exchanger for either chloride reabsorption or oxalate handling by the nephron has yet to be evaluated. It is not known whether there is a specific exchanger for each species of anion transported or whether one or two "common" transporters exist that have different affinities for several anions.

MECHANIMS OPERATING AT THE BASOLATERAL MEMBRANE

*Chloride conductive movement*    Electrophysiological experiments in the amphibian proximal tubule suggest that the basolateral membrane chloride conductance is very low (59, 69). Using ion-selective microelectrodes to measure cellular potassium and chloride activities, Shindo & Spring (69) demonstrated that the basolateral chloride conductance was about 10% of that

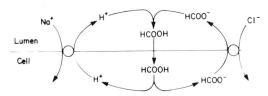

*Figure 1*   Proximal cell model demonstrating the role of formate in mediating electroneutral sodium chloride entry across the apical cell membrane.

for potassium. In addition, they showed that intracellular chloride activity was virtually unchanged by changes in basolateral membrane potential, which suggests the existence of an electroneutral transport step. The negligibly small chloride conductance of the basolateral membrane of proximal tubule cells was confirmed by Guggino et al (40) using cable analysis.

In mammalian proximal tubule, total replacement of peritubular chloride with impermeant anions did not affect cell membrane potentials (18, 20). Depolarization of the basolateral cell membrane with barium also had no effect on NaCl and fluid absorption (9). Both these pieces of evidence indicate a potential-insensitive step for chloride movement from the cell and argue against significant contributions to chloride transport by a channel in the basolateral membrane. However, using patch clamp techniques, Gögelein & Greger (31) recently found evidence of a basolateral channel in the rabbit proximal straight tubule that discriminated poorly between $Na^+$, $K^+$, and $Cl^-$ but was reversibly inhibited by the $Cl^-$ channel blocker diphenylamine-2-carboxylate (DPC). Although this basolateral $Cl^-$ conductive pathway may not play a major role in transcellular chloride movement, these $Cl^-$ channels may be involved in some cellular regulatory processes. Preliminary reports showed that changes in cell volume in the rabbit proximal tubule modulated not only a basolateral $K^+$ conductance, but also a $Cl^-$ conductance (77).

*Cotransport with potassium*    It is tempting to postulate a chloride and potassium cotransport system similar to that described in *Necturus* gallbladder (58). Evidence for such a mechanism has recently been obtained in basolateral membrane vesicles (25) isolated from rabbit kidney cortex, and the recent demonstration of activation of a $Ba^{2+}$-insensitive, furosemide-sensitive potassium efflux by glucose in proximal tubule suspensions is consistent with a component of $K^+$-$Cl^-$ cotransport (42). However, the participation of this cotransport in the basolateral chloride exit step has not been firmly established for the proximal tubule.

*Exchange for an anion*    Evidence was presented some years ago for a $Cl^-$-$HCO_3^-$ exchange system at the basolateral membrane of proximal tubule cells (37, 72). The evidence was based on the inhibitory effects on net chloride transport of disulphonic stilbenes, which as discussed above, may not be sufficiently specific to allow such a conclusion to be drawn. However, a $Cl^-$-$HCO_3^-$ exchanger, has been more directly identified in basolateral membrane vesicles isolated from rabbit kidney cortex (32). pH measurements made with pH-sensitive dyes also indicated the presence of a $Cl^-$-$HCO_3^-$ exchanger, since intracellular pH decreased when peritubular chloride concentration was increased (3). However, measurements of cellular concentrations of bicarbonate and chloride indicate that if there is such a mechanism there would be net entry of chloride into the cell in exchange for bicarbonate (18, 21, 78).

Studies of intracellular pH demonstrate that the exchange may also require the presence of sodium (3), and the recently described sodium bicarbonate cotransport (1, 78) may also be linked to chloride transport. Evidence in support of this idea has been obtained in rat cortical basolateral vesicles (32), but similar experiments have not yet been done in rabbit. In *Necturus* proximal tubules the basolateral $Na^+$-$HCO_3^-$-$Cl^-$ transporter involves transfer of charge (41), but in mammalian proximal tubule it is not known whether or not this transporter is electrogenic. If this exchanger is electroneutral, it may be similar to the $NaCO_3^-$-$Cl^-$ exchange reported in invertebrate cells (13).

## SECRETION OF CHLORIDE INTO THE PROXIMAL TUBULE

In the early proximal tubule bicarbonate is reabsorbed preferentially over chloride, which results in a rise in luminal chloride concentration above that in plasma. Using micropuncture techniques, Bomsztyk showed that in the rat proximal tubule inhibition of bicarbonate reabsorption reduced chloride concentration in the tubule lumen (12). In principle, this could result either from an enhanced chloride reabsorption or an inhibition of net chloride secretion. Interestingly, under these experimental conditions of no net water flux, the metabolic inhibitor cyanide also decreased luminal chloride concentration, which suggests the participation of active chloride *secretion* in the early proximal tubule. These data appear to contradict the observations previously reported by Green et al (33) and Alpern et al (4) that cyanide inhibits net chloride *reabsorption*. However, their experiments were performed in the presence of a chloride concentration gradient.

Clearly, the possibility that chloride secretion is the mechanism responsible for preferential bicarbonate reabsorption over chloride in the early proximal tubule needs further investigation.

## SUMMARY

Our knowledge of chloride transport along the nephron has greatly expanded. Whereas for a long time it was assumed that chloride ions were reabsorbed entirely passively with sodium—the "mendicant" role of chloride, more recent studies suggest that several distinct reabsorptive transport mechanisms operate in parallel. Accordingly, a new model of proximal chloride transport has evolved that includes both active, transcellular as well as passive, intercellular transport pathways. Transcellular chloride reabsorption involves anion exchange mechanisms in both the luminal and peritubular cell membranes, processes that also depend on sodium, hydrogen, and bicarbonate ions. Chloride transport is thus intimately related to sodium and fluid transport as well as to cell acid-base metabolism. Unresolved problems concern the relative magnitude of transcellular and paracellular chloride transport and the details of luminal and basolateral chloride translocation steps.

ACKNOWLEDGMENTS

LS is supported by a fellowship of the Connecticut Heart Association.

*Literature Cited*

1. Alpern, R. J. 1985. Mechanism of basolateral membrane $H^+/OH^-/HCO_3^-$ transport in the rat proximal convoluted tubule: A sodium-coupled electrogenic process. *J. Gen. Physiol.* 86:613–36
2. Alpern, R. J. 1987. Apical membrane Cl/base exchange in the rat proximal convoluted tubule. *J. Clin. Invest.* 79:1026–30
3. Alpern, R. J., Chambers, M. 1987. Basolateral membrane $Cl/HCO_3$ exchange in the rat proximal convoluted tubule: Na-dependent and independent modes. *J. Gen. Physiol.* 89:581–98
4. Alpern, R. J., Howlin, J. J., Preisig, P. A., Wong, K. R. 1985. Active and passive components of chloride transport in the rat proximal convoluted tubule. *J. Clin. Invest.* 76:1360–66
5. Andreoli, T. E., Schafer, J. A., Troutman, S. L., Watkins, M. C. 1979. Solvent drag component of $Cl^-$ flux in superficial proximal straight tubules: Evidence for a paracellular component of isotonic fluid absorption. *Am. J. Physiol.* 237:455–62
6. Aronson, P. S. 1981. Identifying secondary active solute transport in epithelia. *Am. J. Physiol.* 240:F1–F11
7. Aronson, P. S. 1983. Mechanisms of active $H^+$ secretion in the proximal tubule. *Am. J. Physiol.* 245:F647–59
8. Barratt, J. L., Rector, F. C., Kokko, J. P., Seldin, D. W. 1974. Factors governing the transepithelial potential difference across the proximal tubule of the rat kidney. *J. Clin. Invest.* 53:454–64
9. Baum, M., Berry, C. A. 1984. Evidence for neutral transcellular NaCl transport and neutral basolateral chloride exit in the rabbit proximal convoluted tubule. *J. Clin. Invest.* 74:205–11
10. Bello-Reuss, E. 1982. Electrical properties of the basolateral membrane of the straight portion of the rabbit proximal renal tubule. *J. Physiol. London* 326: 49–63
11. Bishop, J. H. V., Green, R. 1978. Effects of a disulphonic stilbene, SITS on anion reabsorption from the proximal tubule of the rat. *J. Physiol. London* 285:45P
12. Bomsztyk, K. 1986. Chloride transport by rat renal proximal tubule: Effects of bicarbonate absorption. *Am. J. Physiol.* 250(19):F1046–54
13. Boron, W. F., McCormick, W. C., Roos, A. 1981. pH regulation in barnacle muscle fibers: Dependence on extracellular sodium and bicarbonate. *Am. J. Physiol.* 240:C80–C89
14. Boulpaep, E. L. 1979. Electrophysiology of the kidney. In *Membrane Transport in Biology,* Vol. IV, pp. 97–144, ed. A. G. Giebisch, D. C. Tosteson, H. H. Ussing. Berlin: Springer-Verlag
15. Boulpaep, E. L., Seely, J. F. 1971. Electrophysiology of proximal and distal tubules in the autoperfused dog kidney. *Am. J. Physiol.* 221:1084–96
16. Brazy, P. C., Gunn, R. B. 1976. Furosemide inhibition of chloride transport in human red blood cells. *J. Gen. Physiol.* 68:583–99
17. Brown, C. D., Murer, H. 1985. Characterization of a Na:K:2Cl cotransport in the apical membrane of a renal epithelial cell line (LLC-PK1). *J. Membr. Biol.* 87(2):131–39
18. Burckhardt, B.-Ch., Sato, K., Frömter, E. 1984. Electrophysiological analysis of bicarbonate permeation across the peritubuluar cell membrane of rat kidney proximal tubule. *Pflüg. Arch.* 401:341–42
19. Cabantchik, Z. I., Rothstein, A. 1972. The nature of the membrane sites controlling anion permeability of human red blood cells as determined by studies with disulfonic stilbene derivatives. *J. Membr. Biol.* 10:311–30
20. Cardinal, J., LaPointe, J.-Y., Laprade, R. 1984. Luminal and peritubular ionic substitutions and intracellular potential

of the rabbit proximal convoluted tubule. *Am. J. Physiol.* 247:F352–64

21. Cassola, A. C., Mollenhauer, M., Frömter, E. 1983. The intracellular chloride activity of rat kidney proximal tubular cells. *Pflüg. Arch.* 399:259–65

22. Chantrelle, B. M., Cogan, M. G., Rector, F. C. 1985. Active and passive components of NaCl absorption in the proximal convoluted tubule of the rat kidney. *Miner. Electrolyte Metab.* 11:209–14

23. Cogan, M. G., Rector, F. C. Jr. 1982. Proximal reabsorption during metabolic acidosis in the rat. *Am. J. Physiol.* 242:F499–F507

24. Corman, B., DiStefano, A. 1983. Does water drag solutes through kidney proximal tubule? *Pflüg. Arch.* 397:35–41

25. Eveloff, J., Warnock, D. G. 1987. KCl cotransport systems in rabbit renal basolateral membrane vesicles. *Am. J. Physiol.* 252:F883–89

26. Frömter, E. E., Gessner, K. 1974. Free-flow potentials profile along rat kidney proximal tubule. *Pflüg. Arch.* 351:69–83

27. Frömter, E. E., Gessner, K. 1974. Active transport potentials, membrane diffusion potentials and streaming potentials across rat kidney proximal tubule. *Pflüg. Arch.* 351:85–98

28. Frömter, E. E., Rumrich, G., Ullrich, K. J. 1973. Phenomenologic description of $Na^+$, $Cl^-$, and $HCO_3^-$ absorption from proximal tubules of the rat kidney. *Pflüg. Arch.* 343:189–220

29. Giebisch, G. H. 1956. Measurement of pH, chloride and inulin concentrations in the proximal tubule of Necturus. *Am. J. Physiol.* 185:171–75

30. Giebisch, G., Aronson, P. S. 1986. The proximal nephron. In *Physiology of Membrane Disorders,* ed. T. E. Andreoli, J. F. Hoffman, D. D. Fanestill, S. G. Schultz, 3:669–710. New York/London: Plenum Medical Book Co. 1060 pp. 2nd ed.

30a. Giebisch, G., Schild, L., Green, R. 1987. Mechanism of chloride transport across mammalian proximal tubule. *Proc. Int. Congr. Nephrol.* In press

31. Gögelein, H., Greger, R. 1986. A voltage-dependent ionic channel in the basolateral membrane of the late proximal tubule of the rabbit kidney. *Pflüg. Arch.* 407(Suppl. 2):S142–48

32. Grassl, S. M., Holohan, P. D., Ross, C. R. 1987. $Cl/HCO_3$ exchange in rat renal cortical basolateral membrane vesicles. *Kidney Int.* 31(1):409 (Abstr.)

33. Green, R., Bishop, J. H. V., Giebisch, G. 1979. Ionic requirements of proximal tubular sodium transport. III. Selective luminal anion substitution. *Am. J. Physiol.* 236(3):F268–77

34. Green, R., Giebisch, G. 1975. Ionic requirements of proximal tubular sodium transport. I. Bicarbonate and chloride. *Am. J. Physiol.* 229:1205–15

35. Green, R., Giebisch, G. 1984. Luminal hypotonicity: A driving force for fluid absorption from the proximal tubule. *Am. J. Physiol.* 246(3):F167–74

36. Green, R., Giebisch, G. 1987. Reflection coefficients for solutes in rat proximal tubules. *Kidney Int.* 31:446 (Abstr.)

37. Green, R., Greenwood, S. L., Giebisch, G. 1980. The role of anions in the regulation of proximal tubular sodium and fluid transport. *Ann. NY Acad. Sci.* 341:125–33

38. Green, R., Moriarty, R. J., Giebisch, G. 1981. Ionic requirements of proximal tubular fluid reabsorption: Flow dependence of fluid transport. *Kidney Int.* 20:580–87

39. Green, R., White, S. J. 1985. The effect of inhibitors of anion exchange and chloride conductance on fluid reabsorption from rat renal proximal tubule. *J. Physiol. London* 361:58P (Abstr.)

40. Guggino, W. B., Boulpaep, E. L., Giebisch, G. 1982. Electrical properties of chloride transport across the *Necturus* proximal tubule. *J. Membr. Biol.* 65:185–96

41. Guggino, W. B., London, R., Boulpaep, E. L., Giebisch, G. 1983. Chloride transport across the basolateral cell membrane of the *Necturus* proximal tubule. Dependence on bicarbonate and sodium. *J. Membr. Biol.* 71:227–40

42. Gullans, S. R., Avison, M. J., Ogino, T., Shulman, R. G., Giebisch, G. 1986. Furosemide-sensitive $K^+$ efflux induced by glucose in the rabbit proximal tubule. *Kidney Int.* 29(1):396 (Abstr.)

43. Howlin, K. J., Alpern, R. J., Berry, C. A., Rector, F. C. 1986. Evidence for electroneutral sodium chloride transport in rat proximal convoluted tubule. *Am. J. Physiol.* F644–48

44. Illsley, N. P., Chen, P. Y., Verkman, A. S. 1987. Renal vesicle chloride transport measured by a novel Cl-sensitive fluorescent indicator. *Kidney Int.* 31(1):437 (Abstr.)

45. Jacobson, H. R., Kokko, J. P. 1976. Intrinsic differences in various segments of the proximal tubule. *J. Clin. Invest.* 57:818–25

46. Jacobson, H. R., Kokko, J. P., Seldin, D. W., Holmberg, C. 1982. Lack of solvent drag of NaCl and $NaHCO_3$ in

rabbit proximal tubules. *Am. J. Physiol.* 243:F342–48

47. Karniski, L. P., Aronson, P. S. 1985. Chloride formate exchange with formic acid recycling: A mechanism of active chloride transport across epithelial membranes. *Proc. Natl. Acad. Sci. USA* 82:6362–65

48. Karniski, L. P., Aronson, P. S. 1987. Evidence for two separate anion exchange pathways for Cl transport in rabbit renal microvillus membrane vesicles. *Kidney Int.* 31(1):438 (Abstr.)

49. Kawamura, S., Imai, M., Seldin, D. W., Kokko, J. P. 1975. Characteristics of salt and water transport in superficial and juxtamedullary straight segments of proximal tubules. *J. Clin. Invest.* 55:1269–77

50. Kimura, G., Spring, K. R. 1982. Transcellular and paracellular tracer chloride fluxes in *Necturus* proximal tubule. *Am. J. Physiol.* 235:F617–25

51. Kokko, J. P. 1973. Proximal tubular potential difference: Dependence on glucose, $HCO_3^-$ and amino-acids. *J. Clin. Invest.* 52:1362–67

52. Kunau, R. T. Jr. 1972. The influence of carbonic anhydrase inhibitor, benzolamide (CL-11,366), on the reabsorption of chloride, sodium and bicarbonate in the proximal tubule of the rat. *J. Clin. Invest.* 51:294–306

53. Lucci, M. S., Warnock, D. G. 1979. Effects of anion-transport inhibitors on NaCl reabsorption in the rat superficial proximal convoluted tubule. *J. Clin. Invest.* 64:570–79

54. Nakhoul, S. A., Boulpaep, E. L. 1986. Apical membrane transport mechanims for Na entry in *Ambystoma* kidney proximal tubule. *Kidney Int.* 29(1):403 (Abstr.)

55. Neumann, K. H., Rector, F. C. Jr. 1976. Mechanism of NaCl and water reabsorption in the proximal convoluted tubule of the rat kidney: Role of chloride concentration gradients. *J. Clin. Invest.* 58:1110–18

56. Rector, F. C. 1983. Sodium, bicarbonate, and chloride reabsorption by the proximal tubule. *Am. J. Physiol.* 244:F461–71

57. Rector, F. C., Martinez-Maldonado, M., Brunner, F. P., Seldin, D. W. 1966. Evidence for passive reabsorption of NaCl in the proximal tubule of the rat kidney. *J. Clin. Invest.* 45:1060 (Abstr.)

58. Reuss, L. 1983. Basolateral KCl cotransport in a NaCl-absorbing epithelium. *Nature* 305:723–26

59. Sackin, H., Boulpaep, E. L. 1981. Isolated perfused salamander proximal

tubule. II. Monovalent ion replacement and rheogenic transport. *Am. J. Physiol.* 241(10):F540–55

60. Schafer, J. A. 1984. Mechanisms coupling the absorption of solutes and water in the proximal nephron. *Kidney Int.* 25:708–16

61. Schafer, J. A., Patlak, C. S., Andreoli, T. E. 1975. A component of fluid absorption linked to passive ion flows in the superficial pars recta. *J. Gen. Physiol.* 66:445–71

62. Schafer, J. A., Troutman, S. L., Andreoli, T. E. 1974. Volume reabsorption, transepithelial potential differences, and ionic permeability properties in mammalian superficial proximal straight tubules. *J. Gen. Physiol.* 64:582–607

63. Schafer, J. A., Troutman, S. L., Watkins, M. C., Andreoli, T. E. 1978. Volume absorption in the pars recta. I. "Simple" active $Na^+$ transport. *Am. J. Physiol.* 3(4):F332–39

64. Schild, L., Giebisch, G., Karniski, L. P., Aronson, P. S. 1987. Effect of formate on volume reabsorption in the rabbit proximal tubule. *J. Clin. Invest.* 79:32–38

65. Schwartz, G. J. 1983. Absence of $Cl^-/OH^-$ or $Cl-/HCO_3^-$ exchange in the rabbit proximal tubule. *Am. J. Physiol.* 245:F462–69

66. Seely, J. F. 1973. Variation in electrical resistance along the length of rat proximal convoluted tubule. *Am. J. Physiol.* 225:48–57

67. Seifter, J. L., Aronson, P. S. 1984. Chloride absorption by renal proximal tubules of *Necturus*. *Am. J. Physiol.* 247:F888–95

68. Seifter, J. L., Knickelbein, R., Aronson, P. S. 1984. Absence of Cl-OH exchange and NaCl cotransport in rabbit renal microvillus membrane vesicles. *Am. J. Physiol.* F753–59

69. Shindo, T., Spring, K. R. 1981. Chloride movement across the basolateral membrane of proximal tubule cells. *J. Membr. Biol.* 58:35–42

70. Shiuan, D., Weinstein, S. W. 1984. Evidence for electroneutral chloride transport in rabbit renal cortical brush broder membrane vesicles. *Am. J. Physiol.* 247:F837–47

71. Spring, K. R., Kimura, G. 1978. Chloride reabsorption by renal proximal tubules of *Necturus*. *J. Membr. Biol.* 38:233–54

72. Ullrich, K. J., Capasso, G., Rumrich, G., Papavassiliou, F. 1977. Coupling between proximal tubular transport processes: Studies with ouabain, SITS and

bicarbonate free solutions. *Pflüg. Arch.* 368:245–52

73. Vari, R. C., Ott, C. E. 1982. In vivo proximal tubular fluid-to-plasma concentration gradient in the rabbit. *Am. J. Physiol.* 242:F575–79

74. Vogh, B. P., Langham, M. R. 1981. The effects of furosemide and bumetanide on cerebrospinal fluid formation. *Brain Res.* 221:171–83

75. Walker, A. M., Bott, P. A., Oliver, J., MacDowell, M. C. 1941. The collection and analysis of fluid from single nephrons of the mammalian kidney. *Am. J. Physiol.* 134:580–95

76. Warnock, D. G., Yee, V. J. 1981. Chloride uptake by brush-border membrane vesicles isolated from rabbit renal cortex: Coupling to proton gradients and $K^+$ diffusion potentials. *J. Clin. Invest.* 67:103–15

77. Welling, P. A., O'Neil, R. G. 1987. Cell swelling increases basolateral membrane $Cl^-$ and $K^+$ conductances of the rabbit proximal straight tubule. *Kidney Int.* 31(1):452 (Abstr.)

78. Yoshitomi, K., Burckhardt, B.-Ch., Frömter, E. 1985. Rheogenic sodium-bicarbonate cotransport in the peritubular cell membrane of rat renal proximal tubule. *Pflüg. Arch.* 405:360–66

*Ann. Rev. Physiol. 1988. 50:111–22*

# CHLORIDE TRANSPORT IN THICK ASCENDING LIMB, DISTAL CONVOLUTION, AND COLLECTING DUCT

*Rainer Greger*

Lehrstuhl II, Physiologie, Albert-Ludwigs-Universität, D-7800 Freiburg, West Germany

## INTRODUCTION

The traditional view in the field of epithelial transport has been to look upon the chloride ion as the obedient passive partner that follows the actively transported $Na^+$ ion. This view has to be modified or even rejected for several epithelia, including different nephron segments. In this volume, Schild et al examine the mechanisms of proximal tubule chloride transport. My contribution briefly summarizes the mechanisms of chloride transport in distal nephron segments. In the reabsorptive processes the $Cl^-$ ion generally takes the transcellular route rather than that between cell. To cross the cell, the $Cl^-$ ion must penetrate the luminal and basolateral cell membranes. In different distal tubular segments various carrier systems and ion channels are responsible for chloride permeation.

Much progress has been made recently in the understanding of the mechanism of NaCl reabsorption in the thick acending limb of the loop of Henle (13, 29). Our knowledge about the mechanisms responsible for NaCl reabsorption in the early distal tubule (19) is much less extensive. With respect to research on the collecting tubule, rapid progress has been made since intracellular microelectrode technology has been applied to the various segments and functionally heterogenous cell types (35, 45, 48). In the collecting tubule, $Cl^-$ transport is closely related to bicarbonate transport. This specific transport process is covered in this volume by Luke & Galla. The

111

0066-4278/88/0315-0111$02.00

present review focuses on the cellular mechanisms of distal tubule $Cl^-$ transport, its regulation, and its inhibition by specific transport inhibitors.

## THICK ASCENDING LIMB

### Mechanism of NaCl Reabsorption

The basic principles of NaCl reabsorption in the thick ascending limb (TAL) have been reviewed recently (13). Figure 1 summarizes these concepts. The reabsorption of $Cl^-$ occurs transcellularly, leading to the generation of the lumen-positive transepithelial voltage. $Na^+$ is reabsorbed transcellularly as well as paracellularly. The latter process is driven by the transepithelial voltage. The energy-consuming component in the reabsorption of NaCl is the basolateral $Na^+$-$K^+$ pump. The cellular uptake of $Cl^-$ is mediated by the $Na^+$-$2Cl^-$-$K^+$ carrier system. $Cl^-$ leaves the cell via the chloride conductance in the basolateral membrane and via an electroneutral KCl transport system. A certain amount of $K^+$, closely corresponding to that taken up by the $Na^+$-$2Cl^-$-$K^+$ carrier, recycles across the luminal membrane. This fairly simple concept was developed from studies in the rabbit (16) and is supported by other studies in a variety of species, including fish (30), bird (42), *Amphiuma* (43), frog (44, 56), mouse (27), and rat (46). It appears that an analogous nephron segment has been conserved meticulously during evolution. The tasks of this nephron segment are (*a*) the reabsorption of NaCl and (*b*) the prevention of water fluxes that generate a concentration gradient for NaCl directed from the peritubular space to the lumen. Thus the term diluting segment (56) accurately describes the function of this nephron segment. Compared to the NaCl reabsorptive mechanisms present in other distal nephron segments, the system based on $Na^+$-$2Cl^-$-$K^+$ cotransport and paracellular reabsorption of $Na^+$ is most economical; the maximum efficiency can be as high as six NaCl transported per ATP consumed (13). It may be this efficiency of NaCl transport work that has helped to conserve this mechanism throughout evolution.

### Luminal $Na^+$-$H^+$ and $Cl^-$-$HCO_3^-$ Exchange

Although the above adequately describes the mechanism for most of the NaCl reabsorption in this nephron segment, some modifications are needed to account for certain experimental observations. For example, in the mouse and the rat cortical TAL segment (10, 12) and in the frog diluting segment (40, 44), it has been shown that the luminal membrane possesses, in addition to a $Na^+$-$2Cl^-$-$K^+$ cotransporter, a $Na^+$-$H^+$ exchanger and probably also a $Cl^-$-$HCO_3^-$ exchanger (mouse cTAL). The combination of the latter two exchangers leads to an additional component of NaCl reabsorption. Interestingly, this fraction of NaCl reabsorption was also blocked by high doses ($10^{-4}$ mol/l) of furosemide (10) and by low doses ($<10^{-6}$ mol/l) of bumetanide (9). If these exchangers work at unequal rates such that the $Na^+$-$H^+$ exchanger predominates, acidic luminal fluid will be generated, as has been observed for the rat cTAL segment (12) and for the amphibian diluting segment (40, 44). In the latter preparation it has been shown that $Na^+$ deficiency due to aldosterone treatment increases the rate of $Na^+$-$H^+$ exchange. This increased acid extrusion from the cell led to intracellular alkalinization, which in turn increased the $K^+$ conductance of the luminal cell membrane and the rate of $K^+$ secretion.

## Luminal $NH_4^+$ Uptake

It has been shown that $NH_4^+$ is reabsorbed along the rat TAL nephron segment (12). This reabsorption appears to occur via the transcellular route, and it may reflect the replacement of $K^+$ by $NH_4^+$ at the $K^+$ binding site of the $Na^+$-$2Cl^-$-$K^+$ carrier (33).

## Basolateral Transport Mechanisms

As stated above, the electroneutral KCl exit mechanism is required to recycle most of the $K^+$ taken up by the $Na^+$-$K^+$ pump. Unfortunately, this transport mechanism has been poorly characterized, in part because no specific inhibitors are known for this system. The existence of yet other transport systems has been postulated based on experimental results in medullary TAL segments in the mouse. It has been shown that the regulatory volume increase caused by an initial osmotic shrinkage of mTAL cells is mediated by uptake of $HCO_3^-$ and probably $Na^+$ (25).

## Attempts to Purify the $Na^+$-$2Cl^-$-$K^+$ Carrier

Currently, several groups are attempting to purify and reconstitute the $Na^+$-$2Cl^-$-$K^+$ cotransport protein. Photoactivation of bumetanide (2, 32), 4-benzoyl-5-sulfanoyl-3-(3-thionyloxy)benzoate (24), and of azido piretanide (6) has been used. The molecular masses of the putative $Na^+$-$2Cl^-$-$K^+$ carrier, or of the loop diuretic binding subunit, range between 17 and 170 kd. Initial attempts to reconstitute the $Na^+$-$2Cl^-$-$K^+$ carrier as well as the $K^+$ channel from renal medullary membranes have been reported recently (4). The similarity of the $Na^+$-$2Cl^-$-$K^+$ carrier with the Tamm-Horsfall protein has been emphasized repeatedly, and it was claimed that the Tamm-Horsfall protein may constitute a component of the $Na^+$-$2Cl^-$-$K^+$ carrier (21). This hypothesis appears attractive since (a) Tamm-Horsfall protein is localized only in the thick ascending limb; (b) Tamm-Horsfall protein binds loops diuretics with $K_d$ values similar to those found for the $Na^+$-$2Cl^-$-$K^+$ uptake mechanism in TAL cells; (c) the interaction of loop diuretics with the Tamm-Horsfall protein requires the presence of $Na^+$, $Cl^-$, and $K^+$, as does the inhibition of the $Na^+$-$2Cl^-$-$K^+$ carrier in intact TAL cells. However, this evidence is circumstantial. It should be noted that very high doses of polyclonal antibodies against Tamm-Horsfall protein were necessary to inhibit NaCl transport in the loop of Henle of rats (21), and no such inhibition was seen with monoclonal antibodies against Tamm-Horsfall protein in rabbit TAL segments perfused in vitro (R. Greger & Ph. Wangemann, unpublished observations). Further, the predicted interaction of Tamm-Horsfall antibodies with the $Na^+$-$K^+$-$Cl^-$ carrier in all the different epithelia and apolar cells possessing this carrier system (13) has not yet been reported.

## Hormonal Regulation of Thick Ascending Limb NaCl Transport

Hormonal regulation of thick ascending limb NaCl transport has been reviewed recently (13, 39). Recent data favor the view that antidiuretic hormone acts via cAMP and thereby increases NaCl reabsorption, mainly in the medullary TAL segment in mice and rats. As to the mechanism of action, it is generally accepted that all membrane transporters outlined in Figure 1 work at higher rates after ADH stimulation. Discrepant outlines of the sequence of these events have been proposed. It has been reported that ADH, acting via cAMP, increases the apical $K^+$ conductance (23). Similarly, it has been suggested that ADH causes an increase in $K^+$ conductance and in the number of functioning $Na^+$-$2Cl^-$-$K^+$ carriers (27, 38). Another study (49) used intracellular impalements to show that cAMP depolarizes the cell, even in the presence of furosemide. It was concluded, therefore, that the primary effect of cAMP is to increase the chloride conductance of the basolateral membrane. Clearly, this does not exclude the possibility that the other components responsible for the reabsorption of NaCl in the TAL cell are also enhanced as a consequence of the increased chloride conductance.

Prostaglandins ($PGE_2$) have been reported to reduce NaCl reabsorption in medullary TAL segments of the mouse. This inhibitory effect occurs through the cAMP-dependent pathway and is mediated by reduced cAMP generation (28). Glucagon and $\beta$-agonists both increase the rate of NaCl rebsorption by stimulating cAMP production.

The action of corticoid hormones has also been reviewed recently (39). Circumstantial evidence points to a glucocorticoid-mediated increase in NaCl reabsorption in the TAL segment. However, no direct data on in vitro perfused TAL tubules are available as yet.

## Specific Transport Inhibitors

LOOP DIURETICS OF THE FUROSEMIDE TYPE    This topic has been reviewed thoroughly (13, 17). Since the appearance of these reviews a few new drugs, classified as loop diuretics, have been introduced. One called torasemide shares some structural similarities with furosemide: The anionic group, which is $COO^-$ in case of furosemide, is a sulfonylurea moiety in case of torasemide. The sulfamoyl moiety of furosemide is replaced by a pyridino nitrogene in torasemide. It is not surprising then that torasemide interferes with the $Na^+$-$2Cl^-$-$K^+$ cotransporter (63). Nevertheless, two differences between furosemide and related compounds as opposed to torasemide are worth noting. Firstly, torasemide is far more lipid soluble than furosemide. This characteristic leads to corresponding changes in its pharmacokinetics, but it may also have a significance with respect to its pharmacodynamics since torasemide and related compounds can gain access to the brain, for example. Secondly, torasemide, at higher concentrations ($3 \times 10^{-5}$ mol/l) blocks the chloride conductance of the basolateral membrane of TAL segments (63). Another new substance, muzolimine, is not structurally related to furosemide, but nevertheless it inhibits loop NaCl transport in the intact organism. Previously, it was shown that muzolimine at concentrations lower than $10^{-4}$ mol/l has no effect on in vitro perfused TAL segments (50). Recent experiments from my laboratory indicate that muzolimine is metabolized to an active compound that inhibits NaCl reabsorption in the thick ascending limb from the luminal side. The fact that the secretion of this active metabolite is inhibited by probenecid suggests that this muzolimine metabolite is also an anion like furosemide and related drugs.

CHLORIDE CHANNEL BLOCKERS    A recent, extensive article (62) covers the structure-activity relationship for this class of drugs. Substances with an affinity of $< 10^{-7}$ mol/l for the basolateral chloride conductance have been found. Chloride channel blockers are structurally related to inhibitors of the $Na^+$-$2Cl^-$-$K^+$ cotransporter and also to inhibitors of the band 3 protein (15, 20). The mechanism of interaction has been studied in some detail in patch-clamp analyses of single chloride channels of the rectal gland (18) and of colon carcinoma cells (14). Chloride channel blockers appear to block the channel from the outside. Their mode of action is comparable to that of amiloride, inasmuch as they induce channel noise (flickering).

# DISTAL CONVOLUTED TUBULE

## Mechanism of NaCl Transport

It is impossible, at this stage, to describe the mechanism of NaCl reabsorption in this nephron segment by a comprehensive model. This dilemma has been phrased in recent reviews (39, 60). It may be summarized as follows: (a) This nephron segment is heterogenous, comprising at least three different substructures with different cell types even within a single substructure. (b) The heterogeneity differs from species to species. (c) The rat, the best-studied animal in in vivo experiments, is probably not a good model for the very early distal segment, since this nephron segment is not accessible to micropuncture, nor for the late distal convolution, where the different cell types intermingle. (*d*) The rabbit distal convoluted tubule has not been studied to a great extent in vitro because the segments are difficult to dissect and are rather short, at least for net-flux studies. A clear subdivison for the rabbit distal convolution on the basis of morphology, hormone responsiveness, and inhibitors was first presented in 1979 (31), but only a few comparable studies have been presented since (1, 19). In the following section, I focus on the very early distal tubule of the rabbit, which commences with a transition from the cTAL cell type to a more palisadal cell type some 200 $\mu$m past the macula densa and which extends to the connecting tubule with a length of some 500 $\mu$m. This nephron segment probably corresponds to the very early distal tubule, the earliest loop in the rat kidney accessible to micropuncture, and probably represents the thiazide-sensitive nephron site. A working hypothesis (19) for NaCl transport in this nephron segment is summarized in Figure 1.

Clear evidence for the existence of the basolateral $Na^+$-$K^+$ pump comes from electrophysiological studies, including intracellular impalements (19), and from the histochemical demonstration of the presence of the Na,K-ATPase in the basolateral membrane of this segment (52). Also, there is little doubt that this membrane possesses a $K^+$ conductance that accounts for the vast majority of the conductance of this cell membrane. Thus the $K^+$ taken up by the $Na^+$-$K^+$ pump is at least partially recycled through this pathway. Less clear are the properties of the luminal cell membrane. Nevertheless, the most striking finding is that the luminal membrane conductance is extremely small in absolute terms, as well as in comparison with that of the basolateral membrane ($< 10\%$). This minute conductance of $<< 1$ mS/cm$^2$ could not be

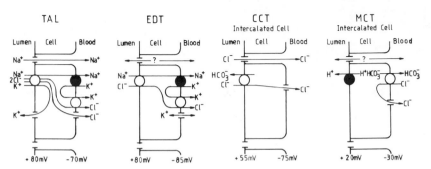

*Figure 1*   Models of ion transport in the thick ascending limb of the loop of Henle (TAL), early distal tubule (EDT), cortical collecting tubule (CCT), and medullary collecting tubule (MCT). ⇌→ channel, $\sigma$→ carrier system, ●→ primary active pump. Data are taken from the following references, 13, 19, 34, and 48.

ascribed with certainty to one ionic species. It became clear, however, that the net reabsorptive fluxes across this epithelium, as they have been deduced from in situ perfusions (61) and from measurements in in vitro perfused segments (R. Greger, unpublished), were too large to be accounted for by the small electrochemical gradient and the small transepithelial conductance. In addition, no corresponding conductance was found in the luminal cell membrane. In view of this, an electroneutral mechanism for $Na^+$ and $Cl^-$ uptake appears likely. However, NaCl uptake via the $Na^+$-$K^+$-$Cl^-$ carrier present in the thick ascending limb of the loop of Henle has been excluded (cf above) since furosemide and related drugs do not hyperpolarize early distal tubule cells. In contrast, it has been shown by in situ perfusions (61) and by preliminary in vitro perfusion experiments that thiazides reduce the rate of NaCl transport in this nephron segment (R. Greger, unpublished). Since it has been shown in another epithelium, flounder urinary bladder (54), that thiazides interfere with an electroneutral NaCl cotransport system, it may be an acceptable working hypothesis that this same NaCl carrier system is responsible for the transcellular NaCl transport in the early distal tubule.

Another obvious question regards the mechanism by which $Cl^-$ leaves the cell. As no chloride conductance was demonstrable in the basolateral membrane by electrophysiological studies (19), one has to assume that chloride leaves the cell electroneutrally. Close inspection reveals that at least some $K^+$ must also leave the cell electroneutrally, even though a $K^+$ conductance is present in this membrane. Since the voltage is high across the basolateral membrane (about $-85$ mV), the driving force for $K^+$ must be small, which makes it necessary to postulate additional mechanisms for $K^+$ transport. Again, the KCl symport in this model is postulated on the basis of indirect evidence; this entire concept is to be regarded as a working model (19).

## Hormonal Control of NaCl Transport in Early Distal Tubule

From dissection studies and measurements of adenylate cyclase it appears that the only hormone of importance in this nephron segment is calcitonin (39). The effects of this hormone on NaCl transport have been reported from in situ microperfusion studies (8; de Rouffignac & Elalouf, this volume).

The possible effects of mineralo- and glucocorticoids are less clearly defined, in part because of the heterogeneity of the rat distal nephron segments. Therefore, functional data are difficult to interpret. No data are available on the effects of mineralocorticoids on this nephron segment in rabbits.

## Inhibitors of NaCl Transport in the Early Distal Tubule

The effect of thiazides has already been mentioned above. It is important to emphasize that loop diuretics of the furosemide type do not block NaCl transport in the early distal tubule and that, conversely, thiazides do not block NaCl reabsorption in the thick ascending limb. Somewhat conflicting results on this issue are found in the literature; however, in those studies reporting an effect of furosemide in the early distal tubule, concentrations as high as $10^{-4}$ mol/l were required. Such high concentrations may interfere with elements other than the $Na^+$-$2Cl^-$-$K^+$ carrier. Clearly, more direct data on thiazide effects on in vitro perfused distal tubules and on luminal membrane vesicles of this nephron segment are needed to characterize this NaCl transport system. Specifically, does NaCl uptake resemble a dual exchanger utilizing $Na^+$-$H^+$ and $Cl^-$-$HCO_3^-$, or does it resemble a NaCl cotransporter? Currently, the latter seems more likely since (a) no effect of thiazides on intestinal NaCl transport, mediated by the double exchanger, has been described thus far and (b) SITS does not alter the membrane voltage of the early distal tubule (H. Velázquez & R. Greger, unpublished), nor is band 3 protein immunologically demonstrable in this nephron segment (7) (see below).

## COLLECTING TUBULE

### Mechanisms of $Cl^-$ Transport in the Collecting Duct System

The collecting duct system is a morphologically and functionally heterogenous epithelium (37). The various segments, cortical collecting tubule (CCT), medullary collecting tubule (MCT), and papillary collecting duct (PCT), follow each other. Within each segment the cells can be classified into principal cells and intercalated cells. However, even this distinction is not sufficient. Type A intercalated cells (found in the CCT) segments are likely different from type B intercalated cells (found in the MCT). Not surprisingly, our understanding of the cellular mechanism of ionic transport in the collecting tubule is still far from complete. Nevertheless, the relative ease with which CCT and MCT segments can be dissected and studied electrophysiologically has greatly contributed to our current understanding of the basic concepts. However, we know little of the mechanisms operating in the PCT.

For the CCT cell, analogies have been drawn to frog skin epithelial cells. Thus the main route for $Cl^-$ was supposed to be paracellular (48). More recently, evidence has accumulated that $Cl^-$ also moves transcellularly in frog skin epithelial cells (41) and CCT cells (34, 48). The transcellular route probably corresponds to the intercalated cells. As is apparent from Figure 1, this transfer is tightly linked to $HCO_3^-$ transport. In fact, the basolateral membrane of the MCT appears to be the only nephron segment possessing immunologically competent band 3 protein (7). The issue of interrelation of $Cl^-$ transport and $H^+$-$HCO_3^-$ transport in this nephron segment is addressed further by Galla & Luke in this volume. The CCT (Figure 1), and specifically, the intercalated cell type, appears to possess the ability to secrete $HCO_3^-$ in alkalosis (3). This cell type possesses a basolateral $Cl^-$ conductance (48, 57). Therefore, the bicarbonate secretion is coupled to $Cl^-$ reabsorption.

The MCT (Figure 1) appears to secrete $H^+$ and reabsorb $HCO_3^-$ under various acid/base conditions (3). The basolateral $HCO_3^-$ exit seems to be driven by $Cl^-$ exchange via band 3 protein (7). The membrane conductances of these MCT intercalated cells have been examined (minority cell type) (34). It was found that the apical membrane has a very low conductance and that the basolateral membrane possesses a predominant $Cl^-$ conductance. One could argue that $Cl^-$ serves only to shuttle $HCO_3^-$ out of the cell and that the $Cl^-$ taken up via $Cl^-$-$HCO_3^-$ exchange leaves the cell via $Cl^-$ channels. In this model, $H^+$ secretion would be viewed as $Na^+$-$H^+$ exchange with $Na^+$ reabsorption occuring in the principal cell and $H^+$ secretion occuring via the intercalated cell. Obviously, much further work is needed to verify this model. In particular, the search for $Cl^-$ conductive pathways must be intensified. A surprising recent report on cultured "Nephronanlagen," which supposedly corresponds to collecting duct cells, claims that $Cl^-$ channels are also present in the apical cell membrane (5).

A comprehensive model for $Cl^-$ transport in the PCT cannot be given at this time. Data in the intact rat kidney favor the view that this segment shares the properties of the above segments, namely (a) the ability to reabsorb $Na^+$ in a fashion controlled by mineralocorticoids, which corresponds to the properties of principal cells (58), and (b) the ability to modulate $H^+$ secretion in response to acid/base disturbances, which corresponds to the properties of intercalated cells (59). Data on the isolated in vitro perfused PCT diverge entirely from these concepts. Recently, in a preliminary set of studies, a furosemide-sensitive $Cl^-$ secretory mechanism has been postulated for this nephron segment (36). Bumetanide-sensitive $Na^+$-$K^+$-$Cl^-$ cotransport has already been reported for papillary epithelial sheets (47) and for dispersed papillary cells (22). There is an urgent need for further work in the PCT as it is thought that atrial natriurectic peptide (ANP) may act at this nephron site (53). However, preparation of in vitro perfused segments may not be the technical solution, since dissection is very difficult in this area of the kidney and since even the most gentle dissection may activate hormonal mechanisms.

## Hormonal Control of $Cl^-$ Transport in the CT Segments

The extensive morphological and functional changes in principal cells in response to mineralocorticoids (37), the antidiuretic hormone– (AVP) and prostaglandin-modulated changes in water permeability (26), and AVP-induced changes in apical $Na^+$ conductance (51) are all beyond the scope of this review. More relevant to the present issue are changes in chloride fluxes in response to the varied NaCl content of the diet (11) and to mineralocorticoid-mediated modulation of $H^+$ secretion (55). (The latter issue is reviewed in this volume by Galla & Luke.) The mechanism by which ANP might mediate increases in PCT NaCl secretion (53) are not yet clear.

ACKNOWLEDGEMENTS

The cited work from the author's laboratory has been supported by Deutsche Forschungsgemeinschaft (DFG, Gr 480/6) and by a grant from the European Community [ST2J-0095-2-D (CD)]. I am indebted to Dr. I. Novak for many helpful suggestions regarding this text. The secretarial assistance by Mrs. E. Viereck is greatly appreciated.

## Literature Cited

1. Almeida, A. J., Burg, M. B. 1982. Sodium transport in the rabbit connecting tubule. *Am. J. Physiol.* 243:F330–34

2. Amsler, K., Kinne, R. 1986. Photoinactivation of sodium-potassium-chloride cotransport in LLC-PK$_1$/Cl 4 cells by bumetanide. *Am. J. Physiol.* 250:C799–C806

3. Atkins, J. L., Burg, M. B. 1985. Bicarbonate transport by isolated perfused rat collecting ducts. *Am. J. Physiol.* 249:F485–89

4. Burnham, C., Karlish, S. J. D., Jørgensen, P. L. 1985. Identification and reconstitution of Na$^+$/K$^+$/Cl$^-$ cotransporter and K$^+$ channel from luminal membranes of renal red outer medulla. *Biochim. Biophys. Acta* 821:461–69

5. Christine, C. W., Laskowski, F. H., Gitter, A. H., Gross, P., Frömter, E. 1987. Chloride-selective single ion channels in the apical membrane of cultured collecting duct principal cells. *Pflüg. Arch.* 408(R32):121 (Abstr.)

6. Di Stefano, A., Wangemann, P., Friedrich, T., Burckhardt, G. Ökonomopoulos, R., Greger, R. 1986. Irreversible inhibition of the Na$^+$2Cl$^-$K$^+$ carrier in in vitro perfused cortical thick ascending limbs of the loop of Henle (TAL) by photoactivated azido derivates of furosemide. *Pflüg. Arch.* 406(R59):222 (Abstr.)

7. Drenckhahn, D., Schlüter, K., Allen, D. P., Bennett, V. 1985. Colocalization of band 3 with ankyrin and spectrin at the basal membrane of intercalated cells in the rat kidney. *Science* 230:1287–89

8. Elalouf, J. M., Roinel, N., de Rouffignac, C. 1983. Stimulation by human calcitonin of electrolyte transport in distal tubules of rat kidney. *Pflüg. Arch.* 399:111–18

9. Friedman, P. A. 1986. Bumetanide inhibition of (CO$_2$+HCO$_3$)-dependent and -independent equivalent electrical flux in renal cortical thick ascending limbs. *J. Pharmacol. Exp. Ther.* 238:407–14

10. Friedman, P. A., Andreoli, T. E. 1982. CO$_2$-stimulated NaCl absorption in the mouse renal cortical thick ascending limb of Henle. *J. Gen. Physiol.* 80:683–711

11. Galla, J. H., Bonduris, D. N., Kirk, K. A., Luke, R. G. 1986. Effect of dietary NaCl on chloride uptake in rat collecting duct segment. *Am. J. Physiol.* 251:F454–59

12. Good, D. W., Knepper, M. A., Burg, M. B. 1984. Ammonia and bicarbonate transport by thick ascending limb of rat kidney. *Am. J. Physiol.* 247:F35–F44

13. Greger, R. 1985. Ion transport mechanisms in the thick ascending limb of Henle's loop of the mammalian nephron. *Physiol. Rev.* 65:760–97

14. Greger, R., Gögelein, H., Hayslett, J. P. 1987. Cl$^-$ channels in the apical cell membrane of colonic carcinoma cells (HT29). *Pflüg. Arch.* 408(R7):19 (Abstr.)

15. Greger, R., Lang, H. J., Englert, H. C., Wangemann, P. 1987. Blockers of the Na$^+$2Cl$^-$K$^+$ carrier and of chloride channels in the thick ascending limb of the loop of Henle. In *Diuretics*, ed. J. B. Puschett. New York: Elsevier

16. Greger, R., Schlatter, E. 1981. Presence of luminal K$^+$, a prerequisite for active NaCl transport in the cortical thick ascending limb of Henle's loop of rabbit kidney. *Pflüg. Arch.* 392:92–94

17. Greger, R., Schlatter, E. 1983. Cellular mechanism of the action of loop diuretics on the thick ascending limb of Henle's loop. *Klin. Wochenschr.* 61:1019–27

18. Greger, R., Schlatter, E., Gögelein, H. 1987. Chloride channels in the luminal membrane of the rectal gland of the dogfish *(Squalus acanthias)*. Properties of the "larger" conductance channel. *Pflüg. Arch.* 409:114–25
19. Greger, R., Velázquez, H. 1987. The cortical thick ascending limb and early distal convoluted tubule in the urinary concentrating mechanism. *Kidney Int.* 31:590–96
20. Greger, R., Wangemann, P., Wittner, M., Di Stefano, A., Lang, H. J., et al. 1987. Blockers of active transport in the thick ascending limb of the loop of Henle. *Diuretics: Basic, Pharmacological and Clinical Aspects*, ed. V. E. Andreucci, A. Dal Canton, pp. 33–38. Boston: Nijhoff
21. Greven, J. 1987. The pharmacological basis of the action of loop diuretics. In *Diuretics II*, ed. J. B. Puschett, A. Greenberg, p. 173. New York: Elsevier
22. Grupp, C., Kinne-Saffran, E., Stokes, J. B., Kinne, R. 1987. Evidence for a furosemide-sensitive Na-K-Cl cotransport system in rat papillary collecting duct cells. *10th. Int. Congr. Nephrol.* (Abstr.) p. 570
23. Guggino, S. E., Suarez-Isla, B. A., Guggino, W. B., Sacktor, B. 1985. Forskolin and antidiuretic hormone stimulate a Ca²⁺-activated K⁺ channel in cultured kidney cells. *Am. J. Physiol.* 249:F448–55
24. Haas, M., Forbush, B. III. 1986. Photolabeling of membranes from dog kidney with a benzophenone analog of bumetamide. *Fed. Proc.* 45(1938):2665 (Abstr.)
25. Hebert, S. C. 1986. Hypertonic cell volume regulation in mouse thick limbs. II. Na⁺-H⁺ and Cl⁻-HCO₃⁻ exchange in basolateral membranes. *Am. J. Physiol.* 250:C920–31
26. Hebert, S. C., Andreoli, T. E. 1980. Interactions of temperature and ADH on transport processes in cortical collecting tubules. *Am. J. Physiol.* 238:F470–80
27. Hebert, S. C., Andreoli, T. E. 1984. Effects of antidiuretic hormone on cellular conductive pathways in mouse medullary thick ascending limbs of Henle: II. Determinants of the ADH-mediated increases in transepithelial voltage and in net Cl⁻ absorption. *J. Membr. Biol.* 80:221–33
28. Hebert, S. C., Andreoli, T. E. 1984. Control of NaCl transport in the thick ascending limb. *Am. J. Physiol.* 246:F745–56
29. Hebert, S. C., Andreoli, T. E. 1986. Ionic conductance pathways in the

30. Hebert, S. C., Friedman, P. A. 1985. Electrophysiological properties of the in vitro perfused "diluting" segment from the peritublar sheath of *Squalus acanthias* kidney. *Bull. Mt. Desert Isl. Biol. Lab.* 25:128–31
31. Imai, M. 1979. The connecting tubule: A functional subdivision of the rabbit distal nephron segments. *Kidney Int.* 15:346–56
32. Jørgensen, P. L., Petersen, J., Rees, W. D. 1984. Identification of a Na⁺,K⁺,Cl⁻-cotransport protein of Mᵣ 34000 from kidney by photolabeling with (³H)bumethanide. The protein is associated with cytoskeleton components. *Biochim. Biophys. Acta* 775:105–10
33. Kinne, R., Koenig, B., Hannafin, J., Kinne-Saffran, E., Scott, D. M., et al. 1985. The use of membrane vesicles to study the NaCl/KCl cotransporter involved in active transepithelial chloride transport. *Pflüg. Arch.* 405:S101–5
34. Koeppen, B. M. 1986. Conductive properties of the rabbit outer medullary collecting duct: Outer stripe. *Am. J. Physiol.* 250:F70–F76
35. Koeppen, B. M., Biagi, B. A., Giebisch, G. H. 1983. Intracellular microelectrode characterization of the rabbit cortical collecting duct. *Am. J. Physiol.* 244:F35–F47
36. Kudo, L. H., Rocha, A. S. 1987. Chloride and sodium secretion by rat papillary collecting duct (PC). *10th. Int. Congr. Nephrology* (Abstr.) p. 574
37. Madsen, K. M., Tisher, C. C. 1986. Structural-functional relationships along the distal nephron. *Am. J. Physiol.* 250:F1–15
38. Molony, D. A., Reeves, W. B., Hebert, S. C., Andreoli, T. E. 1987. ADH increases apical Na⁺,K⁺,2Cl⁻ entry in mouse medullary thick ascending limbs of Henle. *Am. J. Physiol.* 252:F177–87
39. Morel, F., Doucet, A. 1986. Hormonal control of kidney functions at the cell level. *Physiol. Rev.* 66:377–468
40. Münich, G., Dietl, P., Oberleithner, H. 1986. Chloride transport in the diluting segment of the K⁺ adapted frog kidney: Effect of amiloride and acidosis. *Pflüg. Arch.* 407:S60–S65
41. Nagel, W., Beauwens, R., Crabbé, J. 1985. Opposite effects of indacrinone (MK-196) on sodium and chloride conductance of amphibian skin. *Pflüg. Arch.* 403:337–43
42. Nishimura, H., Imai, M., Ogawa, M. 1986. Diluting segment in avian kidney.

I. Characterization of transepithelial voltages. *Am. J. Physiol.* 250:R333–40

43. Oberleithner, H., Giebisch, G., Lang, F., Wang, W. 1982. Cellular mechanism of the furosemide sensitive transport system in the kidney. *Klin. Wochenschr.* 60:1173–79

44. Oberleithner, H., Münich, G., Schwab, A., Dietl, P. 1986. Amiloride reduces potassium conductance in frog kidney via inhibition of $Na^+$-$H^+$ exchange. *Am. J. Physiol.* 251:F66–F73

45. O'Neil, R. G., Sansom, S. C. 1984. Characterization of apical cell membrane $Na^+$ and $K^+$ conductances of cortical collecting duct. *Am. J. Physiol.* 247:F14–F24

46. Ring, T., Beck, F., Dörge, A., Thurau, K. 1987. *Pflüg. Arch.* 408(R45):174 (Abstr.)

47. Sands, J. M., Knepper, M. A., Spring, K. R. 1986. Na-K-Cl cotransport in apical membrane of rabbit renal papillary surface epithelium. *Am. J. Physiol.* 251:F475–84

48. Sansom, S. C., Weinman, E. J., O'Neil, R. G. 1984. Microelectrode assessment of chloride-conductive properties of cortical collecting duct. *Am. J. Physiol.* 247:F291–F302

49. Schlatter, E., Greger, R. 1985. cAMP increases the basolateral $Cl^-$-conductance in the isolated perfused medullary thick ascending limb of Henle's loop of the mouse. *Pflüg. Arch.* 405:367–76

50. Schlatter, E., Greger, R., Weidtke, D. 1983. Effect of "high ceiling" diuretics on active salt transport in the cortical thick ascending limb of Henle's loop of rabbit kidney: Correlations of chemical structure and inhibitory potency. *Pflüg. Arch.* 396:210–17

51. Schlatter, E., Schafer, J. A. 1987. Electrophysiological studies in principal cells of rat cortical collecting tubules. *Pflüg. Arch.* 409:81–92

52. Shaver, J. L. F., Stirling, C. 1978. Ouabain binding to renal tubules of the rabbit. *J. Cell Biol.* 76:278–92

53. Sonnenberg, H. 1986. Mechanisms of release and renal tubular action of atrial natriuretic factor. *Fed. Proc.* 45:2106–10

54. Stokes, J. B. 1984. Sodium chloride absorption by the urinary bladder of the winter flounder. A thiazide-sensitive, electrically neutral transport system. *J. Clin. Invest.* 74:7–16

55. Stone, D. K., Seldin, D. W., Kokko, J. P., Jacobson, H. R. 1983. Mineralocorticoid modulation of rabbit medullary collecting duct acidification. A sodium-independent effect. *J. Clin. Invest.* 72:77–83

56. Stoner, L. C. 1977. Isolated, perfused amphibian renal tubules: The diluting segment. *Am. J. Physiol.* 233(5):F438–44

57. Tago, K., Warden, D. H., Schuster, V. L., Stokes, J. B. 1986. Effects of inhibitors of Cl conductance on Cl self-exchange in rabbit cortical collecting tubule. *Am. J. Physiol.* 251:F1009–17

58. Ullrich, K. J., Papavassiliou, F. 1979. Sodium reabsorption in the papillary collecting duct of rats. *Pflüg. Arch.* 379:49–52

59. Ullrich, K. J., Papavassiliou, F. 1981. Bicarbonate reabsorption in the papillary collecting duct of rats. *Pflüg. Arch.* 389:271–75

60. Velázquez, H., Greger, R. 1986. Electrical properties of the early distal convoluted tubules of the rabbit kidney. *Renal Physiol.* 9:55 (Abstr.)

61. Velázquez, H., Wright, F. S. 1986. Effects of diuretic drugs on Na, Cl, and K transport by rat renal distal tubule. *Am. J. Physiol.* 250:F1013–23

62. Wangemann, P., Wittner, M., Di Stefano, A., Englert, H. C., Lang, H. J., et al. 1986. $Cl^-$-channel blockers in the thick ascending limb of the loop of Henle. Structure activity relationship. *Pflüg. Arch.* 407 (S2):S128–41

63. Wittner, M., Di Stefano, A., Schlatter, E., Delarge, J., Greger, R. 1986. Torasemide inhibits NaCl reabsorption in the thick ascending limb of the loop of Henle. *Pflüg. Arch.* 407:611–14

Ann. Rev. Physiol. 1988. 50:123–40

# HORMONAL REGULATION OF CHLORIDE TRANSPORT IN THE PROXIMAL AND DISTAL NEPHRON

*Christian de Rouffignac and Jean-Marc Elalouf*

Service de Biologie Cellulaire, Département de Biologie, Centre d'Etudes Nucléaires de Saclay, 91191 Gif-sur-Yvette, France

## INTRODUCTION

Hormonal regulation of chloride transport by renal tubules is now being studied extensively. In the recent past, new information in this field was obtained from both in vitro and in vivo investigations of the effects of hormones on proximal and distal tubules. These two complementary approaches have permitted the elucidation of the cellular mechanisms of Cl⁻ transport by various epithelial cells and have provided further insight into integrated nephron functions. In vitro research benefited from the development of physiological, biochemical, and autoradiographic techniques permitting the evaluation of the functional properties of well-defined nephron segments and the localization of the hormone action sites along the nephron. Nephron segments, however, generally present considerable cellular heterogeneity. More recently, introduction of intracellular recordings and patch-clamp techniques directly applicable to single epithelial cells of the mammalian nephron have given fresh impetus to these investigations.

The discovery that several hormones act on the same adenylate cyclase pool and, consequently, on the same target cells in some nephron segments (62) prompted us to modify the method for exploring in vivo the effects of these hormones (14). Since the adenylate cyclase data suggested that each of the hormones acting on common target cells might have the same physiological effects (62), it was clear that suppression of a single hormone from the circulating blood would lead to small or undetectable effects if the other hormones were still present to maintain the cellular response. Basically, it

123

seems to be a general characteristic of the mammalian nephron that in its distal part, i.e. the nephron portion starting with the thick ascending limb of Henle's loop (TALH), several hormones stimulate cAMP production in various epithelial cells. In the rat kidney, four hormones, namely antidiuretic hormone (ADH), calcitonin (CT), glucagon, and parathyroid hormone (PTH), act on the same adenylate cyclase pool in the TALH. ADH and CT may also act on an identical cyclase pool in the cortical collecting ducts. For in vivo studies of the renal effects of each of these four hormones a new model, the so-called hormone-deprived model, was elaborated (14). Rats with diabetes insipidus due to hereditary lack of vasopressin production (Brattleboro strain) were used. PTH and CT were suppressed by acute thyroparathyroidectomy, and glucagon secretion was inhibited by administration of glucose or somatostatin. With this model, the effects of each of the four hormones can be analyzed in the absence of interference from the others. In addition, direct comparison of their physiological effects is possible.

In this review the hormonal effects on $Cl^-$ transport are discussed for each nephron segment: the proximal tubule, the loop of Henle (superficial and juxtamedullary), the distal convoluted tubule, and the collecting ducts (cortical and medullary). Each section begins with a brief analysis of the present knowledge of the cellular mechanisms directly or indirectly responsible for transepithelial $Cl^-$ transport. The effects of the hormones on $Cl^-$ transport are then described.

## PROXIMAL TUBULE

The proximal tubule (including the pars recta) reabsorbs approximately 70% of the filtered $Cl^-$. This reabsorption takes place principally across the intercellular route (shunt pathway), which has a high ionic conductance. The apical $Na^+$-$H^+$ antiporter promotes preferential $HCO_3^-$ reabsorption. Consequently, the $Cl^-$ concentration progressively increases along the proximal tubule until the electrochemical gradient across the conductive shunt pathway becomes favorable to $Cl^-$ diffusion towards the basolateral side. This component of $Cl^-$ reabsorption, secondarily coupled to $H^+$ secretion and bicarbonate reabsorption, represents the major fraction of proximal $Cl^-$ reabsorption. Transcellular reabsorption of $Cl^-$, coupled to $Na^+$ through an electroneutral cotransport at the apical membrane, may represent another component. The mechanisms of $Cl^-$ exit at the basolateral side are not clearly established. In any case, any hormone altering $HCO_3^-$ and $Na^+$ transports, and thus water reabsorption, indirectly modifies $Cl^-$ reabsorption.

It is well established that PTH inhibits $HCO_3^-$ reabsorption along the proximal tubule. As expected, this diminution is accompanied by an inhibition of $Cl^-$ reabsorption (6). However, the inhibition is greater for $Cl^-$ than for $HCO_3^-$. According to Bichara et al (6), this discrepancy suggests that PTH can also inhibit transcellular reabsorption of NaCl. Various cellular events could explain the inhibitory effect of PTH on $Cl^-$ transport. This hormone is known to inhibit the $Na^+$-$H^+$ exchange in the luminal membrane (10). In addition, PTH might increase junctional permeability, which in turn would favor $HCO_3^-$ back-diffusion from the peritubular side (55). The permeability of the shunt pathway is also increased by extracellular volume expansion, and recent experiments suggest that PTH contributes to the expansion-induced inhibition of $Cl^-$ proximal reabsorption (60). That the cellular effects of PTH are dependent on cytosolic $Ca^{2+}$ content is questionable. An influx of calcium into the cell does not seem to be required for PTH inhibition of NaCl transport in the proximal tubule. The ouabain-sensitive component of oxygen consumption (taken as an indication of the Na,K-ATPase activity) of a suspension of rabbit convoluted proximal tubules was inhibited to a similar extent by PTH in the presence of either lanthanum or verapamil, which are held to compete with calcium at its binding sites and to block calcium entry, respectively (17).

Other peptide hormones have also been shown to alter proximal $Cl^-$ reabsorption. In acute thyroparathyroidectomized (TPTX) and in hormone-deprived (HD) rats calcitonin significantly increased the fraction of filtered NaCl remaining at the end proximal site (22, 70). Glucagon exerted similar effects in HD animals (1 and unpublished observations from our laboratory). The cellular mechanism involved is totally unknown. Neither of these two peptides stimulates the adenylate cyclase system of the rat proximal tubule (61). Antidiuretic hormone is without effect on $Cl^-$ transport in the proximal tubule (14, 18). Angiotensin II at physiological concentrations ($10^{-12}$ to $10^{-10}$ M) appears to stimulate NaCl reabsorption by cellular mechanisms not yet established (42). The physiological effect of insulin on proximal NaCl transport has not been unequivocally demonstrated (41). Proximal reabsorption of $Na^+$ may be inhibited in vivo by hyperinsulinemia (13), whereas incubation of primary cultures of proximal tubular cells from rabbit kidney with insulin increases $Na^+$-$H^+$ exchange activity (29), which indicates that $Cl^-$ transport should also be increased.

Since the discovery that renal sympathectomy considerably depresses sodium reabsorption by the rat proximal tubule in vivo, progress has been made in understanding the underlying mechanisms (36). A recent micropuncture study revealed that depression of renal nerve activity inhibits both $HCO_3^-$ and NaCl reabsorptions in the rat proximal tubule (9). According to Morel & Doucet (63), this inhibition corresponds to the suppression of adrenergic control of proximal functions. Several in vitro (4) and in vivo (8, 101) experiments support this interpretation. They demonstrate that norepinephrine, the $\beta$-agonist isoproterenol, and the $\alpha$-agonist phenylephrine stimulate water or $HCO_3^-$ (and thus NaCl) reabsorption in the proximal convoluted tubule. In addition, it was shown by means of simultaneous microperfusion of tubules and peritubular capillaries that norepinephrine directly stimulates $HCO_3^-$ reabsorption, whereas phenoxybenzamine, a specific $\alpha$-adrenergic blocker, inhibits it (8).

Glucocorticoids may alter proximal acidification and thus $Cl^-$ reabsorption. Experiments with brush border membrane vesicles (BBMV) taken from either adrenalectomized (ADX) or ADX dexamethasone-treated rats showed that the synthetic glucocorticoid elicited a significant increase in the initial rate of amiloride-sensitive $Na^+$ entry, whereas aldosterone was inactive (30, 57). It is now well established that long-term thyroid deficiency is accompanied by a progressive decrease in the activity of Na,K-ATPase in renal tissues, including the proximal tubule (see 3, for example). Isotonic fluid reabsorption in the proximal tubules of hypothyroid rats is increased when the animals are treated with low doses [10 $\mu$g/kg body weight (BW)] of triodothyronine for several days (7).

## LOOP OF HENLE

The physiological effects of hormones on $Cl^-$ transport along the different segments of the loop of Henle are only well documented for the thick ascending limb, i.e. the "diluting" segment. We therefore focus our attention on this segment.

### Thick Ascending Limb

The transport mechanism of $Cl^-$ is essentially similar in the cortical (cTALH) and medullary (mTALH) parts of the thick ascending limb (38, 45). In the rabbit cTALH (37) the transcellular transport of $Cl^-$ is mediated at the apical membrane by $Na^+$-$K^+$-$2Cl^-$ cotransporter. $Cl^-$ leaves the cell at the basolateral side by means of a $Cl^-$ conductance and also possibly by a $K^+$-$Cl^-$ electroneutral symport. The activity of the Na,K-ATPase, present in large amounts along the basolateral membrane, generates an inside-negative potential difference and lowers the intracellular $Na^+$ activity. This in turn activates the electroneutral $Na^+$-$K^+$-$2Cl^-$ cotransporter. The $Na^+$ delivered by this transporter is extruded from the cell through the Na,K-ATPase, the $Cl^-$ mainly through the basolateral conductance, and the $K^+$ is recycled through a conductive channel present in the apical membrane. The basolateral depolarizing $Cl^-$ current and the apical hyperpolarizing $K^+$ current explain the lumen-positive transepithelial voltage observed in this segment. Chloride is therefore reabsorbed against an electrochemical gradient. The paracellular pathway is cation-permselective; its conductance is approximately three times higher for $Na^+$ than for $Cl^-$. This permits the transport of up to 50% of the total $Na^+$ reabsorbed through the epithelium, whereas part of the $Cl^-$ reabsorbed in excess of sodium through the transcellular route returns to the lumen via the shunt by a back-diffusion process. As regards the coupling of $Cl^-$ flux with other transport processes, it has been postulated in the mouse that two synchronous membrane antiporters, one exchanging $Na^+$ for cellular $H^+$ and the other exchanging luminal $Cl^-$ for $HCO_3^-$ (or $OH^-$), might operate in parallel. These antiporters might be located in the apical membrane of the cTALH (31) and on the basolateral side of the mTALH (43). There are important species differences, however, in $HCO_3^-$ transport by the TALH. The rabbit TALH does not reabsorb $HCO_3^-$ (50), whereas the rat cTALH and mTALH reabsorb $HCO_3^-$, possibly through the activity of an apical $Na^+$-$H^+$ antiporter (34, 35).

In vivo comparison between the compositions of the fluid collected in early distal and late accessible proximal convolutions belonging to the same super- ficial nephron of hormone-deprived rat kidneys indicated that dDAVP (a synthetic analog of vasopressin) and human calcitonin (HCT) reduce the $Cl^-$ concentration at the early distal site (14, 18, 20, 22), whereas the effect of PTH is insignificant (1, 2). It was recently reported that PTH may increase the $Cl^-$ fractional reabsorption[1] in Henle's loop from 85 to 87% in TPTX rats (6). It is questionable, however, whether this was really a PTH-mediated effect on $Cl^-$ transport in the TALH, since the $Cl^-$ concentration at the early distal site remained unaltered. That glucagon stimulates $Na^+$ and $Cl^-$ transport in the loop escaped attention at first (1). In a recent experimental series (19) conducted in our laboratory, the glucagon-mediated increase of the filtration rate of superficial nephrons was slightly lower than in the previous series (1), and the hormone significantly decreased the $Cl^-$ concentration at the early distal site and also significantly increased the $Cl^-$ fractional reabsorption in the loop. Thus administration of any of the lacking hormones (except PTH) to these hormone-deprived rats enhances the reabsorptive capacity of the loop for $Cl^-$ (and also for $Na^+$). The localization in the TALH of the hormone- mediated effects on $Cl^-$ transport in the loop is facilitated by the fact that (a) the hormones reduce the Cl concentration at the early distal site and (b) the TALH is the sole segment with a cyclase system sensitive to glucagon, calcitonin, and ADH (61). The stimulatory effect of dDAVP on NaCl trans- port in the loop was recently fully confirmed by means of both micro stop-flow techniques in hormone-deprived Brattleboro rats (68) and free flow micropuncture techniques in hormone-deprived Sprague Dawley rats (M. Bichara, personal communication).

The $\beta$-agonist isoproterenol induces a small but significant increase of the adenylate cyclase activity of the rat cTALH (61). Relevant to this observation

[1]The fractional reabsorption is the reabsorbed amount expressed as a percent of the delivered load.

are the data reported by DiBona & Sawin (16) which indicated that low-frequency renal nerve stimulation decreases $Cl^-$ concentration at the early distal site, and those reported by Bencsath et al (5), who observed a reduction in loop NaCl reabsorption following renal sympathectomy.

In vitro microperfusion studies on the effects of peptide hormones on $Cl^-$ transport in the TALH lead to conclusions in agreement with those drawn from in vivo studies. In the rat, few in vitro studies have been made. In this species it is only known that ADH increases the positive transepithelial potential difference (PD) (76, 106) and the net $Cl^-$ reabsorption flux in the mTALH (5a, 106). In the mouse mTALH, ADH increases the transepithelial PD and $Cl^-$ transport (40, 44, 76, 94), and glucagon increases the trans-epithelial PD (94). In a recent study, Wittner & Di Stefano (105) demon-strated in mouse mTALH that glucagon and ADH induce an increase in the positive transepithelial PD ($+ 4$ mV) and a decrease in the transepithelial resistance ($-3\Omega \cdot cm^2$), which reinforces the conclusion that the two hormones have similar physiological effects in the TALH (15). In the mouse cTALH, however, ADH does not alter the transepithelial PD (44). Its effect on $Cl^-$ transport has not been directly evaluated. In the rabbit mTALH, ADH failed to alter the transepithelial PD or the $Cl^-$ efflux (76). This lack of detectable effect may be due to the poor responsiveness of the adenylate cyclase system of this nephron segment to ADH in the rabbit (61). It must be mentioned, however, that calcitonin, which has a large effect on the cyclase, also failed to increase the PD (90). Perhaps in this species the change in PD, which would result from an increase of transcellular $Cl^-$ transport, is masked by a parallel decrease in the transepithelial resistance.

The effects of ADH on the cellular mechanisms of $Cl^-$ transport were analyzed in detail by Hebert et al (45) and Schlatter & Greger (78) in the mouse mTALH. Both teams of workers agree that ADH increases the trans-epithelial conductance and that this effect results from an increase in the $Cl^-$ conductance of the basolateral membrane. However, they propose different sequences of events. According to Hebert et al (45), the primary effect of ADH is to increase the rate of apical $Na^+$-$K^+$-$2Cl^-$ entry, which raises intracellular $Cl^-$ activity and thus indirectly increases $Cl^-$ exit through the basolateral membrane. Schlatter & Greger (78) propose that the primary effect of ADH is an increase in the basolateral $Cl^-$ conductance, which results in a decrease of intracellular $Cl^-$ concentration.

The hormone-stimulated cAMP generation in mTALH might be modulated by either prostaglandins (PGs) or intracellular $Ca^{2+}$. In the mouse, con-centrations of prostaglandin $E_2$ ($PGE_2$) in the nanomolar range reduce the ADH-dependent component of NaCl transport in a dose-dependent fashion (12). This result agrees with the finding of a decrease in ADH-dependent intracellular cAMP generation in isolated rat mTALH after addition of $PGE_2$

(97). In vivo, an increase in $Cl^-$ reabsorption in the superficial loop of Henle was noted during inhibition of prostaglandin synthesis by meclofenamate or indomethacin (48). In vitro, exposure of rabbit mTAL to 2-$\mu$M $PGE_2$ resulted in a fall in net $Cl^-$ transport (87). Preincubation of mouse mTALH with $10^{-5}$ M verapamil, used as a blocker of Ca entry into the cells, reduces the effects of glucagon ($10^{-6}$ M) or AVP (200 $\mu$-units/ml) on both the transepithelial voltage and the intracellular cAMP generation in the presence of 1.8 mM of $Ca^{2+}$ in the medium (94). Verapamil also inhibits the AVP-dependent net $Cl^-$ reabsorptive flux. These results are contradicted by data indicating that $10^{-5}$ M verapamil did not modify the cAMP generation by glucagon and AVP in the presence of 2-mM $Ca^{2+}$ in the medium (93). According to the latter study (93), a high extracellular $Ca^{2+}$ concentration (5 mmol), however, may itself impair AVP-, glucagon-, or forskolin-dependent cAMP production at a post-receptor level.

In the rabbit thick ascending limb, $10^{-6}$M calcitonin increased cytosolic free $Ca^{2+}$ concentration, whereas PTH ($10^{-6}$M), dibutyryl (dB) cAMP ($10^{-4}$M), and forskolin ($2.10^{-5}$M) had no significant effect (64). These experiments were interpreted as indicating that calcitonin elevates cytosolic free $Ca^{2+}$ by a non-cAMP-mediated mechanism and that $Ca^{2+}$ can act as an intracellular second messenger. It should be noted that in rat hepatocytes glucagon stimulates intracellular inositol triphosphate and cAMP generation through so called V1 and V2 receptors, respectively (100, 103). Further studies are therefore needed to determine whether a single intracellular second messenger is generated by peptide hormones in the TALH or whether two such messengers are formed.

Steroids probably control $Cl^-$ reabsorption in the TALH. It is claimed that ADX increases the $Na^+$ concentration at the early distal site, but which steroid, by its absence, is responsible for this effect is unknown. Welch et al (102) found, by micropuncture, that $Cl^-$ reabsorption in the loop of Henle of ADX (4–7 days) rats was less than in sham-operated control rats or ADX rats treated with dexamethasone (5 $\mu$g/100 g BW/day). In contrast, Stanton (85) reported that in in vivo microperfusion studies in the same species ADX (10 days) inhibited $Na^+$ reabsorption by 33%, but that aldosterone (0.5 $\mu$g/100 g BW/day) reversed this inhibition, whereas dexamethasone (1.2 $\mu$g/100 g BW/day) was without effect. The results of Welch and coworkers are in better agreement with the finding that the decreased Na,K-ATPase activity of TALH from ADX rabbits was fully restored after administration of dexamethasone, whereas aldosterone had no effect (28).

## Juxtamedullary Nephrons

Micropuncture studies at the bend of the loop of juxtamedullary nephrons of hormone-deprived rats made it possible to evaluate the effect on $Cl^-$ delivery at this site of each of the peptide hormones that modulate $Cl^-$ transport in the TALH (18, 23–25). In these rats, i.e. in the absence of ADH, PTH, calcitonin, and glucagon, the corticomedullary concentration gradient was greatly reduced; in fact, the fluid at the bend of the loop of juxtamedullary nephrons was close to isotonicity. Accordingly, the tubular fluid to plasma ultrafiltrate concentration ratio (TF/UF) of $Cl^-$ was not significantly different from unity, and the fractional $Cl^-$ delivery (as percent of filtered load) was close to 40%. Administration of ADH, glucagon, or calcitonin increased the osmolality of the fluid at the hairpin turn. The mechanisms responsible for the increase of the tubular fluid osmolality at the bend of the loop were not the same for all the hormones. Glucagon enhanced both the osmolality and the NaCl concentration of the tubular fluid, but left the absolute and fractional water delivery unchanged (24). Its effects, therefore, were entirely attributable to net NaCl entry (secretion) in the tubular lumen. Human calcitonin (25) and dDAVP (23), however, did not increase the $Na^+$ or $Cl^-$ delivery but tended rather to decrease them. Unlike glucagon, they both decreased the water delivery rate. These observations were interpreted as follows: Glucagon, calcitonin, or ADH stimulate NaCl transport in the medullary thick ascending limb, and the NaCl delivered to the interstitium creates a gradient favorable to its return by diffusion into the descending limb. Thus NaCl would undergo a medullary recycling process. Since calcitonin and dDAVP, but not glucagon, both induce water removal along the descending limb, we propose that this water removal favors NaCl escape at some point along the descending limb. This NaCl removal would counterbalance NaCl addition in the descending limb, thus masking the stimulation by dDAVP and calcitonin, but not by glucagon, of NaCl recycling. This hypothesis was fully confirmed (18) in Brattleboro rats subjected to long-term treatment with dDAVP, which greatly increases the concentrating ability of the kidney and, as a consequence, increases water removal along the descending limb. In such rats, fractional NaCl delivery at the hairpin turn was significantly decreased.

## DISTAL TUBULE

The distal tubule displays great cellular heterogeneity. From the macula densa to the cortical collecting duct, five different cell types are encountered. In the rabbit, these cell types are relatively segregated into successive segments. In other species such as the rat, however, no such clear cut segregation is observed. Consequently, the nature of the transport carried out by each cell population is difficult to establish. It is well known that the distal tubule reabsorbs sodium chloride. From in vivo microperfusion studies (99) it was concluded that the cells of the rat distal tubule possess a NaCl cotransport system that differs from the $Na^+$-$K^+$-$2Cl^-$ cotransporter found in the TALH.

$Na^+$ transport can also proceed via a conductive (amiloride-sensitive) pathway (99) located in the late but not in the early portion of the tubule (11, 38). In addition, reduction of the lumen $Cl^-$ concentration increases net $K^+$ secretion through a mechanism insensitive to barium, which suggests the presence of a secretory pathway linking $K^+$ with $Cl^-$ in the luminal membrane of certain cells (26). Recently, Greger & Velasquez (38) succeeded in perfusing rabbit early distal tubules, which contain a relatively homogeneous population of "distal convoluted cells." The transepithelial voltage is lumen-negative and low ($-5$ mV), and the transepithelial resistance is high. According to the authors, NaCl is probably reabsorbed by an electroneutral process. $Cl^-$ efflux would proceed through a KCl symport in the basolateral membrane which contains, in addition to the Na,K-ATPase, a $K^+$ conductance that accounts for the total membrane conductance.

The adenylate cyclase system of the rat distal tubule is sensitive to many hormones and agonists, including ADH, PTH, calcitonin, glucagon, and isoproterenol (63). However, no experiments on the possible additivity of the cyclase response to several hormones have been made on this segment. Micropuncture studies in the distal tubule of hormone-deprived rats revealed that ADH, PTH, and HCT enhanced NaCl reabsorption, whereas the response to glucagon was not significant (2, 20, 21). In TPTX Wistar rats ADH, but not PTH, enhanced $Na^+$ reabsorption (11a). In vitro, no microperfusion experiments have been performed on this nephron segment because microdissection of distal tubules is very difficult in the rat. In the rabbit distal convoluted tubule (DCT), the adenylate cyclase system is only sensitive to calcitonin, and eel calcitonin elicited a decrease of the transepithelial PD (54), whereas isoproterenol left it unchanged (52). In the connecting tubule, dB-cAMP, ADH, and isoproterenol decreased the lumen-negative PD (52, 53), but PTH was without effect (52, 83).

In vivo microperfusion studies on the rat kidney revealed that ADX considerably reduces $Na^+$ reabsorption and that aldosterone (0.5 $\mu$g/100 g BW/ day) increases its reabsorption to control levels (85). In contrast, dexamethasone (1.2 $\mu$g/100 g BW/day) only partially restores $Na^+$ transport. In the ADX rabbit, the Na,K-ATPase activity is decreased by 40% in isolated DCT and is restored after either chronic or acute administration of dexamethasone (28, 33). Aldosterone (up to 10 $\mu$g/kg BW) has no effect on Na,K-ATPase (28, 33). These contradictory results may stem from species differences.

## COLLECTING DUCT SYSTEM

The collecting duct system comprises three main portions with distinct functions: the cortical collecting tubule (CCT); the outer medullary collecting tubule (OMCT), subdivided into two portions located in the outer and inner stripes, respectively; and the inner medullary collecting tubule (IMCT). Each segment throughout the system comprises two main cell types: the principal (light) cells and the intercalated (dark) cells. The principal cells are three to four times more numerous than the intercalated cells in the CCT. The physiological properties of these cells are being studied extensively in vitro with electrophysiological techniques applied to isolated microperfused segments.

## Cortical Collecting Tubule

The paracellular pathway, which is highly conductive to $Cl^-$, is an important route for reabsorption of $Cl^-$ by diffusion down its electrochemical gradient (lumen-negative PD). The functional properties of the principal and intercalated cells are not definitely established. However, it is proposed that in the CCT, probably in the principal cells (66), the apical membrane is conductive to $K^+$ and $Na^+$ but not to $Cl^-$. $K^+$ secretion occurs through a barium-sensitive $K^+$ channel, whereas $Na^+$ reabsorption proceeds via an amiloride-sensitive channel (see 91). The Na,K-ATPase operates at the basolateral side. $Cl^-$ transport seems to occur essentially through the paracellular pathway. However, the recent discovery of a $Cl^-$ conductance at the basolateral side raises the question of a transcellular transport and, especially, of the mode of $Cl^-$ entry at the apical border. The principal cells can probably reabsorb $HCO_3^-$ by means of a mechanism not yet understood, which may involve a proton secretion dependent on $Na^+$ reabsorption ($Na^+$-$H^+$ exchanger) and/or on the transepithelial PD (proton pump). These cells are thought to be sensitive to vasopressin. It now seems feasible to postulate that the intercalated cells are sensitive to the acid-base status of the organism and can secrete $HCO_3^-$ via a $HCO_3^-$-$Cl^-$ exchanger. $HCO_3^-$ secretion is insensitive to $Na^+$ transport or to transepithelial PD but is dependent on the presence of $Cl^-$ in the lumen. In addition, $Cl^-$ is subjected to a self-exchange process, which is itself stimulated by $HCO_3^-$ and/or $CO_2$. The relationship between these two mechanisms, which might be carrier mediated (80, 86, 91, 92), is not yet understood, as it is not established in which membrane the processes take place. It is likely, however, that they operate at the apical border and that the basolateral membrane has a $Cl^-$ selective pathway to facilitate $Cl^-$ exit from the cell. In this scheme, intracellular $HCO_3^-$ would be generated via an active proton pump or a $Na^+$-$H^+$ exchanger, which would transport $H^+$ out of the cell, across the basolateral membrane. These cells are thought to be sensitive to isoproterenol.

In the rabbit, ADH causes a transitory increase followed by a sustained decrease in the transepithelial PD of microperfused CCT, whereas in the rat the hyperpolarization may persist for at least 3 hr (71). The decrease of PD subsequent to ADH-mediated stimulation may result from an increase of prostaglandin $E_2$ biosynthesis by the CCT cells (49). In the rat, the rise in the transepithelial PD is accompanied by a marked (severalfold) increase in net sodium absorption (72, 96) and net potassium (96), or rubidium (77), secretion. The ADH-induced stimulation of $Na^+$ and $K^+$ transport is inhibited by luminal amiloride and barium, respectively, which implies that such transport involves the apical channels. Arginine vasopressin at $10^{-10}$ M causes a greater increase in $Cl^-$ reabsorption in rat CCT than could be caused by the increase in transepithelial PD alone. Thus $Cl^-$ reabsorption cannot be due solely to voltage-driven diffusion of $Cl^-$ through the paracellular pathway (95). Since bradikinin inhibits both net $Na^+$ (96) and net $Cl^-$ (95) reabsorption in this system, with no significant effect on either transepithelial PD or $K^+$ transport, it was concluded that bradykinin may affect an electroneutral transport process and that ADH may stimulate this electroneutral transport (95). In addition, vasopressin consistently alters $HCO_3^-$ transport, inhibiting secretion or even stimulating reabsorption. It is possible that ADH acts by stimulating the putative proton pump (95).

Isoproterenol at $10^{-6}$ M (51, 52, 56) and norepinephrine at $10^{-6}$ M (51) decrease the transepitheial PD in isolated rabbit CCT. This effect is accompanied by an increase in net $Cl^-$ absorption (51), which may result from an increase in the $Cl^-$-$HCO_3^-$ exchange, since Schuster (79, 80) found that cAMP and isoproterenol (but not ADH) stimulate $HCO_3^-$ secretion in rabbit CCT. This secretion was reversibly stopped by elimination of $Cl^-$ from the perfusate, whereas basolateral addition of disulfonic stilbene (DIDS, an inhibitor of $H^+$ secretion) had no effect. In addition, cAMP in the presence of $HCO_3^-$-$CO_2$ increased the diffusive $Cl^-$ permeability by either increasing or inducing a basolateral $Cl^-$ conductive pathway (80, 91). Isoproterenol, but not ADH, also had such an effect, which suggests cellular heterogeneity in this response to cAMP (91). The adenylate cyclase system of the rat CCT, but not that of the rabbit, is also sensitive to calcitonin and glucagon (61), but nothing is known about their effects on ionic transports.

The CCT is the main target site for gluco- and mineralocorticosteroids. In the rat and rabbit, pretreatment with DOCA increased both transepithelial PD and $Na^+$ reabsorption in microperfused CCT (67, 82, 88, 96). The $Na^+$ reabsorption increase resulted exclusively from a rise of the lumen-to-bath unidirectional flux (72). This flux increase may primarily correspond to short-term effects (within one day) of mineralocorticoids involving apical sodium channels (74). The action of DOCA treatment on transepithelial PD and $Na^+$ transport is thought to be also due to an increase in the basolateral membrane area of principal cells (a long-term effect) and the resulting increase in the number of Na,K-ATPase units (27). In support to this idea, Sansom & O'Neil (75) found that the basolateral voltage and the basolateral electrogenic current increased on chronic (2 weeks) elevation of mineralocorticoid levels, which suggests that the activity of the electrogenic $Na^+$ pump increased. Moreover, long-term treatment also decreased the tight junction conductance, resulting in an additional hyperpolarization of the transepithelial voltage (75). Although $Cl^-$ was not measured in these studies, it is possible that the hormone-mediated effects on transepithelial PD alter $Cl^-$ transport through the paracellular pathway, at least during the short-term response. High rates of $HCO_3^-$ secretion can be induced in rabbit CCT by chronic treatment of the animals with DOCA (32). According to Garcia-Austt et al (32), in mineralocorticoid-treated animals it is possible that net $HCO_3^-$ secretion in the CCT balances the mineralocorticoid-stimulated $HCO_3^-$ absorption in the OMCT (see below). The vasopressin-dependent increase of cAMP production in rat CCT is enhanced in tubules dissected from DOCA-treated animals (69). This facilitating action of DOCA results in a rise of the magnitude of the ADH effect on $Na^+$ transport (72).

The effects of aldosterone directly added in vitro gave contradictory results. In one study the steroid was observed to increase the lumen-negative PD (39), whereas in another it failed to alter either the transepithelial PD or the $Na^+$ transport (82). In a more recent study carried out on ADX rabbits, it was found that aldosterone added in vitro produced an increase in $Na^+$ absorption without changing the transepithelial PD, whereas dexamethasone was without effect (104).

## Outer Medullary Collecting Tubule

The outer stripe portion of the outer medullary collecting tubule reabsorbs $Na^+$ and secretes $K^+$, but to a lesser extent than does the CCT. It secretes protons continually, and accordingly, the transepithelial PD is less negative than in the cortical segment. Two cell types can be defined by their elec-trophysiological properties (59). One has a mean basolateral voltage of $-30$ mV, a predominantly $Cl^-$-selective basolateral membrane, and was less frequently encountered (26% of successfull impalements) than the second cell type, which has a mean basolateral voltage of $-60$ mV and a predominantly $K^+$-selective basolateral cell membrane. The first cell type may correspond to the intercalated cells, while the second may represent the principal cells.

The inner stripe portion of the outer medullary collecting tubule has a lumen-positive PD of about $+20$ mV (58). The basolateral membrane voltage is close to $-30$ mV. The apical membrane does not show significant ionic conductance. However, the apical membrane is thought to contain an electrogenic proton pump that is responsible for the lumen-positive PD. The excess of bicarbonate left in the cell by the apical proton transport is thought to be transferred across the basolateral cell membrane by a $HCO_3^-$-$Cl^-$ exchanger (107). $Cl^-$ could be recycled across the basolateral membrane, which is predominantly $Cl^-$ selective (58). The shunt pathway is conductive to several ions, including $Cl^-$. $H^+$ secretion could drive $Cl^-$ secretion in this epithelium, which, on the basis of its electrophysiological properties, appears to contain only one cell type. According to Koeppen (58), cells found in the inner stripe show characteristics similar to those of the intercalated cells of the outer stripe. These cells secrete $H^+$ in the lumen by mechanisms very similar to those of $HCO_3^-$ secretion by the (intercalated) cells of the CCT. However, the proton pump is at the apical border in the OMCT, whereas it is at the basolateral border in the CCT, and the $HCO_3^-$-$Cl^-$ exchanger is at the basolateral border in the OMCT, whereas it is at the apical side in the CCT. The basolateral membrane of both cells presumably contains a $Cl^-$ conductive pathway. In the basolateral membrane of intercalated cells, which reabsorb $HCO_3^-$, the $HCO_3^-$-$Cl^-$ exchanger is presumably included in the membrane (anion-transporting) domain of band 3 protein (81).

Little is known about the hormonal control of $Cl^-$ transport in this nephron segment. ADX reduced the $HCO_3^-$ reabsorptive rate in the inner stripe portion of rabbit OMCT, whereas chronic administration of DOCA to normal rabbits increased it to twice the control value (89). Dexamethasone was without effect. In perfusion experiments in OMCT obtained from ADX rabbits, aldosterone added to the bath $(5.10^{-8}$ M$)$ increased net reabsorption of $HCO_3^-$, whereas dexamethasone had no effect. The effect of aldosterone on $HCO_3^-$ reabsorption was $Na^+$ independent (89). The fact that the lumen-positive PD was unchanged either by in vitro aldosterone administration or by in vivo DOCA administration indicates that an electrical shunt conductance operates in parallel with the electrogenic acidifying system. Diffusion of $Cl^-$ through the paracellular diffusive pathway may play a part in this phenomenon. It is not known whether aldosterone stimulates the activity of the apical $H^+$ pump or basolateral $HCO_3^-$-$Cl^-$ exchanger.

## Inner Medullary Collecting Tubule

Little is known about the functional properties of the IMCT. Most of our knowledge comes from data obtained in vivo by micropuncture of papillary collecting ducts (PCD), which are accessible at the surface of the extrarenal part of the papilla, or by microcatheterization (84). The PCD are quite difficult to dissect. Rocha & Kudo (73) and recently Nonoguchi et al (65), however, have managed to dissect discrete segments of the IMCT, thus creating the possibility of studying their physiology at the cellular level in the near future.

The transepithelial PD of IMCT is close to zero in both rats and rabbits. In the rat, this epithelium displays low $Na^+$ and $Cl^-$ permeabilities ($\sim 1 \times 10^{-5}$ cm sec$^{-1}$) but reabsorbs significant amounts of NaCl (73, 84). Under normal acid-base conditions, the PCD participates in the urinary acidification process

(46), probably by a $H^+$ secretion/$HCO_3^-$ reabsorption mechanism. This reabsorption of NaCl in the absence of a transepithelial PD could be due either to active $Na^+$ reabsorption counterbalanced by electrogenic $H^+$ secretion or to electroneutral NaCl reabsorption. $Cl^-$ transport must be exclusively transcellular. Micropuncture studies on ADX rats receiving a chronic infusion of dexamethasone (5 $\mu$g/100 g BW/day) revealed that the PCD no longer reabsorbed $Na^+$. Aldosterone given to the animals as a bolus (1.5 $\mu$g/100 g BW) and infused throughout the experiment (0.5 $\mu$g/hr), reestablished $Na^+$ reabsorption along the PCD (47). These experiments confirm earlier experiments by Ullrich & Papavassiliou, which demonstrated that sodium reabsorption in the PCD is controlled by mineralocorticoids (98).

Atrial natriuretic factor (ANF) is thought to act on the IMCT cells and the second messenger cGMP (65). In a recent study using a microcatheterization technique in vivo, it was found that synthetic ANF infused at 10 $\mu$g/hr decreased the fractional $Na^+$ reabsorption in the PCD (84). This effect may participate in the natriuretic response induced by the peptide. The mechanism of the inhibition of $Na^+$ reabsorption remains to be established.

ACKNOWLEDGMENTS

The authors acknowledge the skillful secretarial assistance of Mrs. Claudine Belin.

This work was supported in part by a grant from the Commission des Communautés Européennes ST 2J-0095-1-F (CD).

## Literature Cited

1. Bailly, C., Roinel, N., Amiel, C. 1984. PTH-like glucagon stimulation of Ca and Mg reabsorption in Henle's loop of the rat. Am. J. Physiol. 246:F205–12
2. Bailly, C., Roinel, N., Amiel, C. 1985. Stimulation by glucagon and PTH of Ca and Mg reabsorption in the superficial distal tubule of the rat kidney. Pflüg. Arch. 403:28–34
3. Barlet, C., Doucet, A. 1986. Kinetics of tri-iodothyronine action on Na-K-ATPase in single segments of rabbit nephron. Pflüg. Arch. 407:27–32
4. Bello-Reuss, E. 1980. Effect of catecholamines on fluid reabsorption by the isolated proximal convoluted tubule. Am. J. Physiol. 238:F347–52
5. Bencsath, P., Szenasi, G., Takacs, L. 1985. Water and electrolyte transport in Henle's loop and distal tubule after renal sympathectomy in the rat. Am. J. Physiol. 249:F308–14
5a. Besseghir, K., Trimble, M. E., Stoner,

L. 1986. Action of ADH on isolated medullary thick ascending limb of the Brattleboro rat. Am. J. Physiol. 251: F271–77
6. Bichara, M., Mercier, O., Paillard, M., Leviel, F. 1986. Effects of parathyroid hormone on urinary acidification. Am. J. Physiol. 251:F444–53
7. Capasso, G., Lin, J.-T., de Santo, N. G., Kinne, R. 1985. Short term effect of low doses of tri-iodothyronine on proximal tubular membrane Na-K-ATPase and potassium permeability in thyroidectomized rats. Pflüg. Arch. 403:90–96
8. Chan, Y. L. 1980. Adrenergic control of bicarbonate absorption in the proximal convoluted tubule of the rat kidney. Pflüg. Arch. 388:159–64
9. Cogan, M. G. 1986. Neurogenic regulation of proximal bicarbonate and chloride reabsorption. Am. J. Physiol. 250: F22–26
10. Cohn, D. E., Klahr, S., Hammerman, M. R. 1983. Metabolic acidosis and

parathyroidectomy increase $Na^+$-$H^+$ exchange in brush-border vesicles. *Am. J. Physiol.* 245:F217–22

11. Costanzo, L. S. 1984. Comparison of calcium and sodium transport in early and late rat distal tubules: Effect of amiloride. *Am. J. Physiol.* 246:F937–45

11a. Costanzo, L. S., Windhager, E. E. 1980. Effects of PTH, ADH and cyclic AMP on distal tubular Ca and Na reabsorption. *Am. J. Physiol.* 239:F478–85

12. Culpepper, R. M., Andreoli, T. E. 1983. Interactions among prostaglandins $E_2$, antidiuretic hormone, and cyclic adenosine monophosphate in modulating $Cl^-$ absorption in single mouse medullary thick ascending limbs of Henle. *J. Clin. Invest.* 71:1588–1601

13. de Fronzo, R. A., Goldberg, M., Agus, Z. S. 1976. The effects of glucose and insulin on renal electrolyte transport. *J. Clin. Invest.* 58:83–90

14. de Rouffignac, C., Corman, B., Roinel, N. 1983. Stimulation by antidiuretic hormone of electrolyte tubular reabsorption in rat kidney. *Am. J. Physiol.* 244:F156–64

15. de Rouffignac, C., Elalouf, J. M., Roinel, N., Bailly, C., Amiel, C. 1984. Similarity of the effects of antidiuretic hormone, parathyroid hormone, calcitonin, and glucagon on rat kidney. In *Nephrology*, ed. R. R. Robinson, 1: 340–57. New York: Springer-Verlag. 884 pp.

16. DiBona, G., Sawin, L. L. 1982. Effects of renal nerve stimulation on NaCl and $H_2O$ transport in Henle's loop of the rat. *Am. J. Physiol.* 243:F576–80

17. Dolson, G. M., Hise, M. K., Weinman, E. J. 1985. Relationship among parathyroid hormone, cAMP, and calcium on proximal tubule sodium transport. *Am. J. Physiol.* 249:F409–16

18. Elalouf, J. M., Chabane-Sari, D., Roinel, N., de Rouffignac, C. 1987. NaCl and Ca delivery at the bend of the loop of rat deep nephrons decreases during antidiuresis. *Am. J. Physiol.* 252: F1055–87

19. Elalouf, J. M., Chabane-Sari, D., Roinel, N., de Rouffignac, C. 1987. ADH induces homologous desensitization in rat renal thick ascending limb cells. *Proc. 10th Int. Congr. Nephrol.* (Abstr.)

20. Elalouf, J. M., Roinel, N., de Rouffignac, C. 1983. Stimulation by human calcitonin of electrolyte transport in distal tubules of rat kidney. *Pflüg. Arch.* 399:111–18

21. Elalouf, J. M., Roinel, N., de Rouffig-

nac, C. 1984. Effects of antidiuretic hormone on electrolyte reabsorption and secretion in distal tubules of rat kidney. *Pflüg. Arch.* 401:167–73

22. Elalouf, J. M., Roinel, N., de Rouffignac, C. 1984. ADH-like effects of calcitonin on electrolyte transport by Henle's loop of rat kidney. *Am. J. Physiol.* 246:F213–20

23. Elalouf, J. M., Roinel, N., de Rouffignac, C. 1985. Effects of dDAVP on rat juxtamedullary nephrons: Stimulation of medullary K recycling. *Am. J. Physiol.* 249:F291–98

24. Elalouf, J. M., Roinel, N., de Rouffignac, C. 1986. Effects of glucagon and PTH on the loop of Henle of rat juxtamedullary nephrons. *Kidney Int.* 29:807–13

25. Elalouf, J. M., Roinel, N., de Rouffignac, C. 1986. Effects of human calcitonin on water and electrolyte movements in rat juxtamedullary nephrons: Inhibition of medullary K recycling. *Pflüg. Arch.* 406:502–6

26. Ellison, D. H., Velazquez, H., Wright, F. S. 1986. Unidirectional potassium fluxes in renal distal tubule: Effects of chloride and barium. *Am. J. Physiol.* 250:F885–94

27. El Mernissi, G., Chabardes, D., Doucet, A., Hus-Citharel, A., Imbert-Teboul, M., et al. 1983. Changes in tubular basolateral membrane markers after DOCA treatment. *Am. J. Physiol.* 245:F100–9

28. El Mernissi, G., Doucet, A. 1983. Short-term effects of aldosterone and dexamethasone on Na-K-ATPase along the rabbit nephron. *Pflüg. Arch.* 399:147–51

29. Fine, L. G., Badie-Dezfooly, B., Lowe, A. G., Hamzeh, A., Wells, J., et al. 1985. Stimulation of $Na^+$-$H^+$ antiport is an early event in hypertrophy of renal proximal tubular cells. *Proc. Natl. Acad. Sci. USA* 82:1736–40

30. Freiberg, J. M., Kinsella, J. L., Sacktor, B. 1982. Glucocorticoids increase the $Na^+$-$H^+$ gradient-dependent phosphate-uptake systems in renal brush border membrane vesicles. *Proc. Natl. Acad. Sci. USA* 79:4932–36

31. Friedman, P. A., Andreoli, T. E. 1982. $CO_2$-stimulated NaCl absorption in the mouse renal cortical thick ascending limb of Henle. *J. Gen. Physiol.* 80:683–711

32. Garcia-Austt, J., Good, D. W., Burg, M. B., Knepper, M. A. 1985. Deoxyxorticosterone-stimulated bicarbonate secretion in rabbit cortical collecting ducts: Effects of luminal chloride re-

moval and in vivo acid loading. *Am. J. Physiol.* 249:F205–12

33. Garg, L. C., Narang, N., Wingo, C. S. 1985. Glucocorticoid effects on Na-K-ATPase in rabbit nephron segments. *Am. J. Physiol.* 248:F487–91

34. Good, D. W. 1985. Sodium-dependent bicarbonate absorption by cortical thick ascending limb of rat kidney. *Am. J. Physiol.* 248:F821–29

35. Good, D. W., Knepper, M. A., Burg, M. B. 1984. Ammonia and bicarbonate transport by thick ascending limb of rat kidney. *Am. J. Physiol.* 247:F35–44

36. Gottschalk, C. W. 1979. Renal nerves and sodium excretion. *Ann. Rev. Physiol.* 41:229–40

37. Greger, R. 1985. Ion transport mechanisms in thick ascending limb of Henle's loop of mammalian nephron. *Physiol. Rev.* 65:760–97

38. Greger, R., Velasquez, H. 1987. The cortical thick ascending limb and early distal convoluted tubule in the urinary concentrating mechanism. *Kidney Int.* 31:590–96

39. Gross, J. B., Kokko, J. P. 1977. Effect of aldosterone and potassium sparing diuretics on electrical potential differences across the distal nephron. *J. Clin. Invest.* 59:82–89

40. Hall, D. A., Varney, D. M. 1980. Effect of vasopressin on electrical potential difference and chloride transport in mouse medullary thick ascending limb of Henle. *J. Clin. Invest.* 66:792–802

41. Hammerman, M. R. 1985. Interaction of insulin with the renal proximal tubular cell. *Am. J. Physiol.* 249:F1–11

42. Harris, P. J., Navar, L. G. 1985. Tubular transport responses to angiotensin. *Am. J. Physiol.* 248:F621–30

43. Hebert, S. C. 1986. Hypertonic cell volume regulation in mouse thick limbs II. $Na^+$-$H^+$ and $Cl^-$-$HCO_3^-$ exchange in basolateral membranes. *Am. J. Physiol.* 250:C920–31

44. Hebert, S. C., Culpepper, R. M., Andreoli, T. E. 1981. NaCl transport in mouse medullary thick ascending limbs. I. Functional nephron heterogeneity and ADH-stimulated NaCl co-transport. *Am. J. Physiol.* 241:F412–31

45. Hebert, S. C., Reeves, W. B., Molony, D. A., Andreoli, T. E. 1987. The medullary thick limb: Function and modulation of the single-effect multiplier. *Kidney Int.* 31:580–88

46. Higashihara, E., Carter, N. W., Pucacco, L., Kokko, J. P. 1984. Aldosterone effects on papillary collecting duct pH profile of the rat. *Am. J. Physiol.* 246:F725–31

47. Higashihara, E., Kokko, J. P. 1985. Effects of aldosterone on potassium recycling in the kidney of adrenalectomized rats. *Am. J. Physiol.* 248:F219–27

48. Higashihara, E., Stokes, J. B., Kokko, J. P., Campbell, W. B., Dubose, T. D. 1979. Cortical and papillary micropuncture examination of chloride transport in segments of the rat kidney during inhibition of prostaglandin production. Possible role for prostaglandins in the chloruresis of acute volume expansion. *J. Clin. Invest.* 64:1277–87

49. Holt, W. F., Lechene, C. 1981. ADH-$PGE_2$ interactions in cortical collecting tubule. I. Depression of sodium transport. *Am. J. Physiol.* 241:F452–60

50. Iino, Y., Burg, M. B. 1981. Effect of acid base status in vivo on bicarbonate transport by rabbit renal tubules in vitro. *Jpn. J. Physiol.* 31:99–107

51. Iino, Y., Troy, J. L., Brenner, B. M. 1981. Effects of catecholamines on electrolyte transport in cortical collecting tubule. *J. Membr. Biol.* 61:67–73

52. Imai, M. 1979. The connecting tubule: A functional subdivision of the rabbit distal nephron segments. *Kidney Int.* 15:346–56

53. Imai, M. 1981. Effects of parathyroid hormone and $N_6$, $O_2$ - dibutyryl cyclic AMP on $Ca^{2+}$ transport across the rabbit distal nephron segments perfused in vitro. *Pflüg. Arch.* 390:145–51

54. Imai, M., Nakamura, R. 1982. Function of distal convoluted and connecting tubules studied by isolated nephron fragments. *Kidney Int.* 22:465–72

55. Jacobson, H. R. 1979. Altered permeability in the proximal tubule response to cyclic AMP. *Am. J. Physiol.* 236:F71–79

56. Kimmel, P. L., Goldfarb, S. 1984. Effects of isoproterenol on potassium secretion by the cortical collecting tubule. *Am. J. Physiol.* 246:F804–10

57. Kinsella, J. L., Freiberg, J. M., Sacktor, B. 1985. Glucocorticoid activation of $Na^+/H^+$ exchange in renal brush border vesicles: Kinetic effects. *Am. J. Physiol.* 248:F233–39

58. Koeppen, B. M. 1985. Conductive properties of the rabbit outer medullary collecting duct: Inner stripe. *Am. J. Physiol.* 248:F500–6

59. Koeppen, B. M. 1986. Conductive properties of the rabbit outer medullary collecting duct: Outer stripe. *Am. J. Physiol.* 250:F70–76

60. Mercier, O., Bichara, M., Paillard, M., Gardin, J. P., Leviel, F. 1985. Parathyroid hormone contributes to volume

expansion induced inhibition of proximal reabsorption. *Am. J. Physiol.* 248:F100–3

61. Morel, F. 1981. Sites of hormone action in the mammalian nephron. *Am. J. Physiol.* 240:F159–64

62. Morel, F., Chabardes, D., Imbert-Teboul, M., Le Bouffant, F., Hus-Citharel, A., Montegut, M. 1982. Multiple hormonal control of adenylate cyclase in distal segments of the rat kidney. *Kidney Int.* 21:S55–62

63. Morel, F., Doucet, A. 1986. Hormonal control of kidney functions at the cell level. *Physiol. Rev.* 66:377–468

64. Murphy, E., Chamberlin, M. E., Mandel, L. J. 1986. Effects of calcitonin on cystosolic Ca in a suspension of rabbit medullary thick ascending limb tubules. *Am. J. Physiol.* 251:C491–95

65. Nonoguchi, H., Knepper, M. A., Manganiello, V. C. 1987. Effects of atrial natriuretic factor on cyclic guanosine monophosphate and cyclic adenosine monophosphate accumulation in microdissected nephron segments from rats. *J. Clin. Invest.* 79:500–7

66. O'Neil, R. G., Hayhurst, R. A. 1985. Functional differentiation of cell types of cortical collecting duct. *Am. J. Physiol.* 248:F449–53

67. O'Neil, R. G., Helman, S. I. 1977. Transport characteristics of renal collecting tubules: Influences of DOCA and diet. *Am. J. Physiol.* 236:F544–58

68. Peterson, L. N., de Rouffignac, C., Sonnenberg, H., Levine, D. Z. 1987. Thick ascending limb response to dDAVP and atrial natriuretic factor in vivo. *Am. J. Physiol.* 252:F374–81

69. Pettinger, W. A., Fallet, R., Wang, Y., Tam, L.-T., Jeffries, W. B. 1986. Enhanced cAMP response to vasopressin in the CCT of DOCA-Na hypertensive rats. *Am. J. Physiol.* 251:F1096–1100

70. Poujeol, P., Touvay, C., Roinel, N., de Rouffignac, C. 1980. Stimulation of renal magnesium reabsorption by calcitonin in the rat. *Am. J. Physiol.* 239:F524–32

71. Reif, M. C., Troutman, S. L., Schafer, J. A. 1984. Sustained response to vasopressin in isolated rat cortical collecting tubule. *Kidney Int.* 26:725–32

72. Reif, M. C., Troutman, S. L., Schafer, J. A. 1986. Sodium transport by rat cortical collecting tubule. Effects of vasopressin and desoxycorticosterone. *J. Clin. Invest.* 77:1291–98

73. Rocha, A. S., Kudo, L. H. 1982. Water, urea, sodium, chloride, and potassium transport in the in vitro isolated perfused papillary collecting duct. *Kidney Int.* 22:485–91

74. Sansom, S. C., O'Neil, R. G. 1985. Mineralocorticoid regulation of apical cell membrane $Na^+$ and $K^+$ transport of the cortical collecting duct. *Am. J. Physiol.* 248:F858–68

75. Sansom, S. C., O'Neil, R. G. 1986. Effects of mineralocorticoids on transport properties of cortical collecting duct basolateral membrane. *Am. J. Physiol.* 251:F743–57

76. Sasaki, S., Imai, M. 1980. Effects of vasopressin on water and NaCl transport across the thick ascending limb of Henle's loop of mouse, rat and rabbit kidneys. *Pflüg. Arch.* 383:215–21

77. Schafer, J. A., Troutman, S. L. 1986. Effect of ADH on rubidium transport in isolated perfused rat cortical collecting tubules. *Am. J. Physiol.* 250:F1063–72

78. Schlatter, E., Greger, R. 1985. cAMP increases the basolateral $Cl^-$ conductance in the isolated perfused medullary thick ascending limb of Henle's loop of the mouse. *Pflüg. Arch.* 405:367–76

79. Schuster, V. L. 1985. Cyclic adenosine monophosphate-stimulated bicarbonate secretion in rabbit cortical collecting tubules. *J. Clin. Invest.* 75:2056–64

80. Schuster, V. L. 1986. Cyclic adenosine monophosphate-stimulated anion transport in rabbit cortical collecting duct. *J. Clin. Invest.* 78:1621–30

81. Schuster, V. L., Bonsib, S. M., Jennings, M. L. 1986. Two types of collecting duct mitochondria-rich (intercalated) cells: Lectin and band 3 cytochemistry. *Am. J. Physiol.* 251:C347–55

82. Schwartz, G. J., Burg, M. B. 1978. Mineralocorticoid effects on cation transport by cortical collecting tubules in vitro. *Am. J. Physiol.* 235:F576–85

83. Shareghi, G. R., Stoner, I. C. 1978. Calcium transport across segments of the rabbit distal nephron in vitro. *Am. J. Physiol.* 235:F367–76

84. Sonnenberg, H., Honrath, U., Chong, C. K., Wilson, D. R. 1986. Atrial natriuretic factor inhibits sodium transport in medullary collecting duct. *Am. J. Physiol.* 250:F963–66

85. Stanton, B. A. 1986. Regulation by adrenal corticosteroids of sodium and potassium transport in loop of Henle and distal tubule of rat kidney. *J. Clin. Invest.* 78:1612–20

86. Star, R. A., Burg, M. B., Knepper, M. A. 1985. Bicarbonate secretion and chloride absorption by rabbit cortical collecting ducts. *J. Clin. Invest.* 76:1123–30

87. Stokes, J. B. 1979. Effect of prostaglandin $E_2$ on chloride transport across the rabbit thick ascending limb of Henle. *J. Clin. Invest.* 64:495–502

88. Stokes, J. B., Ingram, M. J., Williams, A. D., Ingram, D. 1981. Heterogeneity of the rabbit collecting tubule: Localization of mineralocorticoid hormone action to the cortical portion. *Kidney Int.* 20:340–47

89. Stone, D. K., Seldin, D. W., Kokko, J. P., Jacobson, H. R. 1983. Mineralocorticoid modulation of rabbit medullary collecting duct acidification. A sodium-independent effect. *J. Clin. Invest.* 72:77–83

90. Suki, W. N., Rouse, D. 1981. Hormonal regulation of calcium transport in thick ascending limb renal tubules. *Am. J. Physiol.* 241:F171–74

91. Tago, K., Schuster, V. L., Stokes, J. B. 1986. Regulation of chloride self exchange by cAMP in cortical collecting tubule. *Am. J. Physiol.* 251:F40–48

92. Tago, K., Schuster, V. L., Stokes, J. B. 1986. Stimulation of chloride transport by $HCO_3$-$CO_2$ in rabbit cortical collecting tubule. *Am. J. Physiol.* 251:F49–56

93. Takaichi, K., Uchida, S., Kurokawa, K. 1986. High $Ca^{2+}$ inhibits AVP-dependent cAMP production in thick ascending limbs of Henle. *Am. J. Physiol.* 250:F770–76

94. Takeda, K., Torikai, S., Asano, Y., Imai, M. 1986. Modulation by verapamil of hormonal action on the Henle's loop of mice. *Kidney Int.* 29: 863–69

95. Tomita, K., Pisano, J. J., Burg, M. B., Knepper, M. A. 1986. Effects of vasopressin and bradykinin on anion transport by the rat cortical collecting duct. *J. Clin. Invest.* 77:136–41

96. Tomita, K., Pisano, J. J., Knepper, M. A. 1985. Control of sodium and potassium transport in the cortical collecting ducts of the rat. *J. Clin. Invest.* 76:132–36

97. Torikai, S., Kurokawa, K. 1983. Effect of $PGE_2$ on vasopressin dependent cell cAMP in isolated single nephron segments. *Am. J. Physiol.* 245:F58–66

98. Ullrich, K. J., Papavassiliou, F. 1979. Sodium reabsorption in the papillary collecting duct of rats. *Pflüg. Arch.* 379:49–52

99. Velazquez, H., Wright, F. S. 1986. Effects of diuretic drugs on Na, Cl, and K transport by rat renal distal tubule. *Am. J. Physiol.* 250:F1013–23

100. Wakelam, M. J. O., Murphy, G. J., Hruby, V. J., Houslay, M. D. 1986. Activation of two signal-transduction systems in hepatocytes by glucagon. *Nature* 323:68–71

101. Weinman, E. J., Sansom, S. C., Knight, T. F., Senekjian, H. O. 1982. Alpha and beta adrenergic agonists stimulate water absorption in the rat proximal tubule. *J. Membr. Biol.* 69:107–11

102. Welch, W. J., Ott, C. E., Guthrie, G. P., Kutchen, T. A. 1985. Renin secretion and loop of Henle chloride reabsorption in the adrenalectomized rat. *Am. J. Physiol.* 249:F596–F602

103. Whipps, D. E., Armston, A. E., Pryor, H. J., Halestrap, A. P. 1987. Effects of glucagon and $Ca^{2+}$ on the metabolism of phosphatidylinositol 4-phosphate and phosphatidylinositol 4,5-bisphosphate in isolated rat hepatocytes and plasma membranes. *Biochem. J.* 241:835–45

104. Wingo, C. S., Kokko, J. P., Jacobson, H. R. 1985. Effects of in vitro aldosterone on the rabbit cortical collecting tubule. *Kidney Int.* 28:51–57

105. Wittner, M., Di Stefano, A. 1987. Comparative effects of ADH and glucagon on NaCl reabsorption in isolated perfused medullary thick ascending limbs (mTAL) of mouse kidney; effect of ADH on relative tight junction permselectivity (PNa/PCl). *Proc. 10th. Int. Congr. Nephrol.* (Abstr.)

106. Work, J., Galla, J., Booker, B., Schafer, J., Luke, R. 1985. Effect of ADH on chloride reabsorption in the loop of Henle of the Brattleboro rat. *Am. J. Physiol.* 249:F696–F703

107. Zeidel, M. L., Silva, P., Seifter, J. L. 1986. Intracellular pH regulation in rabbit renal medullary collecting ducts cells. *J. Clin. Invest.* 77:1682–88

*Ann. Rev. Physiol. 1988. 50:141–58*

# CHLORIDE TRANSPORT AND DISORDERS OF ACID-BASE BALANCE[1]

*John H. Galla and Robert G. Luke*

Nephrology Research and Training Center and Division of Nephrology, University Station, Birmingham, Alabama 35294

## INTRODUCTION

The goal of this review is to integrate the possible contributions of changes in total body and plasma chloride and/or renal chloride transport (especially the recently described transport processes examined in detail in other chapters in this section) to the control of acid-base balance by the kidney. We emphasize a new hypothesis based on studies in rat and man that the state of chloride depletion per se is responsible for the maintenance phase of chronic metabolic alkalosis, whereas plasma volume depletion is a commonly associated epiphenomenon. This view is based on our findings that chloride repletion can correct metabolic alkalosis despite the persistence, or even worsening of plasma volume depletion. We also briefly consider metabolic alkalosis caused by potassium depletion or mineralocorticoid excess, one type of renal tubular acidosis, and respiratory acidosis.

## METABOLIC ALKALOSIS

To facilitate the understanding of metabolic alkalosis, one can delineate three pathophysiological phases: generation, maintenance, and recovery (96). *Generation* occurs either by loss of protons from the extracellular fluid (ECF) into the external environment or into the cells or by gain of exogenous or endogenous base. Throughout this review, we pay particular attention to the manner in which alkalosis is generated, including prior dietary changes, because these factors must be considered in the interpretation of the findings.

---

[1]The U.S. Government has the right to retain a nonexclusive royalty-free license in and to any copyright covering this paper.

The disequilibrium state, characterized by bicarbonaturia, may occur transiently during the generation of new bicarbonate when the renal reabsorptive capacity for bicarbonate is exceeded. During *maintenance*, the base excess cannot be excreted due to a variety of factors, which when corrected result in *recovery*. This linkage between maintenance and correction has provided an important device for the study of the factors necessary to maintain alkalosis: A deficit per se cannot explain maintenance if alkalosis can be corrected despite its persistence. Factors responsible for the maintenance of metabolic alkalosis by the kidney must lead to a decrease in filtered bicarbonate load and/or an increase in bicarbonate reabsorption.

## Chloride Depletion

GENERAL BACKGROUND    Chloride was linked to alkalosis when MacCallum et al (74) observed hypochloremia and an increase in "alkali reserve" after the loss of gastric fluid due to pyloric obstruction in dogs. This relationship has been confirmed and extended in other experimental models and in patients (12, 48, 49, 63). Chloride depletion is present in the most common clinical forms of metabolic alkalosis, including those due to the loss of gastric fluid, the use of chloruretic diuretics (such as furosemide, chlorthiazide, and their congeners), and the loss of colonic fluids with a high chloride concentration, as in congenital chloridorrhea and certain villous adenomas. However, because concurrent deficits of sodium, potassium, and fluid as well as chloride usually occur in chloride-depletion alkalosis (CDA), controversy exists as to which of them is responsible for its maintenance.

DEVELOPMENT OF THE CLASSICAL HYPOTHESIS    All of these deficits have been extensively studied in several different models of CDA by balance and clearance techniques. In dogs on chloride-deficient diets rendered alkalotic by $NaNO_3$ infusion (46), gastric drainage (80), or prior hypercapnia (93, 102), the resultant alkalosis can be completely corrected by either NaCl or KCl, despite persisting deficits of either sodium or potassium. Volume contraction was also observed in some of these models (80). Similarly, in men given diuretics or infused with $NaNO_3$ (59) or selectively depleted of gastric HCl (60), alkalosis ensued despite replacement of sodium and potassium losses and was completely corrected with either NaCl or KCl (61). Taken together (94), these studies provide convincing evidence that complete correction of carefully controlled experimental CDA can be effected by chloride without the repletion of either potassium or sodium per se, thus eliminating these deficits, but not necessarily plasma or ECF volume depletion, as causes of maintained alkalosis.

In an effort to separate the correction of volume depletion from chloride repletion, Cohen (23) maintained alkalosis for five days in dogs with ethacrynic acid and a NaCl-deficient diet and then expanded ECF volume with a fluid containing chloride in a concentration no higher than that in plasma during maintenance. This "isometric" infusion excluded the possibility that the plasma anion composition was being altered by the infusate per se and completely corrected alkalosis within 24 hr. Cohen (24) confirmed and extended these findings in a subsequent study of the same model in which the suprarenal aorta was constricted before volume expansion to prevent an increase in glomerular filtration rate (GFR) and hence an increase in filtered chloride load.

A hypothesis for the pathophysiology of the maintenance and correction of CDA by the kidney was developed by integrating all of these studies with the known characteristics of fluid and electrolyte handling in the various nephron segments. According to this hypothesis, the intranephronal redistribution of fluid reabsorption plays a central role, as follows: Volume depletion accompanying alkalosis augments fluid reabsorption in the proximal tubule and, since bicarbonate is preferentially reabsorbed over chloride in this segment, alkalosis is maintained (30). Subsequent volume expansion depresses fluid and bicarbonate reabsorption (64, 83), perhaps in part by enhancing paracellular bicarbonate permeability to passive back-flux (3). More bicarbonate and chloride are delivered to distal nephron segments, which possess a substantial capacity to reabsorb chloride but a limited one for bicarbonate. Chloride is retained, bicarbonate excreted, and alkalosis corrected. Thus chloride administration has only a permissive role for volume expansion, which itself is regarded as the extrarenal impetus to the kidney for correction. Schwartz & Cohen (92), extending this hypothesis to other disorders, later proposed that the rate of urinary acid excretion is dominated by the site and rate of sodium reabsorption rather than by a homeostatic mechanism for acid-base equilibrium.

EVIDENCE AGAINST THE CLASSICAL HYPOTHESIS    In the studies of Cohen (23, 24), both volume expansion *and* chloride repletion were implicit in those protocols. Although the concept of intranephronal redistribution was introduced here (24), in retrospect, it is uncertain that the effects of volume expansion to increase delivery out of the proximal tubule were achieved because it was later shown that aortic clamping after, but not before, volume expansion is associated with decreased proximal tubule reabsorption (31, 52). Furthermore, whether volume expansion influences chloride reabsorption in the proximal tubule differently than it does bicarbonate reabsorption is currently debated (13, 18). In apparent contradiction of this hypothesis, metabolic *acidosis* also has been corrected by volume expansion with "isometric" solutions. (50).

We have examined this classical hypothesis in a series of studies of both acute and chronic CDA in man and rat. In our rat studies, CDA is induced by peritoneal dialysis against a dialysate of 150 mM $NaHCO_3$ and 4 mM $KHCO_3$ 15 ml/100 g body weight. A 30-min single-exchange dialysis results in a chloride deficit of 1.5 to 2.0 mEq, neutral sodium and potassium balances, a plasma chloride concentration of 75–80 mEq/liter, and a plasma bicarbonate concentration of 38–43 mEq/liter (34). CDA can be maintained by chloride restriction (34, 36). Controls dialyzed against a Ringers-bicarbonate solution maintain normal plasma chloride and bicarbonate concentrations.

In balance studies (34), rats drinking 70 mM chloride *ad lib* with either sodium or choline completely recovered from acute CDA within 24 hr, despite negative sodium and potassium balances, decreased body weight, and obligatory bicarbonate loading. In contrast, both control and alkalotic rats drinking 70 mM chloride with ammonium—instead of choline—became acidotic.

In clearance studies with this model, infusion of 80 mM chloride in isotonic solutions at rates sufficiently low to prevent volume expansion corrected alkalosis progressively over six hr (33). When rats with acute CDA were subjected to acute bilateral nephrectomy, chloride infusion did not correct the condition (26). To exclude a role for volume in the maintenance or correction of CDA in this model, both alkalotic and control rats were infused with either 6% albumin or 80 mM chloride (calcium, magnesium, lithium, and potassium salts were used; plasma concentrations were low and did not differ), which were added to 5% dextrose (35). In the rats infused with the albumin-containing solution at 2.5 ml/hr/100 g body weight, alkalosis was maintained, despite a 15% plasma volume expansion and a normal GFR. In contrast, in rats infused with 80 mM chloride at only 0.6 ml/hr/100 g body weight, alkalosis was corrected despite persistent volume contraction and a lower GFR.

In a rat model of chronic CDA maintained for 7–10 days, alkalosis, volume contraction, and decreased GFR were observed (103). Despite negative sodium balance, neutral potassium balance, continued bicarbonate loading, persistent volume contraction, and a further decrease in GFR, complete correction of CDA was achieved over 24 hr with 70 mM choline chloride drink. Again, in this chronic model, CDA in acutely nephrectomized rats was not corrected by chloride infusion, thus excluding an extrarenal mechanism of correction (unpublished results).

In normal men with experimental alkalosis induced by furosemide and maintained by chloride restriction for five days (86), alkalosis was completely corrected as chloride was quantitatively repleted with KCl. These results are similar to those of Kassirer et al (59). In various studies of Schwartz and coworkers, ECF volumes were *calculated by chloride space,* an estimate that is not accurate because of transcellular shifts (70). Therefore, Rosen et al (86) estimated serial plasma volumes by $^{131}$I-albumin space, hematocrit, and plasma protein concentration and showed that the decreased plasma volume that attended the generation of the alkalosis persisted throughout both maintenance and recovery.

Thus, in contradiction to the classical hypothesis, our studies in rat and man that have rigorously separated repletion of volume from that of chloride show that CDA can be corrected by chloride administration without repair of ECF volume contraction and by a renal mechanism in either the acute or chronic CDA model.

SEGMENTAL ANION HANDLING IN CDA    The responses of the various segments of superficial cortical (SC) nephrons to the maintenance and correction of acute and chronic alkalosis have been assessed by in vivo micropuncture. In rats maintained chronically alkalotic by furosemide, a low chloride diet, and NaHCO₃ loading, Mello Aires & Malnic (78, 79) found no differences in fractional fluid or chloride reabsorption in the proximal tubule compared to controls. Similarly, in euvolemic rats with acute CDA that were infused with isotonic solutions containing 80 mM chloride and 40 mM bicarbonate (33), alkalosis was progressively corrected without differences in fluid or chloride reabsorption in the proximal tubule. Furthermore, whether normal and alkalotic rats were volume-expanded or contracted and whether alkalotic rats were maintaining or correcting alkalosis (35), fractional chloride reabsorption in the proximal tubule did not differ.

Cogan & Liu (22) showed that no change occurred in filtered bicarbonate load or absolute bicarbonate reabsorption in the proximal tubule in volume-contracted rats with chronic alkalosis. In their various protocols desoxycorticosterone, a chloride- and potassium-deficient diet, and Na₂SO₄ and NaHCO₃ loading were used to generate alkalosis, so these are not models of "pure" CDA. Nevertheless, Maddox & Gennari (75) also found no difference in bicarbonate reabsorption in the proximal tubule of rats rendered chronically alkalotic by diuretics, chloride-deficient diet, and NaHCO₃ loading compared to normals, at least early in the course of maintained alkalosis. However, after three weeks of alkalosis (76), they observed that proximal bicarbonate reabsorption increased when the GFR had increased to greater than normal. They attributed the increased bicarbonate reabsorption, at least in part, to an increase in the length of the proximal tubule. This may be an adaptive response to a high filtered bicarbonate load with increased delivery of bicarbonate to the late proximal tubule, or it may be an effect of potassium depletion on cell growth.

In rats with acute CDA volume-expanded with 6% albumin in 5% dextrose (35), fractional fluid reabsorption decreased compared to that in normal euvolemic controls. Although absolute proximal bicarbonate reabsorption in alkalotic rats did not differ compared to that in volume-expanded controls, both fractional and absolute bicarbonate delivery out of the proximal tubule increased (Table 1; groups CON-VE and CDA-VE). Nevertheless, alkalosis was maintained. Rats infused with 80 mM chloride in 5% dextrose also had increased fractional and absolute bicarbonate delivery out of the proximal tubule as compared to controls (Table 1; groups CON-CC and CDA-CC), despite maintained volume contraction, but in these circumstances the alkalosis was being corrected. Notwithstanding the absence of differences in absolute proximal bicarbonate reabsorption between normal and alkalotic rats in these studies, regression analysis did show significantly less absolute bicarbonate reabsorption for any given filtered load in alkalotic rats compared to normals, which is consistent with an influence of peritubular bicarbonate concentration (3). Taken together, these data suggest that the major adjustments to chloride and bicarbonate reabsorption in the nephron that maintain or correct CDA are made at distal sites.

The loop segment is that portion of the nephron accessible on the surface of the kidney from the latest proximal to the earliest distal convolution, which includes the proximal straight tubule, the thin descending limb, and the medullary and cortical thick ascending limbs of Henle's loop. In the loop segment, fractional chloride reabsorption did not differ between alkalotic and normal rats during euvolemia (33) and during volume contraction with, or volume expansion without, chloride (35), in agreement with the findings of Mello Aires & Malnic (78). Fractional bicarbonate reabsorption in the loop segment also did not differ between normal and alkalotic rats whether alkalosis was being maintained or corrected (35). Again, despite increased delivery of bicarbonate out of the loop segment during alkalosis with either infusion (Table 1), correction proceeded only when chloride was given. Thus, in the

**Table 1**   Segmental bicarbonate reabsorption during CDA

| Group | Filtered (pEq/min) | Late proximal (%) | Early distal (%) | Late distal (%) |
|---|---|---|---|---|
| CON-CC | 1118 | 83.0 | 95.0 | — |
| CDA-CC[a] | 1282 | 70.8* | 89.5* | — |
| CON-VE | 1145 | 75.9 | 94.7 | — |
| CDA-VE[b] | 1569 | 63.9* | 85.8* | — |
| CDA-DX[c] | 1499 | — | 89.0 | 91.9 |
| CDA-CC/2[d] | 1628 | — | 88.0 | 90.3 |

[a] CDA correcting during volume contraction (35).
[b] CDA maintained during volume expansion (35).
[c] CDA maintained during euvolemia (36).
[d] CDA correcting during euvolemia (36).
* P < 0.05 compared to the appropriate control.

absence of chloride administration, the distal convoluted tubule and the collecting duct segment continued to reabsorb sufficient bicarbonate to maintain the alkalosis.

In our acute CDA model in which alkalosis is maintained by 5% dextrose infusion for at least four hr (36), the addition of 80 mM chloride is associated with a prompt and significant increment in bicarbonaturia and progressive correction of alkalosis. In these recovering animals, the deliveries of chloride and bicarbonate to the early and late distal nephron do not differ from those in rats with maintained alkalosis (Table 1; groups CDA-DX and CDA-CC/2) (36). Net chloride and bicarbonate reabsorption in the distal convolution did not differ and thus appear not to participate in the corrective response.

It is not known whether juxtamedullary (JM) nephrons behave differently than SC nephrons in CDA. Frommer et al (32) showed that JM nephrons contribute a higher bicarbonate load than SC nephrons in a model of acute hypertonic $NaHCO_3$ loading. However, not only does the superimposed hypernatremia confound this interpretation, but also the model is one of base loading rather than maintained CDA.

THE ROLE OF GFR    Evidence for a reduced GFR in alkalosis has been noted since the early 1900s. Studies in man and experimental animals have implicated the liberation of toxins, alkalosis, hypochloremia, and dehydration as the proximate cause of azotemia in alkalosis (4, 12, 25, 39, 48). In contrast, the carefully controlled studies by Kassirer et al (59, 60), Gulyassy et al (46), and Atkins & Schwartz (6) showed no evidence for a decreased GFR in different models of chronic metabolic alkalosis in man and dog.

The idea that reduced GFR and the attendant reduction in filtered bicarbonate load maintain alkalosis has been revived (22). In a model described earlier, Cogan & Liu (22) showed decreased SC nephron GFR in volume-contracted alkalotic rats compared to controls; only partial correction of the alkalosis and the reduced GFR was effected by repair of either the potassium or the chloride deficit. In this model, Cogan (21) later claimed that an increase in GFR alone induced by atrial natriuretic factor corrected alkalosis; however, the chloride-containing vehicle was not controlled in that study, which leaves the conclusion in doubt. In a model of diuretic-induced CDA, Maddox & Gennari observed a decrease in GFR early in the course (75), but after at least three weeks of maintained alkalosis, GFR was actually greater in rats with CDA than in normal rats (75). In our model of chronic CDA, we (103) confirmed the reduction in GFR early in the course during volume contraction.

We have consistently found a 15–20% decrease in GFR in our acute CDA model during euvolemia; thus this decrease is unrelated to volume. In four groups of euvolemic rats, as plasma bicarbonate concentrations were increased from 25 to 43 mEq/liter (37), superficial nephron GFRs determined from distal tubule puncture sites declined significantly and progressively from 40.9 to 28.3 nl/min; those determined from proximal tubule puncture sites did not differ (range: 42.8–46.4 nl/min). These data suggest that the decrease in GFR is mediated by tubuloglomerular feedback (TGF), an intrarenal single nephron mechanism for the control of GFR, whose afferent signal is perceived at the macula densa (107). In early distal tubule fluid, chloride concentration correlated positively and osmolality negatively with the decrease in GFR; these data are consistent with the hypothesis that increasing tubule fluid osmolality at the macula densa acts as a signal for increased TGF (9). In the proximal tubule the responses of stop-flow pressure to an increase in the orthograde perfusion rate of the loop segment did not differ in normal and alkalotic rats, thus suggesting that alkalosis did not alter the sensitivity of TGF (37). Whether this mechanism is active in chronically maintained CDA is uncertain.

Recent studies have shown that GFR decreases in diuretic-induced alkalosis in normal men (11, 86) and does not necessarily return to normal during or after complete correction (86).

CHLORIDE DEPLETION HYPOTHESIS    Considering all of the available evidence, we extend the earlier conclusion of Schwartz and coworkers and conclude that chloride alone is essential for the correction of CDA and that it does so by a renal mechanism. In our view, volume depletion is a commonly associated, but not essential, feature of maintained alkalosis, and its persistence does not preclude correction. This conclusion in no way excludes the possibility that the restoration of depleted volume, if adequate chloride is provided, may hasten correction by increasing GFR and diminishing proximal tubule fluid and bicarbonate reabsorption. In the integrated response to CDA, we propose that intrarenal mechanisms responsive to chloride depletion can account for the maintenance of alkalosis regardless of the status of the ECF volume (Table 2).

**Table 2**    Phases of chloride-depletion alkalosis

Acute chloride depletion with loss of protons or gain of bicarbonate

Disequilibrium with bicarbonaturia (tubuloglomerular feedback decreases GFR)[a]

Maintenance with renal conservation of bicarbonate and chloride; ± plasma volume depletion (accelerated bicarbonate and chloride reabsorption in the collecting duct; continued TGF?; aldosterone effect)

Hypertrophy of proximal tubule (reduction in distal bicarbonate delivery)

Normalization of plasma volume and GFR and positive sodium balance if exogenous sodium available

[a] indicates the renal response.

In the absence of volume depletion, chloride depletion may acutely decrease GFR by TGF by the following mechanism: Because the delivery of bicarbonate to the loop of Henle is increased and that of chloride is decreased, and because bicarbonate is less reabsorbable in the ascending limb, more sodium and solute is delivered to the macula densa, which responds by activating the efferent limb of TGF to reduce GFR. This response, in turn, decreases the absolute delivery of solute to the important final distal regulatory transport sites. Such a protective response by the kidney blunts the losses of fluid and sodium that attend the bicarbonaturia encountered during disequilibrium alkalosis.

Chloride depletion also increases renin secretion by a macula densa mechanism. The resultant increment in aldosterone secretion may be disproportionate to the magnitude of accompanying hypokalemia; this would tend to augment potassium and proton secretion in the collecting duct. Abboud et al (1) have shown that chloride depletion stimulates renin release in the rat despite concurrent volume expansion and potassium loading, two potent renin-inhibiting forces. In comparing a rat infused with NaHCO₃ to one infused with NaCl, we (38) have shown that decreased absolute chloride reabsorption and impaired solute uptake in the loop segment are associated with an increase in plasma renin activity despite volume expansion. Wall et al (104) have recently compared adrenalectomized rats that were glucocorticoid-replaced either with or without aldosterone with intact rats. They found that although increased aldosterone is not essential for maintenance of chronic CDA, a normal level of aldosterone is required. The permissive effect of aldosterone in CDA is suggested by the normal plasma aldosterone concentration in man during maintenance (58) and correction of CDA by KCl or choline chloride despite rising plasma aldosterone concentration (86, 104).

Micropuncture data strongly suggest that key adjustments in anion excretion during the maintenance and correction of CDA occur beyond Henle's loop and most likely in the collecting duct. At least two sodium-independent processes may significantly influence chloride and bicarbonate transport in the collecting duct: secretion of bicarbonate by a luminal chloride-bicarbonate exchange process in the cortical collecting tubule (CCT) (66, 88, 89, 97; this chapter) and electrogenic proton secretion shunted by chloride movement from the interstitium into the lumen in the outer medullary portion (62, 98; this chapter). In the rabbit CCT in vitro, Schuster (89) has shown that bicarbonate secretion exhibits saturation kinetics with a $K_m$ ranging from 4 to 11 mM for luminal chloride. Thus, in each of these segments, luminal chloride concentrations could plausibly participate in the regulation of renal bicarbonate excretion (84). Intracellular chloride concentration in renal tubule epithelial cells, which decreases by nearly 50% in a different model of acute metabolic alkalosis (8), may also influence transport. Catecholamines (53,

88) also may modulate bicarbonate secretion and chloride reabsorption in CDA. Thus in the CCT decreased chloride delivery to luminal chloride/cellular bicarbonate exchange mechanisms may blunt bicarbonate secretion, and increased bicarbonate delivery may accelerate bicarbonate reabsorption by buffering secreted protons and thereby maintain alkalosis. In addition, the sodium-independent bicarbonate reabsorptive mechanism in the medullary collecting duct may also be stimulated (99). The axial arrangement of transport mechanisms may be such that chloride exchanged for bicarbonate or secreted with protons during maintenance may be reclaimed in the papillary collecting duct (29).

With the provision of chloride and an increase in its concentration or delivery to the collecting duct, all of these proposed mechanisms would be reversed. Our data (36) show that, although neither chloride nor bicarbonate delivery to the collecting duct differed significantly between rats correcting or maintaining CDA, chloride delivery was somewhat higher during correction. If intracellular chloride depletion endows at least one cell type of the collecting duct with the capacity for intense chloride conservation, a progressive increment in plasma chloride concentration might be brought about if virtually all of the chloride presented from either the basolateral or luminal aspect of the cell was retained within the cell and then selectively released into the ECF. It is also possible that the ratio of luminal-to-cellular chloride concentration influences bicarbonate secretion in the CCT such that a slight increase in luminal chloride concentration facilitates bicarbonate excretion in the presence of low tubule cell chloride activity, i.e. altered $K_m$. As shown by microinjection (33), chloride reabsorption in the collecting duct segment was accelerated in euvolemic rats during correction of CDA. Urinary chloride excretion in the correcting animal remained minimal until CDA was almost completely corrected (37).

Even though chloride may be given at a concentration less than that found in ambient plasma, mass balance demands a progressive increase in both intracellular and extracellular chloride content. The response almost exclusively results in either a decrease of concomitant acid excretion or an increase in alkali excretion as bicarbonate and other unmeasured anions. Chloride appears to be intensely conserved during both maintenance and correction until the plasma chloride concentration is restored to or near normal levels. How the kidney recognizes the administration of chloride, how transport mechanisms in the distal nephron are signalled, and how their axial arrangements subsequently interact to effect correction of alkalosis are important questions that require further study.

## Mineralocorticoid Excess and Potassium Depletion

Whereas CDA can be corrected by chloride repletion without potassium repletion or despite some degree of persistent potassium depletion (KD), metabolic alkalosis associated with mineralocorticoid excess/KD cannot be corrected by chloride administration without potassium, e.g. by NaCl (71, 100). In mild to moderate KD there may be no chloride deficit, and in such circumstances the associated hypochloremia must be due to movement of chloride intracellularly or, more likely, due to retention of bicarbonate in the ECF (43, 71). In states of selective KD without chloride depletion, metabolic alkalosis is modest (43, 57); in fact in the dog, metabolic acidosis possibly due to the associated secondary hypoaldosteronism has been noted (51). More severe metabolic alkalosis in states of KD-dependent metabolic alkalosis are associated with concomitant chloride depletion (as, for example, when induced by loop-acting diuretics or Bartter's syndrome) and/or with mineralocorticoid excess; KD per se depresses aldosterone secretion (14). In such severe cases administration of potassium without chloride or without cessation of exogenous or endogenous excess mineralocorticoid will not fully correct metabolic alkalosis.

Generation of KD alkalosis is due to the intracellular shift of protons (2, 43). Although KD is associated with enhanced renal ammonia production, there is no evidence for overall enhanced net acid excretion, and hence none for renal generation of metabolic alkalosis (43, 57, 101). Intracellular acidosis in renal tubular cells (56) facilitates bicarbonate reabsorption (proton secretion), opposes bicarbonate secretion, and thus, maintains alkalosis. Enhanced bicarbonate reabsorption in both proximal and distal convoluted tubules has been shown by in vivo microperfusion studies (15, 17). Increased $V_{max}$ for $Na^+$-$H^+$ exchange has been observed in brush border membrane vesicles prepared from potassium-depleted alkalotic rats (95); this finding suggests increased proton transport capacity in response to intracellular acidosis. Maintenance of alkalosis would also be facilitated by KD-associated reduction in GFR (68). The important role of intracellular acidosis in KD alkalosis is supported by the fact that alkalosis can be corrected by potassium infusion without any suppression of renal net acid excretion (71) or indeed by KCl infusion in nephrectomized animals (81); correction is assumed to occur by intracellular movement of potassium and the movement into the ECF of protons that titrate bicarbonate.

Severe KD in man and experimental animals causes renal chloride wasting, depletion of total body chloride, and more severe metabolic alkalosis (22, 40, 73, 100), which can be corrected only by administration of both potassium and chloride (22, 71, 100). We have investigated segmental chloride reabsorption in potassium-depleted rats by free flow micropuncture, microperfusion, and $^{36}Cl$ microinjection (69, 73). As compared to controls, net chloride reabsorption is depressed in the proximal tubule and loop segment; the increase in early distal chloride concentration and the associated urinary concentrating defect are consistent with KD induced impairment of chloride transport in the thick ascending limb (47, 69). The defect in chloride transport at this site is improved but not corrected by indomethacin (69). We speculate that the defect may be related to the impaired recycling of potassium at the luminal membrane, which in turn impairs the effectiveness of the Na, K, 2Cl carrier in facilitating net chloride reabsorption at that site (45, 108). Microinjection data also suggests impaired chloride transport in the collecting duct as compared to even less chloride-depleted control rats (73). Whatever the mechanism of chloride depletion, its effects could clearly be synergistic in maintaining more severe metabolic alkalosis than in KD alone.

## Bartter's Syndrome

The pathophysiology of the sometimes severe metabolic alkalosis seen in Bartter's syndrome (41) may be due to a primary hereditary defect in the coupled Na, K, 2Cl luminal carrier protein in the thick ascending limb of Henle's loop. This can explain the tendency to renal sodium, potassium, and chloride wasting (41, 42), impaired concentrating capacity, magnesium wasting (7), macula densa–(38) and baroreceptor-stimulated activation of the renin-aldosterone system, and high renal production of prostaglandin $E_2$ (27). The latter (27) and severe KD both can further impair coupled NaCl reabsorption in the ascending limb.

The severe metabolic alkalosis is due to potassium and chloride depletion and aldosterone excess. Potassium wasting may be due to impaired potassium reabsorption in the thick ascending limb together with the effects of increased delivery of sodium and fluid to the CCT without adequate reabsorbable anion (i.e. chloride) in the presence of high plasma aldosterone concentrations (85).

Bartter's syndrome is rare but its pathophysiology is important, since it is very similar to some causes of metabolic alkalosis that are commonly concealed by the patient, such as laxative or diuretic abuse or bulimia. Bulimia with surreptitious vomiting, or laxative abuse, can produce similar pathophysiological consequences, but renal conservation of chloride remains normal.

# RENAL TUBULAR ACIDOSIS AND CHLORIDE SHUNT

Distal renal tubular acidosis has been attributed to the failure to maintain a proton gradient due to a permeability defect, a defect in the proton pump, or a "voltage-dependent" defect, presumably in the CCT (5, 65). Another, but rare, condition is termed the "chloride shunt" defect in which mineralocorticoid-resistant hyperkalemia, hypertension, and hyperchloremic acidosis are thought to be due to excess NaCl reabsorption in the CCT with shunting of the voltage-dependent stimulatory effects on potassium and proton secretion and excess retention of NaCl (87).

## RESPIRATORY ACIDOSIS

Respiratory acidosis is another state of chloride depletion characterized by hypochloremia and renal maintenance of a high plasma bicarbonate but with an acid pH both in cells and ECF. The renal response to respiratory acidosis is characterized by chloruresis, negative chloride balance, enhanced fractional and absolute bicarbonate reabsorption, kaluresis, and enhanced net acid including ammonium excretion (16, 19, 20, 67, 82, 105). Chloruresis is detectable within one to three hours of exposure to 8% $CO_2$ in air (72). The renal chloruretic and acid-base response is near maximum at 24 hr in the rat; thereafter, a steady state can be sustained for a week at inspired concentrations of $CO_2$ as high as 15% (16). Chloruresis and a negative chloride balance are not essential for the renal response to respiratory acidosis; rats exposed to a high $P_{CO_2}$ and then maintained on a low chloride diet prior to reexposure to the same degree of respiratory acidosis continue to conserve chloride and have an otherwise normal acid base response (72). A prior low NaCl diet does not prevent increased net acid excretion and (67, 82, 93) chloruresis after exposure to a high $P_{CO_2}$.

Decreases in proximal chloride reabsorption tend to parallel increases in urinary chloride excretion (19, 105). In the isolated, perfused thick ascending limb, a high $P_{CO_2}$ reduces chloride reabsorption (106). The overall effect of respiratory acidosis on collecting duct chloride reabsorption is not yet documented.

In response to a high $P_{CO_2}$, both absolute and fractional reabsorption of bicarbonate in the proximal tubule increase without a change in proximal fluid reabsorption in vitro and in vivo (20, 54, 105). Bicarbonate reabsorption increases in the medullary collecting duct (55), and net acid excretion increases in the inner medullary collecting duct (10). Madsen & Tisher have shown insertion of proton pumps from the subapical cytoplasm into the luminal membrane of outer medullary collecting duct intercalated cells of rat and an increase in the surface area of the luminal membrane after four hours of respiratory acidosis (77). Thus, in respiratory acidosis, the kidney can generate new bicarbonate and retain it.

Schwartz & Al-Awqati (91) have discussed insertion of proton-translocating ATPase in the renal tubule luminal membrane (proximal tubule, CCT, medullary collecting duct) in response to an increase in $P_{CO_2}$ with a resulting increase in net bicarbonate reabsorption. Studies using membrane vesicles support the existence of electrogenic $H^+$-ATPase in the proximal tubule brush border and in renal medullary membranes (62); some of these vesicles contain a chloride channel in parallel with the proton pump (28, 44, 90). It is certainly attractive to link, in collecting duct segments, proton secretion and enhanced bicarbonate reabsorption in response to respiratory acidosis with chloride secretion into the tubular lumen and chloruresis. In this construct, chloruresis will cease when chloride reabsorption is adequately stimulated by chloride depletion in the papillary collecting duct (29).

After recovery from respiratory acidosis, enhanced proximal bicarbonate reabsorption persists for at least one hour (19). These findings are consistent with enhanced proximal cell proton secretory capacity for some time after exposure to respiratory acidosis; the latter will contribute to post-hypercapnic metabolic alkalosis. It is likely however that the most important and common cause of persistent post-hypercapnic metabolic alkalosis is failure to replenish the chloride deficit (93).

Despite these data on changes in bicarbonate and chloride reabsorption within the whole kidney and in various nephron segments, one cannot yet establish the precise timing of and interrelationships between bicarbonate and chloride reabsorption and the sites responsible for the initial chloruresis and subsequent new steady state of chloride balance, and for enhanced bicarbonate reabsorption. It does seem clear that an absolute and fractional reabsorption of bicarbonate is maintained in the proximal tubule; since fluid reabsorption does not change, this would imply a decreased fractional and absolute chloride reabsorption in this segment (19). However, adjustments at more distal sites are necessary to create and maintain a new steady state. Further studies are needed to clarify these relationships and the integrated renal response to respiratory acidosis.

*Literature Cited*

1. Abboud, H. E., Luke, R. G., Galla, J. H., Kotchen, T. A. 1979. Stimulation of renin by acute selective chloride depletion in the rat. *Circ. Res.* 44:815–21
2. Adler, S., Fraley, D. S. 1977. Potassium and intracellular pH. *Kidney Int.* 11:433–42
3. Alpern, R. J., Cogan, M. G., Rector, F. C. Jr. 1983. Effects of extracellular fluid volume and plasma bicarbonate concentration on proximal acidification in the rat. *J. Clin. Invest.* 71:736–46
4. Ariel, I. M., Miller, F. 1950. The effects of hypochloremia upon renal function in surgical patients. *Surgery* 28:552–67
5. Arruda, J. A. L., Kurtzman, N. 1980. Mechanisms and classification of deranged distal urinary acidification. *Am. J. Physiol.* 239:F515–23
6. Atkins, E. A., Schwartz, W. B. 1962. Factors governing correction of the alkalosis associated with potassium deficiency; the critical role of chloride in the recovery process. *J. Clin. Invest.* 41:218–29

7. Baehler, R. W., Work, J., Kotchen, T. A., McMorrow, G., Guthrie, G. 1980. Studies on the pathogenesis of Bartter's syndrome. *Am. J. Med.* 69:933–38
8. Beck, F.-X., Dorge, A., Rick, R., Schramm, M., Thurau, K. 1982. Intracellular element concentrations of renal tubular cells during acute metabolic alkalosis. *Pflügers Arch. Suppl.* 394:R23
9. Bell, P. D., Navar, L. G. 1982. Relationship between tubuloglomerular feedback and perfusate hypotonicity. *Kidney Int.* 22:234–39
10. Bengele, H. H., Schwartz, J. H., McNamara, E. R., Alexander, E. A. 1986. Effect of buffer infusion during acute respiratory acidosis. *Am J. Physiol.* 250:F115–19
11. Berger, B. E., Cogan, M. G., Sebastian, A. 1984. Reduced glomerular filtration and enhanced bicarbonate reabsorption maintain metabolic alkalosis in humans. *Kidney Int.* 26:205–8
12. Berger, E. H., Binger, M. W. 1935. The status of the kidneys in alkalosis. *J. Am. Med. Assoc.* 104:1383–87

13. Bichara, M., Paillard, M., Corman, B., de Rouffignac, C., Level, F. 1984. Volume expansion modulates $NaHCO_3$ and NaCl transport in the proximal tubule and Henle's loop. *Am. J. Physiol.* 247:F140–50

14. Cannon, P. J., Ames, R. P., Laragh, J. H. 1966. Relation between potassium balance and aldosterone secretion in normal subjects and in patients with hypertensive and renal tubular disease. *J. Clin. Invest.* 45:865–79

15. Capasso, G., Kinne, R., Malnic, G., Giebisch, G. 1986. Renal bicarbonate reabsorption in the rat. I. Effects of hypokalemia and carbonic anhydrase. *J. Clin. Invest.* 78:1558–67

16. Carter, N. W., Seldin, D. W., Teng, H. C. 1959. Tissue and renal response to chronic respiratory acidosis. *J. Clin. Invest.* 38:949–60

17. Chan, Y. L., Biagi, B., Giebisch, G. 1982. Control mechanism of bicarbonate transport across the rat proximal convoluted tubule. *Am. J. Physiol.* 242: F532–43

18. Cogan, M. G. 1983. Volume expansion predominantly inhibits proximal NaCl rather than $NaHCO_3$. *Am. J. Physiol.* 245:F272–75

19. Cogan, M. G. 1984. Effects of acute alterations in $PCO_2$ on proximal $HCO_3^-$, Cl⁻, and $H_2O$ reabsorption. *Am. J. Physiol.* 246:F21–26

20. Cogan, M. G. 1984. Chronic hypercapnia stimulates proximal bicarbonate reabsorption in the rat. *J. Clin. Invest.* 74:1942–47

21. Cogan, M. G. 1985. Atrial natriuretic factor ameliorates chronic metabolic alkalosis by increasing glomerular filtration. *Science* 229:1405–7

22. Cogan, M. G., Liu, F.-Y. 1983. Metabolic alkalosis in the rat. Evidence that reduced glomerular filtration rate rather than enhanced tubular bicarbonate reabsorption is responsible for maintaining the alkalotic state. *J. Clin. Invest.* 71:1141–60

23. Cohen, J. J. 1968. Correction of metabolic alkalosis by the kidney after isometric expansion of extracellular fluid. *J. Clin. Invest.* 47:1181–92

24. Cohen, J. J. 1970. Selective Cl retention in repair of metabolic alkalosis without increasing filtered load. *Am. J. Physiol.* 218:165–70

25. Cooke, J. V., Rodenbaugh, F. H., Whipple, G. H. 1916. Intestinal obstruction. VI. A study of non-coagulable nitrogen of the blood. *J. Exp. Med.* 23: 717–38

26. Craig, D. M., Galla, J. H., Bonduris, D. N., Luke, R. G. 1986. Importance of the kidney in the correction of chloride-depletion alkalosis in the rat. *Am. J. Physiol.* 250:F54–57

27. Culpepper, R. M., Andreoli, T. A. 1983. Interactions among prostaglandin $E_2$, antidiuretic hormone, and cyclic adenosine monophosphate in modulating Cl⁻ absorption in single mouse medullary thick ascending limbs of Henle. *J. Clin. Invest.* 71:1588–1601

28. Diaz-Diaz, F. D., LaBelle, E. F., Eaton, D. C., DuBose, T. D. Jr. 1986. ATP-dependent proton transport in human renal medulla. *Am. J. Physiol.* 251:F297–302

29. Diezi, J., Michoud, P., Aceves, J., Giebisch, G. 1973. Micropuncture study of electrolyte transport across papillary collecting duct of the rat. *Am. J. Physiol.* 224:623–34

30. Emmett, M., Seldin, D. W. 1985. Clinical syndromes of metabolic acidosis and metabolic alkalosis. In *The Kidney: Physiology and Pathophysiology*, ed. D. W. Seldin, G. Giebisch, pp. 1611–24 New York: Raven

31. Fitzgibbons, J. P., Gennari, F. J., Garfinkel, H. B., Cortell, S. 1974. Dependence of saline-induced natriuresis upon exposure of the kidney to the physical effects of extracellular fluid volume expansion. *J. Clin. Invest.* 54:1428–36

32. Frommer, J. P., Wesson, D. E., Laski, M. E., Kurtzman, N. A. 1985. Juxtamedullary nephrons during acute metabolic alkalosis in the rat. *Am. J. Physiol.* 249:F107–16

33. Galla, J. H., Bonduris, D. N., Dumbauld, S. L., Luke, R. G. 1984. Segmental chloride and fluid handling during correction of chloride-depletion alkalosis without volume expansion in the rat. *J. Clin. Invest.* 73:96–106

34. Galla, J. H., Bonduris, D. N., Luke, R. G. 1983. Correction of acute chloride-depletion alkalosis in the rat without volume expansion. *Am. J. Physiol.* 244:F217–21

35. Galla, J. H., Bonduris, D. N., Luke, R. G. 1987. Effect of chloride and extracellular fluid volume on bicarbonate reabsorption along the nephron in metabolic alkalosis in the rat: A reassessment of the classical hypothesis of the maintenance of metabolic alkalosis. *J. Clin. Invest.* 80:41–50

36. Galla, J. H., Bonduris, D. N., Luke, R. G. 1987. Mechanism of correction of chloride-depletion alkalosis by Cl: Role of the distal nephron in vivo. *Clin. Res.* 35:635A (Abstr.)

37. Galla, J. H., Bonduris, D. N., Sanders, P. W., Luke, R. G. 1984. Volume-independent reductions in glomerular fil-

tration rate in acute chloride-depletion alkalosis in the rat. Evidence for mediation by tubuloglomerular feedback. *J. Clin. Invest.* 74:2002–8

38. Galla, J. H., Kirchner, K. A., Kotchen, T. A., Luke, R. G. 1981. Effect of hypochloremia on loop segment chloride and solute reabsorption in the rat during volume expansion. *Kidney Int.* 20:569–74

39. Gamble, J. L., Ross, S. G. 1925. The factors in the dehydration following pyloric obstruction. *J. Clin. Invest.* 1:403–23

40. Garella, S., Chazan, J. A., Cohen, J. J. 1970. Saline-resistant metabolic alkalosis or "chloride-wasting nephropathy." *Ann. Int. Med.* 73:31–38

41. Gill, J. R. Jr., Bartter, F. C. 1978. Evidence for a prostaglandin-independent defect in chloride reabsorption in the loop of Henle as a proximal cause of Bartter's syndrome. *Am. J. Med.* 65:766–72

42. Gill, J. R. Jr., Frolich, J. C., Bowden, R. E., Taylor, A., Keiser, H. R., et al. 1976. Bartter's syndrome: A disorder characterized by high urinary prostaglandins and dependence of hyperreninemia on prostaglandin synthesis. *Am. J. Med.* 61:43–51

43. Girard, P., Brun-Pascaud, M., Paillard, M. 1985. Selective dietary potassium depletion and acid-base equilibrium in the rat. *Clin. Sci.* 68:301–9

44. Gluck, S., Al-Awqati, Q. 1984. An electrogenic proton-translocating adenosine triphosphate from bovine kidney medulla. *J. Clin. Invest.* 73:1704–10

45. Greger, R., Wittner, M., Schlatter, E., Gebler, B., Weidtke, C., Di Stefano, A. 1984. Sodium chloride reabsorption in the thick ascending limb of the loop of Henle. In *Nephrology,* ed. R. Robinson, V. W. Dennis, T. F. Ferris, R. J. Glassock, J. P. Kokko, C. C. Tisher, 1:224–41. New York: Springer-Verlag

46. Gulyassy, P. F., van Ypersele de Strihou, C., Schwartz, W. B. 1962. On the mechanism of nitrate-induced alkalosis. The possible role of selective chloride depletion in acid-base regulation. *J. Clin. Invest.* 41:1850–62

47. Gutsche, H. U., Peterson, L. N., Levine, D. Z. 1984. In vivo evidence of impaired solute transport by the thick ascending limb in potassium-depleted rats. *J. Clin. Invest.* 73:908–16

48. Haden, R. L., Orr, T. G. 1923. Chemical changes in the blood of the dog after intestinal obstruction. *J. Exp. Med.* 37:365–75

49. Haden, R. L., Orr, T. G. 1924. The effect of inorganic salts on the chemical changes in the blood of the dog after obstruction of the duodenum. *J. Exp. Med.* 39:321–29

50. Hulter, H. N., Ilnicki, L. P., Harbottle, J. A., Sebastian, A. 1978. Correction of metabolic acidosis by the kidney during isometric expansion of extracellular fluid volume. *J. Lab. Clin. Med.* 92:620–12

51. Hulter, H. N., Sebastian, A., Sigala, J. F., Licht, J. H., Glynn, R. D., et al. 1980. Pathogenesis of renal hyperchloremic acidosis resulting from dietary potassium restriction in the dog: Role of aldosterone. *Am. J. Physiol.* 28:F79–91

52. Ichikawa, I., Brenner, B. M. 1979. Mechanism of inhibition of proximal tubule fluid reabsorption after exposure of the rat kidney to the physical effects of expansion of extracellular fluid volume. *J. Clin. Invest.* 64:1466–74

53. Iino, Y., Troy, J. L., Brenner, B. M. 1981. Effects of catecholamines on electrolyte transport in cortical collecting tubule. *J. Membr. Biol.* 61:67–73

54. Jacobson, H. R. 1981. Effects of $CO_2$ and acetazolamide on bicarbonate and fluid transport in rabbit proximal tubules. *Am. J. Physiol.* 240:F54–62

55. Jacobson, H. R. 1984. Medullary collecting duct acidification. Effects of potassium, $HCO_3$ concentration and $pCO_2$. *J. Clin. Invest.* 74:2107–14

56. Jones, B., Simpson, D. P. 1983. Influence of alterations in acid-base conditions on intracellular pH of intact renal cortex. *Renal Physiol.* 6:28–35

57. Jones, J. W., Sebastian, A., Hulter, H. N., Schambelan, M., Sutton, J. M., et al. 1982. Systemic and renal acid-base effects of chronic dietary potassium depletion in humans. *Kidney Int.* 21:402–10

58. Kassirer, J. P., Appleton, F. M., Chazan, J. A., Schwartz, W. B. 1967. Aldosterone in metabolic alkalosis. *J. Clin. Invest.* 46:1558–71

59. Kassirer, J. P., Berkman, P. M., Lawrenz, D. R., Schwartz, W. B. 1965. The critical role of chloride in the correction of hypokalemic alkalosis in man. *Am. J. Med.* 38:172–89

60. Kassirer, J. P., Schwartz, W. B. 1966. The response of normal man to selective depletion of hydrochloric acid. Factors in the genesis of persistent gastric alkalosis. *Am. J. Med.* 40:10–18

61. Kassirer, J. P., Schwartz, W. B. 1966. Correction of metabolic alkalosis in man without repair of potassium deficiency.

A re-evaluation of the role of potassium. *Am. J. Med.* 40:19–25

62. Kaunitz, J. D., Gunther, R. D., Sachs, G. 1985. Characterization of an electrogenic ATP and chloride-dependent proton translocating pump from rat renal medulla. *J. Biol. Chem.* 260:11567–73

63. Kirsner, J. B., Palmer, W. L. 1941. The role of chlorides in alkalosis. *J. Am. Med. Assoc.* 116:384–90

64. Kurtzman, N. A. 1970. Regulation of renal bicarbonate reabsorption by extracellular volume. *J. Clin. Invest.* 49:586–95

65. Kurtzman, N. A. 1983. Acquired distal renal tubular acidosis. *Kidney Int.* 24:807–19

66. Laski, M. E., Warnock, D. G., Rector, F. C. Jr. 1983. Effects of chloride gradients on total $CO_2$ flux in the rabbit cortical collecting tubule. *Am. J. Physiol.* 244:F112–21

67. Levitin, H., Branscome, W., Epstein, F. H. 1958. The pathogenesis of hypochloremia in respiratory acidosis. *J. Clin. Invest.* 37:1667–75

68. Linas, S. L., Dickmann, D. 1982. Mechanism of the decreased renal blood flow in the potassium-depleted conscious rat. *Kidney Int.* 21:757–65

69. Luke, R. G., Booker, B. B., Galla, J. H. 1985. Effect of potassium depletion on chloride transport in loop of Henle in the rat. *Am. J. Physiol.* 248:F682–87

70. Luke, R. G., Galla, J. H. 1983. Chloride-depletion alkalosis with a normal extracellular fluid volume. *Am. J. Physiol.* 245:F419–24

71. Luke, R. G., Levitin, H. 1967. Impaired renal conservation of chloride and the acid-base changes associated with potassium depletion in the rat. *Clin. Sci.* 32:511–26

72. Luke, R. G., Warren, Y., Kashgarian, M., Levitin, H. 1970. Effects of chloride restriction and depletion on acid-base balance and chloride conservation in the rat. *Clin. Sci.* 38:385–96

73. Luke, R. G., Wright, F. S., Fowler, N., Kashgarian, M., Giebisch, G. H. 1978. Effects of potassium depletion on renal tubular chloride transport in the rat. *Kidney Int.* 14:414–27

74. MacCallum, W. G., Lintz, J., Vermilye, H. N., Leggett, T. H., Boas, E. 1920. The effect of pyloric obstruction in relation to gastric tetany. *Bull. Johns Hopkins Hosp.* 31:1–7

75. Maddox, D. A., Gennari, F. J. 1983. Proximal tubular bicarbonate reabsorption and $PCO_2$ in chronic metabolic alkalosis in the rat. *J. Clin. Invest.* 72:1385–95

76. Maddox, D. A., Gennari, F. J. 1986. Load dependence of proximal tubular bicarbonate reabsorption in chronic metabolic alkalosis in the rat. *J. Clin. Invest.* 77:709–16

77. Madsen, K. M., Tisher, C. C. 1983. Cellular responses to acute respiratory acidosis in rat medullary collecting duct. *Am. J. Physiol.* 245:F670–79

78. Mello Aires, M., Malnic, G. 1972. Micropuncture study of acidification during hypochloremic alkalosis in the rat. *Pflügers Arch.* 331:13–24

79. Mello Aires, M., Malnic, G. 1972. Renal handling of sodium and potassium during hypochloremic alkalosis in the rat. *Pflügers Arch.* 331:215–25

80. Needle, M. A., Kaloyanides, G. J., Schwartz, W. B. 1964. The effects of selective depletion of hydrochloric acid on acid-base and electrolyte equilibrium. *J. Clin. Invest.* 43:1836–46

81. Orloff, J., Kennedy, T. J. Jr., Berliner, R. W. 1953. The effect of potassium in nephrectomized rats with hypokalemic alkalosis. *J. Clin. Invest.* 32:538–42

82. Polak, A., Haynie, G. D., Hays, R. M., Schwartz, W. B. 1961. Effects of chronic hypercapnia on electrolyte and acid-base equilibrium. I. Adaptation. *J. Clin. Invest.* 40:1223–37

83. Purkerson, M. L., Lubowitz, H., White, R. W., Bricker, N. S. 1969. On the influence of extracellular fluid volume expansion on bicarbonate reabsorption in the rat. *J. Clin. Invest.* 48:1754–60

84. Rector, F. C. Jr. 1984. Hydrogen ion transport along the nephron. See Ref. 45, pp. 161–77

85. Rodriguez Portales, J. A., Delea, C. S. 1986. Renal tubular reabsorption of chloride in Bartter's syndrome and other conditions with hypokalemia. *Clin. Nephrol.* 26:269–72

86. Rosen, R. A., Julian, B. A., Dubovsky, E. V., Galla, J. H., Luke, R. G. 1988. On the mechanism by which chloride corrects metabolic alkalosis in man. *Am. J. Med.* In press

87. Schambelan, M., Sebastian, A., Rector, F. C. Jr. 1981. Mineralocorticoid-resistant renal hyperkalemia without salt wasting (type II pseudo-hypoaldosteronism): Role of increased chloride reabsorption. *Kidney Int.* 19:716–27

88. Schuster, V. L. 1985. Cyclic adenosine monophosphate-stimulated bicarbonate secretion in rabbit cortical collecting tubules. *J. Clin. Invest.* 75:2056–64

89. Schuster, V. L. 1986. Cyclic adenosine

monophosphate-stimulated anion transport in rabbit cortical collecting duct. Kinetics, stoichiometry, and conductive pathways. *J. Clin. Invest.* 78:1621–30

90. Schwartz, G. J., Al-Awqati, Q. 1985. $CO_2$ causes exocytosis of vesicles containing $H^+$ pumps in isolated perfused proximal and collecting tubules. *J. Clin. Invest.* 75:1638–44

91. Schwartz, G. J., Al-Awqati, Q. 1986. Regulation of transepithelial $H^+$ transport by exocytosis and endocytosis. *Ann. Rev. Physiol.* 48:153–61

92. Schwartz, W. B., Cohen, J. J. 1978. The nature of the renal response to chronic disorders of acid-base equilibrium. *Am. J. Med.* 64:417–28

93. Schwartz, W. B., Hays, R. M., Polak, A., Haynie, G. D. 1961. Effects of chronic hypercapnia on electrolyte and acid-base equilbrium. II. Recovery, with special reference to the influence of chloride intake. *J. Clin. Invest.* 40:1238–49

94. Schwartz, W. B., van Ypersele de Strihou, C., Kassirer, J. P. 1968. Role of anions in metabolic alkalosis and potassium deficiency. *N. Engl. J. Med.* 279:630–39

95. Seifter, J. L., Harris, R. C. 1984. Chronic K depletion increases Na-H exchange in rat renal cortical brush border membrane vesicles. *Kidney Int.* 25:282A (Abstr.)

96. Seldin, D. W., Rector, F. C. Jr. 1972. The generation and maintenance of metabolic alkalosis. *Kidney Int.* 1:306–21

97. Star, R. A., Burg, M. B., Knepper, M. A. 1985. Bicarbonate secretion and chloride absorption by rabbit cortical collecting ducts. Role of chloride/bicarbonate exchange. *J. Clin. Invest.* 76:1123–30

98. Stone, D. K., Seldin, D. W., Kokko, J. P., Jacobson, H. R. 1983. Anion dependence of rabbit medullary collecting duct acidification. *J. Clin. Invest.* 71:1505–8

99. Stone, D. K., Seldin, D. W., Kokko, J. P., Jacobson, H. R. 1983. Mineralocorticoid modulation of rabbit medullary collecting duct acidification. *J. Clin. Invest.* 72:77–83

100. Struyvenberg, A., DeGraeff, J., Lameijer, L.D.F. 1965. The role of chloride in hypokalemic alkalosis in the rat. *J. Clin. Invest.* 44:326–38

101. Tannen, R. L. 1977. Relationship of renal ammonia production and potassium homeostasis. *Kidney Int.* 11:453–65

102. van Ypersele de Strihou, C., Gulyassy, P. F., Schwartz, W. B. 1962. Effects of chronic hypercapnia on electrolyte and acid-base equilibrium. III. Characteristics of the adaptive and recovery process as evaluated by provision of alkali. *J. Clin. Invest.* 41:2246–53

103. Wall, B. M., Byrum, G. V., Galla, J. H., Luke, R. G. 1987. Importance of chloride for the correction of chronic metabolic alkalosis in the rat. *Am. J. Physiol.* In press

104. Wall, B. M., Galla, J. H., Luke, R. G. 1987. The role of aldosterone in the maintenance of chronic metabolic alkalosis in the rat. *Kidney Int.* 31:417 (Abstr.)

105. Warren, Y., Luke, R. G., Kashgarian, M., Levitin, H. 1970. Micropuncture studies of chloride and bicarbonate absorption in the proximal renal tubule of the rat in respiratory acidosis and in chloride depletion. *Clin. Sci.* 38:375–83

106. Wingo, C. S. 1986. Effect of acidosis on chloride transport in the cortical thick ascending limb of Henle perfused in vitro. *J. Clin. Invest.* 78:1324–30

107. Wright, F. S., Briggs, J. P. 1977. Feedback regulation of glomerular filtration rate. *Am. J. Physiol.* 233:F1–7

108. Wright, F. S., Giebisch, G. 1985. Regulation of potassium excretion. In *The Kidney: Physiology and Pathophysiology*, ed. D. W. Seldin, G. Giebisch, pp. 1123–49. New York: Raven

# COMPARATIVE PHYSIOLOGY

## *FUNCTIONAL AND CHEMICAL PROPERTIES OF HEMOGLOBIN*

*Introduction,* Fred N. White, *Section Editor*

Among the myriad of biological molecules, hemoglobin has provoked the most sustained investigative interests among comparative physiologists. Early efforts centered on describing the functional diversity of this molecule in terms of the form and shape of the hemoglobin dissociation curve, especially in regard to the affinity for oxygen in response to protons (the Bohr effect). Such observations were related to species diversity, stage of development, and environmental factors such as temperature and environmental hypoxia.

Two reviews constitute this year's Comparative Physiology section. Drs. Weber and Jensen present recent perspectives concerning functional adaptations of the hemoglobins of ectothermic vertebrates. Their review correlates environmental and intrinsic factors that are responsible for the modulation of the behavior of the molecule. The review by Dr. Riggs focuses on the most famous of the hemoglobin modulations—the Bohr effect. The emphasis of his review is the nature of the specific chemical groups involved in the Bohr effect and how these groups interact with various allosteric factors. Together these reviews provide perspectives which link environmental and adaptational physiology with the functional and chemical behavior of the molecule.

Ann. Rev. Physiol. 1988. 50:161–79

# FUNCTIONAL ADAPTATIONS IN HEMOGLOBINS FROM ECTOTHERMIC VERTEBRATES

*Roy E. Weber and Frank B. Jensen*

Biology Institute, Odense University, DK 5230 Odense M, Denmark

## INTRODUCTION

Hemoglobin (Hb) increases the $O_2$ carrying capacity of the blood of ectothermic vertebrates by about twenty times compared to physically dissolved $O_2$. This drastically raises the blood $O_2$ capacitance coefficient ($\beta_{O_2} = \Delta C_{O_2}/\Delta P_{O_2}$) and permits corresponding reductions in the cardiac output ($\dot{Q}_h$) required for a given convective $O_2$ transfer ($\dot{V}_{O_2}$) as predicted by the Fick equation ($\dot{V}_{O_2} = \dot{Q}_h \cdot \beta_{O_2} \cdot \Delta P_{O_2}$). The $O_2$ transporting role of Hb, however, also depends on its qualitative properties, namely (*a*) its intrinsic $O_2$ binding properties and (*b*) its interaction with factors that modulate these properties inside the red cells. Ectotherm erythrocytes contain a full complement of cellular apparatus (including nucleus, mitochondria, and endoplasmic reticulum), exhibit high metabolic activity compared to mammalian erythrocytes, and greater potential for feedback regulation of tissue $O_2$ supply via cellular metabolites that affect Hb-$O_2$ affinity.

The molecular properties of Hb have been dealt with in recent treatises (1, 77, 84, 107). This review focuses on the physiological function of ectotherm Hb in the red blood cells, particularly the inter- and intraspecific adaptations to exogenous and endogenous factors like ambient hypoxia (low $O_2$ tension), temperature, activity, and dormancy, and illustrates these with representative examples.

0066-4278/88/0315-0161$02.00

# BASIC CONCEPTS IN HEMOGLOBIN STRUCTURE AND FUNCTION

The Hb molecule is exquisitely engineered to optimize the transport of $O_2$ via cooperative homotropic interactions (which are basic to the sigmoidal Hb-$O_2$ equilibrium curve and increase capacitance), and heterotropic interactions with allosteric effectors like $CO_2$, protons, chloride, and certain polyanionic organic phosphates which decrease $O_2$ affinity (i.e. increase the half-saturation $O_2$ tension, $P_{50}$) (cf Figures 1 and 2). Recent studies demonstrate important roles of cellular responses that modulate Hb function via changes in its erythrocytic microenvironment. In mammalian and avian red cells the major erythrocytic phosphate modulators are 2,3-diphosphoglycerate (DPG) and inositol pentaphosphate (IPP), respectively. In contrast, in ectothermic

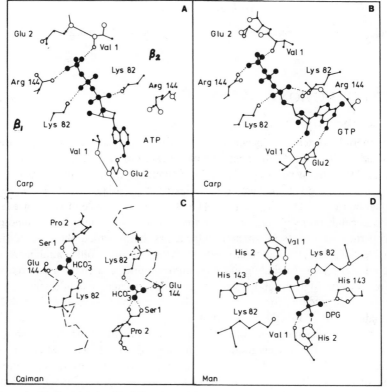

*Figure 1*    Binding sites for (A) ATP and (B) GTP to carp Hb, (C) for $HCO_3^-$ to caiman Hb, and (D) for DPG to human Hb A. Filled circles indicate the individual allosteric effectors (Modified after References 5, 36, and 77.)

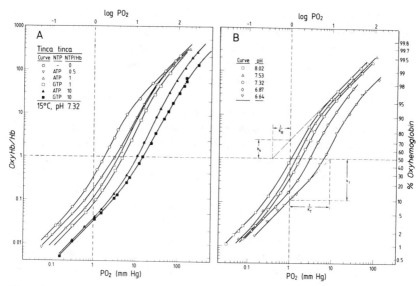

*Figure 2*   Hill plots of precise $O_2$ equilibria of tench Hb at (A) various ATP/Hb and GTP/Hb ratios, and (B) different pH values, showing construction lines for graphical evaluation of the association equilibrium constants for the Hb in T and R states ($K_T$ and $K_R$) and for binding the first and fourth $O_2$ molecules ($k_1$ and $k_4$). (After Reference 102.)

vertebrates the major modulator is ATP. Some ectotherms, however, also have guanosine triphosphate (GTP), other nucleoside triphosphates (NTP), DPG, and/or IPP (6, 41, 65, 99, 105). In crocodilians Hb-$O_2$ affinity is insensitive to organic phosphates but is strongly decreased by bicarbonate ions (7), and in the shark *Squalus* and the toad *Xenopus* the affinity is increased by erythrocytic urea (64, 108).

Most vertebrate Hbs are tetrameric, consisting of two $\alpha$ and two $\beta$ chains; however, cyclostome Hb is monomeric when oxygenated, and Hb from the primitive reptile *Sphenodon* appears to consist of only one type of chain (16, 77, 116). Despite species variation in the number of amino acid residues in the $\alpha$ and $\beta$ chains [142 and 147 in carp, 141 and 140 in adult bullfrog, and 141 and 146 in man (37, 98)], vertebrate Hbs exhibit a characteristic tertiary structure. Oxygenation is associated with a shift in quaternary structure from the tense (T) state (low-affinity, "deoxy") to the relaxed (R) state (high-affinity, "oxy"). Heterotropic ligands lower $O_2$ affinity by preferential binding to the T state, decreasing its $O_2$ affinity and delaying the T → R transition (cf 49, 77; see also Figure 2).

The ligand binding sites in human Hb A are well documented (77) and thus may serve as a basis for understanding molecular adaptations in ectotherms. In Hb A DPG binds to seven $\beta$-chain residues, namely $\beta$1 Val, $\beta$2 His, and

$\beta$143 His of both chains, and to $\beta$82 Lys of one $\beta$ chain. Binding of Bohr protons, which is basic to the Bohr effect (decrease in $O_2$ affinity at low pH that promotes unloading in the tissues), occurs mainly at residues $\alpha$1 Val, $\beta$82 Lys, and $\beta$146 His in the absence of phosphate and additionally at $\beta$2 His and $\beta$143 His in the presence of phosphate. Carbon dioxide undergoes oxylabile binding at the N-terminal residues of $\alpha$ and $\beta$ chains (valines in man) to form carbamate, while chloride binds at $\alpha$1 Val and $\beta$82 Lys (77).

Teleost Hbs have glutamic or aspartic acid at $\beta$2 and arginine at $\beta$144 (versus His at these positions in man), which creates a binding site that is stereochemically complementary to NTP (78). Modelling indicates that ATP forms five hydrogen bonds with carp deoxy-Hb (with $\beta_2$1 Val, $\beta_1$2 Glu, $\beta_1$144 Arg and $\beta_{1+2}$82 Lys). GTP forms an additional bond with $\beta_1$ Val (36; Figure 1), as predicted by the almost twofold greater effect of GTP versus ATP on fish Hb-$O_2$ affinity (36, 104–106). $\beta$93 Ser in fish Hbs (Cys in man) appears to be involved in the Root effect (decreased $O_2$ carrying capacity at low pH), which may be implicated in acid-induced secretion of $O_2$ in the swimbladder and eyes of fish (78). However, $\beta$93 Ser is also present in *Xenopus* Hb, which is reported to lack the Root effect (15).

Crocodilian Hbs bind two $HCO_3^-$ equivalents at the N terminus and adjacent $\beta$-chain residues, namely Ser-Pro in the caiman and Ac-Ala-Ser in the Nile crocodile and alligator (7, 77; Figure 1).

The effects of different ligands thus depend on competition for the same binding sites. Since the oxygenation of Hb is exothermic and linked to binding of $CO_2$ and protons, blood $O_2$ transport is integrally linked with heat, proton, and $CO_2$ transport.

Many ectothermic vertebrates express multiple $\alpha$- and $\beta$-type globin genes, resulting in multiple or heterogeneous Hbs (isoHbs). Hb heterogeneity and "polymorphism" (intraspecific differences in Hbs) provide a basis for a division of labor among component Hbs under different conditions.

## QUANTITATIVE ADAPTATIONS

Increased blood Hb concentrations raise the $O_2$ capacitance coefficient. This is an energetically inexpensive means of adjusting blood $O_2$ transport to increased $O_2$ demand. Parallel increases in viscosity may, however, set an upper limit on Hb concentration. The erythrocytic Hb and hematocrit (Hct) levels are lower in arctic than in temperate fish which may compensate for the higher blood viscosity at low ambient temperatures (114).

The lower blood [Hb] and Hct values in ectothermic than in homeothermic vertebrates accord with their lower metabolic rates but simultaneously confer a greater potential for adaptive increases in $O_2$ carrying capacity in stress situations. In teleosts the increases in blood [Hb] under the stress of severe exercise varies from about 10% in striped bass and tench (53, 72) to 30–35% in trout and yellowtail (94, 127). In contrast to the ubiquitous elevation in blood [Hb] in mammals under high altitude–induced hypoxia, aquatic hypoxia evokes variable responses in fishes: [Hb] remains unchanged in plaice, carp, and tench (57, 104, 122) but increases in eel, trout, and yellowtail (87, 120, 128). The increased [Hb] seen in fish that utilize air breathing (63, 111) may be triggered by associated internal hypoxia-hypercapnia (115). In amphibians $O_2$ capacities increase during exercise (68, 92) and enforced but not voluntary dives (11). The variable exploitation of the quantitative strategy in ectotherms implies the involvement of alternative mechanisms (e.g. $O_2$ affinity modulation).

Hemoconcentration may result from water shifts from the extracellular to the intracellular lactate-loaded tissue compartments, increased diuresis (94, 127), and/or a rapid release of stored erythrocytes via splenic contraction, which in the yellowtail can be visualized through an abdominal window (128). Erythropoeisis and synthesis of new Hb, which require a long time span, presumably can only be involved in long-term adaptation.

# QUALITATIVE ADAPTATIONS

## Organic Phosphate Modulation

Changes in allosteric effectors provide a means of rapidly adapting Hb function to tissue $O_2$ demand. Organic phosphates are the most important heterotropic effectors in ectothermic vertebrates.

$O_2$ AVAILABILITY    Ambient hypoxia decreases red cell [NTP] in fish and amphibians, which raises $O_2$ affinity directly via decreased allosteric interaction and indirectly via an altered Donnan distribution of protons across the red cells that increases red cell pH (32, 55, 87, 104, 119, 120). This response is graded to the ambient $O_2$ tension (90) and serves to safeguard arterial $O_2$ loading and increase $O_2$ capacitance at low $O_2$ tensions. The time required to attain the new steady-state NTP level varies from hours to days (57, 87, 91, 104), depending on the species and the acuteness of the ambient $O_2$ change.

Whereas ATP is the major NTP effector in fish like rainbow trout and dogfish sharks, GTP is the main modulator in species like eel, carp, tench, and goldfish (30, 55, 65, 104–106, 112), which experience a wide variety of ambient $O_2$ tensions in nature. Where both NTPs coexist, a greater modulating role for GTP follows from greater environmentally induced changes in its concentration, (57, 62, 104–106, 111), its greater effect on $P_{50}$ of fish Hb (104–106, 111), and a lesser inhibition of this effect by divalent cations like $Mg^{2+}$ (which form complexes with NTP) and $CO_2$ (which competes with NTP for binding to the $\alpha$-amino groups of the $\beta$ chains) (104, 107).

In the catfish *Hypostomus*, which switches to gut air breathing in hypoxic water, increases in blood $O_2$ affinity via decreased erythrocytic NTP may compensate for lower efficiency of $O_2$ transfer across the gut wall and increase $O_2$ extraction from swallowed air (111). In the estivating lungfish *Protopterus*, on the contrary, the drastic NTP-induced increase in blood $O_2$ affinity (62) may serve to decrease $O_2$ unloading and contribute to the reduction in metabolic rate.

Hb-$O_2$ affinity in burrowing terrestrial ectotherms may similarly be adapted to microenvironmental gas tensions. The apodan amphibian *Boulengerula* inhabiting hypoxic-hypercapnic fossorial habitats has Hb with high intrinsic $O_2$ affinity and small Bohr and phosphate effects (125). Hb of the burrowing reptile, *Amphisbaena* also exhibits high affinity but has high ATP sensitivity, reflecting a large scope for adaptive $O_2$ affinity modulation (60).

Phosphates may also adapt to internal hypoxia resulting from obstruction of gill gas exchange caused by pollutants such as zinc (88) and aluminium in acid water (resulting from acid rain), which in tench elicits a selective reduction in GTP (58).

TEMPERATURE     In ectotherms acute temperature rise decreases $O_2$ affinity directly due to overall exothermy of Hb oxygenation (cf Figure 3), and indirectly due to the associated pH decrease (cf Figure 4). Thus in the alligator the apparent heat of oxygenation $[\Delta H^{app} = R\ln\Delta\log P_{50}/\Delta\,(1/T)]$ at different temperatures and in vivo pH conditions (including the Bohr effect contributions) is almost double that at constant pH $[-47$ and $-24$ kJ/mol $O_2$, respectively (110)].

Temperature acclimation influences erythrocytic NTP and $P_{50}$ and thus temperature sensitivity, but the responses differ. In the Australian blackfish, the eel, neotenic *Ambystoma* salamanders, and the snake *Vipera*, warm

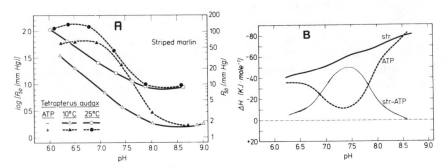

*Figure 3*     (A) Influence of pH and ATP on $P_{50}$ values of striped marlin Hb at 10 and 25°C. (B) $\Delta H$ values calculated for this temperature interval in the absence and presence of ATP, and the difference curve (R. E. Weber, S. C. Wood & C. Daxboeck, unpublished data).

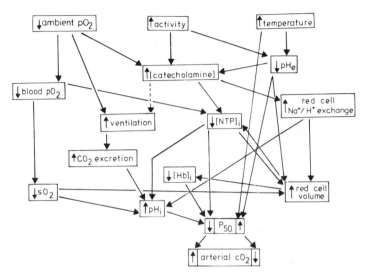

*Figure 4*   Some mechanisms by which ambient $P_{O_2}$, temperature, and activity can influence Hb-$O_2$ affinity in the blood of ectothermic vertebrates. ( ↑ indicates an increase in affinity ↓ indicates a decrease.)

acclimation increases blood NTP and $P_{50}$ measured at the same temperature (23, 61, 119). This causes greater $P_{50}$ changes in acclimated animals than in acutely exposed specimens and suggests adaptive increases in unloading as $O_2$ demand increases with temperature. In the brown bullhead, the killifish, the antarctic *Trematomus,* carp, and pancake tortoise (4, 32, 33, 124), however, the opposite response lowers the temperature effect in fully acclimated animals and may be construed as an adaptation to ensure $O_2$ loading at the respiratory surfaces at high temperature.

ACTIVITY   Little information is available on the effect of activity on phosphate effectors in ectotherms. Neither short-term bursts of activity in tench (54) nor 200 days' sustained swimming in trout (22) alter NTP content. The liberation of stored red cells in fish upon physical exertion (127) could modulate blood affinity given that splenic $O_2$ conditions may influence red cell NTP. The polyanionic phosphates raise the Bohr factor (via increased binding at low pH; cf Figure 3), which increases $O_2$ unloading in response to the slightly lower pH of blood perfusing the highly buffered muscles of fast-swimming fish (24).

ONTOGENETIC DEVELOPMENT   Changes in the red cell phosphate pool, sometimes acting in concert with changes in component Hbs, may be basic to ontogenetic changes in Hb function. The bullfrog tadpole has Hb with high phosphate sensitivity and high red cell concentrations of NTP, DPG, and IPP. These features reflect a large capacity for regulatory control of $O_2$ affinity in its euryoxic aquatic environment (40, 97). In contrast, the adult Hb exhibits low, relatively constant, intrinsic $O_2$ affinity, due in part to the fact that the $\beta$ chains lack the N-terminal amino acids that normally bind the phosphate effectors (40, 89). A parallel situation is encountered in the oviparous Logger-head and Green sea turtles: Late-stage embryos have appreciable red cell DPG concentrations and high-affinity, phosphate-sensitive Hbs, whereas the adults have low DPG and IPP levels and low-affinity, phosphate-insensitive Hbs (51).

Phosphate effects may similarly underly maternal-fetal differences in blood $O_2$ affinity (and thus $O_2$ transfer) in some viviparous ectotherms, as in the apodan amphibian *Typhlonectes compressicauda,* the skink *Phenomorphus quoyii,* and the snake *Agkistrodon piscivorus,* in which the maternal and fetal Hbs appear to be identical (8, 28, 35). Among viviparous teleosts, fetal seaperch *Embiotoca lateralis* have Hbs of higher intrinsic affinity and lower NTP concentrations than do adults (50). In the blenny *Zoarces viviparous* the affinity shift is entirely attributable to differences in the Hb (101).

## Effects and Transport of Protons, $CO_2$ and $HCO_3^-$

PROTONS AND $CO_2$    Metabolic and respiratory acidoses may both increase tissue $O_2$ unloading and hamper $O_2$ loading at the gas exchange surfaces via oxygenation-linked proton and $CO_2$ binding (above). Accordingly, the literature abounds with alleged, often contradictory, examples of inter- and intraspecific adaptations in these effects.

Ambient hypercapnia acutely decreases ectotherm blood pH (and thus $O_2$ affinity), which generally is compensated completely in fish (within one to several days) and partly in amphibians and reptiles, by $HCO_3^-$ accumulation (42). Blood pH may also fall drastically due to lactic acid increases under activity or submersion [up to 200 mM in the turtle *Chrysemys picta bellii* in hypoxic water (95)]. Lactate depresses the $O_2$ affinity of human Hb (38) but exerts no significant specific effect on tench Hb oxygenation (R. E. Weber, unpublished).

The specific effect of $CO_2$ increases at high pH, under which condition the implicated amino groups are uncharged, resulting in lower $CO_2$ Bohr effects ($\phi_{CO_2}$) than fixed-acid Bohr effects ($\phi_{FA}$) in Hb solutions. In teleost Hbs the specific $CO_2$ effect generally is physiologically insignificant because of the low blood $CO_2$ tensions in water breathers and because acetylation of the $\alpha$-amino groups of the $\alpha$ chains limits $CO_2$ binding to the corresponding $\beta$-chain groups, where it must compete with phosphate binding (25, 104). In Hbs of lungfish [in which $CO_2$ tensions may rise to 60 mm Hg during estivation (103)], carp, tench, and of Green and Loggerhead turtles, the $CO_2$

effect is eliminated or drastically reduced by ATP or GTP at physiological pH and NTP/Hb ratios (55, 66, 104, 107). NTP, however, increases the Bohr effect (cf 28, 55, 104, 108) and the Root effect in fish (100), with GTP exerting a greater effect than ATP (96). In eel Hb, moreover, the $CO_2$ Root effect exceeds the fixed-acid Root effect below pH 6.5 (14).

The notion that large Bohr factors correlate with diving, permitting efficient utilization of $O_2$ reserves during submersion, holds true for crocodilians (34, 110); but no such correlation is found in snakes, turtles, or lizards (cf 107, 123).

In ectothermic as in homeothermic vertebrates blood $CO_2$ transport is mediated by the Jacobs-Stewart cycle, in which red cell carbonic anhydrase catalyzes the reversible hydration of $CO_2$ to produce protons that are buffered by Hb, and $HCO_3^-$ that is exchanged with plasma $Cl^-$ (82). The lower blood Hb concentration in ectotherms than in mammals is consistent with a lower blood $CO_2$ capacitance coefficient at the same $P_{CO_2}$ (113) and a lower nonbicarbonate buffer value (2). Apart from their lower concentration, the Hbs of eel, carp, tench, and trout have lower buffer values due to a smaller number of titratable groups in the oxy as well as deoxy conformations at physiological pH (12, 20, 56; F. B. Jensen, unpublished). In these fish Hbs, however, the reduced $H^+$ binding at fixed protein conformation is compensated by larger Haldane effects (greater proton uptake upon deoxygenation). ATP and GTP further increase this oxygenation-linked proton binding (13, 56). The Haldane effect thus seems of greater significance for proton and $CO_2$ transport in fish than in mammals.

$HCO_3^-$ EFFECTS IN CROCODILIANS    In contrast to $O_2$ linked $CO_2$ binding, which increases with pH and lowers $\phi_{CO_2}$, $HCO_3^-$ binding to crocodilian Hb increases with proton concentration (7), raising the $HCO_3^-$ Bohr factor. In the alligator, $\phi_{HCO_3}$ greatly exceeds $\phi_{FA}$ [$-0.95$ and $-0.20$, respectively (110)]. The low $\phi_{FA}$ safeguards the relatively high blood $O_2$ affinity under conditions of large activity-induced acidoses (34, 85, 110). The $HCO_3^-$ effect may, however, represent an adaptation to bone consumption and the associated $Cl^-$ secretion into the stomach in exchange for $HCO_3^-$, which raises blood pH. The binding of $HCO_3^-$ to Hb neutralizes the adverse effects of the "alkaline tide" on $O_2$ unloading and may even contribute to the increased $O_2$ consumption following feeding (110).

The oxygenation-linked unloading of $HCO_3^-$ in the lungs implicit in the $HCO_3^-$ effect indicates a unique role for crocodilian Hb in $CO_2$ transport.

## Control Mechanisms of Allosteric Effectors

As interpreted in terms of the two-state model (69), ATP and GTP at physiological NTP/Hb (tetramer) ratios decrease the $O_2$ affinity of tench Hb by lowering the association equilibrium constant of the T state ($K_T$) without significantly affecting that of the R state ($K_R$) and by increasing the allosteric constant, $L$ (102). These effects are similar to those of DPG on human Hb A (cf 49). In contrast to the DPG effect in Hb A, however, ATP and GTP at high NTP/Hb ratios also decrease $K_R$ (102), correlating with their effects on the Root effect (96, 100). The greater effect of GTP than ATP on the $P_{50}$ of fish Hb thus correlates with greater effects of GTP in the T as well as the R state (102). Increased proton concentrations have similar effects on $K_T$, $K_R$, and $L$ (19, 102), and both NTP and protons delay the major conformational change until the third heme group has been oxygenated (102).

## Temperature Effects and Heat Transport

The overall heat of oxygenation is the sum of the intrinsic heat of oxygenation, $\Delta H^{intr}$, the heat of solution of $O_2$, $\Delta H^{sol}$ (which are exothermic), and endothermic contributions from proton and phosphate dissociation, $\Sigma \Delta X^A \Delta H^A$, where $\Delta X^A$ is the number of effector ions displaced and $\Delta H^A$ is the heat of displacement (cf 49). The temperature sensitivity of Hb oxygenation thus is reduced under natural conditions by endothermic displacement of heterotropic effectors (48, 49, 55, 109; see also Figure 3).

In tench Hb at physiological pH and NTP/Hb ratio, the major release of NTP upon oxygenation of the third heme group renders this step endothermic, even though the overall oxygenation reaction remains exothermic because of the negative $\Delta H$ values at oxygenation steps 1, 2, and 4 (59). In tuna Hb, however, pronounced endothermic release of Bohr protons at both steps 3 and 4 overrides the earlier exothermic oxygenation events (48), whereby the large number of Bohr groups appears to explain the small, inverse temperature effect in tuna Hb (18, 48). In another fast-swimming fish, the striped marlin, $\Delta H^{app}$ is $-78$ kJ/mol $O_2$ at high pH, where ATP and Bohr proton binding is negligible, is reduced to about $-48$ kJ/mol at pH 7.3 as a result of Bohr proton release, and approaches zero in the presence of ATP (Figure 3). Thus the in vivo temperature sensitivity is small due to both ATP and proton displacement. The reduction in $\Delta H$ in the presence of ATP reflects a greater stabilization of the T state by ATP at lower temperatures (59). In trout Hb I the weak temperature sensitivity is attributable to endothermic conformational changes in the T state, which reverses the temperature effect at low saturation (126).

The fact that the oxygenation reaction in blood is usually exothermic implies that the heat liberated at the gas exchange surfaces is transported from the tissues by Hb. The lack of temperature sensitivity in Hbs from tunas and lamnid sharks that are warm-bodied (17) may contribute to heat conservation as well as preventing gas emboly when cold efferent blood enters the warm body core (cf 46).

## Functional Hemoglobin Heterogeneity

Multiple Hbs with different functional properties, as may be encountered in teleosts, amphibians, and turtles (80, 83, 97, 106, 112), increase the scope of $O_2$, proton, and heat transport in blood. In fish like trout, eel, and some catfish (80, 105), cathodal Hb components that have high, pH-insensitive $O_2$ affinities may transport $O_2$ under conditions of internal hypoxia and acidosis, whereas the low-affinity, pH-sensitive anodal Hb components unload $O_2$ under normoxic conditions with high $O_2$ demand.

Alterations in the relative abundances of isoHbs provide a further mechanism for functional adaptation. In teleosts isoHb changes commonly accompany temperature acclimation (47). In trout the abundances of isoHbs also depends on day length and acclimation to hypoxic conditions (93). In the mudfish *Labeo umbratus,* four weeks' hypoxia induces the synthesis of cathodal Hb (39), which has a significantly higher $O_2$ affinity than the anodal Hbs (R. E. Weber, unpublished). Goldfish exhibit two major Hbs at water temperatures $< 10°C$ but three Hbs at higher temperatures. This change, however, also occurs in cell-free conditions, which suggests that altered subunit combination rather than de novo Hb synthesis is involved (47). Mixing of the two major Hbs isolated from the turtle *Chrysemys,* which have distinctly different $O_2$ affinities, results in properties similar to only one of the Hbs (R. E. Weber, unpublished). These findings caution against basing predictions of the functional properties of composite cellular Hbs on the properties of the individual Hbs.

Functional heterogeneity may also result from partial oxidation. Some ectotherms show elevated metHb concentrations (31); in garter snakes a higher $O_2$ affinity in the fetus than in the adult is attributable to metHb (79). Multiple aggregation states may also be responsible for the functional heterogeneity of Hbs. For example, in vitro preparations Hbs of *Squalus acanthias* (shark) and *Liophis Miliaris* (water snake) are dimeric, but they become tetrameric upon deoxygenation and in the presence of ATP (27, 67).

# CELLULAR REGULATORY MECHANISMS

## Organic Phosphate Modulation

Glycolytic synthesis and degradation of 2,3-DPG are well understood in anuclear mammalian erythrocytes (29), whereas the cellular mechanisms involved in the in vivo modulation of ATP and/or GTP in the nucleated red cells of ectotherms remain largely unresolved.

It appears that hypoxia does not decrease blood NTP directly via impeded oxidative phosphorylation *in vivo,* as the NTP pool in fish erythrocytes in vitro is reduced only in the absence of oxygen (32, 57), whereas erythrocytes in vivo are exposed to low capillary $O_2$ tensions for only a few seconds. This observation suggests that other organismic factors are involved (90). [ATP] is reduced in adrenergically stimulated trout red cells (70); however, the [ATP] change may be a transient side effect of increased red cell metabolism. That GTP $\leftrightarrow$ ATP conversion may be involved in the adaptive modulation of Hb-$O_2$ affinity follows from the selective reductions in GTP (see above) and the presence of nucleoside diphosphokinase and nucleoside monophosphate kinase in fish erythrocytes (cf 99). However, as the conversion is an equilibrium reaction, the mechanism regulating NTP abundance may reside at other levels in the biosynthetic and degradative pathways of the nucleotides.

## Donnan Effects

In vertebrates $H^+$, $Cl^-$, and $HCO^-_3$ are generally passively distributed across the red cell membranes (3, 43, 44, 68), and the Donnan distribution ratios are dictated by the nonpermeable negative charges carried by the cellular hemoglobin and organic phosphates. This causes much lower pH values in red cells than in plasma and reduces the dependence of $pH_i$ on $pH_e$ ($\Delta pH_i/\Delta pH_e$ becomes less than unity) in teleosts (4, 55, 90, 121), elasmobranchs (117), and amphibians (64, 118, 119). In contrast, in the lamprey $pH_i$ is actively maintained above $pH_e$, and the $H^+$ and $Cl^-$ distribution ratios show a large difference (71). Under hypoxic conditions this compensates for the lack of phosphate-mediated $P_{50}$ regulation (75).

The hypoxia-induced reduction in erythrocytic organic phosphates in fish and amphibians elevates $r_{H^+}$ ($[H^+]_e/[H^+]_i$) and red cell pH, which increases the blood $O_2$ affinity via the Bohr effect (Figure 4). This pH effect may be more important than the direct allosteric effect (121).

A reduction in the level of Hb-$O_2$ saturation, as occurs in hypoxia, in itself raises red cell pH as a result of the increase in $r_{H^+}$ caused by the Haldane effect (Figure 4). This effect is especially important in teleosts (4, 52), in which Haldane effects are large and red cell buffer capacities are low (52). In tench it predominates between 50 and 100% Hb-$O_2$ saturation because of the uptake and release of most Bohr protons at high Hb saturations (102) and contributes significantly to the increased arterial red cell pH, despite plasma pH decreases, observed in hypoxic fish (58).

## Swelling

Increases in the Donnan distribution ratios of diffusible ions with decreases in plasma pH, the level of Hb-$O_2$ saturation, and cellular organic phosphate concentration raise the erythrocytic concentration of osmotically active particles ($Cl^-$ and $HCO^-_3$), resulting in an influx of water and cell swelling (cf Figure 4).

Red cells of fish subjected to environmental hypoxia swell rapidly and typically remain swollen throughout long-term severe hypoxia (45, 55, 57, 86); they revert to their original volume when normoxia returns (57). Swelling may also occur in fish and amphibians as a result of exercise-stress (68, 72, 81). Although swelling does not alter the NTP/Hb ratio, it decreases the cellular hemoglobin and NTP concentrations and Hb-NTP complexing, all of which promote an increase in blood $O_2$ affinity (99, 112; see Figure 4), as shown for purified carp Hb and ATP (104).

$\beta$-ADRENERGIC SWELLING    Apart from the Donnan effects described above, red cell swelling can be induced by catecholamine binding to glycoproteinaceous $\beta$-adrenergic receptors in the red cell membranes. In teleosts (9, 21, 73) and amphibians (76) the mechanism of swelling is rapid catecholamine activation of a $Na^+$-$H^+$ countertransporter, which causes cellular $Na^+$ influx and $H^+$ efflux. This activates the exchange of cellular $HCO_3^-$ for plasma $Cl^-$ mediated by band 3 protein in the cell membrane, resulting in a net $Na^+$-$Cl^-$ influx coupled with water influx. The $Na^+$-$H^+$ countertransport alkalinizes the red cell cytoplasm, and thus is implicated in the control of $O_2$ affinity, when it overrides the opposite pH effects of the $HCO_3^-$-$Cl^-$ exchange. Under stressful conditions in vivo, catecholamines are released, and provided $Na^+$-$H^+$ exchange dominates, Hb-$O_2$ affinity and capacity are increased via $pH_i$ (Bohr and Root effects), thus safeguarding arterial $O_2$ loading (see Figure 4). Indeed, striped bass (72) and trout (81) subjected to acidotic exercise-stress exhibit higher red cell pH values and arterial $O_2$ contents and lower in vivo $\Delta pH_i/\Delta pH_e$ compared to specimens in which $\beta$-adrenergic responses are blocked by propranolol. Similar effects are induced in trout by in vivo acidosis per se (10) and by hypoxia (26).

The magnitude and importance of this in vivo response, however, vary with species. In tench in normoxic water, $\Delta pH_i/\Delta pH_e$ is not affected by exercise stress, and adrenaline injection neither elevates red cell pH nor causes red cell swelling. During exercise, however, the lack of an $O_2$ affinity response to adrenaline appears to be compensated for by increased arterial $P_{O_2}$ (53). In trout and carp the $\beta$-adrenergic responses depend upon season (74) and low $O_2$ tension, respectively (A. Salama & M. Nikinmaa, unpublished results). Also, in amphibians the responses appear to be absent in vivo (92), despite the demonstrated existence of the ionic exchange mechanisms in vitro.

## CONCLUDING REMARKS

The maze of major direct, indirect, acute, and chronic changes affecting Hb function in ectothermic vertebrates as induced by environmental conditions (e.g. $O_2$ availability, temperature), metabolic states, and endogenous factors (e.g. activity, dormancy, and developmental stage) are summarized in Figure

4. The time constants of the different responses vary. Generally, acute stresses are met with rapid organismic, cellular, and molecular adjustments (e.g. red cell swelling and recruitment, ventilatory alkalosis, and changes in Hb subunit composition), whereas long-term perturbations evoke slower compensatory responses (e.g. qualitative and quantitative changes in allosteric phosphate effectors and de novo Hb synthesis).

ACKNOWLEDGMENTS

This study was supported by grants 11-5553 (REW) and 11-5844 (FBJ) from the Danish Natural Science Research Council.

*Literature Cited*

1. Ackers, G. K., Smith, F. R. 1985. Effects of site-specific amino acid modification on protein interactions and biological function. *Ann. Rev. Biochem.* 54:597–629
2. Albers, C. 1970. Acid-base balance. In *Fish Physiology,* ed. W. S. Hoar, D. J. Randall, 4:173–208. New York/London: Academic
3. Albers, C., Goetz, K. G. 1985. $H^+$ and $Cl^-$ ion equilibria across the red cell membrane in the carp. *Respir. Physiol.* 61:209–19
4. Albers, C., Goetz, K.-H., Hughes, G. M. 1983. Effect of acclimation temperature on intraerythrocytic acid-base balance and nucleoside triphosphates in the carp, *Cyprinus carpio. Respir. Physiol.* 54:145–49
5. Arnone, A. 1972. X-ray diffraction study of binding of 2,3-diphosphoglycerate to human deoxyhemoglobin. *Nature* 237:146–49
6. Bartlett, G. R. 1978. Water soluble phosphates of red cells. *Can. J. Zool.* 56:870–77
7. Bauer, C., Forster, M., Gros, G., Mosca, A., Perrella, M., et al. 1981. Analysis of bicarbonate binding to crocodilian hemoglobin. *J. Biol. Chem.* 256:8429–35
8. Birchard, G. F., Black, C. P., Schuett, G. W., Black, V. 1984. Fetal maternal blood respiratory properties of an ovoviviparous snake the cottonmouth, *Agkistrodon piscivorus. J. Exp. Biol.* 108:247–55
9. Borgese, F., Garcia-Romeu, F., Motais, R. 1986. Catecholamine-induced transport systems in trout erythrocyte. $Na^+/H^+$ countertransport or NaCl cotransport? *J. Gen. Physiol.* 87:551–60
10. Boutilier, R. G., Iwama, G. K., Randall, D. J. 1986. The promotion of catacholamine release in rainbow trout, *Salmo gairdneri,* by acute acidosis: Interactions between red cell pH and haemoglobin oxygen-carrying capacity. *J. Exp. Biol.* 123:145–57
11. Boutilier, R. G., Shelton, G. 1986. Respiratory properties of blood from voluntarily and forcibly submerged *Xenopus laevis. J. Exp. Biol.* 121:285–300
12. Breepoel, P. M., Kreuzer, F., Hazevoet, M. 1980. Studies of the hemoglobins of the eel *(Anguilla anguilla* L.)—I. Proton binding of stripped hemolysate; separation and properties of two major components. *Comp. Biochem. Physiol. A* 65:69–75
13. Breepoel, P. M., Kreuzer, F., Hazevoet, M. 1981. Studies of the hemoglobins of the eel *(Anguilla anguilla)*—III. Proton and organic phosphate binding to the Root effect hemoglobin component. *Comp. Biochem. Physiol. A* 69:709–12
14. Bridges, C. R., Hlastala, M. P., Riepl, G., Scheid, P. 1983. Root effect induced by $CO_2$ and fixed acid in the blood of the eel, *Anguilla anguilla. Respir. Physiol.* 51:275–86
15. Bridges, C. R., Pelster, B., Scheid, P. 1985. Oxygen binding in blood of *Xenopus laevis* (amphibia) and evidence against Root effect. *Respir. Physiol.* 61:125–36
16. Briehl, R. W. 1963. The relation between oxygen equilibrium and aggregation of subunits in lamprey hemoglobin. *J. Biol. Chem.* 238:2361–66
17. Carey, F. G., Teal, J. M., Kanwisher, J. W., Lawson, K. D., Beckett, J. S. 1971. Warm-bodied fish. *Am. Zool.* 11:137–45
18. Cech, J. J., Laurs, R. M., Graham, J. B. 1984. Temperature induced changes in blood gas equilibria in the albacore, *Thunnus alalunga,* a warm-bodied tuna. *J. Exp. Biol.* 109:21–34

19. Chien, J. C. W., Mayo, K. H. 1980. Carp hemoglobin. I. Precise oxygen equilibrium and analysis according to the models of Adair and of Monod, Wyman and Changeux. *J. Biol. Chem.* 255:9790–99

20. Chien, J. C. W., Mayo, K. H. 1980. Carp hemoglobin. II. The alkaline Bohr effect. *J. Biol. Chem.* 255:9800–6

21. Cossins, A. R., Richardson, P. A. 1985. Adrenaline-induced $Na^+/H^+$ exchange in trout erythrocytes and its effects upon oxygen-carrying capacity. *J. Exp. Biol.* 118:229–46

22. Davie, P. S., Wells, R. M. G., Tetens, V. 1986. Effects of sustained swimming on rainbow trout muscle structure, blood oxygen transport and lactate dehydrogenase isoenzymes: Evidence for increased aerobic capacity of white muscle. *J. Exp. Zool.* 237:159–71

23. Dobson, G. P., Baldwin, J. 1982. Regulation of blood oxygen affinity in the Australian blackfish *Gadopsis marmoratus*. II. Thermal acclimation. *J. Exp. Biol.* 99:245–54

24. Dobson, G. P., Wood, S. C., Daxboeck, C., Perry, S. F. 1986. Intracellular buffering and oxygen transport in the Pacific blue marlin *(Makaira nigricans):* Adaptations to high-speed swimming. *Physiol. Zool.* 59:150–56

25. Farmer, M. 1979. The transition from water to air breathing: Effects of $CO_2$ on hemoglobin function. *Comp. Biochem. Physiol. A* 62:109–14

26. Fievet, B., Motais, R., Thomas, S. 1987. Role of adrenergic-dependent $H^+$ release from red cells in acidosis induced by hypoxia in trout. *Am. J. Physiol.* 252:R269–75

27. Fyhn, U. E. H., Sullivan, B. 1975. Elasmobranch hemoglobins: Dimerization and polymerization in various species. *Comp. Biochem. Physiol. B* 50:119–29

28. Garlick, R. L., Davis, B. J., Farmer, M., Fyhn, H. J., Fyhn, U. E. H., et al. 1979. A fetal-maternal shift in the oxygen equilibrium of hemoglobin from the viviparous caecilian, *Typhlonectes compressicaudus*. *Comp. Biochem. Physiol. A* 62:239–44

29. Gerlach, E., Duhm, J. 1972. 2,3-DPG metabolism of red cells: Regulation and adaptive changes during hypoxia. In *Oxygen Affinity of Hemoglobin and Red Cell Acid Base Status*, ed. M. Rorth, P. Astrup, pp. 552–69. Copenhagen: Munksgaard

30. Geoghegan, W. D., Poluhowich, J. J. 1974. The major erythrocytic organic phosphates of the American eel, *Anguilla rostrata*. *Comp. Biochem. Physiol. B* 49:281–90

31. Graham, M. S., Fletcher, G. L. 1986. High concentrations of methemoglobin in five species of temperate marine teleosts. *J. Exp. Zool.* 239:139–42

32. Greaney, G. S., Powers, D. A. 1978. Allosteric modifiers of fish hemoglobins: In vitro and in vivo studies of the effect of ambient oxygen and pH on erythrocyte ATP concentrations. *J. Exp. Zool.* 203:339–50

33. Grigg, G. C. 1969. Temperature induced changes in the oxygen equilibrium curve of the blood of the brown bullhead *Ictalurus nebulosus*. *Comp. Biochem. Physiol.* 29:1203–23

34. Grigg, G. C., Cairncross, M. 1980. Respiratory properties of the blood of *Crocodylus porosus*. *Respir. Physiol.* 41:367–80

35. Grigg, G. C., Harlow, P. 1981. A fetal-maternal shift of blood oxygen affinity in an Australian viviparous lizard, *Spenomorphus quoyii* (Reptilia, Scincidae). *J. Comp. Physiol.* 142:495–99

36. Gronenborn, A. G., Clore, G. M., Brunori, M., Giardina, B., Falcioni, G., Perutz, M. 1984. Stereochemistry of ATP and GTP bound to fish haemoglobins. *J. Mol. Biol.* 178:731–42

37. Grujic-Injac, B., Braunitzer, G., Stangl, A. 1979. Die Sequenz der $\beta_A$- und $\beta_B$-Ketten der Hamoglobine des Karpfens (*Cyprinus carpio* L.) *Hoppe-Seyler's Z. Physiol. Chem.* 360:609–12

38. Guesnon, P., Poyart, C., Bursaux, E., Bohn, B. 1979. The binding of lactate and chloride ions to human adult hemoglobin. *Respir. Physiol.* 38:115–29

39. Hattingh, J. 1976. Haemoglobins in *Labeo umbratus:* The influence of temperature and oxygen. *S. Afr. J. Sci.* 72:27–28

40. Hazard, E. S., Hutchison, V. H. 1978. Ontogenetic changes in erythrocytic organic phosphates in the bullfrog, *Rana catesbeiana*. *J. Exp. Zool.* 206:109–18

41. Hazard, E. S., Hutchison, V. H. 1982. Distribution of acid-soluble phosphates in the erythrocytes of selected species of amphibians. *Comp. Biochem. Physiol. A* 73:111–24

42. Heisler, N. 1986. Comparative aspects of acid-base regulation. In *Acid-Base Regulation in Animals*, ed. N. Heisler, pp. 397–450. Amsterdam: Elsevier

43. Heming, T. A., Randall, D. J., Boutilier, R. G., Iwama, G. K., Primmett, D. R. N. 1986. Ionic equilibria in red blood cells of rainbow trout *(Salmo gairdneri):* $Cl^-$, $HCO_3^-$ and $H^+$. *Respir. Physiol.* 65:223–34

44. Hladky, S. B., Rink, T. J. 1977. pH equilibrium across the red cell membrane. In *Membrane Transport in Red Cells*, ed. J. C. Ellory, V. L. Lew, pp. 115–35. London: Academic
45. Holeton, G. F., Randall, D. J. 1967. The effect of hypoxia upon the partial pressure of gases in the blood and water afferent and efferent to the gills of rainbow trout. *J. Exp. Biol.* 46:317–27
46. Hochachka, P. W., Somero, G. N. 1973. *Strategies in Biochemial Adaptation*. Philadelphia: Saunders
47. Houston, A. H. 1980. Components of the hematological response of fishes to environmental temperature change: A review. In *Environmental Physiology of Fishes*, ed. A. Ali, pp. 241–98. New York: Plenum
48. Ikeda-Saito, M., Yonetani, T., Gibson, Q. H. 1983. Oxygen equilibrium studies on hemoglobin from the bluefin tuna *(Thunnus thunnus)*. *J. Mol. Biol.* 168:673–86
49. Imai, K. 1982. *Allosteric Effects in Hemoglobin*. Cambridge: Cambridge Univ. Press. 275 pp.
50. Ingermann, R. I., Terwilliger, R. C. 1981. Intraerythrocytic organic phosphates of fetal and adult seaperch *(Embiotoca lateralis):* Their role in maternal-fetal oxygen transport. *J. Comp. Physiol.* 144:253–59
51. Isaacks, R. E., Harkness, D. R., Witham, P. R. 1978. Relationship between the major phosphorylated metabolic intermediates and oxygen affinity of whole blood in the Loggerhead *(Caretta caretta)* and the Green sea turtle *(Chelonia mydas)* during development. *Dev. Biol.* 62:293–300
52. Jensen, F. B. 1986. Pronounced influence of Hb-$O_2$ saturation on red cell pH in tench blood in vivo and in vitro. *J. Exp. Zool.* 238:119–24
53. Jensen, F. B. 1987. Influences of exercise-stress and adrenaline upon intra- and extracellular acid-base status, electrolyte composition and respiratory properties of blood in tench *(Tinca tinca)* at different seasons. *J. Comp. Physiol. B* 157:51–60
54. Jensen, F. B., Nikinmaa, M., Weber, R. E. 1983. Effects of exercise stress on acid-base balance and respiratory function in blood of the teleost *Tinca tinca*. *Respir. Physiol.* 51:291–301
55. Jensen, F. B., Weber, R. E. 1982. Respiratory properties of tench blood and hemoglobin. Adaptation to hypoxic-hypercapnic water. *Mol. Physiol.* 2:235–50
56. Jensen, F. B., Weber, R. E. 1985. Proton and oxygen equilibria, their anion sensitivities and interrelationships in tench hemoglobin. *Mol. Physiol.* 7:41–50
57. Jensen, F. B., Weber, R. E. 1985. Kinetics of the acclimational responses of tench to combined hypoxia and hypercapnia. I. Respiratory responses. *J. Comp. Physiol. B* 156:197–203
58. Jensen, F. B., Weber, R. E. 1987. Internal hypoxia-hypercapnia in tench exposed to aluminium in acid water: Effects on blood gas transport, acid-base status and electrolyte composition in arterial blood. *J. Exp. Biol.* 127:427–42
59. Jensen, F. B., Weber, R. E. 1987. Thermodynamic analysis of precisely measured oxygen equilibria of tench *(Tinca tinca)* hemoglobin and their dependence on ATP and protons. *J. Comp. Physiol. B* 157:137–43
60. Johansen, K., Abe, A. S., Weber, R. E. 1980. Respiratory properties of whole blood and hemoglobin from the burrowing reptile, *Amphisbaena alba*. *J. Exp. Zool.* 214:71–77
61. Johansen, K., Lykkeboe, G. 1979. Thermal acclimation of aerobic metabolism and $O_2$-Hb binding in the snake, *Vipera berus*. *J. Comp. Physiol.* 130:293–300
62. Johansen, K., Lykkeboe, G., Weber, R. E., Maloiy, G. M. O. 1976. Respiratory properties of lungfish blood in awake and estivating lungfish, *Protopterus amphibius*. *Respir. Physiol.* 27:335–45
63. Johansen, K., Mangum, C. P., Lykkeboe, G. 1978. Respiratory properties of the blood of Amazonan fishes. *Can. J. Zool.* 56:898–906
64. Jokumsen, A., Weber, R. E. 1980. Hemoglobin-oxygen binding properties in the blood of *Xenopus laevis*, with special reference to the influences of estivation and salinity and temperature acclimation. *J. Exp. Biol.* 80:19–37
65. Leray, C. 1979. Patterns of purine nucleotides in fish erythrocytes. *Comp. Biochem. Physiol. B* 64:77–82
66. Lutz, P. L., Lapennas, G. N. 1982. Effects of pH, $CO_2$ and organic phosphates on oxygen affinity of sea turtle hemoglobins. *Respir. Physiol.* 48:75–87
67. Matsuura, M. S. A., Hatsushika, O., Focesi, A. 1987. Dimer-trimer transition in hemoglobins from *Liophis miliaris*. I. Effect of organic polyphosphates. *Comp. Biochem. Physiol. A* 86:683–87
68. McDonald, D. G., Boutilier, R. G., Toews, D. P. 1980. The effects of enforced activity on ventilation, circulation and blood acid-base balance in the semi-

terrestrial anuran, *Bufo marinus*. *J. Exp. Biol.* 84:273–87
69. Monod, J., Wyman, J., Changeux, J.-P. 1965. On the nature of allosteric transitions: A plausible model. *J. Mol. Biol.* 12:88–118
70. Nikinmaa, M. 1983. Adrenergic regulation of haemoglobin oxygen affinity in rainbow trout red cells. *J. Comp. Physiol.* 152:67–72
71. Nikinmaa, M. 1986. Red cell pH of lamprey *(Lampetra fluviatilis)* is actively regulated. *J. Comp. Physiol. B* 156: 747–50
72. Nikinmaa, M., Cech, J. J. Jr., McEnroe, M. 1984. Blood oxygen transport in stressed striped bass *(Morone saxatilis):* Role of beta-adrenergic responses. *J. Comp. Physiol. B* 154:365–69
73. Nikinmaa, M., Huestis, W. H. 1984. Adreneric swelling of nucleated erythrocytes: Cellular mechanisms in a bird, domestic goose, and two teleosts, striped bass and rainbow trout. *J. Exp. Biol.* 113:215–24
74. Nikinmaa, M., Jensen, F. B. 1986. Blood oxygen transport and acid-base status of stressed trout *(Salmo gairdneri):* Pre- and postbranchial values in winter fish. *Comp. Biochem. Physiol. A* 84:391–96
75. Nikinmaa, M., Weber, R. E. 1984. Hypoxic acclimation in the lamprey, *Lampetra fluviatilis*. *J. Exp. Biol.* 109: 109–19
76. Palfrey, H. C., Greengard, P. 1981. Hormone-sensitive ion transport systems in erythrocytes as models for epithelial ion pathways. *Ann. NY Acad. Sci.* 372:291–308
77. Perutz, M. F. 1983. Species adaptation in a protein molecule. *Mol. Biol. Evol.* 1:1–28
78. Perutz, M. F., Brunori, M. 1982. Stereochemistry of cooperative effects in fish and amphibian hemoglobins. *Nature* 299:421–26
79. Pough, F. H. 1977. Ontogenetic change in molecular and functional properties of blood of garter snakes, *Thamnophilis sirtalis*. *J. Exp. Zool.* 201:47–56
80. Powers, D. A. 1972. Hemoglobin adaptation for fast and slow water habitats in sympatric catastomid fishes. *Science* 177:360–62
81. Primmett, D. R. N., Randall, D. J., Mazeaud, M., Boutilier, R. G. 1986. The role of catecholamines in erythrocyte pH regulation and oxygen transport in rainbow trout *(Salmo gairdneri)* during exercise. *J. Exp. Biol.* 122:139–48
82. Randall, D., Daxboeck, C. 1984. Oxygen and carbon dioxide transfer across

fish gills. In *Fish Physiology,* ed. W. S. Hoar, D. J. Randall, 10A:263–314. Orlando: Academic
83. Reischl, E., Hohn, M., Jaenicke, R., Bauer, C. 1984. Bohr effect, electron spin resonance, and subunit dissociation of the hemoglobin components from the turtle *Phrynops hilarii*. *Comp. Biochem. Physiol. B* 78:251–57
84. Riggs, A. F. 1988. The Bohr effect. *Ann. Rev. Physiol.* 50:181–204
85. Seymour, R. S., Bennett, A. F., Bradford, D. F. 1985. Blood gas tensions and acid-base regulation in the salt-water crocodile *Crocodylus porosus,* at rest and after exhaustive exercise. *J. Exp. Biol.* 118:143–59
86. Soivio, A., Nikinmaa, M. 1981. The swelling of erythrocytes in relation to the oxygen affinity of the blood of the rainbow trout, *Salmo gairdneri* Richardson. In *Stress and Fish,* ed. A. D. Pickering, pp. 103–19. London: Academic
87. Soivio, A., Nikinmaa, M., Westman, K. 1980. The blood oxygen binding properties of hypoxic *Salmo gairdneri*. *J. Comp. Physiol.* 136:83–87
88. Spry, D. J., Wood, C. M. 1984. Acid-base, plasma ion and blood gas changes in rainbow trout during short term zinc exposure. *J. Comp. Physiol.* 154:149–58
89. Tam, L.-L., Gray, G. P., Riggs, A. F. 1986. The hemoglobins of the bullfrog *Rana catesbeiana*. *J. Biol. Chem.* 261: 8290–94
90. Tetens, V., Lykkeboe, G. 1981. Blood respiratory properties of rainbow trout, *Salmo gairdneri:* Responses to hypoxia acclimation and anoxic incubation of blood in vitro. *J. Comp. Physiol.* 145: 117–25
91. Tetens, V., Lykkeboe, G. 1985. Acute exposure of rainbow trout to mild and deep hypoxia: $O_2$ affinity and $O_2$ capacitance of arterial blood. *Respir. Physiol.* 61:221–35
92. Tufts, B. L., Mense, D. C., Randall, D. J. 1987. The effects of forced activity on circulating catecholamines and pH and water content of erythrocytes in the toad. *J. Exp. Biol.* 128:411–18
93. Tun, N., Houston, A. H. 1986. Temperature, oxygen, photoperiod, and the hemoglobin system of the rainbow trout, *Salmo gairdneri*. *Can. J. Zool.* 64: 1883–88
94. Turner, J. D., Wood, C. M., Clark, D. 1983. Lactate and proton dynamics in the rainbow trout *(Salmo gairdneri)*. *J. Exp. Biol.* 104:247–68
95. Ultsch, G. R., Jackson, D. C. 1982. Long-term submergence at 3°C of the

turtle *Chrysemys picta bellii*, in normoxic and severely hypoxic water. I. Survival, gas exchange and acid-base status. *J. Exp. Biol.* 96:11–28

96. Vaccaro, A. M. T., Raschetti, R., Salvioli, R., Riciardi, G., Winterhalter, K. H. 1977. Modulation of the Root effect in goldfish by ATP and GTP. *Biochim. Biophys. Acta* 496:367–73

97. Watt, K. W. K., Riggs, A. 1975. Hemoglobins of the tadpole of the bullfrog, *Rana catesbeiana*. Structure and function of the isolated components. *J. Biol. Chem.* 250:5934–44

98. Watt, K. W. K., Maruyama, T., Riggs, A. 1980. Hemoglobins of the tadpole of the bullfrog, *Rana cateisbeiana*. Amino acid sequence of the $\beta$ chain of a major component. *J. Biol. Chem.* 255:3294–3301

99. Weber, R. E. 1982. Intraspecific adaptation of hemoglobin function in fish to environmental oxygen availability. In *Exogenous and Endogenous Influences on Metabolic and Neural Control*, ed. A. D. F. Addink, N. Spronk, 1:87–102. Oxford: Pergamon

100. Weber, R. E., DeWilde, J. A. M. 1975. Oxygenation properties of haemoglobins from the flatfish plaice *(Pleuronectes platessa)* and flounder *(Platichthys flesus)*. *J. Comp. Physiol.* 101:99–110

101. Weber, R. E., Hartvig, M. 1984. Specific fetal hemoglobin underlies the fetal-maternal difference in blood $O_2$ affinity in a viviparous teleost. *Mol. Physiol.* 6:27–32

102. Weber, R. E., Jensen, F. B., Cox, R. P. 1987. Analysis of teleost hemoglobin by Adair and Monod-Wyman-Changeux models. Effects of nucleoside triphosphates and pH on oxygenation of tench hemoglobin. *J. Comp. Physiol.* 157:145–52

103. Weber, R. E., Johansen, K. 1979. Oxygenation-linked binding of carbon dioxide and allosteric phosphate cofactors by lungfish hemoglobin. In *Animals and Environmental Fitness*, ed. R. Gilles, pp. 49–50. Oxford: Pergamon

104. Weber, R. E., Lykkeboe, G. 1978. Respiratory adaptations in carp blood. Influences of hypoxia, red cell organic phosphates, divalent cations and $CO_2$ on hemoglobin-oxygen affinity. *J. Comp. Physiol.* 128:127–37

105. Weber, R. E., Lykkeboe, G., Johansen, K. 1975. Biochemical aspects of the adaptation of hemoglobin-oxygen affinity in eels to hypoxia. *Life Sci.* 17:1345–50

106. Weber, R. E., Lykkeboe, G., Johansen, K. 1976. Physiological properties of eel

hemoglobin: Hypoxic acclimation, phosphate effects and multiplicity. *J. Exp. Biol.* 64:75–88

107. Weber, R. E., Wells, R. M. G. 1988. Hemoglobin structure and function. In *Comparative Pulmonary Physiology—Current Concepts*, ed. S. C. Wood. New York: Dekker. In press

108. Weber, R. E., Wells, R. M. G., Rossetti, J. E. 1983. Allosteric interactions governing oxygen equilibria in the hemoglobin system of the dogfish, *Squalus acanthias*. *J. Exp. Biol.* 103:109–20

109. Weber, R. E., Wells, R. M. G., Rossetti, J. E. 1985. Adaptations to neoteny in the salamander, *Necturus maculosus*. Blood respiratory properties and interactive effects of pH, temperature and ATP on hemoglobin oxygenation. *Comp. Biochem. Physiol. A* 80:495–501

110. Weber, R. E., White, F. N. 1986. Oxygen binding in alligator blood related to temperature, diving and "alkaline tide". *Am. J. Physiol.* 251:R901–8

111. Weber, R. E., Wood, S. C., Davis, B. J. 1979. Acclimation to hypoxic water in facultative air-breathing fish: Blood oxygen affinity and allosteric effectors. *Comp. Biochem. Physiol. A* 62:125–29

112. Weber, R. E., Wood, S. C., Lomholt, J. P. 1976. Temperature acclimation and oxygen-binding properties of blood and multiple haemoglobins of rainbow trout. *J. Exp. Biol.* 65:333–45

113. Weinstein, Y., Ackerman, R. A., White, F. N. 1986. Influence of temperature on the $CO_2$ dissociation curve of the turtle *Pseudemys scripta*. *Respir. Physiol.* 63:53–63

114. Wells, R. M. G., Ashby, M. D., Duncan, S. J., MacDonald, J. A. 1980. Comparative study of the erythrocytes and haemoglobins in nototheniid fishes from Antarctica. *J. Fish Biol.* 17:517–28

115. Wells, R. M. G., Forster, M. E., Meredith, A. S. 1984. Blood oxygen affinity in the amphibious fish *Neochanna burrowsius* (Galaxiidae: Salmoniformes). *Physiol. Zool.* 57:261–65

116. Wells, R. M. G., Tetens, V., Brittain, T. 1983. Absence of cooperative haemoglobin-oxygen binding in *Sphenodon*, a reptilian relict from the Triassic. *Nature* 306:500–2

117. Wells, R. M. G., Weber, R. E. 1983. Oxygenational properties and phosphorylated metabolic intermediates in blood and erythrocytes of the dogfish *Squalus acanthias*. *J. Exp. Biol.* 103:95–108

118. Wells, R. M. G., Weber, R. E. 1985.

Fixed acid and carbon dioxide Bohr effects as functions of hemoglobin-oxygen saturation and intra-erythrocytic pH in the blood of the frog, *Rana temporaria. Pflüg. Arch. Eur. J. Physiol.* 403:7–12

119. Wood, S. C., Hoyt, R. W., Burggren, W. W. 1982. Control of hemoglobin function in the salamander, *Ambystoma tigrinum. Mol. Physiol.* 2:263–72

120. Wood, S. C., Johansen, K. 1972. Adaptation to hypoxia by increased $HbO_2$ affinity and decreased red cell ATP concentration. *Nature* 237:278–79

121. Wood, S. C., Johansen, K. 1973. Organic phosphate metabolism in nucleated red cells. Influence of hypoxia on eel $Hb-O_2$ affinity. *Neth. J. Sea Res.* 7:328–38

122. Wood, S. C., Johansen, K., Weber, R. E. 1975. Effects of ambient $P_{O_2}$ on hemoglobin-oxygen affinity and red cell ATP concentrations in a benthic fish, *Pleuronectes platessa. Respir. Physiol.* 25:259–67

123. Wood, S. C., Lenfant, C. J. M. 1976. Respiration: Mechanics, control and gas exchange. In *Biology of the Reptillia,* ed. C. Gans, W. R. Dawson, pp. 225–74. New York: Academic

124. Wood, S. C., Lykkeboe, G., Johansen, K., Weber, R. E., Maloiy, G. M. O. 1978. Temperature acclimation in the pancake tortoise *Malacochersus tornieri:* Metabolic rate, blood pH, oxygen affinity and red cell organic phosphates. *Comp. Biochem. Physiol. A* 59:155–60

125. Wood, S. C., Weber, R. E., Maloiy, G. M. O., Johansen, K. 1975. Oxygen uptake and blood respiratory properties of the caecilian *Boulengerula taitanus. Respir. Physiol.* 24:355–63

126. Wyman, J., Gill, S. J., Noll, L., Giardina, B., Colosimo, A., et al. 1977. The balance sheet of a hemoglobin. Thermodynamics of CO binding by hemoglobin trout I. *J. Mol. Biol.* 109:195–205

127. Yamamoto, K., Itazawa, Y., Kobayashi, H. 1980. Sypply of erythrocytes into the circulating blood from the spleen of exercised fish. *Comp. Biochem. Physiol. A* 65:5–11

128. Yamamoto, K., Itazawa, Y., Kobayashi, H. 1985. Direct observation of fish spleen by an abdominal window and its application to exercised and hypoxic yellowtail. *Jpn. J. Ichthyol.* 31:427–33

Ann. Rev. Physiol. 1988. 50:181–204

# THE BOHR EFFECT

*Austen F. Riggs*

Department of Zoology University of Texas Austin, TX 78712

"Whatever you do in one part of the molecule affects the molecule as a whole."

M. F. Perutz (91)

## INTRODUCTION

The control of oxygen binding by hemoglobin (Hb) with pH is of profound importance in facilitating gas exchange in blood. This modulation, known as the Bohr effect, reflects the fact that protons are released upon Hb oxygenation at physiological pH (the alkaline Bohr effect), and protons are taken up upon oxygenation at low pH (the acid or reversed Bohr effect). Reciprocally, changes in pH modulate oxygen affinity. These proton exchanges arise because conformational changes in the Hb associated with ligand binding at the heme result in pK changes in certain acid groups that are distant from the heme. Changes in proton binding also result from differential interaction of buffer ions with oxy- and deoxy-Hb (3, 18). The binding of salt ions can be considered a special kind of Bohr effect (3). Resonance Raman spectroscopy shows that the iron-proximal histidine stretching motion is exquisitely sensitive to amino acid substitutions distant from the heme (34). This review examines recent experiments to determine which groups are responsible for the Bohr effect and how these ligand-linked processes are modulated by other allosteric factors, e.g. buffer ions, organic phosphates, $CO_2$, and chloride, all of which lower the oxygen affinity of Hb by preferential binding to deoxy-Hb. A central problem has been to determine the relative quantitative roles of different ionizable groups responsible for in the Bohr effect. What kinds and numbers of groups are involved? Attempts have been made to calculate pK values by using electrostatic theory. How do such electrostatic calculations compare with other methods for estimating the contributions of different groups?

181

0066-4278/88/0315-0181$02.00

Perutz (89) proposed a stereochemical model that provided a molecular explanation of both the Bohr effect and of cooperativity of oxygen binding. The model rested initially on differences between the x-ray structures determined for horse deoxy- and oxy-like metHb. The model has been modified and refined as a result of many subsequent experiments and higher resolution x-ray analyses on human deoxy-Hb, HbCO, and $HbO_2$ (8, 33, 96, 112). Although the original proposal depended on the structure of metHb, which was found to be isomorphous with $HbO_2$, some differences between the met, CO, and oxy derivatives do exist (33, 112). This is shown most simply by the pronounced differences in solubility: human HbCO is over 40% more soluble than $HbO_2$ in phosphate buffers at 10°C and 67% more soluble than metHb; deoxy-Hb is only one tenth as soluble as HbCO (50). The differences in surface topology responsible for these solubility effects are unknown. However, the distal histidine of the $\alpha$ subunit is much closer to the heme axis in $HbO_2$ than in HbCO (112). Presumably the $HbO_2$-HbCO solubility difference results from interaction of the ligands with the distal histidine; these perturbations are somehow transmitted to the surface of the molecule. The pH-dependent differences in CO and $O_2$ binding have been explained by a charge-dipole interaction between the distal histidine and CO (26).

Four different approaches have been used to identify Bohr groups and to assess their quantitative importance. These are (*a*) direct measurement of the Bohr effect either by equilibrium or kinetic determination of the pH dependence of ligand binding or by titrating proton release associated with ligand binding, (*b*) deuterium and tritium exchange experiments, (*c*) electrostatic calculations based on the relative positions of charged groups determined by x-ray analysis, and (*d*) NMR measurements of the proton resonances in deoxy- and ligated Hbs. Extensive use has been made of mutant and chemically modified Hbs in each of these procedures.

Early studies of the Bohr effect have been thoroughly reviewed (55, see 28 for early history). Site-specific amino acid modifications of hemoglobin have recently been reviewed (2). Comparative aspects of Hb function in different animals have been reviewed (92). The Root effect, a very large Bohr effect that occurs in fish, has been recently surveyed (17). In this review Hb refers to human Hb unless otherwise specified. Positions of amino acid residues are specified either by position along the chain counting from the N-terminus, or by position in a helix or non-helical segment, or by both these ways. Thus $\beta$97 His is the 97th residue, a histidine, of the $\beta$ chain; C5$\alpha$ Lys is the lysine at position 5 of the C helix of the $\alpha$ chain; His HC3 (146) $\beta$ is the histidine at position 3 of the C-terminal segment following the H-helix; position HC3 is also the 146th residue of the chain.

# β146 HISTIDINE

The stereochemical model (89) suggested that a major contributor to the alkaline Bohr effect is His HC3 (146) β. The x-ray data showed that the imidazole group of this residue forms an electrostatic bond ("salt bridge") with Asp FG1(94)β of the same chain in deoxy-Hb that is absent in ligated or metHb. Participation of β146 His in the Bohr effect was clearly foreshadowed by earlier experiments with carboxypeptidase (106). The specific removal of β146 His by carboxypeptidase A or substitution (Hbs Hiroshima (β146 His→Asp) and Cochin-Royal (β146 His→Arg) all reduced the Bohr effect substantially (56, 95, 125). The resonance corresponding to the C-2 protons of β146 histidine was identified by high-resolution NMR spectroscopy (52) by comparing spectra of deoxy-HbA and des-His deoxy-HbA. The measured pK of the group corresponding to the resonance dropped from 8.0 in deoxy-Hb to 7.1 in HbCO. This shift could account for about 50% of the alkaline Bohr effect in 0.2 M phosphate and 0.2 M NaCl at 30°C. Russu et al (108) confirmed a pK of 8.0 for deoxy-Hb but reported that in 0.1 M bis-tris buffers containing only 5–60 mM Cl⁻ the pK of β146 His dropped from 8.0 to 7.85 upon combination of deoxy-Hb with CO. They pointed out that the observed Bohr effect is normal in this buffer. Their result suggested that the β146 histidine mechanism proposed by Perutz could not be unique: the particular residues participating in the Bohr effect must depend on the buffer. Russu et al (109) gave a further detailed analysis of the pH dependence of the resonances corresponding to the histidines of the tetramer in both deoxy-Hb and HbCO, which indicated that multiple histidyl residues participate in the alkaline Bohr effect. These reports gave rise to considerable controversy (41, 54, 97–100, 107–109, 113, 115, 116). Identification of proton resonances depends on the use of mutant and chemically modified Hbs. A major difficulty has been that the resonance patterns show that Hbs chemically modified or substituted with another residue at a single amino acid position often show perturbations of many resonances, which indicates that the effects of substitution are global. Furthermore, the proton resonance patterns for deoxy-Hb and HbCO differ greatly, so it is not obvious which resonance peaks in deoxy-Hb correspond to the peaks in HbCO. This raises questions not only about the identification of the resonances, but also about the assumption that there is a 1:1 relationship between residue and resonance. Russu et al (108) had identified resonance C in HbCO as arising specifically from β146 Histidine. Perutz et al (99) measured the NMR spectra of a variety of mutant and chemically modified Hbs and concluded that resonance C belonged not to β146 His but to β97 His. They assigned resonance H to β146 His because they failed to find it in Hb Cowtown (β146 His→Leu). This identification would, however, produce a pK shift of 1.8 units, which would result in a larger Bohr effect than actually measured, unless some compensating effects exist (107). Russu and Ho (107) then made a detailed investigation of the mutant Hbs and showed conclusively that resonance H cannot be assigned to $\beta 146$ His. Resonance H was found in Hb Cowtown, Hb des-His ($\beta 146$ His deleted), Hb Wood ($\beta 97$ His→Leu), Hb Mälmo ($\beta 97$ His → Gln), Hb Barcelona ($\beta 94$ Asp→His), and Hb Abruzzo ($\beta 143$ His → Arg). Their demonstration that resonance H is present *only* in HbCO but not in $HbO_2$ suggests that it might correspond to the distal histidine. They also showed that the ring-current-shifted resonances associated with the heme pocket were perturbed in *ligated* Hb with amino acid substitutions at the $\beta 146$ position. Shih et al (115, 116) have repeated their NMR measurements and found that resonance H is indeed present in Hb Cowtown. They attributed the discrepancy between their two sets of data to the way the Hb was prepared (resonance H was present in pressure filtered but not dialyzed Hb Cowtown), but the molecular basis for the discrepancy is undetermined. Resonance C, attributed by Russu et al to $\beta 146$ His (108), is present in Hb Cowtown ($\beta 146$ His→Leu) but missing from Hbs with amino acid substitutions at $\beta 143$, $\beta 97$, and $\beta 94$ as well as from des-His ($\beta 146$ His deleted) (41). This means that the original claim that the pK of $\beta 146$ His changed only from 8.0 to 7.85 in bis-tris buffers (108) can no longer be made because it depended on this resonance. We are then left with no identification of the histidine resonance corresponding to $\beta 146$ in HbCO. The difficulties seem to have arisen in large part from the great sensitivity of the NMR resonances to changes in protein structure, the global effects of many amino acid substitutions, and the complex effects of buffers. In addition, the differences between the resonances in $HbO_2$, HbCO, and metHb appear to have provided a further complication. The deuterium and tritium exchange experiments (see below) and oxygen binding data on a number of mutant and modified Hbs, however, provide much support for $\beta 146$ as a major Bohr group. What buffer conditions exist in which the contribution of this group to the Bohr effect may be suppressed? Although this question cannot yet be clearly answered, Bucci & Fronticelli (18) made the important discovery that the Bohr effect can be entirely determined by differential interaction of buffer ions with either oxy- or deoxy-Hb. They measured the Bohr effect in the Good buffers, HEPES, MOPS, and MES (39) and found that the form of the Bohr effect ($H^+$ release/$O_2$ versus pH) was completely different from that obtained in tris-HCL/bis-tris-HCl buffers. How these zwitterionic buffer effects are mediated is not yet clear. It is noteworthy that x-ray analysis of HbCO Kansas ($\beta 102$ Asn→Thr) shows that the $\beta 146$ His–$\beta 94$Asp salt bridge is intact (4), i.e. that ligand binding is not associated with breakage of this salt bridge in Hb Kansas; the pK does not appear to change with formation of HbCO (51).

Although the preceding discussion shows that difficulties exist in the identification of 14 resonances in deoxy-Hb and 19 resonances in HbCO for which pKs have been accurately determined (109), the pKs must together reflect the titration behavior of the surface 22 histidines of the tetramer. The pK values are shown in Figure 1 for deoxy-Hb and HbCO. Ten of the pK values for deoxy-Hb cannot be matched with any pK for HbCO even when the errors, which average $\pm 0.04$, are included. It is difficult to avoid the conclusion that the number of histidines that change their pK values is greater than 2.

Tyrosine HC2 (145) $\beta$ played a pivotal role in the original stereochemical model. The recent determination for the first time of the structure of $HbO_2(112)$ suggests that the perturbation of the pK value of $\beta146$ His is associated with much smaller movements of $\beta145$ Tyr than formerly believed. The newly determined structure shows that this residue is relatively localized and maintains a hydrogen bond with the carbonyl oxygen of Val FG5 (98) $\beta$ in *both* oxy- and deoxy-Hb. The Tyr side chain alternates with Cys F9 (93) $\beta$ for occupancy of an internal pocket between the F and H helices. Such structural heterogeneity may be quite widespread. Recent high-resolution analyses of several proteins (118) show that 6–13% of the side chains are in multiple discrete conformations. Numerous solvent sites appear as multiplets at high resolution, giving rise to mutually exclusive solvent networks. This strong tendency for discrete rather than continuous conformational perturbations may be important for understanding the Bohr effect. Although $\beta146$ His appears to be far removed from Asp FG1 (94) $\beta$ in the

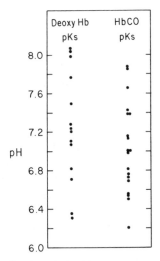

*Figure 1*   Comparison of the pK values obtained for proton resonances of histidine in deoxy-Hb and HbCO (109).

$HbO_2$ structure, the $COO^-$ group of $\beta146$ His forms a salt bridge with Lys HCl (144) $\beta$. The low temperature (4°C) at which the $HbO_2$ structure was determined made it possible to detect a number of salt bridges not previously found. All of the amino acid residues participating in the new salt bridges are polar, and most form bridges between peripheral residues in the same subunit. Some of these linkages may prove to be alternatives between two arrangements where the choice depends on solvent conditions.

## $\alpha1$ VAL AND CHLORIDE

Compelling evidence has shown that $\alpha1$ Val participates in the alkaline Bohr effect in the presence of chloride (31, 83, 123, 124). The $pK_a$ of this group shifts from 8.0 $\pm$ 0.2 in deoxy-Hb to 7.25 $\pm$ 0.05 in HbCO in 100 mM $Cl^-$. The values are 7.5 $\pm$ 0.05 and 7.4 $\pm$ .05, respectively, in 10 mM $Cl^-$ (123). If the $\alpha$-$NH_2$ groups are carbamylated, the remaining Bohr effect becomes $Cl^-$ independent, and 1.3–1.4 protons/tetramer are released (83). These observations show that $Cl^-$ binding is associated with the $\alpha$-$NH_2$ groups. X-ray analysis of hemoglobin specifically carboxymethylated at the $NH_2$ termini ($HbNHCH_2COO^-$) shows the presence of two anion (sulfate) binding sites, one on the $\alpha$ and one on the $\beta$ subunit. The secondary amine of $HbNHCH_2COO^-$ also shows oxygen-linked binding of both chloride and protons at $\alpha1$ Val. The $Cl^-$ binding on the $\beta$-subunit site is between $\beta1$ Val $NH_3^+$ and the $\epsilon$-$NH_3^+$ of $\beta82$ Lys together with the NH groups of the F helix. The $\alpha$-subunit site is between $\alpha1$ Val $\alpha NH_3^+$ and the $\beta$-OH of $\alpha131$ Ser (31). This is in contrast to the earlier suggestion that the $\alpha1$ Val is sufficiently close to 141 Arg of the other $\alpha$ subunit to interact.

Although the $\beta1$ Val/$\beta82$ Lys site contributes to the $Cl^-$-dependent Bohr effect in the absence of organic phosphates, diphosphoglycerate (DPG) would be the dominant anion at this site in vivo. Preferential binding of DPG by deoxy-Hb enhances the alkaline Bohr effect by raising the effective pK of $\alpha1$ Val $\alpha$-$NH_2$ and the $\epsilon$-$NH_2$ of $\beta82$ Lys (55, 104). The DPG binding site constitutes a pocket lined with eight positively charged groups. Substitutions in the DPG binding site show that any such changes have drastic consequences (11, 12, 16, 19, 102). Binding of DPG at this site would raise the pKs of these groups and also modify the pK values of the phosphate groups of DPG, thus giving rise to a DPG-dependent enhancement of the Bohr effect. Differences in the magnitude of this enhancement (122) appear to be responsible for the early finding that the magnitude of the Bohr effect is related to body weight in a series of mammals ranging in size from mouse to elephant (103). The relationship, not apparent in the absence of DPG, has recently been confirmed in studies of a more extensive series of mammalian Hbs (78). Some teleost fish and amphibians have hemoglobins that show only reversed (acid) Bohr effects that are changed to positive alkaline Bohr effects with organic phosphates (13, 105, 128).

The position of His H21 (143) $\beta$ between Lys EF6 (82) $\beta$ and Lys HCl (144) $\beta$ would give rise to an abnormally low pK value; DPG binding would raise the pK. The substitution of $\beta$143 His by Ser in human fetal chains may explain why HbF has a lower $O_2$ affinity than HbA in the absence of DPG. The repulsion of positively charged groups lining the DPG pocket would raise the potential energy of molecules in the deoxy state (100). The His $\rightarrow$ Ser replacement would lower this repulsive potential energy. The greater electrostatic repulsion in deoxy than in oxy HbA would lower the pK of $\beta$143 His and so it would be an acid Bohr group (100). The $\beta$143 His $\rightarrow$ Ser substitution in the $\gamma$ chain would reduce the acid Bohr effect as observed (100).

A central idea of the stereochemical model is that salt bridges are the dominant energetic factor stabilizing deoxy-Hb. However, Chu & Ackers (23) found that the tetramer-dimer association constant for deoxy-Hb was unaffected by changes in [Cl$^-$] between 0.08 and 0.33 M, whereas the corresponding constant for HbO$_2$ varied inversely with [Cl$^-$]. They interpreted this to mean that the salt bridges were not the major energetic stabilizing factor in deoxy-Hb. The release of 1.8 Cl$^-$ ions at pH 7.4 upon oxygenating tetramers is exactly balanced by an uptake of 1.8 Cl$^-$ ions upon dissociation of HbO$_2$ tetramers to dimers.

Bucci & Fronticelli (18) attempted to gain insight into the nature of the Bohr groups by carboxymethylation of either deoxy- or oxy-Hb. They found that, although $\alpha$1 Val and $\beta$146 His were equally alkylated in both forms, carboxymethylation abolished the Bohr effect when HbO$_2$ was used for the reaction but had no effect on the Bohr effect when deoxy-Hb was used. This remarkable finding cannot be explained solely in terms of $\alpha$1 Val and $\beta$146 His and indicates that other Bohr groups must exist.

## CO$_2$ AND THE BOHR EFFECT

Arnone (6) has clearly shown by x-ray crystallography that CO$_2$ binds specifically to the NH$_2$ termini, thus confirming the work of Kilmartin et al (53). The stepwise linkage between CO$_2$ binding and oxygenation has been analyzed by Imaizumi et al (46). The participation of the $\alpha$1 Val $\alpha$-NH$_3^+$ groups in the Cl$^-$-dependent alkaline Bohr effect is strongly modulated by CO$_2$ because of its combination with the uncharged NH$_2$ groups:

$$Hb\text{-}NH_3^+ \rightleftharpoons HbNH_2 + H^+$$

$$HbNH_2 + CO_2 \rightleftharpoons HbNHCOO^- + H^+.$$

Since this process occurs preferentially in deoxy-Hb it will decrease the number of protons bound, i.e. decrease the alkaline Bohr effect. Some Hbs of teleost fish and amphibians have only a reversed "acid" Bohr effect. In these Hbs $CO_2$ *enhances* the reversed Bohr effect for the same reason (32, 38). Oxygen binding by the hemoglobin of crocodiles and their relatives is specifically controlled by bicarbonate binding (9, 10, 93).

## OTHER BOHR GROUPS

Are the residues discussed above the only ones responsible for the Bohr effect? Indeed, does compelling evidence exist that any of the proposed Bohr groups do *not* contribute to the Bohr effect? A central argument concerning specific residues has been as follows. A Bohr group is assigned on the basis of the effects of deletion, substitution, or modification of a particular residue. X-ray analysis apparently shows the structural perturbation to be purely local. This conclusion precludes any other possibility; the functional studies alone cannot unequivocally confirm the assignment of a Bohr group. X-ray studies of many mutant hemoglobins, however, do show perturbations, which are often global (91). Amino acid substitutions at other sites not thought to contribute to the Bohr effect should serve as controls, but mutant Hbs with substitutions distant from putative sites often do have modified Bohr effects. Do other kinds of experiments have the potential to get around this problem?

## TRITIUM AND DEUTERIUM EXCHANGE EXPERIMENTS

Several investigators (65, 79, 84) have attempted to use a hydrogen exchange method based on determination of the pseudo–first order rate constant for the exchange of histidine protons as a function of pH. The conditions under which these experiments have been done make their results difficult to compare with those of other kinds of experiments. Either deoxy-Hb or HbCO was incubated with deuterium or tritium at 37°C for 24–100 hr in buffers at various pHs; the deoxy-Hb solution contained dithionite. Ohe & Kajita (84) separated the $\alpha$ and $\beta$ chains chromatographically after such an incubation with the use of mercurials, after which the chains were digested successively with trypsin and chymotrypsin. Eighteen histidyl peptides were isolated, hydrolyzed, and subjected to amino acid analysis and mass spectrometry. The experiments, in 0.1 ionic strength bis-tris or tris buffers, indicated the following pK shifts in histidyl residues for the deoxy to CO change: $\alpha20$, $-0.6$; $\alpha89$, $-1.6$; $\beta143$, $+0.5$; $\beta146$, $-1.1$. These findings support a role for $\beta146$ in the alkaline Bohr effect and $\beta143$ in the acid Bohr effect. Participation of $\alpha20$ and $\alpha89$ in the Bohr effect has not been reported by others. They found no significant shifts in other histidines, including $\alpha 122$ His. The latter residue had been suggested to be a Bohr group (79) upon analysis of two (A and B) of eleven histidyl peptides. Both contained $\alpha 122$ His: peptide A showed no pK shift between deoxy-Hb and HbCO, whereas peptide B showed a pK shift from 6.6 (deoxy) to 6.1 (CO). This shift would only account for ~10% of the Bohr effect at pH 7.4. The absence of a pK shift in peptide A, attributed to back exchange, suggests that there is a major unsolved methodological problem. Similar experiments in 0.1 M chloride were performed recently in which carboxypeptidase A was used to obtain $\beta 143$ His and $\beta 146$ His (65). The results supported the conclusion that $\beta 146$ His together with $\alpha 1$ Val (see previous sections) could explain 97% of the alkaline Bohr effect. The pK of $\beta 146$ His dropped from 8.0 (deoxy) to 6.5 (CO). They also found that the pK of $\beta 143$ His rose from 5.2 (deoxy) to 6.0 (CO), which would explain about half of the acid Bohr effect. Of course, these experiments can be criticized for examination only of those residues already believed to be important. The selective nature of the experiments, i.e. their investigation of only $\beta 143$ and $\beta 146$ (65) or $\alpha 122$ (79), precludes their use as evidence that other residues do not participate in the Bohr effect. Matsukawa et al (65) made the significant observation that the number of Bohr protons released from des-His Hb ($\beta 146$ deleted) cannot be accounted for simply by the removal of histidine and that there must be large perturbations in the tertiary and/or quaternary structure.

Analogies with results for animal Hbs have been used by Perutz et al (100) to suggest that $\alpha 122$ His is not a Bohr group (llama Hb lacks it) and that $\alpha 89$ His is unlikely to be a Bohr group (cat Hb lacks it but has a normal Bohr effect). Although the conclusions may be correct, the arguments are weak: the animal Hbs differ from human Hb at many residues, and x-ray crystallography has been done only on hemoglobins of four vertebrates: man, horse, deer, and lamprey. Further, cat Hb does not have a completely normal Bohr effect, because its cooperativity is strongly pH dependent (40). It is important that further exchange experiments be made, for the technique seems to hold great promise. Recent exchange measurements (30) under mild conditions indicate that tritium exchange can be an extremely sensitive and powerful tool. The results show that major differences in exchange rates between oxy- and deoxy-Hb are present over the entire pH range.

## ELECTROSTATIC CONSIDERATIONS

Much recent effort has been made to assess the roles of electrostatic interactions, not only in determining protein stability but also in controlling conformational changes and functional properties (42, 67, 68, 90, 126). Oxygenation of tetrameric Hb is associated with conformational changes that modify the relative positions and interactions of many ionizable groups. The energy, $W_{ij}$, required to bring two charges to a distance $r_{ij}$ apart is given by $W_{ij} = Z_iZ_j/r_{ij}D_{ij}$, where $Z_i$ and $Z_j$ are the respective charges and $D_{ij}$ is the dielectric constant that measures the coulombic screening of each charge pair. The $r_{ij}$ values can be obtained from structures determined by x-ray crystallography, but an appropriate $D_{ij}$ value is difficult to define because of the complex nature of the protein-solvent interface. In the Tanford-Kirkwood macroscopic model the electrostatic free energy of a set of discrete point charges is calculated by assuming that the charges are on the surface of a sphere of low dielectric constant surrounded by solvent of high dielectric constant in which mobile counter ions are distributed (68) in accordance with Debye-Hückel theory. A solvent static accessibility parameter (60) was introduced to allow for partial burial of a group. This model has been applied successfully to myoglobin and tetrameric hemoglobin (68). It can predict pK values of individual sites, the overall titration curve, the effects of ionic strength, and specific ion binding sites. This computational capability is presently unique to the modified Tanford-Kirkwood model. This algorithm has been applied most recently to ion binding phenomena in sperm whale aquometmyoglobin (35, 68), which was chosen because of the close similarity of its tertiary structure to that of the subunits of Hb. The calculations showed that the atomic coordinates of five ion binding sites could be predicted from maps at 0.2 Å resolution of the electrostatic potential surface of myoglobin determined as a function of pH and ionic strength; four of these sites have been identified by experiment. Other algorithms have been used for the analysis of different proteins (42). These have independently provided support for the Tanford-Kirkwood model. Matthew et al (69, 70) used this model to calculate pK values of the histidines of deoxy- and ligated hemoglobin. These calculations were criticized (54, 100) for the use of incorrect coordinates for the $HbO_2$ structure and therefore erroneous values of $r_{ij}$. Calculations based on recent high-resolution data on deoxy-Hb and $HbO_2$ appear to be substantially in accord with the observed titration curves of deoxy-Hb and $HbO_2$ (68). This agreement constitutes a quantitatively correct prediction of the Bohr effect. Although more detailed analysis of Hb with the techniques previously applied to myoglobin is not yet complete, it does not appear possible to manipulate the analysis in such a way as to reduce the number of residues participating in the Bohr effect to two, but this remains to be proved. The validity of the individual calculated pK values is unclear because most of the histidines for which pK values have been calculated do not have independent experimental pK assignments. Quantitative agreement with the results of the deuterium exchange experiments (84) is poor, perhaps because of experimental difficulties such as back reactions. Identification of the NMR resonances corresponding to most of the histidines has not yet been made, and uncertainties exist with those that have been identified (see section on $\beta146$ His).

The way in which the dielectric constant is assigned in electrostatic calcula-tions is controversial. The difficulty concerns the nature of the protein-solvent interface and the presence of permanent and induced dipoles. Warshel et al (126, 127) argue that these factors result in large values for the dielectric constant in the neighborhood of a charged group. The basis of their argument is that ionized groups cannot exist inside nonpolar regions of a protein and that any charged groups inside a protein must be in regions of high dielectric constant. High local values of $D_{ij}$ may help explain why many side-chain pK values do not seem to be affected by their only partial exposure to solvent (68).

The importance of electrostatic interactions is underlined by studies (114) of mutant Hbs with substitutions of the highly conserved $\beta101$ Glu, which is at the $\alpha_1\beta_2$ interface but has not been described as forming a salt bridge. Nevertheless, the substitution $\beta101$ Glu$\rightarrow$Gly in Hb Alberta results in a 167-fold increase in the magnitude of the tetramer-to-dimer dissociation constant (71). Similarly, the $\alpha_1\beta_2$ interface of the Hb of a Brazilian water snake (66) has two fewer negative charges. The substitution $\beta101$ Glu$\rightarrow$Val, together with the absence of the salt bridge between $\beta_2$ CD2(43) Glu and $\alpha_1$ FG 4(92)Arg, results in a greatly enhanced tetramer-to-dimer dissociation. Electrostatic interactions are not only important for hemoglobin function, but they also govern the assembly of $\alpha$ and $\beta$ subunits to form dimers (20, 76).

## STEPWISE BOHR EFFECT

Oxygenation of Hb involves both tertiary and quaternary changes in structure. Much effort has gone into attempts to determine how proton release is related to the course of oxygenation. The most detailed and comprehensive investiga-tion to date is that of Chu et al (24), who have made careful measurements of the pH dependence of oxygen binding as a function of protein concentration and have analyzed these data together with measurement of the pH depen-dence of the tetramer-dimer dissociation for both deoxy- and oxy-Hbs. The data were analyzed without use of any constraining model (the simple mass action equilibria associated with the Adair constants are not considered models). Such an analysis requires precise measurement of the equilibria as provided by the automated technique of Imai (44). If one measures oxygen equilibria over a large range of protein concentrations the results will depend not only on the four successive Adair constants but also on the tetramer-to-dimer equilibria of both deoxy- and oxy-Hb and the dimer oxygenation. A large body of self-consistent data are therefore required, all obtained under closely comparable conditions. Chu and colleagues (see 24 and other refer-ences contained therein) have carried out a meticulous analysis of 62 oxygenation curves as a single complete set of data. Arbitrary weighing functions, such as those used by Imai (43), were not incorporated into the analysis because the distribution of residuals for the complete data set showed no correlation with any of the variables. Individual curves may exhibit a systematic bias, but any bias is eliminated by analysis of the complete set.

The results of the analysis (24) of the data at pH 7.4, 21.5°C, 0.1 M Cl$^-$, 1 mM EDTA, and 0.1 M tris are that $0.64 \pm 0.07$ protons per $O_2$ are released in the first step of tetramer oxygenation. Steps 2 and 3 together release a further $1.62 \pm 0.27$ protons. The fourth step is accompanied by no significant proton release ($0.05 \pm 0.06$ H$^+$). The overall proton release is approximately linear with oxygenation because the cooperativity of oxygen binding results in the predominant species being either 100% deoxy-Hb or 100% fully saturated. The tetramer oxygenation results, along with the subunit assembly data, indicate that dimer oxygenation has a Bohr effect about one third as large as that of the tetramer ($0.88 \pm 0.48$ H$^+$/4$O_2$). The dimer Bohr effect reflects tertiary changes in the subunits that presumably correspond to the tertiary changes in the tetramer, although they may not be identical because of constraining interactions within the tetramer.

Earlier studies showed a close correlation between the heat of Bohr proton release for tetramers and the decrease in the enthalpy of oxygenation that comes from subunit assembly (72). This has led to the suggestion (24) that the enthalpic contribution to the free energy of cooperativity of oxygen binding results entirely from the enthalpy of proton release, so that the observed enthalpy of oxygenating tetramers is

$$\Delta H_{observed} = \Delta H_{int} + \Delta \bar{\nu}_4 \Delta H_{H^+},$$

where $\Delta H_{int}$ is the intrinsic enthalpy of oxygenation for isolated subunits, $\Delta \bar{\nu}_4$ is the number of moles of protons released, and $\Delta H_{H^+}$ is the associated enthalpy. The available data are completely consistent with this interpretation.

Allosteric theory states that the equilibrium between the T and R states at ligation state $i$ is given by $L_i = [T]/[R] = L_o (K_R/K_T)^i$, On this basis more than 25% of the Bohr protons would be dissociated before 1/600 of the molecules have switched from the T to R state (96). Almost all the remainder of the protons would be released in steps 2 and 3, when the theory suggests that the T to R shift occurs. Only 5% of the protons would be released during the fourth oxygenation step. This picture, of course, includes all the constraints implicit in the allosteric model. Much of the attractiveness of the allosteric theory rests on the ease with which the parameters of the model can be calculated, and there is no doubt that it has been extremely useful. However, it has become clear that the simplest two-state model is insufficient to describe the oxygenation of Hb (45, 117).

The finding that the fourth step of ligand binding in tetrameric Hb is pH independent is not consistent with kinetic experiments designed to determine the pH dependence of the fourth binding constant, $L_4$, for CO (25, 57, 58). Experiments (57) were performed by (*a*) flash photolysis of 5 and 10% of the HbCO followed by measurement of the recombination rate constant, $l'_4$ and (*b*) measurement of the dissociation rate constant, $l_4$, by replacing CO with NO to yield $L_4 = l'_4/l_4$. The results suggested a substantial pH dependence for $L_4$ for HbA which was greatly diminished in des-His HbA. The pH dependence of $l'_4$ in Hb Cochin—Port Royal ($\beta$146 His $\rightarrow$ Arg) was also reduced.

Could this dependence have resulted from the presence of dimers or the participation of diliganded tetramers? The partial flash determination of $l'_4$ was measured at 40–65 $\mu$M heme; $l_4$ was largely measured at 10 $\mu$M heme. An increase from 10 to 100 $\mu$M heme had no significant effect on the results at pH 6 or 9 (25). This is puzzling since Ackers et al. (1, 73) have shown that even at 100 $\mu$M heme none of the four Adair constants for the tetramer can be satisfactorily determined because of the presence of dimers. DeYoung et al. (25) argued that the absence of concentration dependence meant that the results could not be explained by the presence of dimers unless the properties of the dimers and di- and triliganded tetramers were very similar. Since dimers do appear to have a significant Bohr effect it would seem essential to determine the kinetic constants over as wide a range of concentrations and pH as possible.

If the flash photolysis is random the tetrameric molecules that recombine would be largely a mixture of $Hb(CO)_2$ and $Hb(CO)_3$. If the fraction dissociated is 10% then one seventh of the tetramers would be of the form $Hb(CO)_2$. Although this suggests that the results might have been biased by the inclusion of the pH-dependent third step of ligand binding, the results were not significantly altered by changing the fractional photolysis from 10% to 5%. This change would decrease the amount of $Hb(CO)_2$ from 14% to 7%. The presence of deoxy and singly liganded tetramers would be expected to give rise to significant heterogeneity in the kinetics but the kinetics all appeared homogeneous. Dimers would not be expected to contribute significantly to this heterogeneity because their ligand binding properties are very similar to those for the last step of ligand binding by tetramers. Similar experiments (58) have been performed with des-(Arg 141$\alpha$) HbA. This deletion reduces the apparent pH dependence of $L_4$ by about 80%. Indirect effects on other residues are presumably involved because the sum of the effects of the (separate) removal of $\beta$146 His and $\alpha$141 Arg is more than 100%.

## THE ROOT EFFECT

Two oxygen-pumping structures occur in many teleost fish: (*a*) the countercurrent capillary system (the rete) and an associated gas gland that pumps gas into the swim bladder to maintain neutral buoyancy and (*b*) the choroid rete, which supplies oxygen to the retina. All fish that have these pumps have at least one Hb with an unusually large Bohr effect called the Root effect. Air-equilibrated Hbs that exhibit the Root effect release as much as half of their bound oxygen when brought from pH 8 to 6 (17, 92, 105). The gas gland associated with the rete releases lactic acid, causing a pH drop so that the counter-current system can pump oxygen into the swim bladder against what are often very large pressures. The low oxygen affinity of the Hb at low pH is associated with complete loss of cooperativity (81, 121). Molecules in the low affinity T state appear to be so stabilized at low pH that no conformational change occurs upon oxygenation (81, 88, 121). Fish Hbs have therefore served as useful models for the study of allosteric mechanisms, because Hbs in the T or R states can be obtained simply by changing the pH.

A guiding assumption in the search for a molecular mechanism of the Root effect has been that a small number of key residues dominate allosteric function. This assumption is subject to the same difficulties discussed earlier with regard to the alkaline Bohr effect. We seek to determine how many protons are released from which chains and from which residues upon oxygenation. The pH dependence of oxygen binding in Hbs exhibiting the Root effect strongly suggests that histidine residues are involved. The amino acid sequences of the $\alpha$ and $\beta$ chains of carp Hb show that, in addition to the proximal and distal histidines, the $\beta$ chain has two histidines and the $\alpha$ chain has three histidines. All but one of these positions are also occupied by histidines in human Hb. Since the number of protons released by carp Hb upon oxygenation is much greater than that released by human Hb, it appears that groups other than histidines must play a role, or histidines interact differently with polar residues in carp Hb, or both. Analysis by x-ray crystallography of both oxy and deoxy forms will be required before a choice between these alternatives can be made. Parkhurst et al (86) removed the C-terminal histidine from the $\beta$ chain of carp Hb (des-His Hb) and found that the $\Delta \log P_{50}/\Delta pH$ was halved. The rate of recombination of CO after photolytic dissociation of part of the HbCO is normally faster than the rate observed after full dissociation; this accelerated rate was absent in experiments with des-His Hb. They concluded that removal of His HC3 abolishes *all* phenomena associated with the Root effect. It is noteworthy that Phe replaces the C-terminal His in certain fish Hbs (92); none of these Hbs has a Root effect. Kinetic and equilibrium analysis of hybrid carp-human Hbs has provided some insight into the complexities involved (21, 85). One might suppose that analysis of the Bohr effects of the hybrids $\alpha$ (human) $\beta$ (carp) and $\alpha$ (carp) $\beta$ (human) together with the parent species would permit determination of the individual contributions of the $\alpha$ and $\beta$ chains, but this could not be done (21) because the data were linearly dependent. Although

3.8 $H^+$ and 2.6 $H^+$ were released upon oxygenation at pH 7 from carp and human Hb tetramers, respectively, only 1.6 $H^+$ were released from $\alpha$ (carp) $\beta$ (human) and 2.2 $H^+$ from $\alpha$ (human) $\beta$ (carp). The results show that the number of protons released depends on the identity of and interaction between the $\alpha$ and $\beta$ chains (or $\alpha$-$\beta$ dimers) and is not simply additive. The pH of maximal proton release by carp Hb is shifted to higher values by inorganic and organic phosphates (22, 37, 81, 121).

Although the $\alpha$ and $\beta$ chains of mammalian Hbs do exhibit somewhat different oxygen binding and spectral properties, the differences are masked by the high cooperativity of oxygenation. These differences can be quite large, however, in a number of teleost fish Hbs and are most apparent at low pH, where cooperativity is absent. The Hill coefficient at low pH is $<1.0$ for a number of teleost fish Hbs (14, 80, 82, 87, 105, 110); this appears to reflect different oxygen affinities for the $\alpha$ and $\beta$ chains. Thus CO binding by menhaden Hb, for example, is slow and biphasic at low pH (110). The rates of 0.25 and 0.023 $\mu M^{-1}s^{-1}$ are attributed to the $\alpha$ and $\beta$ chains, respectively. The CO dissociation rates are also biphasic. In contrast, the rates of CO binding and dissociation were homogeneous at alkaline pH.

The Root effect has been interpreted as resulting from a large shift in conformational equilibria induced by pH. Attempts made (110) to observe the R to T transition by measuring spectral changes at the Hb-HbCO isosbestic point during flash photolysis of menhaden HbCO gave a poor correlation between the static or kinetic absorption changes and the parameters calculated from functional measurements on the basis of the allosteric model. They suggested that optical absorption measurements may not give a quantitative measure of quaternary conformation. Alternatively, the model is probably inadequate. No uniformity exists in fish hemoglobins with respect to differences between the spectra of the $\alpha$ and $\beta$ chains. In tuna Hb (74) the spectra of $\alpha_T$ and $\beta_T$ differ and those of $\alpha_R$ and $\beta_R$ do not; since the spectra of $\beta_R$ and $\beta_T$ are the same, oxygenation can be described in terms of just two spectral species. This pattern is reversed in shark Hb. Clearly differences between $\alpha$ and $\beta$ chains and between the spectra of conformers must be taken into account explicitly.

Recent studies of several deep-sea bottom-living rat-tail fish (80) indicate that those fish with swim bladders may have Hbs with two equal populations of hemes that differ as much as 100- to 500-fold in their CO affinities at low pH. The species living at the greatest depths (1700–2900 meters) have hemoglobins with a population of hemes characterized by a $P_{50}$ (CO) of 100 mm Hg, whereas those living at 200–1400 meters had $P_{50}$ (CO) values of only 30 mm Hg for the low-affinity hemes. If the CO/$O_2$ partition coefficient for the very low affinity hemes is about 100, the $P_{50}$ ($O_2$) would be more than 10 atm in the deep-sea species. These appear to be the lowest affinities of any Hb yet studied. Two species lacking swim bladders had Hbs that showed none of this heterogeneity. This suggests a possible relationship between the low-affinity heme groups and the pumping of oxygen into the swim bladder at great hydrostatic pressures.

Perutz & Brunori (94) noticed that the cysteinyl residue at $\beta93$ in mammalian Hbs was replaced by Ser in the $\beta$ chain of carp and trout IV hemoglobins and suggested that the Root effect resulted from an unusual stabilization of the $\beta146$ histidine by formation of a hydrogen bond between the histidyl $COO^-$ group and $\beta93$ Ser and formation of a salt bridge with $C5\alpha$ Lys and a salt bridge between the imidazole of $\beta146$ His and FGl Glu. The cDNA coding for the $\beta$ chain of *Xenopus* globin showed the presence of all these residues, so they predicted that *Xenopus* Hb should possess a Root effect. They measured the pH dependence of oxygen binding by *Xenopus* Hb and reported (94) that it did indeed possess a Root effect. This conclusion, however, required that they use a new, unique diagnostic criterion by which to identify the Root effect in Hbs, namely that of noncooperativity at low pH. Their results do show that *Xenopus* Hb has a very low affinity and is noncooperative at pH 6, but this pH dependence is in no way unusual. The curve for $\log P_{50}$ versus pH for *Xenopus* Hb differs from that for human Hb only by a shift of scale towards lower affinity ($\Delta\log P_{50}\sim0.5$). The *Xenopus* and human Hb data can be superimposed on one another so that no difference in pH dependence is apparent. The Hbs of adult frogs of *Rana esculenta* and *R. catesbeiana* and the Hb of the lungfish *Lepidosiren* all have $\beta93$ Ser, and none has a Root effect by any definition. Explanations for the absence of a Root effect in these Hbs were contrived to preserve the hypothesis: Gly replaces Glu at FGl in *R. catesbeiana* Hb, and Asn replaces Glu in *R. esculenta* Hb. However, the $\beta$ chain of *Lepidosiren* Hb has both $\beta93$ Ser and FGl Glu yet lacks a Root effect. This was explained by supposing that the salt bridge with His $HC3\beta$ was weakened by competition from a histidine at $F6\beta$.

The serine hypothesis was pursued further with the use of site-directed mutagenesis (77) in which a mutant human Hb with a $\beta93$ Cys→Ser substitution was synthesized in *Escherichia coli*. This change was expected to provide human Hb with a Root effect. The results, however, show that the mutant Hb has an essentially unchanged normal Bohr effect. This finding did not, however, kill the hypothesis. Nagai et al (77) concluded that the Cys→Ser substitution is "not sufficient" to generate the hydrogen bond presumed necessary for a Root effect and that "additional replacements may be necessary to bring the serine and histidine together." Crystallographic analysis of the mutant (15) Hb showed that $\beta93$ Ser forms a hydrogen bond with $\beta94$ Asp that is in equilibrium with the salt bridge between $\beta94$ Asp and $\beta146$ His. As a further test one might construct a double mutant of human Hb with both $\beta93$ Ser and FGl Glu, but since the hemoglobin of the lungfish *Lepidosiren* has this combination, it appears that such a double mutant would be unlikely to possess a Root effect. The differences between the tertiary and quaternary structures of human and carp Hb may be sufficient to make it impossible to provide human Hb with a Root effect by changing only a few residues, even if the $\beta 93$ Ser hypothesis proved correct. However, no experimental support yet exists for this hypothesis.

## ASSOCIATION OF TETRAMERS

Substantial evidence now exists for deoxygenation-dependent association of tetramers in many animal Hbs. Such association of tetramers appears to be widespread among birds, amphibians, and some reptiles and to be of considerable physiological importance. This association will contribute to the Bohr effect to the extent that the tetramer-tetramer interaction is pH dependent. The evidence is primarily of two types: (a) direct measurement by ultracentrifugation and (b) indirect indication by finding oxygen equilibria with Hill coefficients greater than four. The best studied system is that of the adult bullfrog *Rana catesbeiana* (119, 120), in which two tetrameric components, B and C, associate upon deoxygenation to form aggregates that appear to be trimers of tetramers of the form $BC_2$ that have an extremely low affinity for oxygen. The trimers dissociate as oxygenation progresses to form B and C tetramers of much higher oxygen affinity. Consequently, the Hill coefficient reaches values of over four at 70–80% oxygenation. Since the $\alpha$ chains differ and the $\beta$ chains appear to be identical (119), formation of $BC_2$ molecules appears to require contacts between unlike $\alpha$ chains. This is consistent with the fact that organic phosphates have no effect upon aggregation (5), since the phosphates bind between two $\beta$ chains. Steric constraints are presumably responsible for limiting the association to trimers. Since trimer formation decreases greatly with an increase in pH, the dissociation of the trimer will make a large contribution to the alkaline Bohr effect. Preliminary estimates suggest that as many as 0.8 protons may be released per tetramer dissociated. The finding of very high Hill coefficients in oxygen binding measurements of whole blood (63) requires that red cells contain both components B and C, because components B and C do not self-associate significantly.

The association of deoxygenated tetramers provides an explanation for the unusually high Hill coefficients obtained for the blood of *R. catesbeiana* and other frogs (49, 63, 130), for the blood of all birds examined and that of some lizards, turtles, and snakes (48, 64, 101, 131), but not salamanders (129). The birds whose blood showed high Hill coefficients include the rhea, mallard, pigeon, chicken, quail, sparrow, and hummingbird (47, 59, 61, 62). Although spuriously high Hill coefficients may result from measurement of oxygen binding in the presence of $O_2$ consumption, Hill coefficients for bird blood remain as high as five even after correction for oxygen consumption (62). Hill coefficients less than four require that tetramer-tetramer association occurs in deoxy-Hb, but no evidence exists that the mechanism for association is the same as in the bullfrog. Chicken hemoglobin $A_I$ self-associates upon deoxygenation (75), but no stoichiometric data are available. Only for bull-frog Hb is it known that two different tetramers are required. It is conceivable that open-ended association might occur in some Hbs in addition to human Hb S, in which aggregation produces a Hill coefficient over five in concentrated solutions (36).

A wide range of pH dependencies of tetramer-tetramer association exists among amphibian Hbs (29). Aggregation of deoxy-Hb from the axolotl shows a much sharper pH dependence than does that in the bullfrog, whereas the association of deoxy tetramers of *Rana esculenta* Hb is independent of pH, and tetramers of newt Hb do no associate at all. Thus the association of deoxy-Hb tetramers must enhance the Bohr effect of hemoglobin from the axolotl and bullfrog but be without effect on the hemoglobin of *R. esculenta*. Human hemoglobin Olympia ($\alpha_2\beta_2 20(B2)$Val→Met) has oxygenation prop-erties somewhat like those of the frog hemoglobin in that it undergoes self-association in the deoxy state (27); the Hill coefficient reaches values as high as four. The association is pH dependent so it must alter the Bohr effect.

## CONCLUSIONS

Many experiments show that the highly conserved N- and C-terminal residues play a crucial role in the Bohr effect of hemoglobin. Substitution or deletion of $\beta146$ histidine leads to a marked reduction in the Bohr effect, but the magnitude of the reduction differs substantially with different substitutions, even though the salt bridge between $\beta146$ and $\beta94$ Asp is presumably broken in all of them. Bohr groups, by definition, have global effects in the sense that their ionization or substitution results in perturbations at other, distant loca-tions in the molecule (e.g. the heme and heme pocket). This makes un-equivocal identification of the sources of ionization difficult to assess because the perturbations are not necessarily purely local. Identification of the N- and C-terminal residues as Bohr groups does not, by itself, exclude simultaneous participation of other groups. This possibility is not completely excluded by present quantitative measurements because the assumption is made that the contributions of the different Bohr groups are independent and additive.

The possibility that $\beta146$ histidine exerts its effect indirectly cannot be completely excluded, but it seems unlikely. If the $\beta146$ His/$\beta94$ Asp salt bridge does break as a consequence of oxygenation, as the x-ray results show, then the pK of $\beta146$ His must drop, thereby making this histidine a Bohr group. Conditions under which this salt bridge does not break are incompletely understood, although human hemoglobin Kansas has a substantial Bohr effect even though the salt bridge is not broken. The experiments of Bucci & Fronticelli (18) indicate that buffer conditions can be found that completely transform the Bohr effect, perhaps by effects on salt bridges. It should also be noted that the hemoglobin of lampreys has a large Bohr effect, yet it has none of the groups presently invoked to explain the Bohr effect. It is not unreasonable to expect shifts in mechanisms with large evolutionary change.

High-precision measurements of oxygen equilibria combined with data on subunit assembly and analysis of intermediates (7, 111) hold great promise for obtaining much detailed information about the energetic pathway of oxygenation and the pH dependence of the steps in this pathway, particularly the roles of each of the ten different ligation states (117) in the Bohr effect. Nevertheless, the oxygen equilibrium technique has depended largely on measurements at single wavelengths. Although measurements have shown linearity between oxygenation and absorbance change (73), they were not based on complete spectra and may not have been of the same precision as the recent determination of highly precise oxygen equilibria that are based on the assumption of linearity.

ACKNOWLEDGMENTS

I thank A. Arnone, B. Garcia-Moreno, C. Ho, R. W. Noble, and M. F. Perutz for manuscripts received prior to publication. I regret that because of space limitations all relevant work could not be included. Studies by the author cited here were supported by NIH grant GM35847, NSF grant DMB-8502857, and Robert A. Welch Foundation grant F-213.

*Literature Cited*

1. Ackers, G. K., Johnson, M. L., Mills, F. C., Halvorson, H. R., Shapiro, S. 1975. The linkage between oxygenation and subunit dissociation in human hemoglobin. Consequences for the analysis of oxygenation curves. *Biochemistry* 14:5128–34

2. Ackers, G. K., Smith, F. R. 1985. Effects of site-specific amino acid modification on protein interactions and biological function. *Ann. Rev. Biochem.* 54:597–629

3. Amiconi, G., Antonini, E., Brunori, M., Wyman, J., Zolla, L. 1981. Interaction of hemoglobin with salts: Effects on the functional properties of human hemoglobin. *J. Mol. Biol.* 152:111–29

4. Anderson, L. 1975. Structures of deoxy and carbonmonoxy haemoglobin Kansas in the deoxy quaternary conformation. *J. Mol. Biol.* 94:33–49

5. Araki, T., Okazaki, T., Kajita, A., Shukuya, R. 1974. Polymerization of oxygenated and deoxygenated bullfrog hemoglobins. *Biochim. Biophys. Acta* 351:427–36

6. Arnone, A. 1974. X-ray studies of the interaction of $CO_2$ with human deoxyhaemoglobin. *Nature* 247:143–44

7. Arnone, A., Rogers, P., Blough, N. V., McGourty, J. L., Hoffman, B. M. 1986. X-ray diffraction studies of a partially liganded hemoglobin, $[\alpha(FeII\text{-}CO)\beta(MnII)]_2$. *J. Mol. Biol.* 188:693–706

8. Baldwin, J. M. 1980. The structure of human carbonmonoxyhaemoglobin at

2.7 Å resolution. *J. Mol. Biol.* 136:103–28

9. Bauer, C., Forster, M., Gros, G., Mosca, A., Perrella, M., et al. 1981. Analysis of bicarbonate binding to crocodilian hemoglobin. *J. Biol. Chem.* 256:8429–35

10. Bauer, C., Jelkmann, W. 1977. Carbon dioxide governs the oxygen affinity of crocodile blood. *Nature* 269:825–27

11. Bonaventura, C., Bonaventura, J. 1980. Anionic control of function in vertebrate hemoglobins. *Am. Zool.* 20:131–38

12. Bonaventura, C., Bonaventura, J., Amiconi, G., Tentori, L., Brunori, M., Antonini, E. 1975. Hemoglobin Abruzzo [$\beta$143 (H21) His→Arg]. Consequences of altering the 2,3-diphosphoglycerate binding site. *J. Biol. Chem.* 250:6273–77

13. Bonaventura, C., Sullivan, B., Bonaventura, J., Bourne, S. 1977. Anion modulation of the negative Bohr effect of haemoglobin from a primitive amphibian. *Nature* 265:474–76

14. Bonaventura, C., Sullivan, B., Bonaventura, J., Brunori, M. 1976. Spot hemoglobin. Studies on the Root effect hemoglobin of a marine teleost. *J. Biol. Chem.* 251:1871–76

15. Bonaventura, F. L., Nagai, K. 1986. Crystallographic analysis of mutant haemoglobins made by *Escherichia coli*. *Nature* 320:555–56

16. Bonaventura, J., Bonaventura, C., Sullivan, B., Godette, G. 1975. Hemoglobin Deer Lodge ($\beta$2 His → Arg). Consequences of altering the 2,3-diphosphoglycerate binding site. *J. Biol. Chem.* 250:9250–55

17. Brittain, T. 1987. The Root effect. *Comp. Biochem. Physiol.* 86B:473–81

18. Bucci, E., Fronticelli, C. 1985. Anion Bohr effect of human hemoglobin. *Biochemistry* 24:371–76

19. Bucci, E., Salahuddin, A., Bonaventura, J., Bonaventura, C. 1978. Characterization of the ionizable groups interacting with anionic allosteric effectors of human hemoglobin. *J. Biol. Chem.* 253:821–27

20. Bunn, H. F., McDonald, M. J. 1983. Electrostatic interactions in the assembly of haemoglobin. *Nature* 306:498–500

21. Causgrove, T., Goss, D. J., Parkhurst, L. J. 1984. Oxygen equilibrium studies on carp-human hybrid hemoglobins. *Biochemistry* 23:2168–73

22. Chien, J. C. W., Mayo, K. H. 1980. Carp hemoglobin II, the alkaline Bohr effect. *J. Biol. Chem.* 255:9800–6

23. Chu, A. H., Ackers, G. K. 1981. Mutual effects of protons, NaCl, and

oxygen on the dimer-tetramer assembly of human hemoglobin. *J. Biol. Chem.* 256:1199–1205

24. Chu, A. H., Turner, B. W., Ackers, G. K. 1984. Effects of protons on the oxygenation-linked subunit assembly in human hemoglobin. *Biochemistry* 23:604–17

25. DeYoung, A., Pennelly, R. R., Tan-Wilson, A. L., Noble, R. W. 1976. Kinetic studies on the binding affinity of human hemoglobin for the 4th carbon monoxide molecule, $L_4$. *J. Biol. Chem.* 251:6692–98

26. Doster, W., Beece, D., Bowne, S. F., Dilorio, E. E., Eisenstein, L., et al. 1982. Control and pH dependence of ligand binding to heme proteins. *Biochemistry* 21:4831–39

27. Edelstein, S. J., Poyart, C., Blouquit, Y., Kister, J. 1986. Self-association of haemoglobin Olympia ($\alpha_2\beta_2$ 20 (B2) Val → Met) A human haemoglobin bearing a substitution at the surface of the molecule. *J. Biol. Chem.* 187:277–89

28. Edsall, J. T. 1972. Blood hemoglobin: The evolution of knowledge of functional adaptation in a biochemical system. Part I. The adaptation of chemical structure to function in hemoglobin. *J. Hist. Biol.* 5:205–59

29. Elli, R., Giuliani, A., Tentori, L., Chiancone, E., Antonini, E. 1970. The hemoglobin of amphibia. X. Sedimentation behavior of frog, triton and axolotl hemoglobins. *Comp. Biochem. Physiol.* 36:163–71

30. Englander, J. J., Englander, S. W. 1987. Hydrogen-tritium exchange survey of allosteric effects in hemoglobin. *Biochemistry* 26:1846–50

31. Fantl, W. J., Donato, A. D., Manning, J. M., Rogers, P. H., Arnone, A. 1987. Hemoglobin specifically carboxymethylated at the $\alpha$- and $\beta$-chain $NH_2$-terminal residues as an analogue of carbamino hemoglobin: X-ray and solution studies. *J. Biol. Chem.* 262:12700–13

32. Farmer, M. 1979. The transition from water to air breathing: Effects of $CO_2$ on hemoglobin function. *Comp. Biochem. Physiol.* 62A:109–14

33. Fermi, G., Perutz, M. F., Shaanan, B., Fourme, R. 1984. The crystal structure of human deoxyhaemoglobin at 1.74 Å resolution. *J. Mol. Biol.* 175:159–74

34. Friedman, J. M. 1985. Structure, dynamics, and reactivity in hemoglobin. *Science* 228:1273–80

35. Garcia-Moreno, B. 1986. Effects of ion-binding and electrostatic interaction on the structure and function of sperm

whale myoglobin. PhD thesis. Indiana Univ.

36. Gill, S. J., Sköld, R., Fall, L., Shaeffer, T., Spokane, R., Wyman, J. 1978. Aggregation effects on oxygen binding of sickle cell hemoglobin. *Science* 201:362–63

37. Gillen, R. G., Riggs, A. 1972. Structure and function of the hemoglobins of the carp, *Cyprinus carpio*. *J. Biol. Chem.* 247:6039–46

38. Gillen, R. G., Riggs, A. 1973. Structure and function of the isolated hemoglobins of the American eel, *Anguilla rostrata*. *J. Biol. Chem.* 248:1961–69

39. Good, N. E., Winget, G. D., Winter, W., Connolly, T. N., Igawo, S., Singh, R. M. M. 1966. Hydrogen ion buffers for biological research. *Biochemistry* 5:467–77

40. Hamilton, M. N., Edelstein, S. J. 1972. Cat hemoglobin: pH-dependent cooperativity of oxygen binding. *Science* 178:1104–5

41. Ho, C., Russu, I. M. 1987. How much do we know about the Bohr effect of hemoglobin? *Biochemistry* 26:6299–6305

42. Honig, B. H., Hubble, W. L., Flewelling, R. F. 1986. Electrostatic interactions in membranes and proteins. *Ann. Rev. Biophys. Biophys. Chem.* 15:163–93

43. Imai, K. 1981. Analysis of ligand binding equilibria. *Meth. Enzymol.* 76:470–86

44. Imai, K. 1981. Measurement of accurate oxygen equilibrium curves by an automatic oxygenation apparatus. *Meth. Enzymol.* 76:438–49

45. Imai, K., Yonetani, T. 1975. pH dependence of the Adair constants of human hemoglobin. Non-uniform contribution of successive oxygen bindings to the alkaline Bohr effect. *J. Biol. Chem.* 250:2227–31.

46. Imaizumi, K., Imai, K., Tyuma, I. 1982. Linkage between carbon dioxide binding and four-step oxygen binding to hemoglobin. *J. Mol. Biol.* 159:703–19

47. Johansen, K., Berger, M., Bicudo, J. E. P. W., Ruschi, A., de Almeida, P. J. 1987. Respiratory properties of blood and myoglobin in hummingbirds. *Physiol. Zool.* 60:269–78

48. Johansen, K., Lykkeboe, G. 1979. Thermal acclimation of aerobic metabolism and $O_2Hb$ binding in the snake, *Vipera berus*. *J. Comp. Physiol.* 130:293–300

49. Johansen, K., Lykkeboe, G., Kornerup, S., Maloiy, G. M. O. 1980. Temperature insensitive $O_2$ binding in blood of the tree frog *Chiromantis petersi*. *J. Comp. Physiol.* 136:71–76

50. Jope, H. M., O'Brien, J. R. P. 1949. Crystallization and solubility studies on human adult and foetal haemoglobins. *Haemoglobin*, ed. F. J. W. Roughton, J. C. Kendrew, pp. 269–78. London: Butterworths

51. Kilmartin, J. V., Anderson, N. L., Ogawa, S. 1978. Response of the Bohr group salt bridges to ligation of the T state of haemoglobin Kansas. *J. Mol. Biol.* 123:71–87

52. Kilmartin, J. V., Breen, J. J., Roberts, G. C. K., Ho, C. 1973. Direct measurement of the pK values of an alkaline Bohr group in human hemoglobin. *Proc. Natl. Acad. Sci. USA* 70:1246–49

53. Kilmartin, J. V., Fogg, J., Luzzana, M., Rossi-Bernardi, L. 1973. Role of the $\alpha$-amino groups of the $\alpha$ and $\beta$ chains of human hemoglobin in oxygen-linked binding of carbon dioxide. *J. Biol. Chem.* 248:7039–43

54. Kilmartin, J. V., Fogg, J. H., Perutz, M. F. 1980. Role of C-terminal histidine in the alkaline Bohr effect of human hemoglobin. *Biochemistry* 19:3189–93

55. Kilmartin, J. V., Rossi-Bernardi, L. 1973. Interaction of hemoglobin with hydrogen ions, carbon dioxide, and organic phosphates. *Phys. Rev.* 53:836–90

56. Kilmartin, J. V., Wooton, J. F. 1970. Inhibition of Bohr effect after removal of C-terminal histidines from haemoglobin $\beta$-chains. *Nature* 228:766–67

57. Kwiatkowski, L. D., Noble, R. W. 1982. The contribution of histidine (HC3)(146$\beta$) to the R state Bohr effect of human hemoglobin. *J. Biol. Chem.* 257:8891–95

58. Kwiatkowski, L. D., Noble, R. W. 1987. The contribution of arginine (HC3) 141$\alpha$ to the Bohr effect of the fourth binding step in the reaction of ligand with human hemoglobin. *Proteins* 2:72–77

59. Lapennas, G. N., Reeves, R. B. 1983. Oxygen affinity of blood of domestic chicken and red jungle fowl. *Resp. Physiol.* 52:27–39

60. Lee, B. K., Richards, F. M. 1971. The interpretation of protein structures: Estimation of static accessibility. *J. Mol. Biol.* 55:349–400

61. Lutz, P. L. 1980. On the oxygen affinity of bird blood. *Am. Zool.* 20:187–98

62. Lutz, P. L., Longmuir, I. S., Schmidt-Nielsen, K. 1974. Oxygen affinity of bird blood. *Resp. Physiol.* 20:325–30

63. Lykkeboe, G., Johansen, K. 1978. An $O_2$-Hb 'paradox' in frog blood? (n-

values exceeding 4.0). *Resp. Physiol.* 35:119–27

64. MacMahon, J. A., Hamer, A. 1975. Effects of temperature and photoperiod on oxygenation and other blood parameters of the sidewinder *(Crotalus cerastes):* adaptive significance. *Comp. Biochem. Physiol.* 51A:59–69

65. Matsukawa, S., Itatani, Y., Mawatari, K., Shimokawa, Y., Yoneyama, Y. 1984. Quantitative evaluation for the role of $\beta$146 His and $\beta$143 His residues in the Bohr effect of human hemoglobin in the presence of 0.1 M chloride ion. *J. Biol. Chem.* 259:11479–86

66. Matsuura, M. S. A., Fushitani, K., Riggs, A. F. 1987. Amino acid sequence of the $\beta$ chain of the hemoglobin of the Brazilian water snake, *Liophis miliaris. Fed. Proc.* 46:2266

67. Matthew, J. B. 1985. Electrostatic effects in proteins. *Ann. Rev. Biophys. Chem.* 14:387–417

68. Matthew, J. B., Gurd, F. R. N., Garcia-Moreno, B., Flanagan, M. A., March, K. L., Shire, S. J. 1985. pH-dependent processes in proteins. *CRC Crit. Rev. Biochem.* 18:91–197

69. Matthew, J. B., Hanania, G. I. H., Gurd, F. R. N. 1979. Electrostatic effects in hemoglobin: Hydrogen ion equilibria in human deoxy- and oxyhemoglobin A. *Biochemistry* 18:1919–28

70. Matthew, J. B., Hanania, G. I. H., Gurd, F. R. N. 1979. Electrostatic effects in hemoglobin: Bohr effect and ionic strength dependence of individual groups. *Biochemistry* 18:1928–36

71. McDonald, M. J., Turci, S. M., Bleichman, M., Stinson, R. A. 1985. Functional and subunit assembly properties of hemoglobin Alberta $(\alpha_2\beta^{101\ Glu\rightarrow Gly})$. *J. Mol. Biol.* 183:105–12

72. Mills, F. C., Ackers, G. K. 1979. Thermodynamic studies on the oxygenation and subunit association of human hemoglobin. Temperature dependence of the linkage between dimer-tetramer association and oxygenation state. *J. Biol. Chem.* 254:2881–87

73. Mills, F. C., Johnson, M. L., Ackers, G. K. 1976. Oxygenation-linked subunit interactions in human hemoglobin: Experimental studies on the concentration dependence of oxygenation curves. *Biochemistry* 15:5350–62

74. Morris, R. J., Gibson, Q. H. 1982. Cooperative ligand binding to hemoglobin. Effects of temperature and pH on a hemoglobin with spectrophotometrically distinct chains *(Tunnus thynnus). J. Biol. Chem.* 257:4869–74

75. Morrow, J. S., Wittebort, R. J., Gurd, F. R. N. 1974. Ligand-dependent aggregation of chicken hemoglobin $A_I$. *Biochem. Biophys. Res. Commun.* 60:1058–65

76. Mrabet, N. T., McDonald, M. J., Turci, S., Sarkar, R., Szabo, A., Bunn, H. F. 1986. Electrostatic attraction governs the dimer assembly of human hemoglobin. *J. Biol. Chem.* 261:5222–28

77. Nagai, K., Perutz, M. F., Poyart, C. 1985. Oxygen binding properties of human mutant hemoglobins synthesized in *Escherichia coli. Proc. Natl. Acad. Sci. USA* 82:7252–55

78. Nakashima, M., Noda, H., Hasegaea, M., Ikai, A. 1985. The oxygen affinity of mammalian hemoglobins in the absence of 2,3-diphosphoglycerate in relation to body weight. *Comp. Biochem. Physiol.* 82A:583–89

79. Nishikura, K. 1978. Identification of histidine-122$\alpha$ in human haemoglobin as one of the unknown alkaline Bohr groups by hydrogen-tritium exchange. *Biochem. J.* 173:651–57

80. Noble, R. W., Kwiatkowski, L. D., De-Young, A., Davis, B. J., Haedrich, R. L., et al. 1986. Functional properties of hemoglobins from deep-sea fish: correlations with depth distribution and presence of a swim bladder. *Biochim. Biophys. Acta* 870:552–63

81. Noble, R. W., Parkhurst, L. J., Gibson, Q. H. 1970. The effect of pH on the reactions of oxygen and carbon monoxide with the hemoglobins of the carp, *Cyprinus carpio. J. Biol. Chem.* 245:6628–33

82. Noble, R. W., Pennelly, R. R., Riggs, A. 1975. Studies of the functional properties of the hemoglobin from the benthic fish, *Antimora rostrata. Comp. Biochem. Physiol.* 52B:75–81

83. O'Donnell, S., Mandaro, R., Schuster, T. M., Arnone, A. 1979. X-ray diffraction and solution studies of specifically carbamylated human hemoglobin A. *J. Biol. Chem.* 254:12204–8

84. Ohe, M., Kajita, A. 1980. Changes in $pK_a$ values of individual histidine residues of human hemoglobin upon reaction with carbon monoxide. *Biochemistry* 19:4443–50

85. Parkhurst, L. J., Goss, D. J. 1984. Ligand binding kinetic studies on the hybrid hemoglobin $\alpha$(human):$\beta$(carp): A hemoglobin with mixed conformations and sequential conformational changes. *Biochemistry* 23:2180–86

86. Parkhurst, L. J., Goss, D. J., Perutz, M. F. 1983. Kinetic and equilibrium studies on the role of the $\beta$-147 histidine in the

Root effect and cooperativity in carp hemoglobin. *Biochemistry* 22:5401–9

87. Pennelly, R. R., Riggs, A., Noble, R. W. 1978. The kinetics and equilibria of squirrel fish hemoblogin. A Root effect hemoglobin complicated by large subunit heterogeneity. *Biochim. Biophys. Acta* 533:120–29

88. Pennelly, R. R., Tan-Wilson, A. L., Noble, R. W. 1975. Structural states and transitions of carp hemoglobin. *J. Biol. Chem.* 250:7239–44

89. Perutz, M. F. 1970. Stereochemistry of cooperative effects in haemoglobin. *Nature* 228:726–39

90. Perutz, M. F. 1978. Electrostatic effects in proteins. *Science* 201:1187–91

91. Perutz, M. F. 1982. Comments. In *Hemoglobin and Oxygen Binding,* ed. C. Ho, pp. 318–19. New York: Elsevier

92. Perutz, M. F. 1983. Species adaptation in a protein molecule. *Mol. Biol. Evol.* 1:1–28

93. Perutz, M. F., Bauer, C., Gros, G., Leclercq, F., Vandecasserie, C., et al. 1981. Allosteric regulation of crocodilian haemoglobin. *Nature* 291:682–84

94. Perutz, M. F., Brunori, M. 1982. Stereochemistry of cooperative effects in fish and amphibian haemoglobins. *Nature* 299:421–26

95. Perutz, M. F., del Pulsinelli, P., TenEyck, L., Kilmartin, J. V., Shibata, S., et al. 1971. Haemoglobin Hiroshima and the mechanism of the alkaline Bohr effect. *Nature New Biol.* 232:147–49

96. Perutz, M. F., Fermi, G., Luisi, B., Shaanan, B., Liddington, R. C. 1987. Stereochemistry of cooperative mechanisms in hemoglobin. *Accounts of Chemical Research* In press

97. Perutz, M. F., Fermi, G., Shih, T.-b. 1984. Structure of deoxyhemoglobin Cowtown [His HC3(146)$\beta$→Leu]: Origin of the alkaline Bohr effect and electrostatic interactions in hemoglobin. *Proc. Natl. Acad. Sci. USA* 81:4781–84

98. Perutz, M. F., Gronenborn, A. M., Clore, G. M., Fogg, J. H., Shih, D. T.-b. 1985. The p$K_a$ values of two histidine residues in human haemoglobin, the Bohr effect, and the dipole moments of $\alpha$-helices. *J. Mol. Biol.* 183:491–98

99. Perutz, M. F., Gronenborn, A. M., Clore, G. M., Shih, D. T.-b., Craescu, C. T. 1985. Comparison of histidine proton magnetic resonances of human carbonmonoxyhaemoglobin in different buffers. *J. Mol. Biol.* 186:471–73

100. Perutz, M. F., Kilmartin, J. V., Nishikura, K., Fogg, J. H., Butler, P. J. G., Rollema, H. S. 1980. Identification of residues contributing to the Bohr effect of human haemoglobin. *J. Mol. Biol.* 138:649–70

101. Pough, F. H., 1969. Environmental adaptations in the blood of lizards. *Comp. Biochem. Physiol.* 31:885–901

102. Poyart, C., Bursaux, E., Arnone, A., Bonaventura, J., Bonaventura, C. 1980. Structural and functional studies of hemoglobin Suresnes (Arg 141$\alpha_2$ → His $\beta_2$). Consequences of disrupting an oxygen linked anion-binding site. *J. Biol. Chem.* 255:9465–73

103. Riggs, A. 1960. The nature and significance of the Bohr effect in mammalian hemoglobins. *J. Gen. Physiol.* 43:737–52

104. Riggs, A. 1971. Mechanism of the enhancement of the Bohr effect in mammalian hemoglobins by diphosphoglycerate. *Proc. Natl. Acad. Sci. USA* 68:2062–65

105. Riggs, A., ed. 1979. The *Alpha Helix* expedition to the Amazon for the study of fish bloods and hemoglobins. *Comp. Biochem. Physiol.* 62A:1–272

106. Rossi Fanelli, A., Antonini, E., Caputo, A. 1964. Hemoglobin and myoglobin. *Adv. Protein Chem.* 19:209–12

107. Russu, I. M., Ho, C. 1986. Assessment of roles of $\beta$146-histidyl and other histidyl residues in the Bohr effect of human normal adult hemoglobin. *Biochemistry* 25:1706–16

108. Russu, I. M., Ho, N. T., Ho, C. 1980. Role of the $\beta$146 histidyl residue in the alkaline Bohr effect of hemoglobin. *Biochemistry* 19:1043–52

109. Russu, I. M., Ho, N. T., Ho, C. 1982. A proton nuclear magnetic resonance investigation of histidyl residues in human normal adult hemoglobin. *Biochemistry* 21:5031–43

110. Saffron, W. A., Gibson, Q. H. 1978. The effect of pH on carbon monoxide binding to menhaden hemoglobin. Allosteric transitions in a Root effect hemoglobin. *J. Biol. Chem.* 253:3171–79

111. Samaja, M., Rovida, E., Niggeler, M., Perrella, M., Rossi-Bernardi, L. 1987. The dissociation of carbon monoxide from hemoglobin intermediates. *J. Biol. Chem.* 262:4528–33

112. Shaanan, B. 1983. Structure of human oxyhaemoglobin at 2.1 Å resolution. *J. Mol. Biol.* 171:31–59

113. Shih, D. T.-b., Jones, R. T., Bonaventura, J., Bonaventura, C., Schneider, R. G. 1984. Involvement of His HC3 (146)$\beta$ in the Bohr effect of human hemoglobin. *J. Biol. Chem.* 259:967–74

114. Shih, D. T.-b., Jones, R. T., Imai, K.,

Tyuma, I. 1985. Involvement of Glu G3(101)$\beta$ in the function of hemoglobin. *J. Biol. Chem.* 260:5919–24

115. Shih, D. T.-b., Perutz, M. F. 1987. Influence of anions and protons on the Adair coefficients of haemoglobins A and Cowtown (His HC3(146)$\beta$→Leu). *J. Mol. Biol.* 195:419–22

116. Shih, D. T.-b., Perutz, M. F., Gronenborn, A. M., Clore, G. M. 1987. Histidine proton resonances of carbonmonoxyhaemoglobins A and Cowtown in chloride-free buffer. *J. Mol. Biol.* 195:453–55

117. Smith, F. R., Ackers, G. K. 1985. Experimental resolution of cooperative free energies for the ten ligation states of human hemoglobin. *Proc. Natl. Acad. Sci. USA* 82:5347–51

118. Smith, J. L., Hendrickson, W. A., Honzatko, R. B., Sheriff, S. 1986. Structural heterogeneity in protein crystals. *Biochemistry* 25:5018–27

119. Tam, L.-T., Gray, G. P., Riggs, A. F. 1986. The hemoglobins of the bullfrog *Rana catesbeiana*. The structure of the $\beta$ chain of component C and the role of the $\alpha$ chain in the formation of intermolecular disulfide bonds. *J. Biol. Chem.* 261:8290–94

120. Tam, L.-T., Riggs, A. F. 1984. Oxygen binding and aggregation of bullfrog hemoglobin. *J. Biol. Chem.* 259:2610–16

121. Tan, A. L., DeYoung, A., Noble, R. W. 1972. The pH dependence of the affinity, kinetics and cooperativity of ligand binding to carp hemoglobin, *Cyprinus carpio. J. Biol. Chem.* 247:2493–98

122. Tomita, S., Riggs, A. 1971. Studies of the interaction of 2,3-diphosphoglycerate and carbon dioxide with hemoglobins from mouse, man and elephant. *J. Biol. Chem.* 246:547–54

123. Van Beek, G. G. M., De Bruin, S. H. 1980. Identification of the residues involved in the oxygen-linked chloride-ion binding sites in human deoxyhemoglobin and oxyhemoglobin. *Eur. J. Biochem.* 105:353–60

124. Van Beek, G. G. M., Zuiderweg, E. R. P., De Bruin, S. H. 1979. The binding of chloride ions to ligated and unligated human hemoglobin and its influence on the Bohr effect. *Eur. J. Biochem.* 99:379–83

125. Wajcman, H., Kilmartin, J. V., Najman, A., Labie, D. 1975. Hemoglobin Cochin-Port Royal: Consequences of the replacement of the $\beta$-chain C-terminal by an arginine. *Biochim. Biophys. Acta* 400:354–64

126. Warshel, A., Russell, S. T. 1984. Calculations of the electrostatic interactions in biological systems and in solutions. *Q. Rev. Biophys.* 17:283–422

127. Warshel, A., Russell, S. T., Churg, A. K. 1984. Macroscopic models for studies of electrostatic interactions in proteins: Limitations and applicability. *Proc. Natl. Acad. Sci. USA* 81:4785–89

128. Watt, K. W. K., Riggs, A. 1975. Hemoglobins of the tadpole of the bullfrog, *Rana catesbeiana*. Structure and function of isolated components. *J. Biol. Chem.* 250:5934–44

129. Weber, R. E., Wells, R. M. G., Rossetti, J. E. 1985. Adaptations to neoteny in the salamander, *Necturus maculosus*. Blood respiratory properties and interactive effects of pH, temperature and ATP on hemoglobin oxygenation. *Comp. Biochem. Physiol.* 80A:495–501

130. Wells, R. M. G., Weber, R. E. 1985. Fixed acid and carbon dioxide Bohr effects as functions of hemoglobin-oxygen saturation and erythrocyte pH in the blood of the frog, *Rana temporaria. Eur. J. Physiol.* 403:7–12

131. Wood, S. C., Lykkeboe, G., Johansen, K., Weber, R. E., Maloiy, G. M. O. 1978. Temperature acclimation in the pancake tortoise, *Malaccochersus tornieri*: Metabolic rate, blood pH, oxygen affinity and red cell organic phosphates. *Comp. Biochem. Physiol.* 59A:155–60

# CELL AND MOLECULAR PHYSIOLOGY

## MODULATION OF MEMBRANE TRANSPORT SYSTEMS

*Introduction,* Joseph F. Hoffman, *Section Editor*

This year's theme of the section on Cell and Molecular Physiology is primarily concerned with factors that modulate membrane transport systems. The characteristics displayed by all membrane transport systems appear to be defined by intrinsic as well as extrinsic determinants. Intrinsic properties are presumably set by the amino acid sequence defining the protein/transport complex structure, while extrinsic determinants are defined by environmental interactions such as with lipids, substrates, and ligands. Most of the articles in this section deal mainly with defining extrinsic determinants because until recently these aspects have been the most experimentally accessible. However, the application of molecular biological techniques to alter transport systems offers ways to evaluate intrinsic determinants. As always, space limitations prevent as complete a survey as desired. Nevertheless it seems clear that combinations as well as extensions of the various approaches discussed here provide considerable insight into the molecular mechanisms that underlie the transport reactions.

*Ann. Rev. Physiol. 1988. 50:207–23*

# MITOGENS AND ION FLUXES

*Stephen P. Soltoff and Lewis C. Cantley*

Department of Physiology, Tufts University School of Medicine, Boston, Massachusetts 02111

## INTRODUCTION

The response of growth-arrested cells to a variety of growth factors and pharmacological mitogens involves a cascade of biochemical and ionic changes that occur within minutes and are believed to play critical roles in the initiation of cell proliferation. In general, investigations of these phenomena have used proliferating cells in culture that can be made to reversibly enter the nonproliferative $G_0/G_1$ state, usually by the withdrawal of serum. The biochemical changes observed within the first few minutes of the addition of growth factors and mitogens include protein phosphorylation, an increased turnover of inositol lipids, and increased transcription of several proto-oncogenes. The ionic alterations include rapid increases in the cytosolic free calcium concentration ($[Ca^{2+}]_i$) from intracellular calcium stores and/or via influx through channels in the plasma membrane and the stimulation of the plasma membrane $Na^+$-$H^+$ exchanger, which promotes an increase in sodium influx and cytoplasmic alkalinization. The relationship between these early changes and the increase in DNA synthesis that occurs many hours later is a key question in the understanding of mitogenesis. This article focuses on the alterations in ion fluxes that have been observed in response to mitogens in a variety of cells. In addition, the association of biochemical events with ion fluxes and the association of these early events with the subsequent initiation of DNA synthesis are discussed. Important considerations that are addressed are whether there are multiple pathways by which different mitogens induce proliferation and whether a single mitogen can induce proliferation by multiple pathways.

207

0066-4278/88/0315-0207$02.00

# BINDING OF GROWTH FACTORS TO RECEPTORS GENERATES SECOND MESSENGERS

The binding of polypeptide growth factors and mitogens to specific receptors on the cell surface results in the production of a variety of intracellular second messengers and metabolites that are believed to have important functions in cell proliferation. Many growth factor receptors, including those for PDGF (platelet-derived growth factor), CSF-1 (macrophage colony stimulating factor), and EGF (epidermal growth factor), share common structural features and possess intrinsic protein tyrosine kinase activity on their cytosolic domains (24, 82). Since the tyrosine kinase activity is stimulated within seconds of the binding of growth factors to their receptors, it has been suggested that the proliferative response of cells to growth factors necessarily depends on the phosphorylation of tyrosine residues on the receptor itself (autophosphorylation) or on the phosphorylation of other proteins. The structural similarities between growth factors/growth factor receptors and various oncogene products (13) have also led to the suggestion that the activation of tyrosine kinases may be a common trait of both the activation of quiescent cells to a state of proliferation and of the persistent proliferative state that characterizes transformed cells.

Within seconds after the addition of some mitogens to cells, the levels of inositol polyphosphates are altered (for review, see 5). Phosphatidylinositol-4,5-bisphosphate ($PIP_2$), a phospholipid located in the inner leaflet of the plasma membrane, is hydrolyzed by phospholipase C, and two biologically active products are formed: diacylglycerol (DAG), which is lipid soluble and remains associated with the membrane, and inositol 1,4,5-trisphosphate ($IP_3$), which is water soluble and can diffuse through the cytosol. Both products can act as second messengers. $IP_3$ increases $[Ca^{2+}]_i$ by causing the release of calcium from the endoplasmic reticulum (5), and DAG activates the calcium- and phospholipid-dependent protein kinase C (47). As discussed below, $IP_3$ can increase $[Ca^{2+}]_i$ in other ways, and protein kinase C can activate the $Na^+$-$H^+$ exchanger in the plasma membrane and increase $pH_i$. Increases in $[Ca^{2+}]_i$ and $pH_i$ are both well-characterized effects of many mitogens that stimulate phosphoinositide breakdown.

There is also an increase in the transcriptional products of several genes, notably c-*myc* and c-*fos*, within minutes after the binding of growth factors to their receptors. The gene product of c-*fos* was shown to be required for proliferation in 3T3 fibroblasts (23), and c-*myc* apparently plays a regulating role in PDGF-stimulated 3T3 cell growth (2). These genes are called proto-oncogenes because they are cellular homologues of retroviral genes that can transform cells. The expression of these gene products can also be regulated by various second messengers (including DAG and $Ca^{2+}$) produced when growth factors bind to their receptors (73).

# MITOGENS RAISE $[Ca^{2+}]_i$

## Release of Calcium from Intracellular Stores

The addition of concanavalin A (con A) to T lymphocytes (72) or of PDGF, EGF, or serum to human fibroblasts (43) promotes a rapid rise in $[Ca^{2+}]_i$, which frequently reaches a level of two to three times the unstimulated value (generally 100–150 nM) and then declines to a new level that is often somewhat higher than the unstimulated value. In sea urchin eggs loaded with the calcium-sensitive dye Fura-2, fertilization promotes an increase in $[Ca^{2+}]_i$ that is about ten times larger than normal, after which $[Ca^{2+}]_i$ declines to a level of almost twice that observed before fertilization (53).

As has been now documented for many cells, including proliferating cells in culture, sea urchin eggs, and cells isolated from various tissues, the link between receptor occupation and the increase in calcium is frequently mediated by the rapid turnover of inositol polyphospholipids (5). The production of $IP_3$ in response to growth factors such as PDGF, bombesin vasopressin, and serum causes the release of calcium from the endoplasmic reticulum, thereby raising $[Ca^{2+}]_i$. In these cases there is a rapid increase in $[Ca^{2+}]_i$ even in the absence of extracellular calcium.

## Activation of Calcium Channels

Some growth factors, notably EGF and FGF (fibroblast growth factor), increase $[Ca^{2+}]_i$ even when very little phosphoinositide breakdown is measurable. The addition of FGF to quiescent CCL39 fibroblasts increased $[Ca^{2+}]_i$ and reinitiated DNA synthesis but did not stimulate an increase in the level of the total inositol phosphates (34). EGF increased $[Ca^{2+}]_i$ (22) and stimulated DNA synthesis (7) in 3T3 fibroblasts but did not alter inositol lipid degradations. For both cell lines, the increase in $[Ca^{2+}]_i$ was dependent on the presence of extracellular calcium. These studies suggest that in cells in which mitogens increase $[Ca^{2+}]_i$ and do not stimulate phosphatidylinositol turnover, the increase in $[Ca^{2+}]_i$ results from channel-mediated calcium influx across the plasma membrane. A similar mechanism was initially postulated to exist in A431 cells. In these cells, which express up to 100-fold more EGF receptors than do other cells, EGF-stimulated increases in $[Ca^{2+}]_i$ (as measured by Quin 2 fluorescence) (38) and $^{45}Ca$ uptake (68) were both blocked by $La^{3+}$, and EFG was reported to either stimulate (68) or have no effect on (33) phosphoinositide turnover. Recent experiments indicate that EGF does stimulate the production of inositol trisphosphate in A431 cells: In response to EGF, $IP_3$ increased 40–50% above the baseline level (21, 52). In one of these studies, the maximal increase in $IP_3$ was reached in 20 sec, after which it rapidly declined (21). EGF produced a sustained elevation of $[Ca^{2+}]_i$ (as measured with Fura 2) in the presence of external calcium. A transitory increase in $[Ca^{2+}]_i$ was observed in the absence of extracellular calcium (21), which suggests that EGF can mobilize calcium through an $IP_3$-mediated release of intracellular calcium. Part of the controversy regarding the effects of EGF on A431 cells stems from the fact that the increase in $IP_3$ is transitory and of a relatively low magnitude. The use of Fura 2, which buffers intracellular calcium less than does Quin 2, may explain the difference in the reports as to the ability of EGF to raise $[Ca^{2+}]_i$ in the absence of external calcium (21). Other mitogens, such as PDGF (43) and serum (38), increase $[Ca^{2+}]_i$ in the absence of extracellular calcium in A431 cells, presumably through the stimulation of phosphoinositide turnover; however, this has not been examined directly.

There is other evidence that mitogens activate a calcium channel. In a human T-cell lymphocytic leukemia cell line (HPB-ALL), $La^{3+}$-sensitive increases in $[Ca^{2+}]_i$ in response to mitogenic antibodies appeared to involve a membrane potential–sensitive calcium channel (48). In the study of A431 cells cited above (21) and in other studies, elevated levels of intracellular calcium may be maintained in the presence of extracellular calcium, but in the absence of calcium the maximal rise in $[Ca^{2+}]_i$ is frequently reduced, and the elevated levels rapidly return to baseline values. These observations suggest that calcium influx is required to maintain the elevated levels of $[Ca^{2+}]_i$. Direct evidence that metabolites of phosphoinositides can activate calcium channels is presented in the next section. However, Putney et al (57) have suggested that extracellular calcium directly enters the $IP_3$-sensitive calcium pool in the endoplasmic reticulum and that this provides a sustained elevation of $[Ca^{2+}]_i$ in response to the receptor-mediated release of calcium. According to this model, the entry of extracellular calcium into the endoplasmic reticulum is activated by a decrease in the calcium content of this organelle.

## Channel Activation by Inositol Polyphosphate Metabolites

Recent studies have shown that in addition to $IP_3$-mediated mobilization of calcium from intracellular stores, receptor-mediated changes in phosphatidy-inositol metabolism can also increase $[Ca^{2+}]_i$ by activating calcium channels in several different ways.

1. In whole-cell patch-clamp studies using cloned human T lymphocytes, the mitogenic lectin PHA (phytohaemagglutinin) activated a voltage-independent, low-conductance calcium channel (28). In excised patches of these cells, a similar conductance was activated by $IP_3$ (27). Thus in these cells an increase in $IP_3$ not only mobilizes intracellular calcium but can also stimulate calcium influx.

2. In human neutrophils platelet-activating factor and fMet-Leu-Phe (fMLP) increase $[Ca^{2+}]_i$ in the absence of extracellular calcium. Patch-clamp studies indicated that these cells possess a nonselective cation channel through which calcium ions can pass (78). This channel was activated by $[Ca^{2+}]_i$ but not by $IP_3$, which suggests that intracellular calcium can act as a positive

modulator to further increase $[Ca^{2+}]_i$ beyond the level produced by $IP_3$-induced mobilization.

3. In sea urchin eggs the injection of inositol 1,3,4,5-tetrakisphosphate ($P_4$, produced from $IP_3$ by inositol 1,4,5-trisphosphate kinase) promoted the raising of the fertilization envelope, an event that depended on the presence of extracellular calcium (25). This finding suggests that $IP_4$ can function as a second messenger and may activate a calcium channel that is responsible for maintaining the elevated calcium levels seen after fertilization (see above), which are necessary for the activation of the egg. Recent studies in mouse thymocytes reported that the phosphorylation of $IP_3$ to $IP_4$ depends on the free calcium concentration (83). Since the injection of $IP_3$ alone into sea urchin eggs is sufficient to raise the fertilization envelope (81), these studies suggest that the production of $IP_3$ initially mobilizes calcium from intracellular stores and that this activates the conversion to $IP_4$, which then promotes a sustained increase in $[Ca^{2+}]_i$ by influx through a calcium channel. However, no direct effect of $IP_4$ on calcium influx has yet been demonstrated.

Thus there are multiple ways in which mitogens can increase intracellular calcium. The existence of calcium channels that can be activated directly and indirectly by metabolites of inositol phospholipids promotes the maintenance of an elevated $[Ca^{2+}]_i$ within cells and prolongs the initial effects that originate when mitogens bind to their receptors.

## Mitogenic Alterations of Channel Expression

Although this subject is only briefly considered here, the expression of ion channels can also be altered by mitogens. The withdrawal of serum from proliferating $BC_3Hl$ myocytes results in differentiation and the expression within five days of functional calcium and sodium channel which are not normally seen during proliferation (9). In addition, cells that were transfected with certain oncogene alleles ($Val^{12}$ c-H-*ras*, or c-*myc* combined with v-*erbB*) and maintained in serum did not express calcium and sodium channels for at least four weeks. This suggests that mitogens and oncogenes suppress differentiation and maintain muscle cells in a state of proliferation. Potassium channels in muscle cells were unaffected by withdrawal of serum or by transfection with oncogene alleles (9). In contrast, murine T lymphocytes, which in the quiescent state express small numbers of potassium channels, have a large number of potassium channels one day after treatment with the mitogen con A (11).

# MITOGENS ACTIVATE $Na^+$-$H^+$ EXCHANGE

In early studies it was observed that serum and growth factors rapidly promoted an increase in uptake of $^{86}Rb$ into cells, and that this uptake was mediated by the $Na^+$ pump (Na,K-ATPase) (66). The increase in $Na^+$ pump activity was due to the stimulation of sodium entry and could be mimicked by monensin (70), an ionophore that promotes sodium entry (in exchange for intracellular $H^+$). Moreover, the stimulation by serum of DNA synthesis was dependent on the concentration of sodium in the extracellular medium, as was the sodium pump activity (70), which suggested that there might be a primary relationship between sodium pump activity and cell proliferation. Subsequently, the contribution of the activated $Na^+$-$H^+$ exchanger to sodium entry and the dependence of the $Na^+$-$H^+$ exchanger on the extracellular sodium concentration were recognized. These realizations, as well as the finding that protein synthesis is dependent on $pH_i$ (55) and the intracellular potassium concentration (8), relegated the stimulation of the sodium pump by mitogens to a secondary response. The increased activity of the sodium pump is such that in the absence of ouabain the intracellular sodium concentration may not be greatly changed in some mitogen-stimulated cells (15, 41), although measurable increases were observed in other cells (61).

An overwhelming number of studies have now shown that growth factors increase $pH_i$ via activation of the $Na^+$-$H^+$ exchanger (for review, see 37, 65), an ion transport system in the plasma membrane that exchanges intracellular $H^+$ for extracellular $Na^+$. Direct evidence for the existence of such an exchange system was first presented by Murer et al (46), who used a membrane vesicle preparation from renal and intestinal cells. In intact cells, the earliest direct indication of the activation of $Na^+$-$H^+$ exchange was in studies of the fertilization of sea urchin eggs. Johnson et al (26) observed that immediately after fertilization there was an efflux of acid ($H^+$), which varied as a function of the extracellular sodium concentration; a stimulation of $^{22}Na$ uptake; and an increase in the $pH_i$ of about 0.3 units. In addition, the $H^+$ efflux and $^{22}Na$ uptake were blocked by amiloride. The sensitivity of these fluxes to amiloride soon became one way in which the activation of the $Na^+$-$H^+$ exchange system was identified in other systems. Johnson et al (26) presciently suggested that changes in intracellular pH might play an important role in the activation of other kinds of quiescent cells in the $G_0$ state.

Subsequent studies found that serum and growth factors stimulate an electrically silent, amiloride-sensitive increase in sodium entry in quiescent fibroblasts (45, 75), neuroblastoma cells (40, 41), A431 epidermoid carcinoma cells (64), pre–B lymphocytes (60, 62), T lymphocytes (61), and other cells. Measurements of $H^+$ efflux (54), 5,5-dimethyl-2,4-oxazoladinedione (DMO) distribution (69), and internalized pH-sensitive dyes (44, 62) demonstrated that mitogen-stimulated sodium entry was linked to $H^+$ efflux and a rise in $pH_i$.

Upon the reintroduction of serum or mitogens to quiescent cells, the reinitiation of DNA synthesis, which occurs hours after the addition of mitogens, is preceded by the stimulation of an amiloride-sensitive sodium uptake, $H^+$ efflux, and an increase in $pH_i$, events which occur during the first several minutes. Two questions are raised by these findings: What is the mechanism by which the $Na^+$-$H^+$ exchanger becomes activated by growth factors? And what is the relationship between the activation of $Na^+$-$H^+$ exchange and DNA synthesis? These questions are addressed in the next sections.

## PROTEIN KINASE C AND $[Ca^{2+}]_i$ CAN REGULATE THE ACTIVATION OF $Na^+$-$H^+$ EXCHANGE

Under physiological conditions $(Na^+]_{out} > [Na^+]_{in}; [H^+]_{out} \le [H^+]_{in})$ the $Na^+$-$H^+$ exchanger mediates a $1:1$ exchange of $Na^+_{out}$ for $H^+_{in}$. In quiescent cells the exchanger is not very active, even though there is a large inwardly directed sodium gradient. However, when the $pH_i$ is lowered, the $Na^+$-$H^+$ exchanger can be disproportionately stimulated above the amount expected due to the increase in the $[H^+]$ as a substrate. This occurs due to the existence of an intracellular $H^+$-modifying site that allows the $[H^+]$ to allosterically activate the $Na^+$-$H^+$ exchanger separately from its role as a substrate (3). In quiescent cells the threshold $pH_i$ for this effect frequently occurs between pH 6.8 and 7.2, which is the normal $pH_i$ range; this explains the relative inactivity of the $Na^+$-$H^+$ exchanger in spite of the inward sodium gradient. Growth factors activate $Na^+$-$H^+$ exchange by increasing the affinity of the exchanger for internal protons, and this raises the threshold $pH_i$ (44, 50). Therefore, in the presence of growth factors the normal $[H^+]$ inside the cell activates $Na^+$-$H^+$ exchange at the allosteric site, and there is an increase in $pH_i$.

In many cells the effect of growth factors on $Na^+$-$H^+$ exchange is due to the increase in phosphatidylinositol turnover that is promoted by the binding of many growth factors to their receptors. As mentioned above, growth factors can stimulate the production of DAG from the hydrolysis of $PIP_2$. Diacylglycerol can activate protein kinase C, a calcium- and phospholipid-dependent enzyme that can phosphorylate serine and threonine residues on proteins (47). In addition, phorbol esters, which are tumor promoting agents, are structural analogs of diacylglycerol and can also activate protein kinase C (47). Several studies suggest that the underlying basis of the activation of $Na^+$-$H^+$ exchange by growth factors is the activation of protein kinase C by diacylglycerol (for review, see 59): (*a*) Phorbol esters stimulate sodium influx in quiescent Swiss 3T3 fibroblasts (12, 76) and 70z/3 pre–B lymphocytes (62). The addition of phorbol ester or exogenous protein kinase C to renal apical membrane vesicles increases amiloride-sensitive sodium uptake (79). (*b*) Both phorbol esters and diacylglycerol produce rapid increases in the $pH_i$ of cultured fibroblasts (42). (*c*) Like growth factors, phorbol esters activate

$Na^+$-$H^+$ exchange by increasing the sensitivity to $pH_i$. For example, the threshold for activation was increased by about 0.2 pH units in lymphocytes (18).

Although the stimulation of $Na^+$-$H^+$ activity by growth factors can occur through the activation of protein kinase C, this may not be a universal occurrence in all systems. FGF activated $Na^+$-$H^+$ exchange and increased $[Ca^{2+}]_i$ in CCL39 lung fibroblasts, but it did not stimulate phosphatidylinositol turnover or activate protein kinase C (34). EGF also activated $Na^+$-$H^+$ exchange in these cells without activating protein kinase C (10). After TPA stimulated an increase in $pH_i$ in Swiss 3T3 cells, EGF increased $pH_i$ even more, which suggested that the effect of EGF on $pH_i$ was not mediated through protein kinase C (22). Moreover, although the addition of phorbol ester or the combination of EGF plus insulin to Swiss 3T3 cells increased $pH_i$ via activation of $Na^+$-$H^+$ exchange, protein kinase C did not appear to be activated by these mitogens (74). In serum-deprived cultured vascular smooth muscle cells, angiotensin II was found to increase $pH_i$ through a protein kinase C–dependent pathway, but in the presence of serum the increase in $pH_i$ was mediated by a protein kinase C–independent pathway (4).

In some cells, the $Na^+$-$H^+$ exchanger appears to be activated by an increase in intracellular calcium, and this may provide an alternative pathway (to protein kinase C) by which the $Na^+$-$H^+$ exchanger can be activated. Treatment of HSWP human fibroblasts with the calcium ionophore A23187 increased sodium entry threefold, compared to the fivefold stimulation by serum (49). In human T-cell leukemia cells (HPB-ALL), mitogenic antibodies against the T3-T cell receptor complex activated a $La^{3+}$-inhibitable calcium influx (48) and increased $pH_i$ (via $Na^+$-$H^+$ exchange). $pH_i$ remained elevated for at least 20 min, and this elevation required the presence of extracellular calcium (61). In these cells PMA caused a transitory increase in $pH_i$ that was not dependent on extracellular calcium. Thus, $Na^+$-$H^+$ exchange could be activated by two separate pathways: a calcium-dependent pathway and a protein kinase C–dependent pathway. The calcium-dependent pathway was inhibited in both HPB-ALL human T cells and rat fibroblasts by the immunosuppressive drug cyclosporine A (63).

Although TPA did not activate $Na^+$-$H^+$ exchange in fibroblasts (49), TPA in combination with submaximal concentrations of A23187 increased sodium influx more than did the calcium ionophore alone (76). These results suggest that protein kinase C may enhance $Na^+$-$H^+$ exchange in cells in which activation of protein kinase C alone is not a sufficient stimulus. The activation of protein kinase C may also have an inhibitory effect on other stimuli. In A431 cells and human fibroblasts, TPA had little or no effect by itself on $Na^+$-$H^+$ exchange, but it blocked the stimulation of $Na^+$-$H^+$ exchange by various mitogens (serum, EGF, vasopressin, and bradykinin) (76, 80). Thus protein kinase C may be able to regulate $Na^+$-$H^+$ exchange in either a positive or negative fashion.

One way in which protein kinase C may inhibit $Na^+$-$H^+$ exchange is by blocking calcium entry into cells that require a rise in $[Ca^{2+}]_i$ to activate the $Na^+$-$H^+$ exchanger. For example, TPA inhibited the serum- and EGF-promoted rise in $[Ca^{2+}]_i$ in A431 cells (38). If the stimulation of $Na^+$-$H^+$ exchange by EGF in A431 cells requires an elevation of intracellular calcium, this may explain the inhibition by TPA of the EGF-stimulated $Na^+$-$H^+$ exchanger (80). Other studies provide further indications of the mechanism(s) by which protein kinase C blocks the activation of $Na^+$-$H^+$ exchange by mitogens. In HPB-ALL T cells, in which $Na^+$-$H^+$ exchange is activated by antibodies to the T3-T cell receptor, an increase in $pH_i$ did not occur if the antibody was added after TPA produced a transient increase in $pH_i$ (61). Since TPA did not prevent antibody from raising $[Ca^{2+}]_i$ (61) in these cells, TPA did not block the activation of $Na^+$-$H^+$ exchange by reducing calcium entry. Moreover, the addition of TPA during the antibody-induced elevation of $pH_i$ (which is normally maintained for $\geq 20$ min) raised the $pH_i$ even more, but the effect was transient, and $pH_i$ was reduced to the level found prior to the initial stimulation by antibody (61). Thus in these cells protein kinase C could both stimulate and block the activation of $Na^+$-$H^+$ exchange.

The molecular mechanism by which mitogens activate $Na^+$-$H^+$ exchange is not known. Grinstein & Rothstein (19) evaluated common properties of various mitogens and activators of $Na^+$-$H^+$ exchange, and pointed out that they all activate protein kinases (tyrosine kinase or protein kinase C). This fact, in combination with observations that the activation of $Na^+$-$H^+$ exchange can be reduced if cells are depleted of ATP (see 19), suggests that a kinase-dependent phosphorylation probably plays an important role in the activation of $Na^+$-$H^+$ exchange.

## AN INCREASE IN $pH_i$ IS NECESSARY BUT NOT SUFFICIENT FOR PROLIFERATION

In sea urchin eggs, fertilization is marked by a rapid increase in $[Ca^{2+}]_i$ (53) and activation of $Na^+$-$H^+$ exchange (26). Fibroblasts and lymphocytes also respond to mitogens with increases in both $pH_i$ and $[Ca^{2+}]_i$ (22). In T lymphocytes, calcium ionophores were unable to stimulate DNA synthesis, but in combination with the phorbol ester TPA they markedly increased DNA synthesis (71). Studies such as these indicate correlations between cell proliferation and increases in both $[Ca^{2+}]_i$ and $pH_i$. Under some conditions, however, increases in $[Ca^{2+}]_i$ may not be required for mitogen-induced proliferation. A proliferative response was obtained when T lymphocytes were exposed to a combination of TPA, which does not raise $[Ca^{2+}]_i$, and PHA, which elicits a mitogenic response only in the presence of extracellular calcium, under conditions in which $[Ca^{2+}]_i$ did not increase (17). This observation may indicate that the activation of protein kinase C, which does not itself stimulate proliferation in these cells, permits mitogens to stimulate a calcium-independent proliferative response.

Several lines of evidence suggest that the activation of the $Na^+$-$H^+$ exchanger or some other mechanism of intracellular alkalinization is necessary for mitogen-induced cell proliferation, as follows.

1. The dose-response relationship of the effect of growth factors (thrombin or serum) on the stimulation of amiloride-sensitive $^{22}Na$ uptake in quiescent fibroblasts was similar to that of the stimulation of DNA synthesis by these factors (16, 54).

2. OAG, a synthetic diacylglycerol that activates $Na^+$-$H^+$ exchange, stimulates DNA synthesis in fibroblasts. In combination with other mitogens it has a synergistic effect on DNA synthesis and cell proliferation (67).

3. Amiloride and amiloride analogs inhibit $Na^+$-$H^+$ exchange in the same rank order of potency as they inhibit growth factor–stimulated DNA synthesis (29).

4. An elegant series of studies performed by Pouyssegur and coworkers demonstrated the interrelationship of the $Na^+$-$H^+$ exchanger, $pH_i$, and cell growth in $HCO_3^-$-free media. In one study (56), mutant CCL39 lung fibroblast cells were selected using a proton-suicide technique that acidified the $pH_i$ from 7.1 to 4.8. The cells that survived this selection pressure were mutants that lacked the $Na^+$-$H^+$ exchanger and, presumably, did not acidify under the imposed conditions, which drove $Na^+$-$H^+$ exchange in the reverse direction in wild-type cells. Once selected, the mutant cells were unable to grow in a neutral or acidic medium (pH $<$ 7.2) but grew normally when exposed to an alkaline medium (pH 8–8.3). The wild-type cells, which possessed the $Na^+$-$H^+$ exchanger, grew over a wide range of external pH values (6.6–8.2).

These results suggested the importance of $Na^+$-$H^+$ exchange in regulating $pH_i$ and cell growth under these conditions. A subsequent study (55) using the same cells demonstrated that the $pH_i$ dependence of DNA synthesis extended over an identical narrow range for both wild-type and mutant CCL fibroblasts in $HCO_3^-$-free media. Below $pH_i$ 7.2, mitogens (thrombin plus insulin) were unable to stimulate DNA synthesis; but at $pH_i$ 7.4, an increase of only 0.2 units, the mitogens stimulated DNA synthesis to 90% of the maximal amount. Thus these experiments demonstrated that $pH_i$ has a permissive effect on processes involved in cell proliferation.

This relationship is not restricted to mammalian cells. In synchronized populations of the cellular slime mold *Dictyostelium discoideum* growing exponentially in culture, increases in $pH_i$ occurred with a periodicity equal to but slightly ahead of cyclical increases in DNA synthesis and cell proliferation (1).

The presence or absence of bicarbonate is a key issue in studies such as these because of the ability of a $Cl^--HCO_3^-$ exchange system to help regulate $pH_i$ in the presence of bicarbonate (31, 58). Mutant CCL39 fibroblasts that lacked $Na^+-H^+$ exchange activity had nearly the same $pH_o$ dependence for growth factor–induced DNA synthesis in bicarbonate-buffered media as did wild-type fibroblasts, but this dependence was widely divergent between mutants and wild types in the absence of bicarbonate (55). These cells (both mutant and wild type) possess a $Na^+$-dependent $Cl^--HCO_3^-$ exchange mechanism that can maintain the $pH_i$ at a permissive level in the absence of the $Na^+-H^+$ exchanger if bicarbonate is present in the extracellular medium (31).

A few studies have suggested that neither activation of the $Na^+-H^+$ exchanger nor an increase in $pH_i$ is necessary for the initiation of proliferation by growth factors, even in the absence of bicarbonate. Under these conditions (no bicarbonate), interleukin 2 (IL-2) acted in a growth factor–like manner on T lymphocytes: It produced a rapid (within 90 sec) increase in $pH_i$ via activation of $Na^+-H^+$ exchange, and there was an increase in DNA synthesis hours later (36). However, DNA synthesis also occurred in the presence of concentrations of amiloride analogs that blocked $Na^+-H^+$ exchange and cytoplasmic alkalinization. Thus IL-2-dependent proliferation in T lymphocytes could occur without the activation of the $Na^+-H^+$ exchanger. In a similar study, EGF-induced DNA synthesis in BALB/c 3T3 cells was not blocked by concentrations of amiloride analogs sufficient to inhibit $Na^+-H^+$ exchange (6). However, since these studies were performed in the presence of bicarbonate, the possibility remained that an EGF-evoked cytoplasmic alkalinization may have occurred by a system other than $Na^+-H^+$ exchange. Thus stimulation of $Na^+-H^+$ exchange per se is not required for the initiation of DNA synthesis.

An increase in $pH_i$ is not sufficient for the initiation of DNA synthesis. In the absence of serum, elevation of the $pH_i$ to 7.4 in human fibroblasts only slightly increases DNA synthesis; but in the presence of serum, a much larger synthetic activity is seen at the same $pH_i$ (39). Similarly, CCL39 fibroblasts at $pH_i$ 7.39, which is sufficient for a nearly maximal amount of DNA synthesis (55), did not exhibit a significant amount of DNA synthesis in the absence of growth factor (30). Thus the proliferative effect of mitogens requires more than simply an increase in $pH_i$.

## DO THE EARLY RESPONSES TO MITOGENS MEDIATE PROLIFERATION?

Many of the biochemical measurements and almost all of the ion fluxes commonly measured after the addition of mitogens to quiescent cells are made in the first several minutes. Since DNA synthesis occurs hours later, it is not apparent that the same signal transduction pathway mediates both the early signals at the plasma membrane and DNA synthesis in the nucleus. In general, cells must be continuously exposed to growth factors for many hours for proliferation to occur. This may indicate that such a period of time is required for the sufficient accumulation of a product critical to proliferation. The increase in IP$_3$ levels is transient and generally rapidly abates, whereas the increase in DAG occurs more slowly and is longer lasting. In some cells, the $[Ca^{2+}]_i$ rises transiently and rapidly returns to baseline levels, but in others it remains elevated for a longer period of time, probably due to the activation of calcium channels in the plasma membrane (see above). Notably, in the sea urchin egg the postfertilization $[Ca^{2+}]_i$ is twice as high as the prefertilization level, and transient peaks during the rest of the cell cycle attest to the continuing association of calcium with mitosis (53).

The possibility that there are multiple mitogenic pathways within the same cell type was suggested by experiments performed using pertussis toxin, which blocks the effects of various mitogens, including bombesin, thrombin, and serum on DNA synthesis and cell proliferation (10, 32). In CCL39 fibroblasts, pertussis toxin selectively blocked the mitogenic effect of serum and thrombin but did not block the effects of FGF (10). Pertussis toxin also inhibited the thrombin-stimulated increase in inositol phosphates and the activation of the $Na^+$-$H^+$ exchanger; however, it did not block the activation of the $Na^+$-$H^+$ exchanger by phorbol ester (TPA) or EGF (51). Pertussis toxin is believed to inactivate a GTP-binding protein that couples membrane receptors to phospholipase C (77). Thus serum and thrombin may mediate their mitogenic effects by stimulating phosphatidylinositol turnover, while EGF and FGF may do so in the same cells by an independent mechanism.

In this light, it is worth considering the role of gene transcripts in the proliferative pathway. Mitogens increase the level of transcripts of proto-oncogenes such as c-*myc* and c-*fos*. In Swiss 3T3 fibroblasts, c-*fos* mRNA was increased by stimuli known to activate protein kinase C (phorbol esters), increase $[Ca^{2+}]_i$ (ionophores), and to elevate cAMP (73). This suggests that c-*fos* gene expression can be regulated by three different second messengers. Since c-*fos* expression normally precedes cell proliferation (23), any or all of these second messengers could be involved in the signal transduction pathway that initiates the proliferative response. Similar conclusions were obtained in this cell line in a study using growth factors. Bombesin and platelet-activating factor, which stimulate phosphatidylinositol turnover and thereby activate protein kinase C, were weak inducers of c-*fos* and c-*myc* when protein kinase C was depleted from the cells; but EGF, which is a relatively poor stimulator of inositol lipid turnover, was a potent inducer of these proto-oncogenes under these conditions (35). Thus the induction of the expression of these proto-oncogenes can occur through multiple pathways, which implies that there are multiple ways in which signal transduction at the plasma membrane can stimulate cell proliferation.

Oncogenes are believed to transform cells by encoding proteins that maintain cells in a highly proliferative state. It has been postulated that one of these proteins may transduce signals from the growth factor receptor to the cytosolic second messenger (24). The *ras* oncogene family may act in this manner. Interestingly, fibroblasts transformed with mutated *ras* genes had elevated levels of the products of $PIP_2$ hydrolysis (14), which suggests that transformation may maintain phospholipase C in a constitutively activated state and that these second messengers may play a critical role in cell proliferation. In addition, the microinjection of activated *ras* p21 into quiescent mouse 3T3 cells produced an increase in $pH_i$ by activating $Na^+$-$H^+$ exchange within 5 min of injection, which suggests that *ras* has a relatively direct effect on the pathway that regulates the exchanger (20).

## CONCLUSIONS

Rapid changes in phospholipid metabolism, ion fluxes, and other biochemical events ensue when quiescent cells are exposed to mitogens. This article has reviewed some of these changes. The ionic events are marked by the stimulation of $Na^+$-$H^+$ exchange and increases in $[Ca^{2+}]_i$ via multiple pathways. The breakdown of phosphatidylinositol into $IP_3$ and DAG can account for the stimulatory effects of many growth factors on the ion fluxes, but the effects of EGF remain less well characterized. Recent studies have shown that multiple pathways exist for mitogen stimulation of the early events at the plasma membrane. Thus there may be multiple pathways by which DNA synthesis and cell proliferation can be initiated.

ACKNOWLEDGMENTS

The authors wish to thank Drs. P. M. Rosoff and M. Whitman for helpful conversations and critically reading the manuscript. This work was supported by NIH grant GM 36133 (to LCC) and fellowship AM07566 (to SPS).

*Literature Cited*

1. Aerts, R. J., Durston, A. J., Moolenaar, W. H. 1985. Cytoplasmic pH and the regulation of the *Dictyostelium* cell cycle. *Cell* 43:643–57
2. Armelin, H. A., Armelin, M. C. S., Kelly, K., Stewart, T., Leder, P., et al. 1984. Functional role for c-*myc* in mitogenic response to platelet-derived growth factor. *Nature* 310:655–60
3. Aronson, P. S., Nee, J., Suhm, M. A. 1982. Modifier role of internal $H^+$ in activating the renal $Na^+$-$H^+$ exchanger in renal microvillus membrane vesicles. *Nature* 299:161–63
4. Berk, B. C., Aronow, M. S., Brock, T.

A., Cragoe, E. C. Jr., Gimbrone, M. A., Alexander, R. W. 1987. Angiotensin II–stimulated $Na^+$-$H^+$ exchange in cultured vascular smooth muscle cells. Evidence for protein kinase C-dependent and independent pathways. *J. Biol. Chem.* 262:5057–64
5. Berridge, M. J., Irvine, R. F. 1984. Inositol trisphosphate, a novel second messenger in cellular signal transduction. *Nature* 312:315–21
6. Besterman, J. M., Tyrey, S. J., Cragoe, E. J. Jr., Cuatrecasas, P. 1984. Inhibition of epidermal growth factor–induced mitogenesis by amiloride and an ana-

logue: Evidence against a requirement for Na$^+$-H$^+$ exchange. *Proc. Natl. Acad. Sci. USA* 81:6762–66

7. Besterman, J. M., Watson, S. P., Cuatrecasas, P. 1986. Lack of association of epidermal growth factor-, insulin-, and serum-induced mitogenesis with stimulation of phosphoinositide degradation in BALB/c 3T3 fibroblasts. *J. Biol. Chem.* 261:723–27

8. Burns, C. P., Rozengurt, E. 1984. Extracellular Na$^+$ and initiation of DNA synthesis: Role of intracellular pH and K$^+$. *J. Cell Biol.* 98:1082–89

9. Caffrey, J. M., Brown, A. M., Schneider, M. D. 1987. Mitogens and oncogenes can block the induction of specific voltage-gated ion channels. *Science* 236:570–73

10. Chambard, J. C., Paris, S., L'Allemain, G., Pouyssegur, J. 1987. Two growth factor signalling pathways in fibroblasts distinguished by pertussis toxin. *Nature* 326:800–3

11. Decoursey, T. E., Chandy, K. G., Gupta, S., Calahan, M. D. 1987. Mitogen induction of ion channels in murine T lymphocytes. *J. Gen. Physiol.* 89:405–20

12. Dicker, P., Rozengurt, E. 1981. Phorbol ester stimulation of Na influx and Na-K pump activity in Swiss 3T3 cells. *Biochem. Biophys. Res. Commun.* 100:433–41

13. Downward, J., Yarden, Y., Mayes, E., Scrace, G., Totty, N., et al. 1984. Close similarity of epidermal growth factor receptor and v-erb-B oncogene protein sequences. *Nature* 307:521–27

14. Fleischman, L. F., Chahwala, S. B., Cantley, L. 1986. *Ras*-transformed cells: Altered levels of phosphatidylinositol-4,5-bisphosphate and catabolites. *Science* 231:407–10

15. Frantz, C. N., Nathan, D. G., Scher, C. D. 1981. Intracellular univalent cations and the regulation of the BALB/c-3T3 cell cycle. *J. Cell Biol.* 88:51–56

16. Frelin, C., Vigne, P., Lazdunski, M. 1983. The amiloride-sensitive Na$^+$-H$^+$ antiport in 3T3 fibroblasts. Characterization and stimulation by serum. *J. Biol. Chem.* 258:6272–76

17. Gelfand, E. W., Cheung, R. K., Mills, G. B., Grinstein, S. 1985. Mitogens trigger a calcium-independent signal for proliferation in phorbol-ester-treated lymphocytes. *Nature* 315:419–20

18. Grinstein, S., Cohen, S., Goetz, J. D., Rothstein, A., Gelfand, E. W. 1985. Characterization of the activation of Na$^+$-H$^+$ exchange in lymphocytes by phorbol esters: Changes in cytoplasmic pH dependence of the antiport. *Proc. Natl. Acad. Sci. USA* 1429–33

19. Grinstein, S., Rothstein, A. 1986. Mechanisms of regulation of the Na$^+$-H$^+$ exchanger. *J. Membr. Biol.* 90:1–12

20. Hagag, N., Lacal, J. C., Graber, M., Aaronson, S., Viola, M. V. 1987. Microinjection of *ras* p21 induces a rapid rise in intracellular pH. *Mol. Cell. Biol.* 7:1984–88

21. Hepler, J. R., Nakahata, N., Lovenberg, T. W., DiGuiseppi, J., Herman, B., et al. 1987. Epidermal growth factor stimulates a rapid accumulation of inositol (1,4,5)-trisphosphate and a rise in cytosolic calcium mobilized from intracellular stores in A431 cells. *J. Biol. Chem.* 262:2951–56

22. Hesketh, T. R., Moore, J. P., Morris, J. D. H., Taylor, M. V., Rogers, J., et al. 1985. A common signal of calcium and pH signals in the mitogenic stimulation of eukaryotic cells. *Nature* 313:481–84

23. Holt, J. T., Gopal, T. V., Moulton, A. D., Nienhuis, A. W. 1986. Inducible production of c-*fos* antisense RNA inhibits 3T3 cell proliferation. *Proc. Natl. Acad. Sci. USA* 83:4794–98

24. Hunter, T., Cooper, J. A. 1985. Protein-tyrosine kinases. *Ann. Rev. Biochem.* 54:897–930

25. Irvine, R. F., Moor, R. M. 1986. Micro-injection of inositol 1,3,4,5-tetrakisphosphate activates sea urchin eggs by a mechanism dependent on external Ca$^{2+}$. *Biochem. J.* 240:917–20

26. Johnson, J. D., Epel, D., Paul, M. 1976. Intracellular pH and activation of sea urchin eggs after fertilisation. *Nature* 262:661–64

27. Kuno, M., Gardner, P. 1987. Ion channel activated by inositol 1,4,5-trisphosphate in plasma membrane of human T-lymphocytes. *Nature* 326:301–4

28. Kuno, M., Goronzy, J., Weyand, C. M., Gardner, P. 1986. Single-channel and whole-cell recordings of mitogen-regulated inward currents in human cloned helper T lymphocytes. *Nature* 323:269–73

29. L'Allemain, G., Franchi, A., Cragoe, E. Jr., Pouyssegur, J. 1984. Blockade of the Na$^+$-H$^+$ antiport abolishes growth factor–induced DNA synthesis in fibroblasts. Structure-activity relationships in the amiloride series. *J. Biol. Chem.* 259:4313–19

30. L'Allemain, G., Paris, S., Pouyssegur, J. 1984. Growth factor action and intracellular pH regulation in fibroblasts. Evidence for a major role of the Na$^+$-H$^+$ antiport. *J. Biol. Chem.* 259:5809–15

31. L'Allemain, G., Paris, S., Pouyssegur, J. 1985. Role of a $Na^+$-dependent $Cl^-$/$HCO_3^-$ exchange in regulation of intracellular pH in fibroblasts. *J. Biol. Chem.* 260:4877–83

32. Letterio, J. J., Coughlin, S. R., Williams, L. T. 1986. Pertussis toxin-sensitive pathway in the stimulation of c-*myc* expression and DNA synthesis by bombesin. *Science* 234:1117–19

33. Macara, I. G. 1986. Activation of $^{45}Ca^{2+}$ influx and $^{22}Na/H^+$ exchange by epidermal growth factor and vanadate in A431 cells is independent of phosphatidylinositol turnover and is inhibited by phorbol ester and diacylglycerol. *J. Biol. Chem.* 261:9321–27

34. Magnaldo, I., L'Allemain, G., Chambard, J. C., Moenner, M., Barritault, D., Pouyssegur, J. 1986. The mitogenic signaling pathway of fibroblast growth factor is not mediated through polyphosphoinositide hydrolysis and protein kinase C activation in hamster fibroblasts. *J. Biol. Chem.* 261:16916–22

35. McCaffrey, P., Ran, W., Campisi, J., Rosner, M. R. 1987. Two independent growth factor-generated signals regulate c-*fos* and c-*myc* mRNA levels in Swiss 3T3 cells. *J. Biol. Chem.* 262:1442–45

36. Mills, G. B., Cragoe, E. J. Jr., Gelfand, E. W., Grinstein, S. 1985. Interleukin 2 induces a rapid increase in intracellular pH through activation of a $Na^+$-$H^+$ antiport. Cytoplasmic alkalinization is not required for lymphocytes proliferation. *J. Biol. Chem.* 260:12500–7

37. Moolenaar, W. H. 1986. Effects of growth factors on intracellular pH regulation. *Ann. Rev. Physiol.* 48:363–76

38. Moolenaar, W. H., Aerts, R. J., Tertoolen, L. G. J., de Laat, S. W. 1986. The epidermal growth factor-induced calcium signal in A431 cells. *J. Biol. Chem.* 261:279–84

39. Moolenaar, W. H., Defize, L. H. K., de Laat, S. W. 1986. Ionic signalling by growth factor receptors. *J. Exp. Biol.* 124:359–73

40. Moolenaar, W. H., de Laat, S. W., van der Saag, P. T. 1979. Serum triggers a sequence of rapid ionic conductance changes in quiescent neuroblastoma cells. *Nature* 279:721–23

41. Moolenaar, W. H., Mummery, C. L., van der Saag, P. T., de Laat, S. W. 1981. Rapid ionic events and the initiation of growth in serum-stimulated neuroblastoma cells. *Cell*:789–98

42. Moolenaar, W. H., Terloolen, L. G. J., de Laat, S. W. 1984. Phorbol ester and diacylglycerol mimic growth factors in raising cytoplasmic pH. *Nature* 312:371–74

43. Moolenaar, W. H., Tertoolen, L. G. J., de Laat, S. W. 1984. Growth factors immediately raise cytoplasmic free $Ca^{2+}$ in human fibroblasts. *J. Biol. Chem.* 259:8066–69

44. Moolenaar, W. H., Tsien, R. Y., van der Saag, P. T., de Laat, S. W. 1983. $Na^+$-$H^+$ exchange and cytoplasmic pH in the action of growth factors in human fibroblasts. *Nature* 304:645–48

45. Moolenaar, W. H., Yarden, Y., de Laat, S. W., Schlessinger, J. 1982. Epidermal growth factor induces electrically silent $Na^+$ influx in human fibroblasts. *J. Biol. Chem.* 257:8502–6

46. Murer, H., Hopfer, U., Kinne, R. 1976. Sodium/proton antiport in brush-border-membrane vesicles isolated from rat small intestine and kidney. *Biochem. J.* 1 54:597–604

47. Nishizuka, Y. 1984. The role of protein kinase C in cell surface signal transduction and tumor promotion. *Nature* 308:693–98

48. Oettgen, H. C., Terhorst, C., Cantley, L. C., Rosoff, P. M. 1985. Stimulation of the T3–T cell receptor complex induces a membrane-potential-sensitive calcium influx. *Cell* 40:583–90

49. Owen, N. E., Villereal, M. L. 1982. Evidence for a role of calmodulin in serum stimulation of $Na^+$ influx in human fibroblasts. *Proc. Natl. Acad. Sci. USA* 79:3537–41

50. Paris, S., Pouyssegur, J. 1984. Growth factors activate the $Na^+$-$H^+$ antiporter in quiescent fibroblasts by increasing its affinity for intracellular $H^+$. *J. Biol. Chem.* 259:10989–94

51. Paris, S., Pouyssegur, J. 1986. Pertussis toxin inhibits thrombin-induced activation of phosphoinositide hydrolysis and $Na^+$-$H^+$ exchange in hamster fibroblasts. *EMBO J.* 5:55–60

52. Pike, L. J., Eakes, A. T. 1987. Epidermal growth factor stimulates the production of phosphatidylinositol monophosphate and the breakdown of polyphosphoinositides in A431 cells. *J. Biol. Chem.* 262:1644–51

53. Poenie, M., Alderton, J., Tsien, R. Y., Steinhardt, R. A. 1985. Changes of free calcium levels with stages of cell division cycle. *Nature* 315:147–49

54. Pouyssegur, J., Chambard, J. C., Franchi, A., Paris, S., Van Obberghen-Schilling, E. 1982. Growth factor activation of an amiloride-sensitive $Na^+$-$H^+$ exchange system in quiescent fibroblasts: Coupling to ribosomal S6

phosphorylation. *Proc. Natl. Acad. Sci. USA* 79:3935–39

55. Pouyssegur, J., Franchi, A., L'Allemain, G., Paris, S. 1985. Cytoplasmic pH, a key determinant of growth factor–induced DNA synthesis in quiescent fibroblasts. *FEBS Lett.* 190:115–19

56. Pouyssegur, J., Sardet, C., Franchi, A., L'Allemain, G., Paris, S. 1984. A specific mutation abolishing $Na^+$-$H^+$ antiport activity in hamster fibroblasts precludes growth at neutral and acidic pH. *Proc. Natl. Acad. Sci. USA* 81:4833–37

57. Putney, J. W., Aub, D. L., Taylor, C. W., Merritt, J. E. 1986. Formation and biological actions of inositol 1,4,5-trisphosphate. *Fed. Proc.* 45:2634–38

58. Roos, A., Boron, W. F. 1981. Intracellular pH. *Physiol. Rev.* 61:296–434

59. Rosoff, P. 1987. Phorbol esters and the regulation of $Na^+$-$H^+$ exchange. In *$Na^+$-$H^+$ Exchange*, ed. S. Grinstein. Boca Raton, Fla.: CRC. In press

60. Rosoff, P. M., Cantley, L. C. 1983. Increasing the intracellular $Na^+$ concentration induces differentiation in a pre-B lymphocyte cell line. *Proc. Natl. Acad. Sci. USA* 80:7547–50

61. Rosoff, P. M., Cantley, L. C. 1985. Stimulation of the T3–T cell receptor–associated $Ca^{2+}$ influx enhances the activity of the $Na^+$-$H^+$ exchanger in a leukemic human T cell line. *J. Biol. Chem.* 260:14053–59

62. Rosoff, P. M., Stein, L. F., Cantley, L. C. 1984. Phorbol esters induce differentiation in a pre-B lymphocyte cell line by enhancing $Na^+$-$H^+$ exchange. *J. Biol. Chem.* 259:7056–60

63. Rosoff, P. M., Terres, G. 1986. Cyclosporin A inhibits $Ca^{2+}$-dependent stimulation of the $Na^+$-$H^+$ antiport in human T cells. *J. Cell Biol.* 103:457–63

64. Rothenberg, P., Glaser, L., Schlesinger, P., Cassel, D. 1983. Epidermal growth factor stimulates amiloride-sensitive $^{22}Na$ uptake in A431 cells. Evidence for $Na^+$-$H^+$ exchange. *J. Biol. Chem.* 258:4883–89

65. Rozengurt, E. 1986. Early signals in the mitogenic response. *Science* 234:161–66

66. Rozengurt, E., Heppel, L. A. 1975. Serum rapidly stimulates ouabain-sensitive $^{86}Rb^+$ influx in quiescent 3T3 cells. *Proc. Natl. Acad. Sci. USA* 72:4492–95

67. Rozengurt, E., Rodriguez-Pena, A., Coombs, M., Sinnett-Smith, J. 1984. Diacylglycerol stimulates DNA synthesis and cell division in mouse 3T3 cells: Role of $Ca^{2+}$-sensitive phospholipid-dependent protein kinase. *Proc. Natl. Acad. Sci. USA* 81:5748–52

68. Sawyer, S. T., Cohen, S. 1981. Enhancement of calcium uptake and phosphatidylinositol turnover by epidermal growth factor in A-431 cells. *Biochemistry* 20:6280–86

69. Schuldiner, S., Rozengurt, E. 1982. $Na^+$-$H^+$ antiport in Swiss 3T3 cells: Mitogenic stimulation leads to cytoplasmic alkalinization. *Proc. Natl. Acad. Sci. USA* 79:7778–82

70. Smith, J. B., Rozengurt, E. 1978. Serum stimulates the $Na^+,K^+$ pump in quiescent fibroblasts by increasing $Na^+$ entry. *Proc. Natl. Acad. Sci. USA* 75:5560–64

71. Truneh, A., Albert, F., Golstein, P., Schmitt-Verhulst, A.-M. 1985. Early steps of lymphocyte activation bypassed by synergy between calcium ionophores and phorbol ester. *Nature* 313:318–20

72. Tsien, R. Y., Pozzan, T., Rink, T. J. 1982. T-cell mitogens cause early changes in cytoplasmic free $Ca^{2+}$ and membrane potential in lymphocytes. *Nature* 295:68–71

73. Tsuda, T., Hamamori, Y., Yamashita, T., Fukumoto, Y., Takai, Y. 1986. Involvement of three intracellular messenger systems, protein kinase C, calcium ion and cyclic AMP, in the regulation of *c-fos* gene expression in Swiss 3T3 cells. *FEBS Lett.* 208:39–42

74. Vara, F., Rozengurt, E. 1985. Stimulation of $Na^+$-$H^+$ antiport activity by epidermal growth factor and insulin occurs without activation of protein kinase C. *Biochem. Biophys. Res. Commun.* 130:646–53

75. Villereal, M. L. 1981. Sodium fluxes in human fibroblasts: Effects of serum, $Ca^{2+}$, and amiloride. *J. Cell. Physiol.* 107:359–69

76. Vincentini, L. M., Villereal, M. L. 1985. Activation of $Na^+$-$H^+$ exchange in cultured fibroblasts: Synergism and antagonism between phorbol ester, $Ca^{2+}$ ionophore, and growth factors. *Proc. Natl. Acad. Sci. USA* 82:8053–56

77. Volpi, M., Naccache, P. H., Molski, T. F. P., Shefcyk, J., Huang, C.-K., et al. 1985. Pertussis toxin inhibits fMet-Leu-Phe- but not phorbol ester-stimulated changes in rabbit neutrophils: Role of G proteins in excitation response coupling. *Proc. Natl. Acad. Sci. USA* 82:2708–12

78. von Tscharner, V., Prod'hom, B., Baggliolini, M., Reuter, H. 1986. Ion channels in human neutrophils activated by a rise in free cytosolic calcium concentration. *Nature* 324:369–72

79. Weinman, E. J., Shenolikar, S. 1986.

Protein kinase C activates the renal apical membrane $Na^+$-$H^+$ exchanger. *J. Membr. Biol.* 93:133–39

80. Whiteley, B., Cassel, D., Zhuang, Y.-X., Glaser, L. 1984. Tumor promoter phorbol 12-myristate 13-acetate inhibits mitogen-stimulated $Na^+$-$H^+$ exchange in human epidermoid carcinoma A431 cells. *J. Cell Biol.* 99:1162–66

81. Whittaker, M., Irvine, R. F. 1984. Inositol 1,4,5-trisphosphate microinjection activates sea urchin eggs. *Nature* 312:630–39

82. Yarden, Y., Escobedo, J. A., Kuang, W.-J., Yang-Feng, T. L., Daniel, T. O., et al. 1986. Structure of the receptor for platelet-derived growth factor helps define a family of closely related growth factor receptors. *Nature* 323:226–32

83. Zilberman, Y., Howe, L. R., Moore, J. P., Hesketh, T. R., Metcalfe, J. C. 1987. Calcium regulates inositol 1,3,4,5-tetrakisphosphate production in lysed thymocytes and in intact cells stimulated with concanavalin A. *EMBO J.* 6:957–62

Ann. Rev. Physiol. 1988. 50:225–41

# VOLTAGE DEPENDENCE OF THE Na-K PUMP

*Paul De Weer*

Department of Cell Biology and Physiology, Washington University, School of Medicine, St. Louis, Missouri 63110

*David C. Gadsby*

Laboratory of Cardiac Physiology, The Rockefeller University, New York, New York 10021

*R. F. Rakowski*

Department of Physiology and Biophysics, University of Health Sciences/The Chicago Medical School, North Chicago, Illinois 60064

## INTRODUCTION

The Na-K pump is electrogenic (for recent reviews see 7, 21, 37, 44, 48, 103, 109). For thermodynamic and kinetic reasons, membrane potential should affect the turnover rate of a pump that transports net charge, and the character of the voltage sensitivity should contain mechanistic information. Because, until recently, this expectation seemed unsupported by experiment, we critically examine here evidence for voltage dependence of the Na-K pump.

## THEORETICAL BACKGROUND

### Equilibrium Potential of the Electrogenic Na-K Pump

The equilibrium potential, $E_{Na/K}$, of a pump transporting $m$Na$^+$ and $n$K$^+$ per molecule of ATP hydrolyzed is defined as the voltage at which the free energy of ATP hydrolysis ($\Delta G_{ATP}$) and the work required for the reversible, stoichiometric transfer of Na$^+$ and K$^+$ are equal and opposite:

225

$0 = \Delta G_{ATP} + m\{-FE_{Na/K} + RT \ \ln([Na]_o/[Na]_i)\} + n\{FE_{Na/K} + RT \ \ln([K]_i/[K]_o)\}$,

where $F$, $R$, and $T$ have their usual meanings. Solving for $E_{Na/K}$:

$$E_{Na/K} = \{(\Delta G_{ATP}/F) + mE_{Na} - nE_K\}/(m-n), \hspace{2cm} 1.$$

where $E_{Na}$ and $E_K$ are the Na$^+$ and K$^+$ equilibrium potentials. Recalling that

$$\Delta G_{ATP} = \Delta G^o_{ATP} + RT \ \ln([ADP][P_i]/[ATP]) \text{ and } \Delta G^o_{ATP} = -RT \ \ln K_{ATP},$$

where $K_{ATP}$ is the hydrolysis constant, we have

$$\Delta G_{ATP}/F = -(RT/F) \ \ln K_{ATP} + (RT/F) \ \ln([ADP][P_i]/[ATP])$$

or

$$E_{ATP} = E^o_{ATP} + (RT/F) \ \ln([ADP][P_i]/[ATP]). \hspace{2cm} 2.$$

By analogy $E_{ATP}$ is termed the ATP driving potential (the electromotive force of an ATP battery, if one could be made, numerically equal to the free energy of ATP hydrolysis expressed in meV/molecule), and $E^o_{ATP}$ is termed the standard ATP driving potential. Substitution of Equation 2 into Equation 1 yields:

$$E_{Na/K} = (E_{ATP} + mE_{Na} - nE_K)/(m-n). \hspace{2cm} 3.$$

Since $E_{Na/K}$ can be estimated experimentally as $V_{rev}$ (the interpolated reversal potential for pump current or net flux), it is obvious from Equation 3 that the pump's stoichiometry can be determined from the simultaneous equations $\delta V_{rev}/ \ \delta E_K = n/(m-n)$ and $\delta V_{rev}/ \ \delta E_{Na} = m/(m-n)$. Approximate values for the terms of Equation 3 in respiring animal cells are $-300$ mV for $E^o_{ATP}$ (54), $-600$ mV for $E_{ATP}$ (11, 22, 107, 113) and $+60$ to $+70$ mV and $-90$ to $-100$ mV for $E_{Na}$ and $E_K$, respectively, yielding $-200$ to $-240$ mV for $E_{Na/K}$, beyond early estimates (10, 13, 65) and, perhaps, experimental reach. If pump current, typically 0.1–1 $\mu$A cm$^{-2}$ near 0 mV, declined linearly with potential to vanish at $E_{Na/K}$, it would contribute $\sim$0.4–4 $\mu$S cm$^{-2}$ to the membrane conductance (32, 64, 98, 104), a small fraction of typical animal cell membrane conductances ($\sim$0.1–1 mS cm$^{-2}$). Constant pump conductance is unlikely, but even a narrow voltage-dependent region should contribute little to total membrane conductance unless the latter is artificially lowered.

## Kinetics

PUMP CYCLE    The Na-K pump is thought to cycle through a series of steps known as the Albers-Post model (for recent reviews see 3, 49, 50, 60, 68). The enzyme can reversibly assume two conformations and can be either unphosphorylated ($E_1$, $E_2$) or phosphorylated ($E_1P$, $E_2P$). One ATP molecule, one $Mg^{2+}$, and three $Na^+$ bind to $E_1$ on the intracellular side of the pump, forming $E_1P$ and "occluding" $Na^+$. After releasing ADP, $E_1P$ exergonically changes to $E_2P$ (a transition prevented by oligomycin or chymotrypsin treatment), delivering $Na^+$ extracellularly and acquiring high affinity for external $K^+$. Binding of two $K^+$ triggers dephosphorylation and $K^+$ occlusion [$E_2(2K)$]. Spontaneous reversion to $E_1$ (which is accelerated by high [ATP]) releases $K^+$ inside the cell, completing the cycle. The separation of $Na^+$ and $K^+$ transfer (via occlusion) permits the enzyme to sustain Na-Na or K-K exchange in the respective absence of $K^+$ or $Na^+$.

PREDICTING STEADY-STATE $I$-$V$ RELATIONSHIPS    If every step in the pump cycle were identified and all transition rate constants and their voltage dependences were known, the pump current-voltage ($I$-$V$) relationship could be formulated from first principles. Absent such knowledge, proposed models have relied on Nernst-Planck diffusion regimes (32), nonequilibrium thermodynamics (12, 15, 16, 79, 98), or explicit kinetic schemes (11, 14, 22, 23, 55, 79–81, 101), some with realistic rate constants (11, 14, 81, 101). Most kinetic modelers have assumed (a) that only translocations of ions or charged "empty" carriers display voltage dependence, which (b) is described by symmetric Eyring barriers (82). But asymmetric barriers (14, 15, 23, 80, 81) and additional voltage-sensitive steps (81, 101) have been considered. The elaborate model of Läuger & Apell (81) includes possible voltage effects on ion binding and on charge movements accompanying ion translocation and protein motion during occlusion/deocclusion. Despite the fact that even a simple, two-state, four–rate constant cycle produces a wide variety of $I$-$V$ curves (22, 23, 53, 55), these generalizations remain: (a) $I$-$V$ curves of unbranched cycles with a single voltage-sensitive step are monotonic, i.e. display only positive conductance; (b) these models behave as either constant-current or constant-voltage circuits over certain voltage ranges, depending on the nature of the rate-limiting step(s); (c) parameters (e.g. the apparent $K_m$) of ligand interactions can be voltage dependent (11, 14, 81, 102); and (d) addition of a step in which charge moves against the field yields $I$-$V$ curves with regions of negative conductance (11, 14, 23, 53, 80, 81, 101). Negative slopes could also reflect "gating" unrelated to the pump cycle (22).

INTERPRETING STEADY-STATE $I$-$V$ RELATIONSHIPS    Obtaining $I$-$V$ curves and extracting information are separate challenges. Pump current must be isolated from other, mostly larger, membrane currents by specifically arresting the Na-K pump with cardiotonic steroids. Controls should show the difference current to be free of non pump components arising from, e.g. concentration changes (mostly external [K]) or time-dependent drifts. The difference current or flux defined by removing Na, K, or ATP ("metabolic poisoning") will rarely equal that obtained by stopping the pump. This lack of equivalence is in part due to signals from other transport systems and, as argued by Chapman et al (14) and Blatt (6), to shifts of pump mode and of $E_{Na/K}$, which may generate false reversal potentials and/or negative slopes. Difficulties also arise in interpreting pump $I$-$V$ plots. Hansen et al (55) proved formally that $n$-state cycles with a single voltage-sensitive step reduce to two-state models with no loss of generality in steady-state $I$-$V$ curve shape. By analogy with enzyme kinetics where multistep reactions are reducible to elementary (e.g. Michaelis-Menten) formulations, the parameters of the simplified model are algebraic combinations of the original rate constants. Thus, a complete monotonic $I$-$V$ curve (i.e. from saturating inward to saturating outward current) yields only the four empirical rate constants of a two-state model, and these will rarely be "true" rate constants in the full model. Without additional data, even the location of the Eyring barrier is indeterminate, and partial $I$-$V$ curves yield correspondingly fewer parameters. $I$-$V$ curves over a range of transported ligand concentrations may resolve an additional rate constant if the ligand effect is saturable, a second if another ligand saturates, a third if they interact, and so on. Whether such additional rate constants are "true" or apparent depends on the details of the cycle (55). For example, the overall voltage dependence of the cycle may reflect that of the rate-limiting step or that of the steady-state level of the intermediate entering that step.

Studies of the Na-K pump can yield information other than net current: Four unidirectional fluxes (Na and K, in and out) can provide additional kinetic constraints, as can analysis of the voltage sensitivity of Na-Na and K-K exchange. Fluxes show, for example, that the pump's forward/backward rates ratio is normally large.

NON-STEADY-STATE ANALYSIS    Charged reaction cycle intermediates must redistribute in response to voltage steps, eliciting transient charge movements (14, 56) whose rate constants will aid further extraction of the cycle's individual rate constants. Since reduction to a two-state model is valid only in the steady state, however, rate constants of current transients need not match those found by steady-state analysis of "reduced" models.

## EXPERIMENTAL EVIDENCE

As the voltage sensitivity of the Na-K pump need not be strong, it may be hard to demonstrate and harder to quantify. So results of experiments to examine it demand careful scrutiny. We discuss results by tissue in the order in which each was used to address this question.

### Nerve

The first researchers to examine the influence of membrane potential on the Na-K pump rate were Hodgkin & Keynes (58, 59). They electrotonically hyperpolarized segments of *Sepia* axons by $\leq 30$ mV to determine whether or not voltage sensitivity might be the cause of the 70% drop in $^{24}$Na efflux seen on switching to K-free seawater, which produced a 5–10 mV hyperpolariza-tion. As $^{24}$Na efflux was reduced an average of 1% for an 18 mV hyperpolarization, Hodgkin & Keynes concluded: "The effect of removing external potassium cannot be due to a change in membrane potential" (59). Using their internal dialysis technique in squid axons, Brinley & Mullins (9) were led to the stronger conclusion: "The Na pump operates independent of membrane potential (at least in the range $-10$ to $-90$ mV)." They measured the effects on total $^{24}$Na efflux and $^{42}$K influx of $\leq 40$ mV hyperpolarizations induced either by raising $[K]_i$ in K-depleted axons or by injecting current and found small reductions in all conditions. Current injection caused Na efflux to drop in the presence of strophanthidin but not in K-free fluid. An axon dialyzed with ADP instead of ATP had a somewhat larger voltage depen-dence, but it was not tested in strophanthidin. It seems fair to state that no clear effect of voltage on Na-K pump rate was shown.

Nakajima & Takahashi (90) showed that in crayfish *(Oronectes)* stretch receptor neurons pump-mediated posttetanic hyperpolarization (PTH) was not accompanied by a change in membrane slope conductance but was bigger at more negative potentials (up to $-90$ mV). They were uncertain whether this effect was direct or indirect (via Na entry) but thought their results were not inconsistent with the pump being a voltage-independent current source. Holloway & Poppele (61) later showed that the PTH decayed exponentially (with a time constant of 4–6 s at 17°C), was abolished by strophanthidin or zero $[K]_o$, and seemed unrelated to Na entry because tetrodotoxin (TTX) had no effect. They proposed a slow voltage-dependent redistribution of active and inactive Na-K pump states. Meunier & Tauc (87) mentioned that *I-V* plots from *Aplysia* neurons with and without strophanthidin showed a pump current "not inactivated by the membrane hyperpolarization" but did not quote the voltage range. Marmor (84) echoed that conclusion after measuring *I-V* curves in *Anisodoris* neurons, and yet three of his four ouabain-sensitive *I-V* plots show current declining $\leqslant 50\%$ between $-40$ and $-100$ mV. Lambert et al (78), using slow current ramps in *Helix aspersa* neurons, found a strophanthidin-sensitive current fivefold greater at $-120$ mV than at $-40$ mV, possibly due to raised K conductance caused either directly by external K accumulation or indirectly via (67, 85) elevation of $[Na]_i$. Kostyuk and coworkers (71–75) ionophoretically injected sodium acetate into voltage-clamped *Helix pomatia* neurons (cf 108) and saw a current increment that was outward near $-50$ mV and declined during slow negative voltage ramps with a variably steep slope but sometimes reversed sign between $-70$ and $-100$ mV (71, 72, 75). The reversal potential was K sensitive (72). The large conductance increase was seen only with Na, not Li or K, injections but was not shown to need an active Na-K pump. Indeed, ouabain alone increased membrane conductance, a result consistent with an effect of raised $[Na]_i$ following pump inhibition (72). The voltage-sensitive current increment probably included both a Na-K pump current and a K current (cf 67, 85) in varying proportions (71–75).

Using Na-sensitive microelectrodes in voltage-clamped *Helix* neurons, Thomas found a fivefold drop in the net Na extrusion rate on hyperpolarizing from $-47$ to $-137$ mV (108) and a lower amplitude and possibly a lower decay rate of current increments after injecting the same amount of Na at increasingly negative voltages (110). Despite his evident disappointment "that the pump is not blocked by a 90 mV hyperpolarization" (108), the results are consistent with a direct slowing of the pump by hyperpolarization, although current-induced external K depletion is not ruled out.

Thomas' pioneering experiments combining current and net Na flux (via $Na^+$ activity) measurements under voltage clamp were extended by Cooke et al (18) on *Aplysia* neurons to include injection of $^{24}Na$. Strophanthidin-sensitive current and $^{24}Na$ efflux were measured simultaneously; their mean ratio was 0.56 rather than the 0.33 expected for 3Na-2K pump stoichiometry, possibly because the pump current was overestimated by inclusion of an inward current shift caused by extracellular K accumulation on pump inhibition. This "pump-clamp" technique, i.e. the simultaneous measurement of cardiotonic steroid-sensitive current and $^{22}Na$ efflux, is ideally suited to squid giant axons (20, 26, 93–97). Initial results in *Loligo pealei* axons internally dialyzed with ATP-rich solutions showed, like those of Cooke et al (18), a current/flux ratio of $\sim 0.5$, presumably because of a similar overestimation of the pump current (94). In axons kept in K-free seawater and dialyzed with $^{42}K$, ADP, and $P_i$, but no ATP or Na, the Na-K pump ran backwards (i.e. pumped $^{42}K$ out and $^{22}Na$ in), generating an inward current. A surprising finding was that hyperpolarization not only slowed the forward-running pump, as expected, but also seemed to diminish the inward current of the backward-running pump (26, 94). Recent improvements of this technique, including elimination of "end effects" (24, 27, 43) and of steroid-sensitive nonpump current (due to K accumulation) with more powerful K channel blockers (27), made it possible to show that the Na-K pump current is strongly voltage dependent in 400 mM Na seawater but only weakly so in Na-free seawater. In both cases this dependency approximately parallels the steroid-sensitive $^{22}$Na efflux between $-60$ and $+20$ mV (27). A reexamination of the voltage dependence of the reverse pump current showed it to increase monotonically with hyperpolarization, saturating near $-90$ mV, with no evidence of a negative slope (25). The negative slope found earlier probably reflected the voltage dependence of uncontrolled "end" currents.

## Muscle

Conway (17) proposed that a "critical energy barrier" impedes active Na extrusion from Na-loaded frog sartorius muscles under unfavorable conditions and that lowering the barrier by reducing $[Na]_o$ or membrane potential (by raising $[K]_o$) allowed net Na loss. Fozzard & Kipnis (35) similarly lowered $[Na]_o$ or raised $[K]_o$ or $[K]_i$ (with hypertonic solutions) and found little alteration in the steady-state electrochemical gradient for Na, which they took to indicate that Na-K pump rate might increase on depolarization. More direct evidence had already been obtained by Horowicz & Gerber (62, 63), who measured rate constants of $^{24}$Na efflux from small bundles of frog semitendinosus muscle fibers exposed to various K or $NaN_3$ concentrations, both of which depolarized and enhanced $^{24}$Na efflux in a manner implying a causal relationship (63). However, Beaugé & Sjodin (4) later showed that dependence of $^{22}$Na efflux on $[K]_o$ was closely similar in muscles "clamped" near $-20$ mV (via a Cl gradient) and in fresh muscles whose membrane potential varied. They concluded: "The activating effect of $[K]_o$ on the Na pump in muscles is independent of any simultaneous change in transmembrane potential."

Tahara et al (106) briefly warmed Na-loaded frog muscles from 2–26°C to elicit Na-K pump hyperpolarizations, which they attempted to compensate by current injection. Ouabain-sensitive I-V curves suggested a reversal potential near $-90$ mV at 10 mM $[K]_o$, which showed a biphasic dependence on $[K]_o$. However, lack of cable corrections or allowance for [K] changes in the T-system (36) severely limit analysis of the data. Lederer & Nelson (83) simultaneously measured ouabain-sensitive $^{22}$Na efflux and current at two potentials 10 mV apart in a voltage-clamped, internally perfused muscle cell of the giant barnacle, Balanus nubilus. The small depolarization seemed not to alter Na efflux, and effects on current were not mentioned. Ouabain-sensitive flux and current in a cell depolarized to $-13$ mV with 114 mM $[K]_o$ were within the range of normal values, but since these varied more than twofold and no cell served as its own control, the result seems inconclusive.

The authors concluded, nevertheless, that "modest changes in membrane potential have no effect on ouabain-sensitive Na efflux."

## Red Cells

Cotterell & Whittam (19) looked at the effect on ouabain-sensitive $^{42}K$ influx and $^{24}Na$ efflux of raising the membrane potential of human red blood cells from $-9$ to $+30$ mV (by replacing external Cl with impermeant anions) and saw up to 20% and 40% drops in the two fluxes, respectively. These were ascribed to technical problems, e.g. that $Cl^{-}$-$OH^{-}$ exchange, in maintaining a reciprocal relationship between $[Cl^{-}]$ and $[H^{+}]$ gradients, probably raised internal pH ($pH_i$). Zade-Oppen et al (115) reexamined the issue using high-potassium sheep erythrocytes; they raised membrane potentials from $-10$ to $+70$ mV by lowering $[Cl]_o$ with or without keeping $[H^{+}]_o \times [Cl^{-}]_o$ constant. Alkaline $pH_i$ inhibited pump fluxes up to 50%, but the membrane potential had no effect at constant $pH_i$. But, they used Na-free external solutions, which attenuates voltage sensitivity of the pump in oocytes (5), cardiac cells (40), and axons (27). Milanick & Hoffman (88) replaced $Cl_o$ with gluconate to shift the membrane potential of human red cells from $-10$ to $+100$ mV, in both Na-containing and Na-free solutions, while clamping $pH_i$ and $pH_o$, and found Na-K exchange to be "only minimally" affected. In later experiments with Na-free solutions, they extended the voltage range to $-100$ mV using K gradients and valinomycin but still found no effect on ouabain-sensitive Na efflux or K influx (89).

## Heart

To minimize changes in ion concentrations, Isenberg & Trautwein (66) used the fast-acting steroid dihydro-ouabain (DHO) in voltage-clamped ($-30$ to $-90$ mV) sheep Purkinje fibers. Even so, the $I$-$V$ curve in DHO took 2 min to record, sufficient time for extracellular K accumulation to reach steady state. Because of inward rectification of cardiac steady-state K currents, raised external $[K]$ will add a positive slope to the $I$-$V$ curve during pump inhibition and hence a negative slope to the DHO-sensitive $I$-$V$ curve. The roughly voltage-independent difference current seen by Isenberg & Trautwein (66) might thus represent the sum of a pump $I$-$V$ curve with positive slope and an increment in K current with negative slope. The same explanation may apply to the later findings by Eisner & Lederer (28) and Glitsch et al (47) of approximately parallel shifts of the $I$-$V$ curve of Na-loaded Purkinje fibers between $-80$ and $-20$ mV (28) and between $-120$ and $-30$ mV (47) as pump current declines, despite substitution of Rb for K (28) or addition of 0.5 mM Ba to the 13.5 mM K fluid (47) to limit K currents. Although neither maneuver completely abolishes K currents, Glitsch et al (47) sometimes saw the difference current decline between $-100$ and $-120$ mV. Recently,

Glitsch & Krahn (45) added 2 mM Ba and 2 mM Cs to remove more K current and found a variable decline of DHO-sensitive current between $-50$ and $-110$ mV in resting Purkinje fibers. Hasuo & Koketsu (57) used highly Na-loaded strips of bullfrog atria, voltage-clamped via a single sucrose gap. They kept the strips in K-free fluid and switched briefly to 2 mM K, 10 mM Rb or Cs, or 40 mM Li to activate the pump and allow $I$-$V$ measurements, which were repeated in ouabain. Difference curves were strongly voltage-dependent and fell 70–85% between $-50$ and $-120$ mV but had various shapes: roughly linear in Cs or Li, curved in Rb, and peaking at $-70$ mV in K, probably due to uncontrolled changes in nonpump currents. Verdonck (114), using another approach, saw no voltage dependence (between $-30$ and $-80$ mV) of the exponential rate of decay of pump current in Na-loaded Purkinje fibers, but small effects might not have been detectable.

Whole-cell current recording in single heart cells has made measurement of Na-K pump current more reliable. With internal and external solutions that sustain the Na-K pump but limit contaminating currents by blocking K and Ca channels and Na-Ca exchange, outward pump current was clearly voltage dependent (38, 42). The current was small at $-140$ mV and grew steadily with voltage to a plateau near 0 mV that seemed level up to $+60$ mV (38). Control experiments showed no other effects of strophanthidin after pump inhibition with K-free solution and no K-sensitive current after pump inhibition with ouabain. Voltage dependence was not due to voltage sensitivity of steroid action since ouabain-sensitive and $[Na]_i$-activated $I$-$V$ curves were closely similar (38). Later measurements showed: (*a*) The pump $I$-$V$ curve is sigmoid with a "foot" at large negative potentials (39, 40), which prevents extrapolation to pump reversal potentials; (*b*) reduction of the internal [Na] lowered (and shifted) pump current but the voltage dependence persisted (40); (*c*) removal of external Na nearly abolished the voltage dependence by enhancing pump current at large negative potentials (40); (*d*) at zero $[Na]_o$, the only effect of changing $[Na]_i$ was to scale the pump $I$-$V$ plot (40); (*e*) with zero $[K]_o$ and $[Na]_i$, inward, reverse Na-K pump current increased on hyperpolarization from almost zero at $+50$ mV to a plateau near 100 mV, with no evidence of a negative slope (2). Stimers et al (105), using voltage-clamped aggregates of chick heart cells, noted that "ouabain-sensitive current was nearly constant between $-70$ and 0 mV, but decreased negative to $-70$ mV". Glitsch et al (46), working with cells from guinea pig and sheep hearts, reported that DHO-sensitive current "was little affected by the membrane potential . . . between 0 and $-100$ mV," whereas Mehrke et al (86) found DHO-sensitive current in guinea pig cells to decrease on hyperpolarization from $-80$ to $-140$ mV. Control tests will help identify the Na-K pump fraction of steroid-sensitive current in these last three cases.

The steady-state data are now complemented by measurements of transient strophanthidin-sensitive charge movements elicited by voltage steps after interruption of the Na-K pump cycle by removal of external K (91). The charge transients needed ATP, $Na_i$, and $Na_o$; were blocked by oligomycin; were equal in the "on" and "off" direction; and decayed exponentially with voltage-dependent rate constants ($\sim 250$ $s^{-1}$ near 0 mV at 37°C). The charge movement was well described by a two-state Boltzmann model for a single positive charge equilibrating across the entire membrane field. A simple interpretation is that the pump's Na binding sites provide two negative charges so that with three $Na^+$ bound a single positive charge remains and makes Na translocation voltage-dependent. The observed voltage-dependent rates suggest that most of the voltage sensitivity is in the backward rate constant (39, 41).

## Oocytes

A strong indication that Na-K pump current is voltage-dependent came from experiments by Turin (111, 112) on *Xenopus laevis* blastomeres whose membrane conductance is extremely low at $pH_o=6.5$. Strophanthidin de-polarized resting cells at $-40$ to $-70$ mV but *hyperpolarized* two cells held near $-100$ mV and $-135$ mV by current injection, which implies that the pump reversal potential may have been exceeded. Later, Béhé & Turin (5) reported that $[K]_o$-dependent or ouabain-sensitive *I-V* curves of voltage-clamped blastomeres were linear from 0 to $-150$ mV and crossed the zero-current axis between $-110$ and $-160$ mV with no change in slope. Also, removing $Na_o$ "suppressed the slope" of the difference *I-V* curve and lowered its amplitude, possibly because $[Na]_i$ fell. Lafaire & Schwarz (76, 77) obtained DHO-sensitive current in *Xenopus* oocytes from $-200$ mV all the way to $+100$ mV. Both fresh and Na-loaded eggs gave average difference curves with positive slopes at negative voltages, peaks at about $+20$ mV, and steep negative slopes (with increased statistical error) positive to the peaks. Attributing this biphasic voltage dependence to the pump, they concluded that its cycle comprises "at least two voltage-dependent steps [which] are oppositely affected by the membrane potential" (77). *I-V* curves in 3 mM $[K]_o$ plus DHO were almost identical to those in zero $[K]_o$ between $-160$ and 0 mV [a crucial control for Béhé & Turin (5)] but had an extra outward current of variable size beyond $+20$ mV. So extracellular K accumulation during pump inhibition might also have elicited the extra outward current, causing the DHO-sensitive curves to have variable negative slopes positive to $+20$ mV. Recent measurements in voltage-clamped *Xenopus* oocytes (92) gave DHO-sensitive *I-V* curves that often simply saturated at positive voltages. Eisner et al (29, 30) obtained a strophanthidin-sensitive current and $^{22}Na$ efflux between $-160$ and $+40$ mV in voltage-clamped *Xenopus* eggs with normal or raised $[Na]_i$. The current/flux ratio at $-40$ mV was $0.35\pm0.17$

(SD), which is close to the value of 0.33 expected for a 3Na-2K pump. Strophanthidin-sensitive current and flux seemed voltage dependent in Na-loaded but not control oocytes, so Eisner et al concluded that "at normal $[Na]_i$, the over-all rate is limited by the availability of $[Na]_i$", but "as $[Na]_i$ is elevated, the voltage-dependent step may become rate-limiting" (30). However, variability of currents and Na efflux may have obscured voltage dependence at normal $[Na]_i$. The steroid-sensitive current fell a little more on hyperpolarization than did the flux, leading the authors to suggest that negative potentials might promote reverse Na translocation (i.e. convert Na-K to Na-Na exchange) (30).

## Reconstituted Na-K Pump

Using partially purified Na,K-ATPase from pig kidney, reconstituted into soybean phospholipid vesicles, Karlish and coworkers (51, 70, 99, 100) examined the voltage dependence of different modes of Na-K pump operation by setting positive membrane potentials with the ionophores valinomycin or AS701 and gradients of [K] or [Li], respectively. $^{22}Na$ uptake into Na-free vesicles, initiated by inside-out Na-K pumps on sudden addition of ATP, was accelerated 30–40% by membrane potentials equivalent to $+130$ to $+180$ mV (for normal orientation) at saturating cytoplasmic [Na] and [ATP] but not at rate-limiting (1 $\mu$M) [ATP] (51, 70). Assuming that at low [ATP] the rate-limiting transport step is the conformational change of the K-occluded state, $E_2(2K) \rightarrow E_1 2K$ [see section on the pump cycle, above], they inferred that it is voltage insensitive and so involves no net charge movement. In agreement with this conclusion, Rb-Rb exchange activated by ATP + $P_i$ was voltage insensitive (51), as were the transition rates (estimated by stopped-flow fluorimetry) and the equilibrium distributions (titrated as cation-induced fluorescence changes) between $E_1K$ and $E_2(2K)$ in tests with reconstituted fluorescein-labelled enzyme (99).

Karlish and coworkers (51, 70) interpreted the voltage dependence of Na flux at high [ATP] as evidence that the conformational change $E_1P(3Na) \rightarrow E_2P3Na$ is voltage sensitive, because it "is at least partially rate limiting," and offered a simple model where "the net charge in the transport domain of the protein when no ions, 2K or 3Na are bound is $-2$, 0, and $+1$, respectively" (51, 70). Positive potentials caused greater acceleration at low cytoplasmic [Na] and increased apparent affinity for Na, an effect they attributed to enhanced intrinsic Na binding. They concluded that Na ions cross part of the field before binding or that voltage affects ion binding by changing the protein's shape (51, 70). The rate of acetyl phosphate–induced fluorescence quenching in the presence of Na and Mg, thought to reflect conversion of $E_1$ to $E_2P$, was accelerated fourfold at $+173$ mV. Rephaeli et al (100) argued that this weak effect was consistent with a single positive charge accompanying "transport of 3 $Na^+$ in the conformational transition." However, absolute potential levels in all these experiments seem uncertain, since recent measurements using the dye oxonol VI reveal the equivalent of a 200–250 mV Na-K pump hyperpolarization in control vesicles without ionophores (51, 52).

Recently, Bamberg and coworkers (30a, 31) and Läuger and coworkers (1, 8) recorded transient currents generated by Na-K pumps in membrane fragments bound to planar lipid bilayers upon photolytic release of ATP from caged ATP. These currents required Mg and Na but not K, were abolished by vanadate or ouabain, and were closely analogous to rapid $^{22}Na$ efflux transients from right-side-out vesicles, measured by Forbush (33, 34), which were also initiated using caged ATP. Because of the capacitive coupling between pump-containing membrane fragments and supporting bilayer (1, 8, 30a, 31) passive circuit parameters must be estimated to extract the transient pump current from the record. Both groups found (1, 8, 30a) that the transient pump current, like Forbush's $^{22}Na$ flux (33), had a fast rising phase ($\sim 60$ s$^{-1}$) and a slower declining phase ($\sim 20$ s$^{-1}$). Saturating dependence of the slower step on [ATP] led Bamberg and coworkers to conclude that it preceded the faster step (30a), whereas the characteristic pH dependence of the faster step led Läuger and coworkers to conclude that it reflected dissociation of caged ATP and thus preceded the slower step (1, 8). The current was not seen in chymotrypsin-treated enzyme, which can occlude Na [$E_1P(3Na)$] but not proceed to $E_2P3Na$. This finding suggests that charge movement accompanies that transition and/or Na release (1, 8). Since the maximum turnover rate at zero [K] is <5 s$^{-1}$, Läuger and coworkers (1, 8) argued, as had Forbush (33), that charge movement and Na transport, respectively, had ceased before the pump had completed a full transport cycle, which implies that these are early events in the cycle. When caged ATP is photolyzed in the presence of external K, a transient burst of $Na^+$ release precedes achievement of the steady-state levels of $^{22}Na$ efflux (34) and current (1, 8, 30a, 31), which indicates that Na translocation and charge movement precede the rate-limiting step in the normal Na-K transport cycle. The same conclusion was reached by Karlish & Kaplan (69), who initiated $^{22}Na$ uptake into inside-out vesicles at 0°C by suddenly adding ATP and demonstrated a transient burst of Na entry.

## SUMMARY AND CONCLUSIONS

Present evidence demonstrates that the Na-K pump rate is voltage dependent, whereas early work was largely inconclusive. The *I-V* relationship has a positive slope over a wide voltage range, and the existence of a negative slope region is now doubtful. Monotonic voltage dependence is consistent with the reaction cycle containing a single voltage-dependent step. Recent measurements suggest that this voltage-dependent step occurs during Na translocation and may be deocclusion of $Na^+$. In addition, two results suggest that K translocation is voltage insensitive: (a) large positive potentials appear to have no influence on Rb-Rb exchange or associated conformational transitions; and (b) transient currents associated with Na translocation appear to involve movement of a single charge, which is sufficient for a 3Na-2K cycle. The simplest interpretation is that the pump's cation binding sites supply two negative charges.

Pre-steady-state measurements demonstrate that Na translocation precedes the pump cycle's rate-limiting step, presumably K translocation. But, because K translocation seems voltage insensitive, the voltage dependence of the steady-state pump rate probably reflects that of the concentration of the intermediate entering this slow step.

Further pump current and flux data (both transient and steady-state), carefully determined over a range of conditions, should increase our understanding of the voltage-dependent step(s) in the Na-K pump cycle.

ACKNOWLEDGMENTS

The authors' work was supported by NIH grants NS11223, NS22979, HL14899, HL36783, and by the Muscular Dystrophy Association. DCG is a Career Scientist of the Irma T. Hirschl Trust.

*Literature Cited*

1. Apell, H.-J., Borlinghaus, R., Läuger, P. 1987. Fast charge-translocations associated with partial reactions of the Na,K-pump. II. Microscopic analysis of transient currents. *J. Membr. Biol.* 97:179–91

2. Bahinski, A., Gadsby, D. C. 1988. Current-voltage relationship of the backward-running Na/K pump in isolated cells from guinea-pig ventricle. In *The Biology of the Isolated Adult Cardiac Myocyte*, ed. W. A. Clark, T. K. Borg, R. S. Decker. New York: Elsevier. In press

3. Beaugé, L. 1984. Sodium pump in squid axons. *Curr. Top. Membr. Transp.* 22:131–75

4. Beaugé, L. A., Sjodin, R. A. 1976. An analysis of the influence of membrane potential and metabolic poisoning with azide on the sodium pump in skeletal muscle. *J. Physiol. London* 263:383–403

5. Béhé, P., Turin, L. 1984. Arrest and reversal of the electrogenic sodium pump under voltage clamp. *Proc. 8th Int. Biophys. Congr.*, p. 304 (Abstr.)

6. Blatt, M. R. 1986. Interpretation of steady-state current voltage curves: Consequences and implications of current subtraction in transport studies. *J. Membr. Biol.* 92:91–110

7. Blaustein, M. P., Lieberman, M., eds. 1984. *Electrogenic Transport: Fundamental Principles and Physiological Implications,* Society of General Physiologists Series, Vol. 38. New York: Raven. 404 pp.

8. Borlinghaus, R., Apell, H.-J., Läuger, P. 1987. Fast charge-translocations associated with partial reactions of the Na,K-pump. I. Current and voltage transients after photochemical release of ATP. *J. Membr. Biol.* 97:161–78

9. Brinley, F. J. Jr., Mullins, L. J. 1974. Effects of membrane potential on sodium and potassium fluxes in squid axons. *Ann. NY Acad. Sci.* 242:406–34

10. Caldwell, P. C. 1973. Possible mechanisms for the linkage of membrane potentials to metabolism by electrogenic transport processes with special reference to *Ascaris* muscle. *Bioenergetics* 4:201–9

11. Chapman, J. B. 1984. Thermodynamics

and kinetics of electrogenic pumps. See
Ref. 7, pp. 17–48

12. Chapman, J. B., Johnson, E. A. 1976.
Current-voltage relationships for theoretical electrogenic sodium pump models. *Proc. Aust. Physiol. Pharmacol.
Soc.* 7:69P (Abstr.)

13. Chapman, J. B., Johnson, E. A. 1978.
The reversal potential for an electrogenic
sodium pump. A method for determining the free energy of ATP breakdown?
*J. Gen. Physiol.* 72:403–8

14. Chapman, J. B., Johnson, E. A., Kootsey, J. M. 1983. Electrical and biochemical properties of an enzyme model of
the sodium pump. *J. Membr. Biol.*
74:139–53

15. Chapman, J. B., Kootsey, J. M., Johnson, E. A. 1979. A kinetic model for
determining the consequences of electrogenic active transport in cardiac muscle.
*J. Theor. Biol.* 80:405–24

16. Chapman, K. M. 1982. The Na-K pump
as a current source—affinity-driven
transport has no reversal potential but its
metabolic cost does. *J. Gen. Physiol.*
80:473–78

17. Conway, E. J. 1960. Critical energy
barriers in the excretion of sodium. *Nature* 187:394–96

18. Cooke, I. M., Leblanc, G., Tauc, L.
1974. Sodium pump stoichiometry in
*Aplysia* neurones from simultaneous current and tracer measurements. *Nature*
251:254–56

19. Cotterell, D., Whittam, R. 1971. The
influence of the chloride gradient across
red cell membranes on sodium and
potassium movements. *J. Physiol. London* 214:509–36

20. De Weer, P. 1974. $Na^+,K^+$ exchange
and $Na^+,Na^+$ exchange in the giant
axon of the squid. *Ann. NY Acad. Sci.*
242:434–44

21. De Weer, P. 1975. Aspects of the recovery processes in nerve. In *MTP International Review of Science, Physiology Series One, Vol III: Neurophysiology,* ed. C. C. Hunt, pp. 231–78. London: Butterworths

22. De Weer, P. 1984. Electrogenic pumps:
Theoretical and practical considerations.
See Ref. 7, pp. 1–15

23. De Weer, P. 1986. The electrogenic
sodium pump: Thermodynamics and
kinetics. *Progr. Zool.* 33:387–99

24. De Weer, P., Gadsby, D. C., Rakowski,
R. F. 1986. Voltage dependence of Na/
K pump-mediated $^{22}Na$ efflux and current in squid giant axon. *J. Physiol. London* 371:144P (Abstr.)

25. De Weer, P., Gadsby, D. G., Rakowski, R. F. 1988. Stoichiometry and volt-

age dependence of the sodium pump. *5th
Int. Conf. on Na,K-ATPase,* Aarhus,
Denmark. New York: Liss. In press

26. De Weer, P., Rakowski, R. F. 1984.
Current generated by backward-running
electrogenic Na pump in squid giant axons. *Nature* 309:450–52

27. De Weer, P., Rakowski, R. F., Gadsby,
D. C. 1987. Current-voltage relationships for the electrogenic sodium pump
of squid giant axon. *Biophys. J.* 51:385a
(Abstr.)

28. Eisner, D. A., Lederer, W. J. 1980.
Characterization of the electrogenic
sodium pump in cardiac Purkinje fibres.
*J. Physiol. London* 303:441–74

29. Eisner, D. A., Valdeolmillos, M.,
Wray, S. 1986. The voltage-dependence
of the Na-K pump in isolated *Xenopus*
oocytes: Simultaneous measurement of
membrane current and $^{22}Na$ efflux. *J.
Physiol. London* 377:84P (Abstr.)

30. Eisner, D. A., Valdeolmillos, M.,
Wray, S. 1987. The effects of membrane potential on active and passive Na
transport in *Xenopus* oocytes. *J. Physiol. London* 385:643–59

30a. Fendler, K., Grell, E., Bamberg, E.
1987. Kinetics of pump currents generated by the $Na^+$, $K^+-ATPase$. *FEBS
Lett.* In press

31. Fendler, K., Grell, E., Haubs, M.,
Bamberg, E. 1985. Pump currents
generated by the purified $Na^+,K^+-$
ATPase from kidney on black lipid
membranes. *EMBO J.* 4:3079–85

32. Finkelstein, A. 1964. Carrier model for
active transport of ions across a mosaic
membrane. *Biophys. J.* 4:421–40

33. Forbush, B. III 1984. $Na^+$ movement in
a single turnover of the Na pump. *Proc.
Natl. Acad. Sci. USA* 81:5310–14

34. Forbush, B. III 1985. Rapid ion movements in a single turnover of the $Na^+$
pump. See Ref. 50, pp. 599–611

35. Fozzard, H. A., Kipnis, D. M. 1967.
Regulation of intracellular sodium concentrations in rat diaphragm muscle. *Science* 156:1257–60

36. Gadsby, D. C. 1982. Hyperpolarization
of frog skeletal muscle fibers and of
canine Purkinje fibers during enhanced
$Na^+-K^+$ exchange: Extracellular $K^+$
depletion or increased pump current. See
Ref. 103, pp. 17–34

37. Gadsby, D. C. 1984. The Na/K pump of
cardiac cells. *Ann. Rev. Biophys. Bioeng.* 13:373–98

38. Gadsby, D. C., Kimura, J., Noma, A.
1985. Voltage dependence of Na/K
pump current in isolated heart cells. *Nature* 315:63–65

39. Gadsby, D. C., Nakao, M. 1987. [Na]

dependence and voltage dependence of Na/K pump current in single heart cells. *Biophys. J.* 51:386a (Abstr.)

40. Gadsby, D. C., Nakao, M. 1987. [Na] dependence of the Na/K pump current-voltage relationship in isolated cells from guinea-pig ventricle. *J. Physiol. London* 382:106P (Abstr.)

41. Gadsby, D. C., Nakao, M. 1988. Voltage dependence of Na/K pump current in isolated cells from guinea-pig ventricle. In *Recent Studies of Ion Transport and Impulse Propagation in Cardiac Muscle*, ed. W. R. Giles. New York: Liss. In press

42. Gadsby, D. C., Noma, A. 1984. Voltage dependence of Na/K pump current in internally dialyzed cells from guinea pig ventricle. *Proc. 8th Int. Biophys. Congr.*, p. 295 (Abstr.)

43. Gadsby, D. C., Rakowski, R. F., De Weer, P. 1986. Voltage dependence of Na/K pump rate in squid giant axon. *Biophys. J.* 49:36a (Abstr.)

44. Glitsch, H. G. 1982. Electrogenic Na pumping in the heart. *Ann. Rev. Physiol.* 44:389–400

45. Glitsch, H. G., Krahn, T. 1986. The cardiac electrogenic pump. *Progr. Zool.* 33:401–17

46. Glitsch, H. G., Krahn, T., Pusch, H. 1987. The Na pump of cardioballs. *Pflüg. Arch.* 408 (Suppl. 1):R10 (Abstr.)

47. Glitsch, H. G., Pusch, H., Schumacher, T., Verdonck, F. 1982. An identification of the K activated Na pump current in sheep Purkinje fibres. *Pflüg. Arch.* 394:256–63

48. Glynn, I. M. 1984. The electrogenic sodium pump. See Ref. 7, pp. 33–48

49. Glynn, I. M. 1985. The $Na^+,K^+$-transporting adenosine triphosphatase. In *The Enzymes of Biological Membranes*, ed. A. N. Martonosi, 3:35–114. London/New York: Plenum. 2nd. ed.

50. Glynn, I. M., Ellory, C., eds. 1985. *The Sodium Pump: 4th. Int. Conf. on Na,K−ATPase*, Cambridge, England: The Company of Biologists. 765 pp.

51. Goldschleger, R., Karlish, S. J. D., Rephaeli, A., Stein, W. D. 1987. The effect of membrane potential on the mammalian sodium-potassium pump reconstituted into phospholipid vesicles. *J. Physiol. London* 387:331–55

52. Goldschleger, R., Karlish, S. J. D., Shahak, Y. 1987. Electrogenic and electroneutral transport modes of the mammalian renal Na/K pump. *J. Physiol. London* 390:98P (Abstr.)

53. Gradmann, D., Hansen, U.-P., Slayman, C. L. 1982. Reaction-kinetic anal-

ysis of current-voltage relationships for electrogenic pumps in *Neurospora* and *Acetabularia*. See Ref. 103, pp. 257–76

54. Guynn, R. W., Veech, R. L. 1973. The equilibrium constants of the adenosine triphosphate hydrolysis and the adenosine triphosphate-citrate lyase reactions. *J. Biol. Chem.* 248:6966–72

55. Hansen, U.-P., Gradmann, D., Sanders, D., Slayman, C. L. 1981. Interpretation of current-voltage relationships for "active" ion transport systems: I. Steady-state reaction-kinetic analysis of Class-I mechanisms. *J. Membr. Biol.* 63:165–90

56. Hansen, U.-P., Tilton, J., Gradmann, D. 1983. Interpretation of current-voltage relationships for "active" ion transport systems: II. Nonsteady-state reaction kinetic analysis for Class-I mechanisms with one slow time-constant. *J. Membr. Biol.* 75:141–69

57. Hasuo, H., Koketsu, K. 1985. Potential dependency of the electrogenic $Na^+$-pump current in bullfrog atrial muscles. *Jpn. J. Physiol.* 35:89–100

58. Hodgkin, A. L., Keynes, R. D. 1954. Movements of cations during recovery in nerve. *Symp. Soc. Exp. Biol.* 8:423–37

59. Hodgkin, A. L., Keynes, R. D. 1955. Active transport of cations in giant axons from *Sepia* and *Loligo*. *J. Physiol. London* 128:28–60

60. Hoffman, J. F., Forbush, B. III 1983. Structure, mechanism, and function of the Na/K pump. *Curr. Top. Membr. Transp.* 19:1043

61. Holloway, S. F., Poppele, R. E. 1984. Post-tetanic hyperpolarization evoked by depolarizing pulses in crayfish stretch receptor neurones in tetrodotoxin. *J. Physiol. London* 350:343–60

62. Horowicz, P., Gerber, C. J. 1965. Effects of external potassium and strophanthidin on sodium fluxes in frog striated muscle. *J. Gen. Physiol.* 48:489–514

63. Horowicz, P., Gerber, C. J. 1965. Effect of sodium azide on sodium fluxes in frog striated muscle. *J. Gen. Physiol.* 48:515–25

64. Hoshiko, T., Lindley, B. D. 1967. Phenomenological description of active transport of salt and water. *J. Gen. Physiol.* 50:729–58

65. Hurlburt, W. P. 1970. Ion movements in nerve. In *Membranes and Ion Transport*, ed. E. E. Bittar, Vol. 2, pp. 95–143. New York: Wiley

66. Isenberg, G., Trautwein, W. 1974. The effect of dihydroouabain and lithium ions on the outward current in cardiac

Purkinje fibers. *Pflüg. Arch.* 350:41–54

67. Kameyama, M., Kakei, M., Sato, R., Shibasaki, T., Matsuda, H., Irisawa, H. 1984. Intracellular $Na^+$ activates a $K^+$ channel in mammalian cardiac cells. *Nature* 309:354–56

68. Kaplan, J. H. 1985. Ion movements through the sodium pump. *Ann. Rev. Physiol.* 47:535–44

69. Karlish, S. J. D., Kaplan, J. H. 1985. Pre-steady-state kinetics of $Na^+$ transport through the Na, K-pump. See Ref. 50, pp. 501–6

70. Karlish, S. J. D., Rephaeli, A., Stein, W. D. 1985. Transmembrane modulation of cation transport by the Na,K-pump. See Ref. 50, pp. 487–99

71. Kononenko, N. I. 1975. Potential-dependent membrane sodium pump current in snail giant neurons. *Neirofiziologiya* 7:428–33. Transl. 1976. *Neurophysiology* 7:333–37

72. Kononenko, N. I., Kostyuk, P. G. 1976. Further studies of the potential-dependence of the sodium-induced membrane currents in snail neurones. *J. Physiol. London* 256:601–15

73. Kostyuk, P. G. 1970. Active transport of ions in a nerve cell and its connection with the electrical processes on surface membrane. *Ukr. Biochem. J.* 43:9–16

74. Kostyuk, P. G., Krishtal (Kryshtal), O. A., Pidoplichko, V. I. 1972. Potential-dependent membrane current during the active transport of ions in snail neurones. *J. Physiol. London* 226:373–92

75. Kostyuk, P. G., Krishtal (Kryshtal), O. A., Pidoplichko, V. I. 1972. Electrogenic sodium pump and the associated changes in conductivity of the surface membrane of neurones. *Biofizika* 17:1048–54

76. Lafaire, A. V., Schwarz, W. 1985. Voltage-dependent, ouabain-sensitive current in the membrane of oocytes of *Xenopus laevis*. See Ref. 50, pp. 523–25

77. Lafaire, A. V., Schwarz, W. 1986. The voltage dependence of the rheogenic $Na^+/K^+$ ATPase in the membrane of oocytes of *Xenopus laevis*. *J. Membr. Biol.* 91:43–51

78. Lambert, J. D. C., Kerkut, G. A., Walker, R. J. 1974. The electrogenic sodium pump and membrane potential of identified neurones in *Helix aspersa*. *Comp. Biochem. Physiol.* 47A:897–916

79. Läuger, P. 1979. A channel mechanism for electrogenic ion pumps. *Biochim. Biophys. Acta* 552:143–61

80. Läuger, P. 1984. Thermodynamic and kinetic properties of electrogenic ion pumps. *Biochim. Biophys. Acta* 779:307–41

81. Läuger, P., Apell, H.-J. 1986. A microscopic model for the current-voltage behaviour of the Na,K-pump. *Eur. Biophys. J.* 13:309–21

82. Läuger, P., Stark, G. 1970. Kinetics of carrier-mediated ion transport across lipid bilayer membranes. *Biochem. Biophys. Acta* 211:458–66

83. Lederer, W. J., Nelson, M. T. 1984. Sodium pump stoichiometry determined by simultaneous measurements of sodium efflux and membrane current in barnacle. *J. Physiol. London* 348:665–77

84. Marmor, M. F. 1971. The independence of electrogenic sodium transport and membrane potential in a molluscan neurone. *J. Physiol. London* 218:599–608

85. Meech, R. W. 1974. The sensitivity of *Helix aspersa* neurones to injected calcium ions. *J. Physiol. London* 237:259–77

86. Mehrke, G., Daut, J., Hartmann, S., Dischner, A. 1987. The effects of dihydro-ouabain on the current-voltage relation of guinea-pig cardiomyocytes. *Pflüg. Arch.* 408 (Suppl. 1):R10 (Abstr.)

87. Meunier, J. M., Tauc, L. 1970. Participation d'une pompe métabolique au potentiel de repos de neurones d'aplysie. *J. Physiol. Paris* 62:192–93 (Abstr.)

88. Milanick, M. A., Hoffman, J. F. 1983. Effects of $pH_i$, $pH_o$, and $V_m$ on the human red blood cell Na/K pump. *Proc. Int. Union Physiol. Sci.* 15:259 (Abstr.)

89. Milanick, M. A., Hoffman, J. F. 1986. Ouabain-sensitive Na/K exchange, Na/Na exchange and uncoupled Na efflux are insensitive to changes in membrane potential, $E_m$, in intact human red blood cells. *Biophys. J.* 49:548a (Abstr.)

90. Nakajima, S., Takahashi, K. 1966. Post-tetanic hyperpolarization and electrogenic Na pump in stretch receptor neurone of crayfish. *J. Physiol. London* 187:105–27

91. Nakao, M., Gadsby, D. C. 1986. Voltage dependence of Na translocation by the Na/K pump. *Nature* 323:628–30

92. Rakowski, R. F. 1987. Voltage dependence of the electrogenic $Na^+/K^+$ pump in *Xenopus* oocytes. *J. Gen. Physiol.* 90:34a (Abstr.)

93. Rakowski, R. F., De Weer, P. 1982. Direct measurement of electrogenic $Na^+/K^+$ pump current and resting inward $Na^+$ current in squid giant axons under voltage clamp control. *Biophys. J.* 37:259a (Abstr.)

94. Rakowski, R. F., De Weer, P. 1982.

Electrogenic $Na^+/K^+$ pump current and flux measurements on voltage-clamped, internally dialyzed squid axons. *Biol. Bull.* 163:402–3 (Abstr.)

95. Rakowski, R. F., De Weer, P. 1982. Forward and reverse electrogenic pumping by the Na/K pump of squid giant axon. *J. Gen. Physiol.* 80:25a (Abstr.)

96. Rakowski, R. F., De Weer, P. 1984. Voltage dependence of the current produced by backward-running sodium pump in squid giant axons. *Proc. 8th. Int. Biophys. Congr.*, p. 289 (Abstr.)

97. Rakowski, R. F., De Weer, P., Gadsby, D. C. 1985. Voltage dependence of backward-running $Na^+$ pump in squid giant axons. See Ref. 50, pp. 511–15

98. Rapoport, S. I. 1970. The sodium-potassium exchange pump: Relation of metabolism to electrical properties of the cell. I. Theory. *Biophys. J.* 10:246–59

99. Rephaeli, A., Richards, D. E., Karlish, S. J. D. 1986. Conformational transitions in fluorescein-labeled (Na,K)ATPase reconstituted into phospholipid vesicles. *J. Biol. Chem.* 261:6248–54

100. Rephaeli, A., Richards, D. E., Karlish, S. J. D. 1986. Electrical potential accelerates the $E_1P(Na)-E_2P$ conformational transition of $(Na,K)-$ATPase in reconstituted vesicles. *J. Biol. Chem.* 261:12437–40

101. Reynolds, J. A., Johnson, E. A., Tanford, C. 1985. Incorporation of membrane potential into theoretical analysis of electrogenic pumps. *Proc. Natl. Acad. Sci. USA* 82:6869–73

102. Sanders, D. 1986. Generalized kinetic analysis of ion-driven cotransport systems: II. Random ligand binding as a simple explanation for non-Michaelian kinetics. *J. Membr. Biol.* 90:67–87

103. Slayman, C., ed. 1982. *Electrogenic Ion Pumps*. In *Curr. Top. Membr. Transp.* 16:1–522

104. Spanswick, R. M. 1972. Evidence for an electrogenic ion pump in *Nitella translucens*. I. The effects of pH, $K^+$,

$Na^+$, light and temperature on the membrane potential and resistance. *Biochim. Biophys. Acta* 288:73–89

105. Stimers, J. R., Shigeto, N., Lobaugh, L. A., Lieberman, M. 1986. Ouabain sensitivity of the Na-K pump in cultured chick heart cells: Voltage clamp and equilibrium binding studies. *J. Gen. Physiol.* 88:56a (Abstr.)

106. Tahara, T., Kimizuka, H., Koketsu, K. 1973. An analysis of the membrane hyperpolarization during action of the sodium pump in frog's skeletal muscles. *Jpn. J. Physiol.* 23:165–81

107. Tanford, C. 1981. Equilibrium state of ATP-driven ion pumps in relation to physiological ion concentration gradients. *J. Gen. Physiol.* 77:223–29

108. Thomas, R. C. 1972. Intracellular sodium activity and the sodium pump in snail neurones. *J. Physiol. London* 220:55–71

109. Thomas, R. C. 1972. Electrogenic sodium pump in nerve and muscle cells. *Physiol. Rev.* 52:563–94

110. Thomas, R. C. 1982. Electrophysiology of the sodium pump in a snail neuron. See Ref. 103, pp. 3–16

111. Turin, L. 1982. Conductance changes associated with sodium pump inhibition in isolated *Xenopus laevis* blastomeres. *J. Gen. Physiol.* 80:60a (Abstr.)

112. Turin, L. 1984. Electrogenic pumping in *Xenopus* blastomeres: Apparent pump conductance and reversal potential. See Ref. 7, pp. 345–51

113. Veech, R. L., Lawson, J. W. R., Cornell, N. W., Krebs, H. A. 1979. Cytosolic phosphorylation potential. *J. Biol. Chem.* 254:6538–47

114. Verdonck, F. 1982. Activation of sodium pump current in rabbit Purkinje fibers. *J. Gen. Physiol.* 80:24a (Abstr.)

115. Zade-Oppen, A. M. M., Schooler, J. M., Cook, P., Tosteson, D. C. 1979. Effects of membrane potential and internal pH on active sodium-potassium transport and on ATP content in high-potassium sheep erythrocytes. *Biochim. Biophys. Acta* 555:285–98

*Ann. Rev. Physiol. 1988. 50:243–56*

# SITE-DIRECTED MUTAGENESIS AND ION-GRADIENT DRIVEN ACTIVE TRANSPORT: On the Path of the Proton

## H. Ronald Kaback

Roche Institute of Molecular Biology, Roche Research Center, Nutley, New Jersey 07110

## INTRODUCTION[1]

The *lac* permease of *Escherichia coli* is a hydrophobic transmembrane protein, encoded by the *lac Y* gene, that catalyzes the coupled translocation of $\beta$-galactosides with $H^+$ (i.e. $H^+$-substrate symport or cotransport) (see 12, 13, and 31 for recent reviews). Thus when a $H^+$ electrochemical gradient ($\Delta\bar{\mu}_{H^+}$) is generated across the cytoplasmic membrane (interior becoming negative and/or alkaline), the permease utilizes free energy released from the downhill translocation of $H^+$ in response to $\Delta\bar{\mu}_{H^+}$ to drive uphill accumulation of $\beta$-galactosides against a concentration gradient (Figure 1A). Conversely, when a concentration gradient of substrate is created in the absence of $\Delta\bar{\mu}_{H^+}$, the permease utilizes free energy released from the downhill translocation of substrate to drive $H^+$ uphill with generation of $\Delta\bar{\mu}_{H^+}$. The polarity of this electrochemical gradient depends on the direction of the substrate concentration gradient: When [substrate]$_{in}$ < [substrate]$_{out}$, $\Delta\bar{\mu}_{H^+}$ is interior positive and acid (Figure 1B); when [substrate]$_{in}$ > [substrate]$_{out}$, $\Delta\bar{\mu}_{H^+}$ is interior negative and alkaline (Figure 1C)]. The *lac* permease is a model system for a wide range of biological machines that transduce free energy

---

[1]Abbreviations: $\Delta\bar{\mu}_{H^+}$, proton electrochemical gradient; NEM, *N*-ethylmaleimide; TDG, $\beta$-D-galactosyl 1-thio-$\beta$-D-galactopyranoside; NPG, *p*-nitrophenyl-$\alpha$-D-galactopyranoside; DEPC, diethylpyrocarbonate; TMG, methyl 1-thio-$\beta$-D-galactopyranoside.

243

0066-4278/88/0315-0243$02.00

stored in an electrochemical ion gradient into work in the form of a concentration gradient. Therefore, the experimental approaches used to study the permease are applicable to other membrane transport proteins from prokaryotes, eukaryotes and their intracellular organelles, as well as highly organized tissues such as epithelia.

The $\beta$-galactoside transport system of *E. coli* was described initially in 1955 (7) and is part of the famous *lac* operon, which allows the organism to utilize the disaccharide lactose. In addition to regulatory loci, the *lac* operon contains three structural genes: (*a*) the *Z* gene, which encodes $\beta$-galactosidase, a cytosolic enzyme that cleaves lactose upon entry into the cell; (*b*) the *Y* gene, which encodes *lac* permease; and (*c*) the *A* gene, which encodes thiogalactoside transacetylase, an enzyme of unknown physiological function that catalyzes acetylation of thio-$\beta$-galactosides using acetyl–coenzyme A as the acetyl donor.

The *lac Y* gene has been cloned and sequenced, and the permease has been purified to a single polypeptide species, reconstituted into proteoliposomes, and shown to be completely functional, thereby demonstrating that the *lac Y* gene product is solely responsible for $\beta$-galactoside transport. Secondary structure models for the permease based on circular dichroic and laser Raman spectroscopy and on analyses of sequential hydropathic character suggest that the polypeptide is organized into 12–14 hydrophobic $\alpha$-helical segments that traverse the membrane in zig-zag fashion, connected by more hydrophilic charged regions containing most of the amino acid residues commonly found in $\beta$ turns (Figure 2) (12, 13). Preliminary evidence supporting certain general

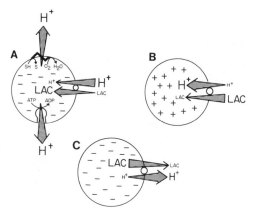

*Figure 1*    Lactose transport in *E. coli*. (A) Uphill lactose transport in response to $\Delta\bar{\mu}_{H^+}$ (interior negative and alkaline) generated either by respiration or ATP hydrolysis. $\sim$ represents a membrane-bound respiratory chain with alternating $H^+$ and electron carriers; $\Omega$ represents the $H^+$-ATPase; $\circ$ is the *lac* permease. (B) Uphill $H^+$ transport in response to an inwardly directed lactose gradient. (C) Uphill $H^+$ transport in response to an outwardly directed lactose gradient.

aspects of the model has been obtained from limited proteolysis studies and from binding studies with monoclonal and site-directed polyclonal antibodies. In view of the subsequent discussion, however, it is clear that only a high resolution crystal structure will reveal the essential structural information.

Although chemical modification of amino acid residues in proteins can provide important information, there are drawbacks to the technique, including the chemical specificity of the reagents and the bulk of the modified residues. Thus, site-directed mutagenesis using bacteriophage M13 single-stranded DNA has been used to introduce single amino acid changes into proteins (33), and during the past few years this approach has been applied to *lac* permease (27). The provocative implication of the studies is that important information can be obtained at the level of individual amino acid residues despite the lack of detailed knowledge of the three-dimensional structure.

## SITE-DIRECTED MUTAGENESIS OF CYS RESIDUES IN *lac* PERMEASE

Based on substrate protection against $N$-ethylmaleimide (NEM) inactivation, Fox & Kennedy (9) postulated that there is an essential sulfhydryl group in the permease located at or near the active site, and Cys148 was later shown to be the critical residue (1). Trumble et al (28) and Viitanen et al (29) cloned *lac Y* into single-stranded M13 phage DNA and, using a synthetic deoxyoligonucleotide primer, converted Cys148 in the permease into a Gly residue. Cells bearing mutated *lac Y* exhibit initial rates of lactose transport that are about one fourth that of cells bearing the wild-type gene on the same recom-

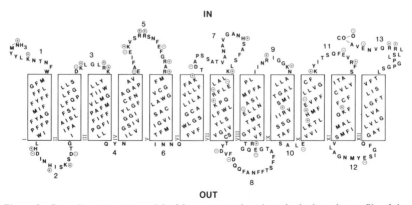

*Figure 2*  Secondary structure model of *lac* permease based on the hydropathy profile of the protein. Hydrophobic segments are shown in boxes as transmembrane, $\alpha$-helical domains connected by hydrophilic segments. The carboxyl terminus and hydrophilic segments 5 and 7 (with the amino terminus as hydrophilic segment 1) have been shown to be on the cytoplasmic surface of the membrane (12, 13).

binant plasmid (Table 1) and steady-state levels of lactose accumulation comparable to that of wild-type cells. Transport activity is considerably less sensitive to inactivation by NEM; however, complete inactivation is observed if sufficient time is allowed, and galactosyl 1-thio-$\beta$-D-galactopyranoside (TDG) affords no protection against inactivation. Furthermore, permease with Ser in place of Cys148 (21, 26) catalyzes transport as well as wild-type permease (Table 1) and exhibits the same properties as Gly148 permease with respect to NEM inactivation and TDG protection. These findings indicate that although Cys148 is important for substrate protection against sulfhydryl inactivation, it is not obligatory for lactose-H$^+$ symport and that another sulfhydryl group elsewhere within the permease is required for full activity.

Site-directed mutagenesis of Cys154 shows that a sulfhydryl group at this position is important for permease activity (20; cf Table 1). Permease with Gly in place of Cys154 exhibits essentially no transport activity, while substitution of Cys154 with Ser also causes marked, though less complete, loss of activity. In contrast, permease with either Gly154 or Ser154 binds the high-affinity ligand p-nitrophenyl-$\alpha$-D-galactopyranoside (NPG) normally. More recently, Brooker & Wilson (5) replaced Cys176 or Cys234 with Ser and Menick et al (19) replaced Cys117, Cys 333, or Cys 353 and Cys355 with Ser, and in each case less than 50% loss in the initial rate of transport is observed (Table 1). Taken as a whole, the results indicate that of the eight Cys residues in *lac* permease, only Cys154 is important for lactose-H$^+$ symport.

In view of the attention paid to the functional importance of sulfhydryl groups in *lac* permease over the past 20 years, this conclusion is particularly

**Table 1**  Summary of transport activities in *lac y* cysteine mutants

| Cys residues | Substitution | Initial rate of transport[a] (% wild type) | Reference |
|---|---|---|---|
| 117 | Ser | 70 | 19 |
| 148 | Gly | 25 | 28 |
|  |  |  | 30 |
| 148 | Ser | 100 | 26 |
| 154 | Gly | 0 | 20 |
| 154 | Ser | 10 | 20 |
| 154 | Val | 30 | — |
| 176 | Ser | 80 | 5 |
| 234 | Ser | 70 | 5 |
| 333 | Ser | 100 | 19 |
| 353, 355 | Ser | ≥50 | 18 |

[a] Initial rate of lactose transport in *E. coli* T184 transformed with the appropriate plasmid.

interesting. In addition to the postulate that a sulfhydryl group at or near the binding site of the permease is essential to its function, other hypotheses implicating Cys residues in *lac* permease function have been put forward. Specifically, it has been suggested that the permease may undergo sulfhydryl-disulfide interconversion during turnover, either as a respiratory intermediate (14) or as a H$^+$ carrier in equilibrium with $\Delta\bar{\mu}_{H^+}$ (15, 24). In this context, the results obtained from site-directed mutagenesis of the Cys residues in *lac* permease place severe restrictions on any theory that invokes disulfide bond formation as part of the catalytic mechanism. Since Cys154 alone appears to be important for activity, it follows that any postulated disulfide bond formation must occur between two *lac* permease monomers. Although there is indirect evidence that is consistent with the notion that the permease may dimerize in the presence of $\Delta\bar{\mu}_{H^+}$, direct evidence supporting this idea is lacking (19). Furthermore, although Ser154 permease is defective, it retains the ability to catalyze lactose accumulation against a concentration gradient at about 10% of the rate of the wild-type molecule. Based on these considerations, it seems highly unlikely that sulfhydryl-disulfide interconversion plays a central role in the mechanism of action of *lac* permease.

Other noteworthy observations include the demonstration that the rate of inactivation of the permease by various maleimides is enhanced by $\Delta\bar{\mu}_{H^+}$ (8) and the finding that this property of the permease is retained or accentuated when Cys148 is replaced with Gly (30). Since Cys154 is the only Cys residue in the permease that is essential for activity, these observations suggest that Cys154 is the residue that exhibits enhanced reactivity to maleimides in the presence of $\Delta\bar{\mu}_{H^+}$. The behavior of the permease in this respect indicates that $\Delta\bar{\mu}_{H^+}$ increases the nucleophilic character of Cys154 and suggests that this residue might be involved in H$^+$ translocation. The following considerations tend to exclude this notion, however. Permease with Ser in place of Cys154 catalyzes lactose accumulation, albeit at 10% of the wild-type rate. Since Ser is similar to Cys in that the hydroxyl group may mimic the sulfhydryl group to an extent, Cys154 was replaced with Val (19). Permease with Val154 catalyzes transport about three times faster than does permease with Ser in place of Cys154 (i.e. at about 30% of the rate of the wild type; cf Table 1). Therefore, although Cys154 appears to be the only Cys residue in the permease whose replacement leads to dramatic loss of activity, the bulk of the evidence suggests that it is not directly involved in either substrate binding or H$^+$ translocation.

## ROLE OF HIS322 IN LACTOSE-H$^+$ SYMPORT

Chemical modification studies with diethylpyrocarbonate (DEPC) and rose bengal provided an initial clue that His residues may play an important role in the coupling of $H^+$ and lactose translocation (12, 13). Subsequently, each of the four His residues in *lac* permease were replaced with Arg by site-directed mutagenesis (22). Replacement of His35 and His39 with Arg has no apparent effect on activity. In contrast, replacement of either His205 or His322 with Arg causes dramatic loss of transport activity, despite the fact that the cell membrane contains a normal complement of permease molecules, as determined by immunoadsorption assays. While substitution of His205 or His322 with Arg results in loss of lactose-$H^+$ symport, permease molecules with Arg at residue 322 facilitate downhill lactose influx at high concentrations of the disaccharide. Furthermore, permease with Arg322 that was purified and reconstituted into proteoliposomes catalyzes facilitated diffusion of lactose at about 50% of the rate of wild-type permease without concomitant translocation of $H^+$ (i.e. the permease is uncoupled); purified permease with Arg205 has no transport activity.

Recently, Lowe et al (16) showed that the side chain of Asn may be superimposed on His in such a manner that the amide nitrogen of Asn occupies the same position as N-1 in His, while the amide nitrogen of Gln may be superimposed on N-3. By site-directed mutagenesis His48 was replaced with Lys, Asn, or Gln in tyrosyl-tRNA synthetase from *Bacillus stearothermophilus*, and it was demonstrated that enzyme with Asn in place of His48 retains normal activity, while enzymes with Lys or Gln at residue 48 are markedly defective. Thus the authors concluded that N-1 of His-48 forms a hydrogen bond with ATP and that electrostatic interaction between the His and ATP is insignificant.

In view of these observations, Püttner et al (23) replaced His205 or His322 in *lac* permease with either Gln or Asn. His205 can be replaced with either Asn or Gln without significant loss of permease activity. These findings, in conjunction with the considerations of Lowe et al (16) and the observation that permease with Arg in place of His205 binds NPG normally (I. B. Püttner & H. R. Kaback, unpublished information), suggest that in all likelihood His205 plays a role in hydrogen bonding within the tertiary structure of the permease. In marked contrast, permease with Arg, Asn, or Gln in place of His205 does not catalyze lactose-$H^+$ symport. Therefore, the results are consistent with the notion that the imidazole ring in His322 must be able to be protonated in order to catalyze symport (i.e. His322 may be directly involved in lactose-coupled $H^+$ translocation).

Measurements of net efflux, exchange, and counterflow are useful for studying permease turnover because specific steps in the overall catalytic cycle can be delineated (12, 13; see below). It is clear from the results of Püttner et al (23) that *lac* permease with Arg in place of His322 is grossly defective in each aspect of translocation.

# HIS322 AND GLU325 AS COMPONENTS OF A CHARGE RELAY SYSTEM

The evidence that His322 may be directly involved in $H^+$ translocation and a secondary structure model suggesting that this residue is located in putative transmembrane $\alpha$-helix X focused attention on Glu325 [Figure 2; see Bieseler et al (2) for more direct evidence that this portion of the permease is in $\alpha$-helical conformation]. If His322 and Glu325 are located in a portion of the permease that is $\alpha$-helical, the functional groups in these residues must be on the same side of the helix and in very close proximity (i.e. within about 1.5 Å; cf Figure 3). In other words, His322 and Glu325 are likely to be ion-paired. In addition, structure/function studies on the serine proteases, and chymotrypsin in particular (3), have led to the notion that Asp and His may function with a Ser residue as components of a charge relay system. Such a mechanism might readily be adapted in part to $H^+$ translocation in transport enzymes such as *lac* permease. For these reasons, Glu325 in *lac* permease was replaced with Ala (6).

As demonstrated for the His322 mutations (22, 23), permease with Ala in place of Glu325 catalyzes downhill lactose influx at high substrate concentrations without translocation of $H^+$. In contrast, permease containing Ala325, like permease containing Arg322, catalyzes neither active lactose transport nor efflux, both of which involve net $H^+$ translocation. Remarkably,

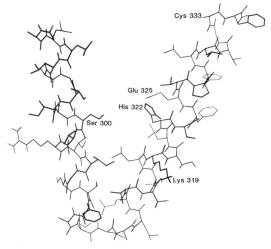

*Figure 3*   Molecular model of helices IX and X in the *lac* permease based on the secondary structure model shown in Figure 1 (generated by Dr. Vincent Madison on an Evans-Sutherland computer).

however, the rate of exchange in vesicles containing Ala325 permease is identical to that observed in vesicles containing wild-type permease. Moreover, membrane vesicles with Ala325 permease catalyze counterflow at the same rate and to the same extent as vesicles containing wild-type permease, but the internal concentration of [1-$^{14}$C]lactose is maintained at high levels for a markedly prolonged period. The effect is consistent with a defect in efflux coupled with unimpaired exchange activity (12, 13).

Mechanistically, the results are easily rationalized by the kinetic scheme shown in Figure 4. Accordingly, efflux down a concentration gradient consists of a minimum of five steps: (1) binding of substrate and H$^+$ on the inner surface of the membrane (order unspecified); (2) translocation of the ternary complex to the outer surface; (3) release of substrate; (4) release of H$^+$; (5) return of the unloaded permease to the inner surface. Alternatively, exchange and counterflow with external lactose at saturating concentrations involve steps 1–3 only (12, 13). Furthermore, release of H$^+$ (step 4) appears to be rate limiting for efflux. (*a*) Downhill lactose translocation, but not exchange, is inhibited by a factor of 3–4 when protium is replaced with deuterium, which indicates that deuterium must affect either the step in which H$^+$ is lost at the surface of the membrane or the step corresponding to return of the unloaded permease. However, the effect of deuterium on influx is abolished when a membrane potential (interior negative) is imposed, which demonstrates that deuterium does not affect the return of the unloaded permease. (*b*) Efflux, but not exchange, is accelerated at alkaline pH. (*c*) In the uncoupled mutant *E. coli* ML308-22, efflux is diminished and is unaffected by pH, while exchange occurs at normal rates.

Since all steps in the mechanism that involve protonation or deprotonation appear to be blocked in the His322 mutants and the primary effect of $\Delta\bar\mu_{H^+}$ on

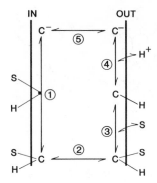

*Figure 4*   Schematic representation of reactions involved in lactose efflux, exchange, and counterflow. C represents the *lac* permease; S is the substrate (lactose). The order of substrate and H$^+$ binding at the inner surface of the membrane is not implied (from Reference 6).

the kinetics of lactose transport (i.e. a decrease in apparent $K_m$) is no longer evident, it seems reasonable to suggest that protonation of His322 is intimately involved in step 1. In contrast, replacement of Glu325 with Ala results in a permease that is defective in all steps involving net $H^+$ translocation but catalyzes exchange and counterflow normally. Clearly, therefore, permease with Ala at position 325 is probably blocked in step 4 (i.e. it is unable to lose $H^+$).

Although it is impossible to prove or disprove the charge relay hypothesis based on the evidence currently available, if such a mechanism is involved in lactose-$H^+$ symport, it would seem reasonable to search for hydroxyl-containing amino acid residues in the vicinity of the postulated His-Glu ion pair in helix X. As indicated in Figure 2, putative helix IX, which must be close to helix X given the length of the connecting hydrophilic segment, contains six Ser and Thr residues. Furthermore, when the amino acid sequence of putative helices IX and X is subjected to three-dimensional molecular modeling (Figure 3), it is apparent that Ser300 is the hydroxyl-containing amino acid residue most likely to be involved if a triad similar to that postulated for chymotrypsin (3) plays a role in *lac* permease. However, when Ser300 is replaced with Ala by site-directed mutagenesis, no change in permease activity is observed (18). Another residue in the vicinity of His322 and Glu325 that might be expected to play an important role is Lys319; however, replacement of this residue with Leu also has no effect on permease activity (18). Although these mutations and replacement of Cys333 with Ser (Figure 3), have no effect on lactose-$H^+$ symport, the results are important for at least two reasons: (1) They highlight the specificity of His322-Glu325, and (2) they support the contention that single amino acid changes do not cause drastic conformational alterations within a relatively localized portion of the permease.

The properties of the Arg322 and Ala325 mutants outlined above provide the basis for a strategy to delineate other residues involved in lactose-coupled $H^+$ translocation. By functional analyses of a population of uncoupled mutants, it should be clear which mutants do and which do not catalyze exchange and counterflow. Alterations in residues involved in steps in the pathway before His322 should not catalyze exchange or counterflow, while alterations in residues after Glu325 should catalyze both reactions. Clearly, this strategy can be used to subclassify uncoupled mutants selected by classical mutagenesis prior to DNA sequencing or to characterize mutants constructed by site-directed mutagenesis.

In this context, it is particularly interesting that replacement of Arg302 with Leu leads to a marked defect in the ability of the permease to catalyze lactose-$H^+$ symport (18). Furthermore, the strategy outlined above has revealed that permease with Leu302 exhibits properties similar to those of permease with Arg substituted for His322. That is, Leu302 permease is defective in efflux, exchange, and counterflow but catalyzes downhill lactose influx without $H^+$ translocation. Therefore, it appears that Arg302 is a component of the putative charge relay system that functions prior to His322.

Arg302 can be moved from the left to the right side of helix IX simply by transferring two amino acid residues (Ala309 and Thr310; Figure 2) from the helix to the hydrophilic segment connecting the helices (Figure 5). Under these circumstances, the guanidino group in Arg302 is sufficiently close to His322 to form a hydrogen bond with the imidazole ring. Minimally, therefore, the putative charge relay in the permease would involve interactions between Arg302, His322, and Glu325 (Figure 5). However, in each of the mutants described the altered permeases are defective in lactose-$H^+$ symport in both directions across the membrane. Given the ordered spatial relationships of the three residues involved and their respective $pK_a$s, $H^+$ would move from Glu325 to His322 to Arg302 but not in the reverse direction. Two possibilities are noteworthy in this regard. First, the $pK_a$s of the respective residues may depend on the conformation of the protein. Second, lactose-coupled $H^+$ translocation may not involve physical movement of $H^+$ from one residue to the next. Instead, His322 may be the only residue immediately involved in $H^+$ translocation, and its $pK_a$ may be influenced by the proximities of Glu325 and Arg302 (i.e. decreased by Glu and increased by Arg).

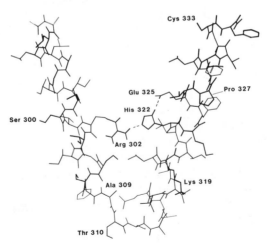

*Figure 5* Modified molecular model of putative helices IX and X in *lac* permease. This model was generated as described for Figure 3, except that Ala309 and Thr310 were transferred from helix IX to hydrophilic segment 10, which connects helices IX and X (cf Figure 2). By this means, the pitch of helix IX was altered so that Arg302 is on the right-hand side of helix IX, where the guanidino group hydrogen bonds to the imidazole ring of His322, which in turn hydrogen bonds to Glu325.

In the hope of discriminating between these possibilities, permease has been engineered to allow assessment of the $pK_a$ of His 322 under various conditions. A *lac* permease molecule has been constructed in which Arg is substituted for His35 and His39 and Gln for His205 (I. B. Püttner & H. R. Kaback, unpublished information). This molecule has a single His residue at position 322 and is completely active. In addition, an analogous molecule has been constructed in which Ala replaces Glu325. Since DEPC and rose bengal react with the unprotonated form of His and both permease constructs catalyze counterflow, these reagents can be used to determine the apparent $pK_a$ of His322 (10). It will be particularly interesting to determine the effects of substrate and the presence or absence of Glu325 on the $pK_a$ of His322. It should be also be enlightening to determine the effect of $\Delta \bar{\mu}_{H^+}$ on the $pK_a$ of His322, especially in the absence of Glu325. If $H^+$ moves from His322 to Glu325 in the presence of $\Delta \bar{\mu}_{H^+}$, the $pK_a$ of His322 may be markedly elevated when Glu325 is replaced with Ala. Functional permease molecules with single His residues could easily be enriched with $^{13}C$ or $^{15}N$ to allow NMR studies if sufficiently high protein concentrations can be obtained.

If His322 and Glu325 are ion-paired residues that function as components in a charge relay system that is important for lactose-$H^+$ symport, the polarity of the residues and the distance between the imidazole and carboxyl groups should be critical. To test this polarity, His322 and Glu325 were interchanged through use of site-directed mutagenesis (I. B. Püttner & H. R. Kaback, unpublished information). Permease altered in this manner is defective in active transport, efflux, exchange, and counterflow. To test the importance of distance, Glu325 was first replaced with Asp, which is one methylene group shorter than Glu, thereby shortening the side-chain containing the carboxylate by about 1.5 Å. Permease with Asp325 catalyzes lactose-$H^+$ symport as well as wild-type permease (N. Carrasco, L. Antes, H. R. Kaback, unpublished information). This result is not surprising since the $pK_a$ of Asp is lower than that of Glu and the side chains of amino acids in proteins are thought to be free to move 1.5–2.0 Å. Interestingly, however, preliminary experiments indicate that the "$pK_a$" for efflux (29) is decreased by about 0.5 pH units in permease with Asp in place of Glu325. More recently, Glu325 was interchanged with Val326, and it was shown that permease with this configuration is inactive (J. A. Lee & H. R. Kaback, unpublished information). Molecular modeling of the residues involved indicates that the distance per se between the imidazole of His322 and the carboxyl of Glu is altered to a relatively minor extent when Glu is moved to position 326. However, the imidazole ring must be rotated significantly to accommodate the putative ion pair. Finally, replacement of Glu325 with Gln yields permease that does not catalyze active lactose transport nor efflux but catalyzes exchange and counterflow (i.e. permease with Gln325 behaves similarly to permease with Ala325) (I. B. Püttner, J. Lolkema, H. R. Kaback, unpublished information). These results support the contention that His322 and Glu325 must have a specific polarity and configuration to support lactose-coupled $H^+$ translocation, that the amino acid residue at position 325 must be acidic, and that ability to hydrogen bond is insufficient for lactose-$H^+$ symport.

Most recently, Pro327 (helix X; Figure 5) has been replaced with Gly, Ala or Leu. Remarkably, permease with Gly or Ala at position 327 catalyzes lactose-$H^+$ symport in a manner similar to that observed with wild type permease, while permease with Leu327 is devoid of activity (J. Lolkema, I. B. Püttner, E. M. Menezes, and H. R. Kaback, unpublished information). Thus, it is apparent that *cis-trans* isomerization of Pro327 is not obligatory for lactose-$H^+$ symport and that it is the bulk of the side chain, rather than its tendency to make (Leu or Ala) or break helices (Pro or Gly) that is important for activity. At present, Pro327 is being replaced with Cys, Val, or Ile.

## IMPLICATIONS FOR OTHER SYMPORTERS

Since the *lac* permease is a model system for cation-substrate symport, it is of interest to examine other bacterial symport proteins, particularly with regard to the presence of potential His-Glu(Asp) ion pairs in analogous positions to those found in *lac* permease. One such system is the melibiose *(mel)* permease of *E. coli,* encoded by the *mel B* gene, which has been cloned and sequenced by Tsuchiya and coworkers (11, 32). This permease catalyzes symport with $Na^+$, $Li^+$, or $H^+$, depending on the substrate [e.g. symport of methyl 1-thio-$\beta$-D-galactopyranoside (TMG) occurs with $Na^+$ or $Li^+$, while symport of melibiose occurs with either $H^+$ or $Na^+$, but not with $Li^+$]. From the nucleotide sequence of the *mel B* gene, the *mel* permease is predicted to consist of 469 residues (the *lac* permease contains 417 residues), resulting in a protein with a molecular weight of 52,029 (the *lac* permease has a molecular weight of 46,504). Like *lac* permease, *mel* permease is very hydrophobic, and the hydropathy profile is similar to that obtained for *lac* permease in that there are a number of long hydrophobic domains in the primary structure that might traverse the membrane in $\alpha$-helical conformation. Despite the predicted structural similarities, homology in the amino acid sequence between the *lac* and *mel* permeases is virtually nonexistent, and there is no homology in the nucleotide sequences of the structural genes for the two permeases. Nonetheless, in the carboxyl-terminal third of the *mel* permease, there are two potential His-Glu(Asp) ion pairs, His357-Glu361 and His442-Asp445. These acidic residues have recently been subjected to site-directed mutagenesis (H. K. Sarkar & H. R. Kaback, unpublished information).

Replacement of Asp445 with Asn or His has no apparent effect on either

Na$^+$-dependent TMG transport or H$^+$-dependent melibiose transport. In contrast, substitution of Glu361 with Gly or Asp inactivates Na$^+$-TMG symport, as well as H$^+$-melibiose symport. Although these results are not conclusive, they suggest that a His-Glu ion pair may also play an important role in the mechanism of action of the *mel* permease.

In addition to *lac Y* and *mel B*, the genes for a few other bacterial symporters have been cloned and sequenced, thereby allowing deduction of primary amino acid sequences and hydropathic profiling of the encoded permeases. Included in the list are the phosphoglycerate permease of *Salmonella typhimurium* (25; G.-q. Yu, D. Goldrick, H. R. Kaback, J.-s. Hong, unpublished information) and the arabinose, xylose, and citrate permeases from *E. coli,* which exhibit a high degree of homology with each other and with the glucose transporter of human erythrocytes (17). None of these molecules has significant amino acid homology with either *lac* permease or *mel* permease, but all manifest hydropathy profiles similar to those of *lac* and *mel* permeases (i.e. multiple hydrophobic domains of sufficient length to traverse the membrane in α-helical conformation). Furthermore, each of these permeases has at least one potential His-Glu(Asp) ion pair in the molecule. It will be interesting to assess the effects of site-directed mutagenesis on the appropriate residues in these proteins.

Finally, I. McMorrow & T. H. Wilson (unpublished information) have recently sequenced the *lac Y* gene in *Klebsiella aerugenes* and observed approximately 60% homology with *lac Y* in *E. coli* K12. Furthermore, in the *Klebsiella* permease, Arg302, His322 and Glu325 are conserved, while Cys154 and His205 are substituted with Ser and Arg, respectively.

In summary, we have reviewed recent applications of oligonucleotide-directed, site-specific mutagenesis to the study of ion-gradient driven transport with the *lac* permease of *E. coli* as a model system. Although it is unlikely that the use of site-directed mutagenesis in itself will fully elucidate the mechanism of lactose-H$^+$ symport, the technique has provided what appears to be an exciting initial glimpse into the chemistry of substrate-coupled H$^+$ translocation. It has revealed that Arg302, His322, and Glu325, neighboring residues in putative helices IX and X of the permease, play an important role in lactose-H$^+$ symport, possibly as components in a charge relay system. Moreover, it has been demonstrated that Cys residues, long thought to play a critical role in the mechanism of the *lac* permease, are probably not directly involved in either substrate binding or H$^+$ translocation. Finally, it is particularly noteworthy that site-directed mutagenesis has now been utilized to introduce 20–30 individual amino acid changes into the *lac* permease, and the results as a whole suggest that conservative single amino acid changes do not lead to marked conformational alterations.

ACKNOWLEDGMENTS

The author is indebted to T. H. Wilson of Harvard Medical School for providing the sequence of the *Klebsiella aerogenes lac Y* gene prior to publication.

## Literature Cited

1. Beyreuther, K., Bieseler, B., Ehring, R., Müller-Hill, B. 1981. In *Methods in Protein Sequence Analysis*, p. 139. Clifton, NJ: Humana
2. Bieseler, B., Prinz, H., Beyreuther, K. 1985. *Ann. NY Acad. Sci.* 456:309
3. Blow, D. M., Birktoft, J. J., Hartley, B. S. 1969. *Nature London* 221:337
4. Brandl, C. J., Deber, C. M. 1986. *Proc. Natl. Acad. Sci. USA* 83:917
5. Brooker, R. J., Wilson, T. H. 1986. *J. Biol. Chem.* 261:11765
6. Carrasco, N., Antes, L. M., Poonian, M. S., Kaback, H. R. 1986. *Biochemistry* 25:4486
7. Cohen, G. N., Monod, J. 1957. *Bacteriol. Rev.* 21:169
8. Cohn, D., Kaczorowski, G. J., Kaback, H. R. 1981. *Biochemistry* 20:3308
9. Fox, C. F., Kennedy, E. P. 1965. *Proc. Natl. Acad. Sci. USA* 54:891
10. Garcia, M.-L., Patel, L., Padan, E., Kaback, H. R. 1982. *Biochemistry* 21:5800
11. Hanatani, M., Yazyu, H., Shiota-Niiya, S., Moriyama, Y., Kanazawa, H., et al. 1984. *J. Biol. Chem.* 259:1807
12. Kaback, H. R. 1986. In *Physiology of Membrane Disorders*, p. 387. New York: Plenum
13. Kaback, H. R. 1986. *Ann. Rev. Biophys. Biophys. Chem.* 15:279
14. Kaback, H. R., Barnes, E. M. Jr. 1971. *J. Biol. Chem.* 246:5523
15. Konings, W. N., Robillard, G. T. 1982. *Proc. Natl. Acad. Sci. USA* 79:5480
16. Lowe, D. M., Fersht, A. L., Wilkinson, A. J., Carter, P., Winter, G. 1985. *Biochemistry* 24:5106
17. Maiden, M. C. J., Davis, E. O., Baldwin, S. A., Moore, D. C. M., Henderson, P. J. F. 1986. *Nature* 325:641
18. Menick, D. R., Carrasco, N., Antes, L., Patel, L., Kaback, H. R. 1987. *Biochemistry*. In press

19. Menick, D. R., Lee, J. A., Brooker, R. J., Wilson, T. H., Kaback, H. R. 1987. *Biochemistry* 26:1132
20. Menick, D. R., Sarkar, H. K., Poonian, M. S., Kaback, H. R. 1985. *Biochem. Biophys. Res. Commun.* 132:162
21. Neuhaus, J. M., Soppa, J., Wright, J. K., Reide, I., Blocker, H., et al. 1985. *FEBS Lett.* 185:83
22. Padan, E., Sarkar, H. K., Viitanen, P. V., Poonian, M. S., Kaback, H. R. 1985. *Proc. Natl. Acad. Sci. USA* 82:6765
23. Püttner, I. B., Sarkar, H. K., Poonian, M. S., Kaback, H. R. 1986. *Biochemistry* 25:4483
24. Robillard, G. T., Konings, W. N. 1982. *Eur. J. Biochem.* 127:597
25. Saier, M. H., Wentzel, D. L., Feucht, B. V., Judice, J. J. 1975. *J. Biol. Chem.* 250:5089
26. Sarkar, H. K., Menick, D. R., Viitanen, P. V., Poonian, M. S., Kaback, H. R. 1986. *J. Biol. Chem.* 261:8914
27. Sarkar, H. K., Viitanen, P. V., Padan, E., Trumble, W. R., Poonian, M. S., et al. 1986. *Meth. Enzymol.* 125:214
28. Trumble, W. R., Viitanen, P. V., Sarkar, H. K., Poonian, M. S., Kaback, H. R. 1984. *Biochem. Biophys. Res. Commun.* 119:860
29. Viitanen, P. V., Garcia, M. L., Foster, D. L., Kaczorowski, G. J., Kaback, H. R. 1983. *Biochemistry* 22:2531
30. Viitanen, P. V., Menick, D. R., Sarkar, H. K., Trumble, W. R., Kaback, H. R. 1985. *Biochemistry* 24:7628
31. Wright, J. K., Seckler, R., Overath, P. 1986. *Ann. Rev. Biochem.* 55:225
32. Yazyu, H., Shiota-Niiya, S., Shimamoto, T., Kanazawa, H., Futai, M., Tsuchiya, T. 1984. *J. Biol. Chem.* 259:4320
33. Zoller, M. J., Smith, M. 1983. *Meth. Enzymol.* 100:468

Ann. Rev. Physiol. 1988. 50:257–71

# EFFECTS OF LIPID ENVIRONMENT ON MEMBRANE TRANSPORT: The Human Erythrocyte Sugar Transport Protein/Lipid Bilayer System[1]

*Anthony Carruthers and Donald L. Melchior*

Department of Biochemistry, University of Massachusetts Medical School, 55 Lake Avenue North, Worcester, Massachusetts 01605

## INTRODUCTION

Membrane transport proteins (carriers) catalyze transmembrane movements of hydrophilic molecular species. To perform this function, carriers employ a variety of mechanisms for transmembrane solute flux that are distinct from and more rapid than leakage or non-Stokesian transbilayer diffusion of solutes (37). The low permeability of the membrane lipid bilayer to most hydrophilic species prevents the rapid dissipation of transbilayer solute gradients co-established by membrane transport systems and intracellular metabolism and thus assists in the maintenance of a cytosolic environment favorable to cellular homeostasis.

In addition to providing a permeability barrier, the membrane lipid bilayer provides a matrix for the attachment of membrane proteins. Most integral membrane proteins contain extensive, hydrophilic (extramembranous) and hydrophobic (membrane spanning) sequences. As a consequence, transverse protein reorientations (flip-flop) within the lipid bilayer are highly improbable

---

[1]Abbreviations: $T_n$, turnover number ($V_{max}$/transport molecule); Ea, activation energy for transport; PC, phosphatidylcholine; PA, phosphatidic acid; PG, phosphatidylglycerol; PS, phosphatidylserine; DMPC, dimyristoyl phosphatidylcholine; DPPC, dipalmitoyl phosphatidylcholine; DSPC, distearoyl phosphatidylcholine; DAPC, diarachidoyl phosphatidylcholine; DEPC, dielaidoyl phosphatidylcholine; DOPC, dioleoyl phosphatidylcholine; DMPG, dimyristoyl phosphatidylglycerol; DPPG, dipalmitoyl phosphatidylglycerol; MPPC, monopalmitoyl phosphatidylcholine.

257

0066-4278/88/0315-0257$02.00

on thermodynamic grounds. A number of integral membrane proteins are additionally anchored to the bilayer by proteinacious cytoskeletal elements. These factors can maintain the appropriate catalytic orientation of transport proteins within the membrane bilayer.

Recent studies indicate that the structural and compositional properties of the bilayer can determine the catalytic properties of membrane transport proteins (7). The lipid bilayer is, in fact, a lipid phase coexisting with an aqueous phase. A large proportion of cellular processes occur in and upon this lipid phase. Just as the activities of water soluble enzymes reflect properties of the aqueous phase in which they exist, so the properties of enzymes existing in the membrane bilayer appear to reflect properties of the lipid phase in which they are embedded. The lipid bilayer is, in a strict sense, a solvent for intrinsic membrane proteins. Whereas cytosolic proteins are dissolved in the cell water, integral membrane proteins are exposed to both aqueous and bilayer phases. Unlike water, the bilayer is an anisotropic system. A self-forming phase in water, the bilayer is a quasi-two-dimensional structure: hydrophilic lipid head groups are exposed to the surrounding aqueous phase and hydrophobic lipid acyl chains form a central hydrocarbon core within the bilayer (Figure 1). Like water, the bilayer is a dynamic structure—its lipid

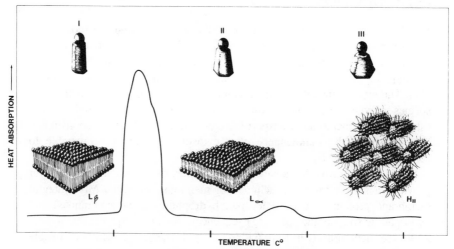

*Figure 1*   The phase behavior of mixed-chain phosphatidylethanolamine in excess water. At low temperature this lipid exists as crystalline bilayers (the $L_\beta$ state). With increasing temperature, the bilayers undergo a reversible endothermic transition commonly called the bilayer phase transition. The resulting state (the or $L_\alpha$ state) is composed of fluid bilayers. The lipid hydrocarbon chains are more disordered in fluid bilayers than in crystalline bilayers. This results in more cone-shaped molecules as illustrated in the top of the figure. With further increase in temperature the lipid molecules become still more cone-shaped and their preferred conformation is the inverted hexagonal $H_{II}$ state. The transition to this state requires less heat than the bilayer phase transition. (From 23.)

components characterized by intermolecular and rotational, translational, and transverse molecular motions (39). Like water, the bilayer structure is modified by temperature and mutually soluble species. The question therefore arises: Are membrane proteins, as is the case with water soluble proteins, affected by the properties of their solvent—the bilayer? Just as the ionization state of an amino acid side chain of a water soluble protein can be affected by pH or protein conformation by ionic strength, can the conformation of an integral membrane protein be modified by the presence in the bilayer of specific lipid head groups or altered lipid acyl chain length and saturation/ unsaturation?

This is not simply an academic question. The forces governing membrane protein structure (and, therefore, presumably activity) are poorly understood. If the bilayer merely provides a structural anchor for membrane proteins, why are lipid compositional asymmetry between hemileaflets of the bilayer and compositional heterogeneity within each hemileaflet of the bilayer common cellular themes (38)?

## THE MEMBRANE BILAYER

Before considering the effects of membrane lipids on membrane transport protein activity, it is useful to examine the properties of lipid bilayers. The lipid bilayer, the underlying foundation of the membrane, is a complex entity whose nature differs markedly from that of other nonlipid macromolecular structures found in biological systems. The subunits of proteins, nucleic acids, and carbohydrates (amino acids, nucleic acid bases, and sugars respectively) are assembled covalently to form essentially linear polymers of fixed primary structure. These chains are then organized into secondary, tertiary, and higher order arrangements. While there can be considerable motion within these macromolecules, the ordering of their subunits is effectively fixed.

In contrast, the associations of the basic structural units of membranes are not covalent in nature, but are physical (26). Unlike proteins, nucleic acids, and carbohydrates, lipid bilayers are sloppy structures. Unlike a linear chain of covalently linked subunits, the bilayer is a quasi-two-dimensional phase. The majority of its component molecules are normally in constant motion, and their spatial relationships to one another are best expressed in time-averaged terms.

A typical membrane is composed of hundreds of different lipid species whose spatial distribution does not appear to be random (16, 38). Regions (domains) of the membrane may be richer in some lipid species than in others because of the mutual solubility properties of the lipids (26). Lipids like cholesterol appear to reorganize lipid packing in the bilayer (24). Cholesterol may further organize the bilayer into regions or domains of differing lipid composition by preferentially associating with certain classes of lipids (13). In a similar manner, certain intrinsic membrane proteins may induce lateral bilayer heterogenity (40). Studies with model bilayer systems demonstrate that certain lipid classes can be precipitated in the plane of the bilayer by divalent cations and thus bring about lateral bilayer heterogeneity (43). In addition to lateral heterogeneity within the bilayer, the two hemileaflets of the bilayer appear to differ in composition (38).

A fundamental property of bilayers formed from a single lipid species is the thermotropic transition (melt) from an ordered, liquid crystalline type state to a disordered, fluid type state (phase transition) (8, 25). Bilayers show a characteristic phase transition temperature ($T_c$) that is dependent both upon lipid acyl chain composition and lipid head group. For example, dipalmitoyl phosphatidylcholine (DPPC[1], a $C_{16}$ disaturate PC) bilayers undergo a phase transition from an ordered to a disordered state at 42°C. During the transition, the arrangement (packing) and mobility of the bilayer lipid molecules are drastically altered (Figure 1). In the ordered bilayer, the acyl chains are roughly parallel and have low mobility and close proximity. Their average molecular cross sectional area normal to the plane of the bilayer is equivalent to that of the phosphorylcholine head group. During and following the bilayer transition, the mobility of the acyl chains is increased, resulting in a lateral expansion of time-averaged lipid molecular area, which in turn thins the bilayer and increases the bilayer surface area (26, 34). This is the most drastic modification of bilayer structure attainable in bilayers formed from a single lipid species.

Unlike water, a bilayer is spatially inhomogeneous and motion within it is anisotropic. Molecular motions within the bilayer are dependent upon molecular class. For example, both membrane lipids and proteins can undergo lateral diffusion in the plane of the bilayer, but only lipids have been observed to move transversely across the membrane (flip-flop) (38).

Under physiological conditions, membranes are disordered and their component molecules are for the most part in constant motion. Phospholipids and steroids diffuse laterally in fluid bilayers at rates of $10^{-8}$ cm$^2$/sec (15, 31, 44) while proteins are less mobile with lateral diffusion rates of $10^{-10}$ cm$^2$/sec (1). Both lipids (20) and proteins (30) undergo rotational motion within the bilayer. Diffusion rates in ordered (crystalline) membranes are low: The lateral diffusion rates of lipids are in the order of $10^{-11}$ cm$^2$/sec (35).

In addition to translational, transverse, and rotational modes of motion, membrane lipids have unique complex internal modes of motion. For instance, while the motions of lipid head groups may be similar to those displayed by the amino acid residues of proteins, the motions of lipid hydrocarbon chains are quite different from those found in molecules such as proteins (39). In bilayers, lipids exist in an array characterized by close intramolecular proximity and significant motional coupling between hydro-carbon chains (29). The motions of molecules such as cholesterol are sub-stantially different than those of the phosphoglycerol- or sphingosine-based lipids (34). The various types of molecular motions occuring in bilayers are not necessarily correlated to one another in a simple manner. For example, a lipid molecule may have rapid rotational movement but not necessarily rapid lateral movement (18). An increase in molecular bilayer lipid disorder can occur without an increase in lipid translational motion (19).

These considerations demonstrate that the molecular motions occurring in a membrane bilayer can be quite diverse. While generalities may be drawn, the modes of movement of any membrane component appear to be quite de-pendent on the particular lipid or protein of interest as well as on overall membrane lipid composition, temperature, or bilayer physical state. An example of this is seen in the study by Rubenstein et al (32) demonstrating the dependence of phospholipid mobility on temperature and bilayer cholesterol content. The bilayer environment of an integral membrane protein is thus both compositionally and structurally complex. As a protein transverses the bilayer, its various domains are exposed to a variety of environments: bulk water, interfacial regions, lipid head group regions, lipid backbone regions, and a bilayer hydrocarbon core region. These membrane environments may vary in both composition and order, according to protein location within lateral and transverse planes of the bilayer.

## THE BILAYER AS A SOLVENT FOR INTRINSIC MEMBRANE PROTEINS

Given that the bilayer is a complex phase and that its properties may be important in determining membrane enzyme activity, what are the most effective means for investigating how bilayer lipids affect membrane enzyme activity? Even a lipid bilayer of homogeneous lipid composition is a complex structure. Classical biochemistry has been concerned with the behavior of water soluble enzymes in aqueous suspension or with aqueous aspects of membrane enzyme function. Because the nature of the bilayer phase is very different from that of the water phase, a priori assumptions regarding which bilayer features affect membrane enzyme behavior are highly speculative.

During initial studies of an enzyme-mediated reaction, it is necessary to define the pH, ionic strength, and divalent cation dependence of the reaction. These parameters have long been known to govern chemical reactions in aqueous environments. When performed rigorously, such studies can provide a wealth of physical data characterizing active centers of catalysis (33). Moreover, these measurements serve to optimize conditions for more de-tailed, kinetic analyses of enzyme function.

Although the above parameters may be suitable for analyses of water soluble systems, one must question their sufficiency for analysis of membrane-spanning enzyme-mediated processes. In the case of intrinsic membrane enzymes, only a portion of the molecule is exposed to an aqueous environment; a significant proportion of the molecule exists in the bilayer phase. Most, if not all, complex integral membrane enzymes lose their catalytic activity when removed from their lipid environment. Indeed, for transport proteins, activity has no meaning in the absence of the bilayer. By analogy with water soluble enzymes, one would expect the activity of integral membrane enzymes to reflect the environment both of protein domains exposed to the aqueous environment and protein domains buried within the core of the membrane lipid bilayer.

A direct approach to this problem is to observe the activity of relevant membrane enzymes reconstituted into bilayers of simple, preselected lipid composition. Simple model systems can be made progressively more complex and hypotheses can be tested. A judicious choice of lipids and conditions may reveal correlations between enzyme activity and bilayer lipid composition/ physical state. For example, in a reconstituted bilayer of a given lipid composition, one can create a system in which the temperature dependency of an enzyme can be studied in the crystalline bilayer, in the fluid bilayer, and during the bilayer transition. In this manner, compositional and physical factors can be separated, and correlations between the results of such studies can be developed into a framework of useful parameters.

An extensive body of knowledge describes the behavior of lipids in model bilayer systems. Studying the behavior of membrane enzymes in bilayers of preselected lipid composition thus not only offers a well-defined system, but also permits utilization of available knowledge on relatively well-characterized systems. These relatively "clean" systems further lend themselves to correlated structure/function studies using physical techniques such as differential scanning calerimetry (DSC), nuclear magnetic resonance (NMR), Fourier transform infrared spectroscopy (FTIR), etc. Hypotheses derived from these various approaches may then be used to evaluate the various existent generalizations deduced from studies on native biomembranes with their heterogeneous lipid populations, diverse protein species, cytoskeletal protein matrices, bilayer lipid and protein structural asymmetries, lateral heterogeneities, etc.

## RECONSTITUTION STUDIES WITH THE GLUCOSE TRANSPORTER

### The Glucose Carrier

As a general class of membrane enzymes, transport proteins may be very useful molecules for investigations of membrane lipid environment/membrane enzyme activity relationships. The use of the human red cell sugar transporter offers a number of advantages (7) in this instance. As a passive transport system, the human hexose transfer protein serves a relatively simple function—to facilitate the net transmembrane movement of sugars down a concentration gradient. The sugar carrier shares structural similarities with other membrane transport proteins. At least 8 to 12 membrane-spanning, hydrophobic domains accounting for some 50% of carrier mass have been predicted from the primary structure of the protein (4, 27). The transporter contains a single cytochalasin B binding site (3). Cytochalasin B binding to this site and catalytic activity are lost when the transporter is irreversibly denatured by removal of lipid (36). Reconstituted transporter activity is proportional to the number of reconstituted cytochalasin B binding sites (2, 6). Determining the number of detectable cytochalasin B binding sites in reconstitution studies permits quantitation of the functional sugar transport protein. By measuring $V_{max}$ for reconstituted, purified transporter activity and the number of reconstituted transporter sites, it is possible not only to calculate the turnover number of the transporter ($t_n$, $V_{max}$/carrier) but also to compare the catalytic efficiency of the transporter in different systems.

## Bilayer Properties

HYDROCARBON CHAINS    Upon reconstitution into a variety of disaturated PC bilayers, the turnover number of the glucose transporter increases during the bilayer phase transition (6). Indeed, catalytic activity is not detectable in crystalline (ordered) dimyristoyl PC (DMPC, $C_{14}$) and DPPC membranes in spite of apparently normal ligand binding. These observations are consistent with the notions that solvent (bilayer) order governs the catalytic activity of the carrier to a greater extent than it does the ligand-binding properties of the transport protein and that substrate binding is not rate limiting for transport. However, a number of findings indicate that bilayer order is not a primary determinant of transporter function. (a) The phase transition in phosphatidylglycerol (PG) bilayers is not associated with altered transporter $T_n$ (see below) (41). (b) $T_n$ for transport in ordered distearoyl PC (DSPC, a $C_{18}$ disaturate) and diarachidoyl PC (DAPC, a $C_{20}$ disaturate) bilayers is as great or even greater than that observed in disordered DMPC and dioleoyl PC ($C_{18}$ a cis-9,10 diunsaturate) bilayers.

Close examination of $T_n$ for transport and the temperature dependence of transport in PC bilayers indicates a linear dependence of $T_n$ and $E_a$ (the activation energy for transport) on PC acyl chain carbon number up to at least $C_{18}$. Bilayer thickness is, to a large extent, determined by bilayer lipid acyl chain carbon number and saturation/unsaturation (34). If bilayer thickness were the major determinant of glucose transporter activity in PC bilayers, the expected activities in the above membranes would be DMPC < DPPC $\cong$

DOL < dielaidoyl PC (DEPC, a trans-9,10 diunsaturate) < DSPC < DAPC. This is almost exactly the activity relationship observed, with the exception that activity in DSPC bilayers is greater than that observed in DAPC bilayers. It is possible that an activity optimum is achieved in $C_{18}$ disaturates. The increase in ordered bilayer thickness per C2 addition to disaturated PC acyl chains is approximately 4 Å (34)—a value approximately equivalent to 1 turn of a proteinaceous alpha helix. Similarly, upon melting DPPC and DMPC bilayers, bilayer thickness falls by approximately 11 and 7 Å respectively (34). This thinning of the bilayer is approximately equivalent to 2 and 1 turns respectively in a polypeptide alpha helix. Although these considerations indicate that altered bilayer order and lipid acyl chain carbon number could have drastic consequences upon protein structure within the bilayer, they also indicate that the relationship between bilayer thickness and carrier activity, if real, is not simple. Activity increases not only with increasing acyl chain carbon number in ordered bilayers (and presumably bilayer thickness) but also during the bilayer crystalline to fluid phase transition (and presumably bilayer thinning).

HEAD GROUP    The influence of bilayer lipid head group on glucose transporter activity has been studied using a series of lipids of homologous acyl chain composition (myristate, a $C_{14}$ disaturate) (41). These lipids are PC, PG, phosphatidylserine (PS), and phosphatidic acid (PA). The turnover number of the glucose carrier at both 20 and 50°C in proteoliposomes formed from these lipids is PC < PG < PS < PA. Similar but less pronounced findings are obtained using lipids with heterogeneous acyl chain composition (egg PC, egg PG, egg PS, and egg PA). The surface potential of bilayers formed from these lipid species also increases in the order PC < PG < PS < PA (17), suggesting that lipid head groups could modify the catalytic activity of the carrier protein through bilayer surface charge effects. However, titration of surface charge using protons or $Na^+$ has quantitatively similar effects on transport in PC and PG bilayers in spite of the clear demonstration of modified phase behavior of DMPG bilayers upon titration of surface potential (41).

The temperature dependence of transporter activity in PC and PG bilayers has been examined for the series dimyristoyl, dipalmitoyl, and distearoyl PC and PG. Unlike DMPG and DPPG bilayers, DMPC and DPPC bilayers are unable to support detectable transport activity in the crystalline, ordered state. During the pre- and main transitions of DMPC and DPPC bilayers, transport activity becomes measurable and increases thereafter with increasing temperature. DMPG and DPPG bilayers, however, support measurable transport activity in the ordered state. In addition, there is no significant increase in transporter turnover number during the crystalline to fluid phase transition of PG bilayers. Rather, $K_{m(app)}$ for transport displays a reversible decrease during the phase transition. With both PC and PG bilayers, the carrier turnover number increases with increasing acyl chain carbon number. These rather dramatic differences between carrier activities in PC and PG bilayers are interesting. PC and PG bilayers display very similar phase transition temperatures when formed from lipids with homologous acyl chain composition, which indicates that the forces determining bilayer structure are very similar. While head group compositional differences are presumably sufficient to account for alterations in transporter activity, the influence of acyl chain composition on transporter properties is still discernable.

BACKBONE    The influence of lipid backbone on sugar transporter activity in proteoliposomes has been studied only in membranes formed from lipids containing glycerol and sphingosine backbones (41). Egg sphingomyelin (containing a sphingosine backbone) bilayers support 10-fold lower activity than do egg PC, PG, and PA (containing a glycerol backbone) bilayers. $K_{m(app)}$ for transport in sphingomyelin bilayers is some 30-fold greater than that observed in PC bilayers, and carrier turnover number increases reversibly during the phase transition of sphingomyelin bilayers.

CHOLESTEROL    Cholesterol is a major lipid component of eukaryotic plasma membranes accounting for almost as much as 42 mol% bilayer lipid (5). Unlike the aforementioned lipids, cholesterol belongs to a class of lipids that by themselves are unable to form bilayers upon hydration but that can interdigitate into bilayers to modify bilayer structure (34). Cholesterol modifies the packing properties of bilayer lipids. At 30–50 mol% bilayer content, cholesterol acts as a membrane plasticizer and transforms membranes to a state intermediate between ordered and disordered (12). Under such conditions, the bilayer phase transition is suppressed (8, 21). Increasing the cholesterol content of DPPC bilayers from 0 to 20 mol% progressively reduces the expansion of bilayer volume occurring during the bilayer phase transition (Figure 2) (24). At about 17.5–18.5 mol% cholesterol, an abrupt decrease in ordered DPPC bilayer volume occurs, but is reversed at 20 mol% cholesterol. At 20 mol% cholesterol, a marked change in bilayer lipid packing occurs. The ordered bilayer is expanded and the disordered bilayer condensed. This progresses to approximately 30 mol% cholesterol when an additional rearrangement of packing is observed (expansion and condensation of ordered and disordered bilayer respectively) that continues monotonically with cholesterol concentrations up to 50 mol%. Above this concentration, cholesterol forms unstable associations with the bilayer.

    The effects of bilayer cholesterol on sugar transporter activity in DPPC membranes are complex (9, 10). Cholesterol is without effect on transport at concentrations of up to 10 mol%. Between 10 and 20 mol% cholesterol, a marked and reversible decrease in carrier turnover number is observed for disordered bilayers and a reversible increase in turnover number for ordered

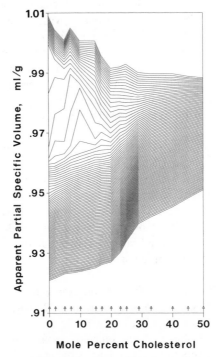

*Figure 2*   The apparent partial specific volume ($V_a$) of pure and cholesterol-containing di-palmitoyl phosphatidylcholine bilayers over the temperature range of 0 to 50°C. $V_a$ is plotted against mol% cholesterol ($X_c$) at half-degree temperature intervals extending 0°C *(bottom)* to 50°C *(top)*. The concentrations of bilayer cholesterol in the dilatometer runs used to construct the plots are indicated by the 15 arrows along the $X_c$ axis at $X_c$ = 0, 2, 5, 7, 10, 15, 17, 20, 23, 25, 29, 33, 40, 45, and 50. Experimental points at these concentrations are connected by straight lines. Since vertical cuts at the arrows reproduce the experimental volume-temperature curves, the vertical spacings between the lines are a measure of the coefficient of expansion at various cholesterol concentrations. (From 24.)

bilayers. Cholesterol is without significant effect on transport between 20 and 30 mol%. Thereafter, cholesterol increases $T_n$ in ordered bilayers and reduces $T_n$ in disordered bilayers. These findings are consistent with the view that carrier activity is related to bilayer order and that cholesterol's actions at high sterol levels reflect its ability to modify lipid packing. At low concentrations (typical of those found in intracellular membranes), cholesterol's effects on transport are less consistent with the sterol's action on bilayer lipid packing. If there is a systematic relationship between bilayer order and transporter activity, transporter turnover number at any bilayer cholesterol concentration should be governed largely by bilayer apparent partial specific volume (a parameter directly related to bilayer disorder). This is not the case (10). In addition, cholesterol at 40 mol% while acting to expand ordered DSPC bilayers in fact reduces the catalytic activity of the transporter under these conditions. These findings argue for a transport-modulating role of bilayer cholesterol that is independent of the sterol's ability to act as a membrane plasticizer.

## Bioactive Lipids

The work described up to this point has been concerned with how lipids modulate the activity of the human sugar transporter by altering overall bilayer properties. Certain bilayer lipids appear to be able to act on the transporter at low bilayer concentrations, behaving as lipid soluble "co-factors" or "allosteric regulators."

Lyso phospholipids are present in red cell membranes at concentrations less than 2 mol%. Intermediates in phospholipid metabolism, lysolipids can be generated by the actions of phospholipase types A1 and A2, which cleave acyl chains from phospholipids at positions 1 and 2 respectively (45). At high concentrations, lyso compounds can act as membrane lytic agents. At lower concentrations, the presence of lyso lipids in the membrane is presumably a consequence of lipid metabolism. Monopalmitoyl PC (MPPC) acts as a reversible, partial uncompetitive inhibitor of exchange glucose transport in human red cells ($K_{m(app)}$ and $V_{max}$ for transport are reduced) (28). The consequence of this action is a stimulation of transport at physiological glucose levels and an inhibition at higher sugar concentrations. $K_{i(app)}$ for MPPC action is reduced by increasing saturation of the glucose carrier with sugar, which indicates a specific interaction of lyso PC with the carrier hexose complex. At 400 mM D-glucose (when the carrier is approximately 85–95% saturated with sugar), half-maximal inhibition of transport is reached at a MPPC bilayer lipid molar ratio of 0.07 mol% and a MPPC-carrier molar ratio of approximately 0.5:1. Similar results have been obtained using reconstituted glucose carrier in a variety of PC bilayers. In addition, this effect has been shown to be specific to lyso lipids with specific head groups and chain lengths. (Inactive PCs include monostearoyl PC, monooleoyl PC; active PEs include monomyristoyl PE; inactive PEs include monopalmitoyl PE, monostearoyl PE; monooleoyl PE produces a small increase in carrier $T_n$ and sphingosine is inactive.) These findings argue strongly against an indirect metabolic or bilayer modulating action of MPPC on transport, but rather indicate a direct mode of action of MPPC on the transport system.

# STUDIES WITH OTHER MEMBRANE TRANSPORT PROTEINS

Studies with sacroplasmic reticulum ($Ca^{2+}$, $Mg^{2+}$)-dependent ATPase find no consistent relationship between bilayer order and ATPase activity (14), although activity does increase during the bilayer phase transition. Rather, activity appears to be related to acyl chain carbon number—a result strikingly similar to that obtained with the reconstituted glucose carrier. The Na-dependent (active) glucose carrier of epithelial cells shows increased activity in DMPC bilayers during and after the bilayer order/disorder transition (11).

These findings support the view that carrier activity is increased in disordered bilayers but that the relationship between activity and bilayer order is not a major determinant of carrier function. An overriding theme is the relationship between lipid acyl chain carbon number and carrier activity.

Using the prokaryotic *Escherichia coli* fatty acid auxotroph T105 whose membrane lipid composition (and therefore phase transition temperature) was varied by supplementation with different fatty acids, Thilo et al (42) studied the consequences of supplementation on bilayer order and proton-$\beta$ glucoside co-transport. Increased co-transport of $\beta$-glucoside was correlated with the bilayer order/disorder transition. The ability of substrate to bind to the permease is unaffected by the bilayer order/disorder transition [P. Overath and co-workers, see reference in (22)], a result very similar to that found with the passive sugar transporter reconstituted into PC bilayers. These studies represent an important demonstration of transport modulation during the order/disorder transition in biological membranes. It is not possible, however, to determine whether this acceleration of transport is the result of decreased bilayer order. During the phase transition, fluid regions of bilayer grow at the expense of ordered bilayer regions; the disordered regions are enriched in low melting point lipids and the ordered regions in high melting point lipids. Membrane proteins partition between fluid and crystalline lipid regions (26) and are, therefore, exposed to environments that vary both in physical state and lipid composition. The carrier could be affected by either or both of these changes in environment.

## CONCLUSIONS

The catalytic activity of membrane transport proteins is markedly sensitive to a variety of membrane lipid bilayer properties. Synthetic bilayers formed from single or mixed lipid species and prokaryotic membrane bilayers undergo characteristic phase transitions from an ordered (crystalline-like) to a disordered (fluid-like) state. The transport proteins that have been studied (the passive glucose carrier, the Na:glucose co-transporter, the $(Ca^{2+}, Mg^{2+})$ATPase and lac permease) can respond to this transition in bilayer order with increased rates of catalytic turnover. In some instances (e.g. the passive sugar transporter) the increase in $T_n$ can be orders of magnitude, whereas under other conditions (e.g. the glucose carrier in PG bilayers) no change in $T_n$ is detectable.

Although bilayer order can be a determinant of transport protein activity, studies with the glucose carrier and the $(Ca^{2+}, Mg^{2+})$ATPase indicate that bilayer lipid acyl chain length may be a more important determinant of catalytic efficiency. Transport activities can differ by orders of magnitude between PC bilayers formed from lipids differing by as little as two in acyl chain carbon number. This effect may reflect protein sensitivity to bilayer thickness. Insufficient data are available to confirm this hypothesis. The head group composition of bilayer lipids can override effects of both bilayer order and lipid acyl chain length on sugar transporter activity. This indicates additional interactions of bilayer lipids with transport proteins. Bilayer-modifying lipids such as cholesterol (a major plasma membrane lipid) can drastically modulate carrier activity.

The preceding discussion demonstrates that the compositional and physical properties of the membrane bilayer have a profound influence on the activities of a variety of membrane transport proteins. Just as the characteristics of the aqueous environment of water soluble enzymes determine enzyme activity, the characteristics of the lipid environment of a membrane protein play a major role in determining activity. Whether transport protein activity may be subject to physiological regulation by modulation of its lipid environment remains an open question. However, studies with the glucose carrier and lyso PC demonstrate that just as very low concentrations of hydrophilic cofactors may modify the activities of water soluble cytosolic proteins, so the lipid bilayer can serve as a solvent phase for hydrophobic species that modulate transporter activity at very low concentrations. The lipid bilayer is, in many respects, a hydrophobic counterpart of cell water. The bilayer provides for much of the structural and compositional requirements of membrane proteins, establishes optimal conditions for activity, and provides a phase for the delivery of hydrophobic factors for physiologic regulation of protein function.

ACKNOWLEDGMENTS

This work was funded by the National Science Foundation, Grant DMB-8416219 (D.L.M.), and the National Institutes of Health, Grant R01 AM36081 (A. C.). We gratefully acknowledge this support. We thank Judith A. Kula for her help in preparing the manuscript.

*Literature Cited*

1. Axelrod, D. 1983. Lateral motions of membrane proteins and biological function. *J. Membr. Biol.* 75:1–10
2. Baldwin, J. M., Gorga, J. C., Lienhardt, G. E. 1981. The monosaccharide transporter of the human erythrocyte. Transport activity upon reconstitution. *J. Biol. Chem.* 256:3685–89
3. Baldwin, S. A., Baldwin, J. M., Lienhard, G. E. 1981. The monosaccharide transporter of the human erythrocyte. Characterization of an improved preparation. *Biochemistry* 21:3836–42
4. Birnbaum, M. J., Haspel, H. C., Rosen, O. M. 1986. Cloning and characterization of a cDNA encoding the rat brain glucose transporter protein. *Proc. Natl. Acad. Sci. USA* 83:3784–88
5. Carruthers, A., Melchior, D. L. 1983. A study of the relationship between bilayer water permeability and bilayer physical state. *Biochemistry* 22:5797–5807
6. Carruthers, A., Melchior, D. L. 1984.

Human erythrocyte hexose transporter activity is governed by bilayer lipid composition in reconstituted vesicles. *Biochemistry* 23:6901–11

7. Carruthers, A., Melchior, D. L. 1986. How bilayer lipids affect membrane protein activity. *Trends Biol. Sci.* 11:331–35

8. Chapman, D., Williams, R. M., Ladbrooke, B. D. 1967. Physical studies of phospholipids. *Chem. Phys. Lipids* 1:445–76

9. Connolly, T. J., Carruthers, A., Melchior, D. L. 1985. Effects of bilayer cholesterol on human erythrocyte hexose transporter protein activity in synthetic lecithin bilayers. *Biochemistry* 24:2865–73

10. Connolly, T. J., Carruthers, A., Melchior, D. L. 1985. Effects of bilayer cholesterol content on reconstituted human erythrocyte sugar transporter activity. *J. Biol. Chem.* 260:2617–20

11. Da Cruz, M.E.M., Kinne, R., Lin, J. T. 1983. Temperature dependence of D-glucose transport in reconstituted liposomes. *Biochim. Biophys. Acta* 732:691–98

12. Demel, R. A., deKruyff, B. 1976. The function of sterols in membranes. *Biochim. Biophys. Acta* 406:97–107

13. Demel, R. A., Jansen, J.W.C.M., van Dijck, P.W.M., van Deenen, L.L.M. 1977. The preferential interaction of cholesterol with different classes of phospholipids. *Biochim. Biophys. Acta* 406:97–107

14. East, J. M., Jones, O. T., Simmonds, A. C., Lee, A. G. 1984. Membrane fluidity is not an important physiological regulation of the $(Ca^{2+}-Mg^{2+})$-dependent ATPase of sarcoplasmic reticulum. *J. Biol. Chem.* 259:8070–71

15. Edidin, M. 1975. Rotational and translational diffusion in membranes. *Ann. Rev. Biophys. Bioeng.* 3:179–201

16. Etemadi, A.-H. 1980. Membrane asymmetry. *Biochim. Biophys. Acta* 604:423–75

17. Hauser, H., Philips, M. C. 1979. Interaction of the polar groups of phospholipid bilayer membranes. *Prog. Surf. Membr. Sci.* 13:297–413

18. Kleinfeld, A. M., Dragsten, P., Klausner, R. D., Pjura, W. J., Matayoshi, E. D. 1981. The lack of relationship between fluorescence polarization and lateral diffusion in biological membranes. *Biochim. Biophys. Acta* 649:471–80

19. Kutchal, H., Chandler, L. H., Zavoico, G. B. 1983. Effects of cholesterol on acyl chain dynamics in multilamellar vesicles of various PC's. *Biochim. Biophys. Acta* 736:137–49

20. Lee, A. G. 1975. Functional properties of biological membranes: A physical-chemical approach. *Prog. Biophys. Mol. Biol.* 29:3–17

21. Mabrey, S., Mateo, P. L., Sturtevant, J. M. 1978. High-sensitivity scanning calorimetric study of mixtures of cholesterol with dimyristoyl and dipalmitoylphosphatidylcholines. *Biochemistry* 17:2464–68

22. McElhaney, R. N. 1982. Effects of membrane lipids on transport and enzymic activities. *Curr. Top. Membr. Transp.* 17:317–80

23. Melchior, D. L. 1982. Lipid phase transitions and regulation of membrane fluidity in prokaryotes. *Curr. Top. Membr. Transp.* 17:263–316

24. Melchior, D. L., Scavitto, F. J., Steim, J. M. 1980. Dilatometry of dipalmitoyllecithin bilayers. *Biochemistry* 19:4828–34

25. Melchior, D. L., Steim, J. M. 1976. Thermotropic transitions in biomembranes. *Ann. Rev. Biophys. Bioeng.* 5:205–38

26. Melchior, D. L., Steim, J. M. 1979. Lipid associated thermal events in biomembranes. *Prog. Surf. Membr. Sci.* 13:211–96

27. Mueckler, M., Caruso, C., Baldwin, S., Panico, M., Blench, I., et al. 1985. Sequence and structure of a human glucose transporter. *Science* 229:941–45

28. Naderi, S., Tefft, R. E. Jr., Carruthers, A., Melchior, D. L. 1987. Submitted for publication

29. Nagel, J. F. 1980. Theory of the main lipid bilayer phase transition. *Ann. Rev. Phys. Chem.* 31:157–95

30. Nigg, E. A., Cherry, R. J. 1979. Labeling of human erythrocyte membranes with eosin probes used for protein diffusion measurements. *Biochemistry* 18:3457–65

31. Rigaud, J. L., Gary Bobo, C. M., Sanson, A., Ptak, M. 1977. Fatty acid diffusion in lecithin multilayers. *Chem. Phys. Lipids* 18:23–38

32. Rubenstein, J.L.R., Owicki, J. C., McConnell, H. M. 1980. Dynamic properties of binary mixtures of phosphatidylcholines and cholesterol. *Biochemistry* 19:569–73

33. Segal, I. H. 1975. *Enzyme Kinetics*. New York: Wiley. 958 pp.

34. Small, D. M. 1986. *Handbook of Lipid Research: The Physical Chemistry of Lipids*. New York: Plenum. 672 pp.

35. Smith, B. A., McConnell, H. M. 1978.

Determination of molecular motion in membranes using periodic pattern photobleaching. *Proc. Natl. Acad. Sci. USA* 75:2759–63

36. Sogin, D. C., Hinkle, P. C. 1978. Characterization of the glucose transporter from human erythrocytes. *J. Supramol. Struct.* 8:447–53

37. Stein, W. D. 1986. *Transport and Diffusion Across Cell Membranes.* New York: Academic. 685 pp.

38. Storch, J., Kleinfeld, A. M. 1985. The lipid structure of biological membranes. *Trends Biol. Sci.* 119:418–21

39. Stubbs, C. D. 1983. Structure and dynamics of membrane lipids. *Essays Biochm.* 19:1–39

40. Taraschi, T. F., deKryuff, B., Verkleij, A., Echteld, C.J.A. 1982. Effect of glycophorin on lipid polymorphism. *Biochim. Biophys. Acta* 685:153–61

41. Tefft, R. E. Jr., Carruthers, A., Melchior, D. L. 1986. Reconstituted human erythrocyte sugar transporter activity is determined by bilayer lipid head group. *Biochemistry* 25:3709–18

42. Thilo, L., Traüble, H., Overath, P. 1977. Mechanistic interpretation of the influence of lipid phase transitions on transport functions. *Biochemistry* 16:1283–90

43. Tokutomi, S., Lew, R., Ohrishi, S. I. 1981. $Ca^{2+}$-induced phase separations in phosphatidylserine, phosphatidylethanolamine and phosphatidylcholine mixed membranes. *Biochim. Biophys. Acta* 643:276–82

44. Traüble, H., Sackman, E. 1972. Studies of the crystalline-liquid phase transition of lipid model membranes III. *J. Am. Chem. Soc.* 94:4499–4503

45. Weltzien, H. U. 1979. Cytolytic and membrane-perturbing properties of lysophosphatidylcholine. *Biochim. Biophys. Acta* 559:259–87

*Ann. Rev. Physiol. 1988. 50:273–90*

# ELECTROCONFORMATIONAL COUPLING: HOW MEMBRANE-BOUND ATPase TRANSDUCES ENERGY FROM DYNAMIC ELECTRIC FIELDS[1]

## Tian Yow Tsong

Department of Biological Chemistry, The Johns Hopkins University School of Medicine, Baltimore, Maryland 21205

## R. Dean Astumian

Laboratory of Biochemistry, National Heart, Lung and Blood Institute, National Institutes of Health, Bethesda, Maryland 20892

## INTRODUCTION

Cells are constantly exposed to or surrounded by electric fields either from self-generating or from external sources. Proteins of cell membranes are thus subjected to influences by these electric fields; two of the most prominent electric fields are the in vivo surface and transmembrane potentials, which have magnitudes of 100–500 kV cm$^{-1}$ (see below). A protein molecule under such an intense electric field will behave quite differently than it would in an homogeneous aqueous solution. It is interesting to compare these values with the dielectric breakdown point of pure water, which is approximately 100 kV cm$^{-1}$. Why a cell should actively maintain such large electric fields across its membranes is a theoretically interesting question since this requires sustained input of free energy. We propose that these fields serve many essential functions.

Starting from the principles of thermodynamics, we summarize how an electric field can interact with a cell membrane and membrane proteins and

[1]The U.S. Government has the right to retain a nonexclusive royalty-free license in and to any copyright covering this paper.

how the energy of such a field can be transduced by these molecules to perform chemical work, e.g. active transport or ATP synthesis. We discuss experiments done in our laboratories concerning the electric activation of membrane associated ATPases. If an enzyme can be activated by an applied electric field, it must likewise respond to endogenous electric fields. The concepts presented here are general and applicable to other thermodynamic variables, although it is expected that the dynamic modulation required for many of the functions described here can be obtained only in the case of the $\Delta\psi$ (where $\psi$ is the membrane potential), which can be rapidly and dramatically changed by the opening or closing of ion channels [for more detailed reviews see (38, 39)].

## ELECTRIC FIELD NEAR THE MEMBRANE INTERFACE

Roughly 10% of membrane lipids are negatively charged. Positively charged lipids are rare. Most commonly occurring lipids with net charges are fatty acids, phosphatidic acids, phosphatidylserines, phosphatidylethanolamines, and cardiolipins. Other constituents of membranes, such as proteins or carbohydrates, also have net charges at neutral pH. These charges do not always (or ever normally) cancel one another. Charges in lipid molecules alone amount to roughly $3 \times 10^{13}$ /cm$^2$ for the bilayer, and by attracting counter ions to their vicinity, an electric double layer that gives rise to a surface potential of 60 mV, i.e. field strength up to 200 kV cm$^{-1}$ within 1 nm from the surface, is formed [see references listed in (39)]. The transmembrane potential arises because of differences in membrane permeability to various ions. The transmembrane potential, typically in the range of $-10$ to $-250$ mV, imposes an electric field strength of roughly $-20$ to $-500$ kV cm$^{-1}$ on molecules of cell membranes if we assume the thickness of membranes ($d$) to be 5–7 nm. The effects on enzyme reactions discussed here were triggered by electric fields of similar or smaller magnitudes than those expected in vivo.

The surface and the transmembrane potentials are endogenous. To study the effect of electric fields on membrane function one can alter these endogenous potentials experimentally. Most of the experimental results discussed here were obtained with the pulsed electric field (PEF) method (21, 37). In this method, cells in suspension are exposed to pulsed electric fields. The applied field ($E$) is distorted in the vicinity of a cell, and if the conductivity of the cytosol and the external medium is much greater than that of the cell membrane, which is almost always the case, a transmembrane potential is generated. For a spherical cell, the induced transmembrane potential is expressed by the Maxwell relation,

$$\Delta\psi = 1.5 \ aE \cos \ \theta, \hspace{3cm} 1.$$

in which $a$ is the outer radius of the membrane vesicle, $\theta$ is the angle between a line from the cell center to the point of interest on the surface of the vesicle and the field vector. For example, when $\theta$ is $0°$, cos $\theta$ is 1 and $\Delta\psi$ is 1.5 $aE$. The effective electric field experienced by a molecule embedded in a bilayer is $\Delta\psi/d$. Thus the maximum electric field experienced by membrane-embedded protein is amplified $\Delta\psi/(dE)$ times. For cells the size of human erythrocytes, this amplification factor is approximately 1000. Equation 1 has been verified to be applicable to lipid vesicles and cells by optical imaging spectroscopy (14) and by measuring the critical breakdown potential of uniform size lipid vesicles (10, 35). For cells with other spheroid shapes deviation from Equation 1 is not severe (11, 14, 22, 23).

## ELECTROCONFORMATIONAL CHANGES OF PROTEINS

Most biological molecules have different accessible conformational states with different electric properties. Such conformational equilibria are thus capable of interacting with an electric field. The thermodynamic relation describing this interaction is given by the generalized van't Hoff equation,

$$\left[ \frac{\delta(\ln K)}{\delta E} \right]_{p,V,T} = \frac{\Delta M}{RT},$$

2.

in which the shift in the chemical equilibrium constant ($K$) by an electric field of strength $E$ is expressed as the function of the difference in the macroscopic electric moment ($\Delta M$) of two different chemical species. For a simple reaction,

$$E_1 \ (u,\alpha) \underset{k_b}{\overset{k_f}{\rightleftharpoons}} E_2 \ (u',\alpha')$$

3.

where $E_1$, and $E_2$ represent enzyme states, $M_1 = u + \alpha E$, $M_2 = u' + \alpha'E$, $u$ is the permanent dipole, and $\alpha$ is the polarizabilities of enzyme species. The field dependence of $K$ and the forward and backward rate coefficients ($k_f$ and $k_b$) may be written in a thermodynamically consistent manner from Equation 2.

$$K_e = K_0 \exp [\Delta M \cdot E/R\ T]$$

4.

$$k_{f,e} = k_{f,0} \exp [r\Delta M \cdot E/R\ T]$$

5.

$$k_{b,e} = k_{b,0} \exp [(r - 1)\Delta M \cdot E/R\ T],$$

6.

in which the subscript 0, denotes zero-field, subscript e denotes under $E$, and $r$ is the apportionment constant, with a value between 0 and 1.

A molecule under an electric field will tend to shift to a state with greater molar electric moment. This can be accomplished by several means, chemical or physical: (a) dissociation of ionizable groups, (b) separation of charges, (c) cooperative alignment of weak dipoles from subunits or monomers of a protein complex in the direction of the field, (d) orientation of permanent dipoles within the molecule, (e) induction of dipoles by the applied field due to the polarizability of the molecule, and (f) structural transition to a conformational state with higher macroscopic dipole moment.

Let us consider proteins in general and membrane proteins in particular. Beside charged amino acids and prosthetic groups, which are obvious targets of electric field interaction, each peptide unit represents an electric dipole of 3.5 Debye (D) (17–19). These peptide dipoles do not cancel each other in a common conformational structure of the protein backbone. For example, in an $\alpha$-helix these small peptide dipoles are aligned almost perfectly to form a macrodipole of strength equivalent to two half charges sitting at the two ends of the helix segment (17, 18). Thus a transmembrane helix 5 nm long is an electric dipole equivalent to 120 D (38, 39). Random coil and beta configurations of a peptide chain, on the other hand, have negligible dipole strengths. Therefore any change in helix orientation or helix content will result in a substantial change of the macrodipole moment of a protein molecule.

In an homogeneous solution where molecules are freely rotating (in the 10 ns time range) and the dimension of molecules is small (diameter in the nm range), electric field effects discussed here are generally insignificant, limited to a few percent shift in the chemical equilibrium. However, these effects are amplified by a few orders of magnitude and become important if the same molecules are embedded in a membrane vesicle of a typical cell dimension (37–39). The significance of the nearly fixed orientation of most membrane proteins will become apparent when we discuss experiments using oscillating electric fields.

Figure 1A shows an energy diagram along the reaction path of a hypothetical reaction. If for Equation 3 under $E$ the $E_2$ state would be additionally stabilized by $\Delta M \cdot E$ and the transition state by $[r\Delta M \cdot E]$ when compared with the $E_1$ state. The forward rate is, thus, greatly increased according to Equation 5. Figure 1B illustrates how the forward rate is dependant on $E$ and $\Delta M$ when the rate at zero field is taken to be unity. The dependence of rate on field strength is not a priori linear (38, 39, 41). This non-linearity plays an important role in energy and signal transductions (see below).

Experimentally, electroconformational changes of biological molecules have been directly detected in several cases. Neumann & Katchalsky (27) reported that the structure of poly(A)·2poly(U) unfolded under an electric field to assume a conformational state with a greater dipole moment. Tsuji & Neumann (40) detected electroconformational change of rhodopsin by ultraviolet absorption. Electroconformational change of channel proteins has been inferred from many single channel experiments. Here, the opening/closing of a channel, a well defined conformational change, is known to depend on the transmembrane electric field (13, 16). Even the acetylcholine receptor, which is not considered a voltage gated channel, has been shown to be potential sensitive (24). Other studies have deduced the conformational change of ion pumps by kinetic analysis (25, 28, 38).

## ELECTRIC ACTIVATION OF MEMBRANE ASSOCIATED ATPases

### Pulsed Electric Field Induced ATP Synthesis

The chemiosmotic hypothesis of Boyer et al links ATP synthesis to movement of protons along the electrochemical potential gradient (4). In other words, ATP synthesis derives its energy from the dissipation of proton electrochemical potential energy. Most biochemical studies confirm movement of protons down the electrochemical potential gradient in the ATP synthetic process. However, in these experiments it is difficult to separate effects that are due to the diffusion potential of protons (0.6 $\Delta$pH) and effects that are due to the electric potential of charge ($F\Delta\psi$ where $F$ is the Faraday constant). Most careful experiments discount the existence of a useful $\Delta$pH in actively respiring mitochondria (12). Thus ATP synthesis most likely is driven predominately by $F\Delta\psi$.

Experiments using the PEF method were designed to see whether ATP synthesis can be induced by applied electric fields alone. Indeed, it has been shown that electric fields of microsecond duration induce ATP synthesis in several energy-transducing membranes, e.g. the chloroplast, mitochondria, thermophilic bacteria, and Escherichia Coli [see (38) for references and (5, 6, 32, 33)]. In these cases, energy sources other than that of applied electric fields either were not present or were blocked by electron transport inhibitors. Experiments were done with either square or exponential waveform short pulses of dc fields. ATP yield in most experiments was less than one molecule per enzyme complex per electric pulse. This fact is regarded as upholding the classical binding energy hypothesis in bioenergetics (15, 20, 31), which postulates that ATP is formed by gaining energy because of its much stronger binding to the enzyme as compared to the binding of substrates ADP and $P_i$. The gain in the binding energy, called the interaction energy (20), presumably derived from enzyme conformational change, must be overcome for the newly formed ATP to release from ATPase. Thus a proton electrochemical potential or an applied electric field is thought to facilitate the release of the tightly bound ATP by restoring the enzyme's initial conformational state.

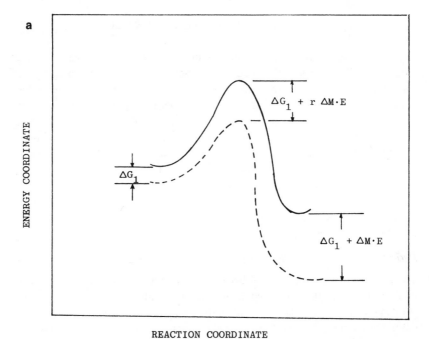

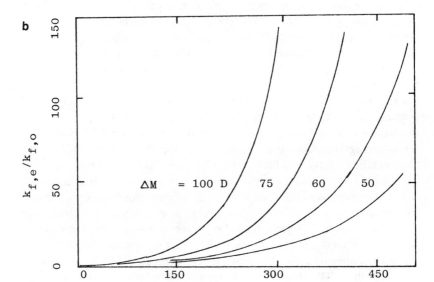

*Figure 1*  (A) Energy diagrams of the reaction $E_1 = E_2$ (see Equation 3) under zero-field condition (solid curve) and under the influence of an electric field, $E$ (dashed curve). The $E_2$ state has a greater molar electric moment than the $E_1$ state ($\Delta M$). Under the electric field $E$, $E_1$ is stabilized by $\Delta G_1$, and $E_2$ is stabilized by $\Delta G_1 + \Delta M \cdot E$. The transition state is stabilized by $\Delta G_1$

Experiments done in our laboratories have produced more ATP per electric pulse than anticipated. We have found that if submitochondrial particles are exposed to a 25–30 kV cm$^{-1}$ electric pulse of about 100 $\mu$s decay time, in the presence of 5 mM dithiothreitol, 5–12 ATP per enzyme complex per pulse is produced (5, 6). Two facts are intuitively puzzling. First, the rate of synthesis is two to three orders of magnitude higher than what one would expect in substrate-linked synthesis. Second, an enzyme turnover by single dc pulse appears to contradict the interpretation given above based on the binding energy mechanism because each turnover would require a conformational relaxation while the enzyme is under the electric field. The first question is explained by dependence of rate on the field strength [Equation 5 and Figure 1B]. The second question is discussed below.

## Electric Field Stimulated $K^+$ and $Rb^+$ Pumping by Na,K-ATPase

Initially our experiment was designed to test the idea that PEF-induced electric pores of red cells occurred at specific transport systems of the cell membranes (23, 34). Inhibitors to various transport activities were used to see if any of them would block the high field-induced transmembrane electric current that was shown to be the result of electroporation. Teissie & Tsong (34) found that ouabain, a potent inhibitor of Na,K-ATPase, blocked 30% of the membrane current, with a half saturation concentration of 0.2 $\mu$M. This concentration agrees with the $K_I$ of ouabain to inhibit Na,K-ATPase. This result indicates that Na,K-ATPase is capable of responding to a transmembrane electric field and suggests that with appropriate designs the enzyme should be reversibly activated by an electric field.

To achieve this goal, Serpersu & Tsong employed low amplitude ac fields of 20 V cm$^{-1}$ at 1 kHz (which can induce a transmembrane potential of 12 mV) to stimulate the activity of Na,K-ATPase in human erythrocytes (29, 30). The stimulated activity was monitored by the uptake of $Rb^+$ and $K^+$ into the erythrocytes against their respective concentration gradients. It was found that at 3° C, where the basal activity of the enzyme was negligible, the maximum stimulated uptake reached approximately 20 $Rb^+$ per enzyme per second (see Figure 2A). When the temperature of the suspension was raised to

←

---

$+ r\Delta M \cdot E$, where $r$ is the apportionment constant, a value in between 0 and 1 (Equation 4). Here $r$ is taken to be 0.5. (B) Because of the alteration in the relative stability of each chemical species involved in (A), the activation barrier of the forward reaction is reduced by $r\Delta M \cdot E$. Here the relative forward rate is plotted against transmembrane potential (assuming membrane thickness of 5 nm) with different values of $\Delta M$ (with $r = 0.5$) expressed in Debye unit. When $\Delta M$ approaches zero, the ratio approaches unity.

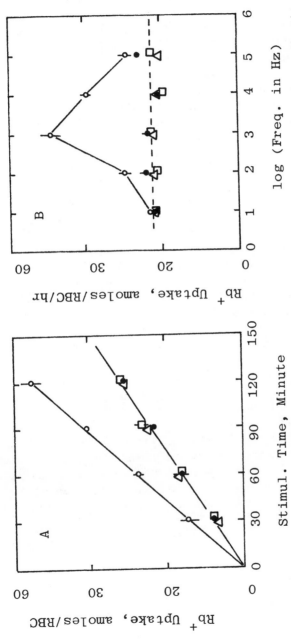

*Figure 2* (*A*) Time course of an ac electric field–stimulated (16 V cm⁻¹, 1 kHz) Rb⁺ uptake by human erythrocytes at 3°C. Uptake of Rb⁺ by samples stimulated with the electric field (○) and not stimulated with the electric field (●); samples preincubated with 50 μM ouabain before electric field stimulation (□) and without electric field stimulation (△) were followed by ⁸⁶Rb⁺ tracer. (*B*) Rb⁺ uptake (1 hour period) was measured for samples stimulated with 20 V cm⁻¹ ac fields of different frequencies. Symbols used are the same as in A. 1 attomole = 1 × 10⁻¹⁸ mole. [After Serpersu & Tsong (29)]

25° C, the electric field stimulated the enzyme activity further, but it was no longer as effective, and at 37° C the effect of voltage stimulation diminished. This is not surprising since one expects that a maximally functioning enzyme would not be susceptible to further stimulation if the voltage activation is relevant to the normal function of the enzyme.

That the PEF-stimulated activity is mediated by the Na,K-ATPase was demonstrated by several experimental criteria. First, effect of the electric field was completely absent when experiments were done with erythrocytes pre-incubated with 50 $\mu$M ouabain for 30 min. Second, $K_m$ of external $K^+$ was 1.7 mM and $K_m$ of internal $Na^+$ was 7 mM for the stimulated activity, which are consistent with $K_m$'s of ATP-linked activity. Third, erythrocytes from an individual who manifested twice basal Na,K-ATPase level also showed twice voltage stimulated activity (33). The stimulated pumping of ions against concentration gradients appears to have derived energy from the ac field since no excess consumption of ATP was detected (33, 34). Similarly, reducing the ATP level to 10 $\mu$M did not have any significant effect on the stimulated activity. Although these results firmly support our contention that Na,K-ATPase is activated by the ac field, we are not pleased by the fact that so far we have been unable to activate the $Na^+$ efflux through the pump by the ac field. This could mean that the two types of transport by the pump are activated by different mechanisms, $Na^+$ transport by ATP hydrolysis and $K^+$ transport by electrogenic transport. It could also mean that activation of $Na^+$ pump occurs at a field strength and frequency we have yet to discover. Nakao & Gadsby (26) observed a strophanthidin-sensitive transient $Na^+$ current in guinea pig ventricle by voltage clamping to potentials between $+60$ and $-100$ mV.[1]

Several experimental facts are especially pertinent to our development of the "electroconformational coupling" concept. It was found that the efficiency of the stimulated $Rb^+$ uptake depended both on field strength and on ac frequency. The optimal field strength was approximately 20 V cm$^{-1}$, and the optimal frequency was around 1 kHz (Figure 2B). Presumably the optimal field strength reflects a conformational factor and the optimal frequency a kinetic factor.

## ELECTROCONFORMATIONAL COUPLING FOR ENERGY TRANSDUCTION

### Energetics of Electroconformational Coupling

Let us consider Equation 3. If the molar electric moment of $E_2$ is greater than $E_1$ by $\Delta M$, an electric field of $E$ will shift the equilibrium constant of Equation

---

[1]$Na^+$ pump has now been activated by an ac field of 20 V cm$^{-1}$ at 1 MHz (D.-S. Liu, R. D. Astumian & T. Y. Tsong, unpublished result).

3 towards $E_2$ according to Equation 2. The amount of energy transferred in the process is $\Delta M \cdot E$. For example, for a $\Delta M$ of 1 D under an electric field of 1 V $cm^{-1}$, the energy transferred is 1 D $\times$ 1 V $cm^{-1}$, which is equal to 3.34 $\times$ $10^{-28}$ J, or $4.8 \times 10^{-5}$ cal $mol^{-1}$. Although this quantity may appear minute, a reaction involving 200 D change in $\Delta M$, under a transmembrane potential change of 200 mV (which is equivalent to a transbilayer electric field of 400 kV $cm^{-1}$), would induce a free energy absorption of 3.85 kcal $mol^{-1}$. As we discuss below, the electric field experienced by a transmembrane protein is most likely dynamic. This would mean that the peak to peak change in the electric field could be 400 mV rather than 200 mV, and the energy transduced by the system could be as much as 7.7 kcal $mol^{-1}$. The translocation of a net single charge across the cell membrane represents effectively a $\Delta M$ of 240 D (39).

## Four State Cyclic Kinetic Model

Having discussed how an electric field can interact with a protein which has two accessible conformational states of different macroscopic electric moments and how free energy contained in an electric field can be absorbed through this interaction, the stage is now set for understanding the experimental results of Na,K-ATPase and mitochondrial $F_0F_1$ATPase using the PEF induction method. Obviously energy absorbed by an enzyme must be efficiently coupled to the chemical process it is designed to catalyze. For Na,K-ATPase, this means to pump $K^+$ against its concentration gradient into the cytoplasmic side of a cell. Let us consider the simple four-state kinetic scheme shown in Equation 7. In the simulations, the charge on the $K^+$ was neglected and substituted with a neutral substrate (S) in order to emphasize the interaction between the enzymes conformational equilibrium and the electric field. This allows us to understand how a neutral substance might be actively transported via Coulombic coupling. Inclusion of charge-field interaction would lead to enhanced energy absorption via enzyme rectification of the time-dependent cyclic driving force (2, 39).

In Equation 7, $E_1$ is a state with low affinity for the internal S, which can convert to $E_2$ when the membrane is depolarized. Depolarization of the membrane is achieved by the first half-cycle of the sinusoidal ac field. $E_2$ has a high affinity for the external S, and it promptly binds an $S_{out}$ to form $E_2S$. When the membrane is polarized in the second half-cycle of the sinusoidal ac field $E_2S$ is converted back to $E_1S$, and at the same time, the bound S is internalized. Since $E_1$ has a low affinity for $S_{in}$, S dissociates and releases into the cytosol. Thus, one cycle of sinusoidal electric field can induce the enzyme to turnover once, although in practice, the yield (turnovers/field cycle) will be usually less than unity.

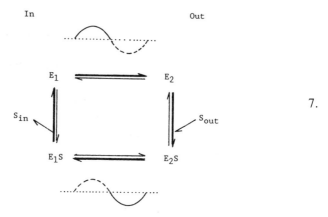

7.

This yield, and thus the rate of enzyme turnover $(s^{-1})$, depends on the matching between kinetic attributes of the system, i.e. the rate coefficients of the four-step cycle and the frequency of the applied field. If binding and dissociation of ligand S are much faster than the two conformational change steps, then the turnover rate is determined by the conformational relaxation of $E_1$ to $E_2$ and $E_2S$ to $E_1S$. Numerical analysis of the four-state model has been carried out (1, 38, 41).

In Figure 3A this scenario is shown in a more quantitative manner. The electric field oscillates sinusoidally as indicated by the dotted curve. Concomitant to each cycle of the ac field, $E_1$ to $E_2$ transition is actuated whenever the electric field is positive and reduced when the field is negative, as indicated by the solid curve. Contrary to this behavior is the $E_2S$ to $E_1S$ transition, which is nearly 180° out of phase of the $E_1$ to $E_2$ transition, as indicated in the dashed curve. The solid and the dashed curves indicate the integrated values of transitions. When the ac field continues to act on the four-state kinetic scheme of Equation 7, clockwise cyclic transitions accumulate, and as a result there is a time-dependent net rise in the internal concentration of S. This is a purely kinetic effect since at no time is there a steady state "driving force" around the cycle (1, 38, 39, 41). Figure 3B reveals some interesting features of this reaction. It appears that the ac induced influx of S is not a monotonic function of the stimulation time, but there are rapid oscillation of $[S]_{in}$. If the kinetic characteristics of the four-state scheme do not match well with the frequency of the ac field, the amplitude of oscillation becomes large, and there is nonconcerted behavior that leads to low efficiency in the energy absorption process. In such case, there will be no net flux of S, as shown in Figure 3C. Effective energy coupling occurs only when the system is in resonance with the ac field.

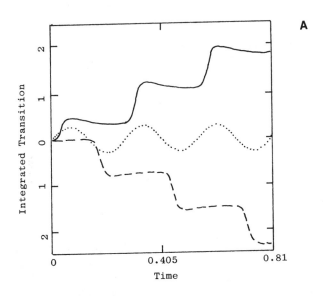

**A**

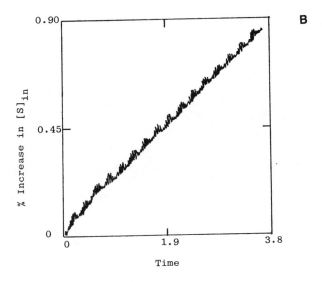

**B**

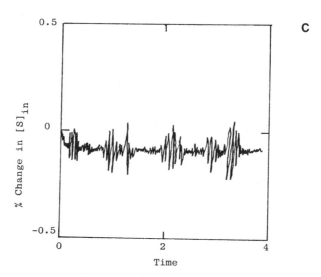

*Figure 3* (*A*) Numerical simulations of an ac field stimulated integrated transitions of Equation 7. The ac field (a transmembrane potential of 142 mV, 7.4 Hz) is indicated by the dotted curve, the $E_1 \rightarrow E_2$ transition by the solid curve, and the $E_2S \rightarrow E_1S$ transition by the dashed curve. In the simulation the bias factor (*b*) of 500 was used. For values of other parameters used in the simulation see Westerhoff et al (41). When the field was positive it induced the first transition, and when the field was negative it induced the second transition. The system cycled clockwise under a well tuned ac field. In the simulation, pumping of a neutral substrate, instead of $K^+$, was investigated. The field interaction was directed toward the enzyme. (*B*) Numerical integration of an ac field stimulated pumping of a neutral substrate. MLAB computer program was used. In the simulation the interaction energy $\Delta M \cdot E$ of 3 kcal $mol^{-1}$ was used. Changes in the internal concentration of substrate is plotted against stimulation time. The frequency and the strength of ac field were adjusted to match the values chosen for the kinetic coefficients of Equation 7 [see Tsong & Astumian (38) for details]. At 300 Hz an effective pumping shown here was observed. (*C*) Concentration fluctuations due to mismatching between the kinetic coefficients of Equation 7 and the frequency of ac field. The same system used in B was investigated, but here the ac frequency was 1500 Hz. No net pumping of substrate was seen. The initial decrease in the $[S]_{in}$ was due to the electric field–induced increase in the binding constant of the substrate to the enzyme.

Another interesting attribute that allows the system to pump S into cytosol instead of pumping in the opposite direction is the difference in the affinity of S for $E_2$ and $E_1$ states. In the simulation shown in Figure 3A, a 500 times greater binding constant of S for $E_2$ than for $E_1$ was assumed. This leads to accumulation of $E_2S$ and $E_1$ under zero-field condition. If the affinity is reversed for $E_2$ and $E_1$, ac stimulation will lead to the pumping of S from in to out. We have termed the factor $[E_1]/[E_2]$ or $[E_2S]/[E_1S]$ the bias factor (b) (7, 39, 41), which is equivalent to what Jencks calls the "interaction energy" (1, 20, 39, 41). This ratio determines the vectorial motion when an external energy source is supplied. If $b$ is close to unity, large oscillations of $[S]_{in}$ will be induced when an ac driving force is applied, but little net pumping of S will result for a symmetric field dependence. Other possibilities for kinetic asymmetry requirements for the four-state model to transduce energy have been discussed in greater detail elsewhere (1, 7, 39).

## Energy Transduction with Stationary Electric Field

The above notion of electroconformational coupling with ac field is in good accord with our intuition. However, we earlier mentioned experiments in which exponentially decaying electric pulses (dc in nature) were used to induce ATP synthesis in submitochondrial particles, with enzyme turnover during a single electric pulse. According to Equation 2, a dc pulse is unable to induce turnover, or recycling, of reactions such as shown in Equation 3 and Equation 7. Indeed, if no mechanisms exist that would allow modulation of stationary potential to an oscillating waveform, enzyme recycling could not possibly take place. Digital simulation of the four-state cyclic model confirmed this verdict. Does this mean then that the experimental results discussed above for Na,K-ATPase are unrelated to the in vivo mechanisms of enzyme action?

Without much reflection, one would assume that the transmembrane potential of a cell is stationary and marks a mean electric potential across the membrane for the whole cell. This, of course, is hardly the case. Except for specialized type of membranes, e.g. the energy-transducing membrane of mitochondrion where curent is transmitted via movement of electrons, current is carried by ions. Ion movement is rate-limited by diffusion, and since cell membranes are abundant in ionic channels or membrane pores, the electric field on the membrane surface is constantly fluctuating and is thus locally oscillatory. Consider for example, a protein embedded in a membrane across which there is a constant electric field, with an ion channel located in its vicinity. If the channel opens and closes with a defined frequency, the protein will experience a fluctuating electric field because of the field attenuation/enhancement cycle due to the channel. Measurements which record the overall potential of the cell would detect only the average stationary electric field. Even if optical methods using potential sensitive probe molecules, e.g. fluorescence optical-imaging method (14), is employed, detection of locally fluctuating electric fields demands real time resolution in millisecond or microsecond time range and a spatial resolution better than one nm. Thus, new designs are in order for experimentally capturing such local, rapid events. However, these considerations are essential if we are to understand the results of the PEF-induced ATP synthesis experiments mentioned above.

When an exponentially decaying dc pulse induces ATP synthesis, with apparent enzyme turnovers during a single pulse period, the enzyme complex or the membrane structure in the vicinity of the complex must be able to modulate the electric field and render it oscillatory. There are several mechanisms by which this modulation can be accomplished: (a) charge translocation through a channel, (b) charge relay through functional groups within the enzyme structure, (c) dynamic enzyme conformational change at a short time scale compared to the electric pulse width, or (d) other mechanisms.

For mitochondrial $F_0F_1$ATPase the immediate thought which came to our mind was potential attenuation by the proton translocator $F_0$ subunit. Here, the closing/opening of the proton channel $F_0$ is assumed to be regulated by the binding/dissociation of nucleotides ADP or ATP. When substrate ADP and $P_i$ bind to the enzyme complex, the $F_0$ channel closes and the complex is prone to the influence of the transmembrane electric field. $(F_0{}^cF_1)$ADP·$P_i$ is now converted into $(F_0{}^cF_1)$*ATP (where c is the closed state and * is the excited state). The enzyme is in an activated state and it has a low affinity for ATP. Upon the dissociation of ATP, the $F_0$ subunit opens its channel, which leads to a local attenuation of the transmembrane electric field. As a result, the enzyme returns from the star state to the relaxed state (non-star). The relaxed state has a high affinity for the substrates ADP and $P_i$. On binding of these substrates, the $F_0$ channel closes again, and the complex again experiences the influence of the electric field. These events can recycle within a single dc electric pulse.

The idea discussed here has been put to a kinetic analysis and shown to work as foreseen (2, 9, 38, 39). In the simulation, it was demonstrated that the enzyme could also respond to positively only oscillating electric field for ATP synthesis (2, 39). Since this is the case, it is still uncertain whether in the experiment proton translocation occured during the PEF ATP synthesis. First, most reliable measurements of the rate of proton translocation across cell membranes indicate a much slower rate, in the millisecond rather than microsecond time range (12). Second, attempts to detect proton translocation during PEF experiments using dye indicator phenol red have not been successful (our unpublished results). Third, there are other efficient means for coupling energy-dissipating processes (electron transport) to ATP synthesis.

The first point may be discounted because the rate of proton translocation could be greatly accelerated by the strong electric field used in the experiments. However, proton translocation during in vivo ATP synthesis could be a consequence of the chemical reaction rather than the driving force. Electron transport itself could be the primary process of membrane polarization and hence, the driving force for ATP synthesis. The proton, in this case, serves only as an electric field–modulating ion. There are organisms in which $Na^+$ or $Cl^-$ translocation is an essential process of ATP synthesis (8, 12, 36). We have also mentioned that enzyme turnover appears to depend on some thiol group(s) in the reduced form. Involvement of a charge relay system in the ATP synthetic process has previously been suggested by Boyer (3). Could thiol group involved in such processes be important for modulating local membrane potential? These possibilities are currently under investigation in our laboratories.

## Transmembrane Electric Noise for Energy and Signal Transduction

Having deliberated how a transmembrane potential conceived as stationary may be locally modulated to be oscillatory, one may want to consider a more realistic situation of a cell membrane. Because a membrane protein or enzyme and its potential modulator are hardly isolated molecules, the actual electric field experienced by the molecule under consideration can not be regularly oscillatory. Instead, the field is likely a composite of many modes of oscillations and may better be described as a fluctuating or noisy electric field (1, 39). Can the enzyme system shown in Equation 7 transduce energy from such kinds of noisy electric fields?

Noises or randomly fluctuating signals must be defined carefully before analysis can be done. We have investigated electric noises whose amplitude distributes around zero, with a standard deviation (1, 39) of 120 mV. The $\Delta\psi$ values are described by standard error function. Fluctuations in either amplitude or duration, or both, have been considered. In all three cases, after a latent period net in-flow of substrate was induced by the electric field (1, 39).

This was a surprising observation. Careful analysis both by Monte Carlo simulation and by analytical methods revealed that energy transduction can only occur if the pattern of the noise is autonomous, i.e. if the noise source is completely or partially unaffected by the presence of the target-interacting molecule. Equilibrium noise does not behave like autonomous noise since the Coulombic interactions will be reciprocal. In this case no free energy can be transduced. However, an autonomous noise generated externally or internally by energy-dissipating processes can do work. In a cell, the time average transmembrane potential is sustained by metabolic energy through ion pumps or electron transport chains. Noises around such a free energy dissipating process can be used to drive other energy-requiring reactions via the electroconformational-coupling mechanisms discussed here (1, 39).

ACKNOWLEDGEMENTS:

This work was supported by NIH Grant GM28795, NSF Grant DCB-8611836 and a contract from ONR to T.Y.T.

*Literature Cited*

1. Astumian, R. D., Chock, P. B., Tsong, T. Y., Chen, Y.-D., Westerhoff, H. V. 1987. Can free energy be transduced from electric noise? *Proc. Natl. Acad. Sci. USA* 84:434–38

2. Astumian, R. D., Chock, P. B., Westerhoff, H. V., Tsong, T. Y. 1987. Energy transduction by electroconformational coupling. In *Recent Development in Enzyme Dynamics and Regulation,* ed. P. B. Chock, C. Huang, L. Tsou, J. H. Wang. Amsterdam: Springer. In press

3. Boyer, P. D. 1984. Correlations of the binding change mechanism with a new concept for proton translocation and energy transmission. In *H⁺-ATPase: Structure, Function, Biogenesis,* ed. S. Papa, K. Altendorf, L. Ernster, L. Packer, Adriatica Editrice, Bari.

4. Boyer, P. D., Chance, B., Ernster, L., Mitchell, P., Racker, E., Slater, E. C. 1977. Oxidative phosphorylation and photophosphorylation. *Ann. Rev. Biochem.* 46:955–1026

5. Chauvin, F., Astumian, R. D., Tsong, T. Y. 1987. Voltage sensing of mitochondrial ATPase in pulsed electric field induced ATP synthesis. *Biophys. J.* 51:243a

6. Chauvin, F., Astumian, R. D., Tsong, T. Y. 1988. Involvement of sulfhydral group(s) in the pulsed electric field ATP synthesis by beef heart submitochondrial particles. Submitted

7. Chen, Y.-D. 1987. Assymmetry and external noise-induced free energy transduction. *Proc. Natl. Acad. Sci. USA* 84:729–33

8. Chernyak, B. V., Dibrov, A. N., Glagolev, A. N., Sherman, M. Yu., Skulachev, V. P. 1983. A novel type of energetics in marine alkali-tolerant bacterium. *FEBS Lett.* 164:38–42

9. Edmonds, D. T. 1986. A two-channel electrostatic model of an ionic counterport. *Proc. R. Soc. London Ser. B* 228:71–84

10. El-Mashak, E. M., Tsong, T. Y. 1985. Ion selectivity of temperature induced and electric field induced pores in dipalmitoylphosphatidylcholine vesicles. *Biochemistry* 24:2884–88

11. Farkas, D. L., Korenstein, R., Malkin, S. 1984. Electroluminescence and the electrical properties of the photosynthetic membrane. *Biophys. J.* 45:363–73

12. Ferguson, S. J., Sorgato, M. C. 1982. Proton electrochemical gradients and energy-transduction processes. *Ann. Rev. Biochem.* 51:185–217

13. Furman, R. E., Tanaka, J. C., Mueller, P., Barchi, R. L. 1986. Voltage-dependent activation in purified reconstituted sodium channels from rabbit T-tubular membranes. *Proc. Natl. Acad. Sci. USA* 83:488–92

14. Gross, D., Loew, L. M., Webb, W. W. 1986. Optical imaging of cell membrane potential changes induced by applied electric fields. *Biophys. J.* 50:339–48

15. Hammes, G. G. 1982. Unifying concept for the coupling between ion pumping and ATP hydrolysis or synthesis. *Proc. Natl. Acad. Sci. USA* 79:6881–84

16. Hartshorne, R. P., Keller, B. U., Talvenheimo, J. A., Catterall, W. A., Montal, M. 1985. Functional reconstitution of the purified brain sodium channel in planar lipid bilayers. *Proc. Natl. Acad. Sci. USA* 82:240–44

17. Hol, W. G. J. 1985. The role of the α-helix dipole in protein function and structure. *Prog. Biophys. Mol. Biol.* 45:149–95

18. Hol, W. G. J., van Duijnen, P. T., Berendsen, H. J. C. 1978. The α-helix dipole and the properties of proteins. *Nature* 273:443–46

19. Honig, B. H., Hubbell, W. L., Flewelling, R. F. 1986. Electrostatic interactions in membranes and proteins. *Ann. Rev. Biophys. Biophys. Chem.* 15:163–93

20. Jencks, W. P. 1980. The utilization of binding energy in coupled vectorial process. *Adv. Enzymol.* 51:75–106

21. Kinosita, K. Jr., Tsong, T. Y. 1977. Hemolysis of human erythrocytes by a transient electric field. *Proc. Natl. Acad. Sci. USA* 74:1923–27

22. Kinosita, K. Jr., Tsong, T. Y. 1977. Voltage induced pore formation and hemolysis of human erythrocytes. *Biochim. Biophys. Acta* 471:227–42

23. Kinosita, K. Jr., Tsong, T. Y. 1979. Voltage induced conductance in human erythrocyte membranes. *Biochim. Biophys. Acta* 554:479–97

24. Labarca, P., Lindstrom, J., Montal, M. 1984. Acetylcholine Receptor in planar lipid bilayers. *J. Gen. Physiol.* 83:473–96

25. Lauger, P. 1985. Ionic channels with conformational substates. *Biophys. J.* 47:581–91

26. Nakao, M., Gadsby, D. C. 1986. Voltage dependence of Na translocation by Na/K pump. *Nature* 323:628–30

27. Neumann, E., Katchalsky, A. 1972. Long-lived conformational changes induced by electric impulses in biopolymers. *Proc. Natl. Acad. Sci. USA* 69:993–97

28. Rephaeli, A., Richards, D. E., Karlish, S. J. D. 1986. Electrical potential accelerates the $E_1P(Na) \rightarrow E_2P$ conformational transition of (Na,K)-ATPase in reconstituted vesicles. *J. Biol. Chem.* 261:12437–12440

29. Serpersu, E. H., Tsong, T. Y. 1983. Stimulation of a ouabain-sensitive $Rb^+$ uptake in human erythrocytes with an external electric field. *J. Membr. Biol.* 74:191–201

30. Serpersu, E. H., Tsong, T. Y. 1984. Activation of electrogenic $Rb^+$ transport of (Na,K)-ATPase by an electric field. *J. Biol. Chem.* 259:7155–62

31. Tanford, C. 1983. Mechanism of free energy coupling in active transport. *Ann. Rev. Biochem.* 52:379–409

32. Teissie, J. 1986. ATP synthesis in E. coli submitted to a microsecond electric pulse. *Biochemistry* 25:368–73

33. Teissie, J., Knox, B. E., Tsong, T. Y., Wehrle, J. 1981. Synthesis of ATP in respiration-inhibited submitochondrial particles induced by microsecond electric pulses. *Proc. Natl. Acad. Sci. USA* 78:7473–77

34. Teissie, J., Tsong, T. Y. 1980. Evidence of voltage-induced channel opening in Na/K ATPase of human erythrocyte membrane. *J. Membr. Biol.* 55:133–40

35. Teissie, J., Tsong, T. Y. 1981. Electric field induced transient pores in phospholipid bilayer vesicles. *Biochemistry* 20:1548–54

36. Tokuda, H., Unemoto, T. 1982. Characterization of the respiration-dependent $Na^+$ pump in the marine bacterium *Vibrio alginolyticus. J. Biol. Chem.* 257:10007–10014

37. Tsong, T. Y. 1983. Voltage modulation of membrane permeability and energy utilization in cells. *Biosci. Rep.* 3:487–505

38. Tsong, T. Y., Astumian, R. D. 1986. Absorption and conversion of electric field energy by membrane-bound ATPases. *Bioelectrochem. Bioenerg.* 15:457–76

39. Tsong, T. Y., Astumian, R. D. 1987. Electroconformational coupling and membrane protein function. *Prog. Biophys. Mol. Biol.* In press

40. Tsuji, K., Neumann, E. 1983. Conformational flexibility of membrane proteins in electric fields. I. Ultraviolet absorbance and light scattering of bacteriorhodopsin in purple membranes. *Biophys. Chem.* 17:153–63

41. Westerhoff, H. V., Tsong, T. Y., Chock, P. B., Chen, Y.-D., Astumian, R. D. 1986. *Proc. Natl. Acad. Sci. USA* 83:4734–4738

*Ann. Rev. Physiol. 1988. 50:291–303*

# MODULATION OF THE Na,K-ATPase BY Ca AND INTRACELLULAR PROTEINS

*Douglas R. Yingst*

Department of Physiology, Wayne State University, Detroit, Michigan 48201

## INTRODUCTION

The Na,K-ATPase is the enzymatic basis of the Na-K pump of the plasma membrane (45, 46). The major function of this pump is to assist in the creation of transmembrane gradients of Na and K. These gradients subserve a number of essential cellular processes such as the maintenance of the resting membrane potential, cell volume control, and the transport of other ions and organic solutes (14). The biochemical and physical properties of the Na,K-ATPase have been extensively studied and reviewed (18, 24, 25).

Recently the mechanisms that regulate the Na,K-ATPase have begun to receive more attention. This article reviews the evidence that intracellular free Ca ($Ca_i$) and intracellular proteins that are associated with changes in $Ca_i$ affect the functioning of the Na,K-ATPase. These results are of interest because they indicate that the Na,K-ATPase could be influenced by physiological changes in $Ca_i$ and by the associated biochemical alterations that have been shown to regulate other cellular enzymes (7, 34, 40).

The resting $Ca_i$ in most cells is in the range of 0.02–0.3 $\mu M$ (40, 49). Hormones and other stimuli cause the $Ca_i$ to rapidly (and transiently) increase to greater than 1 $\mu M$ (49). In many cases, the effects of $Ca_i$ on target enzymes are mediated by intracellular proteins that become active after binding Ca. The best known of these is calmodulin (7). In other cases, the effects are closely associated with the degradation products of inositol phospholipids in the plasma membrane (1, 34). There is now evidence that at least three intracellular proteins could affect the Na,K-ATPase during the time when $Ca_i$

291

0066-4278/88/0315-0291$02.00

is transiently elevated in response to hormones and other stimuli. These three are calnaktin, calmodulin, and protein kinase C. This article reviews the data on these three intracellular proteins and their respective effects on the Na,K-ATPase.

## CALNAKTIN

The ability of Ca to inhibit the Na,K-ATPase has been established for thirty years (44). However, the concentration of Ca reported to inhibit the Na,K-ATPase in different preparations varies: 1–5 $\mu$M for crude rabbit brain (52), 70 $\mu$M for washed human red cell membranes (13), 500 $\mu$M for washed rat brain (48), and almost 2 mM for highly purified dog kidney (22). Interestingly, the least pure ATPase preparation, the rabbit brain homogenate, had the highest sensitivity to Ca and the most purified, dog kidney, had the lowest sensitivity to Ca. It is possible that purification of the Na,K-ATPase may have removed proteins that increase the sensitivity of the Na,K-ATPase to inhibition by Ca. Evidence presented below indicates that intracellular proteins control the sensitivity of Na,K-ATPase to inhibition by Ca and make the enzyme responsive to physiological concentrations of $Ca_i$.

### Effects in Red Cells

Evidence for a protein that increases the sensitivity of the Na,K-ATPase to inhibition by Ca has been found in human red cells (58). This protein was later named calnaktin (60). The idea that such a protein might be present grew out of an attempt to explain why ouabain-sensitive Na efflux through the Na-K pump in hemoglobin-poor resealed ghosts was much more sensitive to inhibition by Ca than the Na,K-ATPase in membrane fragments. For instance, in resealed ghosts containing arsenazo III to monitor $Ca_i$, ouabain-sensitive Na transport is 50% inhibited by 1–5 $\mu$M $Ca_i$ (53, 56). This is at least 15 times more sensitive than the 70 $\mu$M $Ca_i$ required to inhibit the red cell Na,K-ATPase in membrane fragments (13). We found that this difference in sensitivity could be explained by the presence of calnaktin in the resealed ghosts and its absence from the well washed membrane fragments that were used to measure the activity of the Na,K-ATPase. When hemolysate containing calnaktin is added to the membrane fragments, the sensitivity of the Na,K-ATPase to inhibition by Ca is increased to the same level as in the resealed ghosts (58). In well washed membranes from which the calnaktin has been extracted with ethylenedinitrilotetraacetic acid (EDTA), the Na,K-ATPase is inhibited 50% by approximately 50 $\mu$M free Ca (Figure 1). In the presence of calnaktin 50% inhibition is observed at 1 $\mu$M free Ca (Figure 1). The increased inhibition caused by calnaktin is heat-sensitive (58) and reversible, i.e. after exposure to Ca and calnaktin, the activity of the Na, K-ATPase returns to control values upon chelation of the Ca (62). This observation eliminates the possibility that the Ca-dependent inhibition is due to proteolysis or another irreversible process that would impair the Na,K-ATPase. It also is consistent with the conclusion that calnaktin is without effect on the Na,K-ATPase in the absence of Ca. In ghosts from which all the hemolysate has been removed on an agarose column, the readdition of hemolysate containing calnaktin before resealing increases Ca-dependent inhibition of ouabain-sensitive Na efflux through the Na-K pump (53, 55). Thus, calnaktin affects both the enzymatic and ion-transport activities of the Na,K-ATPase.

Calnaktin has been purified from red cells to apparent homogeneity using a combination of Ca-dependent hydrophobic chromatography, anion exchange chromatography, and gel filtration (61, 63). It has an apparent $M_r$ of approximately 35,000 as observed by sodium dodecyl sulfate (SDS) gel electrophoresis run under reducing conditions. Calnaktin is a Ca-dependent protein (61, 63) in the sense that it becomes more hydrophobic in the presence of Ca and more hydrophilic when the Ca is chelated (51). This suggests, but does not prove, that calnaktin binds Ca.

Purified calnaktin has no effect on the Ca-ATPase (61). This observation and its $M_r$ indicate that calnaktin is distinct from calmodulin, an 18,000 $M_r$ protein which is a known stimulator of Ca-ATPase (20, 23). Calnaktin also has no effect on the Mg-ATPase, another enzyme of the red cell membrane

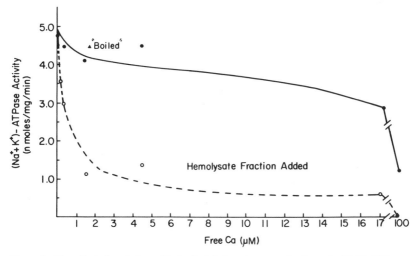

*Figure 1*    The effect of partially purified calnaktin from human red cells on the Na,K-ATPase as a function of free Ca. The symbol marked "Boiled" shows the effect of adding a sample that had been previously heated for 4 min in a bath of boiling water. The assay was carried out as previously described (62). Each point is the mean of two measurements. This Figure is reprinted from Yingst & Polasek (62).

(61), nor does it effect the Na,K-ATPase in the absence of Ca (61). This is consistent with the effects of other Ca-dependent proteins, such as calmodulin (7), which are inactive until they bind Ca.

Calnaktin can be recovered from hemolysate (58), but is present at apparently higher concentrations in low ionic strength extracts of the plasma membrane (54, 59). The membranes of human red cells contain at least 300 $\mu$g of calnaktin per liter cells (61), which is on the order of one molecule of calnaktin per Na-K pump.

## Presence in Other Cells

Calnaktin or a similar protein may be present in other cells. For instance, in myometrial cells the removal of peripheral membrane proteins with SDS decreases the sensitivity of the Na,K-ATPase to inhibition by Ca an order of magnitude (50). Readdition of the solubilized proteins restores the original higher sensitivity to Ca. Dimethyl sulfoxide apparently blocks the removal of this protein by SDS (50). These results are consistent with the removal from the membrane of a protein that confers on the Na,K-ATPase a higher sensitivity to Ca. The identity of the protein(s) responsible for these effects has not yet been reported.

Ca-dependent proteins of approximately 35,000 $M_r$ have also been found in other tissues, including chicken gizzard, eel and rabbit muscle, hamster kidney and liver, and bovine brain, heart, and kidney (32, 33, 57). Homogenates of bovine heart, brain, and kidney increase Ca inhibition of the Na,K-ATPase from human red cells (57). The remainder of the tissues are yet to be tested.

## Possible Effects on Reaction Mechanism

Calnaktin could interact with the Na,K-ATPase via one of the steps in the reaction cycle that are known to be affected by Ca. For instance, Ca blocks pump-mediated ATP-ADP exchange (48), inhibits K-stimulated dephosphorylation (26), competes with Na in the presence and absence of K (4, 15, 48), and substitutes for Mg (15, 48). Most of these effects were discovered in experiments in which millimolar concentrations of Ca were employed in unsided preparations where Ca had access to both the cytoplasmic and extracellular surfaces of the membranes. It is not known which of these effects, if any, might be important in the regulation of the Na,K-ATPase by calnaktin and micromolar concentrations of $Ca_i$

## Relationship of Calnaktin to Other Ca-Dependent Proteins

Calnaktin may be a member of a newly described class of Ca-dependent proteins that are closely associated with the plasma membrane (16). These proteins can be extracted from the internal surface of the membrane, bind to the membrane in the presence of Ca, and have molecular weights in the range 30,000–36,000. Recently there has been considerable interest in the observation that two of these Ca-dependent proteins, one with a $M_r$ of 36,000 and another of 35,000, are major substrates for the transforming protein-tyrosine kinases and growth factor receptors (5). The functions of these Ca-dependent proteins have not yet been established.

## Possible Regulatory Role

Could calnaktin be a physiological regulator of the Na,K-ATPase? By increasing the otherwise low sensitivity of the Na,K-ATPase to Ca, calnaktin could make the Na,K-ATPase sensitive to the physiological concentrations of Ca$_i$ that regulate other enzymes. In the following paragraph I discuss one example where the sensitivity of the Na,K-ATPase to inhibition by Ca could be regulated by calnaktin.

The ability of catecholamines to stimulate the Na,K-ATPase has been known for some time (10, 19). The effects observed at low agonist concentrations that are blocked by the appropriate antagonists appear to be receptor-mediated. In these cases Ca appears to be a necessary co-factor [see reviews by Phyllis & Wu (36) and Clausen (9)]. Recent work in hepatocytes further suggests that Ca may be involved in hormonal stimulation of the pump by a mechanism in which the observed stimulation actually represents a release from Ca inhibition (3). The hormones in question are norepinephrine, vasopressin, and angiotensin (3). At 1.8 mM extracellular Ca the addition of 1 $\mu$M norepinephrine stimulates the Na-K pump via occupancy of $\alpha_1$ receptors and increases Ca$_i$ from the normal level (0.2 $\mu$M) to 0.9 $\mu$M (2, 3). Reducing the Ca$_i$ from 0.2 to 0.04 $\mu$M with quin-2 in the absence of norepinephrine stimulates the pump; this is consistent with the presence of a Na-K pump with a high sensitivity to inhibition by Ca. At the reduced Ca$_i$, the pump is insensitive to norepinephrine; it is already operating at the same level as can be achieved in the presence of hormone and can not be further stimulated. Berthon et al (3) suggest that norepinephrine stimulates the pump by blocking the normal inhibitory action of Ca. This model presupposes that under the normal conditions of 0.2 $\mu$M Ca$_i$, the pump is at least partially inhibited by Ca. For this to be the case, the pump would have to be highly sensitive to Ca, as it is in the presence of calnaktin. If the actions of calnaktin were blocked by norepinephrine, then the pump could indeed be stimulated (compared to its inhibited state) even when Ca$_i$ is increased from 0.2 to approximately 1 $\mu$M. Others suggest that the mechanism by which hormones stimulate the pump may involve protein kinase C (29) rather than a release from Ca inhibition (see below).

# CALMODULIN

## Inhibition

Under some conditions calmodulin appears to increase Ca-dependent inhibition of the Na,K-ATPase (8). David-Dufilho et al (11) showed that the addition of 0.2 $\mu$M calmodulin at 1 $\mu$M free Ca inhibited the ouabain-sensitive ATPase hydrolysis over 50%. Neither calmodulin alone nor Ca alone had any effect on the ouabain-sensitive activity (11). Thus, the observed inhibition of the Na,K-ATPase depends on the presence of both calmodulin and Ca. These experiments were carried out using a crude preparation of the Na,K-ATPase from the hearts of spontaneously hypertensive rats that could have contained calnaktin.

In red cells we have found that similar high concentrations (0.2 $\mu$M and above) of calmodulin can also increase Ca inhibition of the Na,K-ATPase in some preparations of membranes. We have also determined that calmodulin can potentiate the effects of calnaktin under conditions that calmodulin itself has no effect (Figure 2). We think these results indicate that calmodulin may be interacting with the Na,K-ATPase via calnaktin or some other intermediate step. This conclusion is also consistent with the observation that purified calmodulin has no effect on the purified Na,K-ATPase from dog kidney (22). If calmodulin does interact with the Na,K-ATPase via calnaktin, then the effects of high concentrations of calmodulin observed by us and by David-Dufilho et al (11) may be due to the activation of residual calnaktin still present in the tested membranes.

## Stimulation

As discussed above, most data show that Ca inhibits the Na,K-ATPase. Some investigators, however, have found that under certain circumstances (no EDTA present in the assay solution) micromolar additions of Ca and Ca plus calmodulin actually stimulate the Na,K-ATPase in rat brain (37–39). Sub-micromolar additions of Ca to a medium containing no EDTA (and 1–2 $\mu$M contaminating Ca) stimulated the Na,K-ATPase up to 20% compared to the activity observed in the absence of exogenously added Ca (37). Calmodulin potentiated this effect, causing the enzyme to be stimulated a total of 50% compared to the same control values (37). Higher concentrations of Ca ($>$ 10 $\mu$M) reversed the stimulation and inhibited the Na,K-ATPase (38). However, data from the same investigator indicate that the small stimulation seen upon the addition of Ca was on a Na,K-ATPase that was already markedly inhibited by a trace metal that contaminated the original assay solution (38).

This metal could have been Ca. The addition of EDTA to the medium lowered the contaminating free Ca from 1–2 $\mu$M to 0.3 $\mu$M and increased the activity of the Na,K-ATPase over 200% (37). When EDTA was used to buffer Ca, the response to the Na,K-ATPase was altered in two respects.

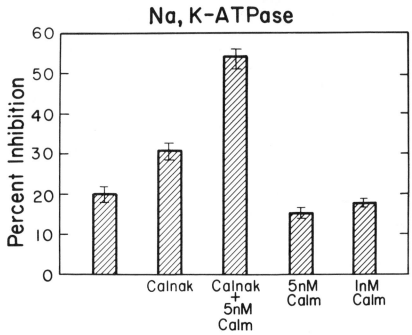

*Figure 2*    The synergistic effect of purified calnaktin and calmodulin on the percent inhibition of the Na,K-ATPase from human red blood cells. The percent inhibition is the reduction of activity at two $\mu$M free Ca compared to zero free Ca. Calnaktin had a final concentration of 3 ng ml$^{-1}$. The assay was carried out and calnaktin was purified as previously described (61). The bars are standard deviations.

First, Ca inhibited the Na,K-ATPase at all concentrations of Ca, including the concentrations that stimulated the enzyme in the absence of EDTA. Second, calmodulin had no effect on the Na,K-ATPase (37, 38). Since EDTA is not normally found in cells and EDTA may affect the sensitivity of other enzymes to Ca, Powis et al suggest that the stimulation of the Na,K-ATPase by Ca and its potentiation by calmodulin represent a physiological response of the Na,K-ATPase (37, 38). An alternative explanation is that both calmodulin and EDTA stimulated the Na,K-ATPase by chelating the contaminating Ca. Since the Na,K-ATPase preparation used by Powis et al was a simple homogenate of rat brain, it may have contained calnaktin and thus have been significantly inhibited by the 1–2 $\mu$M free Ca present in the absence of EDTA. Adding EDTA could then stimulate the Na,K-ATPase by releasing the calnaktin-induced inhibition. Recall that bovine brain contains a Ca-dependent protein of the same $M_r$ as calnaktin and has also been shown to increase inhibition of the Na,K-ATPase by Ca (see above). This explanation, however, does not account for the small stimulation ($\leq$ 20%) observed when Ca was added in the absence of EDTA.

## Effect on Ouabain Inhibition

Ca and calmodulin via other intracellular proteins may also alter the sensitivity of the Na,K-ATPase to inhibition by ouabain, (6, 27, 28) a specific inhibitor of the Na,K-ATPase (42). These observations are significant because differences in sensitivity to ouabain have been used to characterize different molecular forms of the Na,K-ATPase[1] and appear to be involved in the mechanism by which insulin stimulates the Na,K-ATPase in adipocytes (30, 31).

Ca AND CHANGES IN AFFINITY FOR OUABAIN    In murine plasmacytoma cells, the sensitivity of the Na,K-ATPase to inhibition by ouabain can be increased by extracting the membranes in the presence of EDTA (27). The Na,K-ATPase in membranes isolated in the presence of EDTA is inhibited 50% by 1 $\mu$M ouabain, compared to approximately 120 $\mu$M for 50% inhibition when the enzyme is prepared in the absence of EDTA (27). The readdition of the soluble proteins extracted with EDTA to the extracted membranes decreases the sensitivity to ouabain in a Ca-dependent manner (28). $\beta$-actinin (17) or tropomyosin, in the presence of calmodulin and Ca, also restores the low sensitivity to ouabain that is characteristic of the Na,K-ATPase prepared in the absence of EDTA (27). The addition of exogenous calmodulin and Ca alone (in the absence of either $\beta$-actinin or tropomyosin) has no effect on ouabain sensitivity. Thus, calmodulin affects the sensitivity of the Na,K-ATPase to ouabain via other intracellular proteins. Lelievre et al suggest that calmodulin acts as an intracellular receptor for Ca and that the effects of $\beta$-actinin and tropomyosin are exerted via interactions with actin in the cytoskeleton of the cell. Apparently, the manipulations which alter the response of these cells to ouabain do not affect the sensitivity of the Na,K-ATPase to inhibition by Ca (27).

POSSIBLE ROLE IN HORMONE EFFECTS    In adipocytes insulin both stimulates the Na-K pump (41) and increases $Ca_i$ (12, 35). The Na-K pump activity stimulated by insulin can be blocked by low concentrations of ouabain (41). The remainder of the pump activity, whose inhibition requires much higher concentrations of ouabain, is insensitive to insulin (41). Both $\alpha$ and $\alpha+$ forms of the Na,K-ATPase are present in adipocytes (31). It has been suggested that

---

[1]The Na,K-ATPase is composed of two polypeptides: a catalytic subunit ($\alpha$) and an essential glycoprotein ($\beta$) (24). The catalytic subunit is now known to be genetically expressed in three slightly different versions ($\alpha$, $\alpha+$, and $\alpha$III) (43). The Na,K-ATPase containing the $\alpha+$ subunit is considered to be very sensitive to ouabain (47). Na,K-ATPase molecules containing the $\alpha$ type of subunit are much less sensitive (47). Some cells appear to have two types of Na,K-ATPase molecules, one containing the $\alpha$ subunit and the other the $\alpha+$ subunit (31, 47). In these cases the dose-response curve is biphasic, revealing two populations of Na,K-ATPase molecules: one with a high affinity for ouabain and the other with a much lower affinity for ouabain (31, 47).

the $\alpha+$ form could account for the activity that was stimulated by insulin (30). The $\alpha$ form would then be responsible for the activity which was insensitive to insulin. However, the observation that insulin increases Ca$_i$ in adipocytes (12) and that Ca plus calmodulin can alter the affinity of the Na,K-ATPase for ouabain (27) indicate that the situation may be more complex. For instance, the apparent differences in sensitivity to ouabain could be due to differences in the Ca content of the cells, rather than inherent differences in the sensitivity of the $\alpha$ and $\alpha+$ forms for ouabain. Cells with high Ca would have a low affinity for ouabain and would be insensitive to insulin. Cells with low Ca would have a high affinity for ouabain and would be sensitive to insulin. On the other hand, the inherent sensitivity of the Na,K-ATPase to ouabain may indeed reside with the type of catalytic subunit, and Ca$_i$ might control the relative activity of each. For example, when Ca$_i$ was low, the activity of the $\alpha+$ form might predominate. An increase in Ca$_i$, as occurs with insulin, might then shift the equilibrium in favor of the $\alpha$ form. Ca$_i$ could then control the sensitivity of the Na,K-ATPase to stimulation by insulin.

## PROTEIN KINASE C

Phorbol esters stimulate the Na-K pump in hepatocytes (29) and pancreatic acinar cells (21). These results indicate that protein kinase C could stimulate the pump in some cells. Protein kinase C is normally activated by diacylglycerol generated by the hydrolysis of inositol phospholipids in response to hormones binding to specific membrane receptors (34). Phorbol esters can stimulate protein kinase C directly, bypassing the production of diacylglycerol. Hormone binding also increases Ca$_i$ (34). Both Ca$_i$ and diacylglycerol can in turn function as second messengers to regulate other enzymes (34).

In rat hepatocytes the Na-K pump is stimulated by norepinephrine, vasopressin (AVP), and angiotensin II (3, 29). All three of these hormones mobilize Ca$_i$ and generate diacylglycerol (29). It is suggested by Lynch et al (29) that the stimulation of the pump by AVP is due to the production of diacylglycerol rather than an increase in Ca$_i$, because incubating the cells in ethylenebis(oxyethylenenitrilo)tetraacetic acid (EGTA), which reduces Ca$_i$, does not diminish the stimulatory effect of AVP on the pump. In fact, incubating the cells in EGTA actually stimulates the pump, which supports the view of Berthon et al (3) that resting Ca$_i$ may inhibit the pump. The fact that stimulatory effects of AVP and the tumor promoter myristate acetate (PMA) are not additive (29) is evidence that AVP acts via the production of diacylglycerol. However, Lynch et al caution that PMA, in addition to stimulating protein kinase C, can also increase the production of diacylglycerol. Thus the observed stimulation of the pump by PMA could also be due to a general alteration in membrane lipids, rather than a specific stimulation of protein kinase C.

In pancreatic acinar cells the phorbol ester 12-0-tetradecanoyl phorbol-13-acetate (TPA) and the diacylglycerol analog 1-oleoyl-2-lacetoyl-sn-3-glycerol both increase the rate of ouabain binding (21). Under the assay conditions used, Hootman et al claim that the rate of ouabain binding is proportional to the activity of the Na-K pump. Secretagogues such as cholecystokinin and acetylcholine stimulate the Na-K pump, activate protein kinase C, and increase $Ca_i$ (21).

Protein kinase C may be involved in the stimulation of the Na-K pump by cholinergic agents because the stimulation of the pump observed with carbochol plus TPA was less than the effects of either of these agents alone (21). On the other hand, it is difficult to know how differences in $Ca_i$ may have affected the relative responses seen in the presence of carbachol and TPA. First, the response of the pump to $Ca_i$ appears to be complex, with both stimulatory and inhibitory effects observed (21). Second, the level of $Ca_i$ at the time of the comparison was unknown (21).

## SUMMARY

The activity of the Na,K-ATPase can be sensitive to physiological changes in $Ca_i$. Intracellular proteins such as calnaktin, calmodulin, and protein kinase C could regulate the pump during transient changes in $Ca_i$. The mechanisms by which these proteins interact with the Na,K-ATPase, their distribution in different kinds of cells, and their role in regulating the Na,K-ATPase are not yet determined. Preliminary data indicate that an increase in $Ca_i$ within the physiological range could be associated with either a stimulation or an inhibition of enzyme activity or a change in the affinity of the Na,K-ATPase for ouabain. The type of response probably depends on the kind of cell, its associated intracellular proteins, and its physiological state. Ca and intracellular proteins could play a key role in the regulation of the Na,K-ATPase by hormones.

ACKNOWLEDGMENTS

This work was supported by grant GM3223, RCOA DK 01253, and the American Heart Association of Michigan.

### Literature Cited

1. Berridge, M. J. 1984. Inositol triphosphate and diacylglycerol as second messengers. Biochem. J. 220:345–60
2. Berthon, B., Binet, A., Mauger, J., Claret, M. 1984. Cytosolic free $Ca^{2+}$ in isolated rat hepatocytes as measured by $quin^2$. FEBS Lett. 167:19–24
3. Berthon, B., Capiod, T., Claret, M. 1985. Effect of noradrenaline vasopressin and angiotensin on the Na-K pump in rat isolated liver cells. Br. J. Pharmacol. 86:151–61

4. Blostein, R., Burt, V. K. 1971. Interaction of N-ethylmaleimide and $Ca^{2+}$ with human erythrocyte membrane ATPase. Biochim. Biophys. Acta 241:68–74
5. Brugge, J. S. 1986. The p35/p36 substrates of protein-tyrosine kinases as inhibitors of phospholipase $A_2$. Cell 46:149–50
6. Charlemagne, D., Legor, J., Schwartz, K., Geny, B., Zachowski, A., Lelievre, L. 1980. Involvement of tropomyosin in the sensitivity of the $Na^+ + K^+$ ATPase

to ouabain. *Biochem. Pharmacol.* 29: 297–300

7. Cheung, W. Y. 1980. Calmodulin plays a pivotal role in cellular regulation. *Science* 207:19–27

8. Cirillo, M., David-Dufilho, M., Deuynck, M. A. 1984. Calmodulin reduces ouabain-sensitive ATPase of cardiac sarcolemmal membranes: high reduction in spontaneously hypertensive rats. *Clin. Sci.* 67:535–40

9. Clausen, T. 1986. Regulation of active Na$^+$-K$^+$ transport in skeletal muscle. *Physiol. Rev.* 66:542–80

10. Coffey, R. G., Hadden, J. W., Hadden, E. M., Middleton, E. 1971. Stimulation of ATPase by norepinephrine: an alpha-adrenergic receptor mechanism. *Fed. Proc.* 30:A497

11. David-Dufilho, M., Pernollet, M., Sang, H. L., Benlian, P., Mendonca, M. D., Grichois, M. 1986. Active Na$^+$ and Ca$^+$ transport, Na$^+$-Ca$^{2+}$ exchange, and intracellular Na$^+$ and Ca$^{2+}$ content in young spontaneously hypertensive rats. *J. Cardiovas. Pharmacol.* 8 (Supp. 8):S130–35

12. Draznin, B., Kao, M., Sussman, K. E. 1987. Insulin and glyburide increase cytosolic free -Ca$^{2+}$ concentration in isolated rat adipocytes. *Diabetes* 36: 174–78

13. Dunham, E. T., Glynn, I. M. 1961. Adenosine triphosphatase activity and the active movements of alkali metal ions. *J. Physiol.* 156:274–93

14. Dunham, P. B., Hoffman, J. F. 1978. Na and K transport in red blood cells. In *Physiology of Membrane Disorders,* ed. T. E. Andreoli, J. F. Hoffman, D. D. Fanestil, pp. 255–72. New York: Plenum

15. Fukushima, Y., Post, R. L. 1978. Binding of divalent cation to phosphoenzyme of sodium- and potassium-transport adenosine triphosphatase. *J. Biol. Chem.* 253:6852–62

16. Geisow, M. J., Fritsche, U., Hexham, J. M., Dash, B., Johnson, T. 1986. A consensus amino-acid sequence repeat in Torpedo and mammalian Ca$^{2+}$-dependent membrane-binding proteins. *Nature* 320:636–38

17. Geny, B., Paraf, A., Fedon, Y., Charlemagne, D. 1982. Characterization of a β-actinin-like protein in purified non-muscle cell membranes. *Biochim. Biophys. Acta* 692:345–54

18. Glynn, I. M., Karlish, S. J. D. 1975. The sodium pump. *Am. Rev. Physiol.* 37:13–55

19. Godfraind, T., Koch, M. C., Verbeke, N. 1974. The action of EGTA on the catecholamines stimulation of rat brain Na-K-ATPase. *Biochem. Pharmacol.* 23:3505–11

20. Gopinath, R. M., Vincenzi, F.F. 1977. Phosphodiesterase protein activator mimics red blood cell cytpolasmic activator of (Ca$^{2+}$-Mg$^{2+}$)ATPase. *Biochem. Biophys. Res. Commun.* 77:1203–1209

21. Hootman, S.R., Brown, M. E., Williams, J. A. 1987. Phorbol esters and A23187 regulate Na$^+$-K$^+$-pump activity in pancreatic acinar cells. *Am. J. Physiol.* 252:G499–505

22. Huang, W., Askari, A. 1982. Ca$^{2+}$-dependent activities of (Na$^+$ + K$^+$)-ATPase. *Arch. Biochem. Biophys.* 216:741–50

23. Jarrett, H. W., Penniston, J. T. 1977. Partial purification of the Ca$^{2+}$-Mg$^{2+}$ ATPase activator from human erythrocytes: its similarity to the activator of 3':5'-cyclic nucleotide phosphodiesterase. *Biochem. Biophys. Res. Commun.* 77:1210–16

24. Jorgensen, P. L. 1982. Mechanism of the Na$^+$,K$^+$ pump. Protein structure and conformations of the pure (Na$^+$ + K$^+$)-ATPase. *Biochim. Biophys. Acta* 694:27–68

25. Kaplan, J. H. 1985. Ion movements through the sodium pump. *Ann. Rev. Physiol.* 47:535–44

26. Knauf, P. A., Proverbio, F., Hoffman, J. F. 1974. Electrophoretic separation of different phosphoproteins associated with Ca-ATPase and Na,K-ATPase in human red cell ghosts. *J. Gen. Physiol.* 63:325–36

27. Lelievre, L. G., Potter, J. D., Piascik, M., Wallick, E. T., Schwartz, A. 1985. Specific involvement of calmodulin and non-specific effect of tropomyosin in the sensitivity to ouabain of Na$^+$,K$^+$-ATPase in murine plasmocytoma cells. *Eur. J. Biochem.* 148:13–19

28. Lelievre, L., Zachowski, A., Charlemagne, D., Laget, P., Paraf, A. 1979. Inhibition of (Na$^+$ + K$^+$)-ATPase by ouabain: involvement of calcium and membrane proteins. *Biochim. Biophys. Acta* 577:399–408

29. Lynch, C. J., Wilson, P. B., Blackmore, P. F., Eston, J. H. 1986. The hormone-sensitive hepatic Na$^+$-pump. *J. Biol. Chem.* 261:14551–56

30. Lytton, J. 1985. Insulin affects the sodium affinity of the rat adipocyte (Na$^+$ + K$^+$)-ATPase. *J. Biol. Chem.* 260:10075–80

31. Lytton, J., Lin, J. C., Guidotti, G. 1985. Identification of two molecular forms of (Na$^+$ + K$^+$)-ATPase in rat

adipocytes. *J. Biol. Chem.* 260:1177–84

32. Moore, P. B., Dedman, J. R. 1982. Calcium-dependent protein binding to phenothiazine columns. *J. Biol. Chem.* 275:9663–67

33. Moore, P. B., Kraus-Friedman, N., Dedman, J. R. 1984. Unique calcium-dependent hydrophobic binding proteins: possible independent mediators of intracellular calcium distinct from calmodulin. *J. Cell Sci.* 72:121–33

34. Nishizuka, Y. 1986. Studies and perspectives of protein kinase C. *Science* 233:305–12

35. Pershadsingh, H. A., McDonald, J. M. 1984. Hormone receptors coupling and the molecular mechanism of insulin action in the adipocyte: a paradigm for $Ca^{2+}$ homeostasis in the initiation of the insulin-induced metabolic cascade. *Cell Calcium* 5:111–30

36. Phillis, J. W., Wu, P. H. 1981. Catecholamines and the sodium pump in excitable cells. *Prog. Neurobiol.* 17:141–84

37. Powis, D. A. 1985. Failure of calcium to stimulate Na,K-ATPase in the presence of EDTA. *Experientia* 41:1048–51

38. Powis, D. A., Anderson, T. A., Jackson, H., Wattus, G. D. 1983. Stimulation of neuronal $Na^+,K^+$-ATPase by calcium. *Biochem. Pharmacol.* 32:1219–27

39. Powis, D. A., Wattus, G. D. 1981. The stimulatory effect of calcium on Na,K-ATPase of nervous tissue. *FEBS Lett.* 126:285–88

40. Rega, A. F., Garrahan, P. J. 1986. *The $Ca^{2+}$ Pump of Plasma Membranes.* Boca Raton, Florida: CRC Press. 173 pp.

41. Resh, M. D., Nemenoff, R. A., Guidotti, G. 1980. Insulin stimulation of $(Na^+,K^+)$-adenosine triphosphatase-dependent $^{86}Rb^+$ uptake in rat adipocytes. *J. Biol. Chem.* 255:10938–45

42. Schatzmann, H. J. 1953. *Helv. Physiol. Pharmacol. Acta* 11:346–54

43. Shull, G. E., Greeb, J., Lingrel, J. B. 1986. *Biochemistry* 25:8125–32

44. Skou, J. C. 1957. The influence of some cations on an adenosine triphosphatase from peripheral nerves. *Biochim. Biophys. Acta* 23:394–401

45. Skou, J. C. 1960. Further investigations on a $Mg^{++} + Na^+$-activated adenosine triphosphatase, possibly related to the active, linked transport of $Na^+$ and $K^+$ across the nerve membrane. *Biochim. Biophys. Acta* 42:6–23

46. Skou, J. C. 1965. Enzymatic basis for active transport of $Na^+$ and $K^+$ across cell membrane. *Physiol. Rev.* 45:596–617

47. Sweadner, K. J. 1979. Two molecular forms of $(Na^+ + K^+)$-stimulated ATPase in brain. *J. Biol. Chem.* 254:6060–67

48. Tobin, T., Akera, T., Baskin, S. I., Brody, T. M. 1973. Calcium ion and sodium- and potassium-dependent adenosine triphosphatase: Its mechanism of inhibition and identification of the $E_1$-P intermediate. *Mol. Pharmacol.* 9:336–49

49. Tsien, R. Y. 1983. Intracellular measurements of ion activities. *Ann. Rev. Biophys. Bioeng.* 12:91–116

50. Turi, A., Torok, K. 1985. Myometrial $(Na^+ + K^+)$-activated ATPase and its $Ca^{2+}$ sensitivity. *Biochim. Biophys. Acta* 818:123–31

51. Walsh, M. P., Valentine, K. A., Ngai, P. K., Carruthers, C. A., Hollenberg, M. D. 1984. $CA^{2+}$-dependent hydrophobic-interaction chromatography. *Biochem. J.* 224:117–27

52. Whittam, R., Blond, D. M. 1964. Respiratory control by an adenosine triphosphatase involved in active transport in brain cortex. *Biochem. J.* 92:147–58

53. Yingst, D. R. 1982. Effect of cytoplasm on Ca inhibition of the Na-K pump. *Fed. Proc. Fed. Am. Soc. Exp. Biol.* 41:974

54. Yingst, D. R. 1983. Ca-inhibitory protein of the (Na + K)-ATPase attached to the human red cell membrane. *Fed. Proc.* 42:962

55. Yingst, D. R. 1983. Hemolysate increases Ca-inhibition of the $Na^+,K^+$ pump of resealed human red cell ghosts. *Biochim. Biophys. Acta* 732:312–15

56. Yingst, D. R., Hoffman, J. F. 1984. Ca-induced K transport in resealed human red cells containing arsenazo III: transmembrane effects of Na and K and the relationship to the functioning Na-K pump. *J. Gen. Physiol.* 84:19–55

57. Yingst, D. R., Jones, R. M., Polasek, D. M. 1986. The effect of heart, kidney, and brain extracts on Ca-dependent inhibition of the Na,K-ATPase. *Biophys. J.* 49:549a

58. Yingst, D. R., Marcovitz, M. J. 1983. Effect of hemolysate on calcium inhibition of the $(Na^+ + K^+)$-ATPase of human red blood cells. *Biochem. Biophys. Res. Commun.* 111:970–79

59. Yingst, D. R., Polasek, D. M., Marcovitz, M. J. 1984. Ca-dependent inhibitor of the Na + K-ATPase extracted from human red cell membranes: Distinction and independence from calmodulin. In:

*Epithelial Calcium and Phosphate Transport, Molecular and Cellular Aspects,* ed. F. Bonner, M. Peterlik, pp. 127–32. New York: Liss

60. Yingst, D. R., Polasek, D. M., Polasek, P. M. 1985. Identification, reversibility and sensitivity of a Ca-dependent inhibitory of the Na,K-ATPase of human red blood cells. *Biophys. J.* 47:342a

61. Yingst, D. R., Polasek, D. M., Sheiknejade, G. Isolation of calnaktin, a protein from human red cells that increases Ca

inhibition of the Na,K-ATPase. Submitted for publication

62. Yingst, D. R., Polasek, P. M. 1985. Sensitivity and reversibility of Ca-dependent inhibitor of the (Na$^+$ + K$^+$)-ATPase of human red blood cells. *Biochim. Biophys. Acta* 813:282–86

63. Yingst, D. R., Sheiknejade, G., Polasek, D. M. 1987. Identification of an extrinsic membrane protein from human red blood cells associated with Ca-dependent inhibition of the Na,K-ATPase. *Biophys. J.* 51:566a

# SPECIAL TOPIC: RECOMBINANT DNA TO STUDY NEUROPEPTIDE PROCESSING

## General Introduction

*Betty A. Eipper and Richard E. Mains, Section Editors*[1]

Department of Neuroscience, Johns Hopkins Universith, School of Medicine, Baltimore, Maryland 21205

In this Special Topic Section, several aspects of neuropeptide and endocrine peptide biosynthesis are covered. A simple general outline of many of the known steps from initial translation of a prepropeptide to a collection of final product peptides is shown in Figure 1. The signal peptide (solid bar) is removed and core *N*-linked oligosaccharide chains [CHO (pentagon)] are added during or shortly after prepropeptide synthesis (6, 8). In the Golgi apparatus (3, 6), *N*-linked oligosaccharide maturation occurs, O-linked sugar chains are added (rectangle), selected serine/threonine residues are phosphorylated (P) and selected tyrosine residues are sulfated (S) (as discussed by Huttner). Endoproteolytic cleavages producing the hatched and stippled peptides, commonly at paired basic amino acid residues but also at single basic amino acids (mostly Arg), begin either in the Golgi and continue in maturing secretory granules or occur only in secretory granules (Huttner; Fuller et al; 2, 7); it may well be that the initial subcellular site of endoproteolytic cleavage is

---

[1]This section was formerly edited by Edward Herbert who passed away during the production of this volume.

cell type- or peptide-specific. A carboxypeptidase removes COOH-terminal basic amino acids; as discussed by Fricker, the carboxypeptidase in eukaryotic systems acts primarily in secretory granules. If the initial endoproteolytic cleavage is between basic amino acids, an aminopeptidase activity is required (7). In some systems a diaminopeptidase removes amino acids pairwise (Fuller et al). Peptide α-amidation occurs primarily in secretory granules (-NH₂) but may occur as soon as an appropriate -Gly extended substrate is generated (Eipper & Mains). The formation of pyroglutamic acid (pGlu) from Gly and the α-N-acetylation of various HN₂-terminal amino acids (Ac-) are late secretory granule events (1, 4, 5). The subcellular organelles involved in this pathway are discussed in the reviews by Huttner and Fuller et al.

The enzymes involved in prepropeptide processing share many interesting properties. To date, all the extensively studied enzymes have been found to be membrane-bound or to have membrane-associated and soluble forms. Virtually all of the enzymes require a divalent metal ion and are inhibited by chelators such as ethylenediaminetetraacetate (EDTA), although different enzymes require different cations. Most of the enzyme purifications have included a substrate affinity chromatography step and have required purifica-

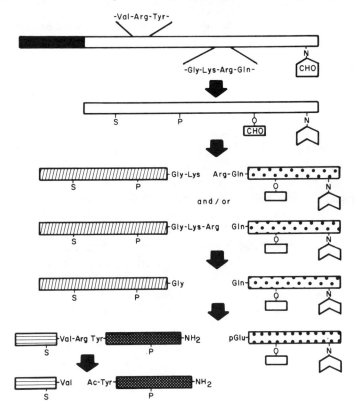

tions in excess of 10,000-fold to reach homogeneity; in general, cells are thought to contain more than a 1000-fold excess of peptide over processing enzyme (2).

The techniques of molecular biology are beginning to yield answers to key questions of peptide processing. As processing enzymes are purified by classical procedures, their cDNAs are cloned and sequenced, providing valuable tools for further studies. Fuller et al describe the use of genetic approaches in studies of yeast peptide processing. Thomas et al describe the use of gene transfer techniques to study peptide processing in eukaryotes. The cDNAs encoding various prepropeptides can be inserted into cell types to evaluate tissue-specific processing. Transfection of cDNAs encoding potential processing enzymes allows evaluation of their enzymatic activity in an appropriate environment. The same methods can be used to examine the role of molecules possibly involved in the routing process, such as the chromogranins, and to examine the function of tissue- and cell-specific regulatory elements (Huttner; Thomas et al). However, major questions remain to be answered. Little is known about the factors underlying tissue-specific processing, the subcellular routing of peptides, the extent to which processing enzymes are generic for many peptides or specific to a few peptides, and to what extent possible modulators of enzyme activity such as metal ion concentration or cofactor levels play an important role in the physiology of peptide processing.

While it is clear that this Special Topic Section and the world of peptide research suffered a great loss with Ed Herbert's untimely death, the personal loss to his family and friends was far greater. Those of us who knew Ed, worked closely with him, and trained under him, including all the authors of this Section, can only hope our efforts live up to Ed's high standards.

*Literature Cited*

1. Busby, W. H. Jr., Quackenbush, G. E., Humm, J., Youngblood, W. W., Kizer, J. S. 1987. An enzyme that converts glutaminyl-peptides into pyroglutamyl-peptides. *J. Biol. Chem.* 262:8532–36
2. Eipper, B. A., Mains, R. E., Herbert, E. 1986. Peptides in the nervous system. *Trends Neurosci.* 9:463–68
3. Farquhar, M. G. 1985. Progress in unraveling pathways of Golgi traffic. *Ann. Rev. Cell Biol.* 1:447–88
4. Fischer, W. H., Spiess, J. 1987. Identification of a mammalian glutaminyl cyclase converting glutaminyl into pyroglutamyl peptides. *Proc. Natl. Acad. Sci. USA* 84:3628–32
5. Gibson, T. R., Glembotski, C. C. 1985. Acetylation of $\alpha$MSH and $\beta$-endorphin by secretory granule-associated acetyltransferase. *Peptides* 6:615–20
6. Kornfeld, R., Kornfeld, S. 1985. Assembly of asparagine-linked oligosaccharides. *Ann. Rev. Biochem.* 54:631–64
7. Loh, Y. P., Brownstein, M. J., Gainer, H. 1984. Proteolysis in neuropeptide processing. *Ann. Rev. Neurosci.* 7:189–222
8. Walter, P., Lingappa, V. R. 1986. Mechanism of protein translocation across the endoplasmic reticulum membrane. *Ann. Rev. Cell Biol.* 2:499–516

Ann. Rev. Physiol. 1988. 50:309–21

# CARBOXYPEPTIDASE E

*Lloyd D. Fricker*

Department of Molecular Pharmacology, Albert Einstein College of Medicine, Bronx, New York 10461

## INTRODUCTION

A large number of peptide hormones and neurotransmitters are initially synthesized as precursor proteins that require enzymatic processing to give rise to the biologically active peptide (4, 24). In many cases, the bioactive peptide is flanked by pairs of basic amino acids in these precursor proteins. The sequential actions of a trypsinlike endopeptidase and a carboxypeptidase B–like exopeptidase would liberate the peptide from the surrounding sequences. The existence of trypsinlike and carboxypeptidase B–like peptide processing enzymes was originally proposed because limited digestion of proinsulin with these pancreatic enzymes produced insulin (21). However, the specificities of both trypsin and carboxypeptidase B are not appropriate for the production of many peptides; trypsin usually cleaves after every basic amino acid within a peptide, and carboxypeptidase B has a moderate affinity for some non-basic amino acids. The enzyme activities that are involved in the processing of peptide precursors are more selective in their substrate specificity than these digestive enzymes and are specific for particular sequences within the precursor (1, 10, 11, 18, 23, 24).

CPE has been proposed to be the carboxypeptidase B–like enzyme associated with the biosynthesis of many peptide neurotransmitters and hormones. Carboxypeptidase E (CPE) is highly specific for C-terminal basic amino acids and has no detectable activity towards other amino acids. This enzyme has been designated EC 3.4.17.10 and is also known as enkephalin convertase and carboxypeptidase H. While there are several important differences between CPE and carboxypeptidase B (CPB), recent studies on CPE have revealed an evolutionary relationship between these enzymes (7) and suggests that the peptide-processing enzymes were originally digestive enzymes. The low overall homology between CPE and CPB (17%) implies that these

309

enzymes diverged a long time ago. An early origin of the peptide-processing enzymes is consistent with the widespread occurrence of paired basic amino acid cleavage sites within prohormone precursors from a variety of species (4, 24).

## HISTORICAL PERSPECTIVES

Evidence for a carboxypeptidase B–like processing enzyme associated with the production of peptide hormones and neurotransmitters came from studies examining the enzymatic activity of secretory granule components. Secretory granules are thought to be a major site of precursor processing, based on peptide analysis. In bovine adrenal chromaffin granules, both enkephalin and C-terminally extended enkephalin precursors (YGGFMR, YGGFMK, and others) are present (32), which suggests that the enzyme activity that removes the C-terminal basic amino acids is also present within these granules. When chromaffin granules were separated from the other subcellular organelles using sucrose density gradient centrifugation, a novel carboxypeptidase B–like enzymatic activity was found to be enriched in the chromaffin granule fractions (10). This chromaffin granule–associated activity differed from other reported carboxypeptidases, including carboxypeptidase B (6), carboxypeptidase N (30), and a carboxypeptidase activity detected in crude chromaffin granule fractions (16) potentially contaminated with lysosomes (10). Further purification of the chromaffin granules on a second sucrose density gradient confirmed that the novel carboxypeptidase B–like activity was present in these granules (14). This enzyme was originally designated both carboxypeptidase E and enkephalin convertase (10).

The chromaffin granule–associated carboxypeptidase differs from other carboxypeptidase activities in several ways. The chromaffin granule enzyme is stimulated by cobalt chloride and inhibited by chelating agents, much like carboxypeptidase B and carboxypeptidase N (CPN). However, CPB and CPN are both maximally active at a neutral pH (6, 30), whereas the chromaffin

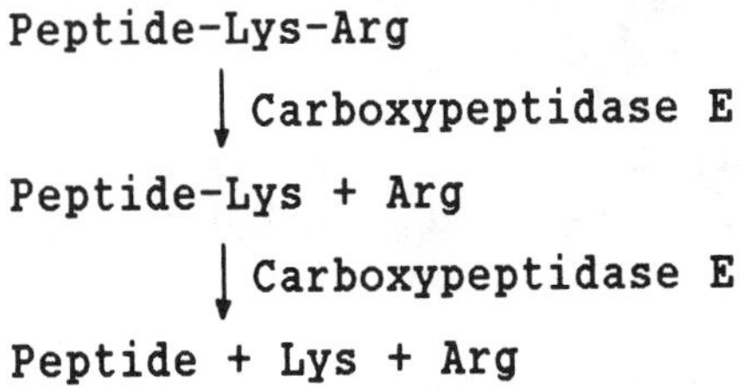

Peptide-Lys-Arg

↓ Carboxypeptidase E

Peptide-Lys + Arg

↓ Carboxypeptidase E

Peptide + Lys + Arg

*Figure 1*    Schematic diagram of carboxypeptidase E processing of a peptide with C-terminal basic amino acids.

granule enzyme is maximally active in the pH 5–6 range (10). The chromaffin granule carboxypeptidase is inhibited by some sulfhydryl reagents, such as *p*-chloromercuriphenyl sulfonate (12, 14). The lysosomal carboxypeptidase is also optimally active in the pH 5–6 range and is inhibited by sulfhydryl reagents (10, 29). However, the lysosomal enzyme is not activated by cobalt chloride or inhibited by chelating agents (10, 14). Thus the unique properties of the chromaffin granule carboxypeptidase allow for the detection of enzymatic activity in tissue homogenates by determining the amount of $Co^{2+}$-stimulated activity at pH 5.6.

Subcellular fractionation studies on rat pituitary and a rat insulin-producing tumor found a $Co^{2+}$-stimulated carboxypeptidase activity with a pH optimum around 5.6 to be present in the peptide-containing secretory granules (3, 18). Within the brain, high levels of a $Co^{2+}$-stimulated activity are detectable in the hypothalamus, hippocampus, striatum, thalamus, and mid brain (10). Lower levels are found in the cerebellum and brain stem (10). Of all the tissues screened, the pituitary has the highest level of a $Co^{2+}$-stimulated carboxypeptidase activity; the activity level in the anterior pituitary is 20 times the average brain level (12). In order to determine whether these carboxypeptidase activities in the different tissues represented the same enzyme, it was necessary to purify and characterize the enzyme from the various tissues.

## PURIFICATION OF CARBOXYPEPTIDASE E

Several things became apparent upon purification of the cobalt-stimulatable carboxypeptidase from the different tissues. First, a similar carboxypeptidase activity was found in both soluble and membrane fractions of the secretory granules or tissue homogenates (10, 35). Repeated freezing and thawing or homogenization in high or low ionic strength buffers could not extract the membrane-associated carboxypeptidase activity (13). The membrane-bound enzyme was solubilized with detergent, and quantitative yields were obtained with 1% Triton X-100 in a buffer containing 1 M sodium chloride (35). After solubilization, the membrane form of CPE was found to have similar physical properties to the soluble form (35). Both forms of CPE are single-chain glycoproteins that bind to concanavalin A and L-Arg affinity columns in a similar manner. The only detectable difference between the two forms is the molecular weight: The membrane form of CPE (52–53 kd) is slightly larger than the soluble form (50 kd) (11, 35). Enzyme isolated from bovine adrenal medulla, brain, and pituitary showed identical physical properties, including this molecular weight difference between the soluble and membrane forms (11, 35).

Purified CPE from the soluble and membrane fractions of the brain, adrenal

**Table 1** Comparison of carboxypeptidases

| Enzyme | pH optimum | Activators | Inhibitors | Substrate specificity (relative rate of hydrolysis) | Ref. |
|---|---|---|---|---|---|
| Carboxypeptidase E (EC 3.4.17.10) | 5.6 | $Co^{2+}$ | Chelating agents | Very selective for C-terminal basic amino acids (Arg>Lys≫His). Does not cleave other amino acids. | 10[a] |
| Carboxypeptidase N (EC 3.4.17.3) | 7–8 | $Co^{2+}$ | Chelating agents | Selective for C-terminal basic amino acids (Lys>Arg>Gly). | 30[b] |
| Carboxypeptidase B (EC 3.4.17.2) | 7–8 | $Co^{2+}$ | Chelating agents | Selective for C-terminal basic amino acids (Arg>Lys>Gly). | 6[b] |
| Carboxypeptidase A (EC 3.4.17.1) | 7–8 | $Co^{2+}$ | Chelating agents | Selective for C-terminal aromatic/aliphatic amino acids. Does not cleave Lys, Arg, Pro. | [c] |
| Lysosomal carboxypeptidase B | 5–6 | Thiols | Thiol blocking reagents | Cleaves all C-terminal amino acids (except Pro) with little selectivity. | 29 |
| Urinary carboxypeptidase | 7.0 | $Co^{2+}$ | Chelating agents | Selective for C-terminal basic amino acids. Does not cleave Phe. | [d] |

[a] N. G. Darby, L. D. Fricker, K. Maruthainar, D. G. Smyth. In preparation.
[b] G. Oshima, J. Kato, E. G. Erdos. 1975. Plasma carboxypeptidase N, subunits and characteristics. *Arch. Biochem. Biophys.* 170:132–38.
[c] J. A. Hartsuck, W. N. Lipscomb. 1971. Carboxypeptidase A. In *Enzymes*, ed. P. D. Boyer III:1–56. New York: Academic. 3rd ed.
[d] R. A. Skidgel, R. M. Davis, E. G. Erdos. 1984. Purification of a human urinary carboxypeptidase (kininase) distinct from carboxypeptidase A, B, or N. *Anal. Biochem.* 140:520–31.

medulla, and pituitary also showed similar enzymatic properties (11, 12, 35). As with the studies on the unpurified secretory granule enzymatic activity, the purified CPE activity is stimulated by $Co^{2+}$ and is inhibited by chelating agents (1 mM 1,10-phenanthroline) and some sulfhydryl reagents (10 $\mu$M $p$-chloromercuriphenyl sulfonate). Several analogs of arginine and lysine that were originally designed as active site directed inhibitors of CPB and CPN were found to be potent inhibitors of CPE (9). Two of these compounds, GEMSA (guanidinoethylmercaptosuccinic acid) and APMSA (aminopropyl-mercaptosuccinic acid), are several hundred fold more potent as inhibitors of CPE than of either CPB or CPN (9). The finding that CPE from the brain, adrenal medulla, and pituitary is similarly inhibited by these compounds is further evidence that the enzymatic activity in these tissues represents the same enzyme protein (11).

Further evidence for the similarity of CPE in the different tissues is provided by the substrate specificities of brain, pituitary, and adrenal CPE. A series of synthetic peptides containing C-terminal arginines are hydrolyzed by CPE from the various tissues with similar kinetic parameters ($K_m$ and $V_{max}$) (11). No differences in substrate specificities could be detected between the soluble and membrane form of CPE (35). Synthetic substrate hydrolysis by CPE from the various tissues is competitively inhibited by enkephalin precursors with C-terminal basic amino acids. The inhibition constants ($K_i$) for different enkephalin precursors show some variation. Peptides with C-terminal arginine residues have lower $K_i$'s than the corresponding peptides with C-terminal lysines. CPE purified from the different tissues showed similar variations between enkephalin precursors. Thus it appears this enzyme is the same in the various tissues examined and is involved in the biosynthesis of many peptide neurotransmitters and hormones.

Only a few synthetic peptides corresponding to the expected naturally occurring biosynthetic intermediates have been tested as substrates for CPE. The early studies on bovine adrenal chromaffin granule CPE found that both met- and leu-enkephalin Arg6 and Lys6 were converted rapidly to met- and leu-enkephalin (10). Prolonged incubation of CPE with enkephalin did not result in any further hydrolysis of the peptide (10), which suggests that CPE is very specific for C-terminal basic amino acids. This specificity has been confirmed in subsequent studies with other peptides. CPE from the rat pituitary is able to convert met-enkephalin Arg6 into met-enkephalin (18). In addition, rat pituitary CPE from the intermediate lobe sequentially removes C-terminal basic amino acids from adrenocorticotropic hormone (ACTH) 1–17 to form the $\alpha$-melanocyte stimulating hormone ($\alpha$-MSH) precursor, ACTH 1–14 (18). CPE isolated from the rat posterior pituitary sequentially removes the Lys and Arg residues from the carboxyl terminus of a vasopressin precursor (18). Partially purified CPE from bovine posterior pituitary was found to sequentially remove a pair of basic amino acids from the carboxyl terminus of an oxytocin precursor (20). Unfortunately, these studies only examined the ability of CPE isolated from a particular tissue to process peptides found in that tissue. The similarity of CPE present in the various tissues can be inferred from the studies with synthetic substrates and inhibitors. Thus it appears that CPE in the different tissues represents a single enzyme activity capable of correctly processing a variety of peptide precursors into the expected products.

## TISSUE DISTRIBUTION

The early studies on CPE detected enzymatic activity only in tissues with high levels of bioactive peptides, such as brain and pituitary. Other tissues with lower levels of peptide hormones and neurotransmitters were screened for CPE activity, but CPE could not be detected in these tissues above the background of other carboxypeptidases. More recent studies have found that CPE is present in many tissues that contain small amounts of peptide hormones or neurotransmitters. [³H]GEMSA binds to CPE with a $K_i$ of 8 nM (9, 34) and tissue levels of membrane-bound CPE can be determined by conventional ligand binding techniques. As GEMSA binds with a high affinity only to CPE, this assay is more specific and sensitive than the enzymatic assay (34). The soluble form of CPE can be quantitated by measuring protein-bound [³H]GEMSA with polyethyleneimine-pretreated filters (34). The ratio of the particulate and soluble forms of CPE is similar in all tissues reported, 2–3 times more GEMSA binds in the membrane fraction than in the soluble fraction (34). Relatively high levels of GEMSA binding are present in all lobes of the pituitary, the salivary gland, and in numerous regions of the brain. Moderate amounts of GEMSA binding are present in the lung, ileum, and the colon. Low levels of GEMSA binding are detectable in many other peripheral tissues, including heart, pancreas, testis, and spleen.

In addition to its use in solution binding assays, [³H]GEMSA can also be used to map the membrane-bound form of CPE with autoradiographic techniques. CPE distribution has been examined by this method in the brain, pituitary, and a variety of peripheral tissues (25–27). The distribution of CPE in the rat brain is similar to that of enkephalin, and the initial mapping studies suggested a selective association of CPE with endephalin-containing neurons (25). Detailed examination of the distribution of GEMSA binding in rat brain, in conjunction with lesioning techniques, revealed CPE to be present in both enkephalinergic and nonenkephalinergic pathways (26). This distribution is consistent with a broad role for CPE in the biosynthesis of many peptide hormones and neurotransmitters.

The distribution of GEMSA binding in peripheral tissues also suggests that CPE is involved in the production of many peptide hormones. In the pancreas,

GEMSA binding is localized to the islets, which are known to produce insulin, glucagon, somatostatin, and other peptides (27). Within the submandibular gland, the majority of GEMSA binding is present in the acinar cells (27). These cells produce atrial natriuretic factor (ANF) and nerve growth factor and are innervated by substance P– and vasoactive intestinal polypeptide–containing neurons. The association of CPE with ANF is evident from the distribution of GEMSA binding in the heart: Both GEMSA binding and ANF are localized to the myocytes in the atrium of rat heart (S. Snyder & D. Lynch, personal communication). The distribution of CPE in the gastrointestinal tract does not correlate with that of any known peptide. In the stomach, colon, and small intestine of the rat, GEMSA binding is enriched in the surface epithelial cells, whereas enkephalins are present in the muscularis layer and in the myenteric plexus (27). It is possible that CPE in the gastrointestinal tract has a function other than the production of bioactive peptides. Alternatively, there may be undiscovered peptides that are processed in these regions.

Although GEMSA binding and enzymatic activity generally correlate fairly well, in the salivary gland the ratio of GEMSA binding to enzymatic activity is severalfold higher than in other tissues (34). Many of the enzymatic properties of the carboxypeptidase in secretory granules from the rat parotid gland (one of the salivary glands) are identical to the properties of CPE from other tissues (36). Also, the properties of the GEMSA binding site in salivary glands are similar to those of the GEMSA binding site in brain and pituitary (34). It is unclear whether all of the GEMSA binding represents enzymatically active CPE, or if GEMSA is able to bind with high affinity to other forms of CPE (such as precursor forms). The latter ability would explain some of the discrepancies between GEMSA binding and CPE enzymatic activity. While it is unlikely that an enzymatically inactive precursor form of CPE is able to bind GEMSA and other ligands with an affinity comparable to that of the active form, this possibility needs to be investigated.

Immunochemical studies with antibodies raised against purified bovine pituitary CPE produce results comparable to those obtained with [$^3$H]GEMSA (19). This antiserum, which does not cross-react with other carboxypeptidases, binds to the soluble and membrane forms of CPE with equal affinity (19). Recently, the antiserum has been used to detect a putative precursor form of CPE that has a larger apparent molecular weight and less acidic pI on two-dimensional gel electrophoresis of bovine adrenal medulla chromaffin granule extracts (22). The antiserum shows a pattern of staining in the rat brain that is similar to the pattern obtained with GEMSA autoradiography (19). This is especially significant because [$^3$H]GEMSA autoradiography only measures the membrane-bound form of CPE, whereas the immunostaining detects the membrane-bound and soluble forms as well as the putative precursor form of CPE. In addition, the antiserum allows for a higher resolution of CPE localization. With electron microscopy, immunoreactive CPE is found in dendrites and nerve terminals that contain secretory granules (19).

## REGULATION

Further evidence for the localization of CPE to the secretory granules comes from studies on the regulation of secretion of CPE activity. Both CPE and a peptidyl-glycine $\alpha$-amidating monooxygenase (PAM) are released from a mouse pituitary corticotropic tumor cell line that secretes large amounts of pro-opiomelanocortin (POMC) derived peptides (28). This release can be stimulated by corticotropin releasing factor (CRF), isoproterenol, or $BaCl_2$ (28). For both CPE and PAM the amount of released enzymatic activity parallels the level of POMC-derived peptides released from the cells, which suggests that both enzymes are stored in the same granules as the peptides. Although cellular levels of PAM and the POMC-derived peptides decrease to 30–35% of control levels upon treatment with dexamethasone for one week, the level of CPE activity is unchanged (28).

Similarly, CPE activity is released from primary cultures of bovine adrenal medullary chromaffin cells (15). This release is stimulated by nicotine and inhibited by hexamethonium, as is the release of met-enkephalin. Interestingly, the ratio of CPE enzymatic activity to CPE immunoreactivity differs between released material and cellular extracts. The ratio of enzyme activity to immunoreactivity is 2–10 fold higher for material released from the cells than for extracts from the soluble or membrane fractions of the cells (15). One possible interpretation of this result is that a precursor of CPE exists in the cells that is immunoreactive with the antisera but not catalytically active. However, to be consistent with the ratio of enzymatic activity to immunoreactivity there would have to be more precursor than CPE inside the cells, and very little of this precursor could be released from the cells.

The possibility that CPE may exist within secretory granules in an inactive form is supported by studies examining the effect of reserpine treatment on CPE in bovine adrenomedullary chromaffin cells. Reserpine apparently increases cellular levels of enkephalin and other small opioid peptides by increasing the processing of the larger enkephalin precursor peptides (5, 37). A 72-hr treatment of chromaffin cells with reserpine causes a threefold increase in the level of $Co^{2+}$-stimulated carboxypeptidase activity within the chromaffin granules, without affecting the level of CPE immunoreactivity (17). Further analyses of the kinetic parameters of substrate hydrolysis have found changes in the apparent $K_m$ for the $Co^{2+}$-stimulated carboxypeptidase (17). However, the subcellular fractions used for these analyses contained considerable quantities of lysosomes. Since the lysosomal carboxypeptidase and CPE have different affinities for the substrate used in these studies (10), the observed change in $K_m$ could be a result of a reserpine-induced increase in the amount of CPE in the subcellular fractions.

Other studies have used [³H]GEMSA autoradiography to examine the regulation of the membrane-bound form of CPE in a variety of systems (33). In the anterior lobe of the rat pituitary, neither adrenalectomy, dehydration, or dexamethasone treatment affected the level of [³H]GEMSA binding sites. Similarly, dehydration or haloperidol treatment had no effect on the number of [³H]GEMSA binding sites in the intermediate pituitary. However, the level of [³H]GEMSA binding sites in the posterior pituitary was substantially decreased by dehydration and was restored by rehydration. This change was attributed to an increase in the rate of CPE secretion, as dehydration causes a depletion of posterior pituitary hormones by stimulating their release. Since levels of [³H]GEMSA binding in hypothalamic areas that project to the posterior pituitary were unaffected by dehydration, it was proposed that the rate of CPE synthesis was not altered by the treatment (33).

In the rat adrenal, the number of [³H]GEMSA binding sites is not affected by hypophysectomy, splanchnic denervation, or treatment with reserpine (33). This discrepancy with the enzymatic studies that reported changes in carboxypeptidase activity upon reserpine treatment could be a difference between in vivo studies on rats and in vitro studies with cultured bovine chromaffin cells. Alternatively, this difference could arise from the methods used to detect CPE. If [³H]GEMSA binds with high affinity to an inactive precursor form of CPE, and this form is as abundant as CPE in the adrenal medulla, then the two experiments would be consistent if reserpine induced a conversion of the inactive form into the active one. The concept of a precursor form of CPE is supported by recent sequence analysis of a cDNA clone encoding CPE (7).

## MOLECULAR BIOLOGY

A cDNA clone encoding CPE was isolated from a bovine pituitary cDNA library with oligonucleotide probes to regions of the enzyme that had been sequenced (7). The first cDNA clone isolated was not full length, although all proteolytic fragments of CPE that had been sequenced were contained within the 434 amino acid open reading frame predicted from the nucleotide sequence. Upon rescreening of the cDNA library, a longer cDNA clone was isolated. The sequence of this clone predicts that CPE is originally produced as a larger precursor (L. D. Fricker, in preparation). In addition to containing a 20–25 residue signal peptide, this precursor also contains a short 15–20 residue N-terminal "pro-peptide." There are five adjacent arginine residues immediately preceding the amino terminus of the active forms of CPE; both the soluble and the membrane forms of CPE have the same partial N-terminal amino acid sequence (7). Since the larger form of CPE with the extended amino terminus has not been isolated and characterized, it is not known whether this form is catalytically inactive. A finding that the precursor is inactive would be consistent with other proteolytic enzymes that are produced from inactive precursors.

In addition to the five adjacent arginines at the amino terminus, there are four pairs of basic amino acids within the sequence of CPE. One of these pairs of basic amino acids is 20 amino acids from the carboxyl terminus of the primary translation product. Cleavage at this pair of basic amino acids may account for the difference between the soluble and membrane-bound forms of the enzyme. Removal of this C-terminal peptide would shorten the protein by 3280 daltons, which is consistent with the observed difference in molecular weight between the two forms (35). Although this C-terminal peptide has no conventional hydrophobic membrane-spanning region, it may contribute to the binding of the membrane form to the lipid bilayer. The predicted secondary structure for this C-terminal region is an amphipathic alpha helix (7).

Only one gene for bovine CPE is apparent on Southern blots, which suggests that both forms of CPE arise from the same gene. Hybridization of the cDNA probes to bovine pituitary mRNA on Northern blots indicates that the predominant species of CPE mRNA is approximately 3300 nucleotides long (7). Shorter species of mRNA are also detected with the CPE cDNA probes, although these forms of CPE mRNA account for less than 5% of the species. The smaller mRNAs presumably arise from alternative sites for polyadenylation within the 3' untranslated region (7).

Although CPE does not appear to be a member of a highly related gene family, it does have significant homology with two other proteins, carboxypeptidases A and B. The overall amino acid homology between CPE and either carboxypeptidase A (CPA) or carboxypeptidase B (CPB) is relatively low (20% and 17%, respectively, for the bovine enzymes); however, all of the amino acids thought to be involved with the catalytic activity of CPA and CPB have been conserved in CPE (7). In addition, several of the amino acids in CPA and CPB that bind to the substrate are also present in comparable positions in CPE (7). The region of greatest homology is that involved in binding the carboxyl terminus of the peptide substrate. In contrast, the region in CPA and CPB that is thought to be involved with binding to the side chain of the substrate's C-terminal amino acid is poorly conserved among the different enzymes, as might be expected for the differing specificities of the enzyme for peptides with different carboxyl-terminal amino acids.

The homology between CPE and the other carboxypeptidases suggests that these enzymes have evolved from a common ancestor. This idea is supported by the homology between the carboxypeptidases from different species. Of the 90 amino acids conserved between bovine CPB, crayfish CPB, bovine CPA, and rat CPA, 35 are conserved in bovine CPE (39% homology) (8). Bovine and rat CPE amino acid sequences are 93% homologous (L. D.

Fricker, J. C. Hutton, J. Douglas, J. P. Adelman, E. Herbert, in preparation). When similar amino acids are included, this homology is ~97%.

The idea that CPE, CPB, and CPA evolved from the same carboxypeptidase ancestor is consistent with the proposal that serine proteases and some peptide hormones may have evolved from the same protein (2, 31). This speculation is based on the small but significant homology between insulin, insulin-related peptides, and serine proteases (2). According to this proposal, ancestral serine proteases that were secreted from the cells as digestive enzymes evolved a secondary function as intercellular messengers. Autodegradation fragments of the proteases may have been the original messengers. Through a series of gene duplications and subsequent rearrangements, the proinsulin gene emerged. Since the ancestral trypsinlike endopeptidase and carboxypeptidase were present in these cells, the proinsulin was processed into insulin. Further evolution of the digestive enzymes gave rise to specific peptide-processing enzymes.

This theory could explain the predominance of basic amino acids as cleavage sites within peptide precursors, since there is no apparent advantage to basic over acidic amino acids. If enzymes that cleaved the precursors at basic amino acids existed along with the first peptides, then other possible processing pathways would be unnecessary. The early divergence of CPE from CPA and CPB supports this theory, but little is known about the evolution of trypsinlike endopeptidases involved in peptide processing. Several of the putative peptide-processing endopeptidases have been described as "trypsinlike" based on their inhibitor specificities (1, 23). However, without amino acid sequence information for these enzymes it is not possible to conclude that they evolved from an ancestral trypsin, and further research is necessary.

## SUMMARY

Carboxypeptidase E appears to be involved in the biosynthesis of a wide range of peptide hormones and neurotransmitters. The evidence for this is: (a) CPE is present in tissues that produce bioactive peptides; (b) in tissues that have been subjected to subcellular fractionation, the CPE activity is associated with peptide-containing secretory granules; (c) CPE is able to remove C-terminal basic amino acids from a variety of synthetic peptides without further hydrolyzing the peptide; (d) CPE is active at pH 5.6, the internal pH of secretory granules.

The CPE activities in various tissues have similar physical and enzymatic properties. Two forms of CPE, soluble and membrane-bound, are present in most tissues with CPE activity. These two forms differ slightly in molecular weight, but have identical enzymatic properties. Both forms arise from the same precursor, which is encoded by a single gene. This gene is a member of a carboxypeptidase gene family that includes CPA and CPB. At the amino acid level, CPE has approximately 20% homology with bovine CPA and 17% homology with bovine CPB. All of the amino acids in CPA and CPB that are thought to be essential for catalytic activity are present in CPE in comparable positions. The homology of CPE with CPA and CPB suggests a common evolutionary origin for the three enzymes. This relationship fits with the theory that certain peptide hormones may have evolved from serine proteases.

Further studies are needed to investigate the processing of proCPE into CPE, and the regulation of CPE activity. While there is some evidence that CPE may be regulated, it does not appear that regulation of CPE activity plays an important role in controlling peptide biosynthesis. However, further studies are necessary before this possibility can be eliminated.

*Literature Cited*

1. Cromlish, J. A., Seidah, N. G., Chretien, M. 1986. Selective cleavage of human ACTH, β-lipotropin, and the N-terminal glycopeptide at pairs of basic residues by IRCM-serine protease 1. *J. Biol. Chem.* 261:868–80
2. de Haen, C., Swanson, E., Teller, D. C. 1976. The evolutionary origin of proinsulin. *J. Mol. Biol.* 106:639–61
3. Docherty, K., Hutton, J. C. 1983. Carboxypeptidase activity in the insulin secretory granule. *FEBS Lett.* 162:137–41
4. Docherty, K., Steiner, D. F. 1982. Post-translational proteolysis in polypeptide hormone biosynthesis. *Ann. Rev. Physiol.* 44:625–38
5. Eiden, L. E., Giraud, P., Affolter, H. U., Herbert, E., Hotchkiss, A. J. 1984. Alternative modes of enkephalin biosynthesis regulation by reserpine and cyclic AMP in cultured chromaffin cells. *Proc. Natl. Acad. Sci. USA* 81:3949–53
6. Folk, J. E. 1971. Carboxypeptidase B. In *Enzymes,* ed. P. D. Boyer, III:57–79. New York: Academic. 3rd ed.
7. Fricker, L. D., Evans, C. J., Esch, F. S., Herbert, E. 1986. Cloning and sequence analysis of cDNA for bovine carboxypeptidase E. *Nature* 323:461–64
8. Fricker, L. D., Herbert, E. 1987. Molecular biology of carboxypeptidase E (enkephalin convertase), a neuropeptide synthesizing enzyme. *Ann. NY Acad. Sci.* 493:391–93
9. Fricker, L. D., Plummer, T. H. Jr., Snyder, S. H. 1983. Enkephalin convertase: Potent, selective, and irreversible inhibitors. *Biochem. Biophys. Res. Commun.* 111:994–1000
10. Fricker, L. D., Snyder, S. H. 1982. Enkephalin convertase: Purification and characterization of a specific enkephalin-synthesizing carboxypeptidase localized to adrenal chromaffin granules. *Proc. Natl. Acad. Sci. USA* 79:3886–90
11. Fricker, L. D., Snyder, S. H. 1983. Purification and characterization of enkephalin convertase, an enkephalin-synthesizing carboxypeptidase. *J. Biol. Chem.* 258:10950–55
12. Fricker, L. D., Supattapone, S., Snyder, S. H. 1982. Enkephalin convertase: A specific enkephalin synthesizing carboxypeptidase in adrenal chromaffin granules, brain, and pituitary gland. *Life Sci.* 31:1841–44
13. Hook, V. Y. H. 1984. Carboxypeptidase B–like activity for the processing of enkephalin precursors in the membrane component of bovine adrenomedullary chromaffin granules. *Neuropeptides* 4:117–25
14. Hook, V. Y. H., Eiden, L. E. 1984. Two peptidases that convert [125-I]-Lys-Arg-(Met)enkephalin and [125-I]-(Met)enkephalin-Arg6, respectively, to [125-I]-(Met)enkephalin in bovine adrenal medullary chromaffin granules. *FEBS Lett.* 172:212–18
15. Hook, V. Y. H., Eiden, L. E. 1985. (Met)Enkephalin and carboxypeptidase processing enzyme are co-released from chromaffin cells by cholinergic stimulation. *Biochem. Biophys. Res. Commun.* 128:563–70
16. Hook, V. Y. H., Eiden, L. E., Brownstein, M. J. 1982. A carboxypeptidase processing enzyme for enkephalin precursors. *Nature* 295:341–42
17. Hook, V. Y. H., Eiden, L. E., Pruss, R. M. 1985. Selective regulation of carboxypeptidase peptide hormone-pro-

cessing enzyme during enkephalin biosynthesis in cultured bovine adrenomedullary chromaffin cells. *J. Biol. Chem.* 260:5991–97

18. Hook, V. Y. H., Loh, Y. P. 1984. Carboxypeptidase B–like converting enzyme activity in secretory granules of rat pituitary. *Proc. Natl. Acad. Sci. USA* 81:2776–80

19. Hook, V. Y. H., Mezey, E., Fricker, L. D., Pruss, R. M., Siegel, R. E., et al. 1985. Immunochemical characterization of carboxypeptidase B–like peptide-hormone-processing enzyme. *Proc. Natl. Acad. Sci. USA* 82:4745–49

20. Kanmera, T., Chaiken, I. M. 1985. Pituitary enzyme conversion of putative synthetic oxytocin precursor intermediates. *J. Biol. Chem.* 260:10118–24

21. Kemmler, W., Peterson, J. D., Steiner, D. F. 1971. Studies on the conversion of proinsulin to insulin. *J. Biol. Chem.* 246:6786–91

22. Laslop, A., Fischer-Colbrie, R., Hook, V., Obendorf, D., Winkler, H. 1987. Identification of two glycoproteins of chromaffin granules as the carboxypeptidase H. *Neurosci. Lett.* 72:300–5

23. Lindberg, I., Yang, H. Y. T., Costa, E. 1984. Further characterization of an enkephalin-generating enzyme from adrenal medullary chromaffin granules. *J. Neurochem.* 42:1411–19

24. Loh, Y. P., Brownstein, M. J., Gainer, H. 1984. Proteolysis in neuropeptide processing and other neural functions. *Ann. Rev. Neurosci.* 7:189–222

25. Lynch, D. R., Strittmatter, S. M., Snyder, S. H. 1984. Enkephalin convertase localization by [3H]guanidinoethyl-mercaptosuccinic acid autoradiography: Selective association with enkephalin-containing neurons. *Proc. Natl. Acad. Sci. USA* 81:6543–47

26. Lynch, D. R., Strittmatter, S. M., Venable, J. C., Snyder, S. H. 1986. Enkephalin convertase: Localization to specific neuronal pathways. *J. Neurosci.* 6:1662–75

27. Lynch, D. R., Strittmatter, S. M., Venable, J. C., Snyder, S. H. 1987. Enkephalin convertase in the gastrointestinal tract and associated organs characterized and localized with [3H]-guanidinoethylmercaptosuccinic acid. *Endocrinology* 121:116–26

28. Mains, R. E., Eipper, B. A. 1984. Secretion and regulation of two biosynthetic enzyme activities, peptidylglycine α-amidating monooxygenase and a carboxypeptidase, by mouse pituitary corticotropic tumor cells. *Endocrinology* 115:1683–90

29. Ninjoor, V., Taylor, S. L., Tappel, A. L. 1974. Purification and characterization of rat liver lysosomal cathepsin B2. *Biochim. Biophys. Acta* 370:308–21

30. Plummer, T. H. Jr., Erdos, E. G. 1981. Human plasma carboxypeptidase N. *Methods Enzymol.* 80:442–49

31. Steiner, D. F., Chan, S. J., Welsh, J. M., Kwok, S. C. M. 1985. Structure and evolution of the insulin gene. *Ann. Rev. Genet.* 19:463–84

32. Stern, A. S., Lewis, R. V., Kimura, S., Rossier, J., Stein, S., et al. 1980. Opioid hexapeptides and heptapeptides in adrenal medulla and brain: Possible implications on the biosynthesis of enkephalins. *Arch. Biochem. Biophys.* 205:606–13

33. Strittmatter, S. M., Lynch, D. R., De Souza, E. B., Snyder, S. H. 1985. Enkephalin convertase demonstrated in the pituitary and adrenal gland by [3H]guanidinoethylmercaptosuccinic acid autoradiography: Dehydration decreases neurohypophyseal levels. *Endocrinology* 117:1667–74

34. Strittmatter, S. M., Lynch, D. R., Snyder, S. H. 1984. [3H]Guanidinoethyl-mercaptosuccinic acid binding to tissue homogenates. *J. Biol. Chem.* 259:11812–17

35. Supattapone, S., Fricker, L. D., Snyder, S. H. 1984. Purification and characterization of a membrane-bound enkephalin-forming carboxypeptidase, "enkephalin convertase". *J. Neurochem.* 42:1017–23

36. von Zastrow, M., Tritton, T. R., Castle, J. D. 1986. Exocrine secretion granules contain peptide amidation activity. *Proc. Natl. Acad. Sci. USA* 83:3297–3301

37. Wilson, S. P., Chang, K. J., Viveros, O. H. 1980. Synthesis of enkephalins by adrenal medullary chromaffin cells: Reserpine increases incorporation of radiolabeled amino acids. *Proc. Natl. Acad. Sci. USA* 77:4364–68

*Ann. Rev. Physiol. 1988. 50:323–32*

# GENE TRANSFER TECHNIQUES TO STUDY NEUROPEPTIDE PROCESSING

*G. Thomas and B. A. Thorne*

Vollum Institute for Advanced Biomedical Research, The Oregon Health Sciences University, Portland, Oregon 97201

*D. E. Hruby*

Department of Microbiology, Oregon State University, Corvallis, Oregon 97331

## OVERVIEW

During the past few years, a great deal of progress has been made in understanding the cellular mechanisms that govern the biogenesis of small peptide hormones and neuromodulators. This area of study has become a focal point toward which a number of research disciplines are converging. In this review, we describe how one of these disciplines, gene transfer technology, is being used to address several fundamental questions regarding neuroendocrine precursor protein maturation.

## INTRODUCTION

Small peptide hormones and neuromodulators are usually synthesized initially as large precursor proteins that undergo tissue-specific posttranslational modifications and proteolytic cleavage to produce mature bioactive peptides (6, 24). The peptides in precursor proteins are typically flanked by pairs of basic amino acids (e.g. Lys-Arg or Lys-Lys). Maturation of the bioactive peptide is generally viewed as a two-step process (40): The paired basic sequence is cleaved by a trypsinlike endopeptidase and then any remaining flanking amino acids are removed by a carboxypeptidase B–like enzyme or a similar

0066-4278/88/0315-0323$02.00

aminopeptidase. Before being released from the cell, the mature peptide may undergo a further series of modification reactions (eg. N-terminal acetylation or C-terminal amidation) (27).

A number of the precursor proteins (Figure 1) contain the sequences of more than one bioactive peptide. A striking example of this type of precursor (known as a polyprotein) is the family of proteins that gives rise to the opioid peptides. Of the more than sixteen opioid peptides characterized to date, all are derived from just three precursor proteins: pro-opiomelanocortin (POMC), proenkephalin A (proenkephalin), and proenkephlin B (pro-dynorphin) (6, 30). Of these proteins, POMC is the best characterized with regard to its synthesis and processing. POMC is expressed in the anterior and neurointermediate lobes of the pituitary, as well as in several regions of the brain and other tissues (6, 18). In the pituitary POMC is processed in a tissue-specific manner to produce a variety of polypeptides: primarily adreno-corticotropin (ACTH), $\beta$-lipotropin ($\beta$-LPH), and N-terminal fragments in the anterior lobe, and $\alpha$-melanocyte stimulating hormone ($\alpha$-MSH), cortico-tropin-like intermediate lobe peptides (CLIP), $\gamma$-lipotropin ($\gamma$-LPH) $\beta$-endorphin, and N-terminal fragments in the neurointermediate lobe.

It is not yet known what accounts for the tissue specificity of the processing reactions. However, there are a number of factors that may be involved, including selective expression of distinct processing enzymes; tissue-specific modification of the precursor proteins, which could govern cleavage-site

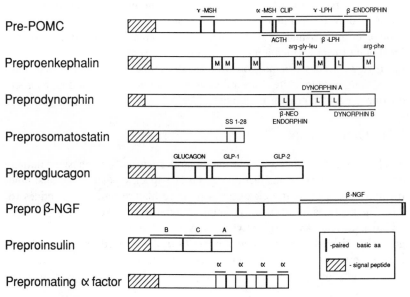

*Figure 1*   Schematic diagram of selected precursor proteins. (Adapted from Reference 6.)

accessibility; and differential compartmentalization of either the enzymes or the precursor protein. With recent advances in gene transfer technology, isolated genes thought to code for a protein involved in the above processes can be expressed in a variety of heterologous cell types. In this way these issues can be addressed in the mammalian cellular environment.

Several gene transfer techniques have been employed to introduce neuroendocrine peptide genes into heterologous cell types. Although it is beyond the scope of this review to present a complete description of each of these techniques, a survey of the essential features of each system is presented. A more detailed account can be found in selected references. In general, gene transfer methods to study neuropeptide processing can be divided into two major categories: those that result in the stable integration of the cloned gene into the genome of heterologous cells and those that produce transient expression of the cloned gene in heterologous cells. Each method has unique advantages and disadvantages.

## STABLE INTEGRATION

Stable transfection of the gene of interest into the genome of heterologous cell types has been a common method for studying neuropeptide processing. This method has been used to examine the proteolytic maturation of proinsulin (33), proenkephalin (3), proglucagon (7), and prosomatostatin (38) in a variety of cell types. In this approach, the cloned gene or cDNA is first engineered into a plasmid such that transcription of the insert is under the control of its own promoter or a heterologous promoter. This plasmid is then cotransfected into a cell population together with a second plasmid containing a gene encoding a dominant selectable phenotype (e.g. Tn5 aminoglycoside phosphotransferase, which confers resistance to the antibiotic G418). Transfection can be accomplished by calcium phosphate precipitation (12), DEAE dextran precipitation, and electroporation (11). Following selection and isolation of clones expressing the dominant selectable marker (e.g. G418 resistance), expression of the gene of interest can be assayed by standard procedures, such as radioimmunoassay or immunostaining.

Although this type of gene transfer approach has been successfully used in a number of laboratories, there are several limitations to its use in the study of the biogenesis of neuroendocrine peptides. First, not all cell types are amenable to established transfection protocols. This limits the cell types that can be readily studied. Second, the efficiency of creating stable transfectants is at best only a few percent. Typically, the efficiency is $10^{-5}$ to $10^{-7}$ (1). Third, neither the gene dosage nor the site of integration of the foreign gene can be regulated. Furthermore, the level of protein expression does not correlate simply with gene dosage.

## Retroviral Vectors

An alternative approach to plasmid transfection that is currently generating a great deal of interest is the use of defective amphotrophic (broad host range) retroviruses (1, 4, 9, 32). Retroviral vectors have been used by Hellerman et al (17) to express preproparathyroid hormone (prepro-PTH) in both 3T3 cells and $GH_4C_1$ cells. The use of retroviral vectors to introduce foreign genes into heterologous cells has several important advantages over classical transfection procedures. First, essentially 100% of a cell population can be transformed with a recombinant retrovirus. This eliminates the requirement of a coexpressed dominant selectable marker. Second, the gene dosage for a population of cells is fairly uniform (1). Unfortunately, there are as yet several disadvantages to this system. First, retroviruses integrate at random sites within the genome. This fact implies that not all cells in a population will express the foreign protein in the same manner. Second, retroviruses frequently undergo deletions during viral replication, and interference between *cis*-acting elements in the foreign gene and the retrovirus vector has been reported (21, 38). Several laboratories are currently attempting to correct these deficiencies. As these drawbacks are overcome, the retrovirus expression system will become increasingly useful.

## TRANSIENT EXPRESSION SYSTEMS

### SV40 Virus

Several transient expression systems have been used to study the cell type–specific expression of neuroendocrine precursor proteins. The first such vector used was SV40 virus (37). Recombinant SV40 has been used to express proinsulin (14) and growth hormone (36) in simian cells. In these experiments SV40 late-region DNA was replaced by the foreign genes. The SV40 recombinants were then coinfected into African green monkey kidney cells together with a tsA helper virus. The helper virus is needed to provide the deleted late gene functions in *trans* to the recombinant virus. Although the expression of foreign proteins by this system is very efficient in simian cells, the SV40 enhancer element does not allow for efficient expression in all mammalian cell types (13). In addition, the gene inserted into SV40 must be very small because of virion packaging restraints (15).

### COS Cells

To circumvent some of the drawbacks in using SV40 virions, Gluzman developed the COS cell lines (10). COS lines were produced by stably integrating replication origin–defective SV40 DNA into the CV-1 genome. This results in the constitutive expression of SV40 large T antigen in the absence of viral replication. Foreign genes inserted into either the early or late regions of SV40 plasmids can then be transfected into the COS cells without helper virus. The transfected DNA is replicated until each cell contains a large number of copies, and the expression of foreign protein can be detected 48–72 hr after transfection. Several neuroendocrine genes and/or cDNAs have been expressed using this system, including those encoding rat (28) and human (25) preproinsulin, anglerfish preprosomatostatin (43), and porcine preproopiomelanocortin (34). Although COS cells transfected with SV40 plasmids generate high levels of foreign gene product, this system allows the study of precursor protein maturation in only a single cell type and hence is not amenable to research addressing tissue-specific processing reactions.

## Vaccinia Virus

The gene transfer systems described above require that the gene of interest be expressed in the nuclear compartment. This necessitates that foreign genes be placed in proper context with respect to promoters, enhancers, splice junctions, polyadenylation sites, and RNA transport signals. Since our understanding of the nature and spatial constraints of eukaryotic regulatory signals is still rudimentary at best, the construction of a highly active chimeric gene remains a challenging proposition. With the vaccinia system, many of these considerations are obviated. Vaccinia has a number of biological attributes that make it uniquely suited for vector work (19): (*a*) Unlike those of other DNA-containing animal viruses, vaccinia virus genes are transcribed and processed in the cytoplasm of infected cells by viral enzymes under the direction of viral regulatory signals. Thus there is no need to incorporate foreign splicing or transport signals. (*b*) The broad host range of vaccinia allows genetic information to be shuttled between a variety of species and cell types. (*c*) The vaccinia virion and genomic DNA molecule are quite large (184 kilobases) and can accomodate large and/or multiple foreign inserts. Unlike other viruses whose capacity for foreign gene inserts is determined by capsid size (e.g. SV40), there does not appear to be any such constraint with vaccinia. (*d*) Vaccinia is a vaccine strain, so it safe to work with in the laboratory.

Several neuroendocrine precursor proteins have been expressed in mammalian cells using the recombinant vaccinia methodology (20). These include human preproenkephalin (41), mouse prepro-opiomelanocortin (our unpublished results) and mouse prepro-$\beta$-nerve growth factor (prepro-$\beta$-NGF) (R. H. Edwards, M. J. Selby, D. E. Hruby, W. J. Rutter, unpublished results). In addition, several processing endopeptidases have been expressed, including the yeast KEX2 endopeptidase and an AtT-20 specific preprokallikrein (our unpublished results).

The main limitations of the present vaccinia virus technology are as follows: (a) Either no selection or at best a negative selection exists for the recombinants of interest. That is, a dominant selectable marker to distinguish vaccinia recombinants from progenitor virus is lacking. This necessitates that the recombinant virus be isolated by classical plaque purification techniques. (b) Like SV40, vaccinia is a live virus that can ultimately kill the infected cell. Research is currently addressing many of these shortcomings (19).

## CURRENT STATUS AND PROSPECTIVES

To date, at least six different gene transfer approaches have been employed to assess the ability of various cell types to process neuroendocrine precursor proteins. The results, which are in close agreement irrespective of the method used, are summarized in Table 1. Several conclusions can be reached from the data. First, fibroblasts lack the capability to process neuroendocrine precursor proteins to smaller peptides, with the notable exceptions of prepro-$\beta$-NGF, prepro-PTH, and somatostatin. The efficient maturation of prepro-$\beta$-NGF by fibroblasts is entirely consistent with published literature describing the synthesis and bioactivity of L cell–derived $\beta$-NGF (2, 44).

**Table 1**  Summary of results using gene transfer to study cell type–specific processing of neuroendocrine precursor proteins[a]

| | Preproinsulin | Preprosomatostatin | Preproenkephlin | Prepro β-NGF | Pre-POMC | Preproglucagon | PreproPTH | Endogenous Prohormone |
|---|---|---|---|---|---|---|---|---|
| BSC-40 | | | — (g) | ++ (k) | — (m) | | | |
| AGMK/COS/CV-1 | — (a,b,c) | + (e) | | | — (n) | | | |
| L | — (d) | | — (g) | ++ (k) | — (m) | | | Pro β-NGF |
| 3T3 | | — (f) | | | | | ++ (p) | |
| BHK21 | | | | | | — (o) | | |
| P388D₁ | | | — (g,*) | | — (m,*) | | | IL-1 |
| GH₄C₁ | | — (f) | — (g) | | — (m) | + (o) | ++ (p) | Prolactin, growth hormone |
| PC12 | | — (f) | | | | | | Neurotensin |
| NG108 | | | | | — (m) | | | Proenkephalin |
| RIN5F | | ++ (f) | | | ++ (m) | | | Proinsulin |
| RIN38 | | | | | | ++ (o) | | Proinsulin |
| AtT-20 | ++ (d) | ++ (f) | ++ (g,h) | ++ (k) | | | | POMC |

[a]—, processing not reported; +, inefficient processing reported; ++, efficient processing reported. References: a, 14; b, 25; c, 28; d, 33; e, 43; f, 38; g, 41; h, 3; k, R. H. Edwards, unpublished results; m, our unpublished results; n, 34; o, 7; p, 17; *, proteolysis after secretion.

Second, several precursor proteins are not processed beyond signal peptide cleavage in fibroblast lines but are efficiently cleaved to small peptides in AtT-20, and/or RIN cell lines (7, 33, 38, 41; our results). The efficient processing of a wide spectrum of precursor proteins by these cell lines suggests that some endoproteolytic enzymes are low-specificity endopeptidases that recognize and cleave several precursor proteins.

The results generated by gene transfer studies to date have set a foundation for several areas of investigation. One exciting research area is the characterization of the determinants that direct neuroendocrine precursor proteins to various compartments in the secretory pathway for: (a) presentation to the cognate endopeptidase and (b) localization of cleaved peptides in storage granules of the regulated secretory pathway (8, 23). Several laboratories are investigating these processes using gene transfer technologies (8). It appears that the N-terminal proregions in some (42), but not all (T. L. Burgess, C. S. Craik, L. Matsuuchi, R. B. Kelly, unpublished results), proproteins contain sorting signals.

The authentication of mammalian neuroendocrine protein processing endopeptidases has proven a formidable task. Several candidate processing activities have been characterized (31), but as yet not one has been convincingly demonstrated to be a bona fide processing enzyme. Many of the difficulties arise from the inability to readily manipulate the phenotype of mammalian cells. In contrast, much greater success has been realized in yeast because they are amenable to genetic manipulations. The ability to perform complementation analysis greatly aided the characterization of the pro-$\alpha$-mating factor endopeptidase KEX2 (22). We have recently determined that recombinant vaccinia virus can be used to readily manipulate the phenotype of mammalian cells. In these experiments a recombinant vaccinia virus that expressed a mammalian neuroendocrine peptide precursor protein (VV:mPOMC) was coinfected with a second vaccinia recombinant that contained the gene for KEX2 (VV:KEX2). When two "maturation deficient" cell lines, BSC-40 (African green monkey kidney) and NG108 (neuroblastoma × glioma), were infected with VV:mPOMC alone, they were unable to process POMC to small bioactive peptides. However, cells coinfected with both VV:mPOMC and VV:KEX2 accurately cleaved the POMC precursor to bona fide POMC-derived peptides (including $\beta$-endorphin). These results show that the recombinant vaccinia system can be used to alter the phenotype of mammalian cell. Furthermore, the recombinant vaccinia virus expression vector system may serve as a tool to express cDNA libraries in mammalian cells to isolate potential processing enzymes.

Except in a few cases, little is known regarding the spatial orientation of cleavage domains on neuroendocrine precursor proteins. This is due to the extremely small amounts of precursor proteins that can be isolated from tissue preparations. However, since the cDNAs for a number of precursor proteins have been cloned, it is now possible to express high levels of each precursor. A variety of vector systems have been used for this purpose, including the vaccinia virus system (19). Bacterial expression plasmids generate high levels of recombinant protein, approaching 10–30% of the total cell protein (33a). Unfortunately, bacteria do not correctly modify mammalian proteins (5). In contrast, recombinant proteins expressed by mammalian cell systems can undergo correct side-group modifications. For example, expression of factor IX in hepatocyte cells with recombinant vaccinia virus results in the $\gamma$-carboxylation step necessary for proper activity (5). However, the level of recombinant protein expression from mammalian cell systems is much lower (0.1%–10% of total cell protein) than that observed with bacterial cell systems. Since proteins expressed in mammalian cell systems can be correctly modified, the accessibility of cleavage domains can be tested by incubating recombinant precursor proteins with isolated candidate processing enzymes in vitro. I. Lindberg (unpublished results) has performed such studies using a candidate proenkephalin endopeptidase, ATLE, isolated from bovine adrenal chromaffin granules (26). Furthermore, in vitro studies of this sort can be complemented with in vivo studies using a defined processing system, such as the KEX2 reconstitution system.

An inherent shortcoming of gene transfer studies to date is that the molecular mechanisms that govern the processing of neuroendocrine precursor protein in heterologous cells differ from those present in homologous cells (29, 38). However, recent advances in germ-line transmission of foreign genes may overcome this problem. Hanahan (16) designed a chimeric gene in which the SV40 T antigen gene was placed under the control of the rat proinsulin promoter. Introduction of the chimeric gene into the germ line of mice resulted in the specific formation of pancreatic $\beta$-cell tumors. The transformed $\beta$ cells produced insulin and were amenable to culture in vitro. Similar experiments have been done with the rat elastase gene (35). Perhaps this technology can next be applied to the establishment of homologous cell types from defined brain nuclei. Using this approach, one would be able to selectively establish a homogeneous cell population in which the processing of a neuroendocrine precursor protein could be studied in its native cell type.

ACKNOWLEDGMENTS

The authors wish to thank L. Thomas for critically reviewing the manuscript, D. Arrington and L. Williams for typing it, and N. Kirkinen for designing the art. GT was supported by a Damon-Runyon Fellowship DRG-797.

## Literature Cited

1. Anderson, W. F. 1984. Prospects for human gene therapy. *Science* 226:401–9
2. Brachet, P., Dicou, E. 1984. L cells potentiate the effect of the extracellular NGF activity in co-cultures with PC12 pheochromocytoma cells. *Exp. Cell Res.* 150:234–41
3. Comb, M., Liston, D., Martin, M., Rosen, R., Herbert, E. 1985. Expression of the human proenkephalin gene in mouse pituitary cells: Accurate and efficient mRNA production and proteolytic processing. *EMBO J.* 4:3115–22
4. Cone, R. D., Mulligan, R. C. 1984. High-efficiency gene transfer into mammalian cells: Generation of helper-free recombinant retroviruses with broad mammalian host range. *Proc. Natl. Acad. Sci. USA* 81:6349–53
5. de la Salle, H., Altenburger, W., Elkaim, R., Dott, K., Dieterle, A., et al. 1985. Active γ-carboxylated human factor IX expressed using recombinant DNA technology. *Nature* 316:268–70
6. Douglass, J., Civelli, O., Herbert, E. 1984. Polyprotein gene expression: Generation of diversity of neuroendocrine peptides. *Ann. Rev. Biochem.* 53:665–715
7. Drucker, D. J., Mosjov, S., Habener, J. F. 1986. Cell-specific posttranslational processing of preproglucagon expressed from a metallothionein-glucagon fusion gene. *J. Biol. Chem.* 261:9637–43
8. Garoff, H. 1985. Using recombinant DNA techniques to study protein targeting in the eucaryotic cell. *Ann. Rev. Cell Biol.* 1:403–45
9. Gilboa, E., Eglitis, M. A., Kantoff, P. W., Anderson, W. F. 1986. Transfer and expression of cloned genes using retroviral vectors. *Biotechniques* 4:504–12
10. Gluzman, Y. 1981. SV40-transformed simian cells support the replication of early SV40 mutants. *Cell* 23:175–82
11. Gorman, C. 1985. High efficiency gene transfer into mammalian cells. In *DNA Cloning, Vol. II, A Practical Approach,* ed. D. Rickwood, B. D. Hames, pp. 143–90. Herndon, VA: IRL Press
12. Gorman, C., Padmanabhan, R., Howard, B. H. 1983. High efficiency DNA-mediated transformation of primate cells. *Science* 221:551–53
13. Gorman, C. M., Merlino, G. T., Willingham, M. C., Pastan, I., Howard, B. H. 1982. The Rous sarcoma virus long terminal repeat is a strong promoter when introduced into a variety of eu-

karyotic cells by DNA-mediated transfection. *Proc. Natl. Acad. Sci. USA* 79:6777–81
14. Gruss, P., Khoury, G. 1981. Expression of simian virus 40–rat preproinsulin recombinants in monkey kidney cells: Use of preproinsulin RNA processing signals. *Proc. Natl. Acad. Sci. USA* 78:133–37
15. Hamer, D. H. 1980. DNA cloning in mammalian cells with SV40 vectors. In *Genetic Engineering,* Vol. 2, pp. 83–101, ed. J. K. Setlow, A. Hollander. New York: Plenum
16. Hanahan, D. 1985. Heritable formation of pancreatic β-cell tumors in transgenic mice expressing recombinant insulin/simian virus 40 oncogenes. *Nature* 315:115–22
17. Hellerman, J. G., Cone, R. C., Potts, J. T., Rich, A., Mulligan, R. C., Kronenberg, H. M. 1984. Secretion of human parathyroid hormone from rat pituitary cells infected with a recombinant retrovirus encoding preproparathyroid hormone. *Proc. Natl. Acad. Sci. USA* 81:5340–44
18. Herbert, E., Comb, M., Thomas, G., Liston, D., Civelli, O., et al. 1987. Biosynthesis of ACTH and related peptides. In *Hormonal Proteins and Peptides,* Vol. XIII, pp. 59–87. ed. C. H. Li. New York: Academic
19. Hruby, D. E., Thomas, G. 1987. Use of vaccinia virus to express biopharmaceutical products. *Pharm. Res.* 4:92–97
20. Hruby, D. E., Thomas, G., Herbert, E., Franke, C. 1986. Use of vaccinia virus as a neuropeptide expression vector. *Meth. Enzymol.* 124:295–309
21. Joyner, A., Keller, G., Phillips, R. A., Bernstein, A. 1983. Retrovirus transfer of a bacterial gene into mouse hematopoietic progenitor cells. *Nature* 305:556–58
22. Julius, D., Brake, A., Blair, L., Kunisawa, R., Thorner, J. 1984. Isolation of the putative structural gene for the lysine-arginine-cleaving endopepsidase required for processing of yeast prepro-α-factor. *Cell* 37:1075–89
23. Kelley, R. B. 1985. Pathways of protein secretion in eukaryotes. *Science* 230:25–32
24. Krieger, D. T. 1983. Brain peptides: What, where and why? *Science* 222:975–85
25. Laub, O., Rutter, W. J. 1983. Expression of the human insulin gene and

cDNA in a heterologous mammalian system. *J. Biol. Chem.* 258:6043–50

26. Lindberg, I., Yang, H.-Y. T., Costa, E. 1982. An enkephalin generating enzyme in bovine adrenal medulla. *Biochem. Biophys. Res. Commun.* 106:186–93

27. Loh, P., Brownstein, M. J., Gainer, Y. H. 1984. Proteolysis in neuropeptide processing and other neural functions. *Ann. Rev. Neurosci.* 7:189–222

28. Lomedico, P. T. 1982. Use of recombinant DNA technology to program eucaryotic cells to synthesize rat proinsulin: A rapid expression assay for cloned genes. *Proc. Natl. Acad. Sci. USA* 79:5798–5802

29. Low, M. J., Lechan, R. M., Hammer, R. E., Brinster, R. L., Habener, J. F., et al. 1986. Gonadotroph-specific expression of metallothionein fusion genes in pituitaries of transgenic mice. *Science* 231:1002–4

30. Lynch, D. R., Snyder, S. H. 1986. Neuropeptides: Multiple molecular forms, metabolic pathways, and receptors. *Ann. Rev. Biochem.* 55:773–99

31. Marx, J. 1987. A new wave of enzymes for cleaving prohormones. *Science* 235:285–86

32. Miller, A. D., Ong, E. S., Rosenfeld, M. G., Verma, I. M., Evans, R. M. 1984. Infectious and selectable retrovirus containing an inducible rat growth hormone minigene. *Science* 225:993–98

33. Moore, H.-P. H., Walker, M. D., Lee, F., Kelly, R. B. 1983. Expressing a human proinsulin cDNA in a mouse ACTH-secreting cell. Intracellular storage, proteolytic processing, and secretion on stimulation. *Cell* 35:531–38

33a. Nicaud, J. M., Mackman, N., Holland, I. B. 1986. The current status of secretion of foreign proteins by microorganisms. *J. of Biotech.* 3:255–70

34. Noel, G., Zollinger, L., Lariviere, N., Nault, C., Crine, P., Boileau, G. 1987. Expression of porcine pro-opiomelanocortin cDNA in heterologous monkey kidney cells. *J. Biol. Chem.* 262:1876–81

35. Ornitz, D. M., Palmiter, R. D., Messing, A., Hammer, R. E., Pinkert, C. A.,

Brinster, R. L. 1985. Elastase I promoter directs expression of human growth hormone and SV40 antigen genes to pancreatic acinar cells in transgenic mice. *Cold Spring Harbor Symp. Quant. Biol.* 50:399–409

36. Pavlakis, G. N., Hizuka, N., Gorden, P., Seeburg, P., Hamer, D. H. 1981. Expression of two human growth hormone genes in monkey cells infected by simian virus 40 recombinants. *Proc. Natl. Acad. Sci. USA* 78:7398–7402

37. Rigby, P. W. J. 1982. Expression of cloned genes in eucaryotic cells using vector systems derived from viral replicons. In *Genetic Engineering*, Vol. 3, pp. 83–141, ed. R. Williamson. New York: Academic

38. Sevarino, K. A., Felix, R., Banks, C. M., Low, M. J., Montminy, M. R., et al. 1987. Cell specific processing of preprosomatostatin in cultured neuroendocrine cells. *J. Biol. Chem.* 262:4987–4993

39. Deleted in proof

40. Steiner, D. F., Quinn, P. S., Chan, S. J., Marsh, J., Tager, H. S. 1980. Processing mechanisms in the biosynthesis of proteins. *Ann. NY Acad. Sci.* 343:1–16

41. Thomas, G., Herbert, E., Hruby, D. E. 1986. Expression and cell type-specific processing of human preproenkephalin with a vaccinia recombinant. *Science* 232:1641–43

42. Valls, L. A., Hunter, C. P., Rothman, J. H., Stevens, T. H. 1987. Protein sorting in yeast: The localization determinant of yeast vacuolar carboxypeptidase Y resides in the propeptide. *Cell* 48:887–97

43. Warren, T. G., Shields, D. 1984. Expression of preprosomatostatin in heterologous cells: Biosynthesis, posttranslational processing, and secretion of mature somatostatin. *Cell* 39:547–55

44. Wion, D., Barrand, P., Dicou, E., Scott, J., Brachet, P. 1985. Serum and thyroid hormones T3 and T4 regulate nerve growth factor mRNA levels in mouse L cells. *FEBS Lett.* 189:37–41

Ann. Rev. Physiol. 1988. 50:333–44

# PEPTIDE α-AMIDATION

*Betty A. Eipper and Richard E. Mains*

Department of Neuroscience, The Johns Hopkins University School of Medicine, 725 North Wolfe Street, Baltimore, Maryland 21205

## INTRODUCTION

About half of the bioactive peptides found in the nervous and endocrine systems possess a C-terminal α-amide group ($-X-NH_2$); for most of these peptides, the presence of the α-amide moiety is important to bioactivity (12, 23, 46). Although almost every amino acid has been found to occur as an amino acid α-amide, α-amidated peptides most often terminate with α-amides of neutral amino acids (1, 23). Nervous systems as primitive as that of the sea anemone contain α-amidated peptides (20), which suggests that this modification may be a very early specialization for use of peptides in communication between cells.

By developing a chemical assay for peptides terminating with an amino acid α-amide, Tatemoto & Mutt were able to demonstrate that such peptides occur exclusively in neuronal and endocrine tissues and possess important biological activities. Peptide histidine isoleucine (PHI), peptide tyrosine tyrosine (PYY), neuropeptide Y (NPY), galanin, neuropeptide K, and pancreastatin were each originally identified in this way (46, 47). Newer methods using reversed phase high performance liquid chromatography (RP-HPLC) to separate dansyl or phenylthiocarbamyl amino acid α-amides should be of use in identifying additional novel peptides with C-terminal α-amide groups (4, 43).

The immediate biosynthetic precursors of all peptides with the structure $-X-NH_2$ investigated to date have the sequence -X-Gly. Thus much of the work on the production of α-amidated peptides has focused on the enzymology and cell biology of the conversion of peptides with the structure -X-Gly into peptides of the form $-X-NH_2$.

333

## ENZYMATIC ACTIVITY

### Enzyme Assay

The assay developed by Bradbury, Finnie and Smyth (6, 7) was critical to the study of the production of peptide $\alpha$-amides. They devised a simple substrate ($^{125}$I-D-Tyr-Val-Gly) stable enough to allow assays on crude homogenates and easily separable from its corresponding amidated product ($^{125}$I-D-Tyr-Val-NH$_2$) using small ion-exchange columns. Other assays in current use are variations on this original scheme, with modifications to lower assay background (11, 35), to separate substrate and product more rapidly by organic extraction (32), to label the substrate with other radioactive groups (33), or to identify amidated product by immunoassay without separation from substrate (2, 22). The validity of these assays has been verified by RP-HPLC and mass spectrometry to identify the reaction products (6, 7, 13, 15, 26, 32, 34, 48, 50). Ascorbate- and copper-catalyzed nonenzymatic production of amidated product can occur with certain His-containing substrates but fails to show specificity for -X-Gly substrates and is blocked by the presence of catalase in the reaction (2).

### Purification

Tissues rich in $\alpha$-amidated peptides have been used as starting material for the purification of $\alpha$-amidation activity. In Table 1 the properties of $\alpha$-amidation activity partially or completely purified from bovine, porcine, and murine pituitary and from frog skin and secretion are compared. In every case, $\alpha$-amidation activity was primarily soluble, with a molecular weight of between 35,000 and 65,000. Upon purification the active enzyme was found to consist of a single subunit. Complete purification of $\alpha$-amidation activity from bovine neurointermediate pituitary (35) was accomplished by ammonium sulfate precipitation, ethanol extraction, metal chelate affinity chromatography, peptide substrate affinity chromatography, and gel filtration; a 20,000-fold purification was required. Complete purification of $\alpha$-amidation activity from frog skin (32) was accomplished by ammonium sulfate precipitation, ion-exchange chromatography, and chromatography on Affi-Gel Blue, Sephacryl S-300, hydroxylapatite, high-performance hydroxylapatite, and Superose 12; an 8400-fold purification was required. Both frog skin and bovine pituitary contained multiple forms of $\alpha$-amidation activity differing in charge and molecular weight, with evidence for heterogeneity at the C-terminal end of the protein (32, 35). The $\alpha$-amidation activity in whole porcine pituitary was purified 620-fold by gel filtration and affinity chromatography (22).

### Properties of the Enzymatic Reaction

In every tissue studied, production of $\alpha$-amidated peptide proceeds as follows:

**Table 1**  Properties of enzymatic amidation

| Tissue source | Assay | $M_r$ (kd) | Extent of purification (-fold) | Metal | Role of[a] Cofactor | Oxygen | Optimal pH | $V_{max}$ (nmol/μg/hr) | $K_m$ (μM) | Ref. |
|---|---|---|---|---|---|---|---|---|---|---|
| Pig pituitary secretory granules | cation exchange ($^{125}$I-D-Tyr-Val-Gly → $^{125}$I-D-Tyr-Val-NH$_2$) | 60 | — | Cu$^{2+}$ only | ascorbate, catechol, NE, DA | yes | 7 | — | — | 7 |
| | radioimmunoassay (D-Tyr-Val-Gly → D-Tyr-Val-NH$_2$) | 64 | 620 | Ni$^{2+}$ only | ascorbate, catechol, ferricyanide, dihydroxyfumarate | yes | 7 | 8.1 | 110 | 22 |
| Beef neurointermediate pituitary | cation exchange ($^{125}$I-D-Tyr-Val-Gly → $^{125}$I-D-Tyr-Val-NH$_2$) | 38 (54) | 21000 | Cu$^{2+}$ only | ascorbate | yes | 8.5 | 84 | 7 | 35 |
| Rat anterior pituitary secretory granules | cation exchange ($^{125}$I-D-Tyr-Val-Gly → $^{125}$I-D-Tyr-Val-NH$_2$) | 50 | 64 | Cu$^{2+}$ only | ascorbate | yes | 7 | 0.13 | 40 | 17 |
| Xenopus laevis skin | organic extraction (Ac-$^{125}$I-Tyr-Phe-Gly → Ac-$^{125}$I-Tyr-Phe-NH$_2$) | 39 (34) | 8400 | Cu$^{2+}$ | ascorbate | — | 6.5 | 1.9 | 0.35 | 32 |
| | cation exchange ($^{125}$I-D-Tyr-Val-Gly → $^{125}$I-D-Tyr-Val-NH$_2$) | 40 | — | Cu$^{2+}$ only | ascorbate | yes | 7 | 0.013 | 60 | 44 |
| secretion | high voltage paper electrophoresis ($^{14}$C-succ-Ala-Phe-Gly → $^{14}$C-succ-Ala-Phe-NH$_2$) | — | 150 | Mn$^{2+}$, Fe$^{3+}$, Cu$^{2+}$ | ascorbate, BH$_4$; pH-dependent | — | — | — | — | 33 |

[a] metal: cations that restore activity after chelation by EDTA, diethyldithiocarbamate, 1,10-phenanthroline; cofactor: major stimulatory reducing agents; NE = norepinephrine; DA = dopamine; oxygen: reaction block by oxygen deprivation or stimulation by pure oxygen atmosphere.

-X-Gly + $O_2$ + ascorbate $\rightarrow$ -X-$NH_2$ + glyoxylate
+ dehydroascorbate + $H_2O$

Bradbury et al (6) prepared substrate containing $^{15}N$-Gly and demonstrated that the $\alpha$-amide nitrogen was derived from the $\alpha$-amino group of glycine. Production of glyoxylate as a reaction product was demonstrated by using substrate containing $^{14}C$-Gly (7) and by RP-HPLC identification of the glyoxylate produced in the reaction (A. S. N. Murthy & B. A. Eipper, unpublished). The reaction in mammalian extracts, frog skin extracts, and with purified pituitary enzyme is blocked by removal of oxygen and stimulated by pure $O_2$ (7, 11, 13, 15, 17, 26, 34–36, 44, 50).

The reaction is stimulated by the presence of a reduced cofactor, and ascorbic acid has usually been found to be the optimal cofactor; as for other ascorbate-catalyzed reactions, catalase must be present during the assay to prevent enzyme inactivation (11, 24, 35). Even with highly purified enzyme, the reaction is not absolutely dependent on exogenous cofactor (32–35, 40). For the purified bovine pituitary enzyme, the amount of ascorbate consumed in the reaction is nearly equimolar with the amount of amidated peptide produced (34); the ascorbate consumed may be oxidized to dehydroascorbate or semidehydroascorbate, as is the case for dopamine $\beta$-hydroxylase (3, 31). As for other ascorbate-stimulated enzymes (24), other reductants will also stimulate the reaction, notably catecholamines (7, 22, 34), tetrahydrobiopterin (33, 34), and $Fe(CN)_6^{4-}$ (22). The ability of other cofactors to substitute for ascorbate is dependent on the assay conditions (33, 34). The properties outlined above have led to the designation of this enzyme as *p*eptidyl-glycine $\alpha$-*a*midating *m*onooxygenase or PAM.

The pH optima of the various enzymes studied range from 5.5 to 8.5 and are dependent on the amino acid at the penultimate position. The presence of a basic residue preceding the C-terminal Gly raises the pH optimum; the presence of an acidic residue lowers the pH optimum (7, 34).

The reaction is blocked by divalent metal ion chelators such as EDTA, 1,10-phenanthroline and diethyldithiocarbamate. The vast majority of reports have shown that cupric ion is the only cation capable of restoring full enzymatic activity (7, 11, 13, 15, 17, 26, 32, 34–36, 40, 44, 48–50), but there are conflicting reports on the same tissues that $Ni^{2+}$, $Co^{2+}$, $Mn^{2+}$, or $Fe^{3+}$ restore activity (22, 33).

The specificity of the enzyme for the C-terminal Gly is quite strict (7). The reaction does not proceed when the C-terminal Gly is replaced by L-Lys, L-Glu, L-Leu, L-Ala, D-Ser, or D-Leu. The reaction proceeds at a reduced rate with D-Ala at the C-terminus, which indicates that the orientation of the substituent attached to the $\alpha$-carbon of the terminal residue is important and that only one of the two $\alpha$-carbon hydrogen bonds is involved in the amidation reaction (7). A primary isotope effect greater than five was demonstrated when the α-hydrogens of Gly were replaced by deuterium, which implies that cleavage of the carbon-hydrogen bond is rate limiting (22). The reaction does not proceed with D-Tyr-Val-Gly-Lys or D-Tyr-Val-$N$-methyl-Gly as substrate (7).

The $K_m$ of the purified bovine enzyme for tripeptide substrates of the type D-Tyr-X-Gly increased in the order X = Trp < Val < Pro << Glu (34). Although highly purified preparations of PAM may consist of a group of closely related enzymes, PAM that was affinity purified by binding to a D-Tyr-Trp-Gly substrate column still catalyzed the amidation of each of the above tripeptides (34). Increasing levels of ascorbate brought about parallel increases in $K_m$ and $V_{max}$, which suggests the presence of an irreversible step separating the interaction of the enzyme with the two substrates (22, 34). With the use of radioactive and nonradioactive monoiodinated substrate, the enzymatic activity has been repeatedly demonstrated to have the same Michaelis constants for unmodified and monoiodinated substrates of the form D-Tyr-X-Gly (17, 26, 35, 48, 50). With approximately 0.25 mM ascorbate, the $K_m$ valves of the purified frog skin, bovine pituitary and porcine pituitary enzymes for peptide substrates of the Tyr-(Val or Phe)-Gly type were 0.35 $\mu$M (32), 1.8 $\mu$M (35), and 40 $\mu$M (22), respectively. The α-amidation of larger natural substrates, such as α-$N$-acetyl-adrenocorticotropin(1–14) and calcitoninyl-Gly, by PAM can be demonstrated as long as the enzyme has been purified adequately to remove contaminating proteolytic activities (7, 17).

PAM and dopamine β-hydroxylase exhibit striking similarities. Both are associated with secretory granules, exhibit ping-pong kinetics, and require copper, ascorbate, and molecular oxygen. Both appear to use reducing equivalents transferred into granules by cytochrome $b_{561}$ (3, 9, 31). The tissue distribution of the two enzymes is different (9, 13, 39, 40). Soluble PAM is a monomer, whereas dopamine β-hydroxylase occurs as a tetramer in both soluble and membrane-bound forms. With the substrate D-Tyr-Glu-Gly, the turnover number for bovine PAM is 1250 per min (34); turnover numbers for pure dopamine β-hydroxylase are in the range of 800–2000 per min (39, 41). A comparison of the DNA encoding the two enzymes, when available, should prove informative.

## PHYSIOLOGY OF PEPTIDE α-AMIDATION

### Tissue Localization

As expected from the widespread distribution of α-amidated bioactive peptides, α-amidation activity has been found in many mammalian tissues. In each of these tissues α-amidation activity exhibits similar properties (requirement for molecular oxygen and copper, stimulation by ascorbate) and thus is referred to here as PAM. Assay of PAM activity in the soluble fraction of tissue homogenates is facilitated by inclusion of $N$-ethylmaleimide in the homogenization buffer and by ammonium sulfate precipitation (22, 40). High levels of soluble PAM activity were found in the anterior, intermediate, and neural lobes of the pituitary and in the hypothalamus, submaxillary and parotid glands, and heart atrium. PAM activity at 1–10% of the pituitary level was found in the thyroid, gastrointestinal tract, and cerebral cortex. PAM activity at <1% of the pituitary value was measured in cerebellum, liver, kidney, skeletal muscle, pancreas, adrenal, lung, spleen, thymus ovaries, testes, adipose, and ventricles (7, 11, 13, 15, 36, 40, 50). When the mass of each tissue is taken into account, it is apparent that gastrointestinal tissue, submaxillary gland, and the central nervous system are major sources of PAM. Substantial levels of PAM are also found in tumors that produce $\alpha$-amidated peptides, such as medullary thyroid carcinomas and pheochromocytomas (50). Frog skin homogenates contained levels of PAM activity of ~15% of those in crude pituitary homogenates (32, 44). PAM activity is easily measured in plasma and cerebrospinal fluid, in secretions from frog skin, and in spent medium from mammalian pituitary cells in culture (26, 44, 49, 50).

## Subcellular Localization

PAM activity has been localized to secretory granules in many neural and endocrine tissues, including pituitary, hypothalamus, parotid gland, neonatal pancreas, and corticotropic tumor cells in culture (7, 11, 15, 17, 22, 26, 35, 36, 48). When rat intermediate pituitary homogenates were fractionated on Percoll gradients, the bulk of the PAM activity migrated with the secretory granule fraction, along with pro-ACTH/endorphin-related peptides (Figure 1). Localization of PAM activity to secretory granules is consistent with the observations of Tatemoto & Mutt on the unique association of $\alpha$-amidated peptides with neuronal and endocrine tissues. In contrast, high levels of $\alpha$-$N$-acetyltransferase activity, another enzyme activity involved in the posttranslational processing of pro-ACTH/endorphin, were found in several regions of the gradient.

## Secretion of PAM Activity

The localization of PAM activity to the soluble fraction of secretory granule lysates is consistent with the presence of PAM activity in plasma, cerebrospinal fluid, secretions from frog skin, and spent culture medium from pituitary corticotropes (13, 26, 27, 33, 44, 49, 50). Studies of corticotropin releasing factor (CRF) or $Ba^{2+}$ plus cAMP-stimulated corticotropic tumor cells and isoproterenol-stimulated parotid secretion demonstrated parallel

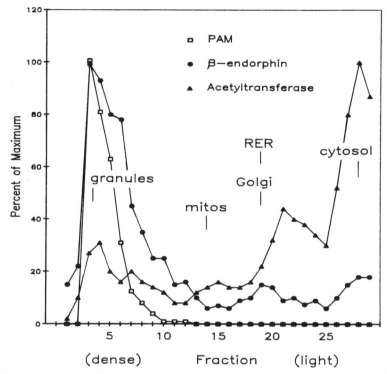

*Figure 1*  Percoll gradient fractionation of rat intermediate pituitary. Rat neurointermediate pituitaries were homogenized in isotonic sucrose buffer and applied to a Percoll density gradient. Fractions were collected from the bottom and assayed for PAM and β-endorphin (11), α-N-acetyltransferase, and marker enzymes (16). Data from the separate analyses were normalized and plotted together.

secretion of PAM activity and other primarily soluble contents of the secretory granules (26, 48). Injection of norepinephrine into the dorsal lymph sac of *Xenopus* stimulated parallel secretion of PAM activity and thyrotropin releasing hormone (TRH) immunoactivity (44).

The level of PAM activity in plasma was not responsive to hypophysectomy, sialectomy, castration, or a number of other surgical manipulations which might have been expected to remove sources of circulating PAM activity. Plasma PAM activity was elevated after thyroidectomy (27), in hypothyroid patients (50), and in patients bearing peptide-secreting tumors (50). Pharmacological blockade of most sympathetic and parasympathetic nervous activity decreased serum PAM activity slightly (27), but the major sources of circulating PAM activity are not yet known. PAM activity in cerebrospinal fluid declined with the progression of Alzheimer's disease, and tissue levels of PAM activity were decreased most in brain regions most severely affected by the dementia (49).

## Ascorbate and Peptide α-Amidation

Early studies on the biosynthesis of pancreatic polypeptide by cultured islet cells indicated rapid loss of ability to α-amidate newly synthesized peptide (37). Subsequent studies on cultured intermediate pituitary melanotropes, hypothalamic neurons, and antral mucosal G cells also demonstrated a declining ability of cultured cells to produce α-amidated products (19, 30, 45). Cells in culture lose ascorbate rapidly, and addition of plasma levels of ascorbate to the culture medium for pituitary, hypothalamic, and antral G cells stimulated α-amidation of product peptides (14, 18, 19, 28, 30, 45). As with purified PAM, ascorbate was not the only cofactor that increased cellular α-amidation of peptides. For example, production of α-amidated peptides by AtT-20 cells was increased when catecholamines, tetrahydrobiopterin, or dehydroascorbate was included in the medium (14). The degree of dependence of peptide α-amidation on ascorbate is tissue specific; the α-amidation of calcitonin, amidorphin, and metorphamide apparently proceeds in the absence of ascorbate and is unaffected by the addition of ascorbate (5, 25). Cultured AtT-20 cells produce α-amidated peptides in the absence of ascorbate, although the extent of amidation is increased upon addition of ascorbate to the medium (14). Scorbutic guinea pigs showed a loss in α-amidation of gastrin when severely deprived of ascorbate (21), although no change in the extent of α-amidation of pituitary peptides was seen when weight loss was minimal (27).

The usual plasma level of ascorbate is $\sim 50$ $\mu$M. Ascorbate is synthesized only in the liver in those animals that can synthesize ascorbate; humans and guinea pigs are among the few species incapable of ascorbate synthesis (24). Ascorbate-dependent peptide-producing cells must take up ascorbate from plasma and transfer the reducing equivalents to the interior of the secretory granule. Pituitary cells and chromaffin cells concentrate ascorbate 20- to 50-fold over plasma levels to achieve millimolar levels (8, 14, 24, 42). Ascorbate uptake has a $K_m$ at or below the plasma concentration of ascorbate and is a saturable process that is sodium dependent and glucose independent (8, 24, 42). It takes many hours for ascorbate uptake into the cytoplasm to reach completion (8, 42). Although secretory granules in many tissues contain a high concentration of ascorbate, it has not been possible to measure direct uptake of ascorbate into the granules, and the route by which ascorbate gains entry into granules is not clear (3, 8, 18, 24, 30, 31, 42). In the case of dopamine $\beta$-hydroxylase, cytoplasmic ascorbate exchanges reducing equivalents with the lumen of the secretory granule via a cytochrome $b_{561}$ activity; cytoplasmic ascorbate could support PAM activity in a similar fashion (3, 9, 24, 31).

## Copper and Peptide $\alpha$-Amidation

In studies to determine the role of copper ions in peptide $\alpha$-amidation in vivo, chronic dietary copper deficiency in adult rats resulted in increased PAM activity in homogenates of anterior pituitary and submaxillary gland and unchanged levels of PAM activity in hypothalamus and neurointermediate pituitary (27). Treatment of adult rats with the relatively selective copper chelator $N,N$-diethyldithiocarbamate or its disulfide dimer, disulfiram (Antabuse), resulted in a dose- and time-dependent decrease in the ability of the anterior and intermediate pituitary to produce $\alpha$-amidated peptides (28). Doses of disulfiram equivalent to those used in humans for alcohol abuse therapy brought about an accumulation of glycine-extended peptides in the pituitary. Diethyldithiocarbamate and disulfiram also blocked the ability of cells in culture to synthesize $\alpha$-amidated peptides (28).

## Glycine-Extended Peptides and the Synthesis of $\alpha$-Amidated Peptides

Peptides with C-terminal glycine residues are the immediate biosynthetic precursors to $\alpha$-amidated peptides in tissues. Studies on the biosynthesis of joining peptide, cholecystokinin, and gastrin have demonstrated that $\alpha$-amidation at the carboxyl terminus can precede or follow removal of N-terminal extensions, with the extent of $\alpha$-amidation increasing in the lower molecular weight products (14, 29, 38). Pituitary and hypothalamic cells in culture when deprived of ascorbate synthesize primarily Gly-extended forms of $\alpha$-melanotropin ($\alpha$-MSH), joining peptide, and TRH (14, 18, 19, 30); extended incubations in nonradioactive medium do not result in detectable $\alpha$-amidation of radiolabeled Gly-extended peptides. Gly-extended peptides can also be final products; Gly-extended forms of gastrin, cholecystokinin, calcitonin, and TRH are found in significant amounts in tissue extracts from normal animals and circulate in plasma (29, 38). In the endocrine pancreas of the anglerfish, a glucagonlike peptide and a NPY/PYY-like peptide occur primarily in Gly-extended forms (1). The mixture of $\alpha$-amidated and Gly-extended peptides secreted from a tissue mirrors their ratio in the secretory granules of that tissue (14, 45). The role of the Gly-extended peptides in plasma is not clear, since Gly-extended forms of peptides that are $\alpha$-amidated usually have <1% of the biological potency of the $\alpha$-amidated peptide and conversion in plasma has not been demonstrated (12, 23, 29, 38, 45).

## Regulation of PAM Activity

In tissues producing pro-ACTH/endorphin-related peptides, levels of PAM activity and production of pro-ACTH/endorphin change in parallel. In corticotropic tumor cells, the dose-dependent suppression of pro-ACTH/

endorphin synthesis by glucocorticoids was accompanied by a parallel decline in PAM activity; levels of another secretory granule associated enzyme, carboxypeptidase E, were unaltered (26). In the intermediate pituitary of rats, production of pro-ACTH/endorphin and levels of PAM activity were stimulated by administration of dopamine blockers such as haloperidol and suppressed by dopamine agonists such as bromocriptine (27). In the pancreas of the rat, levels of PAM activity and TRH immunoactivity showed dramatic and parallel changes during development (36). Treatment of cultured adrenal medullary cells with reserpine led to increased generation of all low–molecular weight enkephalins and, in particular, to a substantial increase in levels of amidorphin and metorphamide, two $\alpha$-amidated peptides produced from proenkephalin (10, 25). In contrast, elevation of proenkephalin synthesis by exposure to high $K^+$ resulted in parallel increases in enkephalin and metorphamide (10). Since the $\alpha$-amidated opiate peptides and the enkephalins differ in their receptor specificity, the ability to regulate their ratio would have physiological significance.

## FUTURE APPROACHES TO THE STUDY OF PEPTIDE AMIDATION

Current efforts are directed at developing the tools required to study regulation of PAM activity by concomitant measurement of mRNA, protein, and activity levels. Utilizing rabbit antibodies to PAM purified from bovine pituitary to screen a bovine intermediate pituitary cDNA expression library in $\gamma$gtll bacteriophage, cDNAs encoding a precursor to PAM have been cloned and sequenced. The 972 amino acid precursor contains an N-terminal signal sequence, a short propeptide, sequences corresponding to active PAM, a lengthy intragranular domain and putative membrane spanning and cytoplasmic domains (14A). The precursor structure is punctuated by 10 pairs of basic amino acids that appear to undergo tissue specific processing (V. May and E. I. Cullen, unpublished observations). Additional $\alpha$-amidated peptides surely await discovery. Exploration of the similarities of PAM, a key enzyme in peptide biosynthesis, and dopamine $\beta$-hydroxylase, a key enzyme in catecholamine biosynthesis, will be facilitated by cloning of the relevant cDNAs and will require a better understanding of cellular handling of ascorbate and copper.

Acknowledgments

This work was supported by grants DA 00097, DA 00098, and DA 00266 from the National Institute on Drug Abuse and by grants DK 32949 and DK 32948 from the National Institutes of Health.

## Literature Cited

1. Andrews, P. C., Hawke, D. H., Lee, T. D., Legesse, K., Noe, B. D., Shively, J. E. 1986. Isolation and structure of the principal products of preproglucagon processing, including an amidated glucagon-like peptide. *J. Biol. Chem.* 261:8128–33

2. Bateman, R. C. Jr., Youngblood, W. W., Busby, W. H. Jr., Kizer, J. S. 1985. Nonenzymatic peptide α-amidation. *J. Biol. Chem.* 260:9088–91

3. Beers, M. F., Johnson, R. G., Scarpa, A. 1986. Evidence for an ascorbate shuttle for the transfer of reducing equivalents across chromaffin granule membranes. *J. Biol. Chem.* 261:2529–35

4. Bennett, H. P. J., Solomon, S. 1986. Use of pico-tag methodology in the chemical analysis of peptides with carboxyl-terminal amides. *J. Chromatogr.* 359:221–30

5. Birnbaum, R. S., Mahoney, W. C., Roos, B. A. 1986. Biosynthesis of calcitonin by a rat medullary thyroid carcinoma cell line. *J. Biol. Chem.* 261:699–703

6. Bradbury, A. F., Finnie, M. D. A., Smyth, D. G. 1982. Mechanism of C-terminal amide formation by pituitary enzymes. *Nature* 298:686–88

7. Bradbury, A. F., Smyth, D. G. 1985. C-terminal amide formation in peptide hormones. In *Biogenetics of Neurohormonal Peptides*, ed. R. Hakanson, J. Thorell, pp. 171–86. London: Academic

8. Cullen, E. I., May, V., Eipper, B. A. 1986. Transport and stability of ascorbic acid in pituitary cultures. *Mol. Cell. Endocrinol.* 48:239–50

9. Duong, L. T., Fleming, P. J., Russell, J. T. 1984. An identical cytochrome $b_{561}$ is present in bovine adrenal chromaffin vesicles and posterior pituitary neurosecretory vesicles. *J. Biol. Chem.* 259:4885–89

10. Eiden, L. E., Zamir, N. 1986. Metorphamide levels in chromaffin cells increase after treatment with reserpine. *J. Neurochem.* 46:1651–54

11. Eipper, B. A., Mains, R. E., Glembotski, C. C. 1983. Identification in pituitary tissue of a peptide α-amidation activity that acts on glycine-extended peptides and requires molecular oxygen, copper, and ascorbic acid. *Proc. Natl. Acad. Sci. USA* 80:5144–48

12. Eipper, B. A., Mains, R. E., Herbert, E. 1986. Peptides in the nervous system. *Trends Neurosci.* 9:463–68

13. Eipper, B. A., Myers, A. C., Mains, R. E. 1985. Peptidyl-glycine α-amidation activity in tissues and serum of the adult rat. *Endocrinology* 116:2497–2504

14. Eipper, B. A., Park, L. P., Keutmann, H. T., Mains, R. E. 1986. Amidation of joining peptide, a major pro-ACTH/endorphin-derived product peptide. *J. Biol. Chem.* 261:8686–94

14a. Eipper, B. A., Park, L. P., Dickerson, I. M., Keutmann, H. T., Thiele, E. A., Rodriquez, H., Schofield, P. R., Mains, R. E. 1987 Structure of the precursor to an enzyme mediating COOH-terminal amidation in peptide biosynthesis. *Mol. Endocrinol.* 1:777–90

15. Emeson, R. B. 1984. Hypothalamic peptidyl-glycine α-amidating monooxygenase. *J. Neuroscience* 4:2604–13

16. Glembotski, C. C. 1982. Characterization of the peptide acetyltransferase activity in bovine and rat intermediate pituitaries. *J. Biol. Chem.* 257:10501–9

17. Glembotski, C. C. 1985. Further characterization of the peptidyl α-amidating enzyme in rat anterior pituitary secretory granules. *Arch. Biochem. Biophys.* 241:673–83

18. Glembotski, C. C. 1986. Characterization of the ascorbic acid–mediated alpha-amidation of alpha-melanotropin in cultured intermediate pituitary lobe cells. *Endocrinology* 118:1461–68

19. Glembotski, C. C., Manaker, S., Winokur, A., Gibson, T. R. 1986. Ascorbic acid increases the TRH content of hypothalamic cell cultures. *J. Neurosci.* 1796–1802

20. Grimmelikhuijzen, C. J. P., Graff, D. 1986. Isolation of <Glu-Gly-Arg-Phe-$NH_2$ (Antho-RFamide), a neuropeptide from sea anemones. *Proc. Natl. Acad. Sci. USA* 83:9817–21

21. Hilsted, L., Rehfeld, J. F., Schwartz, T. W. 1986. Impaired alpha-carboxyamidation of gastrin in vitamin C–deficient guinea pigs. *FEBS Lett.* 196:151–54

22. Kizer, J. S., Bateman, R. C. Jr., Miller, C. R., Humm, J., Busby, W. H. Jr. 1986. Purification and characterization of a peptidyl glycine monooxygenase from porcine pituitary. *Endocrinology* 118:2262–67

23. Kreil, G. 1985. Late reactions in the processing of peptide precursors: Stepwise cleavage of dipeptides and formation of terminal amides. In *The Enzymology of Post-Translational Modification of Proteins*, Vol. 2, pp. 41–51. London: Academic

24. Levine, M. 1986. New concepts in the biology and biochemistry of ascorbic acid. *N. Engl. J. Med.* 314:892–902

25. Lindberg, I. 1986. Reserpine-induced alterations in processing of pro-

enkephalin in cultured chromaffin cells. *J. Biol. Chem.* 261:16317–22

26. Mains, R. E., Eipper, B. A. 1984. Secretion and regulation of two biosynthetic enzyme activities, peptidylglycine α-amidating monooxygenase and a carboxypeptidase, by mouse pituitary corticotropic tumor cells. *Endocrinology* 115:1683–90

27. Mains, R. E., Myers, A. C., Eipper, B. A. 1985. Hormonal, drug, and dietary factors affecting peptidyl glycine α-amidating monooxygenase activity in various tissues of the rat. *Endocrinology* 116:2505–15

28. Mains, R. E., Park, L. P., Eipper, B. A. 1986. Inhibition of peptide amidation by disulfiram and diethyldithiocarbamate. *J. Biol. Chem.* 261:11938–41

29. Matsumoto, M., Park, J., Sugano, K., Yamada, T. 1987. Biological activity of progastrin post-translational processing intermediates. *Am. J. Physiol.* 252:315–19

30. May, V., Eipper, B. A. 1985. Regulation of peptide amidation in cultured pituitary cells. *J. Biol. Chem.* 260:16224–31

31. Menniti, F. S., Knoth, J., Diliberto, E. J. Jr. 1986. Role of ascorbic acid in dopamine β-hydroxylation. *J. Biol. Chem.* 261:16901–8

32. Mizuno, K., Sakata, J., Kojima, M., Kangawa, K., Matsuo, H. 1986. Peptide C-terminal α-amidating enzyme purified to homogeneity from *Xenopus laevis* skin. *Biochem. Biophys. Res. Commun.* 137:984–91

33. Mollay, C., Wichta, J., Kreil, G. 1986. Detection and partial characterization of an amidating enzyme in skin secretion of *Xenopus laevis. FEBS Lett.* 202:251–54

34. Murthy, A. S. N., Keutmann, H. T., Eipper, B. A. 1987. Further characterization of peptidylglycine α-amidating monooxygenase from bovine neurointermediate pituitary. *Mol. Endocrinol.* 1:290–99

35. Murthy, A. S. N., Mains, R. E., Eipper, B. A. 1986. Purification and characterization of peptidylglycine α-amidating monooxygenase from bovine neurointermediate pituitary. *J. Biol. Chem.* 261:1815–22

36. Ouafik, L., Giraud, P., Salers, P., Dutour, A., Castanas, E., et al. 1987. Evidence for high peptide α-amidating activity in neonatal rat pancreas. *Proc. Natl. Acad. Sci. USA* 84:261–64

37. Paquette, T. L., Gingerich, R., Scharp, D. 1981. Altered amidation of pancreatic polypeptide in cultured islet. *Biochemistry* 20:7403–8

38. Rehfeld, J. F., Hansen, H. F. 1986. Characterization of preprocholecystokinin products in porcine cerebral cortex. *J. Biol. Chem.* 261:5832–40

39. Rosenberg, R. C., Lovenberg, W. 1980. Dopamine β-hydroxylase. *Essays Neurochem. Neuropharmacol.* 4:163–209

40. Sakata, J., Mizuna, K., Matsuo, H. 1986. Tissue distribution and characterization of peptide C-terminal α-amidating activity in rat. *Biochem. Biophys. Res. Commun.* 140:230–36

41. Saxena, A., Hensley, P., Osborne, J. C. Jr., Fleming, P. J. 1985. The pH-dependent subunit dissociation and catalytic activity of bovine dopamine β-hydroxylase. *J. Biol. Chem.* 260:3386–92

42. Shields, P. P., Gibson, T. R., Glembotski, C. C. 1986. Ascorbate transport by AtT-20 mouse pituitary tumor cells. *Endocrinology* 118:1452–60

43. Simmons, W. H., Meisenberg, G. 1983. Separation of Dns-amino acid amides: High-performance liquid chromatography. *J. Chromatogr.* 266:483–89

44. Spindel, E. R., Eipper, B. A., Zilberberg, M. D., Mains, R. E., Chin, W. W. 1987. Caerulein mRNA and peptide α-amidation activity in the skin of *Xenopus laevis*: Stimulation by norepinephine. *Gen. Comp. Endocrinol.* 67:67–76

45. Sugano, K., Park, J., Dobbins, W. O., Yamada, T. 1987. Glycine-extended progastrin processing intermediates: Accumulation in cultured G-cells and cosecretion with gastrin. *Am. J. Physiol.* 253:G502–7

46. Tatemoto, K., Efendic, S., Mutt, V., Makk, G., Feistner, G. J., Barchas, J. D. 1986. Pancreastatin, a novel pancreatic peptide that inhibits insulin secretion. *Nature* 234:476–78

47. Tatemoto, K., Mutt, V. 1978. Chemical determination of polypeptide hormones. *Proc. Natl. Acad. Sci. USA* 75:4115–19

48. Von Zastrow, M., Tritton, T. R., Castle, J. D. 1986. Exocrine secretion granules contain peptide amidation activity. *Proc. Natl. Acad. Sci. USA* 83:3297–3301

49. Wand, G. S., May, C., May, V., Whitehouse, P. J., Rapaport, S. I., Eipper, B. A. 1987. Alzheimer's disease: low levels of peptide alpha-amidation activity in brain and CSF. *Neurology* 37:1057–61

50. Wand, G. S., Ney, R. L., Baylin, S., Eipper, B. A., Mains, R. E. 1985. Characterization of a peptide alpha-amidation activity in human plasma and tissues. *Metabolism* 34:1044–52

Ann. Rev. Physiol. 1988. 50:345–62

# ENZYMES REQUIRED FOR YEAST PROHORMONE PROCESSING

*Robert S. Fuller, Rachel E. Sterne, and Jeremy Thorner*

Department of Biochemistry, University of California, Berkeley, California 94720

## INTRODUCTION

In this review we discuss proteolytic processing of precursors to secreted peptides in the unicellular eukaryote *Saccharomyces cerevisiae* (baker's yeast, hereafter, "yeast"), with the aim of illuminating the similar pathways that occur in animal cells. The attractive feature of yeast as an experimental system has been the ability to identify processing enzymes unambiguously by a combination of genetic and biochemical criteria.

General aspects of yeast secretion and cell biology are not considered. Recent reviews are available for: secretion and protein localization (61), glycosylation (3), proteolysis (1, 33), mating physiology (39, 66), and the killer system (71, 81, 86).

## BIOLOGY OF SECRETED PEPTIDES OF *SACCHAROMYCES CEREVISIAE*

### Mating Pheromones

Yeast can exist as one of two haploid cell types, **a** and $\alpha$, which can mate to form an **a**/$\alpha$ diploid. Mating is triggered by the action of secreted oligopeptide pheromones, **a**-factor (produced by **a** haploids) and $\alpha$-factor (produced by $\alpha$ haploids). Cell surface receptors that are specific for the peptide produced by cells of the opposite mating type mediate response to pheromones. Binding of pheromones to their receptors elicits changes in gene expression, in cell physiology, and in cell wall architecture that are required for the mating process.

345

0066-4278/88/0315-0345$02.00

## Killer Toxin

Yeast strains can harbor cytoplasmic double-stranded RNA (dsRNA) molecules, encapsidated in viruslike particles, that encode both a polypeptide toxin and an immunity function (71, 81). The best-studied dsRNA, $M_1$ [1.9 kilobases (kb)], is dependent for its maintenance both on nuclear genes and on another dsRNA, L (4.5 kb). The toxin itself is a disulfide-linked two-chain molecule (like insulin) that kills sensitive cells (other yeast) in two stages: First the toxin binds to a cell wall receptor, probably 1, 6-$\beta$-D-glucan; subsequently it binds to a receptor in the plasma membrane where it forms a channel that discharges the transmembrane proton gradient (81).

# PRECURSOR GENES, PRECURSOR STRUCTURES, AND PATHWAYS OF PROCESSING

## α-Factor

GENES ENCODING α-FACTOR PRECURSORS    Two genes, *MFα1* and *MFα2*, encode closely related α-factor precursors (44, 62). *MFα1* produces the majority of the α-factor secreted (14, 43). The precursors have the following features: (*a*) a pre-region consisting of an *N*-terminal hydrophobic leader that is a signal sequence, (*b*) a pro-segment comprised of a hydrophilic domain containing three consensus sites for addition of Asn-linked carbohydrate (Asn-X-Ser/Thr), and (*c*) a C-terminal region consisting of repeats of the mature α-factor sequence [13 residues (70)] that are separated from the prepro region and from one another by "spacer" segments (Figure 1). The genes differ primarily in the number of α-factor and spacer repeats: *MFα1* has four and *MFα2* has two. Each spacer begins with a pair of basic residues (-Lys-Arg-) and is followed by two or three dipeptides of the form -X-Ala- [where X is Asp or Glu in *MFα1* and Asp, Glu, Asn, or Val in *MFα2*)].

PATHWAY OF BIOSYNTHESIS OF α -FACTOR    Prepro-α-factor (ppαF) is 165 amino acids long and is glycosylated upon entry into the endoplasmic reticulum (ER) by the addition of three *N*-linked core oligosaccharides (19, 23, 36) (Figure 1). In contrast to earlier results based on electrophoretic mobility of unglycosylated precursor from tunicamycin-treated cells (36) or of enzymically deglycosylated precursor generated after mRNA translation and microsome translocation in vitro (14, 31, 36, 58, 84), direct *N*-terminal sequencing of precursor recovered from *sec18$^{ts}$* mutants (blocked in transport from ER to Golgi) (61) indicates that the hydrophobic leader is cleaved by signal peptidase after $Ala_{19}$ (84a).

Upon translocation to the Golgi, a fraction of the ppαF undergoes extensive elongation of the core oligosaccharides (35, 36). No proteolytic processing of ppαF occurs in cells with a mutation in the *KEX2* gene (35); *kex2* mutations

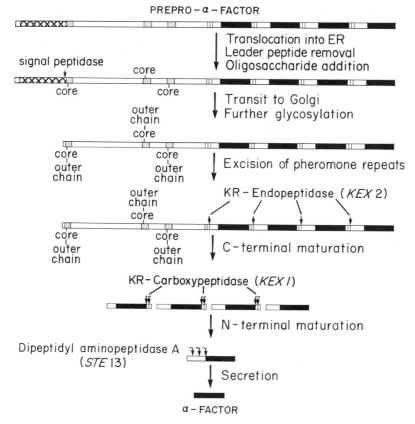

*Figure 1*  Pathway of post-translational processing of prepro-α-factor precursor in yeast. Biosynthesis and processing of prepro-α-factor has been elucidated by biochemical and immunochemical identification of processing intermediates (34–36) and by analysis of the individual processing enzymes and their genes (20, 28, 29, 34, 35). See text for further details.

also prevent production of killer toxin (46, 87). In *sec7^ts* mutants (blocked in transport from Golgi to secretory vesicles), proteolytic cleavage of some ppαF to mature α-factor is found (36). In *sec1^ts* mutants (blocked in fusion of secretory vesicles with the plasma membrane), processing to mature α-factor is virtually complete (36). Thus, proteolytic processing of ppαF likely occurs in a late Golgi compartment, although the "leakiness" of *sec7* mutations (68) leaves open the possibility that processing occurs during formation of secretory vesicles.

Maturation of ppαF by endoproteolytic cleavage at the carboxyl side of the -Lys-Arg- residues is inferred from the absence of processing in *kex2* mutants and from the enzymatic properties of the *KEX2*-encoded protease (see below)

(2, 29, 35). Such cleavage releases peptides slightly larger than $\alpha$-factor that must undergo exoproteolytic processing of two types. Cells carrying a mutation in the *STE13* gene secrete $\alpha$-factor-related peptides that contain remnants of the X-Ala spacer at their *N*-terminal end (34) and are similar in structure to honeybee promellitin (42). Three of the $\alpha$-factor repeat units should also contain C-terminal -Lys-Arg residues. Removal of these residues is blocked in *kex1* mutants (20; see below).

Transit time of intact pp$\alpha$F through the secretory pathway is rapid, $t_{1/2} \leq 4$ min (35), which suggests that secretion occurs by a constitutive pathway rather than by storage in secretory granules and release through a regulated pathway (38).

## a-*Factor*

GENES ENCODING a-FACTOR PRECURSORS    The a-factor secreted by *S. cerevisiae MAT*a cells is a 12-residue peptide that also carries a lipophilic substituent (7, 28). Two genes (*MF* a*1* and *MF* a*2*) encode precursors to a-factor of 36 and 38 amino acids, respectively (13). Each precursor contains only one copy of mature a-factor. These precursors are unusual in that they are extremely short, do not contain a signal sequence (82), and lack sites for *N*-linked glycosylation. Furthermore, secretion of a-factor is much slower than export of other yeast peptides ($\alpha$-factor and killer toxin) and occurs even in temperature-sensitive secretion-defective *sec* mutants (61) at the nonpermissive temperature (28, 67a). These observations indicate that a-factor is processed and exported via a route distinct from the secretory pathway used by pp$\alpha$F (36) and other secreted proteins in yeast (61).

PATHWAY OF BIOSYNTHESIS OF a-FACTOR    Both *N*- and C-terminal proteolytic processing are required to release the 12-residue a-factor segment from its precursor. Several lines of evidence indicate that production of mature a-factor also requires posttranslational covalent modification of the peptide. Synthetic peptides matching the sequence of purified authentic a-factor (6, 7, 13) have little or no biological activity (28, 52, 67a). Treatment of purified native a-factor either with alkaline $NH_2OH$ or with $CH_3I$ + 2-mercaptoethanol eliminates biological activity (R. Sterne and J. Thorner, unpublished results) and converts the molecule to a distinctly less hydrophobic species (6), which suggests that the C-terminal Cys residue of the peptide is linked to an as yet uncharacterized aliphatic moiety. One candidate for such a hydrophobic substituent is the farnesyl group that is thioether-linked to the C-terminal Cys in the peptide pheromones of heterobasidiomycetous yeasts (37).

With respect to the presence of a lipophilic modification, there is a striking parallel between biosynthesis of **a**-factor and maturation of the yeast homolog of the mammalian *ras* oncogene product. Genetic evidence has demonstrated that mutations in the *DPR1* gene (*defective in the processing of RAS*) (also called *RAM1*), which block fatty acid acylation and membrane localization of the yeast *RAS* proteins (26, 55), also prevent production of biologically active **a**-factor (55) and are allelic to a previously identified gene, *STE16*, required for efficient mating of *MAT***a** cells (55, 89). The C-termini of the **a**-factor precursor and the yeast (and mammalian) *RAS* proteins share the consensus, -Cys-HPO-HPO-X-COOH (where HPO is a hydrophobic amino acid and X is an uncharged amino acid). The C-terminal Cys residue is required for subsequent modification and membrane targeting of the *RAS* proteins (19a). Pulse-labelling and immunoprecipitation using anti-**a**-factor antibodies demonstrate that *dpr1* (*ram1*) mutants do not secrete any **a**-factor and accumulate intracellularly intact precursor (67a).

At least two other genes are required for the production of mature **a**-factor, *STE6* and *STE14* (18). Like the *DPR1* gene product, the enzymes encoded by the *STE6* and *STE14* genes are likely to be involved in either proteolytic processing or modification of the **a**-factor precursor because these mutants also do not secrete mature **a**-factor, yet accumulate intracellularly higher molecular weight intermediates (28, 67a).

## Killer Toxin

KILLER TOXIN GENE AND PREPRO-KILLER TOXIN PRECURSOR    The entire $M_1$-dsRNA protein-coding region has been determined by a combination of RNA and cDNA sequence analysis (11, 64). A single open reading frame is responsible for production of both toxin subunits and the immunity function (9, 30, 49, 72).

Prepro-killer toxin (ppKT) is 316 amino acids long (12) and consists of: (*a*) a 44-residue prepro-leader segment (termed δ) that serves as a signal sequence (63), (*b*) the α subunit of the mature toxin, (*c*) an 86-residue spacer region (termed γ ) that contains three sites for addition of *N*-linked oligosaccharides (11, 64), and (*d*) the β subunit of the toxin. *N*-terminal (11) and C-terminal (89a) sequence analysis of the purified α (103 residues) and β (83 residues) toxin subunits defines three processing sites in the precursor: $Pro_{43}Arg_{44}$ (between the δ leader and the *N*-terminus of α), $Arg_{148}Arg_{149}$ (between the C-terminus of α and the γ spacer segment), and $Lys_{232}Arg_{233}$ (between γ and the *N*-terminus of β).

PATHWAY OF TOXIN BIOSYNTHESIS    Entry of ppKT into the ER is marked by core glycosylation at all three sites within γ (12, 17, 30, 48); however, it has not yet been resolved whether the signal peptide is removed (17, 30, 48). Temperature-sensitive *sec* mutations (61) block toxin secretion (17, 48).

The specificity of the Kex2 protease for -Arg-Arg- and -Lys-Arg- sites (2, 29) suggests ppKT undergoes endoproteolytic scission at the doublets of basic residues at the $\alpha$–$\gamma$ and $\gamma$–$\beta$ junctions, followed by removal of the Arg residues from the C-terminus of $\alpha$ by the *KEX1* gene product (20). Thus, a previous conclusion (17) that *KEX1* action precedes that of *KEX2* is likely to be incorrect. Involvement of a tosyl-phenylalanylchloromethylketone-(TPCK) sensitive protease in toxin maturation (17) also is questionable because TPCK also inhibits glycosylation of ppKT (30, 73). A novel enzyme may not be needed for cleavage of the $\delta$–$\alpha$ junction (-Pro-Arg-) because such sites in synthetic peptides can be cleaved by a partially purified preparation of the Kex2 endoprotease at about 25–50% the rate of -Arg-Arg- or -Lys-Arg-sites (51a).

PRODUCTION OF THE IMMUNITY COMPONENT    Production of both the immunity function and the toxin from a single precursor suggests that the pool of newly synthesized ppKT may undergo differential processing (9, 30, 49, 72). The immunity determinant does not reside in the free $\gamma$ segment (11, 81) because nearly all mutations in the ppKT coding sequence that eliminate immunity map in the $\alpha$ subunit (20, 89a) and also inactivate toxin (9, 72). Only one mutation in $\gamma$ is known that affects immunity and the reduction is slight (72). Deletion and nonsense mutations that drastically truncate ppKT confer normal immunity (9) and indicate that most of the precursor molecule distal to $\alpha$ (and perhaps a small portion of $\gamma$) (71, 72) are dispensible for immunity. Hence, immunity may be due to some modification of the precursor other than its alternative proteolytic processing. Because mutations in the *REX1* gene (but not *kex1* or *kex2* mutations) greatly reduce immunity without affecting toxin production (86, 87), the *REX1* gene product may regulate or catalyze this modification.

## PROTEOLYTIC PROCESSING ENZYMES OF YEAST

### Kex2 Endoprotease

PROPERTIES OF *kex2* MUTANTS    In addition to the block in production of killer toxin (86, 87) and $\alpha$-factor (35, 46), several unidentified cell wall proteins display altered mobility in *kex2* mutants (56). Homozygous *kex2/kex2* diploids are defective at a late stage in spore formation (46).

Membrane preparations from normal cells, but not from *kex2* mutants, cleave small peptide substrates on the carboxyl side of -Arg-Arg- and -Lys-Arg- dipeptides (2, 29, 35). Absence of the peptidase cosegregates with the lack of killer toxin and $\alpha$-factor production upon meiosis of a heterozygous *KEX2/kex2* diploid (35). The cloned *KEX2* gene on a multicopy yeast plasmid overproduces this protease activity up to 30-fold (35). Under control of the galactose-inducible *GAL1* promoter on another multicopy plasmid, enzyme activity is overproduced several hundredfold above the level found in wild-type *KEX2* cells (29b). Production of a truncated, but active, form of the protease upon deletion of C-terminal sequences provides direct evidence that the *KEX2* gene encodes this enzyme (29a).

THE Kex2 ENZYME IS A $Ca^{2+}$-DEPENDENT, NEUTRAL SERINE PROTEASE
Activity measured in permeabilized cells (35), crude membrane fractions (2, 35), and more extensively purified preparations (29, 29b, 51a, 83) has the following characteristics. The enzyme is (*a*) membrane associated, but extractable with detergent; (*b*) resistant to high (mM) concentrations of phenylmethylsulfonyl fluoride (PMSF), tosyl-lysyl-chloromethylketone (TLCK), and TPCK, but inhibited by low ($\mu$M) concentrations of Ala-Lys-Arg-chloromethylketone [AKR-CK, formerly ALACK (21)], a covalent inhibitor of certain serine (trypsin) and thiol (cathepsin B) proteases (21); (*c*) inhibited by heavy metals ($Hg^{2+}$, $Zn^{2+}$, and $Cu^{2+}$) and several other thiol-directed reagents; (*d*) inhibited by ethylenediaminetetraacetate (EDTA) and (ethylenedioxy)diethylenedinitrilotetraacetate (EGTA), but not by *o*-phenanthroline, and protected from EGTA by $Ca^{2+}$, but not by $Mg^{2+}$; (*e*) maximally active near neutral pH; and (*f*) resistant to inhibition by *trans*-epoxysuccinic acid derivatives (29) thus, distinguishing the Kex2 protease from mammalian calpains (77). The enzyme is sensitive to moderate (5–10 mM) concentrations of diisopropylfluorophosphate (DFP) (29b) and contains a domain with significant homology to the subtilisins, a class of bacterial serine proteases (29a). Hence, the Kex2 enzyme seems to be a novel type of serine protease. The Kex2 enzyme is unrelated (80) to a soluble enzyme purified from yeast that cleaves between a pair of basic residues (51); however, it has properties identical to a membrane-bound activity partially purified by the same workers (51a).

In small peptide substrates, Kex2 enzyme cleaves after -Lys-Arg- and -Arg-Arg- with about equal efficiency, but it cleaves poorly (if at all) after a single Arg residue or a pair of Lys residues (28, 29b, 35, 51a, 83). The minimal acceptable substrate appears to be X-Lys-Arg or X-Arg-Arg (where X is any amino acid) (2), although larger substrates are readily attacked. For example, partially purified enzyme cleaves proalbumin only at its correct processing site (a doublet of Arg residues) (5). Additional insight concerning specificity comes from the efficacy of processing of hybrid proteins produced by heterologous genes fused to the *MFα1* gene at or near its Kex2 protease cleavage site in the first spacer. Constructions that include the Glu-Ala-repeats immediately following the -Lys-Arg- site display efficient removal of the ppαF leader (8, 15, 22). Constructions that place other sequences immediately adjacent to the -Lys-Arg- are usually cleaved more poorly (65, 90), but in some cases are cleaved well (15, 50). Perhaps the enzyme interacts with one or more residues C-terminal to the cleavage site, or secondary structure may limit accessibility of the cleavage site (or both). The Kex2 enzyme can cleave at both -Lys-Arg- and -Arg-Arg- sites within authentic heterologous proteins introduced into yeast by recombinant methods, including proinsulin (79) and *Aspergillus* glucoamylase (32). When the *KEX2* gene is expressed in mammalian tissue culture cells, active protease that accurately cleaves pro-opiomelanocortin (POMC) to $\gamma$-lipotropin ($\gamma$-LPH) and $\beta$-endorphin$_{1-31}$ is synthesized (see G. Thomas, this volume).

FEATURES OF Kex2 PROTEIN PREDICTED BY NUCLEOTIDE SEQUENCE    The sequence of the *KEX2* gene predicts a polypeptide of 814 amino acids (90 kDa) that contains two markedly hydrophobic sequences (Figure 2). The *N*-terminal sequence is undoubtedly a signal for ER entry. The second hydrophobic segment, near the C-terminus, has features typical of a stop-transfer sequence or transmembrane domain (TMD) (40, 76). The putative TMD divides the protein into two relatively hydrophilic domains: a larger *N*-terminal domain of 660 residues, and a highly charged C-terminal "tail" of 115 amino acids (net charge, $-15$). The larger domain contains the active site, sequences required for activation by $Ca^{2+}$, and sites for addition of both *N*-linked and O-linked carbohydrate (see below). Hence, this domain is within the lumenal space of the secretory compartment and the "tail" is probably in the cytoplasm.

The domain of homology to the subtilisin family of bacterial serine proteases (29a) spans the entire mature subtilisin sequence and corresponds to a region of the Kex2 protein between residues 140 and 440. Identity is only about 30%, but (*a*) homology is significantly greater (up to 60%) when conservative amino acid substitutions are considered, (*b*) good alignments can be obtained with only minor gaps (47), and (*c*) identities cluster in the region of residues thought to be critical for catalytic activity and substrate binding by subtilisin (41, 85). Residues of the charge relay complex (Asp-His-Ser) are present in about the same relative positions in the two sequences.

STRUCTURAL ANALYSIS OF Kex2 PROTEIN    The Kex2 protease can be specifically labeled (29) with an active site–specific covalent affinity reagent [$^{125}$I]Tyr-AKR-CK (formerly [$^{125}$I]TALACK) (21). Rabbit antibody has been raised against a $\beta$-galactosidase-Kex2 hybrid protein that contains the C-terminal 102 amino acids of the Kex2 protein ("anti-tail Ab") (29a, 29b). As detected by either probe (29a, 29b) or estimated from gel filtration (51a, 83), native Kex2 protein in yeast has a $M_r$ ~135 kDa.

Mature Kex2 protein is about 35–45 kDa larger than the predicted primary

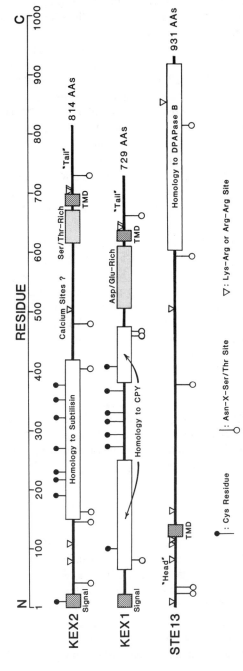

*Figure 2* Schematic depiction of predicted amino acid sequences of yeast precursor processing enzymes. The deduced amino acid sequences, homologies to known proteases, and inferred structural features are derived from the nucleotide sequences of the cloned structural genes, *KEX2* (29a), *KEX1* (20), and *STE13* (C. A. Flanagan and J. Thorner, unpublished data).

sequence. Analysis of Kex2 protein from tunicamycin-treated cells, and endoglycosidase H (or peptide-$N$-glycosidase F) digestion of immunoprecipitated or [$^{125}$I]Tyr-AKR-CK-labeled Kex2 protein, demonstrates that $N$-linked oligosaccharide accounts for only a minor amount (~5 kDa) of this difference, despite five available consensus Asn-linked glycosylation sites in the lumenal domain (29a). As in the low density lipoprotein (LDL) receptor (76), additional mass appears to be due to extensive O-glycosylation of the Ser- and Thr-rich region (40 out of 100 residues) $N$-terminal to the TMD because (*a*) enzyme prepared from tunicamycin-treated cells nevertheless binds to Concanavalin A–Sepharose and is eluted by $\alpha$-methyl mannoside [O-linked carbohydrates in yeast are composed entirely of linear chains of $\alpha$-linked mannosides, (3, 61)], and (*b*) the product of a truncated *KEX2* gene in which the entire Ser- and Thr-rich region (and the remainder of the C-terminus) has been deleted displays a mobility very close to its predicted size (29a).

LOCALIZATION OF Kex2 PROTEIN WITHIN THE YEAST SECRETORY SYSTEM    Kex2 protease appears to reside in an intracellular compartment. Even when overproduced more than 200-fold, Kex2 protease activity can only be detected in whole cells after detergent permeabilization (29, 35); this is in marked contrast to the shunting of vacuolar enzymes to the cell surface upon even modest (3–5-fold) overproduction (59, 69). Mutant Kex2 proteins produced by genes that lack C-terminal sequences are transported to the cell surface. Loss of just the tail sequence results in appearance of a small fraction (~10%) of the protein at the cell surface. An extensive deletion that removes the tail, the TMD, and the Ser- and Thr-rich region causes the majority (60–70%) of the enzyme to be transported to the cell surface (29a). Fusion of the C-terminal third of the *KEX2* gene to the *SUC2* gene that encodes secreted invertase results in retention of invertase activity within cells (P. K. Herman & S. D. Emr, personal communication). Thus, the information for retaining the Kex2 enzyme in the secretory compartment resides in the C-terminal domains.

## Kex1 Carboxypeptidase

CHARACTERIZATION OF THE *KEX1* GENE    Based on differential stability of ppKT in *kex1* versus *kex2* mutants, it was concluded that the *KEX1* gene product acted before the *KEX2* gene product (17) and was likely an endopeptidase (81). This conclusion is refuted by results obtained from cloning of the *KEX1* gene (20). The DNA sequence predicts a 729-residue protein with the following features (Figure 2): (*a*) an apparent signal sequence at the $N$-terminus, (*b*) a potential TMD 100 residues proximal to the C-terminus, (*c*) four potential sites for addition of $N$-linked carbohydrate (three of these on the

$N$-terminal side of the putative TMD), ($d$) in contrast to Kex2 protein, a highly acidic region (52 out of 100 residues) just $N$-terminal to the TMD, and ($e$) a highly charged (but net neutral) C-terminal tail. The sequence also contains two regions of striking homology to the yeast vacuolar serine protease, carboxypeptidase Y (16), which includes the sequence surrounding the active site Ser: Gly-Glu-Ser-Tyr-Ala-Gly (16). Site-directed mutagenesis that changed the corresponding Ser in the *KEX1* sequence to Ala resulted in inactivation of the *KEX1* gene, an observation providing further evidence that it is a serine protease (20).

EVIDENCE THAT Kex1 ENZYME IS A CARBOXYPEPTIDASE B-LIKE PROTEASE    Action of the *KEX1* gene product as an endopeptidase at the $\delta/\alpha$ junction (12) is ruled out because *kex1* mutants are defective for toxin production even when the entire $\delta$ segment is substituted by the efficiently cleaved signal sequence of the *PHO5* gene (20). C-terminal analysis of the $\alpha$ subunit of toxin indicates processing at $Arg_{148}Arg_{149}$, a likely Kex2 protease cleavage site (20, 89a). Given the homology of the *KEX1* gene to a known carboxypeptidase, the revised $\alpha/\gamma$ junction suggested that *KEX1* product might be the exopeptidase responsible for removal of the basic residues after Kex2 enzyme cleavage. This conclusion raised the possibility that *KEX1* might also be required for removal of the -Lys-Arg- residues from the C-termini of three of the four $\alpha$-factor repeats released from pp$\alpha$F (Figure 1) (and the fact that the C-terminus of the last $\alpha$-factor repeat does not require this step presumably would explain why *kex1* mutants still produce some functional $\alpha$-factor) (46, 87).

The total amount of biologically active $\alpha$-factor produced by a *kex1* mutant is significantly reduced compared to wild-type $\alpha$ cells, and crude preparations of $\alpha$-factor from *kex1* cells can be markedly activated by incubation with pancreatic carboxypeptidase B (20). Furthermore, *kex1* mutations completely block production of active $\alpha$-factor when pp$\alpha$F is expressed from an *MF$\alpha$1* gene lacking its terminal repeat; again, latent $\alpha$-factor activity is revealed by treatment of the culture medium of such cells with carboxypeptidase B. The *KEX1* gene product appears to be the same as a membrane-associated carboxypeptidase activity specific for basic residues (called "ysc$\alpha$") detected in vitro (2, 83a).

There is no homology between the predicted Kex1 protein and carboxypeptidase E, a mammalian metalloprotease homologous to both carboxypeptidases A and B (24) found in secretory tissues and thought to be responsible for removal of basic residues during maturation of prohormones and neuropeptides (24, 25). However, unlike the yeast system, it has not been possible by genetic means to establish the essential role in vivo of any mammalian protease in the processing of any hormone precursor.

## Ste13 Exopeptidase

CHARACTERIZATION OF THE *STE13* GENE    Mutations in the *STE13* gene were originally identified because they cause α-specific sterility (67) and result in the secretion of a collection of nonfunctional, incompletely processed forms of α-factor (18) possessing extra N-terminal residues, [Glu(or Asp)-Ala]$_n$, from the spacer regions of the precursor (34).

The *STE13* gene was cloned on the basis of its ability to correct the phenotypic defects of *MATα ste*13 mutants; in addition to the authentic *STE13* gene, another DNA segment (*DAP2* gene) was also cloned that could weakly suppress the mating deficiency and partially restore active pheromone production (34). The complete nucleotide sequence of the *STE13* gene has been determined and predicts a polypeptide of 931 residues (Figure 2) (C. Flanagan & J. Thorner, unpublished results), which can be accommodated by the observed size of the *STE13* transcript (2.9 kb) (4). There is no obvious signal sequence at the N-terminal end of the predicted protein; however, a striking 23-residue TMD (positions 119–141) is indicated by hydropathy plots. The potential TMD divides the molecule into a small hydrophilic N-terminal domain and a large 790-residue hydrophilic C-terminal domain. This topological arrangement is the opposite of that found in the Kex1 and Kex2 enzymes. Also, unlike the Kex1 and Kex2 proteins, the Ste13 molecule lacks Cys residues. Furthermore, unlike Kex1 enzyme, the predicted Ste13 polypeptide has several -Lys-Arg-sites in its catalytic domain (if the large hydrophilic region distal to the TMD represents the lumenal portion of the Ste13 enzyme). This domain also possesses three potential N-glycosylation sites. These features provide clues that the Ste13 protein may be localized to a different secretory compartment than the Kex1 and Kex2 enzymes. Survey of various protein sequence databases has failed to reveal a polypeptide with significant homology to the *STE13* gene.

EVIDENCE THAT Ste13 ENZYME IS A TYPE IV DIPEPTIDYL AMINOPEPTIDASE    The structure of the spacer remnants present on the α-factor-related peptides secreted by *ste13* mutants suggested involvement of a dipeptidyl aminopeptidase (DPAPase) specific for -X-Ala- sequences (type IV enzyme) (42). Using peptide substrates to follow this type of cleavage colorimetrically (74), it was shown that normal yeast cells possess at least two such DPAPases (distinguishable by their sensitivity to heat inactivation) and that *ste13* mutants specifically lacked one of these enzymes (the heat-stable DPAPase A) (34). In a normal cell, DPAPase A comprises about 30% of total activity (39); the majority is the heat-labile DPAPase B, which is a vacuolar enzyme (10, 75). Cells carrying the *STE13* gene on a multicopy plasmid overproduce DPAPase A activity three- to fivefold; cells carrying the DAP2 gene overproduce DPAPase B (34). The simplest interpretation of these findings is that *STE*13 is the structural gene for DPAPase A and that *DAP2* is the structural gene for DPAPase B (75; C. Roberts and T. Stevens, personal communication).

One distinguishing characteristic of DPAPase A is its tight membrane association. Of over a dozen detergents utilized, only a single zwitterionic detergent (Deriphat) solubilizes DPAPase A stably and in good yield from the particulate fraction (R. Kunisawa & J. Thorner, unpublished results). In contrast, Triton X-100 readily solubilizes DPAPase B from vacuolar membrane preparations (T. Stevens, personal communication). Subcellular fractionation of membrane preparations on Percoll gradients indicates that DPAPase A can be completely resolved from both acid phosphatase (accumulated in secretory vesicles) and the Kex2 protease (presumably in the late Golgi) (C. Holcomb & R. Fuller, unpublished results).

It is noteworthy that a dipeptidyl aminopeptidase apparently involved in processing peptide precursors in frog skin secretions is also a large (98,000 $M_r$) glycoprotein (51b).

## CONCLUSIONS AND PERSPECTIVES

The goals of studying precursor maturation are to understand the precursors themselves, the enzymes involved in specific processing, and the interaction of these molecules during the secretory process. Yeast has advantages for the study of these events. First, processing in yeast is relatively simple compared to higher cells. Aside from glycosylation, $\alpha$-factor synthesis, for example, does not involve other modification steps (such as *N*-terminal acetylation, C-terminal amidation, sulfation, or phosphorylation). Second, precursors and enzymes can be identified not only biochemically, but also functionally by genetic criteria. Therefore, the isolation of genes for precursors and processing enzymes is relatively straightforward. Genes encoding the enzymes and precursors are amenable to informative manipulations, as documented here. Third, for biochemical analysis, yeast provides an abundant source of homogeneous "tissue." Fourth, although development of cytological methods and subcellular fractionation has lagged behind procedures available for higher cells, the genetically defined secretory pathway in yeast (61) should facilitate studies of the localization of processing enzymes and transport of precursor molecules.

Although cleavage at pairs of basic residues is a universal feature of precursor maturation, just how similar are the yeast and mammalian processing enzymes and the reactions catalyzed? The Kex2 enzyme, with its neutral pH optimum, probably functions in the yeast Golgi. In contrast, processing of proinsulin may take place in newly forming secretory granules that appear to be undergoing acidification (54). However, the true mammalian processing enzymes have yet to be identified.

Organization of the yeast processing enzymes within secretory compartments remains unknown. Study of their localization may provide a valuable system for probing the structure and assembly of late Golgi-associated components. Identification of the immunity determinant of killer toxin should illuminate the mechanism of alternative processing of a precursor molecule within a single cell. Against this backdrop, synthesis of a-factor stands out as an unprecedented cytoplasmic route for processing and secretion. The resolution of this system should enhance our appreciation for the range of pathways used by eukaryotic cells for the release of bioactive peptides.

ACKNOWLEDGMENTS

For helpful conversations, communication of results prior to publication, and/or gifts of research materials, the authors thank P. Böhni, A. Brake, H. Bussey, S. Emr, J. Rothblatt, R. Schekman, E. Shaw, D. Steiner, T. Stevens, S. Sturley, D. Tipper, and V. MacKay. R.S.F. was supported, in part, by a postdoctoral fellowship from the Helen Hay Whitney Foundation and is currently a Lucille P. Markey Scholar. This work was supported by a grant from the Lucille P. Markey Charitable Trust, by an NCI Predoctoral Traineeship (CA09041) to R.E.S. and by an NIH Research Grant (GM21841) to J. T.

*Literature Cited*

1. Achstetter, T., Wolf, D. H. 1985. Proteinases, proteolysis and biological control in the yeast *Saccharomyces cerevisiae*. *Yeast* 1:139–57
2. Achstetter, T., Wolf, D. H. 1985. Hormone processing and membrane-bound proteases in yeast. *EMBO J.* 4:173–77
3. Ballou, C. E. 1982. Yeast cell wall and cell surface. In *The Molecular Biology of the Yeast Saccharomyces, Metabolism and Gene Expression,* ed. J. N. Strathern, E. W. Jones, J. R. Broach, pp. 335–60. Cold Spring Harbor Lab., NY
4. Barnes, D. A., Thorner, J. 1986. Genetic manipulation of *Saccharomyces cerevisiae* by use of the *LYS2* gene. *Mol. Cell. Biol.* 6:2828–38
5. Bathurst, I. C., Brennan, S. O., Carrell, R. W., Cousens, L. S. Brake, A. J., et al. 1987. Yeast KEX2 protease has the properties of a human proalbumin converting enzyme. *Science* 235:348–50
6. Betz, R., Crabb, J. W., Meyer, H. E., Wittig, R., Duntze, W. 1987. Amino acid sequences of a-factor mating peptides from *Saccharomyces cerevisiae*. *J. Biol. Chem.* 262:546–48

7. Betz, R., Duntze, W. 1979. Purification and partial characterization of a-factor, a mating hormone produced by mating type **a** cells from *Saccharomyces cerevisiae*. *Eur. J. Biochem.* 95:469–75
8. Bitter, G. A., Chen, K. K., Banks, A. R., Lai, P.-H. 1984. Secretion of foreign proteins from *Saccharomyces cerevisiae* directed by α-factor gene fusions. *Proc. Natl. Acad. Sci. USA* 81:5330–34
9. Boone, C., Bussey, H., Greene, D., Thomas, P. Y., Vernet, T. 1986. Yeast killer toxin: site directed mutations implicate the precursor protein as the immunity component. *Cell* 46:105–13
10. Bordallo, C., Schwencke, J., Suarez-Rendueles, M. 1984. Localization of the thermosensitive X-prolyl dipeptidyl amino peptidase in the vacuolar membrane of *Saccharomyces cerevisiae*. *FEBS Lett.* 173:199–203
11. Bostian, K. A., Elliot, Q., Bussey, H., Burn, V. E., Smith, A., et al. 1984. Sequence of the preprotoxin dsRNA gene of type 1 killer yeast: multiple processing events produce a two-component toxin. *Cell* 36:741–51

12. Bostian, K. A., Jayachandran, S., Tipper, D. J. 1983. A glycosylated protoxin in killer yeast: models for its structure and maturation. *Cell* 32:169–80

13. Brake, A. J., Brenner, C., Najarian, R., Laybourn, P., Merryweather, J. 1985. Structure of genes encoding precursors of the yeast peptide mating pheromone a-factor. In *Protein Transport and Secretion*, ed. M. J. Gething, pp. 103–8. Cold Spring Harbor Lab., NY

14. Brake, A. J., Julius, D. J., Thorner, J. 1983. A functional prepro-α-factor gene in *Saccharomyces* yeasts can contain three, four, or five repeats of the mature pheromone sequence. *Mol. Cell. Biol.* 3:1440–50

15. Brake, A. J., Merryweather, J. P., Coit, D. G., Heberlein, U. A., Masiarz, F. A., et al. 1984. α-Factor-directed synthesis and secretion of mature foreign proteins in *Saccharomyces cerevisiae*. *Proc. Natl. Acad. Sci. USA* 81:4642–46

16. Breddam, K. 1986. Serine carboxypeptidases. A review. *Carlsberg Res. Commun.* 5:83–128

17. Bussey, H., Saville, D., Greene, D., Tipper, D. J., Bostian, K. A. 1983. Secretion of the *Saccharomyces cerevisiae* killer toxin; processing of the glycolated precursor. *Mol. Cell. Biol.* 3:1362–70

18. Chan, R. K., Melnick, L. M., Blair, L. C, Thorner, J. 1983. Extracellular suppression allows mating by pheromone-deficient sterile mutants of *Saccharomyces cerevisiae*. *J. Bacteriol.* 155:903–6

19. Deshaies, R. J., Schekman, R. 1987. A yeast mutant defective at an early stage in import of secretory protein precursors into the endoplasmic reticulum. *J. Cell. Biol.* 105:633–45

19a. Deschenes, R. J., Broach, J. R. 1987. Fatty acylation is important but not essential for *Saccharomyces Cerevisiae* RAS function. *Molec. Cell. Biol.* 7:2344–51

20. Dmochowska, A., Dignard, D., Henning, D., Thomas, D. Y., Bussey, H. 1987. Yeast *KEX1* gene encodes a putative protease with a carboxypeptidase B-like function involved in killer toxin and α-factor precursor processing. *Cell.* 50:573–84

21. Docherty, K., Carroll, R., Steiner, D. F. 1983. Identification of a 31,500 molecular weight islet cell protease as cathepsin B. *Proc. Natl. Acad. Sci. USA* 80:3245–49

22. Emr, S. D., Schekman, R., Flessel, M. C., Thorner, J. 1983. An *MFα1-SUC2* (α-factor-invertase) gene fusion for study of protein localization and gene expression in yeast. *Proc. Natl. Acad. Sci. USA* 80:7080–84

23. Emter, O., Mechler, B., Achstetter, T., Muller, H., Wolf, D. H. 1983. Yeast pheromone α-factor is synthesized as a high molecular weight precursor. *Biochem. Biophys. Res. Commun.* 116:822–29

24. Fricker, L. D., Evans, C. J., Esch, F. S., Herbert, E. 1986. Cloning and sequence analysis of cDNA for bovine carboxypeptidase E. *Nature* 323:461–64

25. Fricker, L. D., Snyder, S. H. 1983. Purification and characterization of enkephalin convertase, an enkephalin-synthesizing carboxypeptidase E. *J. Biol. Chem.* 258:10, 950–55

26. Fujiyama, A., Matsumoto, K., Tamanoi, F. 1987. A novel yeast mutant defective in the processing of ras proteins: assessment of the effect of the mutation on processing steps. *EMBO J.* 6:223–28

27. Fujiyama, A., Tamanoi, F. 1986. Processing and fatty acid acylation of *RAS*1 and *RAS*2 proteins in *Saccharomyces cerevisiae*. *Proc. Natl. Acad. Sci. USA* 83:1266–70

28. Fuller, R., Brake, A., Sterne, R., Kunisawa, R., Barnes, D., et al. 1986. Post-translational processing events in the maturation of yeast pheromone precursors. In *Yeast Cell Biology, UCLA Symp. Mol. Cell Biol.*, (NS) 33:519–36. New York: Liss

29. Fuller, R., Brake, A., Thorner, J. 1986. The *Saccharomyces cerevisiae KEX2* gene, required for processing prepro-α-factor, encodes a calcium-dependent endopeptidase that cleaves after Lys-Arg and Arg-Arg sequences. In *Microbiology—1986*, ed. L. Leive, pp. 273–78. Washington, DC: American Society for Microbiology.

29a. Fuller, R. S., Brake, A., Thorner, J. 1987. Molecular features of a prohormone processing enzyme. *Science.* Submitted for publication

29b. Fuller, R. S., Brake, A., Thorner, J. 1987. Yeast precursor convertase (*KEX2* gene product) is a novel class of $Ca^{2+}$-dependent serine protease. *Proc. Natl. Acad. Sci. USA.* Submitted for publication

30. Hanes, S. D., Burn, V. E., Sturley, S. L., Tipper, D. J., Bostian, K. A. 1986. Expression of a cDNA derived from the yeast killer preprotoxin gene: implications for processing and immunity. *Proc. Natl. Acad. Sci. USA* 83:1675–79

31. Hansen, W., Garcia, P. D., Walter, P. 1986. In vitro protein translocation across the yeast endoplasmic reticulum: ATP-dependent post-translational trans-

location of the prepro-α-factor. *Cell* 45:397–406

32. Innis, M. A., Holland, M. J., McCabe, P. C., Cole, G. E., Whittman, V. P., et al. 1985. Expression, glycosylation and secretion of an *Aspergillus* glucoamylase by *Saccharomyces cerevisiae*. *Science* 228:21–26

33. Jones, E. W. 1984. The synthesis and function of proteases in *Saccharomyces:* genetic approaches. *Ann. Rev. Genet.* 18:233–70

34. Julius, D., Blair, L., Brake, A., Sprague, G., Thorner, J. 1983. Yeast α-factor is processed from a larger precursor polypeptide: The essential role of a membrane-bound dipeptidyl aminopeptidase. *Cell* 32:839–52

35. Julius, D., Brake, A., Blair, L., Kunisawa, R., Thorner, J. 1984. Isolation of the putative structural gene for the lysine-arginine-cleaving endopeptidase required for processing of yeast prepro-α-factor. *Cell* 37:1075–89

36. Julius, D., Schekman, R., Thorner, J. 1984. Glycosylation and processing of prepro-α-factor through the yeast secretory pathway. *Cell* 36:309–18

37. Kamiya, Y., Sakurai, A., Tamura, S., Takahashi, N., Tsuchiya, E., et al. 1979. Structure of rhodotorucine A, a peptidyl factor, inducing mating tube formation in *Rhodosporidium toruloides*. *Agric. Biol. Chem.* 43:363–69

38. Kelly, R. B. 1985. Pathways of secretion in eukaryotes. *Science* 230:25–32

39. Klar, A.J.S., Strathern, J. N., Hicks, J. B. 1984. Developmental pathways in yeast. In *Microbial Development*, ed. R. Losick, pp. 151–95. Cold Spring Harbor Lab., NY

40. Klein, P., Kanehisa, M., DeLisi, C. 1985. The detection and classification of membrane-spanning proteins. *Biochim. Biophys. Acta* 81:468–76

41. Kraut, J. 1977. Serine proteases: structure and mechanism of catalysis. *Ann. Rev. Biochem.* 46:331–58

42. Kreil, G., Mollay, C., Kaschnitz, R., Haiml, L., Vilas, U. 1980. Prepromellitin: Specific cleavage of the pre- and propeptide in vitro. *Ann. NY Acad. Sci.* 343:338–46

43. Kurjan, J. 1985. α-factor structural gene mutations in *Saccharomyces cerevisiae:* effects on α-factor production and mating. *Mol. Cell. Biol.* 5:787–96

44. Kurjan, J., Herskowitz, I. 1982. Structure of a yeast pheromone gene (*MFα*): a putative α-factor precursor contains four tandem repeats of mature α-factor. *Cell* 30:933–43

45. Deleted in proof

46. Leibowitz, M. J., Wickner, R. B. 1976. A chromosomal gene required for killer plasmid expression, mating, and spore maturation in *Saccharomyces cerevisiae*. *Proc. Natl. Acad. Sci. USA* 73:2061–65

47. Lipman, D. J., Pearson, W. R. 1985. Rapid and sensitive protein similarity searches. *Science* 227:1435–41

48. Lolle, S. J., Bussey, H. 1986. In vivo evidence for posttranslational translocation and signal cleavage of the killer preprotoxin of *Saccharomyces cerevisiae*. *Mol. Cell. Biol.* 6:4274–80

49. Lolle, S., Skipper, N., Bussey, M., Thomas, D. Y. 1984. The expression of cDNA clones of yeast M1 double stranded RNA in yeast confers both killer and immunity phenotypes. *EMBO J.* 3:1383–87.

50. MacKay, V. L. 1987. Secretion of heterologous proteins in yeast. In *Biological Research on Industrial Yeasts,* Vol. 2. 0:0000–00. CRC. In press

51. Mizuno, K., Matsuo, H. 1984. A novel protease from yeast with specificity towards paired basic residues. *Nature* 309:558–60

51a. Mizuno, K., Nakamura, T., Takada, K., Sakakibara, S., Matsuo, H. 1987. A membrane-bound, calcium-dependent protease in yeast α-cell cleaving on the carboxyl side of paired basic residues. *Biochem. Biophys. Res. Commun.* 144: 807–14

51b. Mollay, C., Vilas, U., Hutticher, A., Kreil, G. 1986. Isolation of a dipeptidyl aminopeptidase, a putative processing enzyme, from skin secretion of *Xenopus laevis*. *Eur. J. Biochem.* 160:31–35

52. Naider, F., Becker, J. M. 1986. Structure-activity relationships of the yeast α-factor. *CRC Crit. Rev. Biochem.* 21:225–48

53. Nakafuku, M., Itoh, H., Nakamura, S., Kaziro, Y. 1987. Occurrence in *Saccharomyces cerevisiae* of a gene homologous to the cDNA coding for the α-subunit of mammalian G proteins. *Proc. Natl. Acad. Sci. USA* 84:2140–44

54. Orci, L., Ravassola, M., Amherdt, M., Madsen, O., Vassalli, J.-D., et al. 1985. Direct identification of prohormone conversion site in insulin-secreting cells. *Cell* 42:671–81

55. Powers, S., Michaelis, S., Broek, D., Santa Anna-A., S., Field, J. et al. 1986. *RAM*, a gene of yeast required for a functional modification of RAS proteins and for production of mating pheromone **a**-factor. *Cell* 47:413–22

56. Rogers, D. T., Saville, D., Bussey, H. 1979. *Saccharomyces cerevisiae* killer

expression mutant *kex2* has altered secretory proteins and glycoproteins. *Biochem. Biophys. Res. Commun.* 90: 187–93
57. Deleted in proof
58. Rothblatt, J. A., Meyer, D. I. 1986. Secretion in yeast: reconstitution of the translocation and glycosylation of α-factor and invertase in a homologous cell-free system. *Cell* 44:619–28
59. Rothman, J. H., Hunter, C. P., Valls, L. A., Stevens, T. H. 1986. Overproduction-induced mislocalization of a yeast vacuolar protein allows isolation of its structural gene. *Proc. Natl. Acad. Sci. USA* 83:3248–52
60. Schauer, I., Emr, S., Gross, C., Schekman, R. 1985. Invertase signal and mature sequence substitutions that delay intercompartmental transport of active enzyme. *J. Cell Biol.* 100:1664–75
61. Schekman, R. 1985. Protein localization and membrane traffic in yeast. *Ann. Rev. Cell Biol.* 1:115–43
62. Singh, A., Chen, E. Y., Lugovoy, J. M., Chang, C. N., Hitzeman, R. A., Seeburg, P. H. 1983. *Saccharomyces cerevisiae* contains two discrete genes coding for the α-factor pheromone. *Nucleic Acids Res.* 11:4049–63
63. Skipper, N., Sutherland, M., Davies, R. W., Kilburn, D., Miller, R. C., et al. 1985. Secretion of a bacterial cellulase by yeast. *Saccharomyces cerevisiae.* *Mol. Cell. Biol.* 6:4274–80
64. Skipper, N., Thomas, D. Y., Lau, P.C.K. 1984. Cloning and sequencing of the preprotoxin-coding region of the yeast M1 double-stranded RNA. *EMBO* 3:107–11
65. Smith, R. A., Duncan, M. J., Moir, D. T. 1985. Heterologous protein secretion from yeast. *Science* 229:1219–24
66. Sprague, G. F. Jr., Blair, L. C., Thorner, J. 1983. Cell interactions and regulation of cell type in the yeast *Saccharomyces cerevisiae. Ann. Rev. Microbiol.* 37:623–60
67. Sprague, G. F. Jr., Rine, J., Herskowitz, I. 1981. Control of yeast cell type by the mating type locus. II. Genetic interactions between *MATα* and unlinked α-specific *STE* genes. *J. Mol. Biol.* 153:323–35
67a. Sterne, R. E., Thorner, J. 1986. Processing and secretion of a yeast peptide hormone by a novel pathway. *J. Cell. Biol.* 103:189a
68. Stevens, T., Esmon, B., Schekman, R. 1982. Early stages in the yeast secretory pathway are required for transport of carboxypeptidase Y to the vacuole. *Cell* 30:439–48

69. Stevens, T. H., Rothman, J. H., Payne, G. S., Schekman, R. 1986. Gene dosage-dependent secretion of yeast vacuolar carboxypeptidase Y. *J. Cell Biol.* 102:1551–57
70. Stötzler, D., Kiltz, H., Duntze, W. 1976. Primary structure of α-factor peptides from *Saccharomyces cerevisiae. Eur. J. Biochem.* 69:397–400
71. Sturley, S. L., El-Sherbeini, M., Kho, S.-H., Levitre, J. L., Bostian, K. A. 1987. Acquisition and expression of the killer character in yeast. In *Viruses of Fungi and Lower Eukaryotes,* ed. Y. Koltin, M. J. Leibowitz. NY: Dekker. In press
72. Sturley, S. L., Elliot, Q., LeVitre, J., Tipper, D. J., Bostian, K. A. 1986. Mapping of functional domains within the *Saccharomyces cerevisiae* type 1 killer preprotoxin. *EMBO J.* 5:3381–89
73. Sturley, S. L., Hanes, S. D., Burn, V., Bostian, K. A. 1986. Maturation and secretion of the $M_1$-dsRNA encoded killer toxin in *S. cerevisiae.* In *Yeast Cell Biology,* ed. J. Hicks, pp. 537–50. New York: Liss
74. Suarez-Rendueles, M. P., Schwencke, J., Garcia-Alvarea, N., Cascon, S. 1981. A new -X-prolyl dipeptidyl aminopeptidase from yeast associated with a particulate fraction. *FEBS Lett.* 131: 296–300.
75. Suarez-Rendueles, P., Wolf, D. H. 1987. Identification of the structural gene for dipeptidyl aminopeptidase yscV (*DAP2*) in *Saccharomyces cerevisiae. J. Bacteriol.* 169:4041–48
76. Sudhof, T. C., Goldstein, J. L., Brown, M. S., Russell, D. W. 1985. The LDL receptor gene: a mosaic of exons shared with different proteins. *Science* 228: 815–22
77. Suzuki, K., Tsuji, S., Ishiura, S. 1981. Effect of $Ca^{2+}$ on the inhibition of calcium-activated neutral protease by leupeptin, antipain, and epoxysuccinate derivatives. *FEBS Lett.* 136:119–22
78. Tamanoi, F., Hseuh, E. C., Goodman, L. E., Cobitz, R. J., Detrick, W. R., et al. 1987. Characterization of *dpr1* mutation which affects processing of H-ras and yeast RAS proteins. *J. Cell. Biochem.* In press
79. Thim, L., Hansen, M. T., Norris, K., Hoegh, I., Boel, E., et al. 1986. Secretion and processing of insulin precursors in yeast. *Proc. Natl. Acad. Sci. USA* 83:6766–70
80. Thorner, J. 1985. Pheromone-processing protease of the yeast *Saccharomyces cerevisiae. Nature* 314:384
81. Tipper, D. J., Bostian, K. A. 1984.

Double-stranded rebonucleic acid killer systems in yeasts. *Microbiol. Rev.* 48:125–56

82. von Heijne, G. 1983. Patterns of amino acids near signal-sequence cleavage sites. *Eur. J. Biochem.* 133:17–21

83. Wagner, J.-C., Escher, C., Wolf, D. H. 1987. Some characteristics of hormone (pheromone) processing enzymes in yeast. *FEBS Lett.* 218:31–34

83a. Wagner, J.-C., Wolf, D. H. 1987. Hormone (pheromone) processing enzymes in yeast: The carboxy-terminal processing enzyme of the mating pheromone α-factor, carboxypeptidase yscα, is absent in α-factor maturation-defective *kex1* mutant cells. *FEBS Letts.* 221:423–26

84. Waters, M. G., Blobel, G. 1986. Secretory protein translocation in a yeast cell-free system can occur post-translationally and requires ATP hydrolysis. *J. Cell Biol.* 102:1543–50

84a. Waters, M. G., Evans, E. A., Blobel, G. 1987. Prepro-α-factor has a cleavable signal sequence. *J. Biol. Chem.* Submitted for publication

85. Wells, J. A., Ferrari, E., Henner, D. J., Estell, D. A., Chen, E. Y. 1983. Cloning, sequencing and secretion of *Bacillus amyloliquefaciens* subtilisin in *Bacillus subtilis*. *Nucleic Acids Res.* 11:7911–25

86. Wickner, R. B. 1974. Chromosomal and nonchromosomal mutations affecting the "killer character" of *Saccharomyces cerevisiae*. *Genetics* 76:423–32

87. Wickner, R. B., Leibowitz, M. J. 1976. Two chromosomal genes required for killing expression in killer strains of *Saccharomyces cerevisiae*. *Genetics* 82:429–42

88. Wilson, K. L., Herskowitz, I. 1986. Sequences upstream of the *STE6* gene required for its expression and regulation by the mating type locus in *Saccharomyces cerevisiae*. *Proc. Natl. Acad. Sci. USA* 83:2536–40

89. Wilson, K. L., Herskowitz, I. 1987. *STE16*, a new gene required for pheromone production by **a** cells of *Saccharomyces cerevisiae*. *Genetics* 155:441–49

89a. Zhu, H., Bussey, H., Thomas, D. Y., Gagnon, J., Bell, A. W. 1987. Determination of the carboxy-termini of the α and β subunits of yeast K1 killer toxin; Requirement of a carboxypeptidase B-like activity for maturation. *J. Biol. Chem.* 262:10, 728–32

90. Zsebo, K. M., Lu, H.-S., Fieschko, J. C., Goldstein, L., Davis, J., et al. 1986. Protein secretion from *Saccharomyces cerevisiae* directed by the prepro-α-factor leader region. *J. Biol. Chem.* 261:5858–65

*Ann. Rev. Physiol. 1988. 50:363–76*

# TYROSINE SULFATION AND THE SECRETORY PATHWAY

*Wieland B. Huttner*

Cell Biology Program, European Molecular Biology Laboratory, Post Office Box 10.2209, 6900 Heidelberg, Federal Republic of Germany

## INTRODUCTION

In addition to proteolytic processing and carboxy-terminal amidation, which are reviewed elsewhere in this volume, neuropeptide processing involves various covalent modifications of amino acid side chains. Glycosylation, phosphorylation, and sulfation are the major such processing reactions. This review focuses on the sulfation of tyrosine, the only amino acid residue of neuropeptides shown to undergo this modification. Tyrosine sulfate is not specific for neuropeptides but has been found in many other proteins as well. Consequently, this review is not restricted to tyrosine sulfation of neuropeptides but includes general aspects of protein tyrosine sulfation that are relevant to this topic. The current status of the field is described in four parts, which deal with the occurrence of tyrosine sulfation, the characteristics of tyrosine-sulfated proteins, the subcellular localization and properties of the sulfating enzyme, and functional aspects of this modification. A comprehensive review and a short summary of the field have recently appeared (42, 43).

## OCCURRENCE OF TYROSINE-SULFATED PROTEINS

Work during the past seven years has established that tyrosine sulfation is an ubiquitous posttranslational modification that occurs in essentially all animal cells containing a Golgi apparatus (35, 40, for review see 43). Up to 1% of the tyrosine residues of the total protein in an organism can be sulfated (9). Thus, sulfation is the most common posttranslational modification known for this amino acid.

363

0066-4278/88/0315-0363$02.00

## Species Distribution

Methods for detecting tyrosine sulfate in proteins have been described in detail (9, 19, 41). Tyrosine-sulfated proteins have been found in every investigated invertebrate and vertebrate species within the animal kingdom (for review see 43). Protein tyrosine sulfation has also been observed in the green alga *Volvox carteri* (W. B. Huttner, S. Wenzl, M. Sumper, unpublished; 76), which raises the possibility that this modification may be widespread in plants. No conclusive evidence has yet been obtained for the occurrence of tyrosine sulfate in proteins of unicellular eukaryotic organisms and prokaryotes. The data obtained so far suggest that during evolution, tyrosine sulfation of proteins first appeared consistently in multicellular eukaryotic organisms.

## Tissue Distribution

Tyrosine-sulfated proteins have been found in all animal tissues studied and in all primary cell cultures and cell lines examined (35, 40, for review see 43). Different cell types contain characteristic sets of tyrosine-sulfated proteins, which suggests that proteins with cell type–specific expression are the main targets for tyrosine sulfation. From the work carried out so far it can be concluded that protein tyrosine sulfation occurs in both single cells and cells that are part of a tissue, in differentiated and undifferentiated cells, and in both normal and transformed cells.

## CHARACTERISTICS OF TYROSINE-SULFATED PROTEINS

### Intracellular and Extracellular Localization

The vast majority of tyrosine-sulfated proteins have not yet been characterized but are only known as sulfated bands on SDS polyacrylamide gels. The tyrosine-sulfated proteins characterized with regard to both localization and function are listed in Table 1. All of these proteins are synthesized by membrane-bound ribosomes in the rough endoplasmic reticulum, and most of them are secretory. Tyrosine sulfate has been found in constitutive as well as regulated secretory proteins.

The frequent occurrence of tyrosine sulfate in secretory proteins is consistent with results obtained with rats in vivo showing that plasma proteins contain much more tyrosine sulfate than tissue proteins (35). In addition, analysis of proteins transported in neurons by fast axonal transport showed that tyrosine sulfate is predominantly found in proteins delivered to nerve terminals, the site of secretion of such proteins (72), and that these tyrosine-sulfated proteins constitute the bulk of the total protein-bound tyrosine sulfate synthesized by neurons (S. B. Por & W. B. Huttner, unpublished data).

**Table 1**  Tyrosine-sulfated proteins

| Protein | Species | Localization[a] | Reference |
|---|---|---|---|
| α-2-antiplasmin | man | sec | 36 |
| α-fetoprotein | man | sec | 57 |
| α-2-macroglobulin | rat | sec | 35 |
| aminopeptidase N | pig | plm | 20 |
| caerulein | frog | sec | 4 |
| cholecystokinin (CCK) | dog, man, pig | sec | 61 |
| C-terminal peptide of pro-CCK | man, rat, pig | sec | 1, 21 |
| complement C4 (α-chain) | man, mouse | sec | 38, 49 |
| dermatan sulfate (core protein) | man | sec | —[b] |
| entactin/nidogen | mouse | sec | 66 |
| factor X | cow | sec | 59 |
| fibrinogen | various species | sec | 15, 35, 46 |
| fibronectin | hamster, man, rat, | sec | 56, 65 |
| gastrin | various mammals | sec | 5, 27 |
| heparin cofactor II | man | sec | 39 |
| hirudin | leech | sec | 67 |
| immunoglobulin A (α-chain) | mouse | sec | —[c] |
| immunoglobulin G 2a (γ-chain) | mouse | sec | 8 |
| immunoglobulin M (μ-chain) | mouse, rat | sec | 11 |
| leucosulfakinin | cockroach | sec | 62 |
| leu-enkephalin | various mammals | sec | 73 |
| maltase-glucoamylase | pig | plm | 20 |
| phyllokinin | frog | sec | 3 |
| procollagen type III | man | sec | 48 |
| procollagen type V | chicken | sec | 22 |
| secretogranin I (chromogranin B) | cow, rat | sec | 53, 70 |
| secretogranin II | cow, rat | sec | 53, 69, 70 |
| S-protein/vitronectin | man | sec | —[d] |
| SG70 | *Volvox* | sec | 76 |
| sucrase-isomaltase | pig | plm | 20 |
| thyroglobulin | mouse, pig, rat | sec | 30, 35 |
| yolk protein 1 | fruit fly | sec | 9 |
| yolk protein 2 | fruit fly | sec | 9 |
| yolk protein 3 | fruit fly | sec | 9 |

[a] Abbreviations: sec, secretory; plm, plasma membrane
[b] H. Kresse, personal communication
[c] P. A. Baeuerle, W. B. Huttner, unpublished
[d] A. Hille, D. Jenne, K. Stanley, W. B. Huttner, unpublished

Recent work indicates that tyrosine sulfation occurs in a wider variety of proteins derived from the rough endoplasmic reticulum than was initially assumed (44). A quantitative study (34) has shown that although most (65–95%) of the total protein-bound tyrosine sulfate synthesized by cells is recovered in secreted proteins, significant amounts of tyrosine sulfate are found in nonsecretory proteins. Several proteins tightly associated with membranes have been found to contain tyrosine sulfate. Some of these [p61 of A431 cells (58); microvillar enzymes of intestinal epithelial cells (20)] are cell surface proteins, whereas others [p150 of the human hepatoma cell line HepG2 (34)] appear to be confined to intracellular membranes. Moreover, a soluble 45-kd glycoprotein of fibroblasts and HepG2 cells that is retained intracellulary in a membrane-enclosed compartment undergoes tyrosine sulfation (33). In contrast to oligosaccharide sulfation (18a), tyrosine sulfation has so far not been reported for lysosomal proteins, but this could be a problem of detection. Proteins not originating from the rough endoplasmic reticulum, such as cytoplasmic, nucleoplasmic, and mitochondrial proteins, do not become tyrosine sulfated under physiological conditions (43, 44).

## Functions

The identified tyrosine-sulfated proteins are functionally diverse (see Table 1). In addition to neuropeptides, which constitute one major functional class, the list of identified tyrosine-sulfated proteins includes cell surface enzymes, proteins of the blood clotting system, of the extracellular matrix, of the immune system, and others. The biological significance of tyrosine sulfation is understood only in the case of a few neuropeptides, as will be discussed below.

## TYROSYLPROTEIN SULFOTRANSFERASE

Tyrosylprotein sulfotransferase catalyzes the sulfate transfer from 3'-phosphoadenosine 5'-phosphosulfate (PAPS) to tyrosine residues of proteins:

protein + PAPS → tyrosine-sulfated protein + PAP

Such an enzymatic activity was first described in PC12 cells, a rat neuroendocrine cell line (53). This enzyme was found to have the correct substrate specificity since it catalyzed the tyrosine sulfation of secretogranin I and secretogranin II, the major tyrosine-sulfated proteins of PC12 cells (53, 70). Subsequent studies have demonstrated that tyrosylprotein sulfotransferase catalyzes the sulfation of a variety of endogenous and exogenous protein substrates in homogenates, membrane fractions, and extracts of numerous cells and tissues, including adrenal medulla tissue, fibroblasts, and AtT-20 cells (54, 55), BHK cells (26), brain tissue (74), A431 cells (58), neuroblastoma-glioma hybrid cells (13), and hybridoma cells (11). Moreover, tyrosylprotein sulfotransferase has been found in membrane fractions of all rat tissues examined (63).

## Subcellular Localization

Tyrosylprotein sulfotransferase, as determined by subcellular fractionation, is localized to the Golgi complex (55). The active site of the enzyme is oriented

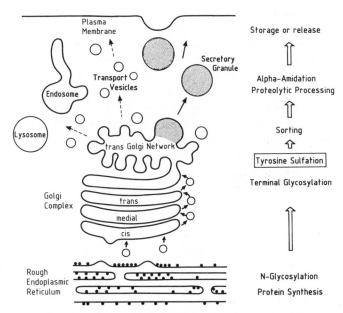

*Figure 1* Tyrosine sulfation, neuropeptide processing, and the secretory pathway. The transport route of neuropeptides along the secretory pathway is indicated by solid arrows. Dashed arrows indicate transport routes not normally taken by neuropeptides. The processing steps are depicted on the right next to the compartments in which they occur, and their sequence is indicated by open arrows.

towards the lumen of the Golgi (55), as one would expect in view of the topology of tyrosine-sulfated proteins. A specific transmembrane carrier system for PAPS from its site of synthesis, the cytosol, to the Golgi lumen supplies the enzyme with its nucleotide cosubstrate (71). Within the Golgi complex, tyrosylprotein sulfotransferase acts specifically in the *trans* Golgi (see Figure 1). This conclusion comes from a study on immunoglobulin M (11) in which the addition of sulfate to tyrosine residues during intracellular transport was compared with the well-characterized steps of processing of N-linked oligosaccharides. Tyrosine sulfation was found to take place in the same compartment as galactosylation and sialylation (i. e. the *trans* Golgi), occurring (at least in part) shortly after these terminal glycosylation reactions. Thus tyrosine sulfation is the last known covalent addition to proteins before their exit from the *trans* Golgi. Tyrosine sulfation has not been found to occur in any other compartment that is part of, or derived from, the secretory pathway. Precursors of tyrosine-sulfated secretory proteins isolated from the rough endoplasmic reticulum and from the *cis* and medial Golgi are not yet tyrosine sulfated (11, 23, 52). Subcellular fractions enriched in lysosomes or secretory granules do not contain significant amounts of tyrosylprotein sulfotransferase activity (55).

The localization of tyrosylprotein sulfotransferase in the *trans* Golgi, together with the notion that proteins secreted by either constitutive or regulated pathways contain tyrosine sulfate, suggests that tyrosine sulfation precedes the sorting of secretory proteins to these pathways, a process thought to occur at the exit site of the Golgi complex (see 29, 50). In the cases where neuropeptides are sorted as precursors and processed proteolytically in secretory granules, tyrosine sulfation precedes, and thus may affect, proteolytic processing of neuropeptide precursors (see Figure 1). In these cases the precursors of neuropeptides rather than the cleaved neuropeptides are the physiological substrates for tyrosylprotein sulfotransferase.

## Properties

Tyrosylprotein sulfotransferase has all the characteristics of an integral membrane protein. It is not extracted from membranes by low ionic strength, high ionic strength, or pH11 treatment but is solubilized by nonionic detergents and partitions into the detergent phase upon Triton X-114 extraction and phase condensation (55, 63). Tyrosylprotein sulfotransferase solubilized from Golgi membranes of bovine adrenal medulla has been studied with an amino acid polymer, $(Glu^{62}, Ala^{30}, Tyr^{8})_n$ (55), with tubulin (55), and with various synthetic peptides (63) that correspond to tyrosine sulfation sites in the cholecystokinin precursor (1, 21) and in secretogranin I (14).

The solubilized enzyme from adrenal medulla has a pH optimum between 6.0 and 6.5 (55). This property fits well with the *trans*-Golgi localization of the enzyme since the *trans* cisternae of the Golgi are known to have a slightly acidic pH (7). With both endogenous and exogenously added substrate proteins, tyrosylprotein sulfotransferase activity is stimulated by the divalent cations $Mg^{2+}$ and $Mn^{2+}$ and is inhibited by EDTA (53, 55). A pH optimum of ~6 and stimulation by $Mn^{2+}$ have also been observed for the nonsolubilized enzyme from rat brain microsomes (74), which has recently been found (75) to be very similar to the enzyme originally characterized in adrenal medulla (54, 55). In contrast, sulfation of an endogenous membrane protein in A431 cells was not inhibited by EDTA (58). The apparent $K_m$ of tyrosylprotein sulfotransferase for various synthetic peptide substrates is in the micromolar range; the lowest value reported is 0.3 $\mu$M for $(Glu^{62}, Ala^{30}, Tyr^{8})_n$ (55, 63, 74, 75). The apparent $K_m$ of solubilized tyrosylprotein sulfotransferase for the cosubstrate PAPS is 5 $\mu$M (55).

## Consensus Features of Tyrosine Sulfation Sites

The sequences surrounding sulfated tyrosine residues are known for several neuropeptides and other secretory proteins. By comparing these sequences, consensus features of tyrosine sulfation sites have been deduced and criteria for predicting tyrosine sulfation sites have been proposed (37, 43, 44; see Table 2).

PRESENCE OF ACIDIC AMINO ACIDS    Sulfated tyrosine residues are usually surrounded by several acidic amino acid residues. Most frequently, an aspartic or glutamic acid is found at position $-1$ of the sulfated tyrosine and at least two more acidic residues are present between positions $-5$ and $+5$ (see footnote to Table 2). The hypothesis (53) that acidic amino acid residues in the vicinity of tyrosine residues are involved in the recognition of substrate proteins by tyrosylprotein sulfotransferase has received experimental support by the demonstration that polymers of tyrosine and glutamic acid are sufficient as substrates for sulfation (55) and by the observations that all of the synthetic peptides found to serve as in vitro substrates (13, 63, 74) contain acidic amino residues, including one in position $-1$. In contrast to the abundance of acidic amino acids, basic amino acids are rarely found in the vicinity of tyrosine sulfate residues (not more than one basic residue between positions $-5$ and $+5$).

PRESENCE OF TURN-INDUCING AMINO ACIDS    All known tyrosine sulfation sites contain amino acids with the potential to induce turns in the polypeptide. At least one proline or glycine, the amino acids with the strongest turn-inducing potential (64), or at least two of the three other amino acids with significant turn-inducing potential [aspartic acid, serine, and asparagine (64)]

**Table 2**    Consensus features of tyrosine sulfation sites[a]

Acidic amino acids
  Presence of an acidic amino acid at position $-1$ and of at least three acidic amino acid residues from $-5$ to $+5$. Paucity of basic amino acid residues (not more than one from $-5$ to $+5$).

Secondary structure
  Presence of turn-inducing amino acid residues from $-7$ to $-2$ and from $+1$ to $+7$ (at least one pro or gly or at least two asp, ser or asn).

Exposure on protein surface
  Paucity of hydrophobic amino acid residues (not more than three from $-5$ to $+5$).

Steric hinderance
  Absence of disulfide-bonded cysteine residues from $-7$ to $+7$. Absence of N-linked glycans near the tyrosine.

[a] For details see References 37, and 43. Negative numbers refer to the sequence position of residues at the N-terminal side of the sulfated tyrosine and positive numbers to those at the C-terminal side. The sulfated tyrosine itself is position 0.

are found in all sulfation sites within positions $-7$ to $-2$ and $+1$ to $+7$ of the tyrosine sulfate residues. The presence of turn-inducing amino acids probably exposes tyrosine residues located near acidic amino acids, thereby facilitating their access to the active site of tyrosylprotein sulfotransferase. Likewise, the scarcity of hydrophobic amino acids in the vicinity of tyrosine sulfate residues presumably reflects the need to expose tyrosine sulfation sites on the surface of substrate proteins.

ABSENCE OF DISULFIDE BONDS AND N-LINKED GLYCANS    No known tyrosine sulfation site contains any cysteine residue between positions $-7$ and $+7$. Most cysteine residues in secretory proteins are involved in formation of disulfide bonds (which are formed in the rough endoplasmic reticulum and thus before the protein reaches the compartment of sulfation). This raises the possibility that disulfide bonds in the vicinity of a tyrosine residue prevent sulfation even if the latter is located in a sequence containing acidic amino acids and turn-inducing amino acids.

No known tyrosine sulfation site is located near an N-glycosylation site (Asn-X-Ser or Asn-X-Thr; see 51). It is likely that N-linked oligosaccharides (which are added to the protein prior to sulfation) prevent sulfation of a nearby tyrosine because of steric hinderance, even if the latter is located in a sequence containing acidic amino acids and turn-inducing amino acids. In mouse IgG2a, a tyrosine residue preceded by two acidic amino acids (tyr 179) adjoins the N-glycosylation site of the constant part of the heavy chain. After inhibition of N-glycosylation, the IgG2a heavy chain becomes tyrosine-sulfated in the constant region (8), presumably at tyr 179, which is now accessible to the tyrosylprotein sulfotransferase.

## Lack of Reversibility of Tyrosine Sulfation in Vivo

The available evidence indicates that tyrosine sulfation is poorly reversible or even irreversible in vivo. For various secretory proteins (e.g. IgM and proteins secreted by fibroblasts) it has been shown that essentially all of the tyrosine sulfate present in the intracellular forms of these proteins at the end of a labelling pulse is recovered when all the labelled secretory proteins had been chased into the medium (11, 34). Certain secretory proteins isolated from secretory granules, e.g. secretogranin I (14), are stoichiometrically tyrosine sulfated. Hence, no significant protein desulfation occurs during transport to the cell surface or in secretory granules. This indicates either the absence of a sulfotyrosylprotein sulfatase or the lack of contact between such an enzyme, if one exists, and the tyrosine-sulfated proteins studied.

The fate of protein-bound tyrosine sulfate after secretion has been in-vestigated in vivo in the case of fibrinogen. The half-life of sulfate-labelled fibrinogen in vivo is the same as that of amino acid–labelled fibrinogen, which indicates that no desulfation of this protein occurs after secretion in the living animal (16). After injection of sulfate-labelled fibrinopeptide B into rabbits, essentially all of the sulfate label was recovered in the urine in the form of free tyrosine sulfate and its deaminated metabolites. This result shows that even after degradation of this tyrosine-sulfated protein there is no significant desulfation (47). This may be true for other tyrosine-sulfated proteins as well, since the amounts of tyrosine sulfate excreted in the urine are too high to be accounted for only by the turnover of fibrinogen (31).

# FUNCTIONAL ASPECTS OF TYROSINE SULFATION

The biological role of protein tyrosine sulfation has been established only in the cases of a few neuropeptides. This is partially due to the fact that studies comparing sulfated and unsulfated forms of proteins (rather than small peptides) are experimentally more difficult; the unsulfated form of a tyrosine-sulfated protein could not easily be obtained. Recently, however, the sulfate analogue chlorate has been shown to be a potent inhibitor of protein sulfation in intact cells (10). The availability of an inhibitor of sulfation will greatly facilitate functional studies on protein tyrosine sulfation.

## Biological Activity of Neuropeptides

Tyrosine sulfation is essential for the biological activity of certain neuropeptides. For example, the hormonal activity of cholecystokinin (CCK) has been shown to depend on the sulfation of the tyrosine residue (60). Sulfated CCK has been found to be 260 times more potent than unsulfated CCK (2, 17). In contrast to the positive effect of sulfation on the hormonal activity of CCK, the biological activity of leu-enkephalin is inhibited by tyrosine sulfation (73).

## Diversification of Translation Products

Tyrosine sulfation can be a means of producing more than one phenotype from a single translation product. This possibility for functional diversification is indeed utilized by gastrin-producing cells, as shown by Brand et al (18). Gastrin requires tyrosine sulfation for its pancreatic secretagogue activity (45), whereas its ability to stimulate gastric acid secretion is unaffected by sulfation (28). Thus a second biological activity of a single translation product results from tyrosine sulfation. The substoichiometric tyrosine sulfation observed in certain proteins, e.g. IgM (11) and factor X (59), may serve a similar purpose in creating subpopulations of molecules that are functionally altered.

## Proteolytic Processing

Tyrosine sulfation can affect the sensitivity of specific sites in proteins to proteolytic cleavage. For example, chymotryptic cleavage in vitro does not occur at the C-terminal side of sulfated tyrosine residues in caerulein and in yolk protein 2 of the fruit fly (12). With regard to a proteolysis-promoting effect, an intriguing correlation has been observed with gastrin (6, 68). The processing of the gastrin precursor varies in different tissues. The extent of processing toward the smallest product correlates with the extent of tyrosine sulfation. Since tyrosine sulfation probably precedes the proteolytic processing of peptide precursors (see Figure 1), one may speculate that sulfation promotes the processing of the gastrin precursor.

## Intracellular Transport of Secretory Proteins

A possible role of tyrosine sulfation in the intracellular transport of a secretory protein has been investigated by site-directed mutagenesis. Vitellogenin 2 of *Drosophila melanogaster* is stoichiometrically sulfated at tyrosine 172 (9, 12). After mutagenesis of tyrosine 172 to phenylalanine, the wild-type and mutated vitellogenin 2 were expressed in fibroblasts, and their sulfation and secretion were studied (24, 25). The wild-type protein was sulfated at the same residue as the vitellogenin 2 synthesized in the fly, whereas the mutated protein produced by fibroblasts was not sulfated (24). The unsulfated vitellogenin 2 was still secreted (24); however, the kinetics of secretion of the unsulfated vitellogenin 2 were markedly reduced compared to those of the sulfated form (25) and suggested an at least twofold slower passage of the unsulfated protein through the *trans* Golgi.

## SUMMARY

Tyrosine sulfation is a widespread posttranslational modification. Most tyrosine-sulfated proteins identified so far are secretory, including several neuropeptides. Tyrosine sulfation occurs in the *trans* Golgi and is one of the last processing steps before proteins exit from the Golgi complex. The sulfation reaction is catalyzed by tyrosylprotein sulfotransferase, an integral membrane protein that recognizes tyrosine residues in exposed protein domains containing acidic amino acids. In the cases studied to date, tyrosine sulfation has been found to be irreversible, resulting in a life-long alteration in the phenotype of the secretory proteins. The biological role of tyrosine sulfation has so far been elucidated in only a few cases. The intracellular transport kinetics of a secretory protein and the biological activity of certain neuropeptides have been found to be affected by this modification. Future functional studies will be greatly facilitated by the use of chlorate, a sulfate analogue that has recently been found to be a potent and nontoxic inhibitor of sulfation in intact cells.

ACKNOWLEDGMENTS

I thank Drs. U. M. Benedum, A. Hille, C. Niehrs, P. Rosa, and S. Tooze for their helpful comments on the manuscript. Work in the author's laboratory was supported by grants from the Deutsche Forschungsgemeinschaft (Hu 275/3-1, Hu 275/3-2, Hu 275/3-3).

## Literature Cited

1. Adrian, T. E., Domin, J., Bacarese-Hamilton, A. J., Bloom, S. R. 1986. Is the C-terminal flanking region of rat cholecystokinin double sulphated? *FEBS Lett.* 196:5–8

2. Anastasi, A., Bernardi, L., Bertaccini, G., Bosisio, G., De Castiglione, R., et al. 1968. Synthetic peptides related to caerulein. Note 1. *Experientia* 24:771–73

3. Anastasi, A., Bertaccini, G., Erspamer, V. 1966. Pharmocological data on phyllokinin (bradykinyl-isoleucyl-tyrosine O-sulphate) and bradykinyl-isoleucyl-tyrosine. *J. Pharmacol. Chemother.* 27: 479–85

4. Anastasi, A., Erspamer, V., Endean, R. 1968. Isolation and amino acid sequence of caerulein, the active decapeptide of the skin of *Hyla caerulea*. *Arch. Biochem. Biophys.* 125:57–68

5. Andersen, B. N. 1984. Measurement and occurrence of sulfated gastrins. *Scand. J. Clin. Lab. Invest.* 44:5–24

6. Andersen, B. N., Stadil, F. 1983. Sulfation of gastrin in Zollinger-Ellison sera: Evidence for association between sulfation and proteolytic processing. *Regul. Peptides* 6:231–39

7. Anderson, R. G. W., Pathak, R. K. 1985. Vesicles and cisternae in the *trans* Golgi apparatus of human fibroblasts are acidic compartments. *Cell* 40:635–43

8. Baeuerle, P. A., Huttner, W. B. 1984. Inhibition of N-glycosylation induces tyrosine sulphation of hybridoma immunoglobulin G. *EMBO J.* 3:2209–15

9. Baeuerle, P. A., Huttner, W. B. 1985. Tyrosine sulfation of yolk proteins 1, 2 and 3 in *Drosophila melanogaster*. *J. Biol. Chem.* 260:6434–39

10. Baeuerle, P. A., Huttner, W. B. 1986. Chlorate—A potent inhibitor of protein sulfation in intact cells. *Biochem. Biophys. Res. Commun.* 141:870–77

11. Baeuerle, P. A., Huttner, W. B. 1987. Tyrosine sulfation is a *trans* Golgi-specific protein modification. *J. Cell Biol.* 105:2655–64

12. Baeuerle, P. A., Lottspeich, F., Hutt-

ner, W. B. 1988. Determination of the site of tyrosine sulfation in yolk protein 2 of *Drosophila melanogaster*. Submitted

13. Barling, P. M., Palmer, D. J., Christie, D. L. 1986. Preparation of desulphated bovine fibrinopeptide B and demonstration of its sulphation in vitro by an enzyme system from neuroblastoma-glioma hybrid cells. *Int. J. Biochem.* 2:137–41

14. Benedum, U. M., Lamouroux, A., Konecki, D. S., Rosa, P., Hille, A., Baeuerle, P. A., Frank, R., Lottspeich, F., Mallet, J., Huttner, W. B. 1987. The primary structure of human secretogranin I (chromogranin B): Comparison with chromogranin A reveals homologous terminal domains and a large intervening variable region. *EMBO J.* 6:1203–11

15. Bettelheim, F. R. 1954. Tyrosine-O-sulfate in a peptide from fibrinogen. *J. Am. Chem.* 76:2838–39

16. Blombäck, B., Boström, H., Vestermark, A. 1960. On the [$^{35}$S]sulphate incorporation in fibrinopeptide B from rabbit fibrinogen. *Biochim. Biophys. Acta* 38:502–12

17. Bodanszky, M., Martinez, J., Priestley, G. P., Gardner, J. D., Mutt, V. 1978. Cholecystokinin (pancreozymin). 4. Synthesis and properties of a biologically active analogue of the C-terminal heptapeptide with epsilon-hydroxynorleucine sulfate replacing tyrosine sulfate. *J. Med. Chem.* 21:1030–35

18. Brand, S. J., Andersen, B. N., Rehfeld, J. F. 1984. Complete tyrosine-O-sulphation of gastrin in neonatal rat pancreas. *Nature* 309:456–58

18a. Braulke, T., Hille, A., Huttner, W. B., Hasilik, A., von Figura, K. 1987. Sulfated oligosaccharides in human lysosomal enzymes. *Biochem. Biophys. Res. Commun.* 143:178–85

19. Christie, D. L., Hill, R. M., Isakow, K., Barling, P. M. 1986. Identification of tyrosine O-sulfate in proteins by reverse-phase high-performance liquid

chromatography: Use of base hydrolysis combined with precolumn derivatization using phenyl isothiocyanate. *Anal. Biochem.* 154:92–99

20. Danielsen, E. M. 1987. Tyrosine sulfation, a posttranslational modification of microvillar enzymes in the small intestinal enterocyte. *EMBO J.* 6:2891–96

21. Eng, J., Gubler, U., Raufman, J.-P., Chang, M., Hulmes, J. D., et al. 1986. Cholecystokinin-associated COOH-terminal peptides are fully sulfated in pig brain. *Proc. Natl. Acad. Sci. USA* 83: 2832–35

22. Fessler, L. I., Brosh, S., Chapin, S., Fessler, J. H. 1986. Tyrosine sulfation in precursors of collagen V. *J. Biol. Chem.* 261:5034–40

23. Fessler, L. I., Chapin, S., Brosh, S., Fessler, J. H. 1986. Intracellular transport and tyrosine sulfation of procollagens V. *Eur. J. Biochem.* 158: 511–18

24. Friederich, E., Baeuerle, P. A., Fritz, H.-J., Lottspeich, F., Huttner, W. B. 1987. Site-specific mutagenesis as an approach to investigate the role of tyrosine sulfation of secretory proteins. *Eur. J. Cell Biol.* 43(Suppl.):17:16

25. Friederich, E. 1987. Mutagenesis of a tyrosine sulfation site in a secretory protein. In *Molecular Mechanism in Protein Secretion, Eur. Mol. Biol. Lab. Res. Rep.*, ed. W. B. Huttner, et al. 1986:19

26. Fukui, S., Numata, Y., Yamashina, I. 1984. Comparison of protein sulfation in control and virus-transformed baby hamster kidney cells. *J. Biochem.* 96: 1783–88

27. Gregory, H., Hardy, P. M., Jones, D. S., Kenner, G. W., Sheppard, R. C. 1964. The antral hormone gastrin. *Nature* 204:931–33

28. Gregory, R. A., Tracy, H. J. 1964. The constitution and properties of two gastrins extracted from hog antral mucosa. *Gut* 5:103–14

29. Griffiths, G., Simons, K. 1986. The *trans* golgi network: Sorting at the exit site of the golgi complex. *Science* 234:438–43

30. Herzog, V. 1985. Secretion of sulfated thyroglobulin. *Eur. J. Cell. Biol.* 39: 399–409

31. Hext, P. M., Thomas, S., Rose, F. A., Dodgson, K. S. 1973. Determination and significance of L-tyrosine O-sulphate and its deaminated metabolites in normal human and mouse urine. *Biochem. J.* 134:629–35

32. Deleted in proof

33. Hille, A., Griffiths, G., Holzer, U., Huttner, W. B. 1987. A 45 kDa soluble

protein residing intracellularly in a membrane-enclosed compartment is tyrosine-sulfated. *Eur. J. Cell Biol.* 43:(Suppl.) 17:25

34. Hille, A., Huttner, W. B. 1988. Tyrosine sulfation occurs in secretory as well as in membrane proteins—a balance sheet. Submitted

35. Hille, A., Rosa, P., Huttner, W. B. 1984. Tyrosine sulfation: A post-translational modification of proteins destined for secretion? *FEBS Lett.* 117:129–34

36. Hortin, G., Fok, K. F., Toren, P. C., Strauss, A. W. 1987. Sulfation of a tyrosine residue in the plasmin-binding domain of α2-antiplasmin. *J. Biol. Chem.* 262:3082–85

37. Hortin, G., Folz, R., Gordon, J. I., Strauss, A. W. 1986. Characterization of sites of tyrosine sulfation in proteins and criteria for predicting their occurrence. *Biochem. Biophys. Res. Commun.* 141:326–33

38. Hortin, G., Sims, H., Strauss, A. W. 1986. Identification of the site of sulfation of the fourth component of human complement. *J. Biol. Chem.* 261:1786–93

39. Hortin, G., Tollefsen, D. M., Strauss, A. W. 1986. Identification of two sites of sulfation of human heparin cofactor II. *J. Biol. Chem.* 261:15827–30

40. Huttner, W. B. 1982. Sulphation of tyrosine residues—a widespread modification of proteins. *Nature* 299:273–76

41. Huttner, W. B. 1984. Determination and occurrence of tyrosine O-sulfate in proteins. *Methods Enzymol.* 107:200–23

42. Huttner, W. B. 1987. Protein tyrosine sulfation. *Trends Biochem. Sci.* 12:361–63

43. Huttner, W. B., Baeuerle, P. A. 1988. Protein sulfation on tyrosine. *Modern Cell Biology*, Vol. 6, ed. B. Satir. pp. 97–140 New York: Liss.

44. Huttner, W. B., Baeuerle, P. A., Benedum, U. M., Friederich, E., Hille, A., et al. 1986. Protein sulfation on tyrosine. In *Hormones and Cell Regulation*, ed. J. Nunez, et al., *Colloque INSERM*, John Libbey Eurotext Ltd., 139, pp. 199–217

45. Jensen, S. L., Rehfeld, J. F., Holst, J. J., Fahrenkrug, J., Nielsen, O. V., Schaffalitzky de Muckadell, O. B. 1980. Secretory effects of gastrins on isolated porcine pancreas. *Am. J. Physiol.* 238:186–92

46. Jevons, F. R. 1963. Tyrosine O-sulphate in fibrinogen and fibrin. *Biochem. J.* 89:621–24

47. Jones, J. G., Dodgson, K. S., Powell, G. M., Rose, F. A. 1963. Studies on

L-tyrosine O-sulphate. 3. The metabolic fate of the L-tyrosine O[$^{35}$S]sulphate residue of $^{35}$S-labelled rabbit fibrinopeptide B. *Biochem. J.* 87:548–53

48. Jukkola, A., Risteli, J., Niemelä, O., Risteli, L. 1986. Incorporation of sulphate into type III procollagen by cultured human fibroblasts. Identification of tyrosine O-sulphate. *Eur. J. Biochem.* 154:219–24

49. Karp, D. R. 1983. Post-translational modification of the fourth component of complement. *J. Biol. Chem.* 258:12745–48

50. Kelly, R. B. 1985. Pathways of protein secretion in eucaryotes. *Science* 230:25–32

51. Kornfeld, R., Kornfeld, S. 1985. Assembly of asparagine-linked oligosaccharides. *Ann. Rev. Biochem.* 54:631–64

52. Kudryk, B., Okada, M., Redman, C. M., Blombäck, B. 1982. Biosynthesis of dog fibrinogen. *Eur. J. Biochem.* 125:673–82

53. Lee, R. W. H., Huttner, W. B. 1983. Tyrosine O-sulfated proteins of PC12 phaeochromocytoma cells and their sulfation by a tyrosylprotein sulfotransferase. *J. Biol. Chem.* 258:11326–34

54. Lee, R. W. H., Huttner, W. B. 1984. Tyrosylprotein sulfotransferase, a novel golgi enzyme involved in the tyrosine sulfation of proteins. *J. Cell Biol.* 99:231a

55. Lee, R. W. H., Huttner, W. B. 1985. (Glu$^{62}$, Ala$^{30}$, Tyr$^8$)$_n$ serves as a high-affinity substrate for tyrosylprotein sulfotransferase: A Golgi enzyme. *Proc. Natl. Acad. Sci. USA* 82:6143–47

56. Liu, M.-C., Lipmann, F. 1985. Isolation of tyrosine-O-sulfate by pronase hydrolysis from fibronectin secreted by Fujinami sarcoma virus-infected rat fibroblasts. *Proc. Natl. Acad. Sci. USA* 82:34–37

57. Liu, M.-C., Yu, S., Sy, J., Redman, C. M., Lipmann, F. 1985. Tyrosine sulfation of proteins from the human hepatoma cell line Hep G2. *Proc. Natl. Acad. Sci. USA* 82:7160–64

58. Liu, N., Baenziger, J. U. 1986. In vivo and in vitro tyrosine sulfation of a membrane glycoprotein. *J. Biol. Chem.* 261:856–61

59. Morita, T., Jackson, C. M. 1986. Localization of the structural difference between bovine blood coagulation factors X$_1$ and X$_2$ to tyrosine 18 in the activation peptide. *J. Biol. Chem.* 261:4008–14

60. Mutt, V. 1980. Cholecystokinin—isolation, structure, and functions. In *Gastrointestinal Hormones*, ed. G. B. J. Glass, pp. 169–221. New York: Raven

61. Mutt, V., Jorpes, J. E. 1968. Structure of porcine cholecystokinin-pancreozymin. *Eur. J. Biochem.* 6:156–62

62. Nachman, R. J., Holman, G. M., Haddon, W. F., Ling, N. 1986. Leucosulfakinin, a sulfated insect neuropeptide with homology to gastrin and cholecystokinin. *Science* 234:71–73

63. Niehrs, C., Huttner, W. B. 1988. Characterization of tyrosylprotein sulfotransferase with synthetic peptide substrates. Submitted

64. Palau, J., Argos, P., Puigdomenech, P. 1982. Protein secondary structure: Studies on the limits of prediction accuracy. *Int. J. Protein Peptides Res.* 91:394–401

65. Paul, J. I., Hynes, R. O. 1984. Multiple fibronectin subunits and their post-translational modifications. *J. Biol. Chem.* 259:13477–87

66. Paulsson, M., Dziadek, M., Suchanek, C., Huttner, W. B., Timpl, R. 1985. Nature of sulphated macromolecules in mouse Reichert's membrane. *Biochem. J.* 231:571–79

67. Petersen, T. E., Roberts, H. R., Sottrup-Jensen, L., Magnusson, S., Badgy, D. 1976. Primary structure of hirudin, a thrombin-specific inhibitor. In *Protides of Biological Fluids*, ed. H. Peeters, 23:145–49. New York: Pergamon

68. Rehfeld, J. F., Larsson, L.-I. 1981. Pituitary gastrins. *J. Biol. Chem.* 256:10426–29

69. Rosa, P., Fumagalli, G., Zanini, A., Huttner, W. B. 1985. The major tyrosine-sulfated protein of the bovine anterior pituitary is a secretory protein present in gonadotrophs, thyrotrophs, mammotrophs, and corticotrophs. *J. Cell Biol.* 100:928–37

70. Rosa, P., Hille, A., Lee, R. W. H., Zanini, A., De Camilli, P., Huttner, W. B. 1985. Secretogranins I and II: Two tyrosine-sulfated secretory proteins common to a variety of cells secreting peptides by the regulated pathway. *J. Cell Biol.* 101:1999–2011

71. Schwarz, J. K., Capasso, J. M., Hirschberg, C. B. 1984. Translocation of adenosine 3'-phosphate 5'-phosphosulfate into rat liver Golgi vesicles. *J. Biol. Chem.* 259:3554–59

72. Stone, G. C., Hammerschlag, R., Bobinski, J. A. 1984. Fast axonal transport of tyrosine-sulfate containing proteins: Preferential routing of sulfoproteins toward nerve terminals. *Cell Mol. Neurobiol.* 4:249–62

73. Unsworth, C. D., Hughes, J., Morley,

J. S. 1982. O-sulphated leu-enkephalin in brain. *Nature* 295:519–22

74. Vargas, F., Frerot, O., Dan Tung Tuong, M., Schwartz, J. C. 1985. Characterization of a tyrosine sulfotransferase in rat brain using cholecystokinin derivatives as acceptors. *Biochemistry* 24:5938–43

75. Vargas, F., Schwartz, J.-C. 1987. Apparent identity of cerebral tyrosylsulfotransferase activities using either a cholecystokinin derivative or an acidic amino acid polymer as substrate. *FEBS Lett.* 211:234–38

76. Wenzl, S., Sumper, M. 1986. Early event of sexual induction in volvox: Chemical modification of the extracellular matrix. *Dev. Biol.* 115:119–28

# SPECIAL TOPIC: GENETIC ANALYSIS OF VOLTAGE-SENSITIVE ION CHANNELS

## General Introduction

*William A. Catterall*, Section Editor

Department of Pharmacology, University of Washington Medical School, Seattle, Washington 98195

The cellular mechanisms of electrical excitability and the functional properties of voltage-sensitive ion channels have been the subject of intense study by physiologists and biophysicists for several decades. This work has provided an increasingly high-resolution description of the ion selectivity, voltage dependence, and physiological and pharmacological modulation of the ion transport activity of this family of membrane proteins. In the past several years, the relationship between their functional properties of ion channels and their structural features has begun to be expored. Biochemical studies have led to the identification and purification of the protein components of ion channels. A combination of classical and molecular genetic experiments have given a high resolution view of their primary structure. The two articles in this section illustrate the application of the methods of classical genetics, somatic cell genetics, and molecular genetics to studies of voltage-sensitive ion channels. In classical genetics as applied to metazoans, mutations induced or arising spontaneously in individual animals are propagated by appropriate mating and selection methods. Analysis of mutations stably inherited in inbred populations then provides insight into the physiological, cellular, and molecular bases for the mutant phenotypes observed. In somatic cell genetics, mutations induced or arising spontaneously in individual somatic cells, usually in cell culture, are propagated by cell growth under selective conditions. Analysis of mutations stably inherited in clonal cell lines can likewise provide insight into the cellular and molecular bases for the mutant phenotypes observed. Molecular genetics has added a new dimension to these older genetic approaches. Cloning of DNA specifying a mutant phenotype can lead to identification of the gene and protein responsible for the genetic lesion, determination of the protein primary structure, and localization of the genetic defect. The combination of biochemical analysis of purified proteins with molecular genetic techniques can lead to the determination of gene and protein structure without classical or somatic cell genetics. The combination of all of these methods has led to an increasingly clear view of the structure of the family of voltage-sensitive ion channels.

Ann. Rev. Physiology. 1988. 50:379–94

# ION CHANNELS IN *DROSOPHILA*

Diane M. Papazian, Thomas L. Schwarz, Bruce L. Tempel,
Leslie C. Timpe, and Lily Y. Jan

Howard Hughes Medical Institute and the Department of Physiology, University of
California, San Francisco, California 94143

## INTRODUCTION

In this review we explore the ways in which the classical and molecular
genetics of *Drosophila melanogaster* can be used to study the structure and
function of ion channels.

Two different approaches can be used to isolate the genes for ion channels
in *Drosophila*. In one approach, classical genetic techniques are used to
generate mutant flies that may have defective channels. Often, these mutants
are initially identified as interesting because they behave abnormally. Subsequently, they are studied electrophysiologically to see whether synaptic
transmission or ionic currents have been affected by the mutation. Once a
physiologically interesting gene has been identified and its chromosomal
location has been determined, the gene can be cloned. This approach can lead
to molecular analysis of channel genes and the proteins they encode, even if
the channel has not previously been purified. In the second approach, channel
genes that have been cloned in other organisms are used to isolate
homologous genes from *Drosophila*. After mapping these genes to chromosomal locations, classical genetic techniques can be used to obtain deletions
and mutations. The phenotype of these mutations can reveal the function of
the wild-type gene product in vivo. This second approach is sometimes
referred to as "reverse genetics."

Once a channel gene has been cloned and mutants have been isolated, the
molecular genetic techniques of *Drosophila* can be applied. For example, P
element–mediated transformation (61, 75) of the wild-type gene into mutant
flies should restore normal function. Furthermore, mutant alleles, generated
in vitro by site-specific mutagenesis of either coding sequences or potential

379

0066-4278/88/0315-0379$02.00

regulatory elements, can be introduced into flies lacking the wild type gene. Such experiments should help to correlate the structure of the gene product with its function and to study the regulaton of the gene's expression during development and in different tissues. These techniques are now used frequently to study *Drosophila* genes and will soon be extended to genes encoding channels.

Below, we briefly discuss the electrophysiological preparations used to study ionic currents in *Drosophila*. Then we review recent progress on four genes. Three of them were isolated on the basis of homology to channel genes that had been cloned previously in other organisms. The fourth is a putative channel gene cloned by the genetic approach, without any prior biochemical information about the gene product. Finally, we summarize findings in some neurological mutants that have not yet been analyzed molecularly. The interested reader is referred to several excellent and more comprehensive reviews that have appeared recently (17, 67, 80, 88).

## Physiological Preparations

Although fruit flies are small, they have surprisingly large muscles. In the larva, the body wall is lined with striated muscle fibers, each about 400 $\mu$m long, 80 $\mu$m wide, and 25$\mu$m thick. Each fiber is innervated by a segmental nerve (38). The neuromuscular junction preparation is thin and can be observed with Nomarski optics, so a variety of intracellular and extracellular recording techniques (38, 90), as well as two-electrode voltage-clamp techniques (91), can be used. This preparation is useful for screening for mutations that may affect synaptic transmission or the propagation of action potentials. During pupal metamorphosis, adult muscles develop de novo. The flight muscle fibers (dorsal longitudinal muscles, DLMs) are large (800 $\times$ 100 $\times$ 50 $\mu$m) and can be voltage clamped using two electrodes. The sequential development of several different currents in these fibers, combined with the elimination of some currents by mutations, allows currents mediated by specific ion channels to be separated (64).

Recently, patch-clamp techniques have been applied to *Drosophila* neurons and muscles (74, 92, 96). Two different primary culture preparations have been used. In one, the larval brain is treated with collagenase and dispersed onto a culture dish, where the neurons settle and sprout neurites (92). In the second, individual mid-gastrula embryos are disrupted and allowed to develop in culture, where both fibrulating muscles and neurons with processes appear, forming neuromuscular junctions and neuronal connections (70). These culture systems offer several advantages: Single-channel currents can be studied, and neuronal currents, which are difficult to voltage clamp in *Drosophila*, can be characterized by patch clamping cell bodies. Furthermore, lethal mutations that disrupt the function of channels necessary for the survival of larvae and adults, may be studied in cultures of embryos (S. E. Germeraad, D. K., O'Dowd, and R. W. Aldrich, personal communication).

The preparations described above can be used to identify individual currents and to compare them in mutant and normal flies. Several other preparations have been used to study neuronal action potentials (79), neuronal connectivity (81), and receptor potentials (57, 59).

## Currents Identified in Drosophila

The ionic currents found in *Drosophila* are similar to those seen in other organisms (Table 1). As in other organisms, the greatest variety is found among $K^+$ currents: Several $K^+$ currents activated by either changes in voltage or calcium concentration have been identified using whole-cell recording techniques. These currents may include components from several channel types, which can only be distinguished at the single-channel level. Some tentative relationships between whole-cell currents and single-channel currents are suggested in Table 1.

The diversity of $K^+$ channels observed physiologically has not yet been explained molecularly. Are the different channels encoded by separate genes or, as suggested by single-gene mutations that affect more than one current (89), do channel genes encode subunits used in more than one type of channel (91)? Nerve and muscle contain similar but not identical inactivating $K^+$ currents (74, 94). Do these differences result from altered expression of one channel gene due to tissue-specific promoters, splice products, or posttranslational modifications of the gene product? These questions will be answered as more currents are defined by single-channel methods and as their relations to newly cloned genes are defined by combining physiological, genetic, and molecular techniques.

# GENES CLONED BY HOMOLOGY: ACETYLCHOLINE RECEPTOR AND SODIUM ION CHANNEL

On the basis of homology to counterparts from other species, three channel genes have recently been isolated from *Drosophila*. The purpose of isolating such genes is to apply the "reverse genetic" approach, although the special advantages of *Drosophila* are just beginning to be exploited. Currently, by comparing the sequences of *Drosophila* and vertebrate genes, one may speculate about the properties of their ancestral genes and learn which regions have been conserved throughout evolution; conserved regions may serve crucial functions.

## Acetylcholine Receptor

Although it is not the transmitter at the *Drosophila* neuromuscular junction, acetylcholine (ACh) is likely to be an important transmitter in the central

**Table 1** Ion currents in $Drosophila$[a]

| Ion | Current[b] | Activation | Preparation | Refs. | Current | Activation | Preparation | Conductance (in pS) | Refs. |
|---|---|---|---|---|---|---|---|---|---|
| | | | | | | | *Single Channel Recordings* | | |
| | *Whole Cell Recordings* | | | | | | | | |
| K$^+$, inactivating | $I_A$ | V | DLM VC | 69, 83 | $I_{A1}$ | V | myotube PC | 16 | 74, 94 |
| | | | larval muscle VC | 91 | $I_{A2}$ | V | neuron PC | 5–8 | 1, 72–74 |
| | $I_R^{(1)}$ | V | DLM VC | 83 | $I_{K_D}$ | V | myotube PC | 15–20 | 94 |
| | $I_{A_{CD}}$ ($I_C$) | Ca$^{2+}$/V | DLM VC | 63, 85 | | V | neuron PC | 13–17 | 72, 73 |
| K$^+$, sustained | $I_K$ | V | larval nerve | 15, 38 | $I_{K_1}$ | V | neuron PC | 20–50 | 73 |
| | | | larval muscle VC | 91 | $I_{K_0}$ | V | myotube PC | 35–40 | 94 |
| | $I_{KC}$ | Ca$^{2+}$/V | DLM VC | 69, 83 | $I_{K_{ST}}$ | stretch | myotube PC | 60–100 | 94 |
| | Inward rectifier | V | DLM VC | 85 | | | | | |
| | | | larval muscle VC | 76 | | | | | |
| Na$^+$ | $I_{Na}$ | V | larval nerve VC | 38, 86 | | | | | |
| | | | CGF | 79 | | | | | |
| | | | neuron PC | 56 | | | | | |
| Ca$^{2+}$ | $I_{Ca}$ | V | larval muscle VC | 78, 91 | | | | | |
| | | | DLM VC | 64 | | | | | |
| | | | neuron PC | 96 | | | | | |
| Na$^+$,K$^+$,Ca$^{2+}$ | $I_P$ | Ca$^{2+}$/V | DLM VC | 64 | | | | | |
| Na$^+$,K$^+$,Mg$^{2+}$ | $I_J$ | L-glutamate | larval NMJ | 38 | | | | | |
| ? | ACh receptor | ACh | CNS | 19, 21, 30, 92, 93 | | | | | |

[a] Abbreviations: V, voltage; VC, voltage clamp; PC, patch clamp; DLM, dorsal longitudinal muscle; CGF, cervical giant fiber; NMJ, neuromuscular junction.

[b] $I_R$ is the residual current seen in $Sh$ null mutations at high gain.

nervous system of flies and other insects (6). An ACh receptor from the locust brain has been purified to homogeneity and reconstituted into lipid bilayers for physiological studies (4, 28, 29).

Two genes homologous to vertebrate ACh receptors have been cloned from *Drosophila* (B. Bossy, L. M. Hall, M. Ballivet, P. Spierer, personal communication; 22, 30). Their sequences have been compared with those of the cloned genes for the vertebrate ACh receptor subunits. One of the *Drosophila* genes predicts a protein with an amino acid sequence that is 46% identical to that of the rat neuronal alpha subunit (30). However, it lacks two cysteines that are thought to form a disulfide bond that is essential to the ACh binding site of the vertebrate alpha subunits (43, 45). Thus this gene may code for a channel subunit that does not bind ACh. [The two cysteines are present, however, in another *Drosophila* gene that also shows extensive homology to the alpha subunit (B. Bossey et al, personal communication).] The predicted protein product of this gene contains a signal peptide and four hydrophobic segments long enough to span the membrane (30). A domain containing the first three hydrophobic segments is highly conserved between *Drosophila* and the rat neural ACh receptor (66% identity) (see 3). In contrast, an adjacent domain thought to be cytoplasmic is less conserved (31% identity) (30). Just before the fourth hydrophobic domain, the two genes share a sequence of eleven identical residues, whose functional significance is unknown. An amphipathic sequence thought to form a membrane-spanning $\alpha$-helix in each of the vertebrate subunits has been hypothesized to line the pore of the channel (12, 23). In the fly, this sequence is only 29% identical to that in the rat neuronal alpha subunit, although its amphipathic character is preserved (30). If this sequence forms the pore, it is surprising that it is not more highly conserved.

## Sodium Ion Channel

A *Drosophila* gene that is highly homologous to vertebrate $Na^+$ channel genes has been isolated by Salkoff et al (65, 66). By sequencing genomic clones that cross-hybridize with a rat $Na^+$ channel cDNA, much of the sequence of a putative *Drosophila* $Na^+$ channel has been determined. As in the vertebrate channels, the predicted protein comprises four tandemly repeated homologous units, each of which contains several putative membrane-spanning segments. The homologous units are connected by domains thought to form large cytoplasmic loops. Within the membrane-spanning domains the amino acid sequence of the fly protein is ~50% identical to the vertebrate sequences, but most of the cytoplasmic loops show little conservation.

Each homologous unit of the vertebrate channel contains one region of special interest, an arginine-rich sequence called S4 by Noda et al (54, 55) that is thought to form a transmembrane helix. Within this sequence positive charges are found at every third position; the intervening residues are hydrophobic. Several groups have proposed that these helices are responsible for the voltage-dependent gating of the channel (8, 20, 24, 54). The conservation of this sequence is nearly perfect between rat and *Drosphila:* In the fourth homology unit, for example, 19 of 22 amino acids are identical. In each domain of the fly channel, basic residues are found at the same positions as in the vertebrate channel.

By in situ hybridization to polytene chromosomes, Salkoff et al localized this gene to the second chromosome at band 60D-E. Several known mutations may affect $Na^+$ channels, but none of these correspond to the cloned gene (see below; 65). There may be additional putative $Na^+$ channels encoded nearby or at other loci (18, 66).

We have discussed the extensive sequence homology between vertebrate and *Drosophila* ion channels, particularly in domains thought to include membrane crossings. This conservation leads us to be optimistic that a channel gene first isolated from *Drosophila*, such as the potential $K^+$ channel subunit described next, will be useful in isolating homologous channels from other species.

## CLONING OF *SHAKER,* A GENE THAT PROBABLY CODES FOR A STRUCTURAL COMPONENT OF A POTASSIUM ION CHANNEL

Despite the ubiquity and variety of $K^+$ channels, detailed molecular analysis has not yet been feasible for any of them: They are rare proteins for which, until recently (7, 27, 32, 52), no high-affinity ligands were known. Analysis of the *Shaker* gene may provide the first description of a structural component of a $K^+$ channel. In addition, *Shaker* is the first putative channel gene to be identified and cloned by the genetic approach.

*Shaker* mutations affect a fast, transient $K^+$ current, the A current, similar to one first described in the somata of molluscan neurons (9, 25). Different *Shaker* alleles reduce, eliminate, or alter $I_A$ (68) without affecting other currents (91); it has been proposed that *Shaker* encodes a structural component of the A channel (62, 79).

Several *Shaker* mutations have been mapped to chromosomal position 16F on the X chromosome (79). A DNA fragment (originally isolated for reasons unrelated to *Shaker*) that hybridized nearby was used to begin a chromosomal "walk" through the locus (42, 58). Overlapping clones were isolated reiteratively from genomic libraries until over 200 kb of genomic DNA had been isolated. To localize the *Shaker* gene, several *Shaker* mutations caused by chromosomal rearrangements were mapped and found within a 65-kilobase (kb) region of the cloned DNA. DNA from this region was then used to screen cDNA libraries (58). The sequences of two *Shaker* cDNAs have been determined (82). They predict that *Shaker* encodes an integral membrane protein of 616 amino acids; hydropathy analysis indicates that the protein has a central hydrophobic core, with hydrophilic domains at its amino and carboxyl termini. The central portion contains six hydrophobic stretches long enough to span the membrane. The predicted *Shaker* protein shares significant homology with voltage-dependent $Na^+$ channels, in the region of the S4 sequence (Figure 1). This sequence may form a seventh membrane crossing in the *Shaker* protein. In all, the *Shaker* protein and the eel $Na^+$ channel are 27% identical over a stretch of 120 amino acids. When conservative amino acid substitutions are included, the proteins are 47% homologous in the region of overlap. The fact that the S4 region is highly conserved between two different voltage-sensitive ion channels enhances the attractiveness of the idea that it is involved in voltage-dependent gating.

Currently, the subunit structure of the A channel is unknown. Genetic experiments suggest that the A channel may be a multimeric protein, containing more than one copy of the *Shaker* gene product (83). It remains to be determined whether the A channel is composed exclusively of one or more copies of the *Shaker* gene product or whether it is a heteromultimer in which the *Shaker* product combines with heterologous subunits. Since all the previously described channels are built from repetitive units, it would not be surprising if additional subunits of the A channel were homologous to the *Shaker* protein.

## Homology of Sodium and Potassium Ion Channels

The homologous portions of the $Na^+$ channel and the predicted A channel protein may constitute a voltage-gating domain that is present in other channels as well. In addition, the homology between the $Na^+$ and A channels suggests that they may be descended from a voltage-sensitive ancestor. Since

*Figure 1*  Sequence comparison of (A) the predicted *Shaker* product (predicted amino acid residues 359–387) and (B) the eel $Na^+$ channel (residues 1415–1443). The putative $K^+$ channel component encoded at the *Shaker* locus contains an arginine-rich sequence (82) that is homologous to the S4 region of the fourth homology unit of the electric eel $Na^+$ channel (55). The homology extends outside the arginine-rich sequence into adjacent hydrophobic regions that are not shown. The regularly spaced positive residues, whose presence is characteristic of S4 domains (20, 24, 54) are designated with an asterisk. Identical residues are enclosed by a solid line; conservative changes are enclosed by a dotted line. Changes were considered conservative if the two amino acids fell within one of the following groups: (Met, Val, Ile, Leu), (Ala, Gly), (Ser, Thr, Gln, Asn), (Lys, Arg), (Asp, Glu), and (Phe, Try) (95).

the homology between these two channels is far less extensive than the homology between the vertebrate and fly $Na^+$ channels or between the ACh receptors (see above), the divergence of the A channel and $Na^+$ channel is probably very ancient (see also 31). It will be interesting to see how the primary structure of a $K^+$ channel that is not voltage-gated, or of a voltage-gated $Ca^{2+}$ channel, fits into this scheme of homologies and evolution.

## OTHER *DROSOPHILA* GENES RELEVANT TO CHANNEL FUNCTION

### Other Mutations Affecting Potassium Channels

As mentioned above, *Shaker* mutations alter $I_A$, leaving other currents unaffected. Mutations that affect other $K^+$ currents, including *ether a go-go (eag), Hyperkinetic (Hk)*, and *slowpoke (slo)*, are listed in Table 2 and have been described in previous reviews (17, 67, 80, 88). Only a few details are mentioned here.

Alleles of *eag* may reduce both $I_A$ and $I_K$ (87, 89); it has been proposed that *eag* encodes a regulatory function or structural component shared by several $K^+$ channels. Therefore, molecular analysis of the *eag* product is eagerly awaited. Recently, new *eag* alleles have been induced by hybrid dysgenesis, which should facilitate cloning of the gene (10, 16).

Voltage-clamp experiments have demonstrated that a *slo* mutation eliminates the rapidly inactivating $Ca^{2+}$-dependent $K^+$ current (11). Some other currents such as $I_A$ are normal, though it is not known whether *slo* alters the slowly inactivating, $Ca^{2+}$-dependent $K^+$ current described by Wei & Salkoff (85). It will be interesting to see whether *slo* is a structural gene for the transient, $Ca^{2+}$-activated $K^+$ channel.

### Bang-Sensitive Mutants

The "bang-sensitive" mutants are temporarily paralyzed by a sudden jolt. Because $nap^{ts}$ (Table 2) suppresses this phenotype, it has been suggested that these mutations cause neuronal hyperexcitability. However, physiological abnormality has been demonstrated only for *bang senseless (bss)* (14, 39).

The genes for *bss, easily shocked (eas)*, and *technical knockout (tko)* are being cloned. The *eas* and *bss* genes have been localized cytologically and isolated in a chromosome walk (41). The *tko* gene was isolated during a walk to the *zeste* locus (50). The location of the gene was pinpointed by transformation with a 3.1-kb segment, which complemented the lethality of the allele $tko^{k11}$ (97). This fragment includes a transcript whose sequence shows substantial homology to ribosomal protein S12 from *Euglena gracilis* chloroplasts and from *Escherichia coli*. A hypothesis has been advanced that *tko* encodes a mitochondrial ribosomal protein; impaired mitochondrial function in neurons and muscle may underlie the behavioral abnormality (97). This result points out that the genetic approach can sometimes identify genes that affect neuronal function indirectly and emphasizes that a well-defined physiological or biochemical phenotype is necessary to provide confidence that the gene being studied is directly relevant to channel structure, synthesis, or regulation.

## Mutations Affecting Sodium Channel Function

Four genes, *paralytic (para)*, *no action potential (nap)*, *seizure (sei)*, and *temperature-induced paralytic E (tip-E)*, may affect $Na^+$ channel function. The evidence comes from neurophysiological experiments on nerve conduction and from saxitoxin binding experiments. The phenotypes of these mutants have been reviewed extensively (17, 67, 80, 88) and are summarized in Table 2. Here we mention only one recent physiological result and consider the possible roles of these genes.

Voltage-clamp studies of $Na^+$ currents in cultured embryonic neurons have shown that both $sei^{ts1}$ and *tip-E* reduce $Na^+$ current density at room temperature to about 70% of the wild-type level (56). This result is consistent with the reduction of saxitoxin binding found in these two mutants (Table 2; 35–37). Curiously $nap^{ts}$, which reduces saxitoxin binding (26, 47) and which has defects in action potential propagation even at room temperature (86), appears to have normal $Na^+$ current in these embryonic neurons.

Do any of these genes code for a voltage-sensitive $Na^+$ channel? As discussed above, a *Drosophila* gene with considerable homology to the vertebrate $Na^+$ channel has been isolated, but it does not map to the chromosomal locations of *para, nap, sei,* or *tip-E*. It is possible that one or more of these genes encodes additional subunits of the channel or molecularly distinct $Na^+$ channels. There is precedent from rat brain for both possibilities, since there $Na^+$ channels consist of a large alpha subunit plus two smaller beta subunits (51), and several different genes encode similar alpha subunits (54).

Alternatively, *para, nap, sei,* and *tip-E* may encode proteins required for the synthesis or regulation of $Na^+$ channels. For example, these proteins may control posttranslational modification of the channel or its insertion into the plasma membrane. In neuroblastoma cells, glycosylation of the alpha subunit is required for normal expression of the channel (84). In rat brain, the existence of a cytoplasmic pool of immature channels suggests that insertion into the plasma membrane is regulated (69a). After *para* (49), *nap, sei,* and *tip-E* (18) are cloned and sequenced, we will know more about their roles in $Na^+$ channel function.

**Table 2**  Neurological mutations that may alter membrane excitability[a]

| Locus and location | Behavioral phenotype | Electrophysiological phenotype | Other information | References |
|---|---|---|---|---|
| *Shaker (Sh)* 1–58 | shaking under ether anesthesia | abnormal, reduced, or abolished $I_A$ (pupal and larval muscle); prolonged action potential (adult & larval nerve) | interacts with *eag*, *nap*[ts]; codes for membrane protein homologous to sodium channel | 14, 15, 40, 44, 68, 79, 83, 91 |
| *ether-a-go-go (eag)* 1–50.0 | shaking under ether anesthesia | abnormal $I_A$ and $I_K$ (larval muscle); spontaneous action potentials (larval nerve) | interacts with *Sh* | 15, 44, 87, 89 |
| *Hyperkinetic (Hk)* 1–30.6 | shaking under ether anesthesia | abnormal $I_A$ (larval muscle); spontaneous action potentials (adult nerve) | suppressed by *nap*[ts] | 14, 33, 34, 44, 76 |
| *slowpoke (slo)* 3–85.0 | uncoordinated; ts sluggish; ether-induced shaking | abolished $I_{A_{CD}}$ (larval muscle) | | 11 |
| *bang-sensitive (bas)* 1–49.5 | bang sensitive | | suppressed by *nap*[ts] | 14 |
| *bang-senseless (bss)* 1–54.0 | bang sensitive | abnormal long-term facilitation (larval nerve) | suppressed by *nap*[ts] | 14, 39 |
| *technical knockout (tko)* 1–0.99 | bang sensitive | | suppressed by *nap*[ts]; codes for S12-like protein | 14, 97 |
| *knockdown (kdn)* | bang sensitive | | suppressed by *nap*[ts] | 14 |

| | | | | |
|---|---|---|---|---|
| *easily shocked (eas)* 1–53 | bang sensitive | | suppressed by *nap*ts | 14 |
| *paralytic (para)* 1–53.9–54.1 | ts paralytic (29–37°C); fast recovery | ts block of action potential (larval nerve) | normal TTX binding | 47, 53, 71, 77, 86 |
| *no action potential (nap)* 2–56.2 | ts paralytic (37.5°C); fast recovery | prolonged refractory period and increased TTX sensitivity at 25°C (larval nerve); ts block of action potential (larval nerve) | reduction of TTX and STX binding in homozygotes | 26, 47, 53, 86, 90 |
| *seizure (sei)* 2–106 | ts paralytic (38°C); paralysis preceded by spontaneous wing and leg movement | | *sei*ts1, ts reduction of STX binding; *sei*ts2, ts alteration of $K_d$; altered pH profile for STX binding | 17, 35, 37 |
| *temperature-induced paralytic (tip-E)* 3–13.5 | ts paralytic (39–40°C) | lowers the restrictive temperature for the ts block of action potential in *para*ts | ts reduction of STX binding in homozygotes | 13, 36, 48 |
| *enhancer of seizure e(sei)* 3–39.1 | sluggish | bursts of ejps (flight muscle) | enhances *sei* | 46 |

[a] Abbreviations: ts, temperature sensitive; ejp, excitatory junctional potential; ttx, tetrodotoxin; stx, saxitoxin

## CONCLUSION

The classical and molecular genetics of *Drosophila* offer several advantages for studying ion channels. Flies contain channels similar to those found in other invertebtrates and vertebrates (Table 1). Mutations affecting $Na^+$ channels and various $K^+$ channels have been isolated (Table 2). These mutations may affect structural genes for channels as well as genes involved in channel expression, synthesis, and regulation. If the chromosomal locations of these genes are known, they can be cloned even though their protein products have not previously been identified.

The emerging picture of strong conservation between ion channels in *Drosophila* and vertebrates is encouraging for two reasons. First, ion channel genes that have been cloned in other species can be used to clone similar genes in *Drosophila*, thereby allowing genetic studies of their function and expression. Second, channel genes that have been cloned for the first time in *Drosophila*, such as *Shaker*, may allow the study of similar channels from other species.

ACKNOWLEDGMENTS

We would like to thank Drs. R. Aldrich, H. Betz, B. Bossy, H. Breer, L. Byerly, B. Ganetzky, J. Hall, L. Hall, L. Salkoff, M. Tanouye, and C. F. Wu for sending us reprints and preprints of their recent work, and we thank Lisa Schulte and Marion Meyerson for preparing the manuscript.

*Literature Cited*

1. Aldrich, R. W., Solc, C. K. 1988. In press
2. Deleted in proof
3. Boulter, J., Evans, K., Goldman, D., Martin, G., Treco, D., et al. 1986. Isolation of a cDNA clone coding for a possible neural nicotinic acetylcholine receptor alpha-subunit. *Nature* 319:368–74
4. Breer, H., Kleene, R., Hinz, G. 1985. Molecular forms and subunit structure of the acetylcholine receptor in the central nervous system of insects. *J. Neurosci.* 5:3386–92
5. Deleted in proof
6. Callec, J. J. 1985. Synaptic transmission in the central nervous system. In *Comprehensive Insect Physiology, Biochemistry and Pharmacology*, Vol 5, pp. 139–79, ed. G. A. Kerkut, L. I. Gilbert. New York: Pergamon
7. Carbone, E., Wanke, E., Pretipino, G., Possani, L. D., Maelicke, A. 1982. Selective blockage of voltage-dependent $K^+$ channels by a novel scorpion toxin. *Nature* 296:90–91
8. Catterall, W. A. 1986. Molecular properties of voltage-sensitive sodium channels. *Ann. Rev. Biochem.* 55:953–85
9. Connor, J. A., Stevens, C. F. 1971. Voltage clamp studies of a transient outward membrane current in gastropod neural somata. *J. Physiol. London* 213: 21–30
10. Drysdale, R., Ganetzky, B. 1985. Cloning of a gene affecting potassium channels in *Drosophila*. *Soc. Neurosci. Abstr.* 11:788
11. Elkins, T., Ganetzky, B., Wu, C.-F. 1986. A *Drosophila* mutation that eliminates a calcium-dependent potassium current. *Proc. Natl. Acad. Sci. USA* 83:8415–19
12. Finer-Moore, J., Stroud, R. M. 1984. Amphipathic analysis and possible formation of the ion channel in an acetylcholine receptor. *Proc. Natl. Acad. Sci. USA* 81:155–59

13. Ganetzky, B. 1986. Neurogenetic analysis of *Drosophila* mutations affecting sodium channels: Synergistic effects on viability and nerve conduction in double mutants involving *tip-E*. *J. Neurogenet.* 3:19–31

14. Ganetzky, B., Wu, C.-F. 1982. Indirect suppression involving behavioral mutants with altered nerve excitability in *Drosophila melanogaster*. *Genetics* 100: 597–614

15. Ganetzky, B., Wu, C.-F. 1983. Neurogenetic analysis of potassium currents in *Drosophila:* Synergistic effects on neuromuscular transmission in double mutants. *J. Neurogenet.* 1:17–28

16. Ganetzky, B., Wu, C.-F. 1984. Mutations of a gene affecting potassium currents induced by transposable elements in *Drosophila*. *Soc. Neurosci. Abstr.* 10:1090

17. Ganetzky, B., Wu, C.-F. 1986. Neurogenetics of membrane excitability in *Drosophila*. *Ann. Rev. Genet.* 20:13–44

18. Gil, D. W., Keen, J. K., Hall, L. M. 1986. Cloning of *Drosophila melanogaster* sequences homologous to the voltage-sensitive sodium channel gene from *Electrophorus electricus*. *Soc. Neurosci. Abstr.* 12:1512

19. Gorczyca, M., Hall, J. C. 1984. Identification of a cholinergic synapse in the giant fiber pathway of *Drosophila* using conditional mutations of acetylcholine synthesis. *J. Neurogenet.* 1:289–313

20. Greenblatt, R. E., Blatt, Y., Montal, M. 1985. The structure of the voltage-sensitive sodium channel. *FEBS Lett.* 193:125–34

21. Greenspan, R. J. 1980. Mutations of choline acetyltransferase and associated neural defects in *Drosophila melanogaster*. *J. Comp. Physiol.* 137:83–92

22. Gundelfinger, E. D., Hermans-Borgmeyer, I., Zopf, D., Sawruk, E., Betz, H. 1986. Characterization of the mRNA and the gene of a putative neuronal nicotinic acetylcholine receptor protein from *Drosophila*. In *Nicotinic Acetylcholine Receptor*, ed. A. Maelicke, pp. 437–46. Berlin/Heidelberg: Springer-Verlag

23. Guy, R. 1984. A structural model of the acetylcholine receptor channel based on partition energy and helix packing calculations. *Biophys. J.* 45:249–61

24. Guy, R. H., Seetharamulu, P. 1986. Molecular model of the action potential sodium channel. *Proc. Natl. Acad. Sci. USA* 83:508–12

25. Hagiwara, S., Saito, N. 1959. Voltage-current relations in nerve cell membrane

of *Onchidium verruculatum*. *J. Physiol. London* 148:161–79

26. Hall, L. M., Wilson, S. D., Gitschier, J., Martinez, N., Strichartz, G. R. 1982. Identification of a *Drosophila melanogaster* mutant that affects the saxitoxin receptor of the voltage-sensitive sodium channel. *Ciba Found. Symp.* 88:207–20

27. Halliwell, J. V., Othman, I. B., Pelchen-Matthews, A., Dolly, J. O. 1986. Central action of dendrotoxin: Selective reduction of a transient K conductance in hippocampus and binding to localized acceptors. *Proc. Natl. Acad. Sci. USA* 83:493–97

28. Hanke, W., Breer, H. 1986. Channel properties of an insect neuronal acetylcholine receptor protein reconstituted in planar lipid bilayers. *Nature* 321:171–74

29. Hanke, W., Breer, H. 1987. Characterization of the channel properties of neuronal acetylcholine receptor reconstituted into planar lipid bilayers. In press

30. Hermans-Borgmeyer, I., Zopf, D., Ryseck, R.-P., Hovemann, B., Betz, H., Gundelfinger, E. D. 1986. Primary structure of a developmentally regulated nicotinic acetylcholine receptor protein from *Drosophila*. *EMBO J.* 5:1503–8

31. Hille, B. 1984. *Ionic Channels of Excitable Membranes*. Sunderland, Mass.: Sinauer Assoc. 426 pp.

32. Hughes, M., Romey, G., Duval, D., Vincent, J. P., Lazdunski, M. 1982. Apamin as a selective blocker of the calcium dependent potassium channel in neuroblastoma cells: Voltage clamp and biochemical characterization of the toxin receptor. *Proc. Natl. Acad. Sci. USA* 79:1308–12

33. Ikeda, K., Kaplan, W. D. 1970. Patterned neural activity of a mutant *Drosophila melanogaster*. *Proc. Natl. Acad. Sci. USA* 66:765–72

34. Ikeda, K., Kaplan, W. D. 1974. Neurophysiological genetics in *Drosophila melanogaster*. *Am. Zool.* 14: 1055–66

35. Jackson, F. R., Gitschier, J., Strichartz, G. R., Hall, L. M. 1985. Genetic modifications of voltage-sensitive sodium channels in *Drosophila:* Gene dosage studies of the *seizure* locus. *J. Neurosci.* 5:1144–51

36. Jackson, F. R., Wilson, S. D., Hall, L. M. 1986. The *tip-E* mutation of *Drosophila* decreases saxitoxin binding and interacts with other mutations affecting nerve membrane excitability. *J. Neurogenet.* 3:1–17

37. Jackson, F. R., Wilson, S. D., Strichartz, G. R., Hall, L. M. 1984.

Two types of mutants affecting voltage-sensitive sodium channels in *Drosophila melanogaster. Nature* 308:189–91

38. Jan, L. Y., Jan, Y. N. 1976. Properties of the larval neuromuscular junction in *Drosophila melanogaster. J. Physiol. London* 262:189–214

39. Jan, Y. N., Jan, L. Y. 1978. Genetic dissection of short-term and long-term facilitation at the *Drosophila* neuromuscular junction. *Proc. Natl. Acad. Sci. USA* 75:515–19

40. Jan. Y. N., Jan, L. Y., Dennis, M. J. 1977. Two mutations of synaptic transmission in *Drosophila. Proc. R. Soc. London Ser. B* 198:87–108

41. Jones, K., Stellar, H., Rubin, G. 1987. Personal communication

42. Kamb, A., Iverson, L., Tanouye, M. 1984. Molecular analysis of the *Shaker (Sh)* gene complex in *Drosophila melanogaster. Soc. Neurosci. Abstr.* 10:1089

43. Kao, P. N., Dwork, A. J., Kaldany, R.-R. J., Silver, M. L., Wideman, J., et al. 1984. Identification of the alpha-subunit half-cystine specifically labeled by an affinity reagent for the acetylcholine receptor binding site. *J. Biol. Chem.* 259:11662–65

44. Kaplan, W. D., Trout, W. E., III. 1969. The behavior of four neurological mutants of *Drosophila. Genetics* 61:399–409

45. Karlin, A. 1980. Molecular properties of nicotinic acetylcholine receptors. *Cell Surf. Rev.* 6:191

46. Kasbekar, D. P., Nelson, J. C., Hall, L. M. 1987. *Enhancer of seizure:* A new genetic locus in *Drosophila melanogaster* defined by interactions with temperature-sensitive paralytic mutations. *Genetics* 116:423–31

47. Kauvar, L. M. 1982. Reduced [³H]-tetrodotoxin binding in the *nap^{ts}* paralytic mutant of *Drosophila. Mol. Gen. Genet.* 187:172–73

48. Kulkarni, S. J., Padhye, A. 1982. Temperature-sensitive paralytic mutations on the second and third chromosomes of *Drosophila melanogaster. Genet. Res.* 40:191–99

49. Loughney, K., Ganetzky, B. 1985. Cloning of a gene affecting sodium channels in *Drosophila. Soc. Neurosci. Abstr.* 11:782

50. Mariani, C., Pirrotta, V., Manet, E. 1985. Isolation and characterization of the *zeste* locus of *Drosophila. EMBO J.* 4:2045–52

51. Messner, D. J., Catterall, W. A. 1985. The sodium channel from rat brain. Sep-aration and characterization of subunits. *J. Biol. Chem.* 260:11597–11604

52. Miller, C., Moczydlowski, E., Latorre, R., Phillips, M. 1985. Charybdotoxin, a protein inhibitor of single $Ca^{2+}$-activated $K^+$ channels from mammalian skeletal muscle. *Nature* 313:316–18

53. Nelson, J. C., Baird, D. H. 1985. Action potentials persist at restrictive temperatures in temperature-sensitive paralytic mutants of adult *Drosophila. Soc. Neurosci. Abstr.* 11:313

54. Noda, M., Ikeda, T., Kayano, T., Suzuki, H., Takeshima, H., et al. 1986. Existence of distinct sodium channel messenger RNAs in rat brain. *Nature* 320:188–92

55. Noda, M., Shimizu, S., Tanabe, T., Takai, T., Kayano, T., et al. 1984. Primary structure of *Electrophorus electricus* sodium channel deduced from cDNA sequence. *Nature* 312:121–27

56. O'Dowd, D. K., Aldrich, R. W. 1988. *J. Neurosci.* In press

57. Pak, W. L., Grabowski, S. R. 1978. Physiology of the visual and flight systems. In *The Genetics and Biology of Drosophila,* Vol. 2a, pp. 553–604, ed. M. Ashburner, T. R. F. Wright. London: Academic

58. Papazian, D. M., Schwarz, T. L., Tempel, B. L., Jan, Y. N., Jan, L. Y. 1987. *Science* 237:749–53

59. Rodrigues, V., Siddiqui, O. 1978. Genetic analysis of chemosensory pathway. *Proc. Indian Acad. Sci. Sect. B* 87:147

60. Deleted in proof

61. Rubin, G. M., Spradling, A. C. 1982. Genetic transformation of *Drosophila* with transposable element vectors. *Science* 218:348–53

62. Salkoff, L. 1983. Genetic and voltage-clamp analysis of a *Drosophila* potassium channel. *Cold Spring Harbor Symp. Quant. Biol.* 48:221–31

63. Salkoff, L. 1983. *Drosophila* mutants reveal two components of fast outward current. *Nature* 302:249–51

64. Salkoff, L. 1985. Development of ion channels in the flight muscles of *Drosophila. J. Physiol. Paris* 80:275–82

65. Salkoff, L., Butler, A., Hiken, M., Wei, A., Giffen, K., et al. 1986. A *Drosophila* gene with homology to the vertebrate $Na^+$ channel. *Soc. Neurosci. Abstr.* 12:1512

66. Salkoff, L., Butler, A., Wei, A., Scavarda, N., Giffen, K., et al. 1987. Genetic organization and deduced amino acid sequence of a putative sodium channel gene in *Drosopohila. Science.* 237:744–49

67. Salkoff, L. B., Tanouye, M. A. 1986. Genetics of ion channels. *Physiol. Rev.* 66:301–29
68. Salkoff, L., Wyman, R. 1981. Genetic modification of potassium channels in *Drosophila Shaker* mutants. *Nature* 293:228–30
69. Salkoff, L. B., Wyman, R. 1983. Ion currents in *Drosophila* flight muscles. *J. Physiol. London* 337:687–709
69a. Schmidt, J. A., Catterall, W. A. 1986. Biosynthesis and processing of the alpha subunit of the voltage-sensitive sodium channel in rat brain neurons. *Cell* 46:437–45
70. Seecof, R. L., Donady, J. J., Teplitz, R. L. 1973. Differentiation of *Drosophila* neuroblasts to form ganglion-like clusters of neurons in vitro. *Cell Differentiation* 2:143–49
71. Siddiqi, O. 1975. Genetic blocks in ·elements of neural networks in *Drosophila*. In *Regulation of Growth and Differentiated Function in Eukaryote Cells*, ed. G. P. Talwar. New York: Raven
72. Solc, C. K., Aldrich, R. W. 1986. Patch clamp analysis of inactivating outward currents in dissociated CNS neurons of wild-type and *Shaker*[5] *Drosophila. Soc. Neurosci. Abstr.* 11:954
73. Solc. C. K., Aldrich, R. W. 1988. *J. Neurosci.* In press
74. Solc, C. K., Zagotta, W. N., Aldrich, R. W. 1987. Single-channel and genetic analyses reveal two distinct A-type potassium channels in *Drosophila. Science* 236:1094–98
75. Spradling, A. C., Rubin, G. M. 1982. Transposition of cloned P elements into *Drosophila* germ line chromosomes. *Science* 218:341–47
76. Sun, Y.-A., Wu, C.-F. 1985. Genetic alterations of single channel potassium currents in dissociated central nervous system neurons of *Drosophila. J. Gen. Physiol.* 86:16a–17a
77. Suzuki, D. T., Grigliatti, T., Williamson, R. 1971. Temperature-sensitive mutants in *Drosophila melanogaster. VII.* A mutation (*para*[ts]) causing reversible adult paralysis. *Proc. Natl. Acad. Sci. USA* 68:890–93
78. Suzuki, N., Kano. M. 1977. Development of action potential in larval muscle fibers in *Drosophila melanogaster. J. Cell. Physiol.* 93:383–88
79. Tanouye, M. A., Ferrus, A., Fujita, S. C. 1981. Abnormal action potentials associated with the *Shaker* complex locus of *Drosophila. Proc. Natl. Acad. Sci. USA* 78:6548–52
80. Tanouye, M. A., Kamb, C. A., Iverson, L. E., Salkoff, L. 1986. Genetics and molecular biology of ionic channels in *Drosophila. Ann. Rev. Neurosci.* 9:255–76
81. Tanouye, M. A., Wyman, R. J. 1980. Motor outputs of giant nerve fiber in *Drosophila. J. Neurophysiol.* 44:405–21
82. Tempel, B. L., Papazian, D. M., Schwarz, T. L., Jan, Y. N., Jan, L. Y. 1987. *Science* 237:770–75
83. Timpe, L. C., Jan, L. Y. 1987. Gene dosage and complementation analysis of the *Shaker* locus in *Drosophila. J. Neurosci.* 7:1307–17
84. Waechter, C. J., Schmidt, J. W., Catterall, W. A. 1983. Glycosylation is required for maintenance of functional sodium channels in neuroblastoma cells. *J. Biol. Chem.* 258:5117–23
85. Wei, A., Salkoff, L. 1986. Occult *Drosophila* calcium channels and twinning of calcium and voltage-activated potassium channels. *Science* 233:780–82
86. Wu, C.-F., Ganetzky, B. 1980. Genetic alteration of nerve membrane excitability in temperature-sensitive paralytic mutants of *Drosophila melanogaster. Nature* 286:814–16
87. Wu, C.-F., Ganetzky, B. 1984. Properties of potassium channels altered by mutations of two genes in *Drosophila. Biophys. J.* 45:77–78
88. Wu, C.-F., Ganetzky, B. 1986. Genes and ionic channels in *Drosophila.* In *Ion Channels in Neural Membranes*, ed. J. M. Ritchie, R. D. Keynes, L. Bolis. New York: Liss
89. Wu, C.-F., Ganetzky, B., Haugland, F. N., Liu, A.-X. 1983. Potassium currents in *Drosophila:* Different components affected by mutations of two genes. *Science* 220:1076–78
90. Wu, C.-F., Ganetzky, B., Jan, L. Y., Jan, Y. N., Benzer, S. 1978. A *Drosophila* mutant with a temperature-sensitive block in nerve conduction. *Proc. Natl. Acad. Sci. USA* 75:4047–51
91. Wu, C.-F., Haugland, F. N. 1985. Voltage clamp analysis of membrane currents in larval muscle fibers of *Drosophila:* Alteration of potassium currents in *Shaker* mutants. *J. Neurosci.* 5:2626–40
92. Wu, C.-F., Suzuki, N., Poo, M.-M. 1983. Dissociated neurons from normal and mutant *Drosophila* larval central nervous system in cell culture. *J. Neurosci.* 3:1888–99
93. Wu, C.-F., Young, S. H., Tanouye, M. A. 1983. Single channel recording of alpha-bungarotoxin resistant acetylcho-

line channels in dissociated CNS neurons of *Drosophila*. *Soc. Neurosci. Abstr.* 9:507

94. Zagotta, W. N., Aldrich, R. W. 1987. Single A-type potassium channels in wild type and *Shaker Drosophila* myotubes. *Soc. Neurosci. Abstr.* 13:578

95. Zuker, C. S., Cowman, A. F., Rubin, G. M. 1985. Isolation and structure of a rhodopsin gene from *D. melanogaster*. *Cell* 40:851–58

## REFERENCES ADDED IN PROOF

96. Leung, H.-T., Byerly, L. 1987. Calcium currents in embryonic cultures of *Drosophila* neurons. *Soc. Neurosci. Abstr.* 13:101

97. Royden, C. S., Pirrotta, V., Jan, L. Y. 1987. The *tko* locus, site of a behavioral mutation in D. *melanogaster*, codes for a protein homologous to prokaryotic ribosomal protein S12. *Cell* 51:165–73

Ann. Rev. Physiol. 1988. 50:395–406

# GENETIC ANALYSIS OF ION CHANNELS IN VERTEBRATES

*William A. Catterall*

Department of Pharmacology, School of Medicine, University of Washington, Seattle, Washington 98195

## INTRODUCTION

### Voltage-Sensitive Ion Channels

Voltage-sensitive ion channels mediate voltage-dependent changes in surface membrane permeability to $Na^+$, $K^+$, and $Ca^{2+}$ in a wide range of cell types. In electrically excitable cells, they are required for generation of propagated action potentials. In inexcitable cells, they participate in regulation of the plasma membrane potential and the intracellular concentrations of $Ca^{2+}$ and monovalent ions. This class of membrane transport proteins is distinguished by three functional characteristics: high selectivity for transported ions, high single-channel conductance, and steep voltage dependence of ion transport activity. The ion transport activity of most voltage-sensitive ion channels is regulated on the millisecond time scale by two experimentally separable processes: *activation,* which controls the rate and voltage dependence of the increase in ion conductance following depolarization, and *inactivation,* which controls the rate and voltage dependence of the return of ion conductance to the resting level during prolonged depolarization. In addition, many voltage-sensitive ion channels are modulated on the time scale of seconds to hours or longer by intracellular second messengers and protein phosphorylation reactions. The molecular basis of these functional properties of voltage-sensitive ion channels and their expression and role in physiological processes are the subject of intense study by both biochemical and genetic methods. The chapter by Papazian et al (44) describes the application of both classical

395

0066-4278/88/0315-0395$02.00

genetic methods and molecular genetic techniques to selection and analysis of ion channel mutants in *Drosophila*. In this chapter, I review somatic cell genetic studies that have contributed to the development of our current understanding of voltage-sensitive ion channels in vertebrates and describe the results of current molecular genetic approaches to this class of ion  .
transport proteins.

## SOMATIC CELL GENETICS

### Somatic Cell Hybrids

In somatic cell genetic experiments, sets of clonal cell populations considered to have stably inherited differences in a phenotype of interest are the starting point for genetic analysis. Cells with such phenotypic diversity may arise with low frequency in the normal cell population or may be generated at high frequency by mutagenesis or formation of somatic cell hybrids between phenotypically distinct parental cell lines. Cell lines with stably inherited differences in phenotype can then be isolated from these sets of clonal populations by application of specific selection procedures for phenotypes of interest or by screening with specific assays designed to recognize phenotypes of interest.

SEPARATE SODIUM AND POTASSIUM CHANNELS    The first somatic cell genetic experiments that yielded information on voltage-sensitive ion channels involved analysis of somatic cell hybrids between mouse neuroblastoma cell lines and nonneuronal cell types (30, 31). Clonal cell lines derived from mouse neuroblastoma C1300 were shown to express many neuronal properties, including the ability to produce regenerative action potentials with a sodium-dependent depolarizing phase and a potassium-dependent repolarization and hyperpolarizing phase (37, 38). These two phases of the neuroblastoma cell action potential are primarily the result of activation of voltage-dependent sodium and potassium channels, respectively (32). These cells were fused with cells from fibroblast lines, and replicating somatic cell hybrids containing genetic elements from both parental cell lines were selected using the hypoxanthine/aminopterin/thymidine (HAT) selection procedure. Analysis of individual clonal isolates revealed a wide variation in the range of neuronal properties inherited by the hybrid cells (30, 31). In particular, some cell lines inherited both the depolarizing and hyperpolarizing phases of the action potential, which are due to voltage-sensitive sodium and potassium channels, respectively; other cell lines inherited only the hyperpolarizing phase of the action potential, which is due to potassium channels; and yet another group of cell lines inherited neither phase of the action potential. At the time of these experiments, it was known that the increases in sodium and potassium permeability during the action potential could be separately blocked by pharmacological agents (28), but direct evidence for physically separate ion permeability pathways had not been obtained. The stable inheritance of separate expression of action potential responses mediated by these two classes of ion channels provided clear evidence in favor of the conclusion that sodium and potassium channels are distinct molecular entities encoded by separate genes. Subsequent work has confirmed that view.

VOLTAGE-SENSITIVE SODIUM CHANNELS ARE NEUROTOXIN RECEPTORS
The functional properties of voltage-sensitive sodium channels are modified by a wide range of biological toxins (2, 9, 10, 33, 46). It is now known that these toxins act at five separate receptor sites on the sodium channel protein. Saxitoxin and tetrodotoxin bind at neurotoxin receptor site 1 and inhibit ion transport by the sodium channel. Veratridine, batrachotoxin, and other lipid-soluble toxins bind at neurotoxin receptor site 2 and cause persistent activation of sodium channels. $\alpha$ scorpion toxins and sea anemone toxins are polypeptides that bind at neurotoxin receptor site 3 and slow or block inactivation of sodium channels. $\beta$ scorpion toxins bind at neurotoxin receptor site 4 and alter sodium channel activation. Toxins from the dinoflaggelate *Ptychodiscus brevis* bind at neurotoxin receptor site 5 and cause repetitive action potentials.

While it is now accepted that these toxins act directly on the sodium channels involved in action potential generation, this interpretation was initially controversial. Neurotoxins acting at receptor sites 2 and 3 depolarize the resting membrane potential of excitable cells by increasing the resting membrane permeability to sodium ions (34, 35, 43, 55). The results of these early experiments did not make it clear whether these toxins acted on "resting membrane sodium channels" that were distinct molecular entities from the sodium channels involved in action potential generation or on the sodium channels involved in action potential generation themselves. Analyses of toxin binding and action on neuroblastoma and somatic cell hybrid cell lines provided direct evidence for the conclusion that these neurotoxins activate the same sodium channels that are involved in action potential generation. The persistent activation of sodium channels by veratridine and other toxins acting at neurotoxin receptor site 2 was measured in a range of neuroblastoma and somatic cell hybrid cell lines that differed in their expression of the depolarizing phase of the action potential mediated by voltage-sensitive sodium channels. These measurements showed that only electrically excitable cells responded to the neurotoxins (14). These results provided early direct evidence that these neurotoxins act on the same sodium channels that are activated during the depolarizing phase of the action potential. The interaction of polypeptide toxins from scorpion venom with their receptor sites can be measured in ligand binding studies (8, 45). Receptor sites for these neurotoxins are only observed in hybrid cell lines that express the depolarizing phase of the action potential (8, 45), which indicates that these toxins also act directly on voltage-sensitive sodium channels involved in action potential generation. Similar results were obtained for the sodium channel inhibitors saxitoxin and tetrodotoxin (13). Considered together, these somatic cell genetic studies provided early direct evidence that the sodium channel protein itself is the receptor for these several different classes of neurotoxins. This conclusion has been clearly verified by subsequent isolation and reconstitution of the functional properties of the channel protein itself using these various neurotoxins as probes (1, 7, 12).

EXPRESSION OF CALCIUM CHANNELS IS ASSOCIATED WITH SYNAPSE FORMATION    A wide range of cell types have been hybridized with neuroblastoma cells, and the resulting neuronal phenotypes have been extensively analyzed (15, 24, 27, 36, 39). A close correlation has been observed between expression of voltage-sensitive calcium channels in various cell lines and the ability of those cells to form functional synapses with postsynaptic targets (39). These results suggest that expression of calcium channels is a critical event in the genetic steps leading to synaptic competency.

## Selection of Somatic Cell Variants

The neurotoxins that cause persistent activation of sodium channels have provided a selection procedure for neuroblastoma cell lines with missing or altered channels. Maintenance of low intracellular sodium and high intracellular potassium concentrations is necessary for cell growth and division. For example, cardiac glycosides that block Na,K-ATPase are cytotoxic and can be used to select variant cell lines that are resistant to their actions (6, 48). The increase in sodium permeability caused by persistent activation of sodium channels with neurotoxins is sufficient to overcome the sodium pump and is therefore cytotoxic (56). Cell lines resistant to the cytotoxic action of veratridine plus scorpion toxin are either sodium channel deficient and lack detectable levels of sodium channels by several functional criteria or are scorpion toxin resistant and have sodium channels with markedly reduced affinity for scorpion toxin (16, 21, 56). The frequency of appearance of both these classes of variants is increased by chemical mutagenesis, which suggests that they result from mutational events (16). The $\alpha$ subunit of the sodium channel was shown to be missing in sodium channel–deficient cells (16), which indicates that this phenotype results from failure to synthesize the protein components of sodium channels. The sodium channels in these cell lines may have major defects that prevent synthesis of an $\alpha$ subunit that can be folded and inserted into the surface membrane normally. In contrast, sodium channels in scorpion toxin–resistant cell lines are functionally normal except for their reduced affinity for the toxin (21). Thus the sodium channels in scorpion toxin–resistant cell lines are likely to have discrete lesions that allow the synthesis of functional channels whose affinity for scorpion toxin is reduced. These methods for selection of variant cell lines with specific lesions in discrete functional properties of sodium channels may provide a valuable approach to mutational analysis of sodium channel function by both somatic cell genetic and molecular genetic approaches.

## MOLECULAR GENETICS

### Molecular Biology of the Sodium Channel

ISOLATION AND CHARACTERIZATION OF cDNA CLONES    The voltage-sensitive sodium channel was the first voltage-sensitive ion channel to be isolated in pure form, as reviewed in References 1, 7, and 12. In the tissues studied to date, the sodium channel consists of a large glycoprotein with an apparent molecular weight of 260,000, designated the $\alpha$ subunit, and one or two additional glycoprotein subunits with apparent molecular weights of 33,000 to 38,000, designated the $\beta$ subunits. At present, the $\alpha$ subunit is the only one for which full-length cDNA clones have been isolated. Two independent cDNA cloning strategies have been pursued. Noda et al (42) determined the amino acid sequence of segments of the sodium channel from electric eel electroplax and screened cDNA expression libraries formed in a plasmid vector with both antisera against the sodium channel from eel electroplax and oligonucleotide probes encoding known short segments of the amino acid sequence of that sodium channel, which had been purified as a single glycoprotein with apparent molecular weight of 260,000 (1). Short cDNAs were isolated and used to identify long cDNA clones, which were subjected to sequence analysis to deduce the complete amino acid sequence of the protein. The inferred sequence consists of 1829 residues with a total molecular weight of 208,321 (42). cDNA clones encoding the electroplax sodium channel were then used to identify and isolate cDNA clones for the $\alpha$ subunits of the rat brain sodium channel (40). Comparison of the inferred amino acid sequences indicated 60% homology between the sodium channels from eel electroplax and rat brain.

Auld et al (4) sought to clone the $\alpha$ subunit of the rat brain sodium channel directly using antibodies to identify cDNA clones in rat brain expression libraries in the bacteriophage vector $\lambda$ gt11 by antibody screening. The amino acid sequence specified by these clones was highly homologous to the sequence of the electroplax sodium channel. Additional cDNA clones were isolated by a combination of screening libraries with cDNA probes and antibodies, and their nucleotide sequence was determined to define segments of the primary structure of the $\alpha$ subunit of the principal sodium channel subtype present in purified preparations from rat brain.

Analysis of the primary structures of the sodium channel $\alpha$ subunits that have been sequenced to date reveals some interesting structural features that have been proposed to relate to specific functional properties of the channel. The polypeptide of 1829–2008 amino acid residues contains four internally homologous domains of 215–272 residues, which suggests that this polypeptide arose during evolution by two gene duplication events (40, 42). All of the proposed transmembrane segments are located in these homologous domains, which indicates that they are the functional core of the sodium channel structure (40, 42). As illustrated in Figure 1 *(left)*, the transmembrane pore of the sodium channel is considered to be formed in the center of a square array of these four homologous domains, with each contributing one or more transmembrane segments to its formation (12, 23, 26, 40, 42). Two ligand-gated ion channels, the nicotinic acetylcholine receptor and the receptor for gamma amino butyric acid (GABA), form a transmembrane pore in the center of a pseudosymmetric array of homologous subunits. The structural motif proposed for the transmembrane pore of the sodium channel formed by the single $\alpha$ subunit polypeptide is therefore analogous to that proposed for the multisubunit receptor proteins. Each proposed pore structure involves a pseudosymmetric array of homologous structural units surrounding the aqueous transmembrane pathway through which transported ions move.

The most unique functional property of the voltage-sensitive ion channels is voltage-dependent gating. Voltage-dependent gating of sodium channels requires that the equivalent of four to six positive charges associated with the channel structure must move across the membrane during the conformational change that leads to sodium channel activation (reviewed in 3). These voltage sensors, or gating charges, must be located within the hydrophobic portion of the membrane in order to respond to changes in the transmembrane electric field. Each of the four homologous domains contains a highly charged sequence in which repeated positively charged residues, usually arginine, are separated by a pair of hydrophobic amino acids to create a segment of approximately 20 amino acid residues (S4) that is both positively charged and hydrophobic (5, 40, 42). The primary structures of these S4 segments are highly conserved between rat brain and eel electroplax (40), and analyses of the predicted secondary structure of the $\alpha$ subunits suggest that these segments are likely to adopt an $\alpha$-helical conformation (23, 26, 40, 42). These characteristics have led to the proposal that these $\alpha$-helices form positively charged transmembrane segments that are involved in sodium channel gating (11, 12, 23, 26, 40). Two closely related models of voltage-dependent gating, termed the sliding helix or helical screw models, have been proposed (11, 12,

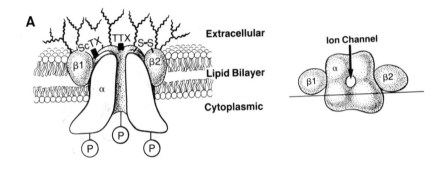

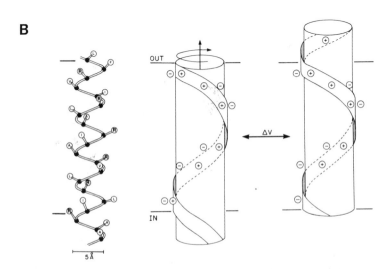

*Figure 1   Models of sodium channel structure and gating.* **A.**   Sodium channel structure. The sodium channel protein from brain is illustrated (left) as associated with the phospholipid bilayer as inferred from biochemical and molecular biological experiments. Sites of glycosylation, phosphorylation (P), and neurotoxin (ScTx, scorpion toxin; TTX, tetrodotoxin) binding are illustrated. The transmembrane pore of the sodium channel is illustrated (right) in *en face* view as formed in the center of the four homologous transmembrane domains (12, 23, 26, 40) of the α subunit.
**B.**   The *Sliding Helix* model of voltage-dependent gating. The S4 segment of domain IV of the electroplax sodium channel is illustrated (left) as a transmembrane α helix: L = lue; F = phe; V = val; I = ileu; A = ala; R = Arg. The transmembrane S4 helix is depicted (right) as a cylinder with ribbon of positive charge formed by the repeating arg residues. Each positive charge is neutralized by a negative charge from surrounding transmembrane helices to form a spiral of ion pairs across the membrane. The force of the membrane electric field stabilizes the ion pairing arrangement by pulling positive charges inward and pushing negative charges outward. Upon depolarization, this force is released and the S4 helices in each of the four homologous domains are proposed to move outward along a spiral path approximately 5 Å with 60° rotation to form new ion pairs. This outward spiral movement transfers at least one gating charge across the membrane in each domain and initiates sequential conformational changes in each domain resulting in activation of the ion channel (11, 12, 26).

26). According to these models, the positively charged S4 transmembrane helices form the gating structures of the sodium channel and move outward under the force of the electric field along a spiral path (Figure 1, *right*). This movement transfers gating charge and initiates sequential conformational changes in each of the four domains of the sodium channel, leading to activation. These models for the structure of the transmembrane pore and for the mechanism of voltage-dependent gating are now being tested by biochemical and molecular genetic methods.

One of the major lines of evidence used in constructing models of sodium channel structure and gating mechanism has been comparison of amino acid sequence of the eel electroplax and rat brain $\alpha$ subunits (11, 40). Recently, amino acid sequences of additional voltage-sensitive ion channels have been determined, providing new data for comparison. As described in the chapter by Papazian et al (44), the amino acid sequence of the *Drosophila* sodium channel has been determined and is strikingly homologous to that of the vertebrate channels studied earlier (47). In particular, it contains four homologous domains with similar hydrophobic segments, and each domain contains a highly positively charged S4 segment (47). Tempel et al (54) have cloned and sequenced a subunit of the A current potassium channel of *Drosophila*. It also has a similar set of hydrophobic segments that are homologous to those of the sodium channel and it contains a homologous, highly positively charged S4 segment. Finally, Tanabe et al (53) have described cloning and primary structure determination of the principal $a_1$ subunit of the voltage-sensitive calcium channel purified from skeletal muscle transverse tubules after radiolabeling with dihydropyridine calcium antagonists and solubilization in digitonin (17, 19, 52). This subunit is also strikingly homologous to the $\alpha$ subunit of the voltage-sensitive sodium channel. It has four homologous domains that each contain similar hydrophobic segments and homologous, positively charged S4 helices (53). The strict conservation of the positively charged S4 helices in these various voltage-sensitive ion channels provides strong, but still indirect, evidence that these unique structural features are indeed the gating units of the channels.

FUNCTIONAL EXPRESSION OF mRNA ENCODING $\alpha$ SUBUNITS OF SODIUM CHANNELS    mRNAs encoding many different ion channels have been successfully expressed by injection into *Xenopus* oocytes, and the resulting ligand- or voltage-gated ion channels have been detected by electrophysiological methods (29, 50, 51). A high–molecular weight fraction of mRNA from rat brain is sufficient to direct the synthesis of functional sodium channels, which suggests that the $\alpha$-subunit mRNA contains all the required information (51). This conclusion has been confirmed by successful expression of $\alpha$-subunit mRNA isolated from rat brain by hybrid selection with cDNA clones encoding the channel (20) and $\alpha$-subunit mRNA

synthesized from cloned cDNA (41, 49). These results indicate that the
$\alpha$-subunit mRNA alone can encode a functional sodium channel, even
though the $\alpha$-subunit protein is associated with $\beta 1$ and $\beta 2$ subunits in rat
brain neurons. This observation will allow analysis of the structural basis
for the functional properties of sodium channels by site-directed mutagenesis approaches.

SODIUM CHANNEL SUBTYPES THAT DIFFER IN PRIMARY STRUCTURE
Determination of the nucleotide sequences of cDNAs encoding the $\alpha$ subunits
of rat brain sodium channels revealed the existence of three separate mRNAs
(40). Two of these were completely sequenced and designated $R_I$ and $R_{II}$.
They predict proteins that are 87% identical in amino acid sequence. The
physiological properties of these sodium channel subtypes have not been
defined, but their differential expression in excitable tissues has been studied
by two different methods. Gordon et al (22) prepared sequence-directed
antibodies against a variable segment of the channel structure. These antibodies recognized the $\alpha$ subunits of either $R_I$ or $R_{II}$ sodium channels specifically,
allowing measurement of their relative expression in different neural and
nonneural tissues. $R_I$ and $R_{II}$ are expressed primarily in the central nervous
system. Sodium channels in skeletal muscle, heart, sympathetic ganglia,
adrenal medulla, and pituitary were not recognized by the antibodies against
$R_I$ and $R_{II}$. These results show that $R_I$ and $R_{II}$ are specific to the central
nervous system (CNS) and indicate that other sodium channel subtypes must
be the major forms expressed in the peripheral nervous system, secretory
cells, heart, and skeletal muscle. The $R_I$ and $R_{II}$ sodium channel proteins are
differentially expressed within the central nervous system as well. The ratio of
$R_{II}$ to $R_I$ is 16 in hippocampus, 6 in cerebral cortex, and 0.4 in lumbar spinal
cord. There is a general increase in $R_I$ expression relative to $R_{II}$ in more
caudal areas of the CNS. In spinal cord, optic nerve, and retina, a substantial
fraction of the sodium channels are not recognized by the anti-$R_I$ and anti-$R_{II}$
antibodies, which suggests that a third sodium channel subtype is expressed in
these regions, consistent with the presence of a third mRNA (40). Although
$R_I$ and $R_{II}$ are expressed in spinal cord, they are not detectable in the sciatic
nerve, which contains the axons of spinal motor neurons. Either the peripherally projecting motor neurons do not express $R_I$ and $R_{II}$ or they express
these channel subtypes only within the boundaries of the CNS.

Grubman et al (25) developed cDNA probes that recognize the 5' ends of
$R_I$ and $R_{II}$ mRNAs specifically. mRNA for $R_{II}$ was detected in brain but not in
skeletal or cardiac muscle, and expression of mRNA for $R_{II}$ was tenfold
greater than that of $R_I$ mRNA in the brain. The isolation of genomic clones
containing the 5' flanking regions of the $R_I$ and $R_{II}$ sodium channel genes
should provide an approach to the analysis of the molecular basis for this
differential regulation.

## CONCLUSION

Application of somatic cell genetic and molecular genetic approaches to studies of voltage-sensitive ion channels in vertebrates has yielded valuable results. Somatic cell genetic experiments helped to demonstrate the existence of distinct sodium and potassium channel macromolecules and provided supporting data for indentification of sodium channel protein components using neurotoxins. Molecular genetics has yielded the full primary structures of a family of voltage-sensitive ion channels and initiated an in-depth analysis of their structure-function relationships and tissue-specific expression. In the future, these two different genetic approaches may come together in mutational analysis of ion channel structure, function, and regulation.

*Literature Cited*

1. Agnew, W. S. 1984. Voltage-regulated sodium channel molecules. *Ann. Rev. Physiol.* 46:517–30
2. Albuquerque, E. X., Daly, J. W. 1976. Batrachotoxin, a selective probe for channels modulating sodium conductances in electrogenic membranes. In *Receptors and Recognition*, ed. P. Cautrecasas, 1:299–336. London: Chapman & Hall
3. Armstrong, C. M. 1981. Sodium channels and gating currents. *Physiol. Rev.* 61:644–82
4. Auld, V., Marshall, J., Goldin, A., Dowsett, A., Catterall, W., et al. 1985. Cloning and characterization of the gene for α subunit of the mammalian voltage-gated sodium channel. *J. Gen. Physiol.* 86:10a–11a
5. Deleted in proof
6. Baker, R. M., Brunette, D. M., Mankovitz, R., Thompson, L. H., Whitmore, G. F., et al. 1974. Ouabain-resistant mutants of mouse and hamster cells in culture. *Cell* 1:9–21
7. Barchi, R. L. 1984. Voltage-sensitive Na$^+$ ion channels: Molecular properties and functional reconstitution. *Trends Biochem. Sci.* 9:358–61
8. Catterall, W. A. 1977. Membrane potential dependent binding of scorpion toxin to the action potential Na$^+$ ionophore. Studies with a toxin derivative prepared by lactoperoxidase catalyzed iodination. *J. Biol. Chem.* 252:8669–76
9. Catterall, W. A. 1980. Neurotoxins that act on voltage-sensitive sodium channels in excitable membranes. *Ann. Rev. Pharmacol. Toxicol.* 20:15–43
10. Catterall, W. A. 1985. The voltage sensitive sodium channel: A receptor for multiple neurotoxins. In *Toxic Dinoflagellates*, ed. D. M. Anderson, A. W. White, D. G. Baden, pp. 329–42. New York: Elsevier Science
11. Catterall, W. A. 1986. Voltage-dependent gating of sodium channels: Correlating structure and function. *Trends Neurosci.* 9:7–10
12. Catterall, W. A. 1986. Molecular properties of voltage-sensitive sodium channels. *Ann. Rev. Biochem.* 55:953–85
13. Catterall, W. A., Morrow, C. S. 1978. Binding of saxitoxin to electrically excitable neuroblastoma cells. *Proc. Natl. Acad. Sci. USA* 75:218–22
14. Catterall, W. A., Nirenberg, M. 1973. Sodium uptake associated with activation of action potential ionophores of cultured neuroblastoma and muscle cells. *Proc. Natl. Acad. Sci. USA* 70:3759–63
15. Christian, C. N., Nelson, P. G., Bullock, P., Mullinax, D., Nirenberg, M. 1978. Pharmacologic responses of cells of a neuroblastoma × glioma hybrid clone and modulation of synapses between hybrid cells and mouse myotubes. *Brain Res.* 147:261–76
16. Costa, M. R., Catterall, W. A. 1982. Characterization of variant neuroblastoma clones with missing or altered sodium channels. *Mol. Pharmacol.* 22:196–203
17. Curtis, B. M., Catterall, W. A. 1984. Purification of the calcium antagonist receptor of the voltage-sensitive calcium channel from skeletal msucle transverse tubules. *Biochemistry* 23:2113–18
18. Deleted in proof
19. Flockerzi, V., Oeken, H.-J., Hofmann, F. 1983. Purification of a functional receptor for calcium channel blockers

from rabbit skeletal muscle microsomes. *Eur. J. Biochem.* 161:217–24

20. Goldin, A. L., Snutch, T., Lubbert, H., Dowsett, A., Marshall, J., et al. 1986. Messenger RNA coding for only the α subunit of the rat brain Na channel is sufficient for expression of functional channels in *Xenopus* oocytes. *Proc. Natl. Acad. Sci. USA* 83:7503–7

21. Gonoi, T., Hille, B., Catterall, W. A. 1984. Voltage clamp analysis of sodium channels in normal and scorpion toxin-resistant neuroblastoma cells. *J. Neurosci.* 4:2836–42

22. Gordon, D., Merrick, D., Goldin, A., Dunn, R., Davidson, N., Catterall, W. A. 1987. Tissue-specific expression of $R_I$ and $R_{II}$ sodium channel subtypes. *Proc. Natl. Acad. Sci. USA* 38:8682–86

23. Greenblatt, R. E., Blatt, Y., Montal, M. 1985. The structure of the voltage-sensitive sodium channel: Inferences derived from computer-aided analysis of the *Electrophorus electricus* channel primary structure. *FEBS Lett.* 193:125–34

24. Greene, L. A., Shain, W., Chalazonitis, A., Breakefield, X., Minna, J., et al. 1975. Neuronal properties of hybrid neuroblastoma X sympathetic ganglion cells. *Proc. Natl. Acad. Sci. USA* 72:4923–27

25. Grubman, S. A., Cooperman, S. S., Begley, M. P., Weintraub, J. L., Goodman, R. H., Mandel, G. 1987. Tissue-specific expression of genes encoding the rat voltage-gated sodium channel, In *Molecular Biology of Ion Channels*, ed. W. Agnew, R. Tsien, New York: Academic

26. Guy, H. R., Seetharamulu, P. 1986. Molecular model of the action potential sodium channel. *Proc. Natl. Acad. Sci. USA* 83:508–12

27. Hammond, D. N., Wainer, B. H., Tonsgard, J. H., Heller, A. 1986. Neuronal properties of clonal hybrid cells lines derived from central cholinergic neurons. *Science* 234:123–40

28. Hille, B. 1970. Ionic channels in nerve membranes. *Prog. Biophys. Mol. Biol.* 21:1–32

29. Houamed, K. M., Bilbe, G., Smart, T. G., Constanti, A., Brown, D. A., et al. 1984. Expression of functional GABA, glycine and glutamate receptors in *Xenopus* oocytes injected with rat brain mRNA. *Nature* 310:318–21

30. Minna, J., Glazer, D., Nirenberg, M. 1972. Genetic dissection of neural properties using somatic cell hybrids. *Nature New Biol.* 235:225–31

31. Minna, J., Nelson, P., Peacock, J.,

Glazer, D., Nirenberg, M. 1971. Genes for neuronal properties expressed in neuroblastoma × L cell hybrids. *Proc. Natl. Acad. Sci. USA* 68:234–39

32. Moolenaar, W. H., Spector, I. 1978. Ionic currents in cultured mouse neuroblastoma cells under voltage-clamp conditions. *J. Physiol.* 278:265–86

33. Narahashi, T. 1974. Chemicals as tools in the study of excitable membranes. *Physiol. Rev.* 54:813–89

34. Narahashi, T., Albuquerque, E. X., Deguchi, T. 1971. Effects of batrachotoxin on membrane potential and conductance of squid giant axons. *J. Gen. Physiol.* 58:54–70

35. Narahashi, T., Shapiro, B. I., Deguchi, T., Scuka, M., Wang, C. M. 1972. Effects of scorpion venom on squid axon membranes. *Am. J. Physiol.* 222:850–57

36. Nelson, P. G., Christian, C. N., Daniels, M. P., Henkart, M., Bullock, P., et al. 1978. Formation of synapses between cells of a neuroblastoma × glioma hybrid clone and mouse myotubes. *Brain Res.* 147:245–59

37. Nelson, P. G., Peacock, H., Amano, T., Minna, J. 1971. Electrogenesis in mouse neuroblastoma cells in vitro. *J. Cell. Physiol.* 77:337–52

38. Nelson, P. G., Ruffner, W., Nirenberg, M. 1969. Neuronal tumor cells with excitable membranes grown in vitro. *Proc. Natl. Acad. Sci. USA* 64:1004–10

39. Nirenberg, M., Wilson, S., Higashida, H., Rotter, A., Krueger, K., et al. 1983. Modulation of synapse formation by cyclic adenosine monophosphate. *Science* 222:794–99

40. Noda, N., Ikeda, T., Kayano, T., Suzuki, H., Takeshima, H., et al. 1986a. Existence of distinct sodium channel messenger RNAs in rat brain. *Nature* 320:188–92

41. Noda, M., Ikeda, T., Suzuki, H., Takeshima, H., Takahashi, T., et al. 1986b. Expression of functional sodium channels from cloned cDNA. *Nature* 322:826–28

42. Noda, M., Shimizu, S., Tanabe, T., Takai, T., Kayano, T., et al. 1984. Primary structure of *Electrophorus electricus* sodium channel deduced from cDNA sequence. *Nature* 312:121–27

43. Ohta, M., Narahashi, T., Keeler, R. F. 1972. Effects of veratrum alkaloids on membrane potential and conductance of squid and crayfish giant axons. *J. Pharmacol. Exp. Ther.* 184:143–54

44. Papazian, D. M., Schwarz, T. L., Tempel, B. L., Timpe, L. C., Jan, L. Y. 1988. Ion channels in *Drosophila*. *Ann. Rev. Physiol.* 50:379–93

45. Ray, R., Catterall, W. A. 1978. Membrane potential dependent binding of scorpion toxin to the action potential sodium ionophore. Studies with a 3-(4-hydroxy 3-[$^{125}$I] iodophenyl) propionyl derivative. *J. Neurochem.* 31:397–407

46. Ritchie, J. M., Rogart, R. B. 1977. The binding of labelled saxitoxin to the sodium channels in normal and denervated mammalian muscle and in amphibian muscle. *J. Physiol. London* 269:341–54

47. Salkoff, L., Butler, A., Wei, A., Seavedra, N., Giffen, K., et al. 1987. Gene organization and deduced amino acid sequence of a *Drosophila* ion channel gene. *Science* In press

48. Siminovitch, L. 1976. On the nature of hereditable variation in cultured somatic cells. *Cell* 7:1–11

49. Stuhmer, W., Methfessel, C., Sakmann, B., Noda, M., Numa, S. 1987. Patch clamp characterization of sodium channels expressed from brain cDNA. *Eur. Biophys. J.* 14:131–38

50. Sumikawa, K., Houghton, M., Emtage, J. S., Richards, B. M., Barnard, E. A. 1981. Active multi-subunit ACh receptor assembled by translation of heterologous mRNA in *Xenopus* oocytes. *Nature* 292:862–64

51. Sumikawa, K., Parker, I., Miledi, R. 1984. Partial purification and functional expression of brain mRNAs coding for neurotransmitter receptors and voltage-operated channels. *Proc. Natl. Acad. Sci. USA* 81:7994–98

52. Takahashi, M., Seagar, M. J., Jones, J. F., Reber, B. F. X., Catterall, W. A. 1987. Subunit structure of dihydropyridine-sensitive calcium channels from skeletal muscle. *Proc. Natl. Acad. Sci. USA* 84:5478–82

53. Tanabe, T., Takeshima, H., Mikami, A., Flockerzi, V., Takahashi, H., et al. 1987. Primary structure of dihydropyridine binding calcium channel from rabbit skeletal muscle. *Nature* 328:313–18

54. Tempel, B. L., Papazian, D. M., Schwarz, T. L., Jan, Y. N., Jan, L. Y. 1987. *Science* 237:770–75

55. Ulbricht, W. 1969. The effect of veratridine on excitable membranes of nerve and muscle. *Ergeb. Physiol. Biol. Chem. Exp. Pharmakol.* 61:18–71

56. West, G. J., Catterall, W. A. 1979. Selection of variant neuroblastoma clones with missing or altered sodium channels. *Proc. Natl. Acad. Sci. USA* 76:4136–40

# ENDOCRINOLOGY

## ENDOCRINE REGULATION OF STEROID HORMONE-SECRETING CELLS

## *Introduction,* Jack L. Kostyo, *Section Editor*

The enzymatic pathways leading to the formation of the steroid hormones in the adrenal cortex, testes, and ovary were described in considerable detail during the 1950s and 1960s. Thus, by the mid 1970s, a rather complete understanding of the steroid hormone biosynthetic process was achieved. Since that time, additional important information has accrued concerning the chemistry of many of the enzymes involved, as well as details of the mechanisms by which steroid hormone-secreting organs obtain cholesterol for use as substrate for hormone formation. Although it was appreciated early on that steroid hormone synthesis by the adrenals and gonads was influenced by tropic hormones, a variety of other circulating agents, and locally produced factors, the mechanisms by which these regulatory substances exert their actions on steroid-secreting cells is not well understood.

During the past few years, knowledge of basic cell biology and the regulation of gene expression has expanded rapidly, providing new concepts and powerful technology with which to explore these regulatory mechanisms at a very fundamental level. As a consequence, important new insights have been gained regarding the molecular mechanisms by which regulatory signals are translated into changes in cell activity and ultimately steroid hormone biosynthesis in the adrenals and gonads. Therefore, the Endocrinology section of this volume has been devoted to five chapters describing recent work on the cellular mechanisms involved in the endocrine regulation of steroid hormone-secreting cells in these organs.

*Ann. Rev. Physiol. 1988. 50:409–26*
*Copyright © 1988 by Annual Reviews Inc. All rights reserved*

# REGULATION OF ALDOSTERONE SECRETION

*Stephen J. Quinn*

Department of Medicine, Brigham and Women's Hospital, Harvard Medical School, 75 Francis Street; and Department of Physiology, Boston University School of Medicine, Boston, Massachusetts 02115

*Gordon H. Williams*

Endocrine-Hypertension Unit, Brigham and Women's Hospital, Harvard Medical School, 75 Francis Street, Boston, Massachusetts 02115

## INTRODUCTION

In contrast to the regulation of hormone secretion in peptide-secreting cells, in which both release and synthesis are important variables, the regulation of steroid secretion requires only an assessment of those factors controlling synthesis. In most steroid-secreting tissues, this process is relatively uncomplicated with one or two factors usually regulating the biosynthetic processes. The single exception is the regulation of aldosterone secretion. Not only are there perhaps more than a dozen factors involved, but these factors exert their effects through potentially all proposed transduction mechanisms, except direct activation of a tyrosine kinase. The mechanisms utilized by the glomerulosa cell include: (*a*) cyclic AMP formation; (*b*) regulation of cytosolic free calcium and protein kinase C activity through the phosphatidylinositol system; (*c*) cytosolic GMP formation; (*d*) ion channel and modification; and (*e*) modification of the membrane potential. Most if not all of these transduction mechanisms create an environment in which phosphorylation of a variety of intracellular proteins is increased. Presumably it is this increased phosphorylation that leads to a change in steroid enzyme activity and aldosterone secretion. The input from each of these transduction mechanisms is probably integrated, although the mechanism of this integration is obscure.

409

0066-4278/88/0315-0409$02.00

The complexity of the regulation of aldosterone secretion is in part related to its function. Aldosterone's major role is to modify sodium (volume) and potassium homeostasis. It accomplishes these tasks primarily by increasing sodium reabsorption, by an energy-dependent process, at the collecting duct and/or distal tubule of the kidney. In response to the increased reabsorption of sodium the excretion of potassium and hydrogen ions is increased.

In general, factors modifying aldosterone secretion do so by changing the activity at one or both of the two major steps in its biosynthetic pathway (2, 8). These steps are termed the early (cholesterol desmolase) and late (18-hydroxylase-isomerase) pathways. It is not known whether any of the acute regulatory factors modify the late pathway; all of them appear to modify the early pathway activity. It is clear, however, that changes in diet primarily affect the late pathway. Specifically, lower sodium and higher potassium intake both enhance the conversion of corticosterone to aldosterone (2, 8).

Substantial progress has been made in defining the specific regulatory factors and the components that transmit the information provided by these factors to the internal synthetic machinery. Little information is available as to how these changes actually modify steroid enzyme function or how the various regulatory factors interdigitate to modify steroidogenesis. Finally, almost no information is available concerning how dietary changes modify aldosterone secretion, which is one of the most important unanswered questions remaining in this area of biology (25). In this review we assess the possibility that regulation of aldosterone secretion may be different in different species, but we primarily focus on the data most likely to be applicable to the regulation of aldosterone secretion in humans.

## FACTORS MODIFYING ALDOSTERONE SECRETION

### Aldosterone Secretagogues

Agents that stimulate aldosterone secretion can be divided into five subgroups, the angiotensins, potassium, pituitary factors, neurotransmitters, and other aldosterone-stimulating factors. Since little is known about this last group, we review only the three most important secretagogues—the angiotensins, potassium, and ACTH—and neurotransmitters.

THE RENIN-ANGIOTENSIN SYSTEM    The renin-angiotensin system is modified by a number of factors, including the adrenergic nervous system, potassium, body fluid volume changes, and sodium. The primary influences on aldosterone are probably through fluid volume, sodium, and potassium, since sodium or volume depletion increases renin release and secondarily increases aldosterone secretion. Angiotensin II (AII) is an octapeptide product of the successive actions of renin and converting enzyme on the angiotensinogen substrate. Angiotensin III (AIII) is the heptapeptide cousin of AII (35). It's effect on the glomerulosa cell appears to be as potent as that of AII.

*Human studies*    The sensitivity threshold to AII infusions in vivo in humans varies from 0.3 to 1 ng AII/kg body weight (BW) min$^{-1}$ in individuals consuming 100–200 mEq of sodium (38). A diet low in sodium increases the sensitivity and the magnitude of the response to AII by as much as threefold. The threshold sensitivity often is reduced to 0.3 ng AII/kg BW min$^{-1}$ or less (38). This infusion rate usually does not produce a measureable change in the circulating AII level, which suggests that the sensitivity of the glomerulosa cell is greater than that of the techniques presently available to measure AII in the circulation. Potassium loading also increases the maximum output of aldosterone in response to AII infusion (39). However, the magnitude of the change in responsiveness induced by changes in dietary potassium intake are less than one third those reportedly induced by changes in sodium intake. With prolonged AII infusion, aldosterone secretion decreases (tachyphylaxis), which may be a secondary effect of potassium depletion (5). However, tachyphylaxis is not as profound with AII as with ACTH (see below). In vitro studies using human tissue are few. Furthermore, because of the profound effect of dietary intake of sodium and potassium on aldosterone secretion in vivo and in vitro, the human studies are difficult to interpret because of the lack of control of these critical variables. However, when normal cells are used, the response is similar to that reported in vivo, e.g. the AII response is modified by dietary sodium intake, and the sensitivity to AII is approximately $10^{-11}$ M (59), Cells obtained from aldosteronomas tend to have an increased sensitivity to sodium and a much greater aldosterone output, primarily because of an increased rate of conversion of corticosterone to aldosterone, i.e. enhanced activity of the late pathway (59).

*Animal studies*    The regulation of aldosterone secretion in vivo has been studied most intensively in sheep, dog, and rat. In general, in all three species the effect of AII on aldosterone secretion is similar to that reported in humans both in terms of the degree of responsiveness and the impact of changes in dietary sodium and potassium intake (2, 24, 32, 50, 54). In contrast, most in vitro studies have used either rat or bovine glomerulosa cells. There are no in vivo bovine studies reported. In general, the rat in vitro studies parallel the results obtained in humans with the single exception of the impact of sodium restriction on AII receptor levels. Sodium restriction increases the number of adrenal AII receptors in rats but decreases the number in primates (no data have been reported in humans)(2). Threshold sensitivities to AII, dose-response relationships, and the impact of changes in dietary sodium and potassium intake on aldosterone response to AII are similar in rat and human glomerulosa cells (2, 59, 61).

An intriguing recent observation is that AII can be generated from tissue renin and converting enzyme within the adrenal itself (48). This adds an additional element of complexity to the role of AII in regulating aldosterone secretion. Tissue renin levels increase in response to lowered sodium intake and potassium loading, at least in rats (24). To date, there have been no studies documenting the presence of a renin-angiotensin system in human adrenal cells.

*Transduction mechanisms*    The stimulatory action of AII is initiated through binding to specific, high-affinity receptors in the plasma membrane (35). The ability of nonhydrolyzable GTP analogues to activate hydrolysis of phosphatidylinositol 4,5-bisphosphate (PIP$_2$) indicates a functional role for G proteins in the transduction mechanism of AII (36). However, identification of the G protein(s) associated with the angiotensin II receptor is still incomplete. Some evidence suggests that the AII receptor may be coupled to more than one G protein, one that stimulates phospholipase C and another that inhibits AMP generation (36)(Figure 1).

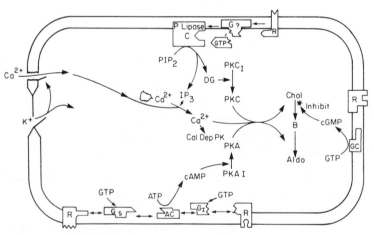

*Figure 1*  Diagram of the relationship between the factors regulating aldosterone secretion. Angiotensin II and vasopressin both activate phospholipase C, as shown at the top of the cell. ACTH at low concentrations may also have this effect. ACTH, MSH, and serotonin all utilize the G$_s$-cAMP system, as shown at the bottom of the cell. Angiotensin II, dopamine, ANP, and somatostatin may use G$_I$ to inhibit adenylate cyclase. ANP may increase cGMP production, but whether or not this is the mechanism by which ANP inhibits aldosterone secretion is unclear. Definitions: PKC = protein kinase C, PKA = protein kinase A, Caldep PK = calmodulin-dependent protein kinase, AC = adenylate cyclase, GC = guanylate cyclase, G$_s$ = stimulatory G protein, G$_I$ = inhibitory G protein, G$_?$ = unidentified other G protein, DG = 1,2-diacylglycerol, B = corticosterone, chol = cholesterol, ANP = atrial natriuretic peptide.

Several lines of evidence suggest that the major transduction mechanism utilized by AII in increasing aldosterone secretion is the hydrolysis of $PIP_2$ by phospholipase C with the formation of inositol trisphosphate ($IP_3$) and 1,2-diacylglycerol (1,2-DG)(28, 29). Activation of phospholipase C is rapid, as evidenced by the reduction in [$^3$H]inositol-labelled $PIP_2$ and the appearance of radioactive labelled $IP_3$ within 5 sec of AII application (30). Most studies have suggested that $IP_3$ levels remain elevated; however, only a limited number of studies have examined the mass of this compound. Most were tracer studies and did not discriminate between the various isomers of $IP_3$. The actual duration of an increased level of this substance appears to be extremely short, although evidence exists for its continued production (6). Recent studies have suggested that AII also stimulates generation of inositol tetrakisphosphate ($IP_4$) in glomerulosa cells (6). If this is true, AII may modify both the release of membrane-bound calcium and the entry of calcium into cells by this mechanism.

Closely linked to the hydrolysis of $PIP_2$ is a rapid elevation of cytosolic free calcium, as measured by fluorescent and bioluminescent indicators (9, 13, 45). The increase in cytosolic calcium is dose dependent and correlates well with aldosterone production (9). The rise in cytosolic calcium may be transient; although some studies suggest that after the initial peak cytosolic calcium does not return to basal levels. Confusion still exists concerning some details, which may in part be related to technical or species differences. For example, in bovine glomerulosa cells, Quin 2 and aequorin signals appear unaffected by nitrendipine except for a decrease in resting calcium concentrations (13, 45). In contrast, dantrolene reduces the signal response to AII (45). In rat glomerulosa cells the AII-induced elevation in cytosolic free calcium detected with Quin 2 appears more sustained, and dantrolene reduces the cytosolic calcium response by almost half. Unlike in the bovine glomerulosa cell, in the rat glomerulosa cell the rise in cytosolic free calcium is also highly dependent on external calcium concentration and is substantially inhibited by nifedipine or nitrendipine administration (9).

There is controversy concerning the effect of AII on the influx of calcium; some studies report a nearly twofold increase in calcium influx, while others found no effect (27, 42). In studies that found that AII enhances calcium influx, the influx was blocked by dihydropyridines, which indicates the involvement of voltage-dependent calcium channels (42). Several studies report membrane depolarization associated with AII stimulation, and action potential activity of sufficient magnitude to activate voltage-dependent calcium channels (13, 53). A decrease in potassium conductance appears to underly this depolarization. However, recent studies using voltage-clamp techniques reveal that AII also increases a voltage-dependent calcium conductance that remains partially open in the resting state (18, 53). In contrast,

**Table 1**  Transduction mechanisms used by aldosterone regulatory factors[a]

| Regulatory Factor | Receptor | Membrane conductance | $Ca^{2+}$ influx | $Ca^{2+}$ release | cAMP | cGMP | $PIP_2$ |
|---|---|---|---|---|---|---|---|
| ACTH | Y | Y | Y | ? | Y | N | ? |
| MSH | Y | ? | ? | ? | Y | N | N |
| Vasopressin | Y | ? | ? | Y | N | N | Y |
| Angiotensin II | Y | Y | Y | Y | I | N | Y |
| Potassium | N | Y | Y | Y | ?Y | N | N |
| Serotonin | Y | ? | N | ? | Y | N | N |
| Dopamine | Y | ? | ? | ? | I or Y | N | ? |
| ANP | Y | ? | ?I | N | I | ?Y | N |
| Somatostatin | Y | ? | ? | ? | I | ? | N |

[a] Y = uses this mechanism; N = does not use this mechanism; I = inhibits this mechanism.

some data suggest that activation of protein kinase C can inhibit calcium influx (14). Thus the mechanism of AII-mediated depolarization is still unclear. Finally, recent studies also have suggested strongly that there is substantial heterogeneity in the time and dose response of the calcium signal to AII in individual glomerulosa cells (19)(Table 1).

AII also causes a slight but demonstrable decrease in cAMP generation; however, this may not be a primary transduction process (36).

*Confounding variables*   As noted above, there are a number of differences that have been reported in terms of the mechanisms underlying AII's effect on glomerulosa cells. At least five variables need to be carefully considered in extrapolating from the results of any study to a statement of the overall regulation of aldosterone secretion.

First, dietary intake of both potassium and particularly sodium has a profound effect on the dose-response relationship and magnitude of the response of the glomerulosa cell to AII (2, 38, 39). In many studies no information is given on these important variables. Specifically, all in vitro studies on bovine tissue lack information on this important element. Since the mechanisms underlying the change in sensitivity and responsiveness to AII with changes in dietary intake are unknown (25), the potential exists that differences in results reported in various experiments are due to this confounding variable.

A second variable is change in the local production of AII. As noted above, there is local generation of AII by the glomerulosa cell itself (24, 48). How this is regulated, and what impact it has on the response of the glomerulosa cell to exogenously administered AII is unclear.

Third, the control of steroid secretion by AII may differ across species. There is evidence for this possibility in the response of fasciculata reticularis cells to AII. Studies of rat and normal human fasciculata reticularis cells in vivo and in vitro give no indication that AII stimulates secretion (10, 38, 59). However, in bovine and pathological human tissue, AII can stimulate cortisol production (44). The implication of these findings in terms of the regulation of aldosterone secretion by AII are uncertain but raise the possibility that differences between bovine and rat or human studies for example, may reflect a fundamental species-specific difference in the regulation of aldosterone secretion.

Fourth, recent studies have reported that individual glomerulosa cells show different calcium signal responses to AII and potassium (19). The reasons for these differences are not clear. It is clear, however, that if there is heterogeneity in tissue responsiveness to aldosterone secretagogues in single, presumably homogeneous, preparations of glomerulosa cells, differences in whole tissue studies could reflect the degree of tissue heterogeneity.

Finally, despite extensive efforts to develop a physiologically responsive glomerulosa cell culture, those that have been described have several deficiencies, and therefore results generated from them should be interpreted cautiously (20). For example, the cultured glomerulosa cell responds poorly to AII. It is not known whether this is due to the loss of AII receptors, the loss of a second messenger, a change in the activity of the tissue renin-angiotensin system, or some other effect.

POTASSIUM    Potassium can stimulate aldosterone secretion and aldosterone can increase the excretion of potassium by the kidney, so it is not surprising that there is a continuous relationship between the level of circulating potassium and that of aldosterone.

*Human studies*    In normal subjects, infusion of 10 mEq of potassium, which does not change measured serum potassium levels, produces a 25% increase in plasma aldosterone levels, reflecting a greater sensitivity of the glomerulosa cell than of the techniques for measuring potassium in humans (37). The steepest part of the dose-response curve is between 3.5 and 6 mEq/liter. Changes in dietary potassium intake for as little as 24 hr substantially modify the response of the adrenal to acute potassium administration: High dietary potassium intake enhances responsiveness, while low potassium intake reduces it (23). Similar effects are not observed with changes in sodium intake (23). The few in vitro studies with human cells have reported a reduced responsiveness of the glomerulosa cell to potassium when compared to that reported in in vivo studies (59). Usually a change of 0.5 mEq/liter of potassium in the incubation medium is required to produce a significant change in aldosterone output. Human in vitro studies have reported greater increases in aldosterone secretion with potassium than with AII (59). It is difficult to make such comparisons in vivo because of the potential toxicity of both agents at high doses.

*Animal studies*    In vivo studies in the rat and sheep have found that the sensitivity of the glomerulosa cell to potassium is similar to that observed in humans. Likewise, dietary potassium intake shifts the dose-response relationship in a similar fashion (8, 32). In rat cells in vitro, as in humans, potassium produces a greater response than AII (10, 59). In contrast, often the bovine adrenal is more responsive to AII than it is to potassium (42, 43). It is uncertain whether this difference is real or simply reflects differences in dietary potassium and sodium intake prior to sacrifice. High levels of potassium in the incubation media (>13 mEq/liter) almost invariably result in a reduction in aldosterone output.

*Transduction mechanisms*    Unlike other aldosterone secretagogues, external potassium acts at the plasma membrane by altering the driving force for potassium across the membrane and in this way modifies the membrane potential (52). The membrane depolarization seen with increasing potassium concentration activates voltage-dependent calcium channels in the plasma membrane as the initial transduction step (43)(Figure 1).

There is evidence for at least two classes of calcium channels in the bovine glomerulosa cell (18). Nitrendipine binds to high- and low-affinity binding sites. The high-affinity binding site has a $K_d$ of 0.48 nM and a capacity of 43 fmol/$10^6$ cells, while the low-affinity binding site has a $K_d$ of 192 nM and a capacity of 122 fmol/$10^6$ cells. Studies examining both binding and inhibition of secretion have found that the $K_d$ and $IC_{50}$ have very similar values, which indicates that the low-affinity binding sites are probably more physiologically important (1). In rat glomerulosa cells only a low-threshold calcium channel has been identified (52). The low-threshold calcium channel is better suited for activation by small changes in membrane potential, as seen with physiological changes in external potassium concentration. If a glomerulosa cell has a resting membrane potential close to the threshold potential for the high-threshold channels, or if potassium stimulation elicits an action potential, the high-threshold calcium channels may also be involved in stimulation of aldosterone production.

As expected, increased calcium influx results in a rise in cytosolic free calcium that is well correlated with aldosterone production (9, 13, 19). Measurements with Quin 2 show this calcium increase to be rapid and sustained for the duration of the stimulation. Cytosolic calcium responses to elevated potassium appear more complicated when observed in individual cells: Different cells demonstrate varied thresholds for potassium stimulation, and some cells do not respond at all (19). Importantly, some glomerulosa cells show a change in cytosolic calcium in response to potassium but not to AII, while others respond only to AII. Cytosolic calcium responses to potassium can be inhibited by nitrendipine, dantrolene, and TMB-8 (9). The inhibition found with dantrolene and TMB-8 suggests that release of cytosolic bound calcium may be involved in the response; however, these agents may have other, uncharacterized effects on calcium metabolism besides blockage of membrane-bound calcium release.

The data concerning the effect of potassium on cAMP are controversial (31, 41). However, the weight of the evidence suggests that potassium affects cAMP generation. It is not clear whether this effect is direct or is secondary to changes in cytosolic calcium levels. No increase in radiolabelled $IP_3$ or tritiated inositol incorporation into phospholipids is observed in the presence of increased concentrations of potassium (63). However, a small, transient decrease in radiolabelled $PIP_2$ has been reported, and an increase in the mass of $IP_3$ lasting for only 10 sec was observed when glomerulosa cells were incubated with 8.7 mmol potassium (43, 56)(Table 1).

PITUITARY FACTORS    Several pituitary factors increase aldosterone secretion. These include a number of products of proopiomelanocortin (POMC), including ACTH, $\alpha$-melanocyte stimulating hormone (MSH), $\beta$-MSH, and $\beta$-endorphins. Vasopressin has also been shown to modify aldosterone secretion. Even though ACTH is the most potent aldosterone secretagogue, it may play only a minor role in the overall regulation of its secretion. There is no negative feedback loop between the pituitary and aldosterone secretion as there is for cortisol output. In addition, aldosterone secretion appears to be normally regulated even in the absence of ACTH.

*Human studies*    Most studies in humans have been limited to the effects of ACTH. ACTH produces a profound, acute increase in aldosterone secretion with a sensitivity threshold of 0.05 mg ACTH/kg BW $min^{-1}$. The response is maximized after 15 min of infusion, as is observed with AII and potassium. Maximum response is produced with an infusion of 0.1 mg of synthetic ACTH (alpha-1-24) over 24 hr (55). In contrast to the effects of AII or potassium stimulation, those of ACTH stimulation are short-lived; a reduction in the adrenal response occurs as early as 6 hr after the initiation of an ACTH infusion. By 24 hr, aldosterone output is actually lower than in the control state (55). The mechanism responsible for this inhibition of aldosterone secretion is unclear. The response of cortisol secretion to ACTH is not biphasic (55). It is also unclear whether or not ACTH inhibition of aldosterone secretion is maintained by pulsatile or very long ACTH infusions or in pathologic conditions, e.g. Cushing's syndrome resulting from excess ACTH production.

Like AII, sodium restriction and potassium loading enhance aldosterone's response to ACTH (55, 60). There have been no reported studies using $\alpha$- and $\beta$-MSH in vivo in humans, but $\beta$-endorphins have been reported to stimulate aldosterone and cortisol production (54). The limited in vitro studies that have been reported with human tissue have provided results similar to those of in vivo studies with a threshold sensitivity to ACTH of $10^{-11}$ to $10^{-12}$ M (59).

*Animal studies*    Studies in experimental animals have provided some data pertinent to the inhibition of aldosterone secretion in response to prolonged ACTH infusion. In sheep following five days of ACTH administration in vivo the cells of the zona glomerulosa appear to transform to a cell type intermediate between glomerulosa and fasciculata (46). This morphological change may transform the cell from an aldosterone- to a cortisol-secreting one.

Both bovine and sheep tissue are less sensitive than rat tissue to ACTH. The sensitivity threshold in rat is between $10^{-13}$ and $10^{-12}$ M ACTH with a peak response at $10^{-10}$ M (10). Both ACTH and $\alpha$-MSH stimulate steroid production in fasciculata and glomerulosa cells (40). However, in vitro, the glomerulosa cell is more responsive than the fasciculata cell to $\alpha$-MSH (57). Both cells are equally responsive to ACTH (54).

*Transduction mechanisms*    ACTH stimulation involves the activation of adenylate cyclase with an increase in intracellular cyclic AMP. A $G_s$ protein is probably an intermediary, since aldosterone production can be stimulated by cholera toxin (31, 44)(Figure 1).

Two populations of ACTH binding sites have been reported on glomerulosa cells: a high-affinity, low-capacity site, and a low-affinity, high-capacity site. The dissociation constant for the high-affinity site is well correlated to the half-maximal concentration of ACTH needed for aldosterone production (33). Based on the observation of two populations of binding sites, models have been proposed that involve dual receptors for ACTH, dual sites within a single receptor molecule, negative cooperativity, dimeric receptors, or a tertiary receptor with interaction of the receptor with another membrane protein, i.e. G protein.

Some studies suggest that the glomerulosa cell response to ACTH uses one of two different pathways depending on the concentration of ACTH used (44). At concentrations lower than $10^{-10}$ M steroid output is stimulated, phospholipase C activity increases, but there is no increase in cAMP. At higher concentrations ($>10^{-9}$ M) adenylate cyclase, but not phospholipase C, activity and steroid secretion are increased. Similar results have been reported with fasciculata cells (65). However, at least two questions remain unanswered. First, the amount of aldosterone produced in response to low doses of ACTH is much smaller than that produced when the cAMP mechanism is involved. Thus the physiological significance of the low-dose effect is questionable. Second, the previously described studies using presumed glomerulosa cells may actually have been measuring the impact of low levels of ACTH on zona fasciculata cells contaminating the glomerulosa cell preparation. No human studies have been reported.

The aldosterone response to ACTH is dependent on external calcium concentration and can be blocked by dihydropyridines and calmodulin inhibitors (1); however, ACTH binding also appears to be calcium dependent (17). ACTH induces a sustained increase in calcium influx (44). However, whether or not it produces changes in cytosolic calcium is unclear (9, 45).

Although the mechanism for ACTH-mediated calcium influx has not been elucidated, some evidence points to the activation of voltage-dependent calcium channels. ACTH can cause depolarization of glomerulosa cells, through a decrease in potassium conductance, with no apparent change in inward calcium current (51). In addition, dihydropyridines can block the calcium influx, though greater concentrations are required than for potassium- or AII-mediated calcium influx (42). The mechanism does not appear to operate through activation of phospholipase C and $PIP_2$ hydrolysis, as neither mass nor isotope measurements change in response to ACTH administration in most studies (56, 63). Where changes in phosphatidylinositol metabolism have been observed in adrenal preparations, fasiculata or reticularis cells appear to be the target cell type, at least in the rat, as noted above (38)(Table 1).

Vasopressin can also stimulate aldosterone secretion. Vasopressin receptors (V-2 type) have been found on glomerulosa cells, and in vitro vasopressin can increase their aldosterone output (7, 64). However, the increase is modest and is not sustained. It has been suggested that the second messenger is phosphatidylinositol because vasopressin can stimulate the breakdown of $PIP_2$ with an accompanying increase in radiolabelled $IP_3$. The hydrolysis of $PIP_2$ is dose dependent with maximum activation at $10^{-6}$ M. However, aldosterone secretion is maximal between $10^{-10}$ and $10^{-9}$ M (64). When secretion is examined during superfusion with $10^{-7}$ M vasopressin, only a transient increase in steroid output is observed (7). If activation of phospholipase C is the sole transduction mechanism for this effect of vasopressin, it is unclear why the hydrolysis of $PIP_2$ does not follow the same dose-dependency as secretion and why maximum stimulation of phospholipase C is associated with a reduced, transient steroid output. Finally, no in vivo effect of vasopressin has been reported.

*Confounding variables*  In addition to the confounding variables noted above, studies using pituitary factors, particularly ACTH, need to consider an additional one—the number of contaminating fasciculata cells. Most pituitary factors induced as much or more steroid (e.g. cortisol and corticosterone) output from fasciculata cells as from glomerulosa cells. Varying the corticosterone content in the incubation medium can influence aldosterone production and its responsiveness to other secretagogues, including ACTH (62).

NEUROTRANSMITTERS    Although the glomerulosa cells are richly innervated, a direct effect of neurotransmitters on aldosterone output has been difficult to prove. There is no known feedback loop involving aldosterone secretion and the neuroadrenergic system. There are no in vivo studies in man or animals reporting an effect of neurotransmitters on aldosterone secretion. However, in vitro studies have documented increased aldosterone production in the presence of serotonin concentrations of $10^{-8}$ M and above (4). This stimulation is dependent on external calcium concentration and is blocked by verapamil but not by dihydropyridine antagonists (34). Cyclic AMP output is well correlated with steroidogenesis except at very low concentrations, which suggests that the mechanism utilized by serotonin is similar to that used by ACTH (4). High concentrations of serotonin do not enhance calcium efflux, thus it is unlikely that a major transduction pathway involves hydrolysis of $PIP_2$. This conclusion is also supported by the absence of a serotonin effect on $^{32}P$ incorporation into elements of the phosphatidylinositol pathway (63). Neither calcium influx nor cytosolic calcium have been examined. Thus, the basis for the external calcium dependency is unknown.

Catecholamines may directly regulate steroid output through $\beta$-type receptors. In cultured bovine glomerulosa cells, catecholamines increase aldosterone secretion, possibly through activation of adenylate cyclase (22). However, since acutely dispersed glomerulosa cells do not respond to adrenergic catecholamines, the physiological relevance of these findings is unclear (22).

## Factors That Inhibit Aldosterone Secretion

All factors known to inhibit aldosterone secretion are natriuretic. In addition to their effect on aldosterone secretion, they also modify vascular contractility and perhaps renal tubular handling of sodium. Thus the inhibition of aldosterone secretion appears to be part of an overall effort to reduce sodium retention. As might be anticipated, the mechanisms underlying the inhibitory effects have been less clearly defined than the transduction mechanisms involved in the stimulation of aldosterone output.

ATRIAL NATRIURETIC PEPTIDES    In vitro, synthetic atrial natriuretic peptide (ANP) directly inhibits aldosterone secretion from rat and bovine glomerulosa cells. This appears to be a receptor-mediated event, but ANP does not interfere with either ACTH or AII binding (21). The effect of ANP mainly is confined to the zona glomerulosa, although some studies have demonstrated inhibition of cortisol production as well (47). It is unclear whether ANP has any effect on basal aldosterone secretion or only affects secretion in response to stimulation by some other factor. ANP inhibits AII, $K^+$, and, in part, ACTH-stimulated aldosterone secretion both in vitro and in vivo in rats (16). Synthetic human ANP also reduces basal aldosterone secretion by aldosterone-producing human adenoma cells and in vivo in humans in response to AII (49).

ANP acts through specific membrane receptors, in which high- and low-affinity binding sites have been identified. The $IC_{50}$ for inhibition is close to $10^{-10}$ M, a value similar to that of the $K_d$ for the high-affinity binding site (21, 58). Interestingly, receptor binding may not be modified by GTP analogues, in contrast to what occurs in vascular tissue (58).

ANP has two well-documented effects on second messengers: It increases cGMP and inhibits adenylate cyclase activity. It is not clear if modulation of either second messenger is the primary mechanism for ANP inhibition of aldosterone secretion. Analogues of cGMP do not inhibit steroidogenesis (26). Thus activation of guanylate cyclase does not appear to mediate the action of ANP, although data on this point are inconsistent. Inhibition of adenylate cyclase has not been examined directly, but it cannot be a common basis for the effect of ANP since it inhibits AII, potassium, and ACTH-induced increases in aldosterone secretion. Yet not all of these agents use cAMP as a second messenger.

There is evidence from other tissues that ANP may act as a calcium channel blocker; however, ANP does not appear to behave in this manner in glomerulosa cells (15). ANP has no effect on the changes in total exchangeable calcium seen with potassium or AII and does not appear to block the increase in cytosolic free calcium induced by these secretagogues; but information on this point is limited.

DOPAMINE   In vivo studies have demonstrated that the dopaminergic system can modulate aldosterone production; the most conclusive evidence is disinhibition of aldosterone secretion in response to the dopamine antagonist metoclopramide (12). There is growing evidence that dopamine may act directly on glomerulosa cells. Dopamine receptors have been located in membrane preparations from zona glomerulosa cells, which indicates the existence of D-2-like and possibly D-1-like receptors (47). Although inhibition of AII-stimulated aldosterone production by dopamine is not always observed in vitro, such inhibition has been observed with high concentrations of dopamine (1 $\mu$M). In addition to direct inhibition by dopamine, some studies report enhanced stimulation by AII in the presence of dopamine antagonists, which indicates a persistent inhibition by dopamine, even in isolated cell preparations.

The mechanism for dopamine inhibition of AII-stimulated aldosterone production has not been firmly established. There are conflicting reports that dopamine stimulates adenylate cyclase through a D-1 receptor, that it inhibits adenylate cyclase activity through a D-2 receptor, and that it has no effect on cAMP generation. One study observed inhibition of AII-stimulated aldosterone production that was blocked by a D-2 antagonist but was not affected by a D-1 antagonist. These observations suggest there may be a link between adenylate cyclase inhibition and steroid output (47). As with ANPs, it is presently unclear how the dopamine inhibition of adenylate cyclase can act to block AII stimulation. Other transduction processes have not been thoroughly examined to evaluate their role in dopamine inhibition of steroidogenesis.

OTHER INHIBITORY FACTORS    The existence of an ouabainlike natriuretic factor has been postulated for more than two decades; however, it has not been identified or isolated. Presumably, such a factor would also inhibit aldosterone secretion by a mechanism similar to that involving ouabain, i.e. inhibition of sodium ATPase activity and equilibration of calcium and sodium concentrations across the membrane (11).

High-affinity binding sites for somatostatin are found on glomerulosa cells of several species, including rat and bovine (3). In addition, low concentrations of somatostatin can inhibit AII-induced aldosterone production in isolated rat glomerulosa cells (3). The transduction mechanism may be an inhibition of adenylate cyclase by activation of an inhibitory G protein similar to that observed in other tissues (36). The mechanism of somatostatin's effect on glomerulosa cells is unclear.

## SUMMARY

Regulation of aldosterone secretion is complex both in terms of the number of secretagogues that can influence its biosynthesis and the number of second messengers utilized by these secretagogues (Table 1, Figure 1). ACTH primarily acts via the adenylate cyclase system through a stimulatory G protein; however, there is evidence that at low concentration it may also activate calcium influx and phospholipase C in some species. The primary effect of AII is activation of phospholipase C, which increases both calcium release from intracellular stores and calcium flux across the cell membrane and activates protein kinase C. Potassium depolarizes the membrane, thereby activating calcium flow through voltage-dependent calcium channels. It also directly or indirectly causes release of calcium from intracellular binding sites. A small change in cAMP levels may also be involved in the sustained secretory response to potassium. Species variation in the regulation of aldosterone secretion probably exists; the control mechanisms in the human appear to be closer to those in the rat than to those in cow and sheep. How changes in dietary sodium and potassium modify aldosterone secretion and the adrenal's responsiveness to secretagogues remains unclear. Yet these effects may be of considerable importance, both in terms of understanding the overall regulation of aldosterone secretion and in resolving the discrepancies in the results obtained under different experimental conditions.

## Literature Cited

1. Aguilera, G., Catt, K. J. 1986. Participation of voltage-dependent calcium channels in the regulation of adrenal glomerulosa function by angiotensin II and potassium. *Endocrinology* 118: 112–28

2. Aguilera, G., Catt, K. J. 1985. Regulation of the sensitivity of the adrenal glomerulosa cell during altered sodium intake. *The Adrenal Gland and Hypertension*, 27:33–40. New York: Raven

3. Aguilera, G., Parker, D. S., Catt, K. J. 1982. Characterization of somatostatin receptors in the rat adrenal glomerulosa zone. *Endocrinology* 111:1376–84

4. Albano, J. D. M., Brown, B. L., Ekins, R. P., Tait, S. A. S., Tait, J. F. 1974. The effects of potassium, 5-hydroxytyramine, adrenocorticotropin and angiotensin II on the concentration of adenosine 3',5'-cyclic monophosphate in suspensions of dispersed rat zona glomerulosa and zona fasciculata cells. *Biochem. J.* 142:391–400

5. Ames, R. P., Borkowski, A. J., Sicinski, A. M., Laragh, J. H. 1965. Prolonged infusions of angiotensin II and norepinephrine and blood pressure, electrolyte balance, and aldosterone and cortisol secretion in normal man and in cirrhosis with ascites. *J. Clin. Invest.* 44:1171–86

6. Balla, T., Baukal, A. J., Guillemette, G., Morgan, R. O., Catt, K. J. 1986. Angiotensin-stimulated production of inositol trisphosphate isomers and rapid metabolism through inositol 4-monophosphate in adrenal glomerulosa cells. *Proc. Natl. Acad. Sci. USA* 83:9323–27

7. Balla, T., Enyedi, P., Spat, A., Antoni, F. A. 1985. Pressor-type vasopressin receptors in the adrenal cortex: Properties of binding, effects on phosphoinositide metabolism and aldosterone secretion. *Endocrinology* 117:421–23

8. Boyd, J. E., Palmore, W. P., Mulrow, P. J. 1971. Role of potassium in the control of aldosterone secretion in the rat. *Endocrinology* 88:556–65

9. Braley, L. M., Menachery, A. I., Brown, E. M., Williams, G. H. 1986. Comparative effect of angiotensin II, potassium, adrenocorticotropin, and cyclic adenosine 3',5'-monophosphate on cytosolic calcium in rat adrenal cells. *Endocrinology* 119:1010–19

10. Braley, L. M., Williams, G. H. 1977. Rat adrenal cell sensitivity to angiotensin II, alpha 1-24-ACTH, and potassium: A comparative study. *Am. J. Physiol.* 233:E402–6

11. Braley, L. M., Williams, G. H., Menachery, A. 1978. The effects of ouabain on steroid production by rat adrenal cells stimulated by angiotensin II, alpha-1-24 adrenocorticotropin, and potassium. *Endocrinology* 103:1997–2005

12. Carey, R. M. 1985. Physiologic and possible pathophysiologic relevance of dopaminergic mechanisms in the control of aldosterone secretion. *The Adrenal Gland and Hypertension*, 27:55–68. New York: Raven

13. Capponi, A. M., Lew, P. D., Jornot, L., Vallotton, M. B. 1984. Correlation between cytosolic free $Ca^{++}$ and aldosterone production in bovine adrenal glomerulosa cells. *J. Biol. Chem.* 259: 8863–69

14. Capponi, A. M., Lew, P. D., Vallotton, M. 1986. Characterization of the $[Ca^{++}]$ response induced in adrenal glomerulosa cells by angiotensin II and potassium. *Experientia* 42:635–39

15. Capponi, A. M., Lew, P. D., Wuthrich, R., Vallotton, M. B. 1986. Effects of atrial natriuretic peptide on the stimulation by angiotensin II of various target cells. *J. Hypertension* 4(Suppl. 2):S61–65

16. Chartier, L., Schiffrin, E., Thibault, G., Garcia, R. 1984. Atrial natriuretic factor inhibits the stimulation of aldosterone secretion by angiotensin II, ACTH and potassium in vitro and angiotensin II-

induced steroidogenesis in vivo. *Endocrinology* 115:2026–28

17. Cheitlin, R., Buckley, D. I., Ramachandran, J. 1985. The role of extracellular calcium in corticotropin-stimulated steroidogenesis. *J. Biol. Chem.* 260:5323–27

18. Cohen, C. J., McCarthy, R. T., Barrett, P. Q., Rasmussen, H. 1987. Two populations of Ca$^{++}$ channels in bovine adrenal glomerulosa cells. *Biophys. J.* 51:224G (Abstr.)

19. Connor, J. A., Cornwall, M. C., Williams, G. H. 1987. Spatially resolved cytosolic calcium response to angiotensin II and potassium in rat glomerulosa cells measured by digital imaging techniques. *J. Biol. Chem.* 262:2919–27

20. Crinello, J. F., Hornsby, P. J., Gill, G. N. 1982. Metyrapone and antioxidants are required to maintain aldosterone synthesis by cultured bovine adrenocortical zona glomerulosa cells. *Endocrinology* 111:469–79

21. DeLean, A., Gutkowska, J., McNicoll, N., Schiller, P. W., Cantin, M., Genest, J. 1984. Characterization of specific receptors for atrial natriuretic factor in bovine adrenal zona glomerulosa. *Life Sci.* 35:2311–18

22. DeLean, A., Racz, K., McNicoll, N., Desrosiers, M. 1984. Direct beta-adrenergic stimulation of aldosterone secretion in cultured bovine adrenal subcapsular cells. *Endocrinology* 115:485–92

23. Dluhy, R. G., Axelrod, L., Underwood, R. H., Williams, G. H. 1972. Studies of the control of plasma aldosterone concentration in normal man. II. Effect of dietary potassium and acute potassium infusion. *J. Clin. Invest.* 51:1950–57

24. Doi, Y., Atarashi, K., Franco-Saenz, R., Mulrow, P. J. 1984. Effect of changes in sodium or potassium balance, and nephrectomy, on adrenal renin and aldosterone concentrations. *Hypertension* (Suppl.) 6:I124–29

25. Douglas, J. G., Brown, G. P., White, C. 1984. Angiotensin II receptors of human and primate adrenal fasciculata and glomerulosa: Correlation of binding and steroidogenesis. *Metabolism* 33:685–91

26. Elliott, M. E., Goodfriend, T. L. 1986. Atrial natriuretic peptide inhibits protein phosphorylation stimulated by angiotensin II in bovine adrenal glomerulosa cells. *Biochem. Biophys. Res. Commun.* 140:814–20

27. Elliott, M. E., Siegel, F. L., Hadjokas, N. E., Goodfriend, T. L. 1985. Angiotensin effects on calcium and steroidogenesis in adrenal glomerulosa cells. *Endocrinology* 116:1051–59

28. Enyedi, P., Buki, B., Mucsi, I., Spat, A. 1985. Polyphosphoinositide metabolism in adrenal glomerulosa cells. *Mol. Cell. Endocrinol.* 41:105–12

29. Farese, R. V. 1984. Phospholipids as intermediates in hormone action. *Mol. Cell. Endocrinol.* 35:1–14

30. Farese, R. V., Larson, R. E., Davis, J. S. 1984. Rapid effects of angiotensin II on phosphoinositide metabolism in the rat adrenal glomerulosa. *Endocrinology* 114:302–4

31. Fujita, K., Aguilera, G., Catt, K. J. 1979. The role of cyclic AMP in aldosterone production by isolated zona glomerulosa cells. *J. Biol. Chem.* 254:8567–74

32. Funder, J. W., Blair-West, J. R., Coghlan, J. P., Denton, D. A., Scoggins, B. A., Wright, R. D. 1969. Effect of plasma (K$^+$) on the secretion of aldosterone. *Endocrinology* 85:381–84

33. Gallo-Payet, N., Escher, E. 1985. Adrenocorticotropin receptors in rat adrenal glomerulosa cells. *Endocrinology* 117:38–46

34. Ganguly, A., Hampton, T. 1985. Calcium-dependence of serotonin-mediated aldosterone secretion and differential effects of calcium antagonists. *Life Sci.* 36:1459–64

35. Goodfriend, T. L., Peach, M. J. 1975. Angiotensin III: (des-aspartic acid$^1$)-angiotensin II. *Circ. Res.* 36,37:138–48

36. Hausdorff, W. P., Sekura, R. D., Aguilera, G., Catt, K. J. 1987. Control of aldosterone production by angiotensin II is mediated by two guanine nucleotide regulatory proteins. *Endocrinology* 120:1668–78

37. Himathongkam, T., Dluhy, R. G., Williams, G. H. 1975. Potassium-aldosterone-renin interrelationships. *J. Clin. Endocrinol. Metab.* 41:153–59

38. Hollenberg, N. K., Chenitz, W. R., Adams, D. F., Williams, G. H. 1974. Reciprocal influence of salt intake on adrenal glomerulosa and renal vascular responses to angiotensin II in normal man. *J. Clin. Invest.* 54:34–42

39. Hollenberg, N. K., Williams, G. H., Burger, B., Hooshmand, I. 1975. Potassium's influence on the renal vasculature, the adrenal, and their responsiveness to angiotensin II in normal man. *Clin. Sci. Mol. Med.* 49:527–34

40. Hyatt, P. J., Bell, J. B. G., Bhatt, K., Chu, F. W., Tait, J. F., et al. 1986. Effects of alpha-melanocyte-stimulating hormone on the cyclic AMP and phos-

pholipid metabolism of rat adrenocortical cells. *J. Endocrinol.* 110:405–16
41. Hyatt, P. J., Tait, J. F., Tait, S. A. S. 1986. The mechanism of the effect of K$^+$ on the steroidogenesis of rat zona glomerulosa cells of the adrenal cortex: Role of cyclic cAMP. *Proc. R. Soc. London* 227:21–42
42. Kojima, I., Kojima, K., Rasmussen, H. 1985. Characteristics of angiotensin II-, K$^+$- and ACTH-induced calcium influx in adrenal glomerulosa cells: Evidence that angiotensin II, K$^+$, and ACTH may open a common calcium channel. *J. Biol. Chem.* 260:9171–76
43. Kojima, I., Kojima, K., Rasmussen, H. 1985. Intracellular calcium and adenosine 3',5'-cyclic monophosphate as mediator of potassium-induced aldosterone secretion. *Biochem. J.* 228:69–76
44. Kojima, I., Kojima, K., Rasmussen, H. 1985. Role of calcium and cAMP in the action of adrenocorticotropin on aldosterone secretion. *J. Biol. Chem.* 260:4248–56
45. Kojima, I., Ogata, E. 1986. Direct demonstration of adrenocorticotropin-induced changes in cytosolic free calcium with aequorin in adrenal glomerulosa cell. *J. Biol. Chem.* 261:9832–38
46. McDougall, J. G., Butkus, A., Coghlan, J. P., Denton, D. A., Muller, J., et al. 1980. Biosynthetic and morphological evidence for inhibition of aldosterone production following administration of ACTH to sheep. *Acta Endocrinol. Copenhagen* 94:559–70
47. Missale, C., Liberini, P., Memo, M., Carruba, M. O., Spano, P. 1986. Characterization of dopamine receptors associated with aldosterone secretion in rat adrenal glomerulosa. *Endocrinology* 119:2227–32
48. Nakamaru, M., Misono, K. S., Naruse, M., Workman, R. J., Inagami, T. 1985. A role for the adrenal renin-angiotensin system in the regulation of potassium-stimulated aldosterone production. *Endocrinology* 117:1772–78
49. Naruse, M., Obana, K., Naruse, K., Yamaguchi, H., Demura, H., et al. 1987. Atrial natriuretic polypeptide inhibits cortisol secretion as well as aldosterone secretion in vitro from human adrenal tissue. *J. Clin. Endocrinol. Metab.* 64:10–16
50. Nicholls, M. G., Tree, M., Brown, J. J., Douglas, B. H., Fraser, R., et al. 1978. Angiotensin II/aldosterone dose-response curves in the dog: Effect of changes in sodium balance. *Endocrinology* 102:485–93
51. Payet, M. D., Gallo-Payet, N., Sauve, R. 1986. Cultured glomerulosa cells from adrenals of rats. Effect of ACTH and TEA. *Biophys. J.* 49:166A (Abstr.)
52. Quinn, S. J., Cornwall, M. C., Williams, G. H. 1987. Electrical properties of isolated rat adrenal glomerulosa and fasciculata cells. *Endocrinology* 120:903–14
53. Quinn, S. J., Cornwall, M. C., Williams, G. H. 1987. Electrophysiological responses to angiotensin II of isolated rat adrenal glomerulosa cells. *Endocrinology* 120:1581–89
54. Rabinowe, S. L., Taylor, T., Dluhy, R. G., Williams, G. H. 1985. β-endorphin stimulates plasma renin and aldosterone release in normal human subjects. *J. Clin. Endocrinol. Metab.* 60:485–89
55. Rayfield, E. J., Rose, L. I., Dluhy, R. G., Williams, G. H. 1973. Aldosterone secretory and glucocorticoid excretory responses to alpha 1–24 (Cortrosyn) in sodium-depleted normal man. *J. Clin. Endocrinol. Metab.* 36:30–35
56. Underwood, R. H., Greeley, R., Glennon, E. T., Menachery, A. I., Braley, L. M., Williams, G. H. 1987. Mass determination of polyphosphoinositides and inositol trisphosphate in rat adrenal glomerulosa cells. *Endocrinology* 120 (Suppl. 1):S189
57. Vinson, G. P., Whitehouse, B. J., Dell, A., Bateman, A., McAuley, M. E. 1983. Alpha-MSH and zona glomerulosa function in the rat. *J. Steroid Biochem.* 19:537–44
58. Waldman, S. A., Rapoport, R. M., Murad, F. 1984. Atrial natriuretic factor selectively activates particulate guanylate cyclase and elevates cyclic GMP in rat tissues. *J. Biol. Chem.* 259:14332–34
59. Williams, G. H., Braley, L. M. 1977. Effects of dietary sodium and potassium intake and acute stimulation on aldosterone output by isolated human adrenal cells. *J. Clin. Endocrinol. Metab.* 45:55–64
60. Williams, G. H., Dluhy, R. G., Underwood, R. H. 1970. Relationship of dietary potassium intake to the aldosterone stimulating properties of ACTH. *Clin. Sci.* 39:489–96
61. Williams, G. H., Hollenberg, N. K., Braley, L. M. 1976. Influence of sodium intake on vascular and adrenal angiotensin II receptors. *Endocrinology* 98:1343–50
62. Williams, G. H., McDonnell, L. M., Tait, S. A. S., Tait, J. F. 1972. The effect of medium composition and in vit-

ro stimuli on the conversion of cortico-sterone to aldosterone in rat glomerulosa tissue. *Endocrinology* 91:948–60

63. Whitley, G. S. J., Bell, J. B. G., Chu, F. W., Tait, J. F., Tait, S. A. S. 1984. The effects of ACTH, serotonin, $K^+$ and angiotensin analogues on 32P incorporation into phospholipids of the rat adrenal cortex: Basis for an assay method using zona glomerulosa cells. *Proc. R. Soc. London* 222:273–94

64. Woodcock, E. A., McLeod, J. K., Johnston, C. I. 1986. Vasopressin stimulates phosphatidylinositol turnover and aldosterone synthesis in rat adrenal glomerulosa cells: Comparison with angiotensin II. *Endocrinology* 118:2432–36

65. Yanagibashi, K. 1979. Calcium ion as "second messenger" in corticoidogenic action of ACTH. *Endocrinology Jpn.* 26:227–32

*Ann. Rev. Physiol. 1988. 50:427–40*

# REGULATION OF THE SYNTHESIS OF STEROIDOGENIC ENZYMES IN ADRENAL CORTICAL CELLS BY ACTH

*Evan R. Simpson and Michael R. Waterman*

Departments of Biochemistry and Obstetrics-Gynecology, and the Cecil H. & Ida Green Center for Reproductive Biology Sciences, The University of Texas Southwestern Medical School, 5323 Harry Hines Boulevard, Dallas, Texas 75235

## INTRODUCTION

The mechanism of steroid hormone regulation of specific gene expression in target cells has provided a major focus of interest for investigators concerned with molecular mechanisms involved in cell regulation. This work has been given renewed impetus by the recent cloning and characterization of several steroid hormone receptors (1–6), the *trans*-acting elements which, upon binding specific ligands, namely the steroid hormones, interact with specific regions of many eukaryotic genes to alter their expression. In contrast, there has been considerably less interest in the mechanisms of regulation of steroid hormone biosynthesis. Yet this is also a topic of great importance, not only because these reactions provide the ligands that interact with the steroid hormone receptors, but also because the steroidogenic enzymes provide excellent model systems for studying the regulation of gene expression by cAMP-dependent mechanisms and by mechanisms involving protein kinase C and tyrosine kinase activity. A variety of mechanisms appear to regulate steroid hydroxylase gene expression in a given cell, and tissue-specific as well as developmental factors play important roles also. In this review, we focus primarily on the regulation of steroid hydroxylase gene expression by cAMP-dependent mechanisms and, in particular, the mechanisms of ACTH regulation of the synthesis of the steroidogenic enzymes present in the adrenal cortex.

427

0066-4278/88/0315-0427$02.00

# PATHWAYS OF STEROID HORMONE BIOSYNTHESIS

The adrenal cortex produces (Figure 1) both glucocorticoids (cortisol and corticosterone) and mineralocorticoids (aldosterone) as well as $C_{19}$ steroids (adrenal androgens), which can serve as precursors to sex hormones in extra-adrenal tissues (7). The cholesterol side-chain cleavage reaction is common to all steroidogenic pathways, including those in the adrenal cortex. It is the initial step in steroid hormone biosynthesis and results in the formation of pregnenolone from cholesterol. This reaction takes place in mitochondria and utilizes three distinct proteins (8). Reducing equivalents from mitochondrial NADPH are transferred by a flavoprotein (adrenodoxin reductase) to an iron-sulfur protein (adrenodoxin). These enzymes are localized in the mitochondrial matrix. Adrenodoxin transfers electrons to a specific form of cytochrome P-450, cholesterol side-chain cleavage cytochrome P-450 (P-450$_{scc}$), localized in the inner aspect of the inner mitochondrial membrane (9, 10). This enzyme catalyzes the cleavage of the cholesterol side-chain to yield pregnenolone. This reaction utilizes three molecules of molecular oxygen and three molecules of NADPH; the first two are required for sequential hydroxylations at positions 22 and 20 (11). The third molecule of oxygen is required for the as yet uncharacterized cleavage of the carbon-carbon bond between these two atoms.

The pregnenolone produced by this reaction leaves the mitochondrion and travels to the endoplasmic reticulum, where it undergoes further transformation. In the adrenal cortex of humans, cows, sheep, and pigs the pregnenolone is converted by a second form of cytochrome P-450 (17$\alpha$-hydroxylase cytochrome P-450, or P-450$_{17\alpha}$) to 17$\alpha$-hydroxypregnenolone. Adrenals of rats, rabbits, hamsters, and guinea pigs do not contain P-450$_{17\alpha}$, and the pregnenolone is converted directly to progesterone by the 3$\beta$-hydroxysteroid dehydrogenase/isomerase. The latter enzyme converts 17$\alpha$-hydroxypregnenolone to 17$\alpha$-hydroxyprogesterone in humans. The progesterone or 17$\alpha$-hydroxyprogesterone then undergoes hydroxylation by a third cytochrome P-450 species (21-hydroxylase cytochrome P-450 or P-450$_{C21}$), which leads to the production of deoxycorticosterone (DOC) and 11-deoxycortisol (S), respectively. The microsomal steroid hydroxylases, P-450$_{17\alpha}$ and P-450$_{C21}$, are reduced by NADPH via the ubiquitous microsomal flavoprotein, NADPH cytochrome P-450 reductase (12). DOC and S then leave the endoplasmic reticulum and enter the mitochondria for the final step in glucocorticoid production, which is catalyzed by the second mitochondrial form of cytochrome P-450 (11$\beta$-hydroxylase cytochrome P-450, or P-450$_{11\beta}$). P-450$_{11\beta}$ is also localized in the inner mitochondrial membrane (9) and utilizes reducing equivalents provided by adrenodoxin and adrenodoxin reductase, as described for P-450$_{scc}$ (13). Thus DOC is converted into corti-

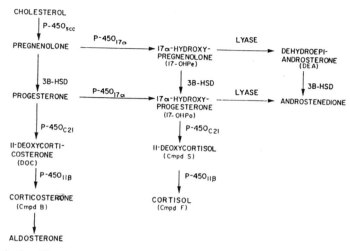

*Figure 1* Steroidogenic pathways in the adrenal cortex leading to the production of glucocorticoids, mineralocorticoids and adrenal androgens. Lyase: 17,20-lyase; 3β-HSD: 3β-hydroxysteroid dehydrogenase.

costerone (B), which is the major glucocorticoid in rodents, while S is converted into cortisol (F), the primary glucocorticoid in humans. These reactions take place in the fasciculata reticularis cells of the adrenal cortex.

In the cells of the zona glomerulosa, a parallel series of reactions takes place, although $P$-$450_{17\alpha}$ is not found in these cells in any species, and corticosterone is converted to aldosterone (the major mineralocorticoid) by an 18-hydroxylation reaction that may also be catalyzed by $P$-$450_{11\beta}$ (14). This is followed by an 18-dehydrogenation reaction that apparently involves insertion of another oxygen atom at the $C_{18}$ position followed by loss of water, and this is perhaps catalyzed by another P-450 species (15). In species having $P$-$450_{17\alpha}$ in the fasciculata reticularis cells of the adrenal cortex (such as man), $C_{19}$ steroids are produced by the 17,20-lyase activity of this enzyme (dehydroepiandrosterone and androstenedione) that can serve as precursors for sex hormones produced by other tissues. Preparations of purified adrenocortical and testicular $P$-$450_{17\alpha}$ possess both the 17α-hydroxylase activity necessary for cortisol production and the 17,20-lyase activity necessary for sex steroid formation (16, 17). The location of both enzymatic activities on the same polypeptide chain has recently been established by expression of $P$-$450_{17\alpha}$ cDNA in COS 1 cells derived from monkey kidney (18).

In testicular Leydig cells and ovarian thecal cells the only representatives of the adrenal steroidogenic pathway present are $P$-$450_{scc}$ and $P$-$450_{17\alpha}$. In the absence of $P$-$450_{C21}$ and $P$-$450_{11\beta}$, no glucocorticoids or mineralocorticoids can be produced; consequently, these tissues produce androgens, namely testosterone and androstenedione. These can be converted to estrogens in the testicular Leydig and Sertoli cells and in ovarian granulosa cells by means of aromatase cytochrome P-450 (P-450$_{arom}$), another P-450 species of the endoplasmic reticulum (19). With the exception of the 3$\beta$-hydroxysteroid dehydrogenase, the enzymes involved in the various steroidogenic pathways are mixed-function oxidases belonging to the cytochrome P-450 gene superfamily. It is readily apparent that the mechanisms involved in regulation of the differential expression of these steroid hydroxylases are important in determining the profile and levels of the various glucocorticoids, mineralocorticoids, and sex hormones, and consequently the tissue specificity associated with these profiles.

## ACUTE AND CHRONIC REGULATION OF STEROIDOGENESIS

Regulation of steroid hormone production involves two responses, which are separable on a temporal basis. The acute response occurs rapidly (within seconds or minutes) and involves mobilization of cholesterol to the mitochondrial cholesterol side-chain cleavage enzyme (20). This rapid mobilization of cholesterol is mediated by cAMP and involves the translocation of cholesterol from storage sites (lipid droplets) to the mitochondria and thence into the inner mitochondrial membrane. The acute response is particularly developed in the adrenal cortex, where it provides for a rapid increase in cortisol secretion in response to stress. Thus ACTH binds to specific cell surface receptors and activates adenylate cyclase, which leads to elevated intracellular cAMP levels, which in turn cause a rapid increase in the levels of cholesterol in the vicinity of P-450$_{scc}$ in the inner mitochondrial membrane.

In addition to the acute response, which regulates substrate supply, steroidogenesis is also regulated by a longer term response to ACTH, which involves maintenance of optimal levels of the steroid hydroxylase enzymes. This chronic action of ACTH was first observed in hypophysectomized rats, in which the levels of steroid hydroxylases decreased in both adrenal cortex and testis (21–23). However, administration of the appropriate peptide hormones to such animals led to recovery of steroidogenic capacity in the respective organ. In our laboratory we have undertaken investigation of the mechanism of this chronic action of peptide hormones, which is apparently mediated by cAMP. It seems clear from our studies and those of others that this action of cAMP serves to maintain optimal steroidogenic capacity in the adrenal cortex. In contrast, in the ovary steroidogenic activity is episodic and cyclical and is precisely coordinated by a number of factors, not all of which have been elucidated.

# REGULATION OF THE SYNTHESIS OF STEROIDOGENIC ENZYMES BY ACTH

As mentioned above, it was apparent that an important element of the long-term action of ACTH in the regulation of adrenal steroidogenesis involved maintenance of optimal levels of the steroid hydroxylases and related enzymes. To investigate the mechanism of this action of ACTH, we utilized primary cultures of bovine adrenal cortical cells as a model system. Utilizing polyclonal antibodies raised against the various steroidogenic forms of cytochrome P-450 as well as adrenodoxin, we found that ACTH treatment resulted in increased rates of synthesis of all of these enzymes, namely P-450$_{scc}$ (24), P-450$_{11\beta}$ (25), P-450$_{C21}$ (26), P-450$_{17\alpha}$ (27), and adrenodoxin (28). The rates increased four- to fivefold and generally reached a maximum value 24–36 hr after initiation of ACTH treatment. There was detectable synthesis of P-450$_{scc}$, P-450$_{11\beta}$, and P-450$_{C21}$ in control cells. In the case of P-450$_{17\alpha}$, synthesis was not detected in the absence of ACTH. Consequently, the increase in synthesis of this protein induced by ACTH was manyfold greater than that of the others. ACTH did not affect the turnover of any of these proteins (29), and the action of ACTH was mimicked by cAMP analogues, such as dibutyryl cAMP and 8-bromo-cAMP (30). These results indicate that the action of ACTH to increase the synthesis of these enzymes is mediated by cAMP. In subsequent studies, it was found that ACTH and cAMP had a similar action on the synthesis of the flavoproteins involved in the steroidogenic pathway, namely adrenodoxin reductase in the mitochondrion (31) and NADPH cytochrome P-450 reductase in the endoplasmic reticulum (32).

Furthermore, it was established for each of these enzymes that the increase in synthesis brought about by the action of ACTH and cAMP was associated with increased levels of translatable mRNA species encoding each of these proteins (24–28). In such experiments, RNA was extracted from bovine adrenal cortical cells maintained in the absence or presence of ACTH or dibutyryl cAMP for various periods of time. This RNA was used to program a rabbit reticulocyte cell-free translation system in the presence of [$^{35}$S]methionine from which the appropriate enzymes were immunoprecipitated. The immunoprecipitates were then subjected to SDS-polyacrylamide gel electrophoresis and visualized by autoradiography. It was found that ACTH and dibutyryl cAMP caused an increase in the levels of translatable mRNA encoding each of the enzymes tested, namely P-450$_{scc}$, P-450$_{11\beta}$, P-450$_{C21}$, P-450$_{17\alpha}$, and adrenodoxin.

The mitochondrial components of the adrenocortical steroidogenic pathway are encoded by nuclear genes and like many mitochondrial proteins are synthesized as higher molecular weight precursors (33–35). These precursors are proteolytically cleaved to their mature forms as they are taken up by mitochondria (36). In vitro processing experiments with isolated mitochondria and radiolabeled precursor proteins synthesized in in vitro translation systems have been used to characterize this maturation process. Adrenocortical mitochondria take up and process the P-450$_{scc}$, P-450$_{11\beta}$, and adrenodoxin precursors (37, 38), whereas kidney, heart, and liver mitochondria take up and process only the adrenodoxin precursor. Such specificity with respect to mitochondrial processing has not previously been observed and suggests that specific receptors for P-450$_{scc}$ and P-450$_{11\beta}$ are found exclusively on steroidogenic mitochondria. Apparently, P-450$_{scc}$ and P-450$_{11\beta}$ can be recognized and processed by the same system, since corpus luteum mitochondria (which contain no P-450$_{11\beta}$) are as efficient at processing P-450$_{11\beta}$ as they are at processing P-450$_{scc}$ (38). The protease required for mitochondrial processing of these precursor proteins appears to be localized in the mitochondrial matrix (39).

## EFFECT OF ACTH ON LEVELS OF mRNA ENCODING STEROIDOGENIC ENZYMES

Based on the above results, it is apparent that ACTH causes an increase in the synthesis of the enzymes in the steroidogenic pathway and that this seems to be a consequence of increased levels of translatable mRNA encoding these enzymes. Furthermore, it appears that cAMP mediates these responses. Changes in the level of translatable mRNA could be a consequence of increased synthesis of the specific mRNA, increased stability of existing mRNA, increased efficiency of translation of existing mRNA, or any combination of these. In order to understand the mechanism of the long-term action of ACTH in more detail, it was necessary to clone and characterize cDNA sequences complementary to the mRNA species encoding these enzymes. Such cDNA sequences could then be used as hybridization probes to measure the levels of mRNA for each of these enzymes directly. They could also be used to study the rate of transcription of the genes encoding these enzymes and to isolate and characterize these genes. cDNA probes specific for these enzymes have been isolated and characterized recently in several laboratories, including our own.

The first of the steroid hydroxylase cytochrome P-450 species to be cloned was bovine P-450$_{scc}$ (40, 41). Subsequently, cDNA clones specific for bovine P-450$_{17\alpha}$ (42), P-450$_{11\beta}$ (43), P-450$_{C21}$ (44–46), and adrenodoxin (47) were characterized, as were cDNA clones for human P-450$_{scc}$ (48), human P-450$_{17\alpha}$ (49, 50), and mouse P-450$_{C21}$ (51). We have utilized steroid hydroxylase cDNA clones as hybridization probes to determine mRNA levels in RNA extracted from bovine adrenocortical cells in primary culture. It was established that ACTH treatment leads to accumulation of RNAs specific for each of these enzymes, namely P-450$_{scc}$ (41), P-450$_{17\alpha}$ (42), P-450$_{11\beta}$ (43), P-450$_{C21}$ (46), and adrenodoxin (47). In cases where the time course was determined, it was found that an increase in mRNA levels could be detected in as little as 4 hr after initiation of ACTH treatment. These actions of ACTH could be mimicked by dibutyryl cAMP, indicative that cAMP also mediates these actions of ACTH. Similar results have been found in studies of the action of ACTH on human fetal adrenal cells in culture (52, 53). Such an action of ACTH to increase the levels of mRNA species encoding these enzymes could be the result of increases in the rates of transcription of the respective genes, increases in the half-life of the mRNA, or both of these. The half-lives of mRNA species encoding P-450$_{C21}$, P-450$_{17\alpha}$, P-450$_{11\beta}$, and adrenodoxin were determined to be unchanged in bovine adrenal cortical cells upon addition of ACTH. However, it was found that ACTH did lead to a fivefold increase in the half-life of P-450$_{scc}$ mRNA (V. Boggaram, unpublished).

It appears, therefore, that a major action of ACTH to regulate the levels of mRNA species encoding these enzymes might be at the level of expression of these genes. To establish this, nuclear run-on assays have been conducted utilizing nuclei isolated from bovine adrenal cortical cells maintained in the absence or presence of ACTH (54). These experiments demonstrate that ACTH causes an increase in the number of transcripts encoding the various steroidogenic enzymes. We may conclude, therefore, that the accumulation of mRNA species encoding these various steroid hydroxylase enzymes is the result of increased transcription of the genes encoding these proteins. Thus the cAMP-mediated, long-term action of ACTH in the adrenal cortex is exerted by regulation of the transcription of the genes encoding the various steroidogenic enzymes. This pathway provides another example of cAMP-mediated gene expression, the mechanism of which is entirely unknown.

These results raise an important question: Is this action of cAMP a direct one or does it require ongoing protein synthesis (which would indicate a mediatory role for short-lived protein factors)? To address this issue, we have investigated the action of cycloheximide, an inhibitor of RNA translation, on the increase in steroid hydroxylase mRNA levels induced by ACTH (54, 55). Cycloheximide was found to inhibit the accumulation induced by ACTH of RNA species encoding the steroidogenic cytochrome P-450s, as well as adrenodoxin, under conditions that did not affect total mRNA levels. This result indicates that the regulation of the expression of the steroidogenic genes by cAMP requires the mediation of some short-lived protein factor(s). There are several possible ways in which this could happen. For example, a cAMP-mediated event might induce the synthesis of the regulatory protein, which would then interact directly with the steroidogenic genes to induce their expression. Alternatively, this regulatory protein might act in parallel with the cAMP-mediated series of events. In this context, it is noteworthy that several eukaryotic genes are thought to be regulated by a putative eukaryotic cAMP binding protein (56); it is possible that the steroid hydroxylase enzymes fall into this class of proteins. In any case, the cAMP-mediated accumulation of steroid hydroxylase mRNA requires a protein that undergoes rapid turnover, as determined by the use of cycloheximide. cAMP probably initiates a cascade of events leading to the production of an unknown factor that regulates the mRNA levels of the steroid hydroxylase regulatory protein. This regulatory protein has been tentatively named SHIP (steroid hydroxylase inducing protein) (55) (Figure 2). At the present time it is not known whether there exists a different SHIP for each steroid hydroxylase protein or whether one SHIP can service the genes for all of these steroid hydroxylase enzymes.

Consensus sequences have been established in the regulatory regions of a number of eukaryotic genes regulated by cAMP and are believed to mediate the action of cAMP (56). At present there is no clear indication as to whether a common cAMP consensus sequence exists in steroid hydroxylase genes. It is clearly pertinent in this context to determine whether such a consensus sequence, or indeed any other consensus sequence, exists among the steroid hydroxylase genes regulated by this nucleotide.

## STUDIES OF THE GENES ENCODING STEROIDOGENIC ENZYMES

At present, the only genes encoding steroidogenic forms of cytochrome P-450 whose characterization has been reported are those for P-450$_{C21}$ (53, 57–61)

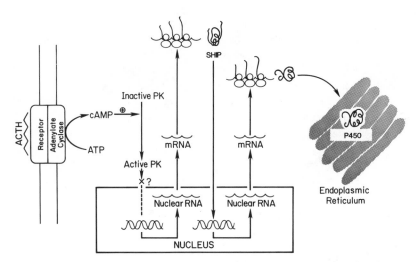

*Figure 2*   Proposed mechanism of cAMP-mediated regulation of steroid hydroxylase gene expression in the adrenal cortex. SHIP: steroid hydroxylase inducing protein.

and P-450$_{scc}$ (62). The gene encoding P-450$_{C21}$ has been studied in mice, cows, and humans; in each species two forms of the gene have been detected, one of which apparently exists as a pseudogene. In the mouse, the inability of this latter gene to be transcribed is due to the presence of a 215-nucleotide deletion spanning the second exon (63). Both the mouse and human genes lie within a duplicated portion of the class V region of the major histocompatibility complex (MHC) (57, 58). Deletion mutations of the functional gene have been implicated in some cases of steroid 21-hydroxylase deficiency, the most common cause of congenital adrenal hyperplasia. In addition, a specific sequence has been established within the 5' untranscribed region of the mouse gene that is believed to be important in the determination of tissue specificity (64). There have been several unpublished reports on the characterization of the bovine and human P-450$_{17\alpha}$ genes (B. Adler & M. Kagimoto, unpublished), the bovine adrenodoxin gene (M. Kagimoto, unpublished), and the P-450$_{11\beta}$ gene (Y. Fujii-Kuriyama, unpublished). Thus common structural features among these genes, including consensus sequences, will likely be revealed in the near future.

Based on sequence homology between the various steroidogenic forms of cytochrome P-450, it is clear that P-450$_{scc}$, P-450$_{17\alpha}$, and P-450$_{C21}$ are members of different gene families within the overall cytochrome P-450 gene superfamily. The differences between these genes are illustrated by a comparison of the genes encoding P-450$_{C21}$ and P-450$_{17\alpha}$ (Figure 3). Some of the cytochrome P-450 gene families involved in steroidogenesis have been designated as follows (64): P-450$_{11\beta}$ is the product of the P450XI gene; P-450$_{17\alpha}$ is the product of the P450XVII gene; P-450$_{C21}$ is the product of the P450XXI gene; and P-450$_{scc}$ is the product of the P450XXII gene. It is estimated that these genes diverged from one another between 600 and 900 million years ago (65). Interestingly, as the various steroidogenic forms of cytochrome P-450 diverged from one another to catalyze specific steroid hydroxylase activities, each exhibiting a high degree of substrate specificity, a common mechanism for their regulation involving cAMP and SHIP was conserved.

## OTHER ENZYMES REGULATED BY ACTH

In addition to the enzymes directly involved in this steroidogenic pathway, other proteins are also required for steroid hormone synthesis. These include enzymes involved in cholesterol biosynthesis, such as HMG CoA reductase, an important rate-limiting enzyme in the biosynthetic pathway leading to cholesterol; the LDL receptor, which is required for lipoprotein cholesterol uptake from the circulating plasma; cholesterol ester hydrolase, which provides a readily available source of free cholesterol from cholesterol esters stored in the lipid droplets; and sterol carrier protein 2 (SCP$_2$), which is

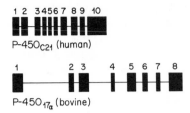

P-450$_{C21}$ (human)

P-450$_{17\alpha}$ (bovine)

*Figure 3*  Structures of the genes encoding cytochrome human P-450$_{C21}$ and bovine P-450$_{17\alpha}$. The human P-450$_{C21}$ gene is approximately 3.2 kb in length (60) while the bovine P-450$_{17\alpha}$ gene is approximately 6.7 kb in length (B. Adler, unpublished). The blackened bars indicate exons while the lines indicate introns.

required to transport cholesterol from the lipid stores to the mitochondria. The rate of cholesterol biosynthesis is extremely low in bovine adrenocortical cells in culture (66, 67). This is reflected in low rates of HMG CoA reductase activity, which respond little to the presence of ACTH in the culture medium. However, in human fetal adrenal cells in culture, cholesterol biosynthesis and HMG CoA reductase are extremely active and both are increased severalfold in response to ACTH in the culture medium (68). In these cells, ACTH stimulates HMG CoA reductase activity and increases the level of HMG CoA reductase as determined by Western blot analysis. These effects were prevented by addition of clotrimazole, an inhibitor of cholesterol side-chain cleavage (69). Since HMG CoA reductase activity, which reflects the level of HMG CoA reductase protein, appears to be related to the requirement of the cell for cholesterol, these results suggest that the increase in HMG CoA reductase in response to ACTH treatment is secondary to the depletion of cellular cholesterol brought about by the action of ACTH, and thus is not a direct effect of ACTH or cAMP.

The number of LDL receptors in bovine adrenal cortical cells is also increased in response to ACTH treatment, which indicates the importance of LDL cholesterol as a source of cholesterol precursors for steroid hormone biosynthesis in these cells (66, 67). This action of ACTH is only partially inhibited by aminoglutethimide, an inhibitor of cholesterol side-chain cleavage (67). Thus it is unclear whether this action of ACTH is mediated by depletion of cholesterol, as is its action on HMG CoA reductase.

In addition, we studied the effects of ACTH on the synthesis of SCP$_2$ (70) and found that ACTH causes a two- or threefold increase in the rate of synthesis of this protein in bovine adrenal cortical cells in culture, as well as in rat adrenal cells in culture. The product of in vitro translation immunoprecipitated with SCP$_2$ antibody has a higher molecular weight than the mature protein. This may indicate that SCP$_2$ is initially synthesized as a precursor of higher molecular weight, but the nature and site of precursor processing are unknown.

Thus it appears that in addition to the enzymes directly involved in the conversion of cholesterol to steroid hormones, enzymes and proteins involved in the provision of cholesterol as a precursor for steroid hormones are also subject to ACTH regulation in the adrenal cortex. In contrast, the levels and activities of many of the enzymes of the adrenal cortical cell are unaffected by ACTH. Thus, many of the enzymes involved in the supply of reducing equivalents for the steroid hydroxylase enzymes, such as enzymes involved in glycolysis, gluconeogenesis, and the Krebs cycle, are totally unaffected by ACTH treatment of bovine adrenal cortical cells in culture (R. Frenkel, unpublished). These results suggest that the action of ACTH to regulate gene transcription in the adrenal cortex is limited to the enzymes directly involved in the steroidogenic pathway and ancillary proteins involved in optimizing the supply of cholesterol to this pathway.

## OTHER FACTORS THAT REGULATE STEROIDOGENIC FORMS OF CYTOCHROME P-450

In this chapter, we focused on the regulation of the genes encoding steroidogenic forms of cytochrome P-450 by ACTH, whose action is mediated by cAMP. This mechanism is required for the maintenance of optimal steroidogenic capacity in the adrenal cortex. However, other factors can modify the expression of these genes in vitro, many of which do not operate via increases in the levels of cAMP (71, 72). This is particularly true in the ovary, where steroid hormone secretion is episodic in nature and is clearly governed by a variety of factors (73). Whereas the gonadotropins LH and FSH act via increases in cAMP, other factors, including growth factors (such as IGF-I, EGF, PDGF, and FGF), GnRH, and phorbol esters, act via other second messengers, e.g. tyrosine kinase, phospholipid turnover, calcium movement, and protein kinase C.

In addition to these factors, many of which act within the same cell, e.g. the ovarian granulosa cell, it is clear that tissue-specific regulation of the expression of these genes also occurs. Thus $P-450_{11\beta}$ and $P-450_{C21}$ are expressed only in the adrenal cortex, whereas $P-450_{scc}$ is expressed in the adrenal cortex, the ovarian theca, the ovarian corpus luteum, testicular Leydig cells, and placenta. $P-450_{17\alpha}$ is expressed in the zona fasciculata of the adrenal cortex, the ovarian theca, and in testicular Leydig cells, whereas $P-450_{AROM}$ is expressed in ovarian granulosa cells, testicular sertoli cells, Leydig cells, placenta, adipose tissue, and brain. As mentioned earlier, Parker and colleagues have begun to elucidate the nature of these tissue-specific regulatory elements in the mouse $P-450_{C21}$ gene (64).

Recently we identified a third level of regulation in the fetal adrenal. This identification was based on the observation that in adrenals of anencephalic human fetuses (in which the adrenal is chronically underexposed to ACTH due to the absence of a functional hypothalamic-pituitary axis) the levels of steroidogenic forms of P-450 and adrenodoxin are the same as those in normal fetal adrenals (74). This is in spite of the fact that adenylate cyclase in such adrenals is essentially nonfunctional (75) and the levels of other proteins regulated by cAMP, such as the LDL receptor and HMG CoA reductase, are very low (68). We have termed this phenomenon fetal imprinting. This type of regulation of steroidogenic enzymes apparently involves initiation of expression of certain genes in the fetus prior to the development of cAMP-mediated regulation.

As in the case of cAMP-mediated regulation of gene expression, the mechanisms whereby these other regulatory pathways alter the rate of expression of these genes will only be determined when various *trans-* and *cis-*acting elements associated with these genes, which mediate these diverse actions, are defined.

ACKNOWLEDGMENTS

The authors wish to recognize their superb colleagues who over the years have been responsible for the research output of this laboratory. This work was supported, in part, by USPHS Grants AM28350, HD13234, and HD11149.

*Literature Cited*

1. Miesfield, R., Orret, S., Wikstrom, A. C., Wrange, O., Gustafsson, J.-A., Yamamoto, K. R. 1984. *Nature* 312: 779–81

2. Hollenberg, S. M., Weinberger, C., Ong, E. S., Cerelli, G. O., Oro, A., et al. 1985. *Nature* 318:635–41

3. Green, S., Walter, P., Kumar, V., Krust, A., Barnet, J.-M., et al. 1986. *Nature* 320:134–39

4. Krust, A., Green, S., Argos, P., Kumar, V., Walter, P., Bornet, J. M. 1986. *EMBO J.* 5:891–97

5. Jeltsch, J. M., Krozowski, Z., Quirin-Stricker, C., Gronemeyer, H., Simpson, R. J., et al. 1986. *Proc. Natl. Acad. Sci. USA* 83:5424–28

6. Conneely, O. M., Sullivan, W. P., Taft, D. O., Birnbaumer, M., Cook, R. G., et al. 1986. *Science* 233:767–70

7. Waterman, M. R., Simpson, E. R. 1985. In *Adrenal Cortex,* ed. D. C. Anderson, J. S. D. Winter, pp. 57–85. London: Butterworths

8. Simpson, E. R. 1979. *Mol. Cell. Endocrinol.* 13:213–27

9. Churchill, P. F., de Alvare, L. R., Kimura, T. 1978. *J. Biol. Chem.* 253:4924–29

10. Mitani, F., Shimizu, T., Ueno, R., Ishimura, Y., Izumi, S., et al. 1982. *J. Histochem. Cytochem.* 20:1066–74

11. Burstein, S., Middleditch, B. S., Gut, M. 1974. *Biochem. Biophys. Res. Commun.* 61:642–47

12. Hiwatashi, A., Ichikawa, Y. 1979. *Biochim. Biophys. Acta* 580:44–63

13. Omura, T., Sanders, E., Estabrook, R. W., Cooper, D. Y., Rosenthal, O. 1966. *Arch. Biochem. Biophys.* 117: 660–73

14. Watanuki, M., Tilley, B. E., Hall, P. F. 1977. *Biochim. Biophys. Acta* 483:236–47

15. Kramer, R. E., Gallant, S., Brownie, A. C. 1980. *J. Biol. Chem.* 255:3442–47

16. Nakajin, S., Hall, P. F. 1981. *J. Biol. Chem.* 256:3871–76

17. Nakajin, S., Hall, P. F., Onoda, M. 1981. *J. Biol. Chem.* 256:6134–39

18. Zuber, M. X., Simpson, E. R., Waterman, M. R. 1986. *Science* 234:1258–61

19. Thompson, E. A., Siiteri, P. K. 1974. *J. Biol. Chem.* 249:5364–72

20. Privalle, C. T., Crivello, J. F., Jefcoate, C. R. 1983. *Proc. Natl. Acad. Sci. USA* 80:702–6

21. Kimura, T. 1969. *Endocrinology* 285: 492–99

22. Purvis, J. L., Canick, J. A., Mason, J. I., Estabrook, R. W., McCarthy, J. L. 1973. *Ann. NY Acad. Sci.* 212:319–42

23. Purvis, J. L., Canick, J. A., Latif, S. A., Rosenbaum, H. A., Hologgita, J., Menard, R. H. 1973. *Arch. Biochem. Biophys.* 159:39–49

24. DuBois, R. N., Simpson, E. R., Kramer, R. E., Waterman, M. R. 1981. *J. Biol. Chem.* 256:7000–5

25. Kramer, R. E., Simpson, E. R., Waterman, M. R. 1983. *J. Biol. Chem.* 258:3000–5

26. Funkenstein, B., McCarthy, J. L., Dus, K. M., Simpson, E. R., Waterman, M. R. 1983. *J. Biol. Chem.* 258:9398–9405

27. Zuber, M. X., Simpson, E. R., Hall, P. F., Waterman, M. R., 1985. *J. Biol. Chem.* 260:1842–48
28. Kramer, R. E., Anderson, C. M., Peterson, J. A., Simpson, E. R., Waterman, M. R. 1982. *J. Biol. Chem.* 257:14921–25
29. Boggaram, V., Zuber, M. X., Waterman, M. R. 1984. *Arch. Biochem. Biophys.* 231:518–23
30. Kramer, R. E., Rainey, W. E., Funkenstein, B., Dee, A., Simpson, E. R., Waterman, M. R. 1984. *J. Biol. Chem.* 259:707–13
31. Kramer, R. E., Anderson, C. M., McCarthy, J. L., Simpson, E. R., Waterman, M. R. 1982. *Fed. Proc.* 41:1298
32. Dee, A., Carlson, G., Smith, C., Masters, B. S. S., Waterman, M. R. 1985. *Biochem. Biophys. Res. Commun.* 128:650–56
33. DuBois, R. N., Simpson, E. R., Tuckey, J., Lambeth, J. D., Waterman, M. R. 1981. *Proc. Natl. Acad. Sci. USA* 78:1028–32
34. Kramer, R. E., DuBois, R. N., Simpson, E. R., Anderson, C. M., Kashiwagi, K., et al. 1982. *Arch. Biochem. Biophys.* 215:478–85
35. Nabi, N., Omiera, T. 1980. *Biochem. Biophys. Res. Commun.* 97:680–86
36. Matocha, M. F., Waterman, M. R. 1985. *J. Biol. Chem.* 260:12259–65
37. Matocha, M. F., Waterman, M. R. 1984. *J. Biol. Chem.* 259:8672–78
38. Matocha, M. F., Waterman, M. R. 1986. *Arch. Biochem. Biophys.* 250:456–60
39. Kumamoto, T., Ito, A., Omura, T. 1986. *J. Biochem.* 100:247–54
40. Morohashi, K., Fujii-Kuriyama, K., Okada, Y., Sogawa, Y., Hirose, T., et al. 1984. *Proc. Natl. Acad. Sci. USA* 81:4647–51
41. John, M. E., John, M. C., Ashley, P., MacDonald, R. J., Simpson, E. R., Waterman, M. R. 1984. *Proc. Natl. Acad. Sci. USA* 81:5628–32
42. Zuber, M. X., John, M. E., Okamura, T., Simpson, E. R., Waterman, M. R. 1986. *J. Biol. Chem.* 26:2475–82
43. John, M. E., John, M. C., Simpson, E. R., Waterman, M. R. 1985. *J. Biol. Chem.* 260:5760–67
44. White, P. C., New, M. I., DuPont, B. 1984. *Proc. Natl. Acad. Sci. USA* 81:1986–90
45. Yoshioka, H., Morohashi, K., Sogawa, K., Yamane, Y., Kominami, S., et al. 1986. *J. Biol. Chem.* 261:4106–9
46. John, M. E., Okamura, T., Dee, A., Adler, B., John, M. C., et al. 1986. *Biochemistry* 25:2846–53
47. Okamura, T., John, M. E., Zuber, M. X., Simpson, E. R., Waterman, M. R. 1986. *Proc. Natl. Acad. Sci. USA* 82:5705–9
48. Chung, B. C., Matteson, K. J., Voutilainen, R., Mohandas, T. K., Miller, W. L. 1986. *Proc. Natl. Acad. Sci. USA* 83:8962–66
49. Chung, B. C., Picardo-Leonard, J., Haniu, M., Bienkowski, M., Hall, P. F., et al. 1987. *Proc. Natl. Acad. Sci. USA* 84:407–11
50. Bradshaw, K. D., Waterman, M. R., Couch, R. T., Simpson, E. R., Zuber, M. X. 1987. *Mol. Endocrinol.* 1:348–54
51. Carroll, M. C., Campbell, D., Porter, K. R. 1985. *Proc. Natl. Acad. Sci. USA* 82:521–25
52. John, M. E., Simpson, E. R., Waterman, M. R., Mason, J. I. 1986. *Mol. Cell. Endocrinol.* 45:197–204
53. Voutilainen, R., Miller, W. L. 1986. *J. Clin. Endocrinol. Metab.* 63:1145–50
54. John, M. E., John, M. C., Boggaram, V., Simpson, E. R., Waterman, M. R. 1986. *Proc. Natl. Acad. Sci. USA* 83:4715–19
55. Waterman, M. R., Simpson, E. R. 1985. In *Microsomes and Drug Oxidations*, ed. A. R. Boobis, J. Caldwell, F. de Matties, C. R. Elcombe, pp. 136–44. London: Taylor & Francis
56. Wynshaw-Boris, A., Lugo, T. G., Short, J. M., Fornier, R. E. K., Hanson, R. W. 1984. *J. Biol. Chem.* 259:12161–69
57. White, P. C., Chaplin, D. D., Weis, J. H., DuPont, B., New, M. I., Seidman, J. C. 1984. *Nature* 312:465–67
58. Amor, M., Tosi, M., Cuponchel, C., Sternetz, M., Meo, T. 1985. *Proc. Natl. Acad. Sci. USA* 82:4455–57
59. Chung, B.-C., Matteson, K. J., Miller, W. L. 1986. *Proc. Natl. Acad. Sci. USA* 83:4243–47
60. White, P. C., New, M. I., DuPont, B. 1986. *Proc. Natl. Acad. Sci. USA* 83:511–15
61. Higashi, Y., Yoshioka, H., Vamane, M., Gotoh, O., Fujii-Kuriyama, Y. 1986. *Proc. Natl. Acad. Sci. USA* 83:2841–45
62. Morohashi, K., Sogawa, K., Omura, T., Fujii-Kuriyama, Y. 1987. *J. Biochem.* 101:879–87
63. Chaplin, D. D., Galbraith, L. J., Seidman, J. G., White, P. C., Parker, K. L. 1986. *Proc. Natl. Acad. Sci. USA* 83:9601–5
64. Parker, K. L., Schimmer, B. P., Chaplin, D. D., Seidman, J. G. 1986. *J. Biol. Chem.* 261:15353–55
65. Nebert, D. W., Adesnik, M., Coon, M.

J., Estabrook, R. W., Gonzalez, F. J., et al. 1987. *DNA* 6:1–12

66. Kovanen, P. T., Faust, J. R., Brown, M. S., Goldstein, J. L. 1979. *Endocrinology* 104:599–609

67. Ohashi, M., Simpson, E. R., Kramer, R. E., Carr, B. R. 1982. *Arch. Biochem. Biophys.* 215:199–205

68. Carr, B. R., Simpson, E. R. 1981. *Endocrine Rev.* 2:306–26

69. Rainey, W. E., Shay, J. W., Mason, J. I. 1986. *J. Biol. Chem.* 261:7322–26

70. Trzeciak, W. H., Simpson, E. R., Scallen, T. J., Vahouny, G. V., Waterman, M. R. 1987. *J. Biol. Chem.* 262:3713–17

71. Veldhuis, J. D., Rodgers, R. J., Dee, A., Simpson, E. R. 1986. *J. Biol. Chem.* 261:2499–2502

72. Trzeciak, W. H., Duda, T., Waterman, M. R., Simpson, E. R. 1987. *Mol. Cell. Endocrinol.* 52:43–50

73. Hsueh, A. J., Jones, P. B., Adashi, E. Y., Wang, C., Zhuang, L. Z., Welsh, T. H. Jr. 1983. *J. Reprod. Fertil.* 69:325–42

74. John, M. E., Simpson, E. R., Carr, B. R., Magnus, R. R., Rosenfeld, C. R., et al. 1987. *Mol. Cell. Endocrinol.* 50: 263–68

75. Carr, B. R. 1986. *J. Clin. Endocrinol. Metab.* 63:31–35

*Ann. Rev. Physiol. 1988. 50:441–63*

# MOLECULAR ASPECTS OF HORMONE ACTION IN OVARIAN FOLLICULAR DEVELOPMENT, OVULATION, AND LUTEINIZATION

*Joanne S. Richards and Lars Hedin[1]*

Department of Cell Biology, Baylor College of Medicine, One Baylor Plaza, Houston, Texas 77030

## INTRODUCTION

The biological challenge to be met by the mammalian ovary is to maintain the continuous development of small follicles and, at the same time, to allow other follicles to ovulate and become corpora lutea. The dynamics of this are orchestrated by many interwoven processes that allow less than 1% of the follicles contained within the ovary to ovulate. The key to the development of a follicle that succeeds in ovulating is its ability to gain new functional capabilities. As summarized in recent reviews (52, 95), the synthesis and action of estradiol in preovulatory follicles, combined with enhanced production of cAMP in response to gonadotropins, appear to be fundamental for the development of a preovulatory follicle.

As a developmental system dependent on gonadotropic hormone action, the ovarian follicle is a challenging area of study that requires the integration of physiology, endocrinology, and molecular biology. Molecular biological techniques have been used to clone the genes that encode the gonadotropic hormones (a topic too broad to be covered herein) and to isolate the cDNA for gonadotropin releasing hormone (GnRH) and the GnRH-associated peptide (GAP) (85). In one elegant study, hypogonadal (hpg) mice that lack a functional GnRH gene (76) were used for gene therapy (78). When heterozygous (hpg/+) transgenic mice bearing the GnRH gene were mated,

---

[1]Current address: Department of Physiology, University of Göteborg, Göteborg, Sweden

441

0066-4278/88/0315-0441$02.00

they produced heterozygous (hpg/+), homozygous (+/+), and (hpg/hpg) transgenic offspring, all of which had well-developed gonads and become sexually mature. This study represents a milestone in the integration of molecular biology and reproductive endocrinology.

## HORMONE ACTION

### Steriod Hormone Receptors

The ovarian follicle not only synthesizes estradiol (95) but also responds to estradiol via estradiol receptors (93, 94). Likewise, the corpus luteum of the rat (94) and rabbit (122) contains receptors for estradiol, a luteotropic hormone in these two species (40, 95, 103). Although the receptors for estradiol (45, 46, 81) and progesterone (18) were cloned using other tissues from other species, the cDNAs and the purified receptors can be used to analyze the sites of estradiol action in regulating the induction of specific genes in ovarian granulosa cells and luteal cells. Estradiol has been shown to be obligatory for induction of synthesis of specific proteins in rat granulosa cells in response to follicle stimulating hormone (FSH) and luteinizing hormone (LH) (52, 95, and discussion below). The mechanism by which estradiol acts synergistically with the gonadotropins remains unclear. The amino acid sequence of the estradiol receptor reveals potential phosphorylation sites for cAMP-dependent protein kinase (45, 46). This information suggests that the synergism between estradiol and cAMP may in part be due to phosphorylation (activation?) of the estradiol receptor. Thus, although previously estradiol was considered to enhance the actions of gonadotropins in granulosa cells, it may be that FSH and/or cAMP enhances the actions of estradiol. With the isolation of ovary-specific genes and the availability of purified, cloned steroid receptors and protein kinase subunits (see below), some insight into the regulation of gene expression by steriods and cAMP in the ovary will be forthcoming.

### Protein Hormone Receptors

It is now well established that the response of ovarian cells to gonadotropins is dependent not only on the concentration of these hormones in serum, but also on the content of their receptors in the target cells (95). Furthermore, hormones can up- or down-regulate the content of their own receptors (homologous regulation) or the content of receptors for other hormones (heterologous regulation). In the ovarian follicle, estradiol, FSH, and the slight increases in serum LH that precede the LH surge are obligatory for the induction of receptors for LH in granulosa cells of preovulatory follicles (8, 95, 96). The slight increases in LH preceding the ovulatory LH surge also act to increase the number of LH receptors in theca cells of preovulatory follicles (8, 95, 96). Conversely, the LH surge decreases the content of both FSH and

LH receptors but increases the content of prolactin receptors (PRL) (95). When low concentrations of human chorionic gonadotropin (hCG) (2.5 IU) are administered to pregnant rats, follicular growth and the acquisition of LH receptors in granulosa cells of these follicles is induced, whereas the content of LH receptors in corpora lutea of the same rats is reduced more than 90% (8). These results clearly document the tissue-specific and developmental stage–specific responses of ovarian cells to the same amount of hormone (hCG).

Studies in vitro have documented that the induction of LH receptor in granulosa cells is dependent on estradiol and cAMP (52, 90), can be modified by anti-estrogens and peptides that inhibit the actions of cAMP (52), and may involve cell-cell contact (35).

Currently several laboratories are attempting to isolate and purify the gonadotropin receptors (3, 24, 28, 55, 60, 65–67, 83). Current data indicate that the intact LH receptor has an apparent $M_r$ of 90,000–95,000 (3, 28, 65, 67, 83), is inactivated by reducing agents (3, 65, 65a), and is a transmembrane protein with a cytoplasmic domain of $M_r$ 20,000 (65a). Other peptides (55, 60) found to have receptor activity (i.e. that have been cross-linked to labeled hCG) most likely represent proteolytic fragments of the LH receptor (3, 65, 65a, 66). Purification of the FSH receptor has proven to be a more difficult task, but recent work has shown that a stable, functional receptor can now be solubilized (24). With the isolation of purified receptors, the generation of receptor-specific antibodies, and the characterization of specific amino acid sequences, the pathway to the successful cloning of these receptors is now open.

## Adenylyl Cyclase

The response of ovarian follicular cells to gonadotropins is dependent not only on the content of FSH and LH receptors but also on the composition of the adenylyl cyclase system. For example, the increase in adenylyl cyclase activity (62, 96) and cAMP production (95) in response to FSH in granulosa cells of rat preovulatory follicles occurs in the absence of a change in the number of FSH receptors per granulosa cell. Rather, there appears to be a change in the adenylyl cyclase system itself. Preliminary results from a study by J. Abramowitz & B. Jena (unpublished) show that granulosa cells of preantral and preovulatory follicles possess similar amounts of a pertussis toxin substrate ($G_i$). However, granulosa cells of preovulatory follicles that exhibit an increase in adenylyl cyclase in response to FSH also show an increase in the content of $G_s$ ($M_r = 46,000$), as measured by NADP ribosylation of $G_s$ subunit and quantitation by one-dimensional SDS PAGE, autoradiography, and densitrometric scanning. Similar changes may occur in other species. Hunzicker-Dunn & LaBarbera (54) recently reported unique properties of an FSH-sensitive adenylyl cyclase in granulosa cells of small (nonovulatory) porcine follicles. Whether the anomalies reside in the cyclase subunit composition or in associated proteins remains to be resolved.

Various regulatory component subunits of the adenylyl cyclase system have been purified, characterized, and cloned (41, 47, 56, 79). Several G proteins have been identified, most notably $G_s$ (stimulatory), $G_i$ (inhibitory), $G_k$ (potassium channel), and $G_o$, a brain-specific regulatory subunit of unknown function. No doubt more G proteins regulating other facets of cell function will be described. Some already known include: the *ras* gene products, a transducer for protein kinase C, and regulators of other ion channels. The isolation and purification of the gonadotropin receptors combined with greater information on changes in the adenylyl cyclase system in developing follicles should bring new insight into the regulation of this obligatory transduction system.

## Cyclic AMP–Dependent Protein Kinases

Granulosa cells of preovulatory follicles are characterized by increased content of receptors for LH, enhanced responsiveness of adenylyl cyclase to FSH and LH, and a marked increase in the content of the regulatory (R) subunit of cAMP-dependent protein kinase type II, designated $RII_{51}$ ($M_r = 51,000$). This $RII_{51}$ (now $RII_\beta$) subunit has been shown to be structurally and immunologically similar (identical) to the RII subunit found in rat brain (57–59) and bovine brain (57–59) but is distinct from $RII_{54}$ ($M_r = 54,000$) (now $RII_\alpha$), the R subunit characteristic of rat heart (58) and bovine heart (57–59).

Because the content of $RII_{51}$ and its isoelectric variants $RII_{51.5}$ ($M_r = 51,500$) and $RII_{52}$ ($M_r = 52,000$) is increased in granulosa cells by estradiol and FSH and subsequently decreased as a consequence of the LH surge (102, 105), this protein has been selected as a molecular marker for hormone action in granulosa cells. To clone the cDNA for $RII_{51}$, a rat granulosa cell cDNA expression library was constructed using poly(A)+ RNA from granulosa cells of hypophysectomized rats treated with estradiol and FSH as the template for cDNA synthesis and $\lambda$gtll as the expression vector (57). Recombinant phage plaques that were immunopositive for affinity-purified RII antisera were isolated, plaque-purified, and subcloned. Nucleotide sequence analyses showed that one $RII_{51}$ cDNA contained greater than 95% of the coding region. The deduced amino acid sequence for rat $RII_{51}$ showed striking homologies to known amino acid sequences of bovine heart $RII_{54}$ and RI, especially in the two putative cAMP binding regions contained in the C-terminal region of the protein. Less homology was seen among these R subunits in the N-terminal region (57).

cDNA clones for $RII_{51}$, RI (70), and two catalytic subunits, $C_\alpha$ (115) and $C_\beta$ (116), have been used to analyze the content, tissue distribution, and hormonal regulation of these protein kinase subunits during follicular development and luteinization (49, 100). $RII_{51}$ is present in both granulosa cells and theca cells of small antral follicles, is increased in both cell types during the development of preovulatory (PO) follicles, and is dramatically decreased within 7 hr after an LH/hCG surge (49). In contrast, the level of mRNAs for RI and $C_\alpha$ showed a transient increase in theca cells of PO follicles but was decreased in granulosa cells of PO follicles and corpora lutea (49).

The induction of $RII_{51}$ mRNA in theca and granulosa cells of preovulatory follicles and in granulosa cells of hypophysectomized (H) rats treated with estradiol and FSH, as well as the marked decrease in $RII_{51}$ mRNA in corpora lutea, correspond to similar changes observed in $RII_{51}$ protein levels (101, 105). Likewise, there is no demonstrable change in the level of $C_\alpha$ mRNA nor protein in differentiating granulosa cells and luteal cells, as measured by radioimmuno labeling of Western transfers (97) and by histone phosphorylation assays (97). In contrast, whereas RI mRNA content appeared to decrease in granulosa cells of developing follicles and remain low in corpora lutea, previous studies using [$^{32}$P]azido-cAMP for photo-affinity labeling of ovarian R subunits found a small increase in the content of RI protein during the early stages of luteinization (97). A comparison of the relative content of R subunit proteins and mRNA molecules per cell demonstrated additional striking differences between the regulation of $RII_{51}$ and RI. When regulatory subunits of cAMP-dependent protein kinase were purified from the ovaries of H rats treated with estradiol and FSH, RI represented ~5% of the total R Protein, whereas $RII_{51}$ represented 85% and $RII_{54}$ 10% (58, 59). This disproportionate amount of the R subunit proteins contrasted with the nearly equal numbers of RI and $RII_{51}$ mRNAs present in total nucleic acid extracts of these cells (49). These observations suggest that the content of RI protein in granulosa cells, like that for RI in S49 lymphoma cells (112) may be influenced by rapid degradation of free RI subunits.

Hormone-treated H rats have been used to show that the increase in $RII_{51}$ mRNA in granulosa cells of preovulatory follicles is dependent on endogenous estradiol as well as on gonadotropins (49). For example, a low dose (1 $\mu$g) of FSH administered first intravenously (hour 0) and then subcutaneously at hour 12, 24, and 36 was ineffective in increasing $RII_{51}$ mRNA in granulosa cells of H rats whereas the same treatment regime of FSH increased $RII_{51}$ mRNA five- to tenfold within 6 hr in granulosa cells of H rats treated with estradiol (HE). Furthermore, the increase in $RII_{51}$ mRNA was associated with increased binding of [$^3$H]cAMP to RII (104). The peak of $RII_{51}$ mRNA at 24 hr precedes the maximum accumulation of RII at 48 hr (104). The decline in $RII_{51}$ mRNA at 48 hr may indicate that these cells are entering an early phase of luteinization (102, 105).

Dose-response studies show that FSH can increase $RII_{51}$ mRNA three- to sevenfold in granulosa cells of H rats if administered intravenously in doses of 2 $\mu$g or greater (49). However, at all doses of FSH given, the amount of $RII_{51}$

mRNA in estradiol-primed granulosa cells remained three to four times greater than that in granulosa cells of H rats. Taken together the time-course and dose-response studies indicate that granulosa cells of H rats require more FSH to initiate the induction of $RII_{51}$ mRNA and never gain the same concentration of $RII_{51}$ mRNA. The enhanced response of estradiol-primed granulosa cells to FSH may be associated, in part, with the increased ability of FSH to activate adenylyl cyclase activity in estradiol-primed granulosa cells, as shown in studies using membrane preparations (62, 100), whole cells in culture (95), and granulosa cells in vivo (95). In addition, granulosa cells of HE rats have been shown to possess more receptors for estradiol (93). Thus, the ability of cells to generate more cAMP and to increase the expression of estradiol receptors may be involved in regulating the intracellular content of $RII_{51}$ mRNA. In further support of this idea, higher doses of FSH, which were found to increase $RII_{51}$ mRNA in granulosa cells of H rats, also increased endogenous estradiol synthesis (as revealed by uterine ballooning), which indicates the presence of LH in the FSH preparation.

The mechanisms by which estradiol and FSH regulate $RII_{51}$ mRNA content and gene transcription are not yet known. Studies using granulosa cells in serum-free culture have shown that estradiol and either FSH, forskolin, or 8-bromo-cAMP increase the content (90) and synthesis (89) of $RII_{51}$ mRNA and its isoelectric variants ($RII_{51.5}$ and $RII_{52}$) (Figure 1). Pulse-chase experiments in cultured granulosa cells documented further that the $RII_{52}$ variant was either more stable than $RII_{51}$ or was derived from $RII_{51}$ by posttranslational modification. These two alternatives need not be mutually exclusive but rather may be part of a complementary regulatory mechanism of R subunit metabolism. The latter possibility is supported by several observations. $RII_{51}$, but not the variants, was synthesized in vitro from granulosa cell poly(A)$^+$ RNA (89) and from hybrid-selected mRNA (57). In granulosa cells cultured in the presence of [$^{32}$P]orthophosphate, RII is a major cellular phosphoprotein (90), and $RII_{52}$ contains more $^{32}$P than does $RII_{51.5}$, which contains more than $RII_{51}$ (89). Conversely, when purified $RII_{51}$ and its variants were incubated with potato acid phosphatase for 0.5–1 hr, $RII_{52}$ and $RII_{51.5}$ were markedly decreased, whereas $RII_{51}$ was retained. In addition, phosphorylation has been clearly associated with the variants of RI (112), $RII_{54}$ from rat tracheal smooth muscle, and $RII_{54}$ from bovine heart (59).

The nature of the kinase responsible for phosphorylating $RII_{51}$ in granulosa cells in vivo and in culture remains unclear. For example, all three $RII_{51}$ variants are equally labeled by the catalytic (C) subunit of cAMP-dependent protein kinase (i.e. $RII_{52}$ is not generated from $RII_{51}$) when the C subunit is added to granulosa cell cytosol (102, 105) or to purified ovarian R subunits (58). Because autophosphorylation of $RII_{51}$ by the C subunit does not explain the presence of the variants generated in situ, granulosa cell $RII_{51}$ appears to

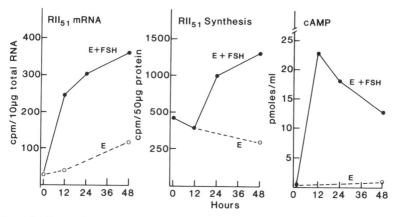

*Figure 1* Changes in $RII_{51}$ mRNA content, de novo synthesis, and cAMP in granulosa cells cultured in serum-free medium (DMEM : F12) containing 10 nM estradiol (E) alone or E and 25 ng/ml FSH. $RII_{51}$ mRNA was quantitated by dot-blot hybridization and counting. $RII_{51}$ synthesis was analyzed by [$^{35}$S]methionine incorporation into partially purified $RII_{51}$ using cAMP-Sepharose chromatography. cAMP was measured by radio immuno assay (RIA). (From Ref. 89.)

be phosphorylated by another kinase(s). Direct proof of conversion of $RII_{51}$ to $RII_{52}$ by phosphorylation awaits the isolation and purification of this other kinase(s).

Recently, a genomic fragment of the rat $RII_{51}$ gene containing 5' coding sequences and putative 5' flanking sequences has been isolated. The next step will be to determine if estradiol and cAMP regulatory domains can be identified and, if so, what the nature of these DNA sequences are. This information may help elucidate the manner in which estradiol and cAMP act synergistically in granulosa cells to regulate the transcription of the $RII_{51}$ gene and other genes, such as the LH receptor.

## Summary

The development of preovulatory follicles is associated with enhanced responsiveness to the gonadotropins. This is mediated by the induction of receptors for LH, by enhanced activation of adenylyl cyclase by FSH and LH, and by other unknown mechanisms. Why is there an increase in $RII_{51}$, an inhibitor of the catalytic subunit of cAMP-dependent protein kinase, when it is likely to decrease the response of granulosa cells and theca cells to cAMP? It may represent a biochemical feedback mechanism to ensure that the catalytic subunit remains regulated by R subunit. This would prevent inappropriate activation of the catalytic subunit in the absence of cAMP. In the ovarian follicle this may be an important way for the follicle to synchronize specific cAMP-mediated events, such as ovulation and luteinization, and to ensure that they do not occur prematurely but only in response to the LH surge and markedly increased concentrations of intracellular cAMP. Although data obtained in previous studies do not support the notion that the induction of $RII_{51}$ is associated with a marked shift in the cAMP dose-response activation of protein kinase (112), the hypothesis remains attractive. Transfection studies using an $RII_{51}$ expression vector will provide a useful approach to reexamine this question in greater detail.

## STEROIDOGENESIS

As stated previously, the synthesis of estradiol and the actions of estradiol on granulosa cells are obligatory for the growth of preovulatory follicles and the differentiation of granulosa cells. Below we examine how the synthesis of this steroid hormone is regulated.

### 17α Hydroxylase Cytochrome P450

The advent of serum-free tissue culture adapted for granulosa cells (52) and low-serum cultures for theca cells and granulosa cells (98) has allowed clear documentation of the two-cell theory of steroidogenesis (95, 100). It has been shown that FSH or cAMP (in the presence of testosterone) induces aromatase activity exclusively in granulosa cells (52, 98), whereas LH induces $17\alpha$-hydroxylase cytochrome P450 ($P450_{17\alpha}$) activity in theca cells (11, 31, 98). Recent purification (84), cloning (124), and subsequent transfection studies (125) have shown that $P450_{17\alpha}$ is a single peptide that contains two enzymatic functions, the $17\alpha$-hydroxylase and $C_{17-20}$ lyase activity, which converts progesterone to androstenedione. Conversion of androstenedione to testosterone by 17-ketosteroid reductase occurs in both theca cells and granulosa cells (7). Recent studies have shown that unlike aromatase and $P450_{17\alpha}$, 17-ketosteroid reductase appears to be a constitutive enzyme present in granulosa cells of all types of follicles, including those present following hypophysectomy (7). On a per-follicle basis, there is more 17-ketosteroid reductase in granulosa cells than in theca cells (7). This may ensure that most of the conversion of androstenedione to testosterone occurs close to the site of conversion of testosterone to estradiol, thereby minimizing circulating levels of active androgens.

Localization of the steroidogenic enzymes within the follicle and demonstration of their regulation by hormones in culture does not identify the initial event that determines when and in which follicles estradiol biosynthesis will occur. Based on a number of different physiological studies (8, 11, 96), it has been shown that slight increases in serum LH and LH stimulation of androgen production are the rate-limiting factors regulating the initial increase in estradiol biosynthesis in small antral follicles of the rat. For example, androgen biosynthesis is increased in small antral follicles of pregnant rats injected with low doses (2.5 IU) of hCG given twice daily for 2 days (8, 11). Recent studies have shown that the increase in follicular $P450_{17\alpha}$ activity is associated with increased content of the enzyme, as measured by Western blots (50, 109) using a $P450_{17\alpha}$ antibody (84), and increased content of $P450_{17\alpha}$ mRNA (50), as measured by filter hybridization using a $P450_{17\alpha}$ cDNA (124, 125). The androgens produced are then rapidly aromatized to estradiol by aromatase maintained by FSH in small antral follicles. Increased synthesis of estradiol, combined with continued gonadotropin actions, subsequently leads to a further marked increase in aromatase activity as well (18, 96, 99).

Following the LH surge estradiol biosynthesis declines. This decline has recently been shown to be associated with a decrease in $P450_{17\alpha}$ activity (29), $P450_{17\alpha}$ content as measured by Western blots (50, 109), and $P450_{17\alpha}$ mRNA (50). Therefore, low doses of LH/hCG increase $P450_{17\alpha}$ content, presumably by cAMP regulation of $P450_{17\alpha}$ gene transcription (124), whereas the LH surge or ovulatory doses of hCG decrease the content of the enzyme and transcription of the $P450_{17\alpha}$ gene. This biphasic regulation of cytochrome $P450_{17a}$ by LH represents a physiological pattern that is unique to the ovary (compared to adrenal and testis) and is not mimicked by other microsomal (HMG CoA reductase and aromatase) or mitochondrial [cholesterol side-chain cleavage cytochrome P450 (P450scc) and adrenodoxin] enzymes involved in follicular steroidogenesis (42, 50, 99, 109). However, this biphasic pattern is reminiscent of that observed for the hormonal regulation of $RII_{51}$ protein and mRNA in granulosa cells (describe above). The molecular factors mediating the effects of high versus low levels of LH/cAMP in theca cells remain to be resolved.

The LH-mediated loss of $P450_{17\alpha}$ in luteinized theca, however does not appear to be an irreversible process of differentiation. Preovulatory theca isolated 7 hr after an ovulatory dose of hCG (at a time when the levels of $P450_{17\alpha}$ protein and mRNA are already reduced; 50) and placed in tissue culture regain their ability to synthesize androgens and maintain it for as long as 30 days, even in the absence of LH or agents, such as forskolin, that increase cAMP (98). These same theca also produce large amounts of progesterone for 30 days in culture in the absence of hormones or cAMP (98). Thus both theca and granulosa cells appear to luteinize and to maintain their steroidogenic capacity in a constitutive manner. Although PRL has previously been shown to inhibit androgen production by dispersed ovarian cells in serum-free culture (31), PRL had little or no effect on androgen biosynthesis by more purified thecal explants (50). Therefore, the loss of $P450_{17\alpha}$ and continued low production of androgen by corpora lutea in situ may involve the action of PRL on cells other than theca cells.

## Aromatase Cytochrome P450

In contrast to $P450_{17\alpha}$, aromatase cytochrome P450 (P450arom) is localized exclusively to granulosa cells of rat ovarian follicles and is maintained by FSH in the presence of low amounts of androgen (52, 95). Antibodies against purified human placental P450arom (33) and a 62-mer-deoxyoligonucleotide probe synthesized from amino acid sequence information derived from peptide cleavage products (16) have been used to isolate cDNA clones for the human placental enzyme (15, 33) and the rat ovarian enzyme (99). Preliminary data indicate that the rat P450arom mRNA is 3.3 kilobases (kb), is present at low levels in granulosa cells of PO follicles, and is markedly elevated in corpora lutea of pregnant rats on day 15 of gestation (99). The elevated content of P450arom mRNA in rat corpora lutea may explain the abundance of aromatase activity in rat corpora lutea in vivo (30) and the apparent constitutive maintenance of this enzyme in luteinized rat granulosa cells in culture (98).

## Cholesterol Side-Chain Cleavage P450

The cholesterol side-chain cleavage cytochrome P450 (P450scc) enzyme converts cholesterol to pregnenolone, a rate-limiting step in ovarian cell progesterone biosynthesis (120) that is regulated by hormones (52, 95, 100). Recently, antibodies raised against purified rat P450scc have been used for (34) immunofluorescent localization of cytochrome P450scc in specific ovarian tissues (123), granulosa cells in culture (43), and within the inner mitochondrial membrane of these cells (34). These studies have demonstrated that the amount of cytochrome P450scc present in preovulatory follicles is greater than that present in small antral (SA) follicles but is greatest in corpora lutea (123). Western blot analysis of both rat (50) and bovine (109) follicles and corpora lutea have demonstrated further that whereas cytochrome P450scc content markedly increases during luteinization, the content of the electron donor for this enzyme, namely adrenodoxin, exhibits only a small change.

A human cDNA probe (80) and an affinity-purified rat P450scc antibody were employed to isolate a rat cytochrome P450scc cDNA clone, which was used to analyze the hormonal regulation of cytochrome P450scc mRNA during ovarian follicular development and luteinization (42, 100). Estradiol alone, given either in vivo or in vitro, did not increase the content of cytochrome P450scc mRNA in rat granulosa cells. Furthermore, when FSH alone was administered to hypophysectomized rats, the increase in cytochrome P450scc mRNA levels in granulosa cells was marginal and only clearly demonstrable 10 hr after a dose (50 μg) was used (42) that produces maximal cAMP production in vivo (101). This dose also stimulated some endogenous estradiol synthesis (as evidenced by uterine morphology), which indicates that the effect of FSH on granulosa cell levels of P450scc mRNA in hypophysectomized rats was associated with endogenous estradiol action. When FSH was administered to estradiol-treated hypophysectomized rats, increased cytochrome P450scc mRNA was observed 10 hr after doses of 10 and 50 $\mu$g were given. The amount of P450scc mRNA induced by 50 $\mu$g of FSH in estradiol-treated cells was five- to tenfold that observed in untreated cells. The enhancement of FSH induction of P450scc in estradiol-treated cells was also demonstrated clearly by the in vivo time-course study (42). Whereas little or no cytochrome P450scc mRNA was induced when 1 $\mu$g of FSH was given twice daily for two days, cytochrome P450scc mRNA was increased within 24 hr in estradiol-treated rats given the same dosage. Similarly, cytochrome P450scc mRNA levels increased rapidly in granulosa cells cultured in serum-free medium with estradiol and forskolin or estradiol and FSH but not with estradiol alone.

The impact of hormones and cAMP on the expression of $P450_{scc}$ mRNA is even more dramatic during luteinization. Cytochrome P450scc mRNA is increased fivefold in theca and granulosa cells within 7 hr after the LH/hCG surge (42, 100), and this elevated expression of cytochrome P450scc mRNA appears to be remarkably stable in both cell types in vivo and in vitro (98, 119). Cytochrome P450scc mRNA is expressed constitutively in luteinized cells in vivo, as evidenced by the constant presence of cytochrome P450scc mRNA and enzyme in corpora lutea of pregnant rats throughout gestation and the first day following parturition (day 23), despite the marked decline in serum progesterone at this time (42). The constitutive exression of cytochrome P450scc mRNA is also supported directly (119) and indirectly (98) by in vitro studies. For example, when theca and granulosa cells are isolated from rat PO follicles 7 hr after an ovulatory dose of hCG and placed in separate cultures, they maintain an elevated rate of progesterone synthesis for 30 days, even in the absence of hormones (FSH, LH, PRL) and agonists that increase cAMP (98). In contrast, theca and granulosa cells isolated from either SA or PO follicles and cultured under similar conditions fail to synthesize progesterone unless hormones or forskolin is added to the culture media (98). These observations extend the pioneering work of Channing (13) and more recent studies by Voutilainen et al (119), who have shown that progesterone biosynthesis and cytochrome P450scc mRNA synthesis, respectively, are maintained by luteinized human granulosa cells for at least 10 days. These changes in the expression of cytochrome P450scc mRNA in ovarian cells contrast with the those in the adrenal (61) and placenta (19), in which cytochrome P450scc is regulated by cAMP alone and is not enhanced by estradiol. Therefore, the factors and mechanisms involved in the switch from hormone-dependent regulation of cytochrome P450scc mRNA in granulosa and theca cells of PO follicles to a stable, constitutive (cAMP-independent?)

mode in corpora lutea appears to be unique to ovarian tissue. This finding raises the possibility that the luteotropic effects of estradiol and PRL in the rat (95) and of LH in the primate (95) may act in vivo to inhibit luteolytic events that do not occur in tissue culture. The results of the in vivo and in vitro studies suggest further that the marked changes that occur in serum concentrations of progesterone during pregnancy in the rat are governed at additional sites in the steroidogenic pathway, including conversion to 20$\alpha$-dihydroprogesterone (20$\alpha$-DHP) (44), and by other agents including somatomedin C (1), estradiol (39), lipoproteins (110) and their receptors (39), and cholesterol transport (114). These latter agents have also been implicated in the maintenance of steroidogenesis in a Leydig cell tumor cell line (R2C). In this cell line P450scc was constitutively expressed, and its synthesis was not markedly altered by protein synthesis inhibitors, whereas pregnenolone accumulation was blocked by the inhibitors (37). The identification of this rapidly turning over regulatory protein has yet to be obtained.

## OVARIAN PEPTIDES

Protein purification (38, 71, 107, 108), antibody preparation (106), and recombinant DNA technology (36, 75, 77) have allowed the identification of the elusive inhibin molecule, whose activity was first proposed in 1932 (82). It is a protein with an apparent molecular weight of 32,000 that is composed of two subunits linked by disulfide bonds (38, 71, 107, 108).

Comparison of amino acid sequences deduced from cloning studies (36, 75, 77) of inhibin subunits ($\alpha$ and $\beta_A$ or $\beta_B$) with each other and with other proteins showed a striking homology between inhibin $\alpha$, inhibin $\beta$, and TGF-$\beta$ (transforming growth factor $\beta$). The homology to TGF-$\beta$ further suggests that inhibin homodimers ($\beta_A$, $\beta_B$), as well as the heterodimers ($\alpha$, $\beta$), may be biologically active (75). In fact, bioassay data reveal that $\alpha\beta$ inhibin inhibits FSH release, whereas the $\beta\beta$ dimer (also called follicular regulatory protein or activin) stimulates FSH release. Because both of these forms are synthesized by granulosa cells (6) and are present in follicular fluid (72), it is now easy to understand why the original crude fractions of follicular fluid often gave conflicting and confusing bioassay data. Work is currently being done to determine if these hetero- and homodimers also have specific functions within the ovary.

Müllerian inhibiting substance (MIS) (12), a glycoprotein produced by the embryonic male gonad that causes regression of the Müllerian duct (63), has been purified and cloned. MIS is produced by granulosa (118) and Sertoli (118) cells in culture. MIS contains two subunits (12), one of which has significant amino acid sequence homology with the $\beta$ subunits of TGF and inhibin (12, 75, 77). Although the functional role of this protein during embryogenesis is well known, the mechanisms by which it acts remain to be resolved. The ability of MIS to inhibit growth of certain ovarian tumor cell lines suggests a possible functional role within the ovary—perhaps as a mediator of atresia (i.e. inhibition of cell growth), as an intraovarian regulator of the initiation of follicle growth, or [as suggested by Jost (63) and Donahoe and colleagues (113)] as a mediator of meiosis.

No discussion of ovarian peptides would be complete without mention of relaxin because relaxin was the first ovarian protein for which cDNA clones were obtained (53). Relaxin is a major secretory product of the rat corpus luteum during the second half of gestation. It regulates the softening of the pubic symphysis (in guinea pigs) (27) and of the uterine cervix and is a potent inhibitor of smooth muscle contraction, via alteration of myosin light-chain kinase activity (26). Increased synthesis of preprorelaxin by the rat corpus luteum on days 15–20 of pregnancy is associated with increased preprorelaxin mRNA levels (21, 22). The hormones regulating relaxin biosynthesis are not all known, but estrogen appears to be important for maintenance of elevated preprorelaxin mRNA concentrations in rat corpora lutea (22). The corpus luteum also appears to contain (synthesize?) oxytoxin and vasopressin (121).

Many other fascinating peptides are being localized to, and are synthesized by, the ovary. These include pro-opiomelanocortin (POMC) (14), insulinlike growth factor 1 (IGF-1) (1, 117), vasoactive intestinal peptide (VIP) (2), and GnRH-like peptides (4). IGF-1 and VIP have been shown to enhance granulosa cell function in vitro (1, 4, 25), whereas GnRH and GnRH-like compounds either inhibit (4, 52) or stimulate this function (69) depending on the time course, dose, and endpoint.

## OVULATION

Ovulation is the process by which the female germ cell is ultimately released from the ovarian follicle at the surface of the ovary. This process, initiated by the LH surge, has been compared to an inflammatory response (for review see 32), in which the key regulators appear to be the prostaglandins, plasminogen activators, and collagenase.

The types, activities, content, tissue distribution, and hormonal regulation of plasminogen activator (PA) in ovarian follicles have been examined extensively (5, 9, 15, 73, 86, 91, 92). Studies indicate that granulosa cells secrete primarily the tissue type of PA (t-PA) in response to gonadotropins, FSH, and LH and that t-PA activity increases in response to the LH surge preceding ovulation. However, granulosa cells also secrete the urokinase type of PA (u-PA). cDNA probes for t-PA (88) have been used to show that the content of t-PA mRNA is increased greater than 50-fold following administration of LH to pregnant mare's serum gonadotropin–treated (PMSG) immature rats (87). Thus t-PA mRNA appears to be induced in granulosa cells by the LH surge. Tissue PA has also recently been localized to oocytes of preantral follicles (73). This finding suggests that synthesis of t-PA in the follicle may not be restricted to granulosa cells and that this protease may regulate events in addition to the putative activation of procollagenase to collagenase and the consequent facilitation of follicular rupture.

Recent studies have documented that collagenase activity increases in follicles at the time of ovulation (23, 91). However, because the increase in collagenase and t-PA activities appears to be independent of prostaglandin synthesis (23, 91), it alone is not sufficient to permit ovulation to occur. Therefore, prostaglandins appear to act on other obligatory steps in the ovulation process.

Prostaglandins are associated with (20, 51, 68), and required for, LH-induced ovulation in the rat, rabbit, and pig (for review see 32). It is not clear what biochemical and hormonal mechanisms regulate the synthesis of prostaglandins in follicles at specific developmental stages (96) and at specific times after the LH surge; however, indirect evidence suggests an important role for prostaglandin synthase (PGS) (20). This enzyme catalyzes the rate-limiting step in the conversion of arachidonic acid to prostaglandins $E_2$ and $F_{2\alpha}$, thromboxane $A_2$, and prostacyclin ($PGI_2$) (111). The enzyme purified from sheep seminal vesicles has an apparent subunit molecular weight of 72,000.

Using affinity-purified anti-ovine PGS IgG and immunoblotting techniques, recent studies have documented unequivocally that the synthesis of prostaglandins in PO follicles exposed to an ovulatory dose of hCG (96) is directly associated with increases in the follicular content of PGS (48; Figure 2). In addition, the induction by hCG of PGS was demonstrated to occur

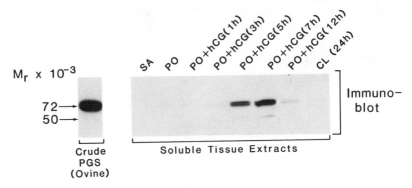

*Figure 2*   Prostaglandin endoperoxide synthase (PGS) induction by human chorionic gonadotropin (hCG) in preovulatory (PO) follicles preceding ovulation. PGS content in soluble cell extracts (200 μg protein) of small antral (SA), and PO hCG-treated (1–12h) follicles and corpora lutea was measured by immunoblot analysis using an affinity-purified PGS antibody. (From Ref. 48.)

primarily in granulosa cells and not in theca cells of ovulating follicles (48). In contrast to PGS, prostacyclin synthase (ISN), the enzyme that converts $PGH_2$ to $PGI_2$, was localized primarily in theca cells and remained unchanged in response to hCG. This distribution within the follicles, as well as the high concentration of ISN in the rat aorta, suggests that ISN may be predominantly localized in the vascular tissue of the theca layer. However, granulosa cells of H rats were clearly immunopositive for ISN (48).

Induction of PGS by hCG in granulosa cells was dose dependent (48). Doses of hCG capable of stimulating ovulation (2–10 IU) also increased the PGS content, whereas non–ovulation inducing doses of hCG (0.25–0.5 IU) only slightly increased it. Furthermore, hCG was capable of stimulating ovulation and inducing PGS in PO follicles but had no effect in SA follicles. The results are consistent with previous observations that prostaglandin E and prostaglandin $F_{2\alpha}$ synthesis increases in PO follicles, but not SA follicles, incubated for 6 hr with LH or FSH (96). The molecular basis of hCG's induction of PGS in PO follicles but not in SA follicles remains to be clearly defined. Estradiol alone administered to hypophysectomized immature rats was not sufficient to induce PGS in granulosa cells (48). Estradiol and FSH administered in a regime known to mimic the functional differentiation of granulosa cells of preovulatory follicles (95, 100) also were insufficient to induce a marked increase in the enzyme. When hCG was given to HEF rats, the content of PGS was markedly increased within 7 hr, a response identical to the effects of hCG on PO follicles in intact rats.

The pattern of hormone induction of PGS in SA and PO follicles, as well as in H, HE, and HEF rats, indicates that the induction of PGS requires levels of hCG (48) high enough to elevate intracellular [cAMP] (95) and a differentiated granulosa cell treated with estradiol and FSH and possessing the functional capabilities of luteinization and promoting ovulation. The ability of phorbol esters to increase production of prostaglandins in rat granulosa cells (64) and the ability of GnRH to induce ovulation in perfused rat ovaries (69) suggest that other intracellular mediators, including the protein kinase C pathway, may facilitate either the induction of PGS or provide sufficient substrate (arachidonic acid) for prostaglandin synthesis.

The induction of PGS is even more intriguing because the increase that was rapidly induced by hCG was transient (48). The content of PGS reached a maximal level prior to ovulation, had begun to decrease by the time of ovulation (12–14 hr), and was low within 24–48 hr following the LH/hCG surge (Figure 2). The biochemical mechanism regulating the decrease in PGS content in ovulating and luteinizing follicles remains unknown and appears specific for PGS, and possibly t-PA. Other proteins known to be regulated in granulosa cells by the LH/hCG surge either increase or decrease in a more permanent fashion. For example, the LH/hCG surge induces a marked increase in cholesterol side-chain cleavage P450 enzyme (P450scc) within 7 hr in PO follicles (42, 100). P450scc protein and mRNA continue to be constitutively expressed in functional corpora lutea (42, 100) and in luteinized theca and granulosa cells in culture (98). Conversely, the LH/hCG surge shuts off the synthesis of receptors for FSH (95) and $RII_{51}$, the regulatory subunit of cAMP-dependent protein kinase type II (102, 105). In the case of $RII_{51}$, the decline in $RII_{51}$ protein is associated with a loss of $RII_{51}$ mRNA (49, 100).

In summary, the induction of PGS in rat ovarian follicles is tissue specific and exhibits time- and dose-dependent responses to hCG (48). The induction of PGS precedes ovulation, is transient, and appears to depend on hCG-induced elevation of intracellular cAMP (48).

## SUMMARY

As stated earlier, the mammalian ovary maintains the continuous development of follicles, but only a few are selected to ovulate and form corpora lutea. These processes are regulated primarily by the gonadotropins and involve specific, sequential changes in the function of theca cells and granulosa cells. Data from recent studies (summarized in Figure 3) show that specific genes are turned on or off at different stages of follicular growth in response to estradiol and different amounts of gonadotropins and cAMP.

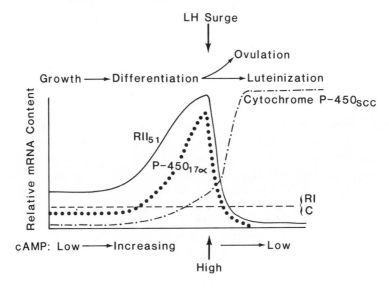

*Figure 3* Schematic diagram of the relative changes in mRNA content for cAMP-dependent protein kinase subunits ($RII_{51}$, RI, and $C_\alpha$), $P450_{17\alpha}$, and P450scc during follicular development, ovulation, and luteinization. P450 aromatase appears to follow a pattern similar to P450scc. Prostaglandin endoperoxide synthase (PGS) and tissue plasminogen activator (t-PA) are expected to follow a different pattern: a rapid induction followed by a rapid decline. (From Ref. 100.)

For example, mRNA for $RII_{51}$ in granulosa cells and theca cells increases in association with small increased in cAMP but is markedly reduced by the LH surge and high cAMP. The content of mRNA for other kinase subunits, RI and $C_\alpha$, show little or no change during similar hormonal changes. In theca cells, mRNA for $17\alpha$-hydroxylase increased and decreased in a manner similar to that for $RII_{51}$. In contrast, levels of mRNA for P450scc increased only gradually in follicles but were markedly increased by the LH surge and high concentrations of cAMP and then appeared to be constitutively expressed in rat corpora lutea in a cAMP-independent manner. PGS and t-PA appear to follow yet another pattern: rapid induction by the LH surge followed by a rapid decline in association with ovulation.

One major task for reproductive endocrinologists and molecular biologists now is to determine how low and high concentrations of cAMP act to turn on and turn off the expression of these specific genes at specific times during follicular maturation. A working model of the molecular events occurring in theca and granulosa cells of PO follicles is shown in Figure 4. LH acts on theca cells via cAMP ro regulate both P450scc and $P450_{17\alpha}$ mRNA levels, leading to increased biosynthesis of androstenedione. The mechanisms by which cAMP acts in theca cells remain to be determined but appear to involve an increase in the content of $RII_{51}$, P450scc, and $P450_{17\alpha}$. In granulosa cells, androstenedione is converted to estradiol by the aromatase P450 enzyme system (95). Estradiol, in turn, binds to estradiol receptors present in these cells (93) and may thereby regulate gene expression. However, despite the

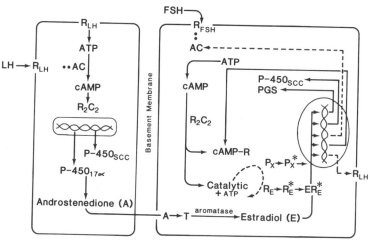

*Figure 4*   Schematic representation of the molecular events coordinating estradiol, FSH, and LH action in theca and granulosa cells of preovulatory follicles. See text for discussion. (From Ref. 100.)

presence of estradiol and estradiol receptors, little or no effect of estradiol is observed unless FSH acts via the FSH receptor to increase intracellular concentrations of cAMP (95). In a manner not yet understood, cAMP appears to enhance the actions of estradiol. The action of estradiol may be enhanced by cAMP-dependent phosphorylation of the estradiol receptor, since recent cloning of the estradiol receptor (45, 46, 81) has revealed putative sites for cAMP-dependent phosphorylation. Alternatively, increased cAMP may lead to the phospshorylation of other *trans*-acting regulatory proteins that in conjunction with the estradiol receptor increase the transcription of the LH receptor, adenylyl cyclase components, $RII_{51}$, PGS, P450scc, and P450arom. It is also possible that one or more of the *trans*-acting regulatory proteins phosphorylated by cAMP-dependent protein kinase are induced by estradiol or by the sequential actions of estradiol and cAMP. Such a mechanism would explain the developmental changes in the response of granulosa cells to the same signal (i.e. cAMP) provided in different strengths (low versus high concentrations). Identification of such putative *trans*-acting proteins (74) and isolation of the genomic sequences containing regulatory domains for estradiol and cAMP in specific genes expressed in the ovary will be just a beginning.

## Literature Cited

1. Adashi, E. Y., Resnick, C. E., P'Eicole, A. J., Svoboda, M. E., Van-Wyck, J. J. 1985. Insulin-like growth factors as intraovarian regulators of granulosa cell functions. *Endocr. Rev.* 6:400–20
2. Ahmed, C. E., Dees, W. L., Ojeda, S. R. 1985. The immature rat ovary is innervated by vasoactive intestinal peptide (VIP) containing fibers and responds to VIP with steroid secretion. *Endocrinology* 118:1682–89
3. Ascoli, M., Segaloff, D. L. 1986. Effects of collagenase on the structure of the lutropin/chorionic gonadotropin receptor. *J. Biol. Chem.* 261:3807–15
4. Aten, R. F., Williams, A. T., Behrman, H. R. 1986. Ovarian-gonadotropin-releasing hormone like proteins(s): Demonstration and characterization. *Endocrinology* 118:961–67
5. Beers, W. H., Strickland, S., Reich, E. 1975. Ovarian plasminogen activator: Relationships to ovulation and hormonal regulation. *Cell* 6:387–94
6. Bicsak, T. A., Tucker, E. M., Cappel, S., Vaughan, J., Rivier, J., et al. 1986. Hormonal regulation of granulosa cell inhibin biosynthesis. *Endocrinology* 119:2711–19

7. Bogovich, K., Richards, J. S. 1984. Androgen synthesis during follicular development: Evidence that rat granulosa cell 17-ketosteroid reductase is independent of hormonal regulation. *Biol. Reprod.* 31:122–31
8. Bogovich, K., Richards, J. S. Reichert, L. E. Jr. 1981. Obligatory role of luteinizing hormone (LH) in the initiation of preovulatory follicular growth in the pregnant rat: Specific effects of human chorionic gonadotropin and follicle-stimulating hormone on LH receptors and steroidogenesis in theca, granulosa and luteal cells. *Endocrinology* 109:860–67
9. Canipari, R., Strickland, S. 1985. Plasminogen activator in the rat ovary. *J. Biol. Chem.* 260:5121–25
10. Deleted in proof
11. Carson, R. S., Richards, J. S., Kahn, L. E. 1981. Functional and morphological differentiation of theca and granulosa cells during pregnancy in the rat: Dependence on increased basal luteinizing hormone activity. *Endocrinology* 109:1433–41
12. Cate, R. L., Mattaliano, R. J., Hession, C., Tizard, R., Farber, N. M., et al. 1986. Isolation of the bovine and human genes for Müllerian inhibiting substance

and expression of the human gene in animal cells. *Cell* 45:685–98

13. Channing, C. P. 1969. Steroidogenesis and morphology of human ovarian cell types in tissue culture. *J. Endocrinol.* 45:297–308.

14. Chen, C.-L. C., Chang, C.-C., Krieger, D. T., Bardin, C. W. 1986. Expression and regulation of proopiomelanocortin-like gene in the ovary and placenta: Comparison with testis. *Endocrinology* 118:2382–89

15. Chen, S., Besman, M. J., Shively, J. E., Hall, P. F. 1987. Identification and characterization of a cDNA clone for aromatase. *Steroids* In press

16. Chen, S., Shively, J. E., Nakajin, S., Shinoda, M., Hall, P. F. 1986. Amino acid terminal sequence analysis of human placenta aromatase. *Biochem. Biophys. Res. Commun.* 135:713–19

17. Deleted in proof

18. Conneely, O. M., Sullivan, W. P., Toft, D. O., Birnbaumer, M., Cook, R.E.G., et al. 1986. Molecular cloning of the chicken progesterone receptor. *Science* 233:767–70

19. Chung, B. C., Matteson, K. J., Voutilainen, R., Mohandas, T. K., Miller, W. L. 1986. Human cholesterol side-chain cleavage enzyme P450scc: cDNA cloning, assignment of the gene to chromosome 15 and expression in the placenta. *Proc. Natl. Acad. Sci. USA* 83:8962–66

20. Clark, M. R., Marsh, J. M., LeMaire, W. J. 1978. Mechanism of luteinizing hormone regulation of prostaglandin synthesis in rat granulosa cells. *J. Biol. Chem.* 253:7757–61

21. Crish, J. F., Soloff, M. S., Shaw, A. R. 1986. Changes in relaxin precursor mRNA levels in the rat ovary during pregnancy. *J. Biol. Chem.* 261:1909–13

22. Crish, J. F., Soloff, M. S., Shaw, A. R. 1986. Changes in relaxin precursor messenger ribonucleic acid levels in ovaries of rats after hysterectomy and removal of conceptuses and during the estrous cycle. *Endocrinology* 119:1222–28

23. Curry, T. E. Jr., Clark, M. R., Dean, D. D., Woessner, J. F., LeMaire, W. J. 1986. The preovulatory increase in ovarian collagenase activity in the rat is independent of prostaglandin production. *Endocrinology* 118:1823–28

24. Dattatreyamurty, B., Schreyer, A., Reichert, L. E. Jr. 1986. Solubilization of functional and stable follitropin receptors from light membranes of bovine calf testis. *J. Biol. Chem.* 261:13104–13

25. Davoren, J. B., Hseuh, A.J.W. 1985.

Vasoactive intestinal peptide: A novel stimulator of steroidogenesis in cultured rat granulosa cells. *Biol. Reprod.* 33:37–52

26. Downing, S. J., Sherwood, O. D. 1985. The physiological role of relaxin in the pregnant rat. II. The influence of relaxin on uterine contractile activity. *Endocrinology* 116:1206–14

27. Downing, S. J., Sherwood, O. D. 1985. The physiological role of relaxin in the pregnant rat. III. The influence of relaxin on cervical extensibility. *Endocrinology* 116:1215–20

28. Dufau, M.., Ryan, D. W., Baukal, A. J., Catt, K. J. 1975. Gonadotropin receptors. Solubilization and purification by affinity chromatography. *J. Biol. Chem.* 250:4822–24

29. Eckstein, B., Tsafriri, A. 1986. The steroid C-17,20 lyase complex in isolated Graafian follicles: Effects of human chorionic gonadotropin. *Endocrinology* 118:1266–70

30. Elbaum, D., Keyes, P. L. 1976. Synthesis of 17$\beta$-estradiol by isolated ovarian tissues of the pregnant rat: Aromatization in the corpus luteum. *Endocrinology* 99:573–79

31. Erickson, G. F., Magoffin, D. A., Dyer, C., Hofeditz, C. 1985. The ovarian androgen producing cells: A review of structure function relationships. *Endocr. Rev.* 6:371–99

32. Espey, L. L. 1980. Ovulation as an inflammatory reaction—A hypothesis. *Biol. Reprod.* 22:73–106

33. Evans, C. T., Ledesma, D. B., Schulz, T. Z., Simpson, E. R., Mendelson, C. R. 1986. Isolation and characterization of a complementary DNA specific for human aromatase-system cytochrome P450 mRNA. *Proc. Natl. Acad. Sci. USA* 83:6387–91

34. Farkash, Y., Timberg, K., Orly, J. 1986. Preparation of antiserum to rat cytochrome P450 cholesterol side-chain cleavage and its use for ultrastructural localization of the immunoreactive enzyme by protein A gold technique. *Endocrinology* 118:1353–56

35. Farookhi, R., Desjardins, J. 1986. Luteinizing hormone receptor induction in dispersed granulosa cells requires estrogen. *Mol. Cell. Endocrinol.* 47:13–24

36. Forage, R. G., Ring, J. W., Brown, R. W., McInerney, B. V., Cobon, G. S., et al. 1986. Cloning and sequence analysis of cDNA species coding for the two subunits of inhibin from bovine follicular fluid. *Proc. Natl. Acad. Sci. USA* 83:3091–95

37. Freeman, D. A. 1987. Constitutive ster-

oidogenesis in the R2C Leydig tumor cell line is maintained by the adenosine 3',5'-monophosphate independent production of a cycloheximide-sensitive factor that enhances mitochrondrial pregnenolone biosynthesis. *Endocrinology* 120:124–32

38. Fukuda, M., Miyamoto, K., Hasegawa, Y., Nomura, M., Igarashi, M., et al. 1986. Isolation of bovine follicular fluid inhibin of about 32K DA. *Mol. Cell. Endocrinol.* 44:55–60

39. Gibori, G., Chan, Y. D., Khan, I., Azhar, S., Reaven, G. M. 1984. Regulation of luteal cell lipoprotein receptors, sterol contents and steroidogenesis by estradiol in the pregnant rat. *Endocrinology* 114:609–17

40. Gibori, G., Richards, J. S. 1978. Dissociation of two distinct luteotropic effects of prolactin: Regulation of luteinizing hormone receptor content and progesterone secretion during pregnancy. *Endocrinology* 102:767–74

41. Gilman, A. 1987. G proteins: Transducers of receptor-generated signals. *Ann. Rev. Biochem.* In press

42. Goldring, N. B., Durica, J. M., Lifka, J., Hedin, L., Ratoosh, S. L., et al. 1987. Cholesterol side-chain cleavage P450 (P450scc) mRNA: Evidence for hormonal regulation in rat ovarian follicles and constitutive expression in corpora lutea. *Endocrinology* 120:1942–50

43. Goldring, N. B., Farkash, Y., Goldschmidt, D., Orly, J. 1986. Immunofluorescent probing of the mitochondrial cholesterol side-chain cleavage cytochrome P450 in differentiating granulosa cells in culture. *Endocrinology* 119:2821–32

44. Goldring, N. B., Orly, J. 1985. Concerted metabolism of steroid hormones produced by cocultured ovarian cell types. *J. Biol. Chem.* 260:913–21

45. Green, S., Walter, P., Kumar, R., Kurst, A., Bornert, J. M., et al. 1986. Human estrogen receptor cDNA: Sequence expression and homology to v-erb-a. *Nature* 320:134–39

46. Greene, G. L., Gilna, P., Waterfield, M., Baker, A., Hart, Y., Shine, J. 1986. Sequence and expression of human estrogen receptor complementary cDNA. *Science* 231:1150–54

47. Harris, B. A., Robishaw, J. D., Mumby, S. M., Gilman, A. G. 1985. Molecular cloning of complementary cDNA for the alpha subunit of the G protein that stimulates adenylate cyclase. *Science* 229:1274–77

48. Hedin, L., Gaddy-Kurten, G., Kurten, R., DeWitt, D. L., Smith, W. L.,

Richards, J. S. 1987. Prostaglandin endoperoxide (PGH) synthase in rat ovarian follicles: Content, cellular distribution and evidence for hormonal induction preceding ovulation. *Endocrinology* 121:722–31

49. Hedin, L., McKnight, G. S., Lifka, J., Durica, J. M., Richards, J. S. 1987. Tissue distribution and hormonal regulation of mRNA for regulatory and catalytic subunits of cAMP-dependent protein kinases during ovarian follicular development and luteinization in the rat. *Endocrinology* 120:1928–35

50. Hedin, L., Rodgers, R. J., Simpson, E. R., Richards, J. S. 1987. Changes in content of cytochrome $P450_{17\alpha}$, cytochrome $P450_{scc}$ and HMG CoA reductase in developing rat ovarian follicles and corpora lutea: Correlation to theca cell steriodogenesis. *Biol. Reprod.* 38: 211–23

51. Holmes, P. V., Hedin, L., Janson, P. O. 1986. The role of cyclic 3',5'-monophosphate in the ovulatory process of the in vitro perfused rabbit ovary. *Endocrinology* 118:2195–2202

52. Hseuh, A.J.W., Adashi, E. Y., Jones, P.B.C., Welsh, T. H. Jr. 1984. Hormonal regulation of the differentiation of cultured ovarian granulosa cells. *Endocr. Rev.* 5;76–127

53. Hudson, P., Haley, J., Cronk, M., Shine, J., Niall, H. 1981. Molecular cloning and characterization of cDNA sequences coding for rat relaxin. *Nature* 291:127–31

54. Hunzicker-Dunn, M., LaBarbera, A. R. 1986. Unique properties of the follicle-stimulating hormone– and cholera toxin-sensitive adenylyl cyclase of immature granulosa cells. *Endocrinology* 118: 302–11

55. Hwang, J., Menon, K.M.J. 1984. Characterization of the subunit structure of gonadotropin receptor in luteinized rat ovary. *J. Biol. Chem.* 259:1978–85

56. Itoh, H., Kozasa, T., Nagata, S., Nakamura, S., Katada, T., et al. 1986. Molecular cloning and sequence determination of cDNAs for alpha subunits of the guanine nucleotide binding proteins $G_s$, $G_i$, and $G_o$ from rat brain. *Proc. Natl. Acad. Sci. USA* 83:3776–80

57. Jahnsen, T., Hedin, L., Kidd, V. J., Beattie, W. G., Lohmann, S. M., et al. 1986. Molecular cloning, cDNA structure and regulation of the regulatory subunit of type II cAMP-dependent protein kinase from rat ovarian granulosa cells. *J. Biol. Chem.* 261:12352–61

58. Jahnsen, T., Hedin, L., Lohmann, S. M., Walter, U., Richards, J. S. 1986.

The neural type II regulatory subunit of cAMP-dependent protein kinase is present and regulated by hormones in the rat ovary. *J. Biol. Chem.* 261:6637–39

59. Jahnsen, T., Lohmann, S. M., Walter, U., Hedin, L., Richards, J. S. 1985. Purification and characterization of hormone-regulated isoforms of the regulatory subunit of type II cAMP-dependent protein kinase from rat ovaries. *J. Biol. Chem.* 260:15980–87

60. Ji, I., Bock, J. H., Ji, T. H. 1985. Composition and peptide maps of cross-linked human choriogonadotropin-receptor complexes on porcine granulosa cells. *J. Biol. Chem.* 260:12815–21

61. John, M. E., John, M. C., Boggaram, V., Simpson, E. R., Waterman, M. R. 1986. Transcriptional regulation of steroid hydroxylase genes by corticotropin. *Proc. Natl. Acad. Sci. USA* 83:4715–19

62. Jonassen, J. A., Bose, K., Richards, J. S. 1982. Enhancement and desensitization of hormone-responsive adenylate cyclase in granulosa cells of preantral and antral ovarian follicles: Effects of estradiol and follicle stimulating hormone. *Endocrinology* 111:74–79

63. Jost, A., Vigier, B., Prepin, J., Perchellet, J. P. 1973. Studies on sex differentiation in mammals. *Recent Prog. Horm. Res.* 29:1–41

64. Kawai, Y., Clark, M. R. 1985. Phorbol ester regulation of rat granulosa cell prostaglandin and progesterone accumulation. *Endocrinology* 116:2320–26

65. Keinänen, K. P., Kellokumpu, S., Metsikkö, M. K., Rajaniemi, H. J. 1987. Purification and partial characterization of rat ovarin lutropin receptor. *J. Biol. Chem.* 262:7920–26

65a. Keinänen, K. P., Rajaniemi, H. J. 1986. Rat ovarian lutropin receptor is a transmembrane protein: Evidence for an $M_r = 20,000$ cytoplasmic domain. *Biochem. J.* 239:83–87

66. Kellokumpu, S., Rajaniemi, H. J. 1985. Involvement of plasma membrane enzymes in the proteolytic cleavage of luteinizing hormone receptor. *Endocrinology* 116:707–14

67. Kim, I. G., Ascoli, M., Segaloff, D. L. 1987. Immunoprecipitation of the lutropin/chorionic receptor from biosynthetically labeled Leydig tumor cells. *J. Biol. Chem.* 262:470–77

68. Koos, R. D., Jaccarino, F. J., Magaril, R. A., LeMaire, W. J. 1984. Perfusion of the rat ovary in vitro: Methodology, induction of ovulation and pattern of steroidogenesis. *Biol. Reprod.* 30:1135–41

69. Koos, R. D., LeMaire, W. J. 1985. The effects of a GnRH agonist on ovulation and steroidogenesis during perfusion of rabbit and rat ovaries in vitro. *Endocrinology* 116:628–32

70. Lee, D. C., Carmichael, D. F., Krebs, E. G., McKnight, G. S. 1983. Isolation of a cDNA clone for the type I regulatory subunit of bovine cAMP-dependent protein kinase. *Proc. Natl. Acad. Sci. USA* 80:3608–12

71. Ling, N., Ying, S.-Y., Ueno, N., Esch, F., Denoroy, L., Guillemin, R. 1985. Isolation and partial characterization of a $M_r = 32,000$ protein with inhibin activity from porcine follicular fluid. *Proc. Natl. Acad. Sci USA* 82:7217–21

72. Ling, N., Ying, S.-Y., Ueno, N., Shimasaki, S., Esch, F., et al. 1986. Pituitary FSH is released by a heterodimer of β-subunits from the two forms of inhibin. *Nature* 321:779–82

73. Liu, Y.-X., Ny, T., Sarkar, D., Loskutoff, D., Hseuh, A.W.J. 1986. Identification and regulation of tissue plasminogen activator activity in rat cumulus-oocyte complexes. *Endocrinology* 119:1578–87

74. Maniatis, T., Goodbourn, S., Fischer, T. A. 1987. Regulation of inducible and tissue specific gene expression. *Science* 236:1237–44

75. Mason, A. J., Hayflick, J. S., Ling, N., Esch, F., Ueno, N., et al. 1985. Complementary cDNA sequences of ovarian follicular fluid inhibin show precursor structure and homology with transforming growth factor-β. *Nature* 318:659–663

76. Mason, A. J., Hayflick, J. S., Zoeller, R. T., Young, II, W. S., Phillips, H. S., et al. 1986. A deletion truncating the gonadotropin-releasing hormone gene is responsible for hypogonadism in the hpg mouse. *Science* 234:1366–71

77. Mason, A. J., Niall, H. D., Seeburg, P. H. 1986. Structure of two human ovarian inhibins. *Biochem. Biophys. Res. Commun.* 135:957–64

78. Mason, A. J., Pitts, S. L., Nikolics, K., Szonyi, E., Wilcox, J. N., et al. 1986. The hypogonadal mouse: Reproductive functions restored by gene therapy. *Science* 234:1372–78

79. Mattera, R., Codina, J., Crozat, A., Kidd, V., Woo, S.L.C., Birnbaumer, L. 1986. Identification by molecular cloning of two forms of the alpha subunit of human liver stimulatory (Gs) regulatory component of adenylyl cyclase. *FEBS Lett.* 206:36–42

80. Matteson, K. J., Chung, B., Miller, W. L., 1984. Molecular cloning of DNA complementary to bovine adrenal

P450$_{scc}$ mRNA. *Biochem. Biophys. Res. Commun.* 120:264–70

81. Maxwell, B. L., McDonnell, D. P., Conneely, O. M., Schulz, T. Z., Greene, G. L., O'Malley, B. W. 1987. Structural organization and regulation of the chjicken estrogen receptor. *Mol. Cell. Endocrinol.* 1:25–35

82. McCullagh, G. R. 1932. Dual endocrine activity of the testes. *Science* 76:19–20

83. Metsikko, M. K., Rajaniemi, H. J. 1984. Immunoprecipitation of the lutropin receptor. *Biochem. J.* 224:467–71.

84. Nakajin, S., Hall, P. F. 1981. Microsomal P450 from neonatal pig testis. Purification and properties of C21 steroid side-chain cleavage (17 α hydroxylase-C$_{17-20}$ lyase) *J. Biol. Chem.* 256:3871–76

85. Nikolics, K., Mason, A. J., Szonyi, E., Ramachandran, J., Seeburg, P. H. 1985. A prolactin-inhibiting factor within the precursor for human gonadotropin-releasing hormone. *Nature* 316:511–17

86. Ny, T., Bjersing, L., Hseuh, A.W.J., Loskutoff, D. J. 1985. Cultured granulosa cells produce two plasminogen activators each regulated differently by gonadotropins. *Endocrinology* 116:1666–68

87. O'Connell, M. L., Canipari, R., Strickland, S. 1987. Hormonal regulation of tissue plasminogen activator secretion and mRNA levels in rat granulosa cells. *J. Biol. Chem.* 262:2339–44

88. Pennica, D., Holmes, W. E., Kohr, W. J., Harkins, R. N., Vehar, G. A. et al. 1983. Cloning and expression of human tissue–type plasminogen activator cDNA in *E. coli. Nature* 301:214–21

89. Ratoosh, S. L., Likfa, J., Hedin, L., Jahnsen, T., Richards, J. S. 1987. Hormonal regulation of the synthesis and mRNA content of the regulatory subunit of cyclic AMP-dependent protein kinase type II in cultured rat ovarian granulosa cells. *J. Biol. Chem.* 262:7306–13

90. Ratoosh, S. L., Richards, J. S. 1985. Regulation of the content and phosphorylation of RII by adenosine 3'5'-monophosphate, follicle stimulating hormone, and estradiol in cultured granulosa cells. *Endocrinology* 117:917–27

91. Reich, R., Miskin, R., Tsafriri, A. 1985. Follicular plasminogen activator: Involvement in ovulation. *Endocrinology* 116:516–21

92. Reich, R., Miskin, R., Tsafriri, A. 1986. Intrafollicular distribution of plasminogen activators and their hormonal regulation in vitro. *Endocrinology* 119:1588–1601

93. Richards, J. S. 1975. Estradiol receptor content in rat granulosa cells during follicular development: Modification by estradiol and gonadotropins. *Endocrinology* 97:1174–84

94. Richards, J. S. 1975. Content of nuclear estradiol receptor complex in rat corpora lutea during pregnancy: Relationship to estradiol concentrations and cytosol receptor availability. *Endocrinology* 96:227–30

95. Richards, J. S. 1980. Maturation of ovarian follicles: Action and interactions of pituitary and ovarian hormones on follicular cell differentiation. *Physiol. Rev.* 60:51–89

96. Richards, J. S., Bogovich, K. 1982. Effects of human chorionic gonadotropin and progesterone on follicular development in the immature rat. *Endocrinology* 111:1429–38

97. Richards, J. S., Haddox, M., Tash, J. S., Walter, U., Lohmann, S. M. 1984. Adenosine 3',5'-monophosphate-dependent protein kinase and granulosa cell responsiveness to gonadotropins. *Endocrinology* 114:2190–98

98. Richards, J. S., Hedin, L., Caston, L. 1986. Differentiation of rat ovarian thecal cells: Evidence for functional luteinization. *Endocrinology* 118:1660–68

99. Richards, J. S., Hickey, G. J., Chen, S., Shively, J. E., Hall, P. F., et al. 1987. Hormonal regulation of estradiol biosynthesis, aromatase activity and aromatase mRNA in rat follicles and corpora lutea. *Steroids* In press

100. Richards, J. S. Jahnsen, T., Hedin, L., Lifka, J., Ratoosh, S. L., et al. 1987. Ovarian follicular development: From physiology to molecular biology. *Recent Prog. Horm. Res.* 43:231–76

101. Richards, J. S., Jonassen, J. A., Rolfes, A. I., Kersey, K., Reichert, L. E. Jr. 1979. Adenosine 3',5'-monophosphate, luteinizing hormone receptor and progesterone during granulosa cell differentiation: Effects of estradiol and follicle-stimulating hormone. *Endocrinology* 104:765–73

102. Richards, J. S., Kirchick, H. J. 1984. Changes in content and phosphorylation of cytosol proteins in luteinizing follicles and corpora lutea. *Biol. Reprod.* 30:737–51

103. Richards, J. S., Midgley, A. R. Jr. 1976. Protein hormone action: A key to understanding ovarion follicular and luteal cell development. *Biol. Reprod.* 14:82–94

104. Richards, J. S., Rolfes, A. I. 1980. Hormonal regulation of cyclic AMP binding

to specific receptor proteins in rat ovarian follicles. *J. Biol. Chem.* 255:5481–89

105. Richards, J. S., Sehgal, N., Tash, J. S. 1983. Changes in the content and phosphorylation of specific proteins in granulosa cells of preantral and preovulatory ovarian follicles and corpora lutea. *J. Biol. Chem.* 258:5227–32

106. Rivier, C., Rivier, J., Vale, W. 1986. Inhibin-mediated feedback control of follicle-stimulating hormone secretion in the female rat. *Science* 234:205–8

107. Rivier, J., Spiess, J., McClintock, R., Vaughan, J., Vale, W. 1985. Purification and partial purification of inhibin from porcine follicular fluid. *Biochem. Biophys. Res. Commun.* 133:120–27

108. Robertson, D. M., Foulds, L. M., Leversha, L., Morgan, F. J., Hearn, M.T.W., et al. 1985. Isolation of inhibin from bovine follicular fluid. *Biochem. Biophys. Res. Commun.* 126:220–26

109. Rodgers, R. J., Waterman, M. R., Simpson, E. R. 1986. Cytochrome P450scc, P450$_{17\alpha}$, adrenodoxin and reduced nicotinamide adenine dinucleotide phosphate P450 reductase in bovine follicles and corpora lutea. Changes in specific contents during the ovarian cycle. *Endocrinology* 118:1366–77

110. Schuler, L. A., Langerberg, K. K., Gynne, J. T., Strauss, J. F. III 1981. High density lipoprotein utilization by dispersed rat luteal cells. *Biochem. Biophys. Acta* 664:583–601

111. Smith, W. L. 1986. Prostaglandin biosynthesis and its compartmentation in vascular smooth muscle and endothelial cells. *Ann. Rev. Physiol.* 48:251–62

112. Steinberg, R. A., Agard, D. A. 1981. Studies on the phosphorylation of type I regulatory subunit of cAMP-dependent protein kinase in intact S49 lymphoma cells. *J. Biol. Chem.* 256:11356–64

113. Takahashi, M., Hayashi, M., Manganaro, T. F., Donahoe, P. K. 1986. The ontogeny of Müllerian inhibiting substance in granulosa cells of the bovine ovarian follicle. *Biol. Reprod.* 35:447–53

114. Tanaka, T., Billheimer, J. T., Strausss, J. F. III 1984. Luteinized rat ovaries contain a sterol carrier protein. *Endocrinology* 114:533–40

115. Uhler, M. D., Carmichael, D. F., Lee, D. C., Chrivia, J. C., Krebs, E. G., McKnight, G. S. 1986. Isolation of cDNA clones for the catalytic subunit of mouse cAMP-dependent protein kinase. *Proc. Natl. Acad. Sci. USA* 83:1300–4

116. Uhler, M. D., Chrivia, J. C., McKnight, G. S. 1986. Evidence for a second isoform of the catalytic subunit of cAMP-dependent protein kinase. *J. Biol. Chem.* 261:15360–62

117. Veldhuis, J. D., Rodgers, R. J., Furlanetto, R. W. 1986. Synergistic action of estradiol and the insulin-like growth factor somatomedin-C on swine ovarian (granulosa) cells. *Endocrinology* 119:530–38

118. Vigier, B., Picard, J.-Y., Tran, D., Legeai, L., Josso, N. 1984. Production of anti-Müllerian hormone: Another homology between Sertoli and granulosa cells. *Endocrinology* 114:1315–20

119. Voutilainen, R., Tapanainem, J., Chung, B. C., Matteson, K. J., Miller, W. L. 1986. Hormonal regulation of P450scc (20, 22 desmolase) and P450$_{17\alpha}$ (17α hydroxylase/17, 20 lyase) in cultured human granulosa cells. *J. Clin. Endocrinol. Metab.* 63:202–7

120. Waterman, M. R., Simpson, E. R. 1985. Regulation of the biosynthesis of cytochromes P450 involved in steroid hormone synthesis. *Mol. Cell. Endocrinol.* 39:81–89

121. Wathes, D. C., Swann, R. W., Birkett, S. D., Porter, D. G., Pickering, B. T. 1983. Characterization of oxytocin, vasopressin and neurophysin from the bovine corpus luteum. *Endocrinology* 113:693–98

122. Yuh, K.-C. M., Keyes, P. L. 1979. Properties of nuclear and cytoplasmic estrogen receptor in rabbit corpus luteum. Evidence for translocation. *Endocrinology* 105:690–96

123. Zlotkin, T., Farkash, Y., Orly, J. 1986. Cell specific expression of immunoreactive cholesterol side-chain cleavage cytochrome P450 during follicular development in the rat ovary. *Endocrinology* 119:2809–20

124. Zuber, M. X., John, M. E., Okamura, T., Simpson, E. R., Waterman, M. R. 1986. Bovine adrenal cytochrome P450$_{17\alpha}$: Regulation of gene expression by ACTH and elucidation of primary sequence. *J. Biol. Chem.* 261:2475–82

125. Zuber, M. X., Simpson, E. R., Waterman, M. R. 1986. Expression of bovine 17α-hydroxylase cytochrome P-450 cDNA in nonsteroidogenic (COS 1) cells. *Science* 234:1258–61

Ann. Rev. Physiol. 1988. 50:465–82

# ENDOCRINE REGULATION OF THE CORPUS LUTEUM

*P. L. Keyes and M. C. Wiltbank*

Department of Physiology and Reproductive Endocrinology Program, 7793 Medical Science II, The University of Michigan, Ann Arbor, Michigan 48019-0622

## INTRODUCTION

The corpus luteum is a small gland that develops rapidly from the ovulated follicle and performs a vital function in the reproductive process, namely, the secretion of progesterone, which is necessary for implantation of the blastocyst. Following implantation, the continued secretion of progesterone is essential to maintain a quiescent uterus and an intrauterine environment that is conducive to continued development of the embryo (29). If fertilization or implantation does not occur, the corpus luteum regresses, and the consequent withdrawal of progesterone leads to increased frequency of pulsatile luteinizing hormone (LH) secretion, increased follicular estrogen synthesis, and a new follicular phase (56). If implantation occurs, then the embryo signals the corpus luteum either directly or indirectly to continue to secrete progesterone and to prevent the corpus luteum from regressing (78). Thus, the corpus luteum can be viewed as the terminal stage of the ovarian follicle, which after shedding the oocyte, continues to nurture the (fertilized) egg indirectly by producing progesterone. The progestational changes in the uterus must precede the arrival of the preimplantation embryo and require the rapid conversion of the predominantly estrogen-producing follicle to a predominantly progesterone-producing corpus luteum. This is accomplished by the preovulatory "surge" of luteinizing hormone, which serves the dual role of stimulating both ovulation and the conversion of the follicle into a corpus luteum, a process known as luteinization (57).

   This review concentrates on certain aspects of the regulation of the corpus luteum that represent relatively new directions in research, and emerging concepts. For more information about the regulation of the corpus luteum in

0066-4278/88/0315-0465$02.00

different species and in pregnancy, and for information about intracellular mechanisms for the control of steroidogenesis, the reader may refer to recent reviews (10, 11, 30, 42, 47, 57, 73, 77, 78, 80, 81, 97, 104, 107).

## DISCOVERY OF THE CORPUS LUTEUM

The first detailed description of the corpus luteum was published in 1672 by de Graaf (102) who referred to "globular bodies" (corpora lutea) that formed in the place of "ova" (follicles). He provided accurate drawings of the sheep corpus luteum, and noted that in the rabbit these "globules," are present only after ovulation. The term "corpus luteum" was introduced by Malpighi (102), who took note that the cow ovary has a "yellow body" that is probably glandular in nature. Had Malpighi studied the ovaries of another species, he might have named the corpus luteum differently, perhaps "corpus rubrum," since in many species the corpus luteum appears reddish because of its high vascularity. The mysteries of the corpus luteum remained undisclosed for over two centuries until Prenant (91) proposed that it was a gland of internal secretion. But Fraenkel & Cohn (31) and Magnus (65) published the first scientific evidence for the physiological role of the corpus luteum. Inspired by the ideas of their teacher, Gustav Born (102), these investigators removed the corpora lutea from pregnant rabbits and observed that the pregnancies were terminated, whereas in operated control animals, pregnancies survived (31, 65). Years later, the active principle was isolated, identified, and named progesterone (2).

## STEROIDOGENESIS DURING LUTEINIZATION

An intrinsic property of the luteal cell is the capacity for de novo steroidogenesis (98), which is inherited from its progenitors, the granulosa cell and theca cell (24, 41). The granulosa cell of a mature follicle measures about $10 \mu m$ in diameter and has sparse agranular endoplasmic reticulum (41). Yet, these cells are steroidogenic, synthesizing progesterone de novo when placed in culture (19) and possessing the microsomal enzyme complex, aromatase, that converts androgens to estrogens (19). By the time a follicle has reached maturity, its constituent granulosa cells have acquired receptors for LH through the combined actions of follicle stimulating hormone (FSH) and estrogen (95). The preovulatory LH surge stimulates these cells to differentiate into luteal cells, i.e. to luteinize (57). This involves cell hypertrophy (the mature luteal cell is $20-40 \mu m$ in diameter), an increase in cytoplasmic to nuclear ratio, a marked expansion of agranular endoplasmic reticulum, and the appearance of large numbers of lipid droplets that contain sterol esters (16, 24, 41, 107). Thus, the differentiating luteal cell has a greatly expanded capacity for the synthesis of progesterone. In some species, such as the rabbit (116) and cow (43), aromatase activity in luteinizing cells disappears within a few days after ovulation; in other species, such as the human (72) and rat (20), the corpus luteum retains aromatase activity and produces estrogen.

Having embarked upon a course of differentiation and growth, the young corpus luteum must either have intrinsic capability for sustained progesterone synthesis or rely upon extrinsic signals (luteotropic hormones). For the first few days after ovulation, the corpora lutea of most species continue a normal course of development and secrete progesterone unaided by known luteotropic hormones. The most convincing evidence, reviewed by Rothchild (97), comes from experiments in which animals were hypophysectomized just after ovulation: the corpora lutea continued to produce progesterone for periods varying from a few days to two weeks in some species, and then regressed. The steroidogenic activity of differentiating corpora lutea in culture is revealing. When rabbit corpora lutea were placed in culture the day after ovulation, they produced increased amounts of progesterone for two days, and continued to synthesize progesterone for at least another eight days without the benefit of serum, growth factors, lipoproteins, or added hormones (118).

The above observations are consistent with the view that the luteinizing granulosa cells undergo a rapid amplification of their steroidogenic activity as a result of the initial ovulating stimulus by LH. This increased steroidogenic activity is associated with cell growth (hypertrophy), but a specific stimulus for steroidogenesis in these luteinizing cells has not been identified. Rothchild (97) refers to this as "autonomous progesterone secretion," on the grounds that the corpus luteum survives and secretes progesterone in the absence of pituitary hormones. Although cells in the early stages of luteinization do not appear to require pituitary hormones—other than the initial stimulus by LH—for steroidogenesis, other potential regulators should be taken into consideration. For example, it is well established that ovarian cells require lipoprotein-derived cholesterol to maintain high rates of steroidogenesis (6, 99, 107). The requirement for lipoprotein is also observed in human luteinizing granulosa cells placed in culture (108). Somatomedin C (110) and insulin (66, 85) have trophic actions upon granulosa cells and luteal cells in vitro, including the stimulation of progesterone synthesis and the enhancement of responses to other trophic hormones. Somatomedin C has been reported to stimulate the synthesis of cholesterol side-chain cleavage P-450 and adrenodoxin in swine granulosa cells (112). Estrogen has been shown to stimulate progesterone synthesis in well-differentiated granulosa cells and in luteinizing cells in culture, and to enhance responsiveness to other hormones (111). The interactions of these nonpituitary factors in luteinizing cells are not understood, but it is sufficient to say that their actions in granulosa cells (47) at least make them candidates for the regulation of steroidogenesis in luteinizing cells. Alternatively, luteinizing cells, undergoing a limited program of differentiation initiated by LH, may not require extrinsic factors for completion of this program and for steroidogenesis for several days.

## LUTEOTROPIC HORMONES

As pointed out by Rothchild (97), the corpus luteum in any species does not survive long in the absence of pituitary hormones. For example, when the rabbit is hypophysectomized the day after ovulation, the corpora lutea develop normally and and secrete progesterone for only three days; by the fifth day, the secretion of progesterone has ceased and the corpora lutea have regressed structurally (117). This brief period of activity represents only about one third of the normal luteal phase, which lasts 16 to 18 days (57). The term "luteotrophins" or "luteotropins" has been given to those pituitary or placental hormones that promote the growth of the corpus luteum and stimulate the secretion of progesterone (4, 97).

Two pituitary hormones are readily identifiable as luteotropic hormones—prolactin and LH. Prolactin has long been known to promote progesterone secretion in the rat (4, 97), and more recently has been reported to stimulate progesterone production in short-term incubations in the presence of lipoproteins (69). LH has steroidogenic activity in corpora lutea and is considered the most important luteotropic hormone in most species (80). The contrast between these two hormones, each recognized as having luteotropic activities, illustrates the complexity and apparent diversity of mechanisms that have evolved in different species to regulate the corpus luteum. LH exerts its acute steroidogenic effect primarily through the activation of adenylyl cyclase, the enhancement of intracellular cyclic AMP (cAMP) concentrations, and the stimulation of cholesterol movement into mitochondria (49, 80, 88). On the other hand, the steroidogenic effect of prolactin is mediated by mechanisms that do not appear to involve an increase in cAMP (101). In most species, LH has acute steroidogenic effects in luteal tissue that are readily demonstrable in short-term incubations (47, 80, 88); prolactin does not increase steroidogenesis acutely in most species (97), but can stimulate progesterone production in dispersed rat luteal cells in the presence of lipoproteins (69). In two species, the rat (6) and rabbit (46), LH has acute steroidogenic effects in luteal tissue, yet the direct action of LH on luteal cells is not required for the corpus luteum to function normally after ovulation (12, 36, 58, 63). In the rabbit, estrogen is the only hormone known to be required for a normal luteal phase (12); in the rat, prolactin and estrogen are the two essential luteotropic hormones (37, 58). Estrogen receptors are present in the sheep corpus luteum (38a), although a physiological role for estrogen in the corpus luteum of this species is not clearly defined.

The list of luteotropic hormones or effectors, i.e. those capable of eliciting an acute increase in steroidogenesis in luteal cells or of maintaining progesterone secretion, can be extended beyond prolactin, LH, and estrogen to include catecholamines (17, 55, 84), prostaglandin $E_2$ (53, 78, 81), human chorionic gonadotropin (80), and other hormones derived from fetal and maternal placental tissues (32, 35). No doubt, the growth of this list will force a continual evaluation of the physiological importance of molecules that promote steroidogenesis in the corpus luteum.

As indicated above, in vitro activity of a hormone does not necessarily imply an obligate physiological role of the hormone. LH is a good case in point. Because LH is universally active in stimulating progesterone synthesis in luteal tissue or cells in vitro, it is indeed tempting to view LH as having a universally important role in the regulation of the corpus luteum beyond the time of ovulation. As noted above, the rabbit and rat, in which the action of LH appears to be subserved by estrogen, are two exceptions. But it is important to note that in both species LH has an essential indirect role: to stimulate the synthesis of estrogen required by the corpus luteum (36, 57).

Catecholamines present a conceptual problem similar to that of LH. Luteal tissue possesses catecholamine receptors of the $B_1$ or $B_2$ subtype (83, 89), catecholamine-sensitive adenylyl cyclase is present in luteal tissue (48), and catecholamines stimulate the production of progesterone by luteal cells in vitro (17, 55, 84). Yet with the possible exception of the cat (115), a physiological role for catecholamines in the regulation of the corpus luteum in other species is unknown (33). The corpus luteum of the Rhesus monkey does not possess catecholamine-sensitive adenylyl cyclase at mid-luteal phase, which casts doubt upon a physiological role of catecholamines in the well-differentiated corpus luteum in this species (25). A review of current concepts of catecholamine regulation of ovarian function has been published (103).

## LUTEOTROPIC HORMONE RELATIONSHIPS IN THE MONKEY

For purposes of illustrating the complexity of luteotropic mechanisms, we present here some current information concerning the monkey. The reader may also refer to a comprehensive review on the corpus luteum in this species (73).

The primate corpus luteum has the interesting characteristic of producing progesterone as well as estrogens (72, 105); this dual steroidogenic capacity is correlated with the presence of both luteinized granulosa and theca cells (24, 41, 60, 72). In theory, the luteinized theca cells produce androgen, which is aromatized by the luteinized granulosa cells. There is some doubt that estrogen is luteotropic in the primate corpus luteum, since estrogen receptors do not appear to be present (43a). The evidence is compelling that the primate corpus luteum is regulated principally by LH. The administration of an antiserum against LH caused the cessation of progesterone synthesis and premature termination of the luteal phase (73). The withdrawal of exogenous gonadotropin-releasing hormone (GnRH) from monkeys with experimentally induced hypothalamic lesions caused immediate disappearance of LH from the circulation and loss of progesterone secretion (52). The remarkable finding was that interruption of LH secretion did not prevent the resumption of progesterone secretion when GnRH infusion was resumed three days later. Further, the length of the luteal phase was not altered by this three-day hiatus in LH stimulation (52). These observations provide important new perspectives on the regulation of the corpus luteum. Clearly, progesterone secretion is stimulated and maintained by gonadotropin (presumably LH), whereas the structural integrity of the corpus luteum and the presence of steroidogenic enzymes are not critically dependent upon gonadotropin. As the authors point out (52), other pituitary hormones, such as prolactin or growth hormone, might be involved in maintaining luteal cell integrity and functions other than steroidogenesis. Since the length of the luteal phase was not altered by interruption of LH stimulation and of progesterone secretion, physiological aging of the corpus luteum, including the acquisition of capacity for regression, may be dissociated from steroidogenesis and LH stimulation at least for a three-day period. In view of the presence of progesterone receptors in primate luteal tissue (43a), an intriguing possibility is that progesterone may act as an autocrine in the primate corpus luteum.

The mechanism of regression of the primate corpus luteum has been shrouded in mystery for years, but progress on this problem is now evident. The frequency of LH pulses declines to one pulse per four to eight hours as the luteal phase advances (22, 92), and one is tempted to speculate that the reduced LH pulse frequency is responsible for physiological regression of the corpus luteum. This does not appear to be the case, however, since imposition of one LH pulse per eight hours on day three and for the remainder of the luteal phase (to mimic the pulse frequency late in the luteal phase) did not alter either the profile of serum progesterone or the duration of the luteal phase in three of four animals (51). Indeed, the maintenance of LH pulse frequency at one pulse per hour throughout the luteal phase results in a normal profile of serum progesterone and a normal course of luteal regression (51, 59).

If luteal regression cannot be attributed to a change in LH secretion, and in view of the evidence that the uterus does not play a role in luteal regression (75), then intrinsic or intraluteal mechanisms assume greater importance. As the corpus luteum ages it becomes less responsive to gonadotropin stimulation (106). Estrogen, which is produced by the monkey corpus luteum (105), has been suggested as an intraluteal luteolytic agent. However, recent investigations cast doubt upon this hypothesized role of estrogen. Neither an aromatase inhibitor (23) nor an estrogen antagonist (1) prolongs the functional lifespan of the corpus luteum. Furthermore, estrogen does not cause premature luteal regression in monkeys in which LH secretion is stimulated by exogenous pulsatile infusion of GnRH (50). Prostaglandin $F_{2\alpha}$, produced by the uterus, is considered to be the primary luteolysin in a number of species (11, 30, 53, 68, 104), but the role of prostaglandin $F_{2\alpha}$ in the monkey has been controversial. Recently, Auletta et al (5) reported that infusions of prostaglandin $F_{2\alpha}$ directly into the monkey corpus luteum induced premature luteal regression, and that the luteal ovary produced increased amounts of the metabolite 13, 14-dihydro-15-keto-prostaglandin $F_{2\alpha}$ at the time of naturally occurring luteal regression. These observations are consistent with the idea that prostaglandin of luteal origin is an active luteolysin in the primate. It may be useful to think of normal luteal regression as programmed cell death (62) or the final phase of luteal cell differentiation that includes the means for self-destruction through the synthesis of a luteolysin or through other mechanisms (86). The activation of luteolytic mechanisms can be held in abeyance by intense stimuli such as chorionic gonadotropin (73), or by other hormones of pregnancy (10, 78), which allows the corpus luteum to survive until parturition (39, 60).

# REGULATION OF THE LUTEAL VASCULATURE

## Angiogenesis

The Graafian follicle has a basal lamina separating the avascular interior of the follicle from a profuse network of blood vessels that lie in the theca interna. At the time of ovulation, the basal lamina, which is composed of type IV collagen, laminin, and fibronectin (8), breaks down; this allows the rapid ingrowth of capillaries from the thecal capillary wreath (9). The invading capillaries form by both migration (9) and by mitoses (34) of the endothelial cells, which show increased tritiated thymidine incorporation by seven to eight hours after ovulation (34). As a result of the proliferation of endothelial cells, a profuse network of new sinusoidal vessels is formed, endowing the corpus luteum with an exceptionally high blood flow (see below). Although angiogenesis is a prominent feature of luteinization, it can also occur after the corpus luteum is formed. For example, at mid-pregnancy the rat corpus luteum triples in size, and serum progesterone concentrations increase as a result of stimulation by placental hormones (14, 97). Accompanying this growth is a sixfold increase in blood flow (14), a threefold increase in luteal endothelial cells (71), and a fivefold increase in labelling index of luteal endothelial cells after incorporation of tritiated thymidine (107a).

The source and identity of angiogenic factors that are responsible for vessel growth in the corpus luteum have been investigated by using such tests as vessel formation in chick allantoic membrane and rabbit cornea, or in vitro endothelial cell migration or proliferation. Angiogenic activity has been detected in medium from incubated luteal tissue and in luteal tissue of several species (28, 61, 93). The angiogenic activity is relatively specific for corpus luteum (61) and does not appear to be due to steroids (93). An angiogenic factor isolated from the bovine corpus luteum accounts for about 84% of the angiogenic activity in crude corpus luteum extracts (40). The factor is an amino-terminally truncated form of fibroblast growth factor (FGF), with its first 17 amino acid residues identical to residues 16–33 of bovine brain and pituitary FGF (40). Angiogenesis in the corpus luteum might be controlled by multiple factors such as prostaglandin $E_1$, epidermal growth factor, endothelial growth factor, endothelium-stimulating factor, angiogenin, insulin, transferrin, and alpha thrombin, all of which have been reported to affect endothelial cell proliferation (28, 64). Some of these factors, as well as luteotropic hormones, may play roles in luteal angiogenesis, either by a direct action on endothelial cells or by modulating the expression of angiogenic activity by the luteal cells.

## The Vasculature of the Differentiated Corpus Luteum

In 1898, Prenant (91) hypothesized that the corpus luteum was an endocrine gland because of "its abundant vascularity, a sign by which the histologist characterizes a gland of internal secretion pouring its products into the internal environment of the organism via the blood." Prenant's impression of the abundant vascularity of the corpus luteum was confirmed much later by actual measurement: blood flow (per gram of tissue) to the corpus luteum is greater than to any other gland or major organ, and accounts for approximately 90% of total ovarian blood flow during the mid-luteal phase (13–15, 45, 79, 82, 114). Vascular space occupies about 20% of the volume of the corpus luteum, and about 60% of each luteal cell's surface directly faces a capillary (18). Structural projections on the luteal cell membrane, uneven capillary endothelium, and the dense network of capillaries provide a short diffusion distance between luteal cell plasma membrane and blood (18).

The rapid acquisition of a blood supply and high rate of blood flow raise fundamental questions about the regulation of the vasculature in the corpus luteum. One hypothesis is that luteotropic hormones, i.e. those maintaining progesterone synthesis as well as the overall integrity of the luteal cells, also promote blood flow (21). We have tested this hypothesis in the rabbit, a species in which estrogen is the luteotropic hormone (12, 57). Estrogen seemed a particularly attractive candidate as a regulator of luteal blood flow in view of its stimulatory effects on blood flow in other estrogen-responsive tissues (70). The effects of acute withdrawal of estrogen on serum progesterone concentration and on blood flow are shown in Figure 1. Removal of

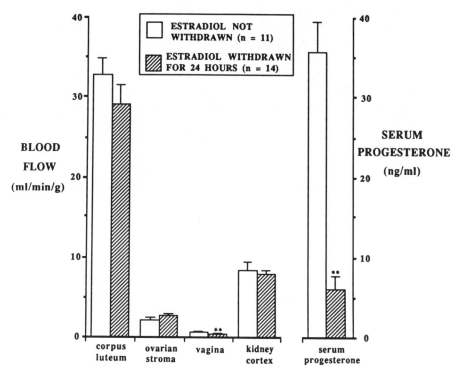

*Figure 1*   Blood flow and serum progesterone concentrations in rabbits on Day 11 of pseudo-pregnancy. Estradiol-filled implants were inserted subcutaneously on Day 1 of pseudopregnancy (Day 0 = Day of ovulation) and on Day 10 the implants were either removed or not removed. On Day 11, blood flow was determined by the reference sample withdrawal technique using radioactive microspheres; serum progesterone was quantitated by radioimmunoassay. Although not shown, the serum progesterone concentrations for the two groups were not significantly different on Days 3, 6, 9, or 10 of pseudopregnancy. Data expressed as mean ± standard error; ** = significantly lower values in animals from which estradiol was withdrawn.

a Silastic constant-release capsule filled with 17β-estradiol caused a precipitous decline in serum progestrone within 24 hours, a finding that confirmed previous results (44); however, luteal blood flow did not change. Figure 1 also illustrates the high rate of blood flow in the corpus luteum (4-fold higher than in kidney, 11-fold higher than in ovarian stroma, and 75-fold higher than in vagina), and documents the significant decline in vaginal blood flow after removal of the estradiol-filled capsule. Although not shown here, the readministration of estradiol (replacement of the estradiol-filled capsule) stimulated an increase in blood flow in uterus, vagina, and ovarian stroma, but caused no change in luteal blood flow.

We have also tested the effect of human chorionic gonadotropin (hCG) on ovarian blood flow. An injection of hCG (10 IU) caused a threefold increase in serum progesterone within 0.5 hour, a threefold increase in ovarian stromal blood flow, but no change in luteal blood flow. Blood flow in the rat corpus luteum also remains unchanged after an injection of hCG or LH, whereas in ovarian stroma, blood flow increases 2.5-fold (82). The above observations indicate that blood flow in the corpus luteum is not acutely regulated by luteotropic hormones, and that steroidogenesis in the corpus luteum can be acutely increased or decreased without concomitant changes in blood flow.

Blood flow in the corpus luteum might be regulated by the autonomic nerves that supply the ovary (109). However, evidence for direct neural control of the luteal vascular bed has not been forthcoming. Nerves have not been observed in the corpus luteum (109), and sympathetic denervation of the ovary of the rat on day 14 of pregnancy did not affect blood flow to the corpora lutea (38).

The apparent lack of innervation in the corpus lutuem (109) and the lack of acute changes in blood flow in response to changes in luteotropic stimuli suggest that the vasculature in the corpus luteum may not be acutely controlled. This idea is further supported by the observation that blood flow to the corpus luteum fluctuates according to changes in mean arterial pressure (54). Most organs autoregulate blood flow to adjust for changes in pressure and for consequent changes in metabolic requirements. Thus, the luteal vasculature can be viewed as immature vessels that have not developed the functional and structural characteristics (e.g. smooth muscle) of mature vessels. Without the means to alter resistance, these vessels behave passively.

With these observations in mind, we developed a hypothetical model for the regulation of blood flow in the ovary containing the corpus luteum. According to this model, the vascular resistance within the corpus luteum is much lower than in stroma and is not acutely regulated. Instead, the regulation of corpus luteum blood flow is mediated through changes in the resistance arteries or arterioles lying outside the corpus luteum. The major vascular resistance to the nonluteal or stromal tissue is through the small arterioles within the stromal tissue. An explanation, therefore, for the high blood flow to the corpus luteum is the high density of luteal capillaries, established during active angiogenesis at the time of luteinization. If these vessels lack the means of regulation because of the absence of autonomic innervation (109) and vascular smooth muscle, then blood flow in the corpus luteum can be viewed as controlled primarily by extraluteal vessels. Utilizing this hypothetical model, one can understand the failure of luteotropic hormones to stimulate luteal blood flow (see above): the luteal vessels are maximally dilated at mid-luteal phase, and more importantly, luteal vessels cannot respond acutely. Likewise, the failure of luteal blood flow to diminish upon withdrawal of the luteotropic hormone, 17$\beta$-estradiol (see above), is understandable, since its major effect is upon steroidogenesis in the luteal cell, which would not necessarily alter the activity of resistance vessels in ovarian stroma.

However, it should be emphasized that the above hypothetical model does not preclude the regulation of luteal vessels, either through the later acquisition of vascular smooth muscle as the corpus luteum ages, for example in pregnancy, or through the actual proliferation or regression of capillaries to coincide with increased or decreased activity of the corpus luteum.

## The Vasculature During Luteal Regression

The status of the luteal vasculature at the time of regression of the corpus luteum has been the subject of investigation and much speculation. One theory holds that a decrease in luteal blood flow is the primary event leading to luteal regression (90, 94). Another theory is that a decrease in luteal blood flow is a secondary event, which accompanies or follows primary regressive changes in the luteal cells (87). In some species, such as the sheep (15, 79, 94) and guinea pig (45, 114), luteal regression is accompanied by a precipitous decline in luteal blood flow. For example, in sheep, luteal blood flow falls from 11.2 ml/min/g luteal tissue on day 14 of the estrous cycle to 1.2 ml/min/g on day 16 (15).

The question here is whether the decline in blood flow precedes the loss of steroidogenesis and incipient regressive changes in the luteal cells. Luteal blood flow has been reported to decrease prior to the decrease in progesterone synthesis (114), and in other reports progesterone secretion decreases prior to a change in blood flow (45). Using prostaglandin $F_{2\alpha}$, which is a vasoconstrictor and considered the luteolytic agent in several species (68), changes in luteal blood flow have preceded diminution in progesterone secretion (76) and vice versa (13, 67). Thus, the issue as to the primacy of blood flow changes in luteal regression remains unsettled. Some of the apparent disparate observations may relate to the source and identity of putative luteolysins: in some species such as the sheep, pig, and guinea pig, the uterus produces prostaglandin $F_{2\alpha}$, which causes luteal regression (11, 68); in other species such as the monkey (75) and rabbit (57), the presence of the uterus is not essential for regression, and the identity of the luteolytic agent is unknown. Luteal tissue itself is a source of prostaglandin (97), and therefore in some species a local or paracrine action of prostaglandin might be involved in regression.

If we assume that at least in certain species, prostaglandin $F_{2\alpha}$ is the luteolytic agent, then what is known about its action on the luteal vasculature? Prostaglandin $F_{2\alpha}$ receptors are localized on luteal cells (100). It seems to follow that a primary action of prostaglandin might be expected on the luteal cells, and that changes in luteal blood flow would ensue secondarily from alterations in luteal cell activity. Blood flow in the corpus luteum might also be changed by the vasoconstrictive action of prostaglandin on ovarian stromal arterioles from which luteal blood is derived. The luteal vascular system may be subject to rapid alterations in structure, perhaps providing a clue to the regression process. Luteal regression is accompanied by dramatic losses in the number of luteal endothelial cells (7, 26, 79). This loss of endothelial cells resembles the process of apoptosis because some endothelial cells begin to protrude into the capillary lumen and form adherens junctions across the capillary lumen. These endothelial cells then show nuclear and cytoplasmic condensation and fragmentation with subsequent disruption of the plasma membrane and cell organelles. Some of these degenerating endothelial cells are then engulfed by viable endothelial cells (7). It is tempting to speculate that the decrease in luteal blood flow during luteolysis is related primarily to this regression of luteal capillaries rather than vasoconstriction.

## CONCLUDING REMARKS

The list of major reviews on the corpus luteum published within the past five years (see the *Literature Cited* section of this chapter) attests to the vitality of this field and to the explosion of new knowledge concerning many species. In this review we highlighted only a few of the many areas of research that could be discussed. Conspicuously absent from our review are discourses on the dynamics and characteristics of cell populations within the corpus luteum and on the synthesis of peptide hormones by the corpus luteum, which have been the subject of recent reviews (30, 42, 100, 113). It is appropriate to mention these important areas of research in closing because they illustrate certain characteristics of the corpus luteum that should be reflected upon and considered in future research. Firstly, the abundant evidence for different steroidogenic luteal cell populations, each with distinctive receptor populations and with different responses (42, 96, 100), opens entirely new vistas in our understanding of corpus luteum regulation. Not only can a cell population change its response to a given hormone as it differentiates and ages, but one cell population potentially can influence another. Secondly, the early evidence of a luteolytic effect of oxytocin (3), coupled with the knowledge that oxytocin is synthesized in luteal tissue (113), leads to a new awareness that the corpus luteum might participate in its own demise via oxytocin (30). Another peptide, relaxin, which is produced by the corpus luteum, has also been shown to cause luteolysis through pathways that are unknown at present (74). Finally, the secretion of relaxin in hysterectomized pigs at the time of expected parturition (27) is consistent with the idea that the corpus luteum has its own timetable for certain events.

The above observations suggest that the corpus luteum has intrinsic mechanisms for its own regulation that we are only beginning to understand. Because it is an ephemeral gland, the corpus luteum has unusual requirements in that it must prepare for its own destruction while fulfilling its crucial role of progesterone secretion. The challenge for the future is to discover those intracellular and intercellular events that allow the corpus luteum to play out this scenario.

## ACKNOWLEDGMENTS

Grants NIH-HD-07127 and P30-HD-18258 supported the original research reported herein (Figure 1). M. C. Wiltbank was the recipient of a University of Michigan Rackham Dissertation Grant and a Reproductive Endocrinology Program Fellowship (Training Grant HD-07048).

## Literature Cited

1. Albrecht, E. D., Pepe, G. J. 1984. Effect of the antiestrogen ethamoxytriphetol (MER-25) and luteectomy on serum progesterone concentrations in pregnant baboons. *Endocrinology* 115: 1717–21

2. Allen, W. M. 1974. Recollections of my life with progesterone. *Gynecol. Invest.* 5:142–82

3. Armstrong, D. T., Hansel, W. 1959. Alteration of the bovine estrous cycle with oxytocin. *J. Dairy Sci.* 42:533–42

4. Astwood, E. B. 1941. The regulation of corpus luteum function by hypophysial luteotrophin. *Endocrinology* 28:309–20

5. Auletta, F. J., Kamps, D. L., Wesley, M., Gibson, M. 1984. Luteolysis in the rhesus monkey: ovarian venous estrogen, progesterone, and prostaglandin $F_{2\alpha}$-metabolite. *Prostaglandins* 27:299–310

6. Azhar, S., Menon, K. M. J. 1981. Receptor-mediated gonadotropin action in the ovary. Rat luteal cells preferentially utilize and are acutely dependent upon the plasma lipoprotein-supplied sterols in gonadrotropin-stimulated steroid production. *J. Biol. Chem.* 256:6548–55

7. Azmi, T. I., O'Shea, J. D. 1984. Mechanism of deletion of endothelial cells during regression of the corpus luteum. *Lab. Invest.* 51:206–17

8. Bagavandoss, P., Midgley, A. R., Jr., Wicha, M. 1983. Developmental changes in the ovarian follicular basal lamina detected by immunoflourescence and electron microscopy. *J. Histochem. Cytochem.* 31:633–40

9. Basset, D. L. 1943. The changes in the vascular pattern of the ovary of the albino rat during the estrous cycle. *Am. J. Anat.* 73:251–91

10. Bazer, F. W., Vallet, J. L., Roberts, R. M., Sharp, D. C., Thatcher, W. W.

1986. Role of conceptus secretory products in establishment of pregnancy. *J. Reprod. Fertil.* 76:841–50

11. Behrman, H. R., Aten, R. F., Luborsky, J. L., Polan, M. L., Miller, J. G. O., Soodak, L. K. 1986. Purines, prostaglandins and peptides—Nature and cellular mechanisms of action of local assist and assassin agents in the ovary. *J. Anim. Sci.* 62 (Suppl. 2):14–24

12. Bill, C. H. II, Keyes, P. L. 1983. 17β-estradiol maintains normal function of corpora lutea throughout pseudopregnancy in hypophysectomized rabbits. *Biol. Reprod.* 28:608–17

13. Bruce, N. W., Hillier, K. 1974. The effects of prostaglandin $F_{2\alpha}$ on ovarian blood flow and corpora lutea regression in the rabbit. *Nature* 249:176–77

14. Bruce, N. W., Meyer, G. T., Dharmarajan, A. M. 1984. Rate of blood flow and growth of the corpora lutea of pregnancy and of previous cycles throughout pregnancy in the rat. *J. Reprod. Fertil.* 71:445–52

15. Bruce, N. W., Moor, R. M. 1976. Capillary blood flow to ovarian follicles, stroma, and corpora lutea of anaesthetized sheep. *J. Reprod. Fertil.* 46:299–304

16. Christensen, A. K., Gillim, S. W. 1969. The correlation of fine structure and function in steroid-secreting cells, with emphasis on those of the gonads. In *The Gonads*, ed. K. W. McKerns, pp. 415–88. New York: Plenum, 792 pp.

17. Condon, W. A., Black, D. L. 1976. Catecholamine-induced stimulation of progesterone by the bovine corpus luteum in vitro. *Biol. Reprod.* 15:573–78

18. Dharmarajan, A. M., Bruce, N. W., Meyer, G. T. 1985. Quantitative ultrastructural characteristics relating to

transport between luteal cell cytoplasm and blood in the corpus luteum of the pregnant rat. *Am. J. Anat.* 172:87–99

19. Dorrington, J. H., Armstrong, D. T. 1979. Effects of FSH on gonadal functions. *Recent Prog. Horm. Res.* 35:301–42

20. Elbaum, D. J., Keyes, P. L. 1976. Synthesis of 17β-estradiol by isolated ovarian tissues of the pregnant rat: aromatization in the corpus luteum. *Endocrinology* 99:573–79

21. Ellinwood, W. E., Nett, T. M., Niswender G. D. 1978. Ovarian vasculature: Structure and function. In *The Vertebrate Ovary*, ed. R. E. Jones, pp. 583–614. New York: Plenum

22. Ellinwood, W. E., Norman, R. L., Spies, H. G. 1984. Changing frequency of pulsatile luteinizing hormone and progesterone secretion during the luteal phase of the menstrual cycle of rhesus monkeys. *Biol. Reprod.* 31:714–22

23. Ellinwood, W. E., Resko, J. A. 1983. Effect of inhibition of estrogen synthesis during the luteal phase on function of the corpus luteum in rhesus monkeys. *Biol. Reprod.* 28:636–44

24. Enders, A. C. 1973. Cytology of the corpus luteum. *Biol. Reprod.* 8:158–82

25. Eyster, K. M., Stouffer, R. L. 1985. Adenylate cyclase in the corpus luteum of the Rhesus monkey. II. Sensitivity to nucleotides, gonadotropins, catecholamines, and nonhormonal activators. *Endocrinology* 116:1552–58

26. Farin, C. E., Moeller, C. L., Sawyer, H. R., Gamboni, F., Niswender, G. D. 1986. Morphometric analysis of cell types in the ovine corpus luteum throughout the estrous cycle. *Biol. Reprod.* 35:1299–1308

27. Felder, K. J., Molina, J. R., Benoit, A. M., Anderson, L. L. 1986. Precise timing for peak relaxin and decreased progesterone secretion after hysterectomy in the pig. *Endocrinology* 119:1502–9

28. Findlay, J. K. 1986. Angiogenesis in reproductive tissues. *J. Endocrinol.* 111:357–66

29. Finn, C. A., Booth, J. E. 1977. The physiological effects of estrogens and progesterone. In *The Ovary*, ed. S. Zuckerman, B. J. Weir, 3:151–225. New York/London: Academic, 457 pp.

30. Flint, A. P. F., Sheldrick, E. L., Theodosis, D. T., Wooding, F. B. P. 1986. Role of luteal oxytocin in the control of estrous cyclicity in ruminants. *J. Anim. Sci.* 62 (Suppl. 2):62–71

31. Fraenkel, L., Cohn, F. 1901. Experimentelle Untersuchungen über den Einfluss des Corpus luteum auf die Insertion des Eies. *Anat. Anz.* 20:294–300

32. Gadsby, J. E., Keyes, P. L. 1984. Control of corpus luteum function in the pregnant rabbit: role of the placenta ("placental luteotropin") in regulating responsiveness of corpora lutea to estrogen. *Biol. Reprod.* 31:16–24

33. Gadsby, J. E., Keyes, P. L., Schwartz, T. S., Bill, C. H. II, Lucchesi, B. 1985. Do catecholamines play a physiologic role in regulating corpus luteum function in the pseudopregnant rabbit? *Biol. Reprod.* 32:907–15

34. Gaede, S. D., Sholley, M. M., Quattropani, S. L. 1985. Endothelial mitosis during the initial stages of corpus luteum neovascularization in the cycling adult rat. *Am. J. Anat.* 172:173–80

35. Gibori, G., Basuray, R., McReynolds, B. 1981. Luteotropic role of decidual tissue in the rat: dependency on intraluteal estradiol. *Endocrinology* 108:2060–66

36. Gibori, G., Keyes, P. L., Richards, J. S. 1978. A role for intraluteal estrogen in the mediation of luteinizing hormone action on the rat corpus luteum during pregnancy. *Endocrinology* 103:162–69

37. Gibori, G., Richards, J. S., Keyes, P. L. 1979. Synergistic effects of prolactin and estradiol in the luteotropic process in the pregnant rat: regulation of estradiol receptor by prolactin. *Biol. Reprod.* 21:419–23

38. Gibson, W. R., Roche, P. J. 1986. Blood flow in the ovary and oviduct of rats after sympathetic denervation. *J. Reprod. Fertil.* 78:193–99

38a. Glass, J. D., Fitz, T. A., Niswender, G. D. 1984. Cytosolic receptor for estradiol in the corpus luteum of the ewe: variation throughout the estrous cycle and distribution between large and small steroidogenic cell types. *Biol. Reprod.* 31:967–74

39. Goldsmith, L. T., Essig, M., Sarosi, P., Beck, P., Weiss, G. 1981. Hormone secretion by monolayer cultures of human luteal cells. *J. Clin. Endocrinol. Metab.* 53:890–92

40. Gospodarowicz, D., Cheng, J., Lui, G. M., Baird, A., Esch, F., Bohlen, P. 1985. Corpus luteum angiogenic factor is related to fibroblast growth factor. *Endocrinology* 117:2383–91

41. Gulyas, B. J. 1984. Fine structure of the luteal tissue. In *Ultrastructure of Endocrine Cells and Tissues*, ed. P. M. Motta, pp. 238–54. Boston: Nijhoff

42. Hansel, W., Dowd, J. P. 1986. New concepts of the control of corpus luteum function. *J. Reprod. Fertil.* 78:755–68

43. Henderson, K. M., Moon, Y. S. 1979. Luteinization of bovine granulosa cells and corpus luteum formation associated with loss of androgen-aromatizing ability. *J. Reprod. Fertil.* 56:89–97

43a. Hild-Petito, S., West, N. B., Stouffer, R. L., Brenner, R. M. 1987. Progesterone but not estrogen receptors are present in preovulatory follicles and luteal tissue of the monkey ovary. In *The Primate Ovary*, ed. R. Stouffer, R. Brenner, C. Phoenix. New York: Plenum

44. Holt, J. A., Keyes, P. L., Brown, J. M., Miller, J. B. 1975. Premature regression of corpora lutea in pseudopregnant rabbits following the removal of polydimethylsiloxane capsules containing 17β-estradiol. *Endocrinology* 97:76–82

45. Hossain, M. I., Lee, C. S., Clarke, I. J., O'Shea, J. D. 1979. Ovarian and luteal blood flow, and peripheral plasma progesterone levels, in cyclic guinea-pigs. *J. Reprod. Fertil.* 57:167–74

46. Hoyer, P. B., Keyes, P. L., Niswender, G. D. 1986. Size distribution and hormonal responsiveness of dispersed rabbit luteal cells during pseudopregnancy. *Biol. Reprod.* 34:905–10

47. Hsueh, A. J. W., Adashi, E. Y., Jones, P. B. C., Welsh, T. H. Jr., 1984. Hormonal regulation of the differentiation of cultured ovarian granulosa cells. *Endocr. Rev.* 5:76–127

48. Hunzicker-Dunn, M. 1982. Epinephrinesensitive adenylyl cyclase activity in rabbit ovarian tissues. *Endocrinology* 110:233–40

49. Hunzicker-Dunn, M., Birnbaumer, L. 1976. Adenylyl cyclase activities in ovarian tissues. IV. Gonadotropin-induced desensitization of the luteal adenylyl cyclase throughout pregnancy and pseudopregnancy in the rabbit and rat. *Endocrinology* 99:211–22

50. Hutchison, J. S., Kubik, C. J., Nelson, P. B., Zeleznik, A. J. 1987. Estrogen induces premature luteal regression in rhesus monkeys during spontaneous menstrual cycles, but not in cycles driven by exogenous gonadotropin releasing hormone. *Endocrinology* 121:466–74

51. Hutchison, J. S., Nelson, P. B., Zeleznik, A. J. 1986. Effects of different gonadotropin pulse frequencies on corpus luteum function during the menstrual cycle of rhesus monkeys. *Endocrinology* 119:1964–71

52. Hutchison, J. S., Zeleznik, A. J. 1985. The corpus luteum of the primate menstrual cycle is capable of recovering from a transient withdrawal of pituitary gonadotropin support. *Endocrinology* 117:1043–49

53. Inskeep, E. K., Murdoch, W. J. 1980. Relation of ovarian functions to uterine and ovarian secretion of prostaglandins during the estrous cycle and early pregnancy in the ewe and cow. *Int. Rev. Physiol.* 22:325–56

54. Janson, P. O., Damber, J.-E., Axen, C. 1981. Luteal blood flow and progesterone secretion in pseudopregnant rabbits. *J. Reprod. Fertil.* 63:491–97

55. Jordan, A. W. III, Caffrey, J. L., Niswender, G. D. 1978. Catecholamine-induced stimulation of progesterone and adenosine 3'5'-monophosphate production by dispersed ovine luteal cells. *Endocrinology* 103:385–92

56. Karsch, F. J., Bittman, E. L., Foster, D. L., Goodman, R. L., Legan, S. J., Robinson, J. E. 1984. Neuroendocrine basis of seasonal reproduction. *Recent Prog. Horm. Res.* 40:185–232

57. Keyes, P. L., Gadsby, J. E., Yuh, K.-C.M., Bill, C. H. 1983. The corpus luteum. *Int. Rev. Physiol.* 27:57–97

58. Keyes, P. L., Possley, R. M., Brabec, R. K. 1987. The roles of prolactin and testosterone in the development and function of granulosa lutein tissue in the rat. *Biol. Reprod.* 37:699–707

59. Knobil, E., Plant, T. M., Wildt, L., Belchetz, P. E., Marshall, G. 1980. Control of the rhesus monkey menstrual cycle: permissive role of hypothalamic gonadotropin-releasing hormone. *Science* 207:1371–1373

60. Koering, M. J., Wolf, R. C., Meyer, R. K. 1973. Morphological and functional evidence for corpus luteum activity during late pregnancy in the Rhesus monkey. *Endocrinology* 93:686–93

61. Koos, R. D., LeMaire, W. J. 1983. Evidence for an angiogenic factor from rat follicles. In *Factors Regulating Ovarian Function*, ed. G. S. Greenwald, P. F. Terranova, pp. 191–95. New York: Raven. 481 pp.

62. Lockshin, R. A., Beaulaton, J. 1974. Programmed cell death. *Life Sci.* 15:1549–65

63. Macdonald, G. J. 1978. Maintenance of pregnancy in the rat in the absence of LH. *Proc. Soc. Exp. Biol. Med.* 159:441–43

64. Maciag, T. 1984. Angiogenesis. In *Progress in Hemostasis and Thrombosis*, ed. T. H. Spaet, pp. 167–82. Orlando: Grune & Stratton

65. Magnus, V. 1901. Ovariets betydning for svangerskabet med saerligt hensyn til corpus luteum. *Nor. Mag. Laegevidensk.* 62:1138–45

66. May, J. V., Schomberg, D. W. 1981. Granulosa cell differentiation in vitro: effect of insulin on growth and functional integrity. *Biol. Reprod.* 25:421–31

67. McCracken, J. A., Glew, M. E., Scaramuzzi, R. J. 1970. Corpus luteum regression induced by prostaglandin $F_{2\alpha}$. *J. Clin. Endocrinol. Metab.* 30:544–46

68. McCracken, J. A., Schramm, W., Barcikowski, B., Wilson, L. Jr. 1981. The identification of prostaglandin $F_{2\alpha}$ as a uterine luteolytic hormone and the hormonal control of its synthesis. *Acta Vet. Scand. Suppl.* 77:71–88

69. Menon, M., Peegel, H., Menon, K. M. J. 1985. Lipoprotein augmentation of human chorionic gonadotropin and prolactin stimulated progesterone synthesis by rat luteal cells. *J. Steroid Bicohem.* 22:79–84

70. Meschia, G. 1983. Circulation to female reproductive organs. In *Handbook of Physiology, Section 2, The Cardiovascular System, Vol. III, The Peripheral Circulation, Part 1*, ed. J. T. Shepherd, R. M. Abbond, pp. 241–69. Baltimore: Waverly Press

71. Meyer, G. T., Bruce, N. W. 1979. The cellular pattern of corpus luteal growth during pregnancy in the rat. *Anat. Rec.* 193:823–30

72. Mori, T., Nihnobu, K., Takeuchi, S., Onho, Y., Tojo, S. 1983. Interrelation between luteal cell types in steroidogenesis *in vitro* of human corpus luteum. *J. Steroid Biochem.* 19:811–15

73. Moudgal, N. R. 1984. Corpus luteum of the nonhuman primate. *Adv. Vet. Sci. Comp. Med.* 28:343–66

74. Musah, A. I., Schwabe, C., Anderson, L. L. 1987. Acute decrease in progesterone and increase in estrogen secretion caused by relaxin during late pregnancy in beef heifers. *Endocrinology* 120:317–24

75. Neill, J. D., Johansson, E. D. B., Knobil, E. 1969. Failure of hysterectomy to influence the normal pattern of cyclic progesterone secretion in the Rhesus monkey. *Endocrinology* 84:464–65

76. Nett, T. M., Niswender, G. D. 1981. Luteal blood flow and receptors for LH during $PGF_{2\alpha}$-induced luteolysis: production of $PGE_2$ and $PGF_{2\alpha}$ during early pregnancy. *Acta Vet. Scand. Suppl.* 77:117–30

77. Niswender, G. D., Farin, C. E., Gamboni, F., Sawyer, H. R., Nett, T. M. 1986. Role of luteinizing hormone in regulating luteal function in ruminants. *J. Anim. Sci.* 62 (Suppl. 2):1–13

78. Niswender, G. D., Fitz, T. A. 1980. Maintenance of the corpus luteum of early pregnancy. In *Functional Correlates of Hormone Receptors in Reproduction*, ed. V. Mahesh, T. Muldoon, B. Saxena, pp. 291–301. New York: Elsevier/North Holland

79. Niswender, G. D., Reimers, T. J., Diekman, M. A., Nett, T. M. 1976. Blood flow: A mediator of ovarian function. *Biol. Reprod.* 14:64–81

80. Niswender, G. D., Sawyer, H. R., Chen, T. T., Endres, D. B. 1980. Action of luteinizing hormone at the luteal cell level. In *Advances in Sex Hormone Research*, ed. J. A. Thomas, R. L. Singhal, 4:153–85. Baltimore: Urban & Schwarzenberg

81. Niswender, G. D., Schwall, R. H., Fitz, T. A., Farin, C. E., Sawyer, H. R. 1985. Regulation of luteal function in domestic ruminants: new concepts. *Recent Prog. Horm. Res.* 41:101–51

82. Norjavaara, E., Olofsson, J., Gafvels, M., Selstam, G. 1987. Redistribution of ovarian blood flow after injection of human chorionic gonadotropin and luteinizing hormone in the adult pseudopregnant rat. *Endocrinology* 120:107–14

83. Norjavaara, E., Rosberg, S., Gafvels, M., Selstam, G. 1984. β-adrenergic receptor concentration in corpora lutea of different ages obtained from pregnant mare serum gonadotropin-treated rats. *Endocrinology* 114:2154–2159

84. Norjavaara, E., Seltsam, G., Ahren, K. 1982. Catecholamine stimulation of cyclic AMP and progesterone production in rat corpora lutea of different ages. *Acta Endocrinol.* 100:613–22

85. O'Shaughnessy, P. J., Wathes, D. C. 1985. Characteristics of bovine luteal cells in culture: morphology, proliferation and progesterone secretion in different media and effects of LH, dibutyryl cyclic AMP, antioxidants and insulin. *J. Endocrinol.* 104:355–61

86. Paavola, L. 1979. Cellular mechanisms involved in luteolysis. *Adv. Exp. Med. Biol.* 112:527–33

87. Pang, C. Y., Behrman, H. R. 1979. Relationship of luteal blood flow and corpus luteum function in pseudopregnant rats. *Am. J. Physiol.* 237:E30–E34

88. Payne, A. H., Quinn, P. G., Stalvey, J. R. D. 1985. The stimulation of steroid biosynthesis by luteinizing hormone. In *Luteinizing Hormone Receptors*, ed. M. Ascoli, pp. 135–72. Boca Raton, Fla: Chemical Rubber Co.

89. Perkins, S. N., Cronin, M. J., Veldhuis, J. D. 1986. Properties of β-adrenergic receptors on porcine corpora lutea and

granulosa cells. *Endocrinology* 118: 998–1005

90. Pharriss, B. B., Cornette, J. C., Gutknecht, G. D. 1970. Vascular control of luteal steroidogenesis. *J. Reprod. Fertil. Suppl.* 10:97–103

91. Prenant, A. 1898. La valeur morphologique du corps jaune. Son action physiologique et therapeutique possible. *Rev. Gen. Sci. Pure Appl.* 9:646–50

92. Reame, N., Sauder, S. E., Kelch, R. P., Marshall, J. C. 1984. Pulsatile gonadotropin secretion during the human menstrual cycle: evidence for altered frequency of gonadotropin-releasing hormone secretion. *J. Clin. Endocrinol. Metab.* 59:328–37

93. Redmer, D. A., Rone, J. D., Goodman, A. L. 1985. Evidence for a non-steroidal angiotropic factor from the primate corpus luteum: Stimulation of endothelial cell migration in vitro. *Proc. Soc. Exp. Biol. Med.* 179:136–40

94. Reynolds, L. P. 1986. Utero-ovarian interactions during early pregnancy: role of conceptus-induced vasodilation. *J. Anim. Sci.* 62 (Suppl. 2):47–61

95. Richards, J.S . 1980. Maturation of ovarian follicles: actions and interactions of pituitary and ovarian hormones on follicular cell differentiation. *Physiol. Rev.* 60:51–89

96. Rodgers, R. J., O'Shea, J. D., Findlay, J. K. 1985. Do small and large luteal cells of the sheep interact in the production of progesterone? *J. Reprod. Fertil.* 75:85–94

97. Rothchild, I. 1981. The regulation of the mammalian corpus luteum. *Recent Prog. Horm. Res.* 37:183–298

98. Savard, K. 1973. The biochemistry of the corpus luteum. *Biol. Reprod.* 8:183–202

99. Schreiber, J. R., Hsueh, A. J. W., Weinstein, D. B., Erickson, G. F. 1980. Plasma lipoproteins stimulate progestin production by rat ovarian granulosa cells cultured in serum free medium. *J. Steroid Biochem.* 13:1009–14

100. Schwall, R. H., Sawyer, H. R., Niswender, G. D. 1986. Differential regulation by LH and prostaglandins of steroidogenesis in small and large luteal cells of the ewe. *J. Reprod. Fertil.* 76:821–29

101. Shiota, K., Wiest, W. G. 1979. On the mechanism of prolactin stimulation of steroidogenesis. In *Ovarian Follicular and Corpus Luteum Function, Adv. Exp. Med. Biol.*, ed. C. P. Channing, J. M. Marsh, W. A. Sadler, 112:169–78. New York: Plenum

102. Short, R. V. 1977. The discovery of the ovaries. In *The Ovary*, ed. S. Zuckerman, B. J. Weir, 1:1–39. New York/ London: Academic. 517 pp.

103. Spicer, L. J. 1986. Catecholaminergic regulation of ovarian function in mammals: current concepts. *Life Sci.* 39: 1701–11

104. Stormshak, F., Zelinski-Wooten, M. B., Abdelgadir, S. E. 1987. Comparative aspects of the regulation of corpus luteum function in various species. In *Regulation of Ovarian and Testicular Function*, ed. V. B. Mahesh, pp. 327–60. New York/London: Plenum

105. Stouffer, R. L., Bennett, L. A., Hodgen, G. D. 1980. Estrogen production by luteal cells isolated from Rhesus monkeys during the menstrual cycle: correlation with spontaneous luteolysis. *Endocrinology* 106:519–25

106. Stouffer, R. L., Nixon, W. E., Gulyas, B. J., Hodgen, G. D. 1977. Gonadotropin-sensitive progesterone production by rhesus monkey luteal cells *in vitro:* a function of age of the corpus luteum during the menstrual cycle. *Endocrinology* 100:506–12

107. Strauss, J. F. III, Schuler, L. A., Rosenblum, M. F., Tanaka, T. 1981. Cholesterol metabolism by ovarian tissue. *Adv. Lipid Res.* 18:99–157

107a. Tamura, H., Greenwald, G. S. 1987. Angiogenesis and its hormonal control in the corpus luteum of the pregnant rat. *Biol. Reprod.* 36:1149–1154

108. Tureck, R. W., Strauss, J. F. III. 1982. Progesterone synthesis by luteinized human granulosa cells in culture. The role of de novo sterol synthesis and lipoprotein-carried sterol. *J. Clin. Endocrinol. Metab.* 54:367–73

109. Unsicker, K. 1974. Qualitative and quantitative studies on the innervation of the corpus luteum of rat and pig. *Cell Tissue Res.* 152:513–24

110. Veldhuis, J. D., Furlanetto, R. W. 1985. Trophic actions of human somatomedin C/insulin-like growth factor I on ovarian cells: In vitro studies with swine granulosa cells. *Endocrinology* 116:1235–42

111. Veldhuis, J. D., Klase, P. A., Hammond, J. M. 1981. Direct actions of 17β-estradiol on progesterone production by highly differentiated porcine granulosa cells in vitro. II. Regulatory interactions of estradiol with luteinizing hormone and cyclic nucleotides. *Endocrinology* 109:433–42

112. Veldhuis, J. D., Rodgers, R. J., Dee, A., Simpson, E. R. 1986. The insulin-like growth factor, somatomedin C, induces the synthesis of cholesterol side-

chain cleavage cytochrome P-450 and adrenodoxin in ovarian cells. *J. Biol. Chem.* 261:2499–2502

113. Wathes, D. C. 1984. Possible actions of gonadal oxytocin and vasopressin. *J. Reprod. Fertil.* 71:315–45

114. Wehrenberg, W. B., Dierschke, D. J., Rankin, J. H. G., Wolf, R. C. 1978. Variations in "functional" blood flow as related to corpus luteum activity in cyclic guinea pigs. *Biol. Reprod.* 19:380–84

115. Wheeler, A. G., Walker, M., Lean, J. 1987. Influence of adrenergic receptors on ovarian progesterone secretion in the pseudopregnant cat and oestradiol secretion in the oestrous cat. *J. Reprod. Fertil.* 79:195–205

116. Younglai, E. V. 1973. Biotransformation of pregnenolone and progesterone by rabbit ovarian follicles and corpora lutea. *Acta Endocrinol.* 74:775–82

117. Yuh, K.-C. M., Bill, C. H. II, Keyes, P. L. 1984. Transient development and function of rabbit corpora lutea after hypophysectomy. *Am. J. Physiol.* 247:E808-E814

118. Yuh, K.-C. M., Possley, R. M., Brabec, R. K., Keyes, P. L. 1986. Steroidogenic and morphological characteristics of granulosa and thecal compartments of the differentiating rabbit corpus luteum in culture. *J. Reprod. Fertil.* 76:267–77

*Ann. Rev. Physiol. 1988. 50:483–508*

# ENDOCRINE REGULATION AND COMMUNICATING FUNCTIONS OF THE LEYDIG CELL[1]

## Maria L. Dufau

Molecular Endocrinology Section, Endocrinology and Reproduction Research Branch, National Institute of Child Health and Human Development, National Institutes of Health, Bethesda, Maryland 20892

## INTRODUCTION

The control of steroid production by the Leydig cell is dependent upon the concerted action of gonadotropin. The episodic secretion of luteinizing hormone (LH) supports the steroidogenic function of the Leydig cell through interaction with LH receptors on the cell surface, and through subsequent stimulation of mainly cyclic AMP (cAMP) -dependent events (31). The cAMP pathway appears to be highly compartmentalized (35) and may be affected by non-cAMP pathways at the membrane and intracellular levels (36, 37, 87). The gonadotropic stimulatory event can be influenced by the action of peptide hormones that cause negative modulation of cAMP generation through activation of the nucleotide inhibitory (Ni) subunit of adenylate cyclase (57) and by non-cAMP mediated mechanisms (36, 37, 54, 87). The trophic actions of LH include the regulation of surface receptors for LH and prolactin (18, 31).

In addition to the positive regulation of membrane receptors and steroidogenesis caused by physiological increases in endogenous hormone, major elevations in circulating gonadotropin can cause down-regulation of homologous LH receptors and desensitization of steroid responses in the target cell (18, 31, 43). Prolactin also has modulatory effects on the Leydig cell probably by potentiation of LH-stimulated responses exerted in part through the control of the number of LH receptors (18, 19, 101). Growth hormone, singly and in combination with prolactin, has been shown to affect

483

LH binding sites and to prevent the loss of LH receptors following hypophysectomy (19, 101). Follicle stimulating hormone (FSH), presumably through its tubular actions and through factors and hormones produced by the tubule, may play an important role in Leydig cell differentiation and function (15, 84, 96). Androgen produced in the Leydig cells plays a major role in the control of spermatogenesis and in many aspects of epididymal function (44).

The Leydig cell synthesizes steroids, neuropeptides, and other proteins. These hormonal and nonhormonal factors can exert autocrine regulation and paracrine actions that may affect tubular function.

## SYSTEMS FOR THE STUDY OF LEYDIG CELL RECEPTORS AND FUNCTION

Because of its interstitial localization and its relative low abundance, a number of purification techniques have been developed for isolation of Leydig cells. The dispersion of the interstitial cell fraction from rat testis by collagenase digestion yields preparations containing 25–50% Leydig cells that are highly responsive for acute studies in suspension and in short-term cultures (63). This type of preparation, without further purification, has been used for the development of highly sensitive bioassays based on the acute dose-related testosterone response of Leydig cells in suspension to gonadotropin in vitro (34, 38, 41, 86).

Preparations of purified Leydig cells have been of considerable value for the analysis of hormonal regulation of gonadotropin receptors and control of androgen biosynthesis. Most methods have employed Metrizamide (26, 29) or Percoll gradients (80). The recovery and degree of purity of the final Leydig cell preparation, as well as the number of cell bands obtained, depend on the range of Metrizamide or Percoll concentrations used in the gradients. However, since less than 100 million interstitial cells can be resolved on each gradient, a considerable number of gradients must be performed to prepare large quantities of pure Leydig cells. This limitation of the density gradient method led most recently to evaluation of the efficacy of centrifugal elutriation (6). It is clear that this technique provides a rapid and convenient method for purification (90–95% purity) of large quantities of metabolically intact Leydig cells since up to 1 billion interstitial cells can be procesed in less than 1 hour (6, 7). The contaminating cells in this step were pachytene spermatocytes ($\sim$ 5%) and a variable proportion (0–2%) of lymphocytes, which reflects their ability to bind selectively to the Leydig cells and form typical rosette structures in vitro. Further, the combination of centrifugal elutriation and centrifugation on gradients of Metrizamide yields 100% pure rat Leydig cell preparations.

Early studies (29) demonstrated that density gradients on 14–32% metrizamide resolved interstitial cells of adult rats in five distinct visible cell bands. Three bands (II, III, IV) displayed specific binding of the labeled hormone fractions. Fraction I contained debris and nonsteroidogenic cells and fraction V consisted entirely of red cells. Band II ($1.078$ g cm$^{-3}$), showing lower binding than bands III ($1.085$ g cm$^{-3}$) and IV ($1.105$ g cm$^{-3}$), consisted of a less responsive cell population that results from the presence of damaged cells in the interstitial cell preparation and could be removed during density gradient. Bands III and IV contained almost homogenous active Leydig cells and sedimented as two adjacent bands with similar hormonal responses (29). Centrifugal elutriation can separate the active Leydig cells ($> 12$ mm/h.g.) from unresponsive cells ($< 12$ mm/h.g.). The competent Leydig cell fraction is composed of cells of different sedimentation velocities with similar morphology and biological activity. The unresponsive Leydig cells, which corresponded to the band resolved in Metrizamide gradients ($1.078$ g cm$^{-3}$), showed a major proportion of damaged Leydig cells displaying $^{125}$I-human chorionic gonadotropin (hCG) specific binding activity to membrane and damaged cells (6, 7). Such structural damage has been also most recently recognized in Percoll gradients (60).

Desensitization of Leydig cells in adult rats can be evoked by the acute in vivo action of a gonadotropin upon the testis, which induces loss of LH receptors and a receptor-independent decrease of in vitro maximum pregnenolone and testosterone responses to hCG in isolated Leydig cells (see also below). A redistribution of Leydig cells with significant reduction of their flotation densities was observed after treatment with desensitizing doses of hCG by subfractionation of elutriation-purified Leydig cells in 16–24% Metrizamide gradients. In comparison to control cells, the concentration of desensitized Leydig cells in bands of densities 1.089, 1.098, and 1.110 g cm$^{-3}$ was decreased, whereas the concentration of band density 1.072 g cm$^{-3}$ was increased. The shifting of a significant proportion of desensitized Leydig cells could arise from changes in the lipid content following gonadotropin treatment since the cell size was not significantly affected (6, 7).

The cited differences of binding and response of the band ($1.078$ g cm$^{-3}$) with variable cell damage, and the redistribution of Leydig cells during desensitization led to the interpretation that functionally different adult Leydig cell populations were resolved by gradient sedimentation (72). However, detailed experimental evidence obtained by dual purification (centrifugal elutriation followed by Metrizamide gradient) has clearly demonstrated that the active Leydig cell population of the adult rat intestinal tissue is composed of cells with different densities and sedimentation velocities that show similar morphology, biological activity and susceptibility to desensitization by gonadotropins (6, 7).

In contrast to the adult rat, Leydig cells from fetal testis were resolved by centrifugal elutriation into two distinct populations. The fraction collected with sedimentation velocities 12–16.8 mm/h.g. showed the presence of a small population of partially differentiated transitional cells with lower cytoplasm to nuclear ration. The fractions eluted at above 19.3 mm/h.g. showed the presence of a cell population with typical fetal Leydig cell characteristics, such as smooth endoplasmic reticulum, tubularlike mitochondria, and abundant cytoplasmic droplets. Both fetal Leydig cell types possess gonadotropin receptors and cAMP and testosterone responses to hCG in vitro (91).

Although adult rat Leydig cells have been used for acute and short-term studies in culture, in general they are not ideal models for long-term study of hormonal effects. Such cells usually lose their LH receptors after 1–3 days in culture along, with a parallel decline of $17\alpha$-hydroxylase/17,20-desmolase activities. Consequently, these cultures do not produce testosterone or other C19 steroids although they maintain a significant level of pregnenolone and progesterone production for up to 15 days (32). Adult Leydig cell cultures maintained in the absence of trophic hormone for 6 days (3) or cell cultures from hypophysectomized rats (54) regain their steroidogenic responsiveness to hCG, but the testosterone levels in these cultures were 1/50–1/200 of those observed with adult cells incubated in suspension (63). In this regard, pig Leydig cells can maintain most of their functions for longer periods; however they appear to possess only some aspects in common with adult rat Leydig cells (79).

Rebois (76) and Ascoli (9) established cell lines from mouse Leydig cell tumors that are of value for studies of receptors and coupling functions. However, the findings derived from these systems cannot be extrapolated to the freshly prepared rat Leydig cells. Although both cell types appeared to have equal number of LH/hCG receptors, the normal adult rat Leydig cells possess LH/hCG receptors in excess (spare receptors) of those required for maximal steroidogenic responses to trophic hormones (17); maximal stimulation of testosterone production occurs when less than 1% of the LH/hCG receptors are occupied (63). Consequently only marked reduction of surface receptors caused changes in the sensitivity of the hormonal stimulus (21). In contrast, in the murine tumor culture, maximal stimulation of progesterone production occurs when 60–70% of the receptors are occupied (46). Furthermore, since the mouse tumor cultured cells secrete predominantly progesterone and $20\alpha$-dehydroprogesterone, such cells cannot be employed for studies on hormonal desensitization of steroidogenic pathways (late lesion).

In contrast with the situation in the adult rat, the fetal Leydig cell can be maintained in long-term culture (for up to 78 days) with preservation of receptor-activated steroidogenic responses. Therefore the fetal Leydig cell provides a good model system for studies of hormone action in the testis. This type of culture is of particular value for studies of gonadotropin and gonadotropin releasing hormone (GnRH) action (37), and for developmental studies for elucidation of molecular mechanisms of gonadotropin-induced estradiol–mediated desensitization (92). Furthermore, recent studies in fetal cultures have demonstrated the absence of $\beta$-endorphin degradation, which is evident in the adult cells. For this reason, the fetal Leydig cell culture is also an excellent model for evaluating testicular $\beta$-endorphin production and its modulation in vitro (59).

## LH RECEPTORS, EARLY MEMBRANE EVENTS, AND cAMP GENERATION

Leydig cell receptors have been identified as glycoproteins with a minor but important phospholipid component. The LH receptors of rat testis have been purified to homogeneity on Affigel-10 (39) and more recently on hCG-Sepharose (64). The pure receptor was resolved in SDS electrophoresis under reducing conditions as a single protein band of $M_r$ 90,000. These findings are consistent with results from studies on chemical cross-linking of hormone-receptor complexes (64, 78) and biosynthetic labeling of receptors (11). The native LH/hCG receptors appear to be composed of two identical subunits of $M_r$ 90,000 (64) associated by noncovalent interactions. Although the individual subunits can bind hormones, it is conceivable that the dimeric form is necessary for signal transduction. The pure receptor can be phosphorylated in vitro by the catalytic subunit of cAMP-dependent protein kinase ($\sim$ 0.3 mol of phosphate per mol of receptor), an event that may be involved in regulating hormone action (64). The LH receptor binding capacity of the adult rat testis is about 1 pmol $g^{-1}$ which is equivalent to 20,000 binding sites per Leydig cell (31). Autoradiograph analysis of $^{125}$I-hCG has demonstrated a predominantly surface location of the hormone-receptor complexes over the microvillous area (2, 29). After saturation of Leydig cell receptors with $^{125}$I-hCG in vivo, internalization of the hormone-receptor complexes is a relatively slow process. Only a small proportion of the bound hormone is internalized at 6 h and significant loss of binding sites does not occur until about 18 h. After in vitro uptake by Leydig cells, the intracellular hormone was mainly associated with endocytic vesicles and lysosomes and was only occasionally located in coated pits or vesicles (2).

Biochemical studies are in general agreement with morphological findings (2, 13, 29) and have shown only minor internalization of the hormone during incubation for 3 h with a saturating concentration of $^{125}$I-hCG. Ninety percent of the labeled hormone bound to adult Leydig cells was released from the cell surface by treatment with acid (pH 3) or heat (65°C for 30 min); the results were identical whether the cells were in culture or in suspension (13). The higher percentage of surface bound hormone after incubation for 3–6 h is in contrast with the rapid internalization of bound hCG reported in cultured porcine cells (62) and in murine Leydig tumor cells (46). This discrepancy could arise from the difference in species and/or between normal and cultured tumoral cells. In either case, normal rat Leydig cells clearly internalize the bound hormone quite slowly, a rate consistent with the delayed onset of receptor down-regulation in vivo after treatment with LH or hCG. The dissociation rate of the bound hormone from Leydig cell membrane is also quite slow, and a progressive reduction in the release of labeled hCG from intact Leydig cells (13) or from cell membrane "tight binding" occurs with increasing duration of incubation at 37°C (18). This tight binding could be related to the termination of peptide hormone action (i.e. receptor uncoupling and/or desensitization of membrane events) and would favour subsequent processing and internalization of the occupied receptor sites.

The specific LH receptor sites in testicular Leydig cells undergo functional coupling to adenylate cyclase within the plasma membrane after occupancy by LH/hCG. Among the processes initiated in the plasma membrane are hormone-induced guanyl nucleotide binding (30), hormone-GTP dependent membrane phosphorylation (36, 43), and adenylate cyclase activation (30). The cAMP pathway may be influenced by non-cAMP pathways at the membrane and intracellular levels. The Leydig cell enzyme is almost totally dependent upon added guanyl nucleotides for hormonal responses, and stimulation of adenylate cyclase by LH or hCG is greatly magnified in the presence of Gpp(NH)p (30). Analysis of [$^3$H]Gpp(NH)p binding to purified Leydig cell membrane fractions revealed a high affinity binding site with $K_a = 1$–$3 \times 10^7$ M$^{-1}$ and binding capacity of 5–20 pmol mg$^{-1}$ membrane protein. LH and hCG stimulate the binding of Gpp(NH)p to Leydig cell membranes in a dose-related manner ($10^{-11}$–$10^{-8}$M), with increases of up to 200% in binding capacity and no appreciable change in binding affinity for the nucleotide. This finding has provided direct evidence for interaction of the hormone-receptor complex with the guanyl nucleotide regulatory sites (30). In addition, there was a close correlation between hormone-stimulated nucleotide binding and activation of adenylate cyclase in the Leydig cell membranes (30, 43).

Rapid membrane events in the gonadotropin-activated Leydig cell included GTP-induced phosphorylation of a 44,500 $M_r$ protein. This phosphorylation is modulated by Ca$^{2+}$, increased at low (nM) concentrations of free Ca$^{2+}$, but inhibited at high ($\mu$M) concentrations. At submaximal levels of GTP ($10^{-4}$ M), LH increased membrane phosphorylation 30% over control levels. The endogenous phosphorylation activity was shown to be a rapid (10 s–20 min, at 18–20°C) cAMP independent event. Adenylate cyclase activity, also modulated by Ca$^{2+}$ in a similar biphastic manner, and its changes were associated with the number of enzyme units activated by the hormone (36, 43).

These results indicate that a $Ca^{2+}$-dependent kinase system exists in the purified Leydig cell membrane and suggest that these events could directly or indirectly influence the hormone-dependent, guanyl nucleotide stimulatory, subunit-mediated interactions in the plasma membrane.

## cAMP POOLS AND HORMONAL ACTIVATION OF PROTEIN KINASE

The rapid stimulation of adenylate cyclase in the Leydig cell plasma membrane appears to be responsible for mediating the steroidogenic and trophic actions of LH upon the Leydig cell via activation of protein kinase and subsequent phosphorylation of regulatory proteins that control the steroidogenic enzymes involved in androgen biosynthesis. Gonadotropin concentrations in the range that produce a graded testosterone response are accompanied by a simultaneous increase of all cAMP pools (intracellular, extracellular, and bound) (30, 31). Very small increases in hormone-stimulated endogenous cAMP bound to the intracellular receptor protein are sufficient to cause activation of protein kinase (99) and the subsequent cascade of protein phosphorylation in intact Leydig cells (40).

Early studies postulated a functional compartmentalization of cAMP action during hormone stimulation. This conclusion was derived from experiments in which small increases of cAMP (25%) bound to the regulatory subunit caused maximal stimulation of the testosterone response. In contrast, comparable increases brought about by choleragen were less effective in stimulating testosterone production, and maximal responses were only observed at the higher occupancy of the subunit (35). These findings indicated either a functional compartmentalization of the cAMP response to the hormone beyond the guanyl nucleotide stimulatory unit ($G_s$) or a facilitatory effect of the hormonal stimulus independent of cAMP action. Recent studies have demonstrated that LH provokes rapid increases in $IP_3$ accumulation in luteal cells (28) as a consequence (most likely) of stimulating $PIP_2$ hydrolysis.

The effect of LH on phosphoinositide metabolism in the ovary does not appear to be mediated by increases in cAMP; this finding indicates that the phosphoinositide metabolism is initiated through a LH receptor–mediated pathway independent of adenylate cyclase (28). Also, LH elicited early increases in cytosolic free $Ca^{2+}$ in luteal cells (28) and Leydig cells (87), with little participation of cyclic nucleotides in the former. However, in the Leydig cells, dose-related stimulatory effects of LH and cAMP on intracellular free $Ca^{2+}$ levels, which indicate that changes in intracellular $Ca^{2+}$ could be mediated by cAMP, were clearly established. The contribution of extracellular $Ca^{2+}$ on LH increase of cytosolic free $Ca^{2+}$ appears to be negligible at physiological concentrations of the hormone; the concentration is significant at supramaximal concentrations (87). Although the contribution of the LH-stimulated phosphoinositide pathway to steroidogenesis is not at all clear, metabolites from this pathway may contribute to a facilitatory or potentiation effect of the cAMP-mediated stimulus in the Leydig cell.

Forskolin increases cAMP production, presumably by its action on the catalytic subunit of adenylate cyclase, (82) and consequently elevates testosterone responses in Leydig cells (58). This is observed at concentrations of 1–10 $\mu$M; lower concentrations (a narrow range around $10^{-7}$ M) have no effect per se, but potentiate the LH/hCG-induced cAMP and testosterone responses. These effects are believed to occur through a high affinity site on the catalytic subunit of adenylate cyclase and through consequent facilitation of interaction with the $G_s$ subunit (82). Forskolin-induced increases in cAMP-bound were less effective than those elicited by hCG in stimulating steroidogenesis in presence of comparable increases on cAMP bound to the regulatory subunit of protein kinase by $10^{-6}$M forskolin. These results could indicate a facilitatory effect of the hormone independent of cAMP action; alternatively forskolin at $10^{-6}$–$10^{-5}$ M concentration could have an inhibitory component in its action at a site distal to cAMP generation.

In addition to the known potentiation effects of forskolin, dose-dependent inhibitory effects of forskolin ($ID_{50}$, $10^{-12}$ M) on basal and hCG-stimulated cAMP pools and testosterone production were demonstrated (58). Maximal inhibition was attained at $10^{-11}$ M and was maintained with concentrations up to $10^{-9}$. This effect of forskolin affected the hormonal stimulus over the dose-range of hCG stimulation, and there was a two-fold decrease in the sensitivity for the hormonal response on cAMP. The observed inhibition of cAMP pools and testosterone production was largely prevented by pertussis toxin and was reversed by addition of 8-bromo-cAMP. Furthermore, forskolin significantly decreased the activity of GTP, LH, and GTP-stimulated adenylate cyclase; this inhibition was also prevented by pertussis toxin. Thus, the reduction of cAMP levels are attributable to the inhibition of adenylate cyclase in the plasma membrane (58).

Seamon et al (82) demonstrated the presence of two binding sites through studies of [$^3$H]forskolin in rat brain membranes: a high affinity site ($K_d = 15$ nM) related to the hormonal potentiation of forskolin action and low affinity site ($K_d = 1.1$ $\mu$M) related to the direct actions of forskolin. Furthermore, the functional studies on Leydig cells (58) have suggested that forskolin has an additional higher-affinity site of action ($K_d \sim$ pM) (of location yet to be determined) that favors the interaction of the catalytic subunit and the Gi-$\alpha$ subunit, or the dissociation of the $\beta\gamma$-subunits of Gi with consequent inhibition of the Gs $\alpha$-subunit.

The above findings are of special interest since inhibitory hormones are thought to negatively modulate the gonadotropin stimulatory actions in the Leydig cell. Early studies have indicated arginine-vasotocin inhibited the steroidogenic effect of hCG in vitro on cultured Leydig cells from hypophysectomized adult rats (1). Recent studies have demonstrated the presence of functional angiotensin II (AII) receptors of high affinity ($K_a = 1.7 \times 10^{-10}M^{-1}$) and low capacity (2000 sites per cell) (57). AII inhibits GTP- and LH-stimulated adenylate cyclase in Leydig cell membranes. This hormone also acutely inhibits (as early as .25–1 h) gonadotropin stimulation of cAMP pools and testosterone production in purified Leydig cells incubated in suspension. These effects were prevented by incubation with pertussis toxin and reversed by 8-bromo-cAMP additions, which indicates that the nucleotide inhibitory unit mainly mediates the inhibitory effect of AII and modulates LH stimulation of the Leydig cell (57).

A number of studies have provided evidence for the presence of a renin-angiotensin system in reproductive tissues. Immunoreactive renin has been detected in Leydig cells of rat and human testes and has been found to be pituitary-dependent in rat (65, 71). Similarly, more recent studies have shown the presence of renin and angiotensin I and II in normal rat Leydig cells and a murine Leydig cell line (70). Furthermore, angiotensin-converting enzyme activity was demonstrated in rat testis and shown to be localized predominantly in the germinal cells, while only minor activity was found in the purified adult rat Leydig and Sertoli cells (95). Also, [³H]captopril bound specifically to cellular fractions enriched in germinal cells (95). The biochemical evidence is consistent with findings from immunofluorescence studies on swine testis (100) showing the presence of converting enzyme in spermatids and other stages of germinal cells. Because of the predominant localization of angiotensin-converting enzyme in the testicular tubular elements, it is likely that AII possesses a physiological paracrine regulatory function, and the locally-produced hormone also could effectively exert an homologous negative modulatory influence on hormone-stimulated events in the Leydig cells (57, 95).

# HORMONAL CONTROL OF LEYDIG CELL FUNCTION

Testicular steroidogenesis has two active phases during development. In fetal and neonatal life androgens are actively produced by the Leydig cells. Cells become quiescent until puberty when the second active phase of testicular steroidogenesis that is maintained through the adult life begins (55, 91). In the adult cell, the ability of the Leydig cell to respond to sustained gonadotropin stimulation with increased androgen production is limited by the development of a refractory state associated with loss of the LH receptors and steroidogenic responses (18, 22, 31, 32, 35, 43, 53, 69, 93). Unlike the adult testis, the fetal (91, 92, 98) and immature (55) testis are refractory to the desensitization process.

In the adult cell, gonadotropin induces a dual control of Leydig cell function: Low doses of LH maintain receptors and steroidogenic enzymes in the up-regulated state, while higher doses of hormone cause receptor down-regulation and desensitization.

This decreased receptor-binding, or down-regulation, demonstrated in detail in vivo (31) has also been reproduced in in vitro culture of adult rat (67) and mouse Leydig cells (9) and is associated in the rat with impaired responsiveness of the target cell due to defined steroidogenic lesions (8, 18, 22, 31, 32, 35, 43, 51, 56, 67, 69, 93). Receptor up-regulation, a phenomenon in which exposure to the hormone increases the subsequent binding of the homologous ligand, has been reported for several hormones including hCG (13, 93). At least two different mechanisms appear to be involved in this positive regulation. Short-term treatment of animals or the single administration of physiological doses of LH or hCG increased the number of homologous receptors in rat Leydig cells (93). Such increases in receptor-binding capacity occurred one or two days after administration of the hormone and were sustained for several days. In contrast, administration of a single supraphysiological dose of hCG (1–10 $\mu$g) to intact animals induced a rapid and transient increase in testicular LH receptors from 3–6 h after hormone treatment. The former slow increase may result from the trophic action of the hormone, with consequent maintenance and/or stimulation of receptors. The rapid increases in LH receptors seems to be caused by exposure of a pre-synthesized pool since it is not prevented by inhibitors of protein synthesis, steroidogenesis, or microtubule and microfilament function.

The early up-regulation of LH receptors previously reported in vivo can be reproduced in vitro when the Leydig cells are attached to a solid substratum (13). hCG treatment of plated cells in culture significantly increased the number of sites measured in suspension at 2 h; at 6 h the number reached 140% of control. This up-regulation was not prevented by preincubation with inhibitors of protein synthesis, steroidogenesis, or microfilament function. This increase in binding was preceded by an early decrease (15 min) reaching 60% of control levels at 90 min. Such transient reduction of sites could be due to a rapid aggregation or cointernalization of free binding sites with a small proportion of occupied sites (13).

Recent studies in vivo have indicated that up-regulation of the receptors induced by a dose of hCG that subsequently causes loss of more than 50% receptor down-regulation is associated with major early increases (1–6 h) in extracellular, intracellular, and bound cAMP (43). However, receptors un-masked by treatment with larger concentrations of hormone do not appear to be effectively coupled to cAMP production, possibly because of the desensitization of adenylate cyclase components (43). It is clear that in vivo such desensitization of adenylate cyclase occurs in Leydig cell membranes within 6–12 h of hCG treatment (43). It is of particular interest that this decrease in enzyme responsiveness was accompanied by a prominent fall in LH-induced stimulation of nucleotide-binding capacity. However, it is not yet clear whether an early desensitization of adenylate cyclase in vivo accounts for the lack of increased cAMP responses during the early up-regulation caused by high hCG treatment dose.

Cultured mouse tumor Leydig cells (77) exhibited a 50% loss in hCG-stimulated adenylate cyclase activity in membranes after 30 min exposure to hCG although the receptor number remained near control levels (77). As in the case of the trophic hormone, exposure of the cells to active phorbol esters and diacylglycerol also causes desensitization of the hCG response, and was similar to homologous hormone desensitization in this system. The findings suggest covergence of the individual functional pathways (77).

Gonadotropin-induced steroidogenic lesions in the adult rat include reduced conversion of progesterone to androgen "late lesion" leading to decreased testosterone response to gonadotropin stimulation in vitro. In addition, with supramaximal doses of hCG an additional "early lesion" is also observed at the level of conversion of cholesterol to pregnenolone and leads to decreased in vitro pregnenolone and testosterone response to hCG (8, 18, 31, 35, 43, 51, 53, 69). Both lesions were initially recognized after in vivo treatment of adult rats with a single subcutaneous low (2.5 $\mu$g) and high dose (10 $\mu$g) of hCG respectively (18, 31, 32, 35, 43, 53, 69), and subsequently were reproduced after in vitro treatment of Leydig cells in short-term culture (67).

An early step in the mechanism by which LH stimulates steroid synthesis in the testis is believed to involve increased transport of cholesterol to the inner mitochondrial membrane in order to gain accesibility to the side-chain cleavage enzyme (49, 85, 88). This transport process requires calmodulin and $Ca^{2+}$; it has been suggested that calmodulin could influence the function of actin, which according to early studies includes the intracellular transport of cholesterol to the mitochondria (48–50). The relative importance of intracellular cholesterol synthesis and circulating lipoprotein cholesterol in the biosynthesis of adrenal and gonadal steroid hormone was initially investigated by Anderson & Dietschy (4) who treated rats with 4-amino-pyrazolo-pyrimidine (4-APP) in order to reduce plasma cholesterol concentrations to a level where impairment of steroid hormone secretion is manifested. During treatment, the rate of endogenous sterol synthesis was increased markedly in the adrenal gland (42-fold), but to a much smaller degree in the ovary (2.7-fold), and was unchanged in the testis. Because gonadotropin-stimulated sterol synthesis in the ovaries and testis of 4-APP-treated rats and infusion of high density lipoprotein suppressed these changes, the availability of lipoprotein cholesterol, rather than newly-synthesized cholesterol, was proposed as a major factor for biosynthesis of steroid hormones in the gonads of the rat, as well as in the adrenal gland (4). Although this conclusion appeared to be valid for the adrenal and probably also for the corpus luteum of the ovary, this seems not to be the case for the Leydig cell. Subsequent findings have demonstrated that testicular HMG-CoA reductase, in contrast to the adrenal enzyme, is not regulated by changes in circulating cholesterol (20). The ability of Leydig cells from 4-APP-treated animals to continue androgen biosynthesis in vivo and in vitro indicated that these cells possess an active steroidogenic pathway from precursors prior to cholesterol and that the marked fall in circulating testosterone in 4-APP-treated animals was largely attributable to decreased LH secretion (20). This drug apparently has an selective inhibitory action on the synthesis and/or release of GnRH with consequent decrease in GnRH receptors (20).

The diminished production of pregnenolone early lesion during desensitization is only minimally related to a reduced activity of HMG-CoA reductase and is not related to inhibition of other enzymes in the pathway from mevalonate to cholesterol (20). Furthermore, the cholesterol content of the Leydig cell inner mitochondria membrane was even higher (by 100%) in desensitized animals with early lesion than in control animals (8). The early lesion appears to be caused by an hCG-regulated, mitochondrial inhibitory protein present in the normal Leydig cell (Stokes radius = 4.8 mm and PI 5.5) that is markedly increased by hCG and is probably located at the inner mitochondrial membrane where it influences electron transport among one or more components of the side-chain cleavage enzyme (51). This inhibitory substance that competitively modulates the activity of cholesterol side-chain cleavage enzyme appears to contribute to the early steroidogenic lesion and to serve as an endogenous modulator of steroid hormone biosynthesis.

It has been shown that steroidogenesis in the rat Leydig cell and corpus luteum is influenced by LH at three levels, namely hydrolysis of cholesterol esters, transport of cholesterol to the inner mitochondrial membrane to increase the steroidogenic cholesterol pool, and the direct activation of the cholesterol side-chain cleavage enzyme system. In a recent in vitro study, aminoglutethimide promoted the accumulation of metabolically available cholesterol in isolated Leydig cells even in the absence of exogenous gonadotropins. This finding suggests that the transport of cholesterol to the inner mitochondrial membrane, which leads to the synthesis of basal steroid levels, takes place irrespective of the presence of the gonadotropic stimulus (8). Thus, it appears that there is a continuous supply of steroidogenic cholesterol in the Leydig cell mitochondrion regardless of the presence of gonadotropin, a process probably regulated by the levels of endogenous steroids.

The accumulation of cholesterol in the absence of gonadotropin could be attributable to the aminoglutethimide-induced suppression of biosynthetic products (including testosterone), which were shown to exert a pronounced influence on the rate of side-chain cleavage activity. These substances may participate in a short feedback mechanism that controls the metabolic pool of cholesterol in the mitochondrion. Although it is conceivable that the hormonal stimulus would increase the rate of cholesterol transport, it is likely that the most critical steps in the tropic action of LH and hCG lie beyond the transport of cholesterol to the side-chain cleavage enzyme system. The tropic hormone could then stimulate transport and subsequent steps [i.e. induction and/or activation of cholesterol side-chain cleavage (3), microsomal cytochrome P-450 (37)], evoking the five to ten fold increase in the production of pregnenolone and testosterone observed during acute in vitro stimulation with gonadotropin.

The late steroidogenic lesion of the microsomal enzymes $17\alpha$-hydroxylase 17,20-desmolase in the adult rat Leydig cells caused by gonadotropin is estrogen mediated (22, 67–69) and can be prevented by inhibitors of aromatase activity (5, 8) and by the estrogen antagonist tamoxifen (22, 67, 68). This inhibition is preceded by a cAMP-mediated activation of aromatase activity (89, 90), with consequent increased estrogen production, nuclear translocation of estrogen receptors (68, 69), and activation of RNA polymerase (5, 8) and is followed by increased synthesis of an estrogen-regulated protein of $M_r$ 27,000 (23, 24, 67). These events preceded the reduction of microsomal cytochrome P-450 and the decrease of $17\alpha$-hydroxylase and 17,20-desmolase activities, with consequent reduction of testosterone stimulation by hCG in vitro and consequent accumulation of progesterone and $17\alpha$-OH progesterone (Figs. 1 and 2). The acute activation of aromatase activity observed during the early phase of both in vivo and in vitro hCG treatment was accompanied by a significant increase in estrogen formation (22, 69, 89, 90). 8-Bromo cAMP and forskolin induced a significant increase in aromatase activity within 30 min, which suggested that the acute enzyme activation is mediated through cAMP action (90). In vitro experiments have demonstrated that after an initial increase in estradiol ($E_2$) production at 30 min, levels remained constant until 2 h, when a sharp rise parallel to that of testosterone was observed. This biphasic pattern suggested the involvement of a least two factors: enzyme activation and substrate availability (90). The early activation of aromatase induces a significant small and possibly compartmentalized initial increase in the estradiol level that triggers the chain of events leading to estrogen-mediated Leydig cell desensitization. The subsequent large increase in testosterone level is probably responsible for the secondary rise in the estradiol level observed between 2–4 h after hCG treatment since this rise parallels that of testosterone even when aromatase activity remains at control levels. This secondary increase in $E_2$ presumably further sustains the desensitization process.

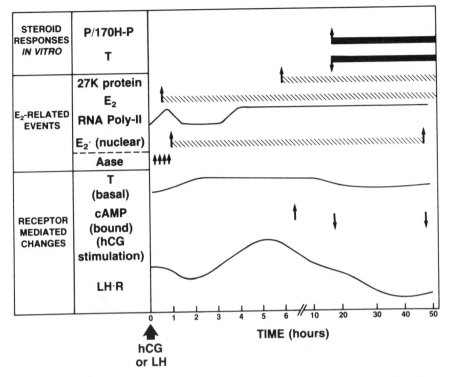

*Figure 1*   Time sequence of receptor down-regulation and densensitization of the Leydig cell distal steroidogenic pathway (late lesion) in the adult rat.

Gonadotropin treatment with 2.5 $\mu$g hCG caused initial decrease of LH receptors, followed by up-regulation (3–6 h) and subsequent down-regulation of receptors ($\sim$ 50–60% decrease). cAMP production by cells stimulated with hCG in vitro is increased or decrease concurrent with up- and down-regulation of receptors. Testosterone basal levels are not changed or slightly increased. Gonadotropin- and cAMP-mediated early increase of aromatase activity leads to an initial small increase in $E_2$ production. Major $E_2$ increases are subsequently observed with increased substrate availability (testosterone). $E_2$, through nuclear actions ($E_2$ nuclear receptor translocation, activation of RNA polymerase II activity), caused increase of 27,000 $M_r$ protein (6 h), reduction of cytochrome P-450, 17$\alpha$-hydroxylase, 17,20-desmolase, and of testosterone production with increases in progesterone and 17$\alpha$-OH progesterone (8–24 h).

P = progesterone; 170H-P: 17$\alpha$-hydroxyprogesterone; T = testosterone; 27K = $E_2$-induced protein $M_r$ = 27,000; Aase = aromatase; cAMP bound to regulatory subunit of protein kinase; LH = luteinizing hormone, R = receptor; $\uparrow$ increase; $\downarrow$ decrease.

The above findings of an $E_2$-mediated desensitization of microsomal enzymes by gonadotropin treatment (late lesion) and an additional estrogen-independent early lesion (with reduced conversion of cholesterol to pregnenolone) at higher gonadotropin doses differ from two other proposed mechanisms of desensitization in the testis (74, 75). An early study in the rat

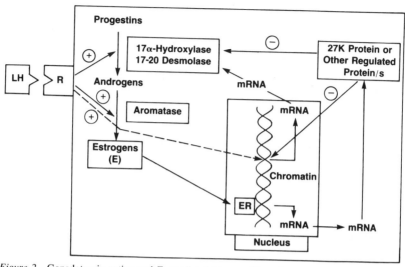

*Figure 2*  Gonadotropin action and $E_2$-mediated late steroidogenic lesion. Gonadotropin supports cytochrome P-450 17α-hydroxylase 17,20-demolase and also causes negative regulation of this enzyme through nuclear actions of estradiol.

suggested that gonadotropin-induced steroidogenic desensitization could be completely reversed by high density lipoprotein (HDL) (75), whereas more recent studies in the mouse attributed the decrease in microsomal P-450 enzyme activities (17α-hydroxylase/17,20-desmolase) to direct or indirect inactivation of P-450 by reactive oxygen-free radicals derived from breakdown of the interaction of pseudosubstrate (testosterone) with P-450 in the presence of oxygen (P-450-pseudosubstrate-oxygen complex) (74). However, in the latter study, the low oxygen tension (1% vs 19% $O_2$) reported to prevent the densensitization of enzyme activities induced by gonadotropin treatment was ineffective in preventing the marked reduction of testosterone responses to hCG in vitro (74). These studies are difficult to interpret for the following reasons. First, reversal by HDL was not confirmed in a subsequent study (51), but in any case the lipoprotein would not be expected to correct the late lesion (17α-hydroxylase/17,20-desmolase). Consequently any reversal by HDL of the inhibition of steroidogenesis should be partial rather than complete as reported. Second, in regard to the latter study (74) indicating that the lesion is microsomal, which contradicts the earlier study by the same group (75), prevention of inactivation of cytochrome P-450 by antioxidants and/or low $O_2$ tension should also reverse the inhibition of androgen responses to hCG in vitro, which is not the case. It is possible that the latter findings are confined to the cultured mouse Leydig cell and are not operative in vivo either in the mouse or rat testis (72).

Fetal Leydig cells appear in the testis during the final third of gestation and decline during the first 10–15 days after birth; the adult Leydig cell generation gradually begins to increase at this time. Electron micrographic analysis of the freshly prepared fetal testicular fractions after centrifugal elutriation has demonstrated the existence of two types of Leydig cells in the fetal testis, a transitional Leydig cell and a fetal Leydig cell (see also above) (91). The transitional Leydig cell morphology resembled a new cell type recently found in the 15-day old rat testis, where the presence of a predominant population (about 90%) of transitional cells and only a small proportion of adultlike Leydig cells (4–5%) were reported. These transitional fetal cells, unlike the transitional cell of immature animals, displayed an adultlike steroidogenic function, such as the induction of a gonadotropin-induced steroidogenic lesion associated with the $E_2$-mediated action. The inability of the fetal cells and cells from immature animals to be desensitized by gonadotropin, a characteristic of the adult cell, is attributed to low aromatase activity with undetectable $E_2$ production, low levels of estrogen receptors, and a minimally detectable level of an $E_2$-induced protein (89, 92). Aromatase activity is barely detectable in fetal life and early post-natal life although it increases with age. In contrast, aromatase is high in Sertoli cells during fetal and early post-natal life (89). The highest levels of aromatase activity were found in the adult rat Leydig cells and transitional cells of the fetal testis (89, 91, 92).

The fetal Leydig cells contain one-tenth of the amount of estrogen receptor found in the adult rat Leydig cell (91, 92). A similar high affinity estrogen receptor ($K_a = 0.5 \times 10^9 \ M^{-1}$) is also present from fetal to adult Leydig life (91, 92); comparable results were observed for both $E_2$ and moxestrol used as the ligand (91, 92). $E_2$ treatment of functional fetal Leydig cell cultures maintained with LH additions (1 $\mu$g) every third day caused up-regulation of $E_2$ receptor, an increase in the $E_2$-regulated protein, induction of a steroidogenic lesion at the microsomal level, and finally a decrease in androgen production (92). This estrogen-mediated enzyme inhibition resembled that observed in the gonadotropin-desensitized adult Leydig cell. Also, estrogen receptor content, which was very low in control fetal Leydig cells, was significantly elevated in cell cultures treated with daily doses of LH (1 $\mu$g) or high doses (5 $\mu$g) every third day. Also, aromatase activity was stimulated up to 160% by hCG after daily doses of LH (1 $\mu$g) or high doses (5 $\mu$g) every third day. However, these fetal cells [treated with LH (1 $\mu$g) daily or high doses (5 $\mu$g) every 3 days] were unresponsive to acute hCG stimulation (91). The induction of aromatase activity, presumably with increased estradiol production, caused the observed up-regulation of estrogen receptor and the impaired activity of microsomal enzymes 17$\alpha$-hydroxylase/17,20-desmolase, with reduction of testosterone production in the fetal Leydig cell treated daily and/or higher doses of LH. Thus, treatment of fetal Leydig cell cultures with multiple or frequent high doses of LH (5 $\mu$g) but not with a low dose of LH (1 $\mu$g every three days) elevated aromatase activity to necessary levels for desensitization (91).

Immunocytochemical studies have demonstrated the induction of an estrogen-regulated protein after exogenous $E_2$ treatment following the concurrent activation of estrogen receptor and the induction of the steroidogenic lesion in the fetal cultured cells (92). Although there is no evidence that this estrogen-regulated protein is involved in the process of desensitization, the 27,000 $M_r$ protein provides a sensitive index of receptor-mediated estrogen action. The $E_2$-mediated desensitization process could involve the 27,000 $M_r$ estradiol-induced protein or an as yet unidentified regulatory protein. This protein could participate in the inhibition of transcription of cytochrome P-450, dependent 17$\alpha$-hydroxylase, 17,20-desmolase, or inhibit directly this enzyme system or its translation. Furthermore, a direct involvement of $E_2$ on gene transcription of microsomal P-450 and related enzymes should also be considered (Fig. 2).

## PARACRINE AND AUTOCRINE EFFECTS ON LEYDIG CELL FUNCTION

Testicular GnRH-like activity has been suggested to be a secretory product of Sertoli cells and to exert a paracine effect on Leydig cells (84). Although, the levels of this peptide in the circulation are below the limit of detection of the present methods and the testicular content of GnRH-like activity was estimated to be less of 15 pg per rat testis, it is conceivable that testicular GnRH could exert a modulatory influence on Leydig cell function in the rat.

There is now a general recognition of the existence of GnRH receptor sites in the Leydig cells of the rat testis (25, 74). The physiological significance of the presence of these receptors in the rat is still unclear since the receptor and direct actions of GnRH have not been readily demonstrable in the human and mouse testes. Studies of the binding of an $^{125}$I-GnRH-analog to adult Leydig cells purified by centrifugal elutriation showed a single class of binding sites with a $K_a = 2.4 \times 10^9$ M$^{-1}$ and a binding capacity of 3000 sites per cell (10, 37).

GnRH and its agonist analogues caused direct inhibitory changes in testicular function via specific receptors. Such effects of GnRH on androgen production were initially demonstrated in vivo during treatment of hypophysectomized rats (25). In contrast, the acute inhibitory actions of GnRH observed in vivo in intact animals were mainly due to the late steroidogenic lesion caused by LH action in the testis (32, 33). In addition, a prolonged treatment of intact animals with the peptide profoundly reduced gonadal function by causing pituitary desensitization. In this case the direct inhibitory effects of GnRH in the gonads presumably are also present (18). Some of the direct early effects of GnRH in the testis have been demonstrated in acute culture of adult Leydig cells (56, 84). These have mainly been stimulatory since the inhibitory effects are not readily demonstrable during short-term incubations (56, 83, 84); however, inhibitory effects have been observed in cultured fetal Leydig cells (37) and cultures of interstitial cells from hypophysectomized animals (54).

The cited GnRH acute stimulatory action (56, 84) was associated with increased phospholipid turnover and does not appear to be mediated by prostaglandins (27). The GnRH agonist–stimulated steroidogenesis is inhibited, like that of LH, by lipoxygenase inhibitors (27). However, this apparent action of the peptide could be due to a nonspecific effect of the inhibitors on Leydig cell metabolic processes. Other studies have suggested that arachidonic acid may be important in mediating the direct stimulatory effects of GnRH on Leydig steroidogenesis while its metabolism would not be required for this action (61).

GnRH receptors were not detectable in homogenates of acutely excised 20.5 day fetal testes or in freshly prepared fetal Leydig cells (20.5 day), but they are detectable from 3 days to 70 days of culture. These receptors were also readily detectable postnatally in the testes of 5-day old rats and increased markedly during maturation at 30–40 days (37, 42). These receptors were increased by GnRH treatment of fetal Leydig cell cultures and were negatively modulated by gonadotropin (37). These in vitro effects are consistent with the in vivo regulation of gonadal GnRH receptors, since GnRH and its agonist analogs increase GnRH receptors in testicular interstitial tissue and pituitary gonadotropin reduces the testicular content of GnRH receptors. Also, pituitary gonadotropin reduced, while hypophysectomy increased, the testicular content of GnRH receptors (16).

GnRH agonist treatment of fetal cultures inhibited LH-dependent steroid production in a dose-dependent fashion and abolished the acute testosterone response to hCG (37). This was observed as early as 12 hours after treatment and was markedly enhanced at 3–4 days. The major component of the steroid inhibitory effect of the GnRH agonist occurs beyond cAMP production. A distal lesion in the microsomal enzymes ($17\alpha$-hydroxylase, 17,20-desmolase) of the androgen pathway is largely responsible for the GnRH-induced decreases in LH-supported androgen production (37). Also, GnRH has a marked inhibitory effect on $17\beta$-hydroxysteroid dehydrogenase as shown by the profound inhibition of the conversion of androstenedione to testosterone. The steroidogenic lesion observed during GnRH action shared some features with the lesion observed during trophic hormone desensitization (37).

The presence of functional GnRH receptors and inhibitory actions of GnRH on cultured fetal and neonatal Leydig cells indicate that GnRH-related peptides can influence the actions of gonadotropins on the fetal Leydig cell population (37). It is likely that maternal GnRH contained in the milk as well as the low endogenous LH levels (near undetectable by conventional radioimmunoassay and bioassay) could be responsible for the quiescent state of the postnatal fetal Leydig cell population. This is in marked contrast to the highly active state of the Leydig cell during late fetal life. Also, GnRH could exert modulatory actions on the transition from the fetal Leydig cell population to the adult population at 15–30 days of age.

Most recently there is increasing evidence for the existence of a number of other protein factors from the tubules that can modulate the function of Leydig cells. Verhoeven and Cailleau have demonstrated that spent media derived from Sertoli cell-enriched cultures contain a protein that stimulates androgen production in adult and immature Leydig cells. The production of this factor is enhanced by cAMP derivatives, FSH, L-isoproterenol and glucagon. The active substance is a termolabile trypsin-sensitive protein with $M_r > 10,000$ (96). Transforming growth factor $\beta$- (TGF$\beta$) like activity is also released in Sertoli cell–conditioned media. This active factor, as well as TGF$\beta$, exerts a biphasic regulatory effect on Leydig cell androgen production through specific TGF$\beta$ receptors (15). Inhibin, whose $\beta$-subunit gene displays homology with TGF-$\beta$ and mullerian duct inhibitin substance, is secreted by cultured Sertoli cells (81). Recent studies have demonstrated that the heterodimer and homodimer of inhibin enhance and inhibit respectively the LH stimulation of androgen production by cultured testicular cells (52).

The presence of functional AII receptors have been demonstrated in the Leydig cells (57). The same studies provided evidence for its acute inhibitory effect of basal and hormone stimulated responses which include inhibition of adenylate cyclase, cAMP generation, and steroid production. These studies also suggest that tubular and locally produced AII could negatively modulate LH stimulation of Leydig cells (57) (see above). Epidermal growth factor (EGF) receptors have been identified in the Leydig cells, and treatment of mouse tumor cultures with murine EGF caused down-regulation of hCG receptors. This receptor decrease mediated the observed reduction of the maximal progesterone response and decreased sensitivity of the cells to the hormonal stimulus (10). More recently an additional early cAMP-independent stimulatory action of EGF on steroidogenesis has been described (10, 97).

The presence of oxytocin has been demonstrated in the testes of several species (47), and oxytocin was found to increase the spontaneous contractile movements of the seminiferous tubules in vitro. Treatment of animals with ethylene-dimethane sulphonate, an agent that destroys the Leydig cell population of the testis, was accompanied by marked reduction in the spontaneous contractile activity of the seminiferons tubules in vitro. Such tubular movements were restored by addition of oxytocin to the incubation medium (66).

Increasing evidence indicates that a line of communication between interstitial and seminiferous elements of the testis may operate through opioid peptides (i.e. $\beta$-endorphin, dynorphin). Immunohistochemical studies have indicated that $\beta$-endorphin is present in the Leydig cells of fetal, neonatal, and adult mice, and hamsters (14). In vivo experiments suggest that hCG and/or testosterone may increase the synthesis and release of the peptide from the Leydig cell compartment (94). Recent studies using fetal Leydig cell cultures have demonstrated that Leydig cells are a site of $\beta$-endorphin synthesis in vitro and that testicular $\beta$-endorphin is under direct control of gonadotropins (59). Acute stimulation of Leydig cells by hCG can markedly enhance $\beta$-endorphin secretion. These changes are not mediated by testosterone. In contrast, testosterone or its metabolites may exert a negative autocrine modulation of $\beta$-endorphin production since inhibition of steroid biosynthesis markedly increased basal and hCG-stimulated $\beta$-endorphin output (by 100–200%). In addition, $\beta$-endorphin did not affect testosterone production, and opiate binding was not detected on Leydig cells (59). Also, corticotropin releasing factor, recently indentified in the Leydig cell (12), may contribute to the regulation of $\beta$-endorphin production. Since functional $\beta$-endorphin receptors and opioid inhibition of FSH stimulated androgen binding protein (ABP) production were demonstrated in Sertoli cells (45), the $\beta$-endorphin produced in the Leydig cell may have paracrine effects that contribute to the quiescent state of the testis from early life to sexual maturation. It could also be involved in the modulation of tubule function during adult life.

## SUMMARY

Activation and regulation of Leydig cell function is exerted primarily by LH, which is secreted in pulses of high biological activity and interacts with membrane receptors. Other hormones and factors secreted by the Leydig cell or from the tubular compartment can influence Leydig cell differentiation and acute or chronic actions of LH on steroidogenesis. Conversely, hormones produced in the Leydig cell could modulate tubular function (e.g. $\beta$-endorphin, oxcytocin). The LH receptor has been purified to homogeneity in sufficient quantities to allow its peptide sequence to be determined and its gene structure to be elucidated as well as functional reconstitution studies to be performed. The LH receptor subunit of $M_r$ 90,000 can be phosphorylated by cAMP-dependent protein kinase. The native receptor appears to exist in the membrane as a dimer of identical subunits associated by noncovalent interactions. It is likely that receptor dimerization and further aggregation are necessary for signal transduction to occur, and receptor phosphorylation by one or more kinases may be involved in regulating gonadotropin action.

Stimulation of the androgen pathway occurs mainly through a cAMP-mediated mechanism. The stimulatory event can be negatively influenced by the action of certain peptide hormones through the guanyl nucleotide inhibitory subunit of adenylate cyclase. Such an inhibitory action of angiotensin has further emphasized the importance of the cAMP pathway in the Leydig cell. The hormone also appears to facilitate androgen production by a cAMP-independent mechanism located at the plasma membrane or intracellular sites. A $Ca^{2+}$ sensitive kinase system is present in the Leydig cell membranes. The presence of nM amounts of $Ca^{2+}$ induces membrane phosphorylation of a protein $M_r$ 45,000. Adenylate cyclase activation also is affected by $Ca^{2+}$. Membrane phosphorylation may be a modifier of LH-stimulated adenylate cyclase activity and possibly other LH-induced actions in the activated Leydig cell membrane.

In the adult rat testis, the ability of Leydig cells to respond to sustained gonadotropic stimulation with increased androgen production is limited by the development of a refractory state associated with loss of LH receptors and steroidogenic enzymes. Gonadotropin-induced steroidogenic lesions in adult rat testes include a late steroidogenic lesion at the site of conversion of progesterone to androgen and an early lesion before pregnenolone formation that leads to a decreased in vitro pregnenolone and testosterone response to hCG. The early lesion appears to be caused by an hCG-regulated mitochondrial protein, probably located at the inner mitochondrial membrane where it can influence electron transport among one or more components of the side-chain cleavage enzyme. The late steroidogenic lesion of microsomal enzymes 17α-hydroxylase and 17,20-desmolase in the adult Leydig cell caused by gonadotropin is estrogen mediated. Gonadotropin activates the androgen pathway with increased testosterone production. Furthermore, early cAMP activation of aromatase activity followed by increased substrate availability increases $E_2$ production. A short loop feed-back control of the androgen pathway is exerted via the nuclear actions of estrogen. Unlike the adult Leydig cell, the fetal and immature Leydig cells are refractory to this desensitizing process and maintains up-regulated LH receptors and steroidogenic function; their resistance to desensitization by gonadotropin is attributed to the absence of an estrogen-mediated regulation of the androgen pathway. The fetal testis possess, in addition to the predominant fetal Leydig cell population, a small population of transitional cells with functional capacities of the adult cell. After appropriate treatment of fetal Leydig cultures (i.e. estrogen and frequent or high gonadotropin doses), a functional adultlike cell type emerges from the fetal Leydig cell population.

The cultured fetal Leydig cell system provides a useful model to elucidate LH and GnRH action, β-endorphin regulation, and the biochemical steps involved in the development of gonadotropin-induced estradiol-mediated desensitization of steroidogenesis.

## 504    DUFAU

## Literature Cited

1. Adashi, E. Y., Hsueh, A. J. W. 1981. Autoregulation of androgen production biosynthesis by organic-vasopressin. *Endocrinology* 109:1793–95
2. Amsterdam, A., Naor, Z., Knecht, M., Dufau, M. L., Catt, K. J. 1981. Hormone action and receptor redistribution in endocrine target cells: Gonadotropin and gonadotropin-releasing hormone. In *Receptor Mediated Binding and Internalization of Toxins and Hormones*, ed. J. L. Middlebrook, L. D. Kohn, pp. 61–105. New York: Academic
3. Anderson, C. M., Mendelson, C. R. 1984. Regulation of the synthesis of cholesterol side-chain cleavage cytochrome P-450 and adrenodoxin in rat Leydig cells in culture. In *Hormone Action and Testicular Function*. ed. K. J. Catt, M. L. Dufau, pp. 259–68. New York Acad. Sci.
4. Andersen, J. M., Dietschy, J. M. 1978. Relative importance of high and low density lipoproteins in the regulation of cholesterol synthesis with adrenal gland, ovary, and testis of the rat. *J. Biol. Chem.* 253:9024–32
5. Aquilano, D. R., Dufau, M. L. 1983. Changes in RNA-polymerase activities in gonadotropin treated Leydig cells: An estradiol mediated process. *Endocrinology* 113:94–103
6. Aquilano, D. R., Dufau, M. L. 1984. Functional and morphological study on isolated Leydig cells: purification by centrifugal elutriation and metrizamide fractionation. *Endocrinology* 114:499–510
7. Aquilano, D. R., Dufau, M. L. 1984. Studies on Leydig cell purification. In *Hormone Action and Testicular Function*, ed. K. J. Catt, M. L. Dufau, 438:237–57. New York Acad. Sci.
8. Aquilano, D. R., Tsai-Morris, C.-H., Hattori, M., Dufau, M. L. 1985. Mitochondrial cholesterol availability during tropic hormone-induced Leydig cell desensitization. *Endocrinology* 116:1745–54
9. Ascoli, M. 1981. Regulation of gonadotropin receptors and responses in a clonal strain of Leydig cells tumor cells by epidermal growth factor. *J. Biol. Chem.* 203:179
10. Ascoli, M., Euffa, J., Segaloff, D. L. 1987. Epidermal growth factor activates steroid biosynthesis in cultured Leydig tumor cells without affecting the levels of cAMP and potentiates the activation of steroid biosynthesis by chorionic gonadotropin and cAMP. *J. Biol. Chem.* 262:9196–203
11. Ascoli M., Segaloff, D. L. 1986. Effects of collagenase on the structure of the lutropin/choriogonadotropin receptor. *J. Biol. Chem.* 261:3807–15
12. Audhya, T., Schlesinger, D., Hutchinson, B., Brown, C., Hollander, C. S. 1987. Corticotropin-releasing factor in the testis is structurally identical. *Clin. Res.* 35:645A (Abstr.)
13. Barañao, J. L. S., Dufau, M. L. 1983. Gonadotropin-induced changes in the luteinizing hormone receptors of cultured Leydig cells. *J. Biol. Chem.* 258:7322–30
14. Bardin, C. W., Shara, C., Mather, J., Salomon, Y., Margioris, A. N. et al. 1984. Identification and possible function of pro-opiomelanocortin-derived peptides in the testis. In *Hormone Action and Testicular Function*, ed. K. J. Catt, M. L. Dufau, 28:346–64. New York Acad. Sci.
15. Benahmed, M., Morera, A. M., Chauvin, M. A., Cochet, C. 1987. Paracrine control of Leydig cell function by TGFβ like activity from Sertoli cells. *Endocrinology* 120:6 (Abstr.)
16. Bowie, G. A., Marshall, J. C. 1984. Anterior pituitary hormone regulation of testicular gonadotropin-releasing hormone receptors. *Endocrinology* 115:723–27
17. Catt, K. J., Dufau, M. L. 1973. Spare gonadotropin receptors in the rat testis. *Nat. New Biol.* 244:219–21
18. Catt, K. J., Harwood, J. P., Clayton, R. N., Davies, T. F., Chan, V. et al 1980. Regulation of peptide hormone receptors and gonadal steroidogenesis. *Recent Prog. Horm. Res.* 36:557–622
19. Chan, V., Katikinemi, M., Davies, T. F., Catt, K. J. 1981. Hormonal regulation of testicular luteinizing hormone and prolactin receptors. *Endocrinology* 108:1607–12
20. Charreau, E. H., Calvo, J. C., Nozu, K., Pignataro, O., Catt, K. J., Dufau, M. L. 1981. Hormonal modulation of 3-hydroxy-3-methylglutaryl coenzyme A reductase activity in gonadotropin-stimulated and desensitized testicular Leydig cells. *J. Biol. Chem.* 256:12719–24
21. Cigorraga, S. B., Dufau, M. L., and Catt, K. J. 1980. Regulation of luteinizing hormone receptors and steroidogenesis in gonadotropin-desensitized Leydig cells. *J. Biol. Chem.* 253:4297–4304

22. Cigorraga, S. B., Sorrell, S., Bator, J., Catt, K. J., Dufau, M. L. 1980. Estrogen dependence of a gonadotropin-induced steroidogenic lesion in rat testicular Leydig cells. *J. Clin. Invest.* 65:699–705

23. Ciocca, D., Dufau, M. L. 1984. Monoclonal antibody to MCF-7 cell line recognizes an estrogen-dependent Leydig cell protein. *Science* 226:445–46

24. Ciocca, D., Winters, C., Dufau, M. L. 1986. Expression of an estrogen-regulated protein rat testis Leydig cells. *J. Steroid Biochem.* 24:219–29

25. Clayton, R. N., Katikinemi, M., Chan, V., Dufau, M. L., and Catt, K. J. 1980. Direct inhibition of testicular function by gonadotropin-releasing hormone mediation by specific gonadotropin releasing hormone receptors in interstitial cells. *Proc. Natl. Acad. Sci. USA* 77:4459–63

26. Conn, M. P., Tsuruhara, T., Dufau, M. L. Catt, K. J. 1977. Isolation of highly purified Leydig cells. *Endocrinology* 101:639–42

27. Cooke, B. A., Dix, C. J., Habberfield, A. D., Sullivan, M. H. F. 1984. Control of steroidogenesis in Leydig cells: Role of $Ca^{2+}$ and lypoxygenase products in LH and LHRH agonist action. *Ann. NY Acad. Sci.* 438:269–82

28. Davis, J. S., Weakland, L. L., Farese, R. V., West, L. A. 1987. Luteinizing hormone increases inositol trisphosphate and cytosolic free $Ca^{2+}$ in isolated bovine luteal cells. *J. Biol. Chem.* 262:8515–21

29. Dehejia, A., Nozu, K., Catt, K. J., Dufau, M. L. 1982. Luteinizing hormone receptors and gonadotropic activation of purified rat Leydig cells. *J. Biol. Chem.* 257:13781–86

30. Dufau, M. L., Baukal, A. J., Catt, K. J. 1980. Hormone-induced guanyl nucleotide binding and activation of adenylate cyclase in the Leydig cell. *Proc. Natl. Acad. Sci. USA* 77:5837–41

31. Dufau, M. L. Catt, K. J. 1978. Gonadotropin receptors and regulation of steroidogenesis in testis and ovary. *Vitam. Horm. (NY)* 36:461–600

32. Dufau, M. L., Cigorraga, S. B., Baukal, A. J., Bator, J. M., Sorell, S. H. et al. 1979. Steroid biosynthetic lesions in gonadotropin-desensitized Leydig cells. *J. Steroid Biochem.* 11:193–99

33. Dufau, M. L., Cigorraga, S., Baukal, A. J., Sorrel, S., Bator, J. M., et al. 1979. Androgen biosynthesis in Leydig cells after testicular desensitization by luteinizing hormone-releasing hormone and human chorionic gonadotropin. *Endocrinology* 10:1314–21

34. Dufau, M. L., Hodgen, G. D., Goodman, A. L., Catt, K. J. 1977. Bioassay of circulating luteinizing hormone in the rhesus monkey: Comparison with radioimmunoassay during physiological changes. *Endocrinology* 100:1557–65

35. Dufau, M. L., Horner, K. A., Hayashi, K., Tsuruhara, T., Conn, P. M., et al. 1978. Actions of choleragen and gonadotropin in isolated Leydig cells. *J. Biol. Chem.* 253:3721–29

36. Dufau, M. L., Khanum, A., Winters, C. A., Tsai-Morris, C.-H. 1987. Multistep regulation of Leydig cell function. *J. Steroid Biochem.* 26. In press

37. Dufau, M. L., Knox, G. F. 1985. Fetal Leydig cell culture an *in vivo* system for the study of trophic hormone and GnRH receptors and actions. *J. Steroid Biochem.* 23:743–55

38. Dufau, M. L., Pock, R., Neubauer, A., Catt, K. J. 1976. *In vitro* bioassay of LH in human serum: The rat interstitial cell testosterone (RICT) assay. *J. Clin. Endocrinol. Metab.* 42:958–69

39. Dufau, M. L., Ryan, D. W., Baukal, A., and Catt, K. J. 1975. Gonadotropin receptors solubilization and purification by affinity chromatography. *J. Biol. Chem.* 250:4822–25

40. Dufau, M. L., Sorrell, S. H., Catt, K. J. 1981. Gonadotropin-induced phosphorylation of endogenous proteins in the Leydig cell. *FEBS Lett.* 131:229–34

41. Dufau, M. L., Veldhuis, J. D. 1987. Pathophysiological relationships between the biological and immunological activities of luteinizing hormone. In *Clinical Endocrinology and Metabolism: Reproductive Endocrinology,* ed. H. G. Burger, pp. 153–176. London: Tindall

42. Dufau, M. L., Warren, D. W., Knox, G. F., Loumaye, E., Castellon, M., et al. 1984. Receptors and inhibitory actions of gonadotropin-releasing hormone in the fetal Leydig cell. *J. Biol. Chem.* 259:2896–99

43. Dufau, M. L., Winters, C. A., Hattori, M., Aquilano, D., Baranao, J. L. S., et al. 1984. Hormonal regulation of androgen production by the Leydig cell. *J. Steroid Biochem.* 20:161–73

44. Ewing, L., Zirkin, B. 1983. Leydig cell structure and steroidogenic function. *Recent Prog. Horm. Res.* 29:599–635

45. Fabbri, A., Tsai-Morris, C. H., Luna, S., Fraioli, F., Dufau, M. L. 1985. Opiate receptors are present in the rat testis identification and localization in Sertoli cells. *Endocrinology* 117:2544–46

46. Freeman, D. A., Ascoli, M. 1981. Desensitization to gonadotropins in cul-

tured Leydig tumor cells involves loss of gonadotropin receptors and decreased capacity for steroidogenesis. *Proc. Natl. Acad. Sci. USA* 78:6309–13

47. Guldenaar, S. E. F., Pickering, B. T. 1985. Immunocytochemical evidence for the presence of oxytocin in rat testis. *Cell Tissue Res.* 240:485–87

48. Hall, P. H., Charponmer, C., Nakamura, M., Gabliani, G. 1979. The role of microfilaments in the response of Leydig cells to luteinizing hormone. *J. Steroid Biochem.* 11:1361–66

49. Hall, P. H., Osawa, S., Mrotek, J. 1981. The influence of calmodulin on steroid synthesis in Leydig cells from rat testis. *Endrocrinology* 109:1677–82

50. Hall, P. H., Osawa, S., Thomasson, C. L. 1981. A role for calmodulin in the regulation of steroidogenesis. *J. Cell Biol.* 90:402–7

51. Hattori, M., Aquilano, D. R., Dufau, M. L. 1984. An early steroidogenic defect in hormone-induced Leydig cell desensitization. *J. Steroid Biochem.* 21:265–77

52. Hsueh, A. J. W., Dahl, K. D., Vaughan, J., Tucker, E., Rivier, J., et al. 1987. Heterodimers and homodimers of inhibin subunits have different paracrine action in the modulation of luteinizing-hormone-stimulated androgen biosynthesis. *Proc. Natl. Acad. Sci.* 84:5082–86

53. Hsueh, A. J. W., Dufau, M. L., Catt, K. J. 1976. Regulation of luteinizing hormone receptors in testicular cells by gonadotropins. *Biochem. Biophys. Res. Comm.* 72:1145–52

54. Hsueh, A. J. W., Schaffer, J. M. 1985. Gonadotropin-releasing hormone as a paracrine hormone and neurotransmitter in extra-pituitary sites. *J. Steroid Biochem.* 25:757–64

55. Huhtaniemi, I. T., Warren, D. W., Dufau, M. L., Catt, K. J. 1984. Functional maturation of rat testis Leydig cells. In *Hormone Action and Testicular Function.* ed. K. J. Catt, M. L. Dufau, 438:263–303. New York Acad. Sci.

56. Hunter, M. G., Sullivan, M. H. F., Dix, C. J., Aldred, L. F., Cooke, B. A. 1982. Stimulation and inhibition by LHRH analogues of cultured rat Leydig cell function and lack of effect on mouse Leydig cells. *Mol. Cell. Endocrol.* 27:31–44

57. Khanum, A., Dufau, M. L. 1987. Inhibitory action of angiotensin II in rat Leydig cell. *Endocrinology* 120 (Abstr.):1022

58. Khanum, A., Dufau, M. L. 1980. Inhibitory action of forskolin on adenylate cyclase activity and cyclic AMP generation. *J. Biol. Chem.* 25:11456–59

59. Knox, G., Fabbri, A., Buzko, E. 1987. β-endorphin release from fetal Leydig cells *in vitro:* modulation by hCG and testosterone synthesis inhibitors. *Endocrinology* 120A:1026 (Abstr.)

60. Laws, A. O., Wreford, N. G. M., de Kretser, D. M. 1985. Morphological and functional characteristics of rat Leydig cells isolated on Percoll gradients: is Leydig cell heterogeneity *in vitro* an artifact? *Mol. Cell. Endocrinol.* 42:73–90

61. Lin, T. 1985. Mechanism of action of gonadotropin-releasing hormone stimulated Leydig cell steroidogenesis. The role of arachidonic acid and Ca/phospholipid dependent protein kinase. *Life Sci.* 36:1255–64

62. Mather, J. P., Saez, J. M., Haour, F. 1982. Regulation of gonadotropin receptors and steroidogenesis in cultured porcine Leydig cells. *Endocrinology* 110:933–40

63. Mendelson, C., Dufau, M. L., Catt, K. J. 1975. Gonadotropin binding and stimulation of cyclic adenosine 3'-5'-monophosphate and testosterone production in isolated Leydig cells. *J. Biol. Chem.* 250:8818–23

64. Minegishi, T., Kusuda, S., Dufau, M. L. 1987. Purification and characterization of Leydig cell luteinizing hormone receptor. *J. Biol. Chem.* 262:17138–43

65. Naruse, K., Murakoshi, M., Osamura, R. Y., Naruse, M., Toma, H., et al. 1985. Immunohistological evidence for renin in human endocrine tissues. *J. Clin. Endocrinol. Metab.* 61:172–77

66. Nicholson, H. D., Worley, R. T. S., Guldenaar, S. E. F., Pickering, B. T. 1985. Depletion of Leydig cells leads to reductions of testicular oxytocin and semicinerous tubule involvement in the rat. *Front. Neuroendocrinol. Symp., Edinburgh* (Abstr.)

67. Nozu, K., Dehejia, A., Zawistowich, L., Catt, K. J., Dufau, M. L. 1981. Gonadotropin-induced receptor regulation and steroidogenic lesions in cultured Leydig cells. Induction of specific protein synthesis by chronic gonadotropin and cultured. *J. Biol. Chem.* 256:12875–82

68. Nozu, K., Dufau, M. L., Catt, K. J. 1981. Estradiol receptor-mediated regulation of steroidogenesis in gonadotropin-desensitized Leydig cells. *J. Biol. Chem.* 256:1915–22

69. Nozu, K., Matsuura, S., Catt, K. J., Dufau, M. L. 1981. Modulation of

Leydig cell androgen biosynthesis and cytochrome P-450 levels during estrogen treatment and hCG-induced desensitization. *J. Biol. Chem.* 256:10012–17

70. Pandey, K. N., Inagami, T. 1986. Regulation of renin angiotensin by gonadotropic hormones in culture murine Leydig cell tumor cells. *J. Biol. Chem.* 261:3934–38

71. Parmentier, M., Inagami, T., Pochet, R., Desclin, J. C. 1983. Pituitary-dependent renin immunolike-immunoreactivity in the rat testis. *Endocrinology* 112:1318–23

72. Payne, A. H., Downing, J. R., Wong, K. L. 1980. Luteinizing hormone receptors and testosterone synthesis in two distinct populations of Leydig cells. *Endocrinology* 106:1424–29

73. Perrin, M. H., Vaughan, J. M., Rivier, J. E., Vale, W. W. 1980. High affinity GnRH binding to testicular membrane homogenates. *Life Sci.* 26:2251–56

74. Quinn, P. G., Payne, A.H. 1984. Oxygen-mediated damage of microsomal cytochrome P-450 enzymes in cultured Leydig cells. *J. Biol. Chem.* 259:4130–35

75. Quinn, P. G., Dombrausky, L. J., Chen, Y.-D. I., Payne, A. H. 1981. Serum lipoproteins increase testosterone production in hCG-desensitization Leydig cells. *Endocrinology* 109:1790–92

76. Rebois, R. V. 1982. Establishment of gonadotropin-responsive murine Leydig tumor cell line. *J. Cell Biol.* 94:70–76

77. Rebois, R. V., Patel, J. 1985. Phorbol esters causes desensitization of gonadotropin responsive adenylate cyclase in a murine Leydig cell turmor line. *J. Biol. Chem.* 260:8026–31

78. Rebois, R. V., Omedeo-Sale, F., Brady, R. O., Fishman, P. H. 1981. Covalent crosslinking of human chorionic gonadotropin to its receptor in rat testes. *Proc. Natl. Acad. Sci. USA* 78:2066–69

79. Saez, S. M., Benahmed, M., Reveritos, J., Bommelaer, M. C., Monbrial, C., et al. 1983. Hormonal regulation of pig Leydig cells in culture. *J. Steroid Biochem.* 19:375–84

80. Schumacher, M., Schafer, F., Holstein, A. F., Hiltz, H. 1978. Rapid isolation of mouse Leydig cells by centrifugation in Percoll gradients with complete retention of morphological and biochemical integrity. *FEBS Lett.* 91:333–38

81. Steinberger, A., Steinberger, E. 1976. *Endocrinology* 98:918–20

82. Seamon, K. B., Vaillaneourt, R., Edwards, M., Daly, J. W. 1984. Binding of [3H] forskolin to rat brain membranes. *Proc. Natl. Acad. Sci. USA* 81:5081–85

83. Sharpe, R. M., Cooper, I. 1982. Stimulatory effect of LHRH and its agonists on Leydig cell steroidogenesis *in vitro*. *Molec. Cell. Endocrol.* 26:141–50

84. Sharpe, R. M., Frazer, H. M., Cooper, I., Rommerts, F. F. G. 1981. Sertoli-Leydig cell communication via an LHRH-like factor. *Nature* 290:785–87

85. Simpson, E. R., McArthy, J. L., Peterson, J. A. 1978. Evidence that the cycloheximide-sensitive site of adrenocorticotropic hormone action is in the mitochondrion. *J. Biol. Chem.* 253:3135–39

86. Solano, A. R., Dufau, M. L., Catt, K. J. 1979. Bioassay and radioimmunoassay of serum luteinizing hormone in the male rat. *Endocrinology* 105:372–81

87. Sullivan, M. H. F., Cooke, B. A. 1986. The role of $Ca^{2+}$ by lutropin (LH), luliberin (LHRH) agonist and cyclic AMP. *Biochem. J.* 236:45–51

88. Toaff, M. E., Strauss, J. F., Flinkinger, G. L., Strattil, S. J. 1979. Relationship of cholesterol supply to luteal mitochondrial steroid synthesis. *J. Biol. Chem.* 254:3977–82

89. Tsai-Morris, C.-H., Aquilano, D., Dufau, M. L. 1985. Cellular localization of rat testicular aromatase activity during development. *Endocrinology* 116:38–46

90. Tsai-Morris, C.-H., Aquilano, D., Dufau, M. L. 1985. Gonadotropic regulation of aromatase activity in the adult rat testis. *Endocrinology* 116:31–37

91. Tsai-Morris, C.-H., Knox, G. F., Dufau, M. L. 1987. Acquisition of hormone-mediated mechanisms regulating testicular steroidogenesis during development. In *Cell Biology of the Testis and Epididymis,* ed. M.-C. Orgebin-Crist, B. Danzo. New York Acad. of Sciences. In press

92. Tsai-Morris, C.-H., Knox, G., Luna, S., Dufau, M. L. 1986. Acquisition of estradiol-mediated regulatory mechanism of steroidogenesis in cultured fetal Leydig cells. *J. Biol. Chem.* 261:3471–74

93. Tsuruhara, T., Dufau, M. L., Cigorraga, S., Catt, K. J. 1977. Hormonal regulation of testicular luteinizing hormone receptors. *J. Biol. Chem.* 252:9002–9

94. Valenca, M. M., Negro-Vilar, A. 1986. Proopiomelonocortin-derived peptides in testicular interstitial fluid: characterization and changes in secretion after human chorionic gonadotropin or luteinizing hormone-releasing hormone

analog treatment. *Endocrinology* 118: 32–35

95. Velletri, P. A., Aquilano, D. R., Bruckwick, E., Tsai-Morris, C.-H., Dufau, M. L., et al. 1985. Control and cellular localization of rat testicular angiotensinconverting enzyme. *Endocrinology* 116: 2516–22

96. Verhoeven, G., Cailleau, J. 1985. A factor in spent media from Sertoli cell-enriched cultures that stimulates steroidogenesis in Leydig cells. *Mol. Cell. Endocrol.* 40:57–68

97. Verhoeven, G., Cailleau, J. 1986. Stimulatory effects of epidermal growth factor on steroidogenesis in Leydig cells. *Mol. Cell. Endocrol.* 47:99–106

98. Warren, D. W., Dufau, M. L., Catt, K.

J. 1982. Hormonal regulation of gonadotropin receptors and steroidogenesis in cultured fetal rat testes. *Science* 218: 375–77

99. Winters, C. A., Dufau, M. L. 1984. Characterization of Leydig cell protein kinase. *FEBS Lett.* 178:73–78

100. Yotsumoto, H., Sato, S., Shibuya, M. 1984. Localization of angiotensin converting enzyme in swine sperm by immunofluorescence. *Life Sci.* 35:1257–61

101. Zipf, W. B., Wukie, J. J. 1983. Role of prolactin and growth hormone in the maintenance of normal Leydig cell function. In *Male Reproduction and Fertility,* ed. A. Negro-Vilar, pp. 65–73. New York: Raven

# CARDIOVASCULAR PHYSIOLOGY

## NEURAL REGULATION OF THE CARDIOVASCULAR SYSTEM

*Introduction,* Lynne C. Weaver and Harvey V. Sparks, Jr., *Section Editors*

The cardiovascular system is regulated by a complex balance of neural, humoral, and metabolic factors. Tonic and reflex actions of the sympathetic nervous system provide control that is crucial to cardiovascular homeostasis. Cannon (1) stated that "of the autonomic system, the symapthetic division is especially concerned with keeping the organs fit for action"; this statement aptly describes sympathetic control of cardiovascular function. Investigators have been challenged for many years in their attempts to understand the central nervous system organization underlying sympathetic control of the heart and blood vessels. The following reviews summarize recent significant gains in that understanding.

In the past few years considerable attention has focussed on a region in the medulla oblongata that has been proposed as the site of origin of resting or basal sympathetic vasoconstrictor discharge. The research is reviewed and evaluated by Calaresu and Yardley. The sympathetic control of blood vessels can be highly specific, leading to selective regulation of different vascular beds. Jänig provides a thorough comparison of distinctive responses of vasoconstrictor neurons innervating skeletal muscle, skin, and visceral organs. The degree of sympathetic influence on the heart or on a blood vessel is determined in part by the degree and pattern of firing of individual sympathetic preganglionic neurons. Such firing is affected greatly by properties of the neurons themselves, such as the type of ionic channels within their membranes. Polosa and colleagues review the properties of spinal sympathetic neurons discovered only recently because of advances in electrophysiological techniques. Although neurotransmitters released by symathetic neurons in the periphery have been known for many years, the chemicals within the central nervous system that excite or inhibit the spinal sympathetic preganglionic neurons have been a subject of controversy. McCall summarizes the recent literature on the functional role of putative neurotransmitters in regulating the discharge of spinal sympathetic neurons. Sympathetic vasomotor control in humans now can be investigated using direct microneurographic recordings of postganglionic sympathetic discharge. In the past few years, this approach has yielded a wealth of information that has been reviewed by Wallin and Fagius. The importance of an intact sympathetic nervous system to cardiovascular control is emphasized when this control is disrupted by spinal cord lesions. Mathias and Frankel describe the disordered cardiovascular control that exists in tetraplegic patients. Cardiovascular control by the sympathetic nervous system functions in unison with other physiological systems, and integration of the sympathetic system with other motor and sensory neural systems is an important consideration in overall neural control of the circulation. Feldman and Ellenberger review mechanisms by which control of cardiovascular function is coordinated centrally with control of respiration. Finally, Foreman and Blair summarize recent investigations of the central nervous system organization responsible for cardiovascular responses to pain. These topics demonstrate that advances in our understanding of cardiovascular control span from new information about channels in sympathetic neuronal membranes to direct observations of human sympathetic responses to everyday stimuli.

## Literature Cited

1. Cannon, W. D. 1929. The sympathetic division of the autonomic nervous system in relation to homeostasis. *Arch. Neurol. Psychiatry* 22:282–94

*Ann. Rev. Physiol. 1988. 50:511–24*
*Copyright © 1988 by Annual Reviews Inc. All rights reserved*

# MEDULLARY BASAL SYMPATHETIC TONE

*Franco R. Calaresu*

Department of Physiology, University of Western Ontario, London, Ontario, Canada N6A 5C1

*Christopher P. Yardley*

John P. Robarts Research Institute and Department of Physiology, University of Western Ontario, London, Ontario, Canada N6A 5K8

## Introduction

Blood is distributed to different tissues under different physiological demands by complex and often overlapping control systems that have been categorized as follows: myogenic (local), humoral (local and remote), and neural. One of the key cardiovascular variables that is maintained within a narrow range is arterial blood pressure. The commonly accepted view is that an important neural factor in the maintenance of arterial pressure within the physiological range is tonic discharge of spinal vasoconstrictor neurons, which is in turn maintained by the tonic discharge of neurons located in the medulla (medullary vasomotor tone).

While the intended purpose of this review is to summarize the findings of the last few years, one must remember that the medulla has been identified as the source of basal vasomotor tone for over 100 years (78). Although this view has remained essentially correct over this long period, it is only since the study by Guertzenstein & Silver (69), who demonstrated that severe arterial hypotension could be elicited by very small lesions in a discrete area of the ventrolateral medulla, that any significant advances have been made in identifying the location of such neurons within the medulla. In this brief review we attempt to define precisely the anatomical location and the functional characteristics of medullary neurons involved in the maintenance of

511

0066-4278/88/0315-0511$02.00

tonic discharge to spinal vasoconstrictor neurons. Because of space limitations we confine our analysis to selected recent experiments; the literature has been covered up to early 1987. Other recent reviews have considered some aspects of this topic (25, 27, 30, 37, 38, 42, 79, 124).

## Where is Vasomotor Tone Generated?

In the quest for the source of vasomotor tone we must first consider whether we are searching for one or more sites. Indeed, it has been suggested that such neurons are not localized to any particular site within the brain but are spread diffusely along the rostro-caudal extent of the neuraxis: " . . . the resting level of blood pressure would seem to be largely determined by the ordinary level of activity generated in the brainstem defence areas and relayed in the pathway in the caudal medulla" [Hilton (78)]. This conclusion was based on studies that clearly identified supramedullary regions from which electrical stimulation elicited cardiovascular responses including an increase in arterial blood pressure and differential changes in regional blood flows (77). Although the efferent pathway for this pattern of response, the defense reaction, clearly relays in the ventrolateral medulla (80, 81, 155), tonic activity from these supramedullary structures does not appear to be essential for maintaining arterial pressure at resting levels, because lesions of the efferent pathway for the defense reaction at a midbrain level do not result in a sustained fall in resting arterial pressure (1). The idea of a diffuse source of vasomotor tone, with a forebrain generator source, has very recently received some support (86), but the overwhelming body of evidence accumulated over the last few years supports the hypothesis that *tonic* vasomotor tone is generated from within a site or sites in the medulla. This now appears to be the generally accepted view (79). The precise location is still to be determined, for although many regions including the A5 region (71, 95, 117, 135, 152), the area postrema (57, 140), locus coeruleus (49, 64, 70), and the nucleus of the tractus solitarius (NTS; 14, 133, 134) have all been implicated as playing a role in regulating the cardiovascular system, they do not appear to be essential for the maintenance of basal levels of arterial pressure. Such a role is thought to be limited to comparatively small areas of the medulla. In particular, two regions, separated on a dorsoventral plane, have been suggested: the rostral ventrolateral medulla (RVLM), identified as the source by a number of investigators using a variety of terms to describe its precise location (15, 29, 32, 42, 56, 72, 79, 80, 106, 107, 124, 146), and a region in the dorsal medulla that has received little attention in comparison with the RVLM (9, 11, 60, 91).

The RVLM, initially because of the observation that direct application of pentobarbitone sodium or glycine (54, 69) to the ventral surface of the medulla caused a profound fall in arterial pressure, has been subjected to extensive investigations in recent years. For instance, localized electrical stimulation was used to locate regions within the RVLM from which increases in blood pressure could be evoked (44, 80, 125, 127). Additional studies demonstrated that relatively discrete electrolytic lesions within the RVLM reduced arterial pressure to a level seen in animals immediately after cervical spinal cord transection (14, 44, 68, 69, 80). The obvious interpretation was that neurons close to the surface of the ventrolateral medulla were responsible for organizing cardiovascular responses and generating vasomotor tone.

Almost in parallel to this initial exploration of the ventral medulla, a group searching for the source of the vasomotor component of the pressor response to cerebral ischemia (91) identified sites in the dorsal medulla that in addition to initiating the pressor response to cerebral ischemia also appeared to be maintaining arterial pressure. At the time, even though electrical stimulation and electrolytic lesions could not distinguish between the involvement of cell bodies and of fibers of passage, it was concluded that the sites in the dorsal medulla in which lesions were effective (nucleus parvocellularis, dorsal part of the nucleus gigantocellularis, and the ventromedial portion of the medial vestibular nucleus) actually contained the neurons responsible for generating the basal vasomotor tone. This hypothesis was quickly rejected following additional experiments in the rabbit (44) that showed that lesions in the dorsal medulla attenuated pressor responses elicited from stimulation of sites in the RVLM. Such findings led to the view that the dorsal medulla was not a generator of basal vasomotor tone but was merely part of a pathway mediating such tone generated from within the RVLM and coursing dorsally before projecting to the spinal cord. Subsequently, the majority of investigators directed their attention exclusively to the RVLM, as demonstrated by the wealth of literature on the RVLM in recent years. The dorsal medulla, although reemerging as a possible site generating vasomotor tone (9, 11, 60, 65), has received limited attention during this period and is therefore discussed after the RVLM. We concentrate on the experimental results that have accumulated over the last few years to support the RVLM as the site of neurons generating vasomotor tone, and on the possible role of the caudal ventrolateral medulla (CVLM) in regulating the activity of RVLM.

## Rostral Ventrolateral Medulla

Following the initial exploration of the RVLM with electrical stimulation, it was confirmed that neurons rather than fiber tracts are crucial for vasomotor tone. Microinjection of excitatory amino acids into restricted regions of the RVLM elicited dramatic increases in arterial blood pressure. Such effects have been demonstrated in the cat (56, 101, 106, 107), the rabbit (41, 42, 119), and the rat (125, 127, 146, 151). Moreover, several electrophysiological studies in these species have identified neurons within the ventrolateral medulla whose frequency of firing is modulated by baroreceptor inputs, is related to cardiac activity, and is altered by stimulation of buffer nerves. These neurons project to the spinal cord (28, 29, 35, 72, 92, 100, 102, 136, 137) and have been traced electrophysiologically to the intermediolateral column (IML; 10, 32, 33, 105) and central autonomic area (31) of the spinal cord, a region known to contain the preganglionic sympathetic neurons (48, 118). Additional support has come from neuroanatomical findings showing that neurons in the cat, the rabbit, and the rat (2, 17, 41, 53, 98, 115, 125, 126) are grouped within the regions of the RVLM from which cardiovascular responses are evoked by microinjections of excitatory amino acids, and these neurons project to the IML column of the spinal cord. Analysis of the precise anatomical locations within the RVLM reveals that the various sites, described by such terms as nucleus paragigantocellularis lateralis (PGL; 3, 28, 72, 79, 101), C1 region of the RVLM (15, 123–125), subretrofacial nucleus (SRF; 105–107), rostral ventrolateral pressor area (VLPA; 120–122, 150), are all contained in a relatively small region in the RVLM, extending from the caudal pole of the facial nucleus caudally to include the rostral third of the inferior olive. This region is limited dorsally by the nucleus ambiguus and medially by the inferior olive. It has also become apparent that these neurons are affected by the application of drugs to the "glycine sensitive" region on the ventral surface of the medulla (15, 153).

More controversial is the question whether the neurons within the general area of the RVLM described above project to and thereby control selective sympathetic outflows. Such a proposal (79) is based on the findings that when regional blood flows or sympathetic nerve discharges are recorded, microinjection of excitatory amino acids can produce selective activation (43, 101) or even changes in opposite directions such as vasodilatation in skeletal muscle and vasoconstriction in renal and mesenteric vascular beds (101). Although the muscle vasodilatation may be due to the release of catecholamines from the adrenal glands (63, 79, 101, 107), such studies do not detract from the idea that the RVLM is involved in generating vasomotor tone; they merely suggest that the organization is perhaps more complex than the simple notion that the RVLM consists entirely of neurons firing en masse to produce an equal activation of all sympathetic outflows. Additional support for this view has been provided by demonstrating that the activity of approximately one third of VLM neurons is differentially related to the discharge of postganglionic nerve pairs (12).

The electrophysiological and neuronanatomical studies reviewed above have conclusively demonstrated that neurons within the RVLM project to the sympathetic outflow in the cord and are capable of increasing blood pressure above resting levels, but they do not demonstrate that the tonic activity of such neurons maintains vasomotor tone. Such a role has, however, been demonstrated in other studies in which the activity of neurons in these areas is inhibited by the application of glycine to the surface of the ventral medulla or by microinjection of glycine into the RVLM. Both in the cat (46, 69, 80, 143) and the rat (15, 124, 127), glycine will reduce arterial pressure to that seen immediately after cervical spinal cord transection; as demonstrated in the cat, it will also abolish cardiovascular responses evoked from supramedullary sites in the hypothalamus and midbrain (46, 80). In the cat, this reduction of blood pressure by topical application of glycine to the ventral medulla is due to abolition of sympathetic vasoconstrictor nerve activity supplying the renal, splanchnic, and skeletal muscle vascular beds (46). In addition, the use of kainic acid, an amino acid that first excites and then destroys neurons (116), has also demonstrated that the activity of neurons in the RVLM is essential for maintaining arterial blood pressure above the level seen in the spinal animal. Following the application of kainic acid onto the ventral medullary surface (15, 108) or its injection into the RVLM (127, 155), a large increase in blood pressure occurs as the amino acid initially excites neurons, but then blood pressure gradually falls as the neurotoxic actions of the drug became manifest. Similarly, inactivation of neurons in this area by cooling (141) or with the neurotoxin tetrodotoxin also lowers pressure to spinal levels (66, 67, 124).

To consider the RVLM a vasomotor center, its involvement in the general regulation of the cardiovascular system must also be discussed because, to function effectively, a vasomotor center needs to be a site of convergence of major inputs from other cardiovascular regulatory regions. Indeed, the RVLM is such a site, and a number of cardiovascular responses that are initiated from other regions are known to relay in the RVLM. For example, the vasodepressor response elicited by stimulation of arterial baroreceptors has been shown to involve the RVLM as electrolytic or chemical lesions of the RVLM abolish the baroreceptor reflex (68, 108, 124). In addition, damage to the RVLM abolishes the rise in arterial pressure produced by lesions in the NTS (14). Further support for the role of the RVLM in neural control of the circulation is provided by the following demonstration: when the RVLM is lesioned either electrolytically or chemically, or when neuronal activity is inhibited by the application of glycine to the ventral surface of the medulla, one can abolish cardiovascular responses elicited by cerebral ischemia (44, 73, 75), stimulation of peripheral nerves (103, 104), carotid chemoreceptor stimulation (46, 103), and defense area stimulation (46, 80, 108, 155). Electrophysiological and neuronanatomical studies confirm that neurons in the RVLM receive inputs from the NTS (34, 128), lateral hypothalamus (35, 138), supramedullary defense areas (81, 93, 102), and buffer nerves (31, 33).

The role of the RVLM, both in generating vasomotor tone and in cardiovascular regulation, has been further elucidated by recent pharmacological investigations. The putative inhibitory neurotransmitter, gamma-aminobutyric acid (GABA), or other GABA receptor agonists lowers arterial pressure (15, 25, 55, 89, 127, 143, 146, 148, 149, 151, 154) when applied directly to the ventral medullary surface or microinjected discretely into the RVLM. Moreover, when the GABA antagonist bicuculline is delivered in a similar manner to the RVLM neurons, arterial pressure increases (15, 25, 89, 127, 147, 148, 153, 154). These results suggest the existence of a tonic inhibitory input utilizing GABA released by nerve terminals in the RVLM. Application of bicuculline also blocks the baroreceptor reflex and suggests that the same RVLM neurons are involved in baroreceptor modulation of vasomotor tone (153). This viewpoint has been refuted (110). It cannot be determined whether this effect is produced by the activation of GABAergic neurons located within the NTS or by the short local interneurons in the vicinity of the RVLM (129). The projection of GABAergic neurons from the NTS to RVLM has been questioned (114). Additionally, other inhibitory systems utilize GABA (111).

## Caudal Ventrolateral Medulla

The caudal ventrolateral medulla (CVLM) overlaps at its most rostral extent with the pressor neurons of the RVLM and contains the A1 noradrenergic cell group (4, 36, 40, 84, 126). It is a region containing cell bodies and, when activated, it elicits a fall in arterial blood pressure (20, 146, 147, 149, 151). It has been suggested that this fall is mediated by an inhibition of RVLM vasomotor neurons (66, 67, 120, 124, 149, 151). Additionally, because destruction of the CVLM elevates arterial pressure (20, 21, 50, 66, 67, 144) and because this effect can be blocked in the rat by the application of tetrodotoxin into the RVLM (66, 67, 124), it has been suggested that the neurons of the depressor region exert a tonic inhibition on the RVLM vasomotor neurons and thereby influence arterial pressure (124). The finding of groups of catecholamine containing neurons in both areas of the medulla, the C1 adrenergic neurons of the RVLM and the A1 noradrenergic neurons of the CVLM, has tempted some investigators to link the two; they hypothesize that the C1 neurons provide vasomotor tone, via their direct projection to the IML of the spinal cord, and that the activity of these neurons is inhibited by a tonic input from rostrally projecting A1 neurons of the CVLM.

The evidence in support of this hypothesis comes mainly from the laboratory of Reis and has been summarized in a recent review (124). Such a hypothesis meets with some criticisms. First, there is no reason to exclude neurons that are not adrenergic from mediating pressor responses induced by microinjections of excitatory amino acids into the RVLM. Second, it has been found that epinephrine inhibits rather than excites sympathetic preganglionic neurons in the IML (39, 74, 130). In this respect, other transmitters can be viewed as potential mediators of excitatory inputs to IML neurons in the spinal cord. These include NPY (82, 83), substance P (5, 62, 76, 88, 97, 99, 139). 5HT (62, 85, 90, 96, 109), and vasopressin (61), but at present the role of each one still has to be resolved. It is possible that no single transmitter is sufficient and that corelease of transmitter substances is required by medullary vasomotor neurons to exert excitatory influences on the IML neurons (18, 52, 79).

The pharmacological evidence for the role of A1 neurons in inhibiting vasomotor neurons in the RVLM is stronger. In the rat, local applications into RVLM of the adrenergic agonist alpha-methyl-norepinephrine ($\alpha$-MNE) or of tyramine, which releases endogenous catecholamines, produce a fall in arterial pressure (66, 67, 124). These findings suggest that the alpha adrenergic receptors in RVLM are sites at which the hypotensive agent clonidine exerts its effects (24), particularly in view of the abundance of $\alpha$2-adrenergic receptors in the region (51).

Some inconsistencies must be resolved before these hypothetical mechanisms involving the A1 and C1 areas are fully accepted. Norepinephrine itself, which according to this hypothesis should be released from the A1 terminals to inhibit the C1 neurons via activation of $\alpha$-receptors, does not have hypotensive effects when administered into RVLM of cats (22, 26). Similarly $\alpha$-MNE, a selective $\alpha$2-adrenoreceptor agonist, which should presumably act on the same receptors as clonidine (22), does not produce hypotension when administered into the RVLM of the cat (23, 25). This is in direct contrast, as reported above, to the hypotensive effects produced in the rat (66, 67, 124). The reasons for the different findings in the two species are not obvious, but for further details on the central actions of clonidine readers are referred to a recent review (25). Such findings do not detract from the fact that the CVLM is a region from which a fall in pressure can be evoked; they merely highlight some of the problems of attributing precise functions to cell groups containing the same neurotransmitters. This difficulty is compounded by the claim that the depressor area within CVLM does *not* correspond to the A1 catecholamine cell group (45) and by the anatomical findings that nonadrenergic neurons of the CVLM (112, 125) and some A1 neurons project directly to the spinal cord (87). Therefore it is possible that not all vasodepressor effects elicited from the CVLM have to be exerted through inhibition of RVLM vasomotor neurons.

## Dorsal Medulla

After an initial period when the dorsal medulla was given equal consideration with the RVLM as the source of vasomotor tone (91), this region was, perhaps prematurely, dismissed as a primary source of vasomotor tone and viewed only as a pathway mediating pressor responses from RVLM (44, 53). Recent developments have, however, returned the dorsal medulla to the limelight. By analyzing resting sympathetic nerve activity, identifying any consistent frequency components of discharge, and then searching for neuronal elements within the brainstem with a discharge locked to that of sympathetic nerve activity, Barman & Gebber (8, 59) located units in the rostral dorsal medulla with firing patterns that were correlated to sympathetic discharge. They suggested that such neurons provide an excitatory input to IML neurons. The spinal cord and forebrain were ruled out as sites of origin of the 2–6 Hz rhythm seen in sympathetic nerves under basal condition, because mid-collicular decerebration did not eliminate this rhythm in the sympathetic nerves (7) while high spinal cord transection did (58). Recently, although groups of neurons with a firing pattern that correlated with sympathetic nerve activity were found both in the RVLM (9, 12) and in the dorsal medulla (60), Barman & Gebber concluded that the dorsal medullary neurons within the lateral tegmental field generated the 2–6 Hz rhythm (9, 11). These dorsal neurons then activated those in the RVLM to generate the 2–6 cps rhythm in the sympathetic nerves. Such conclusions were based on the finding that neurons within the lateral tegmental field of the dorsal medulla did not appear to project directly to the IML (17, 60), while those in the RVLM did (10). Additionally, using spike-triggered averaging and post R-wave interval analysis to identify single neurons with spontaneous discharges temporally related to those in renal or inferior cardiac sympathetic nerves, the dorsal medullary neurons were shown to fire before those in the RVLM (9, 11).

These investigations of the dorsal medulla, although not conclusive, demonstrate that neurons in this region are spontaneously active and fire in a manner that may contribute to the genesis of basal sympathetic discharge. Additional support for this suggestion comes from the recent finding that microinjections of L-glutamate into an identical region of the dorsal medulla in the rabbit elicit profound increases in arterial pressure (65). This confirmation of the presence of cell bodies within the dorsal medulla that can increase arterial pressure is in direct contrast to the earlier conclusions (44, 53) and firmly reestablishes the dorsal medulla as a potential generator of vasomotor tone. In comparison with the RVLM, there have been comparatively few studies of the anatomical connections of the pressor region of the dorsal medulla. The few that have been done indicate that this region does not project directly to the spinal cord (17), does not receive projections from the NTS (13, 94), and does not contain catecholamine fluorescent cells (4, 16, 19, 84, 145). All these findings suggest that the dorsal medulla acts through the RVLM, although even this hypothesis has yet to be confirmed anatomically. The dorsal medulla obviously has received little attention in comparison to the RVLM, and further efforts probably will be made to investigate the roles of both areas in the generation of vasomotor tone.

## Role of the Spinal Cord in Generating Vasomotor Tone

The IML neurons in the spinal cord represent the final common pathway for any region of the brain involved in generating vasomotor tone or any pattern of sympathetic activity required for a variety of physiological functions. They have been the subject of recent reviews (6, 131, 142). In relation to the origin of vasomotor tone, the most important consideration is whether any of these IML neurons are tonically active when acutely separated from supraspinal inputs and therefore contribute directly to the generation of vasomotor tone. In the cat after transection of the spinal cord at the first cervical segment, sympathetic nerve activity is decreased in renal and cardiac nerves (113). On the other hand, in the spinal rat it has been shown that renal nerve activity almost doubles (132). In addition, Dembowsky et al (47) have shown that spinal transection in the cat reduces but does not eliminate excitatory postsynaptic potentials, which were still able to fire spinal preganglionic neurons. Although such findings illustrate that spinal preganglionic neurons (SPNs) can be spontaneously active when detached from supraspinal influences, at least in the rat, they do not indicate whether this sustained activity is contributing to vasomotor tone. In this respect, the role of the spinal cord in generating vasomotor tone independently from supraspinal regions remains unresolved, at least until the activity remaining after transection of the cord can be positively linked with the maintenance of vasomotor tone.

The most important recent contribution to the neurophysiology of inputs to spinal preganglionic neurons has shown that in addition to primary afferents and propriospinal pathways there are at least five bulbo-spinal pathways infringing on SPNs (47). Again, the role of these inputs to SPNs in the maintenance of vasomotor tone remains unknown.

A large number of recent studies focus on the effect of catecholamines, serotonin, a number of amino acids, and substance P and other peptides on SPNs (reviewed in 131), but their significance in the maintenance of vasomotor tone cannot be assessed without demonstrating that these substances act on vasoconstrictor neurons.

## Conclusions

Neurohumoral control of the circulation is under the influence of several discrete sites in the central nervous system that integrate sensory signals and produce reflex neurohumoral responses that are appropriate for different physiological demands. Cardiovascular reflexes mediated by the medulla oblongata have fairly well established pathways and are essential for the maintenance of cardiovascular homeostasis. On the other hand long-loop supramedullary reflexes exhibit a high degree of complexity both in terms of the anatomical pathways and their functional properties; more experiments are needed to provide information on their anatomical connections and their function.

In the last few years new anatomical, physiological, and pharmacological techniques have made possible an explosive growth of research in the area of central control of the circulation. Additional impetus has come from studies searching for pathological derangements of normal control mechanisms as possible causes of hypertension.

In this review we have attempted to evaluate the physiology and neuroanatomy of selected regions of the medulla that are associated with basal vasomotor tone. The current status of research in this area may be summarized as follows.

1. Spinal sympathetic preganglionic neurons in the IML are the final common pathway for the maintenance of basal vasomotor tone.
2. The firing rate of spinal IML neurons is maintained by supraspinal inputs because acute section of the neuraxis at the medullo-spinal junction leads to arterial hypotension and disappearance of the 2–6 Hz rhythm present in sympathetic nerves of the intact animal.
3. The essential tonic input to IML neurons from the medulla that are responsible for maintaining vasomotor tone is located in a small anatomically, physiologically, and pharmacologically well-defined area in the RVLM.
4. A small area in the caudal ventrolateral medulla (CVLM) is likely to play a role in vasomotor tone, because its stimulation elicits a drop in arterial pressure that has been attributed to inhibition of vasomotor neurons in the RVLM.
5. A small area in the dorsomedial medulla may also play a major role in the maintenance of vasomotor tone, but more investigations are needed to establish its precise role.
6. The output of RVLM neurons to IML neurons probably does not produce equal activation of all sympathetic nerves.

ACKNOWLEDGMENTS

We thank Kim Clarke for excellent typing and Adria Calaresu for help with the bibliography. The preparation of this review was supported by the Medical Research Council of Canada.

## Literature Cited

1. Abrahams, V. C., Hilton, S. M., Zbrozyna, A. W. 1960. *J. Physiol.* 154:491–513
2. Amendt, K., Czachurski, J., Dembowsky, K., Seller, H. 1979. *J. Auton. Nerv. Syst.* 1:103–17
3. Andrezik, J. A., Chan-Palay, V., Palay, S. L. 1981. *Anat. Embryol.* 161:373–90
4. Armstrong, D. M., Ross, C. A., Pickel, V. M., Joh, T. H., Reis, D. J. 1982. *J. Comp. Neurol.* 212:173–87
5. Backman, S. B., Henry, J. H. 1984. *Can. J. Physiol. Pharmacol.* 62:248–51
6. Barman, S. M. 1984. In *Nervous Control of Cardiovascular Function,* ed. W. C. Randall, pp. 321–45. New York: Oxford Univ. Press
7. Barman, S. M., Gebber, G. L. 1980. *Am. J. Physiol.* 239:R42–R47
8. Barman, S. M., Gebber, G. L. 1981. *Am. J. Physiol.* 240:R335–47
9. Barman, S. M., Gebber, G. L. 1983. *Am. J. Physiol.* 245:R438–47
10. Barman, S. M., Gebber, G. L. 1985. *J. Neurophysiol.* 53 (6):1551–61
11. Barman, S. M., Gebber, G. L. 1987. *J. Neurophysiol.* 57: 1410–24
12. Barman, S. M., Gebber, G. L., Calaresu, F. R. 1984. *Am. J. Physiol.* 247:R513–19
13. Beckstead, R. M., Morse, J. R., Norgren, R. 1980. *J. Comp. Neurol.* 190:259–82
14. Benarroch, E. E., Granata, A. R., Giuliano, R., Reis, D. J. 1986. *Hypertension* 8(Suppl. I):56–60
15. Benarroch, E. E., Granata, A. R., Ruggiero, D. A., Park, D. H., Reis, D. J. 1986. *Am. J. Physiol.* 250:R932–45
16. Blessing, W. W., Chalmers, J. P., Howe, P. R. C. 1978. *J. Comp. Neurol.* 179:407–23
17. Blessing, W. W., Goodchild, A. K., Dampney, R. A. L., Chalmers, J. P. 1981. *Brain Res.* 221:35–55
18. Blessing, W. W., Howe, P. R. C., Joh, T. H., Oliver, J. R., Willoughby, J. O. 1986. *J. Comp. Neurol.* 248:285–300
19. Blessing, W. W., Jaeger, C. B., Ruggiero, D. A., Reis, D. J. 1984. *Brain Res. Bull.* 9:279–86
20. Blessing, W. W., Reis, D. J. 1982. *Brain Res.* 253:161–71
21. Blessing, W. W., West, M. J., Chalmers, J. P. 1981. *Circ. Res.* 49:949–58
22. Bousquet, P., Bloch, T., Feldman, J., Schwartz, J. 1979. In *Nervous System and Hypertension,* ed. P. Meyer, H. Schmitt, pp. 363–70. New York: Wiley
23. Bousquet, P., Feldman, J., Bloch, R., Schwartz, J. 1981. *Eur. J. Pharmacol.* 69:389–92
24. Bousquet, P., Feldman, J., Schwartz, J. 1984. *J. Pharmacol. Exp. Ther.* 230:232–36
25. Bousquet, P., Feldman, J., Schwartz, J. 1985. *J. Auton. Nerv. Syst.* 14:263–70
26. Bousquet, P., Schwartz, J. 1983. *Biochem. Pharmacol.* 32 (9):1459–65
27. Brody, M. J., Alper, R. H., O'Neil, T. P., Porter, J. P. 1986. In *Handbook of Hypertension—Pathophysiology of Hypertension: Regulating Mechanisms,* ed. A. Zanchetti, R. C. Tarazi, pp. 1–25. Amsterdam: Elsevier
28. Brown, D. L., Guyenet, P. G. 1984. *Am. J. Physiol.* 247:R1009–16
29. Brown, D. L., Guyenet, P. G. 1985. *Circ. Res.* 56:359–69
30. Calaresu, F. R., Ciriello, J., Caverson, M. M., Cechetto, D. F., Krukoff, T. 1984. In *Hypertension and the Brain,* ed. G. P. Guthrie, T. A. Kotchen, pp. 3–21. Mount Kisco, NY: Futura
31. Caverson, M. M., Ciriello, J., Calaresu, F. R. 1983. *Brain Res.* 274:354–58
32. Caverson, M. M., Ciriello, J., Calaresu, F. R. 1983. *J. Auton. Nerv. Syst.* 9:451–75
33. Caverson, M. M., Ciriello, J., Calaresu, F. R. 1984. *Am. J. Physiol.* 247:R872–79
34. Ciriello, J., Caverson, M. M. 1986. *Brain. Res.* 367:273–81
35. Ciriello, J., Caverson, M. M., Calaresu, F. R. 1985. *Brain Res.* 347:173–76
36. Ciriello, J., Caverson, M. M., Park, D. H. 1986. *J. Comp. Neurol.* 253:216–30
37. Ciriello, J., Caverson, M. M., Polosa, C. 1986. *Brain Res. Rev.* 11:359–91
38. Coote, J. H. 1985. *J. Auton. Nerv. Syst.* 14:255–62
39. Coote, J. H., Macleod, V. H., Fleetwood-Walker, S. M., Gilbey, M. P. 1981. *Brain Res.* 215:135–45
40. Dahlström, A., Fuxe, K. 1964. *Acta Physiol. Scand.* 62(Suppl. 232): 1–55
41. Dampney, R. A. L., Goodchild, A. K., Robertson, L. G., Montgomery, W. 1982. *Brain Res.* 249:223–35
42. Dampney, R. A. L., Goodchild, A. K., Tan, E. 1985. *J. Auton. Nerv. Syst.* 14:239–54
43. Dampney, R. A. L., McAllen, R. M. 1986. *J. Physiol.* 377:P59
44. Dampney, R. A. L., Moon, E. A. 1980. *Am. J. Physiol.* 239:H349–58

45. Day, T. A., Ro, A., Renaud, L. P. 1983. *Brain Res.* 279:299–302
46. Dean, C., Coote, J. H. 1986. *Brain Res.* 377:279–85
47. Dembowsky, K., Czachurski, J., Seller, H. 1985. *J. Auton. Nerv. Syst.* 13:201–44
48. Dembowsky, K., Czachurski, J., Seller, H. 1985. *J. Comp. Neurol.* 238:453–65
49. Drolet, G., Gauthier, P. 1985. *Can. J. Physiol. Pharmacol.* 63:599–605
50. Elliott, J. M., Kapoor, V., Cain, M., West, M. J., Chalmers, J. P. 1985. *Clin. Exp. Hypertens.* A7:1059–82
51. Ernsberger, P. R., Mann, J. J., Reis, D. J. 1986. *Fed. Proc.* 45(3):563.
52. Everitt, B. J., Hökfelt, T., Terenius, L., Tatemoto, K., Mutt, V., Goldstein, M. 1984. *Neuroscience* 251:283–90
53. Farlow, D. M., Goodchild, A. K., Dampney, R. A. L. 1984. *Brain Res.* 298:313–20
54. Feldberg, W., Guertzenstein, P. G. 1972. *J. Physiol.* 224:83–103
55. Gatti, P. J., Gillis, R. A. 1985. *Fed. Proc.* 44:1345.
56. Gatti, P. J., Norman, W. P., Da Silva, A. M. T., Gillis, R. A. 1986. *Brain Res.* 381:281–88
57. Gatti, P. J., Souza, J. D., Da Silva, A. M. T., Quest, J. A., Gillis, R. A. 1985. *Brain Res.* 346:115–23
58. Gebber, G. L. 1980. *Am. J. Physiol.* 239:H143–55
59. Gebber, G. L., Barman, S. M. 1981. *Am. J. Physiol.* 240:R348–55
60. Gebber, G. L., Barman, S. M. 1985. *J. Neurophysiol.* 54 (6):1498–1512
61. Gilbey, M. P., Coote, J. H., Fleetwood-Walker, S. M., Petersen, D. F. 1982. *Brain Res.* 251:283–90
62. Gilbey, M. P., McKenna, K. E., Schramm, L. P. 1983. *Neurosci. Lett.* 41:157–59
63. Goadsby, P. J. 1985. *Brain Res.* 327:241–48
64. Goadsby, P. J., Lambert, G. A., Lance, J. W. 1983. *Brain Res.* 278:175–83
65. Goodchild, A. K., Dampney, R. A. L. 1985. *Brain Res.* 360:24–32
66. Granata, A., Kumada, M., Reis, D. J. 1985. *J. Auton. Nerv. Syst.* 14:387–95
67. Granata, A. R., Numao, Y., Kumada, M., Reis, D. J. 1986. *Brain Res.* 377:127–46
68. Granata, A. R., Ruggiero, D. A., Park, D. H., Joh, T. H., Reis, D. J. 1985. *Am. J. Physiol.* 248:H547–67
69. Guertzenstein, P. G., Silver, A. 1974. *J. Physiol.* 242:489–503
70. Gurtu, S., Pant, K. K., Sinha, J. N., Bhargava, K. P. 1984. *Brain Res.* 301:59–64
71. Guyenet, P. G. 1984. *Brain Res.* 303:31–40
72. Guyenet, P. G., Brown, D. L. 1986. *Am. J. Physiol.* 250:R1081–94
73. Guyenet, P. G., Brown, D. L. 1986. *Brain Res.* 364:301–14
74. Guyenet, P. G., Cabot, J. B. 1981. *J. Neurosci.* 1:908–17
75. Haselton, J. R., Haselton, C. L., Vera, P. L., Ellenberger, H. H., LeBlanc, W. G., et al. 1985. *Brain Res.* 335:315–20
76. Helke, C. J., Neil, J. J., Massari, V. J., Loewy, A. D. 1982. *Brain Res.* 243:147–52
77. Hilton, S. M. 1979. In *Integrative Functions of the Autonomic Nervous System*, ed. C. McC. Brooks, K. Koizumi, A. Sato, pp. 444–49. Tokyo: Univ. Tokyo Press
78. Hilton, S. M. 1980. *Adv. Physiol. Sci.* 8:1–12
79. Hilton, S. M. 1986. In *Central and Peripheral Mechanisms of Cardiovascular Regulation*, ed. A. Magro, W. Osswald, D. Reis, P. Vanhoutte, pp. 465–86. New York: Plenum
80. Hilton, S. M., Marshall, J. M., Timms, R. J. 1983. *J. Physiol.* 345:149–66
81. Hilton, S. M., Smith, P. R. 1984. *J. Auton. Nerv. Syst.* 11:35–42
82. Hökfelt, T., Lundberg, J. M., Lagercrantz, H., Tatemoto, K., Mutt, V., et al. 1983. *Neurosci. Lett.* 36:217–22
83. Hökfelt, T., Lundberg, J. M., Tatemoto, K., Mutt, V., Terenius, L., et al. 1983. *Acta Physiol. Scand.* 117:315–18
84. Howe, P. R. C., Costa, M., Furness, J. B., Chalmers, J. P. 1980. *Neuroscience* 5:2229–38
85. Howe, P. R. C., Kohn, D. M., Minson, J. B., Stead, B. H., Chalmers, J. P. 1983. *Brain Res.* 270:29–36
86. Huang, Z.-S., Gebber, G. L., Barman, S. M., Varner, K. J. 1987. *Am. J. Physiol.* 252:R645–52
87. Hudson, M. E., Fuxe, K., Goldstein, M., Kalia, M. 1986. *Soc. Neurosci.* 12 (1):535 (Abstr.)
88. Keeler, J. R., Helke, C. J. 1985. *J. Auton. Nerv. Syst.* 13:19–33
89. Keeler, J. R., Shults, C. W., Chase, T. N., Helke, C. J. 1984. *Brain Res.* 297:217–24
90. Krukoff, T. L., Ciriello, J., Calaresu, F. R. 1985. *J. Comp. Neurol.* 240:103–16
91. Kumada, M., Dampney, R. A. L., Reis, D. J. 1979. *Circ. Res.* 44:63–70
92. Lebedev, V. P., Krasyukov, A. V., Nikitin, S. A. 1986. *Neuroscience* 17:189–203
93. Li, P., Lovick, T. A. 1985. *Exp. Neurol.* 89:543–53

94. Loewy, A. D., Burton, H. 1978. *J. Comp. Neurol.* 181:421–50
95. Loewy, A. D., Marson, L., Parkinson, D., Perry, M. A., Sawyer, W. B. 1986. *Brain Res.* 386:313–24
96. Loewy, A. D., McKellar, S. 1981. *Brain Res.* 211:146–52
97. Loewy, A. D., Sawyer, W. B. 1982. *Brain Res.* 245:379–83
98. Loewy, A. D., Wallach, J. H., McKellar, S. 1981. *Brain Res. Rev.* 3:63–80
99. Lorenz, R. G., Saper, C. B., Wong, D. L., Ciaranello, R. D., Loewy, A. D. 1985. *Neurosci. Lett.* 55:255–60
100. Lovick, T. A. 1985. *Pflügers Arch.* 404:197–202
101. Lovick, T. A., Hilton, S. M. 1985. *Brain Res.* 331:353–57
102. Lovick, T. A., Smith, P. R., Hilton, S. M. 1984. *J. Auton. Nerv. Syst.* 11:27–33
103. Marshall, J. 1986. *Pflügers Arch.* 406:225–31
104. McAllen, R. M. 1985. *J. Physiol.* 368:423–33
105. McAllen, R. M. 1986. *J. Auton. Nerv. Syst.* 17:151–64
106. McAllen, R. M. 1986. *Neuroscience* 18 (1):43–49
107. McAllen, R. M. 1986. *Neuroscience* 18 (1):51–59
108. McAllen, R. M., Neil, J. J., Loewy, A. D. 1982. *Brain Res.* 238:65–76
109. McCall, R. B. 1983. *Brain Res.* 289:121–27
110. McCall, R. B. 1986. *Am. J. Physiol.* 250:R1065–73
111. McCall, R. B., Humphrey, S. J. 1985. *Brain Res.* 339:356–60
112. McKellar, S., Loewy, A. D. 1982. *Brain Res.* 241:11–29
113. Meckler, R. L., Weaver, L. C. 1985. *Brain Res.* 338:123–35
114. Meeley, M. P., Ruggiero, D. A., Ishitsuka, T., Reis, D. J. 1985. *Neurosci. Lett.* 58:83–89
115. Miura, M., Onai, T., Takayama, K. 1983. *J. Auton. Nerv. Syst.* 7:119–39
116. Nadler, J. V. 1979. *Life Sci.* 24:289–300
117. Neil, J. J., Loewy, A. D. 1982. *Brain Res.* 241:271–78
118. Oldfield, B. J., McLachlan, E. M. 1981. *J. Comp. Neurol.* 196:329–45
119. Pilowsky, P., West, M., Chalmers, J. 1985. *Neurosci. Lett.* 60:51–55
120. Punnen, S., Sapru, H. N. 1985. *Brain Res.* 336:180–86
121. Punnen, S., Willette, R. N., Krieger, A. J., Sapru, H. N. 1984. *Neuropharmacology* 23:939–46
122. Punnen, S., Willette, R. N., Krieger, A. J., Sapru, H. N. 1986. *Brain Res.* 382:178–84
123. Reis, D. J., Granata, A. R., Joh, T. H., Ross, C. A., Ruggiero, D. A., Park, D. H. 1984. *Hypertension* 6 (5):7–15.
124. Reis, D. J., Ruggiero, D. A., Granata, A. 1986. In *Central Nervous Systems Control of the Heart,* ed. T. Stober, K. Schimrick, D. Ganten, D. G. Sherman, pp. 19–36. The Hague: Nijhoff
125. Ross, C. A., Ruggiero, D. A., Joh, T. H., Park, D. H., Reis, D. J. 1983. *Brain Res.* 273:356–61
126. Ross, C. A., Ruggiero, D. A., Joh, T. H., Park, D. H., Reis, D. J. 1984. *J. Comp. Neuro.* 228:168–85
127. Ross, C. A., Ruggiero, D. A., Park, D. H., Joh, T. H., Sved, A. F., Fernandez-Pardal, J., Saavedra, J. M., Reis, D. J. 1984. *J. Neurosci.* 4 (2): 474–94
128. Ross, C. A., Ruggiero, D. A., Reis, D. J. 1985. *J. Comp. Neurol.* 242:511–34
129. Ruggiero, D. A., Meeley, M. P., Anwar, M., Reis, D. J. 1985. *Brain Res.* 339:171–77.
130. Sangdee, C., Franz, D. N. 1983. *Neurosci. Lett.* 37:167–73
131. Schramm, L. P. 1986. In *Central and Peripheral Mechanisms of Cardiovascular Regulation,* ed. A. Magro, W. Osswald, D. Reis, P. Vanhoutte, pp. 303–52. New York: Plenum
132. Schramm, L. P., Livingstone, R. H., Knuepfer, M. M. 1985. *Soc. Neurosci.* 11:35 (Abstr.)
133. Spyer, K. M. 1981. *Rev. Physiol. Biochem. Pharmacol.* 88:23–124
134. Spyer, K. M. 1982. *J. Exp. Biol.* 100:109–28
135. Stanek, K. A., Neil, J. J., Sawyer, W. B., Loewy, A. D. 1984. *Am. J. Physiol.* 246:H41–51
136. Sun, M.-K., Guyenet, P. G. 1985. *Am. J. Physiol.* 249:R672–80
137. Sun, M.-K., Guyenet, P. G. 1986. *Am. J. Physiol.* 250:R910–17
138. Sun, M.-K., Guyenet, P. G. 1986. *Am. J. Physiol.* 251:R798–R810
139. Takano, Y., Martin, J. E., Leeman, S. E., Loewy, A. D. 1984. *Brain Res.* 291:168–72
140. Undesser, K. P., Hasser, E. M., Haywood, J. R., Johnson, A. K., Bishop, V. S. 1985. *Circ. Res.* 56:410–17
141. Van de Graaff, W. B., Prabhakar, N. R., Mitra, J., Cherniack, N. S. 1985. *Fed. Proc.* 44:1197
142. Weaver, L. C., Meckler, R. L., Tobey, J. C., Stein, R. D. 1986. In *Central Peripheral Mechanisms of Cardiovascular Regulation,* ed. A. Magro, W.

Osswald, D. Reis, P. Vanhoutte, pp. 269–301. New York: Plenum

143. Wennegren, G., Öberg, B. 1980. *Pflügers Arch.* 387:189–95

144. West, M. J., Blessing, W. W., Chalmers, J. P. 1981. *Circ. Res.* 49:959–70

145. Westlund, K. N., Bowker, R. M., Ziegler, M. G., Coulter, J. D. 1983. *Brain Res.* 263:15–31

146. Willette, R. N., Barcas, P. P., Krieger, A. J., Sapru, H. N. 1983. *Neuropharmacol.* 22 (9): 1071–79

147. Willette, R. N., Gatti, P. A., Sapru, H. N. 1984. *J. Cardiovasc. Pharmacol.* 6:476–82

148. Willette, R. N., Krieger, A. J., Barcas, P. P., Sapru, H. N. 1983. *J. Pharmacol. Exp. Ther.* 226 (3):893–99

149. Willette, R. N., Punnen, S., Krieger, A.

J., Sapru, H. N. 1984. *Brain Res.* 321:169–74

150. Willette, R. N., Punnen, S., Krieger, A. J., Sapru, H. N. 1984. *J. Pharmacol. Exp. Ther.* 231:457–63

151. Willette, R. N., Punnen-Grandy, S., Krieger, A. J., Sapru, H. N. 1987. *J. Auton. Nerv. Syst.* 18:143–51

152. Woodruff, M. L., Baisden, R. H., Whittington, D. L. 1986. *Brain Res.* 379:10–23

153. Yamada, K. A., McAllen, R. M., Loewy, A. D. 1984. *Brain Res.* 297:175–80

154. Yamada, K. A., Norman, W. P., Hamosh, P., Gillis, R. A. 1982. *Brain Res.* 248:71–78

155. Yardley, C. P., Redfern, W. S., Marson, L., Hilton, S. M. 1986. *Neurosci. Lett. Suppl.* 24:S15

*Ann. Rev. Physiol. 1988. 50:525–39*

# PRE- AND POSTGANGLIONIC VASOCONSTRICTOR NEURONS: Differentiation, Types, and Discharge Properties

*W. Jänig*

Physiologisches Institut, Christian-Albrechts-Universität zu Kiel, Olshausenstrasse 40, 2300 Kiel, West Germany

## INTRODUCTION

Stimulation of noradrenergic neurons that innervate blood vessels causes vasoconstriction. In many vessels the vasoconstriction is preceded by excitatory junction potentials which, depending on the frequency of sympathetic firing and the type of vascular bed, initiate either local responses or propagating action potentials leading to constriction along the entire length of vessels. The neuronal effect on the vascular smooth muscle is mediated by norepinephrine released from the varicosities of the postganglionic axons. This neurally released norepinephrine may have restricted actions on postjunctional sites on the vascular smooth muscle, and it does not act primarily on extrajunctional adrenergic receptors to initiate electrical and mechanical responses under physiological conditions (23). Recent findings show that almost all varicosities of the perivascular noradrenergic axons of the anterior cerebral artery and the arterioles of the submucosa of the guinea pig ileum form close neuromuscular junctions with the vascular smooth muscle cells (46, 48). Though there are considerable differences between blood vessels (57), it is likely that the neurovascular transmission is highly specific under physiological conditions in many vessels (e.g. those regulating resistance; 23). This specificity justifies use of the term vasoconstrictor (VC) neurons to describe noradrenergic neurons that induce vasoconstriction when excited.

0066-4278/88/0315-0525$02.00

Despite the specificity of neurovascular transmission, circulating norepinephrine also acts on the blood vessels, but via extrajunctional adrenergic receptors. Vasoconstriction can be initiated via this mechanism with little or no intracellular potential change (26). Other compounds may also be released by the noradrenergic nerve fibers, e.g. neuropeptide Y and ATP (13, 47). Finally, substances released by the noradrenergic postganglionic axons on the vascular smooth muscle may have roles in addition to their conventional transmitter role, such as regulation of the density of ionic channels and other processes of the vascular smooth muscle (22).

This review focuses on the discharge characteristics and some other functional properties of pre- and postganglionic sympathetic neurons that are most likely involved in vasoconstriction. I will argue that these discharge characteristics that are dependent on the organization of the VC systems in spinal cord and brain stem are specific for VC neurons.

The following limitations should be made on the use of the term vasoconstrictor neuron: It is practically impossible to prove in an experiment in vivo that a postganglionic neuron that displays a typical VC pattern of discharge activity innervates a blood vessel. Technically it appears to be nearly impossible to record the activity of a single postganglionic neuron (either intracellularly with a microelectrode or extracellularly from its axon without interrupting its connection to the target organ) in order to determine its discharge pattern and identify its function. Nor is it feasible to stimulate the same neuron and observe the response of the target organ. The latter approach would require that the junction potentials in vascular smooth muscles be recorded, since it appears unlikely that the excitation of a single VC axon can elicit a change of blood flow or resistance to flow in its target vascular bed.

The following aspects of the VC neurons are reviewed: (a) the discharge (reflex) patterns of functionally different types of VC neurons; (b) the distinction of the VC neurons from other types of sympathetic neurons; (c) the impulse transmission from pre- to postganglionic VC neurons.

Most of the data on which this review is based come from studies conducted in the author's laboratory on pre- and postganglionic neurons of the lumbar sympathetic outflow of the cat. The neurons of this sympathetic outflow supply skin, skeletal muscle, and viscera (colon and pelvic organs). The respective vasoconstrictor (VC) neurons will be called cutaneous VC (CVC), muscle VC (MVC), and visceral VC (VVC) neurons. Most cell bodies of these preganglionic VC are situated in the pars principalis and pars funicularis of the lumbar intermediolateral cell column (5–7, 36, 37). The data are only briefly summarized and discussed, and reference is made to recent reviews that concentrate on the functional characteristics of sympathetic pre- and postganglionic neurons in other contexts (28–31, 38, 42).

# THE DISCHARGE PATTERNS OF VASOCONSTRICTOR NEURONS

VC neurons exhibit distinct discharge characteristics according to the functions of their target vessels. These discharge characteristics depend on the central organization of the neuron systems innervating specific targets and can be identified when firing of the VC neurons is analyzed as a function of specified afferent inputs or correlated with phrenic nerve activity (which indicates the phases of respiration; 54) or cardiovascular parameters. This point of view is somewhat arbitrary yet these criteria used for classification provide a matrix that may reflect the functional organization of VC systems and other sympathetic systems in the periphery (29, 30). Table 1 lists some relevant functional properties of the VC neurons supplying skeletal muscle of the cat hindlimb, hairy and hairless skin of the cat hindlimb, tail, and viscera (colon, pelvic organs, and kidney). These systems have been extensively analyzed and may also be representative of VC neurons that project to other visceral organs, other areas of skin, other skeletal muscles, and the head.

## Ongoing Activity in Vasoconstrictor Neurons and Its Continuous Modulation

Many VC neurons exhibit ongoing activity in animals and humans (29, 42). This activity may exhibit grouping of impulses related to the pulse pressure wave (cardiac rhythmicity) and to respiration (respiratory rhythmicity). The cardiac rhythmicity is initiated by the pulsatile activation of the arterial baroreceptors, which then leads to a pulsatile inhibition of the activity of the VC neurons. This rhythmicity of the activity can easily be quantified and is an expression of the potency of the phasic inhibitory baroreceptor influence (12, 42). Usually this effect is large in MVC and VVC neurons and small in CVC neurons (28). Some CVC neurons may also have large cardiac rhythmicity in their firing, and in certain pathophysiological conditions most CVC neurons may exhibit this rhythmicity (10, 11).

Respiratory modulation of VC activity is complex. It depends on several interacting components that are difficult to separate and poorly investigated: (a) "Respiratory" and "cardiovascular" neurons in the lower brain stem are synaptically coupled. This component of the respiratory modulation of the VC activity can be measured after the vagal, aortic, and carotid sinus nerves had been cut (see 35). The activity of these neurons increases during inspiration. (b) Rhythmic ventilation (occurring either actively or passively by positive pressure ventilation) produces rhythmic excitation of lung afferents during inflation of the lung and rhythmic activation of the arterial baroreceptors by

**Table 1** Properties of vasoconstrictor neurons[a]

| Properties, responses to stimulation | CVC neurons | MVC neurons | VVC neurons | |
|---|---|---|---|---|
| Main functions | thermoregulation | regulation of resistance | Colon, pelvic organ | Kidney |
| | | | regulation of resistance and of blood flow through mucosa | regulation of resistance, of JGA, of tubular secretion |
| **Conduction velocity of axons (m/s)** | | | | |
| Preganglionic | 6.7 ± 2.9 (79)[b] 1.6 ± 0.7 (18)[b] | 3.4 ± 1.9 (59) | 2.8 ± 2.5 (49) | — |
| Postganglionic | 0.59 ± 0.13 (193) | 0.79 ± 0.22 (55) | — | — |
| **Ongoing activity (impulses/s)** | | | | |
| Preganglionic | 0.9 ± 0.6 (47) | 1.8 ± 1.3 (26) | 1.6 ± 0.9 (46) | — |
| Postganglionic | 1.2 ± 0.7 (44) | 0.5–3.0 | 1.2 ± 1.1 (12)[c] | 2.4 ± 1.5 (28) |
| **Arterial baroreceptors** | | | | |
| Cardiac rhythm (%)[d] | | | | |
| preganglionic | 23 ± 39 (43) | 127 ± 61 (26) | 139 ± 62 (44) | — |
| postganglionic | 55 ± 26 (54) | 131 ± 69 (33) | 180 ± 43 (14) | 100 ± 47 (22) |
| Stimulation in blind sac | ∅ or → some ↓ (post) | ↓ (post) | ↓ (pre) | — |
| **Arterial chemoreceptors** | | | | |
| Direct stimulation[e] | ↓ or ∅ (post) some ↑ (post) | ↑ (post) | ↑ (pre) | ↑ (post) |
| **Systemic hypoxia[f]** | | | | |
| preganglionic | ↓ 0.38 ± 0.27 × (44)[g] | ↑ 3.3 ± 2.2 × (19) | ↑ (small) | ↓ ~2.1× |
| postganglionic | ↑ 1.7 ± 0.5 × (6)[g] (post) | | ↑ (small) | ↑ (post) |
| Systemic hypercapnia[h] | weak or absent (post) | ↑ (post) | — | ↑ (post) |
| Coupling to respiratory system | some strong (post) | strong (post) | some strong (pre) | strong (post) |

| | | | | |
|---|---|---|---|---|
| Thermoreceptors[i] | | | | |
|   Spinal cord | | | | |
|     warm | ↓ (post) | ∅ (post) | — | — |
|     cold | ↑ or ∅ (post) | ∅ (post) | — | — |
|   Hypothalamus | | | | |
|     warm | ↓ (post) | ∅ (post) | — | — |
|     cold | ↑ or ∅ (post) | ∅ (post) | — | — |
| Cutaneous receptors | | | | |
|   Nociceptors | | | | |
|     preganglionic | ↓ | ↑ | | |
|     postganglionic | ↓ | ↑ | | ↑ |
|   Hair follicle | | | | |
|     preganglionic | ↑ | → | | |
|     postganglionic | ↑ | → | | |
| Visceral receptors | | | | |
|   Urinary bladder[j] | → (post) | ↑ (post) | ↑ (some) | — |
|   Colon[j] | → (post) | ↑ (post) | ∅ | — |
|   Anus | → (post) | ↑ (post) | ↑ (some) | — |
| References | 11, 12, 21, 28, 35, 43, 44 | 11, 12, 21, 28, 35, 43, 44 | 2, 3, 28, 31, 41 | 4, 17 |

a ↑↑/↓↓ = large, small increase/decrease of activity; ∅ = no effect. All numerical values: mean ± SD (number); (post); (pre) indicates result obtained only in post- or preganglionic neurons (other values were measured in pre- and postganglionic neurons). Measurements performed on cats (MVC, CVC, VVC) and rabbits (kidney VVC) in chloralose anesthesia.

b Two separate groups of preganglionic axons (43, 44).

c Lumbar splanchnic nerves cut on one side (41).

d Cardiac rhythmicity of activity evaluated from post-R-wave histograms, activity in 48 ms of maximum minus activity in 48 ms of minimum divided by mean activity in 48 ms times 100 (12).

e Arterial chemoreceptors directly stimulated by bolus injections of 0.5-1 ml $CO_2$-enriched saline solution through lingual artery close to glomus caroticum (12).

f Respiration of the animal with a hypoxic gas mixture of 8% $O_2$ in $N_2$ for 2 min.

g CVC neurons separated into those inhibited and those excited during stimulation of arterial chemoreceptors (11).

h Respiration of the animal with a hypercapnic gas mixture of 7.5% $CO_2$ and 21% $O_2$ in $N_2$ for 2–8 min.

i Stimulation of thermoreceptors in spinal canal and hypothalamus.

j Distension and isovolumetric contraction of organs.

the rhythmic increase of the arterial blood pressure. These changes of afferent activity with respect to ventilation modulate the respiratory rhythmicity of the VC activity by influencing "respiratory" and "cardiovascular" neurons in the lower brain stem. Several types of mutual interaction between the afferent inputs and the neurons in the medulla oblongata are possible.

The activity of MVC neurons exhibits pronounced respiratory rhythmicity. The activity peak during the inspiratory phase (as indicated by the phrenic nerve discharges) is followed by a depression of activity in the postinspiratory phase (see 53) and preceded by a short decrease of activity. The temporal profile of the activity in the MVC neurons may indicate a replication of the activity profile of certain medullary respiratory neurons (see 54).

In principle, the activity in VVC neurons supplying colon, pelvic organs (2), and kidney (4, 17) is also modulated by respiration. VVC activity increases during inspiration, and the activity of VC neurons to the kidney is depressed during early inspiration and the postinspiratory phase (4). The degree to which respiratory rhythmicity in VVC neurons is comparable to that found in MVC neurons has yet to be determined.

The activity of most CVC neurons is only weakly modulated by respiration, although some CVC neurons show a strong respiratory modulation (29, 37).

Many preganglionic neurons contained in the cervical sympathetic trunk in cats and rats exhibit some respiratory modulation of their activity. They discharge maximally either during phrenic nerve discharge (i.e. in the inspiratory phase) or during phrenic nerve silence (i.e. in the expiratory phase). Other functional properties were not tested in these neurons, thus it is unclear whether they were VC neurons (19, 51, 52; see Section III in 15a).

## Vasoconstrictor Neurons Supplying Skeletal Muscle

The reflexes in MVC neurons are very stereotyped. The MVC activity is inhibited by stimulation of arterial baroreceptors (e.g. by increasing the pressure in an innervated, isolated carotid blind sac; 12). Stimulation of most other afferent inputs (e.g. from arterial chemoreceptors, cutaneous nociceptors, and spinal visceral lumbar and sacral afferents supplying urinary bladder, colon, and anal canal) induces reflex excitations in MVC neurons. Only air jet stimuli that excite hair follicle afferents produce a short lasting inhibition of MVC activity (29). This inhibition is probably part of an arousal reaction that is largely masked by the anesthesia. The maximal discharge rates which have been observed in pre- and postganglionic MVC neurons during a strong activation of arterial chemoreceptors by general hypoxia (ventilation of the animals with a gas mixture of 5–8% $O_2$ in $N_2$) are about 10–15 Hz (12, 21, 43).

## Vasoconstrictor Neurons Supplying Viscera

The discharge pattern of VVC neurons produced by stimulation of arterial baro- and chemoreceptors is in many respects similar to that of MVC neurons (2, 17, 28, 41). In the cat the chemoreceptor reflexes of VVC neurons that project to colon and pelvic organs are smaller than those of MVC neurons (2, 28). The maximal discharge rates observed during strong activation of arterial chemoreceptors are about 4–6 impulses in pre- and postganglionic VVC neurons projecting to colon and pelvic organs and about 5–10 impulses in VVC neurons supplying the kidney in the rabbit (2, 17, 41). Otherwise the discharge pattern of VVC neurons has been less well analyzed than that of the MVC neurons. In particular, relatively little is known about the reactions of these neurons to natural stimulation of spinal afferent inputs from skin, deep somatic tissues, and viscera. For example, it is possible that VVC neurons supplying the kidney can be divided into subtypes that react specifically to natural stimulation of renal afferents. These subtypes may be associated with different target organs in the kidney, such as the juxtaglomerular apparatus and resistance vessels (20).

## Vasoconstrictor Neurons Supplying Skin

The discharge patterns of most CVC neurons differ from those of MVC and VVC neurons. This is not surprising considering the main function(s) of the CVC neurons. The inhibitory influence of the arterial baroreceptors on the CVC activity is normally weak or absent in animals with no disruption of the neuraxis. Some CVC neurons may be under strong inhibitory baroreceptor control (12). Natural stimulation of most afferent inputs from the skin (nociceptive afferents, vibration receptors) and the interior of the body (spinal visceral afferents, central warm receptors) decreases the CVC activity. Only central cooling or air jets stimulating hair follicle afferents elicit small transient excitations of the CVC neurons. A small fraction of postganglionic CVC neurons have a reflex pattern similar to that of MVC neurons (i.e. strong inhibitory control by arterial baroreceptors, excitation by stimulation of arterial chemoreceptors and probably by stimulation of cutaneous nociceptors) (12, 21). This could mean that different sections of the cutaneous vascular bed (including the subcutis) are supplied by different types of CVC neurons or that the pattern of CVC neurons is controlled by different parts of the brain stem and hypothalamus and that the control from the lower brain stem (which would lead to a reflex pattern typical of MVC and VVC neurons) is normally suppressed. There is circumstantial evidence for the latter hypothesis: (a) After decerebration (mid-mesencephalic transection of the brain stem) CVC neurons are excited by stimulation of arterial chemoreceptors (21). (b) After chronic lesion of cutaneous nerves, the reflex pattern in CVC neurons supplying hairy skin may be converted to that of MVC neurons (i.e. pronounced inhibitory control by arterial baroreceptors, excitation on stimulation of arterial chemoreceptors, no effect or excitation on stimulation of cutaneous nociceptors) (10, 11).

## The Effects of Anesthesia

All the data summarized above and in Table 1 were obtained in anesthetized animals. It must be assumed that centrally acting anesthetics affect the activity of the VC neurons. The distortion caused by this effect probably depends on the VC system tested, the anesthetic used, and the reaction tested (see 39). As judged from some studies in which the effects of anesthetics on specific autonomic reflexes were tested in cats and rabbits (17, 39) and from comparisons of the sympathetic activity to skin and skeletal muscle in unanesthetized human beings with that in cats, many reactions are quantitatively distorted. Ongoing activity and reflexes may be depressed or enhanced by an anesthetic. Reactions that depend on the integrity of higher brain areas (such as limbic system structures and hypothalamus) are certainly more readily affected than those that depend on the lower brain stem and spinal cord (17, 39, 42). The distortion of the reactions introduced by the anesthetic cannot be avoided by decerebration or spinalization of the animals. These procedures change the central neural machineries and therefore the reactions of the VC neurons.

## THE DISTINCTION BETWEEN VASOCONSTRICTOR NEURONS AND OTHER SYMPATHETIC NEURONS

### Functionally Identified Pre- and Postganglionic Sympathetic Neurons

The sympathetic outflow regulates cardiovascular effector organs not only via noradrenergic vasoconstrictor neurons and noradrenergic neurons to the heart, but also via nonadrenergic postganglionic neurons. Furthermore, it regulates other effector organs, such as glands (sweat glands, salivary glands, glands in the gastrointestinal tract), nonvascular smooth muscles (e.g. erector pili muscles, smooth muscles of pelvic organs, the gastrointestinal tract, and the eye), and even other neurons (e.g. neurons in the enteric nervous system and the pelvic ganglia). Consequently, some pre- and postganglionic sympathetic neurons are expected to have discharge characteristics that differ from those of the VC neurons and that can be associated with nonvascular effector organs and nonvascular functions.

The neurons of the lumbar sympathetic outflow that project through the distal lumbar and sacral sympathetic trunk to skeletal muscle and skin and through the lumbar splanchnic nerves to hindgut and pelvic organs have been extensively analyzed. Six types of nonvasoconstrictor neurons were identified: Three types of neurons are silent and can only be activated under very specific conditions (e.g. vasodilator neurons supplying skeletal muscle and skin, pilomotor neurons). Most neurons of the other three types have ongoing discharge activity and exhibit very specific reflexes in response to visceral and cutaneous stimuli (e.g. sudomotor neurons and two types of "motility regulating" neurons supplying viscera). The functional characteristics of these sympathetic neurons have been described in great detail (1–3, 8, 29–31).

## Silent Sympathetic Neurons Without Reflexes

Many preganglionic neurons that project into the lumbar sympathetic trunk (43, 44), the lumbar splanchnic nerves (3), and the cervical sympathetic trunk (40) have no ongoing discharge and do not respond to afferent stimuli. Some of these neurons have very specific functions [such as inducing active vasodilation in skin and skeletal muscle, piloerection in the skin (29), and contraction of the internal reproductive organs (3)]. The simplest assumption is that many of these quiescent preganglionic neurons that project into the distal sympathetic trunk or the sacral sympathetic trunk also have vasoconstrictor function and that they are activated during specific functional states of the organism, e.g. during severe exposure to cold, hypoxia, or special emotional states. An experimental factor that may contribute to the high percentage of silent preganglionic sympathetic neurons is the anesthesia used (mostly chloralose). Intracellular measurements in the cat show that almost all sympathetic preganglionic neurons in the thoracic segment T3 exhibit continuous synaptic activity; in about 50% of these neurons this synaptic activity has a low frequency and is of less than 5 mV (16).

## IMPULSE TRANSMISSION FROM PRE- TO POSTGANGLIONIC VASOCONSTRICTOR NEURONS

### The Relay Function of Sympathetic Ganglia

The patterns of discharge that characterize the different types of VC have been found in the preganglionic neurons (2, 43, 44) and postganglionic neurons (29, 31, 41). Functionally different types of preganglionic axons have different conduction velocities (3, 29, 44), so there are probably specific synaptic connections between functionally related pre- and postganglionic VC neurons in the para- and prevertebral sympathetic ganglia. Thus there are likely to be functionally separate sympathetic pathways between spinal cord and the periphery that consist of separate preganglionic as well as postganglionic populations of neurons dedicated to specific target organs.

Functional and morphological studies have revealed distinct neurophysiological and neurochemical properties of sympathetic neurons in lumbar paravertebral ganglia and in the inferior mesenteric ganglion in guinea pig and rat: (*a*) Nearly all paravertebral neurons receive one or two strong (suprathreshold) preganglionic synaptic inputs, a few weak subthreshold preganglionic synaptic inputs, and probably no synaptic (afferent) inputs from the periphery. Almost all paravertebral neurons discharge phasically at the onset of prolonged depolarizing currents and contain neuropeptide Y. (*b*) In contrast, most neurons in the inferior mesenteric ganglion receive many weak (subthreshold) preganglionic inputs from the spinal cord and many weak afferent synaptic inputs from the periphery (e.g. from the colon). These prevertebral neurons respond tonically to prolonged depolarizing currents, and most of them do not contain neuropeptide Y. Only some neurons in the inferior mesenteric ganglion have the same biophysical and neurochemical properties as most paravertebral postganglionic neurons. The difference in discharge patterns in response to depolarizing currents is caused by different populations of voltage-sensitive potassium channels in the neurons (14, 15, 24, 25, 49).

Most paravertebral sympathetic neurons project to blood vessels in skin, skeletal muscle, and the viscera and have VC function (see 29, 38), whereas only some neurons in the inferior mesenteric ganglion have discharge properties of VC neurons which suggests that they project to blood vessels in colon and pelvic organs (31, 41). This distribution of postganglionic VC neurons, combined with the biophysical and neurochemical properties of para- and prevertebral sympathetic neurons (see above) and the finding that varicosities of adrenergic postganglionic neurons on blood vessels contain neuropeptide Y (47) whereas those associated with the enteric plexuses do not, strongly suggests that postganglionic VC neurons are phasic, contain neuropeptide Y, and receive one or a few strong (suprathreshold) synaptic preganglionic inputs from the spinal cord and no synaptic inputs from the periphery. Impulses may therefore normally be transmitted from pre- to postganglionic VC neurons without alteration in the ganglia. The same may be true for paravertebral sympathetic systems that induce active vasodilation, sweating, and piloerection (29). In contrast, prevertebral sympathetic postganglionic neurons involved in regulation of motility and secretion and in absorption of water and electrolytes integrate synaptic inputs from the spinal cord, from the periphery, and possibly from interneurons in the ganglia (55, 56).

## Nonnicotinic Cholinergic Transmission to Postganglionic Vasoconstrictor Neurons

Synaptic transmission in sympathetic ganglia of amphibia and mammals and its underlying ionic, pharmacological, and metabolic mechanisms have been investigated as models for different types of synaptic transmission in the brain because the autonomic neurons are relatively accessible and simple. Electrical stimulation of sympathetic preganglionic axons elicits not only fast cholinergic nicotinic excitatory synaptic potentials, but also slow cholinergic muscarinic and slow noncholinergic excitatory postsynaptic potentials and in some neurons even inhibitory postsynaptic potentials (see 18, 45, 50). The functions of these nonnicotinic synaptic mechanisms in the neural regulation of the sympathetic target organs are unknown.

Recent experiments have addressed the question of whether the nonnicotinic excitatory potentials occur in vivo in functionally identified postganglionic neurons in the hind limb and tail of the cat and whether the neurons can be activated or their activity can be modulated physiologically by these nonnicotinic synaptic mechanisms. Repetitive electrical stimulation of preganglionic axons with short trains of stimuli elicits (early) high frequency nicotinic responses and (late) low frequency nonnicotinic responses in many postganglionic neurons. The nonnicotinic responses have the following properties: (*a*) They occur only in VC neurons and not in pilomotor nor sudomotor neurons. (*b*) In decentralized preparations (preganglionic axons cut central to the stimulation electrode) they last up to 1 min or longer following a 2-s train of 50 preganglionic stimuli. (*c*) In intact preparations the ongoing activity in VC neurons can be enhanced for 4–40 min following electrical stimulation of preganglionic axons with 50 stimuli at 25 Hz. (*d*) The nonnicotinic responses can only be elicited when preganglionic axons having high thresholds and conducting at less than 3–4 m/s are stimulated. (*e*) At least 5–6 stimuli at 5–10 Hz are necessary to elicit these responses. (*f*) Stimulation of arterial chemoreceptors by hypoxia (ventilation of the animal with a gas mixture of 8% $O_2$ in $N_2$) leads to a reflex activation of postganglionic muscle VC neurons after complete blockade of the nicotinic cholinergic transmission by hexamethonium. (*g*) Late, low-frequency responses, enhancement of ongoing activity, and reflex activation of postganglionic MVC neurons (after blockade of nicotinic transmission) were sometimes, but not always, completely or partially blocked by atropine. These responses were therefore produced by muscarinic and noncholinergic transmission through paravertebral ganglia (9, 27, 32–34, 44).

The membrane processes that mediate long-term synaptic processes and the transmitter(s) that mediates the noncholinergic discharges in the VC neurons are unknown (see 18, 45). Therefore intracellular recordings from postganglionic VC neurons in vivo are needed. Furthermore, we know nothing of the functional contexts in which these nonnicotinic transmissions are used during neural regulation of blood vessels. Theoretically, the central nervous system (CNS) could modulate the level of ongoing firing of postganglionic VC neurons by short, high-frequency bursts of preganglionic activity at long intervals.

## CONCLUSION: THE FINAL COMMON SYMPATHETIC VASOCONSTRICTOR PATHS

1. The neuron chains consisting of pre- and postganglionic VC constitute final common sympathetic VC paths to blood vessels (Figure 1). There are functionally separate peripheral VC paths to skin, skeletal muscle, and viscera. The neurons of each VC path exhibit characteristic discharge patterns according to the function and central organization of the respective system (see Table 1).

2. The preganglionic neurons in the thoraco-lumbar spinal cord integrate the descending excitatory and inhibitory inputs from the brain stem and hypothalamus and the activity in spinal afferent nerves from skin, viscera and deep somatic tissues. The combination of inputs contributing to this final integration is different for each system (see 29, 30).

3. In the sympathetic ganglia the activity in the preganglionic neurons is transmitted synaptically in a direct fashion to postganglionic VC neurons. The activity in these postganglionic neurons is probably dominated by the synaptic input from one or a few preganglionic axons. Other preganglionic synaptic inputs are weak. The postganglionic VC neurons probably do not receive additional synaptic inputs from peripheral afferents.

4. Activity in postganglionic VC neurons to skeletal muscle and skin can also be influenced by cholinergic muscarinic and noncholinergic synaptic mechanisms. This synaptic influence requires repetitive activation of preganglionic neurons and leads to long-term changes in the excitability of the postganglionic neurons for up to several tens of minutes. It is unknown whether these modes of long-term activation or modulation are used during neural regulation of blood flow.

5. At least in some blood vessels (e.g. resistance vessels) the postganglionic activity is transmitted to the vascular smooth muscles via a very specific neuroeffector apparatus, leading in this way to precise neural regulation of blood flow and resistance to flow. The remote neural control of blood vessels

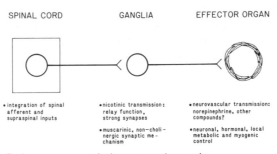

SPINAL CORD          GANGLIA          EFFECTOR ORGAN

• integration of spinal        • nicotinic transmission:        • neurovascular transmission:
  afferent and                   relay function,                  norepinephrine, other
  supraspinal inputs             strong synapses                  compounds?

                               • muscarinic, non-choli-        • neuronal, hormonal, local
                                 nergic synaptic me-              metabolic and myogenic
                                 chanism                          control

*Figure 1*   The final common sympathetic vasoconstrictor path.

by VC neurons interacts with the remote hormonal control and local metabolic and myogenic controls.

6. To summarize, at least three different types of final common sympathetic VC paths transmit the activity from the spinal cord to the blood vessels. The neuronal messages from the CNS are only slightly changed in the sympathetic ganglia and interact at the vascular smooth muscle with remote hormonal, local metabolic, and local myogenic controls.

ACKNOWLEDGMENT

The author's work is supported by the Deutsche Forschungsgemeinschaft.

*Literature Cited*

1. Bahr, R., Bartel, B., Blumberg, H., Jänig, W. 1986. Functional characterization of preganglionic neurons projecting in the lumbar splanchnic nerves: Neurons regulating motility. *J. Auton. Nerv. Syst.* 15:109–30

2. Bahr, R., Bartel, B., Blumberg, H., Jänig, W. 1986. Functional characterization of preganglionic neurons projecting in the lumbar splanchnic nerves: Vasoconstrictor neurons. *J. Auton. Nerv. Syst.* 15:131–40

3. Bahr, R., Bartel, B., Blumberg, H., Jänig, W. 1986. Secondary functional properties of lumbar visceral preganglionic neurons. *J. Auton. Nerv. Syst.* 15:141–52

4. Bainton, C. R., Richter, D. W., Seller, H., Ballantyne, D., Klein, J. P. 1985. Respiratory modulation of sympathetic activity. *J. Auton. Nerv. Syst.* 12:77–90

5. Baron, R., Jänig, W., McLachlan, E. M. 1985. The afferent and sympathetic components of the lumbar spinal outflow to the colon and pelvic organs in the cat. I. The hypogastric nerve. *J. Comp. Neurol.* 236:135–46

6. Baron, R., Jänig, W., McLachlan, E. M. 1985. The afferent and sympathetic components of the lumbar spinal outflow to the colon and pelvic organs in the cat. II. The lumbar splanchnic nerves. *J. Comp. Neurol.* 236:147–57

7. Baron, R., Jänig, W., McLachlan, E. M. 1985. The afferent and sympathetic components of the lumbar spinal outflow to the colon and pelvic organs in the cat. III. The colonic nerves, incorporating an analysis of all components of the lumbar prevertebral outflow. *J. Comp. Neurol.* 236:158–68

8. Bartel, B., Blumberg, H., Jänig, W. 1986. Discharge patterns of motility-regulating neurons projecting in the lumbar splanchnic nerves to visceral stimuli in spinal cats. *J. Auton. Nerv. Syst.* 15:153–63

9. Blumberg, H., Jänig, W. 1983. Enhancement of resting activity in postganglionic vasoconstrictor neurones following short-lasting repetitive activation of preganglionic axons. *Pflüg. Arch.* 396:89–94

10. Blumberg, H., Jänig, W. 1983. Changes of reflexes in vasoconstrictor neurons supplying the cat hindlimb following chronic nerve lesions: A model for studying mechanisms of reflex sympathetic dystrophy? *J. Auton. Nerv. Syst.* 7:399–411

11. Blumberg, H., Jänig, W. 1985. Reflex patterns in postganglionic vasoconstrictor neurons following chronic nerve lesions. *J. Auton. Nerv. Syst.* 14:157–80

12. Blumberg, H., Jänig, W., Rieckmann, C., Szulczyk, P. 1980. Baroreceptor and chemoreceptor reflexes in postganglionic neurones supplying skeletal muscle and hairy skin. *J. Auton. Nerv. Syst.* 12:223–40

13. Burnstock, G. 1986. The changing face of autonomic neurotransmission. *Acta Physiol. Scand.* 126:67–91

14. Cassell, J. F., Clark, A. L., McLachlan, E. M. 1986. Characteristics of phasic and tonic sympathetic ganglion cells of the guinea pig. *J. Physiol. London* 372:457–83

15. Cassell, J. F., McLachlan, E. M. 1986. The effect of a transient outward current $(I_A)$ on synaptic potentials in sympathetic ganglion cells of the guinea pig. *J. Physiol. London* 374:273–88

15a. Ciriello, J., Calaresu, F. R., Renaud, L. P., Polosa, C. (eds) 1987. Organization of the autonomic nervous system.

Central and peripheral mechanisms. New York: Liss. 475 pp

16. Dembowsky, K., Czachurski, J., Seller, H. 1985. An intracellular study of the synaptic input to sympathetic preganglionic neurones of the third segment of the cat. *J. Auton. Nerv. Syst.* 13:201–44

17. Dorward, P. K., Burke, S. L., Jänig, W., Cassell, J. 1987. Reflex responses to baroreceptor, chemoreceptor and nociceptor inputs in single renal sympathetic neurones in the rabbit and the effect of anaesthesia on them. *J. Auton. Nerv. Syst.* 18:39–54

18. Elfvin, L.-G., ed. 1983. *Autonomic Ganglia.* Chichester: Wiley. 527 pp.

19. Gilbey, M. P., Numao, Y., Spyer, K. M. 1986. Discharge patterns of cervical sympathetic preganglionic neurones related to central respiratory drive in the rat. *J. Physiol. London* 378:253–65

20. Gottsckalk, C. W., Moss, N. G., Colindres, R. E. 1985. Neural control of renal function in health and disease. In *The Kidney: Physiology and Pathophysiology,* ed. D. W. Seldin, G. Giebisch, pp. 581–611. New York: Raven. 2162 pp.

21. Gregor, M., Jänig, W. 1977. Effects of systemic hypoxia and hypercapnia on cutaneous and muscle vasoconstrictor neurones to the cat's hindlimb. *Pflüg. Arch.* 368:71–81

22. Hill, C. E., Hirst, G. D. S., Silverberg, G. D., van Helden, D. F. 1986. Sympathetic innervation and excitability of arterioles originating from the rat middle cerebral artery. *J. Physiol. London* 371:305–16

23. Hirst, G. D. S., De Gleria, S., van Helden, D. F. 1985. Neuromuscular transmission in arterioles. *Experientia* 41:874–79

24. Hirst, G. D. S., McLachlan, E. M. 1984. Post-natal development of ganglia in the lower lumbar sympathetic chain of the rat. *J. Physiol. London* 349:119–34

25. Hirst, G. D. S., McLachlan, E. M. 1986. Development of dendritic calcium currents in ganglion cells of the rat lower lumbar sympathetic chain. *J. Physiol. London* 377:349–68

26. Hirst, G. D. S., Neild, T. O. 1980. Evidence for two populations of excitatory receptors for noradrenaline on arteriolar smooth muscle. *Nature* 283:767–68

27. Hoffmeister, B., Hussels, W., Jänig, W. 1978. Long-lasting discharge of postganglionic neurones to skin and muscle of the cat's hindlimb after repeti-

tive activation of preganglionic axons in the lumbar sympathetic trunk. *Pflüg. Arch.* 376:15–20

28. Jänig, W. 1984. Vasoconstrictor systems supplying skeletal muscle, skin, and viscera. *Clin. Exp. Hypertension A* 6:329–46

29. Jänig, W. 1985. Organization of the lumbar sympathetic outflow to skeletal muscle and skin of the cat hindlimb and tail. *Rev. Physiol. Biochem. Pharmacol.* 102:119–213

30. Jänig, W. 1986. Spinal cord integration of visceral sensory systems and sympathetic nervous system reflexes. *Prog. Brain Res.* 67:255–77

31. Jänig, W. 1987. Functional organization of the lumbar sympathetic outflow to pelvic organs and colon. See Ref. 15a, pp. 57–66

32. Jänig, W., Krauspe, R., Wiedersatz, G. 1982. Transmission of impulses from pre- to postganglionic vasoconstrictor and sudomotor neurons. *J. Auton. Nerv. Syst.* 6:95–106

33. Jänig, W., Krauspe, R., Wiedersatz, G. 1983. Reflex activation of postganglionic vasoconstrictor neurones supplying skeletal muscle by stimulation of arterial chemoreceptors via non-nicotinic synaptic mechanisms in sympathetic ganglia. *Pflüg. Arch.* 396:95–100

34. Jänig, W., Krauspe, R., Wiedersatz, G. 1984. Activation of postganglionic neurones via non-nicotinic synaptic mechanisms by stimulation of thin preganglionic axons. *Pflüg. Arch.* 401:318–20

35. Jänig, W., Kümmel, H., Wiprich, L. 1980. Respiratory rhythmicities in vasoconstrictor and sudomotor neurones supplying the cat's hindlimb. In *Central Interaction Between Respiratory and Cardiovascular Control Systems,* ed. H. P. Koepchen, S. M. Hilton, A. Trzebski, pp. 128–35. Berlin: Springer-Verlag. 244 pp.

36. Jänig, W., McLachlan, E. M. 1986. The sympathetic and sensory components of the caudal lumbar sympathetic trunk in the cat. *J. Comp. Neurol.* 245:62–73

37. Jänig, W., McLachlan, E. M. 1986. Identification of distinct topographical distributions of lumbar sympathetic and sensory neurons projecting to end organs with different functions in the cat. *J. Comp. Neurol.* 246:104–12

38. Jänig, W., McLachlan, E. M. 1987. Organization of the lumbar spinal outflow to the distal colon and pelvic organs. *Physiol. Rev.* 67:1332–1404

39. Jänig, W., Räth, B. 1980. Effects of anaesthetics on reflexes in the cat's paws elicited by natural stimulation of Pacinian corpuscles and of cutaneous nociceptors. *J. Auton. Nerv. Syst.* 2:1–14

40. Jänig, W., Schmidt, R. F. 1970. Single unit responses in the cervical sympathetic trunk upon somatic nerve stimulation. *Pflüg. Arch.* 314:199–216

41. Jänig, W., Schmidt, M., Schnitzler, A., Wesselmann, U. 1987. Functional types of sympathetic postganglionic neurones projecting into the hypogastric nerves of the cat. *J. Physiol. London* In press

42. Jänig, W., Sundlöf, G., Wallin, B. G. 1983. Discharge patterns of sympathetic neurons supplying skeletal muscle and skin in man and cat. *J. Auton. Nerv. Syst.* 7:239–56

43. Jänig, W., Szulczyk, P. 1980. Functional properties of lumbar preganglionic neurones. *Brain Res.* 186:115–31

44. Jänig, W., Szulczyk, P. 1981. The organization of lumbar preganglionic neurons. *J. Auton. Nerv. Syst.* 3:177–91

45. Karczmar, A. G., Koketsu, K., Nishi, S. 1986. *Autonomic and enteric ganglia. Transmission and its pharmacology.* New York: Plenum. 514 pp.

46. Luff, S. E., McLachlan, E. M., Hirst, G. D. S. 1987. An ultrastructural analysis of the sympathetic neuromuscular junctions on arterioles of the submucosa of the guinea pig ileum. *J. Comp. Neurol.* 257:578–95

47. Lundberg, J. M., Hökfelt, T. 1986. Multiple co-existence of peptides and classical transmitters in peripheral autonomic and sensory neurones—functional and pharmacological implications. *Prog. Brain Res.* 68:241–62

48. Matsuyama, T., Shiosaka, S., Wanaka, A., Yoneda, A., Kimura, K., et al. 1985. Fine structure of peptidergic and catecholaminergic nerve fibers in the anterior cerebral artery and their inter-relationship: An immunoelectron microscopic study. *J. Comp. Neurol.* 235:268–76

49. McLachlan, E. M., Llewellyn-Smith, I. J. 1986. The immunohistochemical distribution of neuropeptide Y in lumbar pre- and paravertebral sympathetic ganglia of the guinea pig. *J. Auton. Nerv. Syst.* 17:313–24

50. North, A. 1986. Mechanisms of autonomic integration. *Handbook of Physiology. The Nervous System,* Vol. IV: *Intrinsic Regulatory Systems of the Brain,* ed. F. E. Bloom, pp. 115–53. Bethesda, Maryland: Am. Physiol. Soc.

51. Preiss, G., Kirchner, F., Polosa, C. 1975. Patterning of sympathetic preganglionic neurone firing by central respiratory drive. *Brain Res.* 87:363–74

52. Preiss, G., Polosa, C. 1977. The relation between end-tidal CO and discharge patterns of sympathetic preganglionic neurons. *Brain Res.* 122:255–67

53. Richter, D. W., Ballantyne, D. 1983. A three phase theory about the basic respiratory pattern generator. In *Central Neurone Environment and the Control Systems of Breathing and Circulation,* ed. M. E. Schläfke, H. P. Koepchen, W. R. See, pp. 164–74. Berlin: Springer-Verlag

54. Richter, D. W., Ballantyne, D., Remmers, J. E. 1986. How is the respiratory rhythm generated? A model. *News Physiol. Sci.* 1:109–12

55. Simmons, M. 1985. The complexity and diversity of synaptic transmission in the prevertebral sympathetic ganglia. *Prog. Neurobiol.* 24:43–93

56. Szurszewski, J. H. 1981. Physiology of mammalian prevertebral ganglia. *Ann. Rev. Physiol.* 43:53–68

57. van Helden, D. F. 1987. Pre- and postsynaptic mechanisms in neurovascular and neuromuscular transmission. *Neurosci. Lett. Suppl.* 27:S34–S35

Ann. Rev. Physiol. 1988. 50:541–51

# ELECTROPHYSIOLOGICAL PROPERTIES OF SYMPATHETIC PREGANGLIONIC NEURONS

## C. Polosa

Department of Physiology, McGill University, McIntyre Medical Sciences Building, Montreal, Quebec H3G 1Y6, Canada

## M. Yoshimura and S. Nishi

Department of Physiology, Kurume University School of Medicine, Kurume, Japan

## Introduction

The level of sympathetic outflow to cardiovascular effector cells is determined by the number of sympathetic preganglionic neurons (SPNs) that are firing and by the level and pattern of their firing. In turn, properties of the synaptic input as well as of the neuron itself determine whether and how the neuron will fire. The best illustration of the importance of neuron properties in determining response to input is provided by the observation of tonic and phasic responses of neurons of a same population to the stimulus provided by a long intracellular current pulse: The tonic neurons respond with a spike train that lasts as long as the stimulus, while the phasic neurons respond with a burst of spikes at the onset of the pulse and are silent for the rest of the stimulus duration (5, 42). Neuron properties most relevant to the control of firing are the types of ionic channels present in the neuron membrane. This information is usually obtained by means of intracellular recording.

The development of the slice preparation has made SPNs (40) and most neurons of the central nervous system (CNS) (14) more accessible to intracellular recording and has made possible experiments not feasible with standard in vivo preparations. This development has coincided with a marked improvement in the quality of the published in vivo intracellular recordings (11, 12). From both approaches a picture of the ionic channels present in the

541

0066-4278/88/0315-0541$02.00

somatodendritic membrane of the SPNs has begun to emerge. This review summarizes the experimental observations from which this picture has been obtained.

## Resting Membrane Potential

The sympathetic preganglionic neurons of the intermediolateral nucleus of cat or rat upper thoracic cord are the only ones studied in vivo or in vitro with intracellular microelectrodes. In vivo, these neurons receive continuous synaptic input (11), which precludes the assessment of a true "resting" potential. In addition, this region of the spinal cord is difficult to stabilize because of the intrathoracic pressure fluctuations associated with pulmonary ventilation, and cell impalements are likely to be associated with some injury current. These factors may account for the large scatter of resting potential values (from $-40$ to $-80$ mV) reported in studies performed in vivo (7, 11, 12, 30). In contrast, intracellular recordings from the same neurons in the slice preparation show very little spontaneous synaptic activity and are very stable. Therefore they presumably provide a better estimate of the resting potential of the neuron than the in vivo recordings. Mean values of $-61.3$ mV, at an extracellular K concentration of 3.6 mM, have been reported for SPNs in the adult cat (42) and of $-52$ mV, at an extracellular K concentration of 3.1 mM, in the neonatal rat (26). The resting membrane potential of cat SPNs varies inversely with extracellular K concentration, which suggests that it is mainly determined by the transmembrane potassium flux. The fact, however, that at these K concentrations the K equilibrium potential, estimated from the reversal of the early component of the afterhyperpolarization (43), is considerably more negative than the resting potential suggests that other factors, as yet undetermined, also contribute to the resting potential.

## Steady-State Current-Voltage Relations

In the in vitro spinal cord slice preparation of the cat, the current-voltage relation of the SPN membrane is approximately linear in the voltage range from $-25$ to $+5$ mV, relative to a resting potential of $-61$ mV (42). Mean values of input resistance of the neuron ($R_N$) within this voltage range are 67.5 and 105.7 M$\Omega$ in the cat (42) and rat (26), respectively. Membrane depolarization or hyperpolarization outside this range produces a decrease in $R_N$ (42). The ionic conductances underlying these rectifying effects have not been characterized. The rectification caused by large hyperpolarizations may be due to activation of a current analogous to the H current (a mixed Na-K current) described in dorsal root ganglion cells (29). As for the rectification due to depolarization, it may be due to an M current, i.e. to a noninactivating K conductance turned on by depolarization. The rectification caused by large hyperpolarizations has also been observed in in vivo preparations (12). In these preparations values of $R_N$ in a range from 12 to 50 MΩ have been reported for cat SPNs (12, 30), and tonically firing SPNs had lower "resting" membrane potential and $R_N$ than nonfiring (silent) SPNs (12). The time constant of the cat SPN membrane was 11.5 ± 1.2 ms in the in vitro preparation (42). In vivo, values of 4–26 ms (30) and 10–25 ms (12) were reported.

## Steps in Action Potential Generation

The action potential, evoked by antidromic, orthodromic, or intracellular stimulation and recorded by an intrasomatic microelectrode in vivo (7, 12, 18, 30), has a peak amplitude of 70–80 mV. The action potential usually has an inflection on the upstroke at a voltage 20–40 mV positive to the resting potential. Moderate hyperpolarization of the soma during antidromic stimulation blocks a large component of the action potential in an all-or-none fashion, and only a smaller component, of a peak amplitude comparable to that of the above-mentioned inflection on the upstroke, is recorded. With further hyperpolarization this smaller component is also blocked in an all-or-none fashion. This finding suggests that the action potential recorded by an intrasomatic electrode is composed of a lower threshold, smaller amplitude component, which reflects the action potential of the initial segment of the axon, and of a higher threshold, larger amplitude component, which reflects the action potential of the somadendritic membrane (4).

## Ionic Basis of the Action Potential

The action potential of the SPN, evoked by intracellular, antidromic, or orthodromic stimulation and recorded intracellularly in the SPNs of a spinal cord slice superfused with normal Krebs solution (42), has an average duration of 3.03 ms at 37°C and a repolarization phase with a transient slowing or "shoulder." The threshold depolarization for action potentials evoked by intracellular or orthodromic stimulation was between 15 and 20 mV positive to the resting potential. There is evidence that the action potential of the SPN results from Na, Ca, and K currents. The depolarizing phase of the action potential results from influx of both Na and Ca (42). In the in vitro preparation, superfusion with tetrodotoxin (TTX), a blocker of voltage-dependent Na channels (32), eliminates the fast component of the SPN action potential, leaving an action potential of higher threshold (30–50 mV positive to the resting potential), slower rise time, and reduced amplitude. This TTX-resistant action potential is blocked by cobalt, a blocker of calcium channels (1), or by lowering extracellular Ca concentration. Conversely, cobalt or low extracellular Ca concentration, in the absence of TTX, eliminate the "shoulder" on the repolarizing phase of the action potential, reducing its duration. This shorter-lasting action potential is abolished by TTX. Therefore Na influx accounts for the fast component of the normal action potential, whereas Ca influx accounts for a slower component that is responsible for the "shoulder" on the repolarization phase. This inward Ca current associated with the action potential is important for the resulting increase in internal Ca concentration, which then turns on the Ca-activated K conductance responsible for the slow component of the afterhyperpolarization (43). In addition, in the presence of catecholamines, this Ca current, by causing an increase in internal Ca concentration, turns on a Ca-activated Na current, which generates a prolonged afterdepolarization and promotes burst firing (45). The role in the activation of these two conductances of the inward Ca current associated with the action potential is to increase internal Ca concentration. This is shown by experiments with intracellular injection of a Ca chelator (EGTA; 45): Both SPN responses are blocked in this situation, although the inward Ca current, as judged by the shape of the action potential, is still present. The repolarization phase of the action potential is prolonged by superfusion with tetraethylammonium or barium or by intracellular injection of cesium, agents that block K channels (2, 16), which suggests that this phase of the action potential involves an outward K current. These prolonged action potentials are markedly reduced in duration by low Ca or cobalt. Thus, when this outward K current is depressed, the inward Ca current is prolonged.

## After-Hyperpolarization

The somadendritic action potential of the SPN is followed by a long-lasting afterhyperpolarization (AHP). In the spinal cord slice in vitro (43) the AHP that follows a single action potential has an average duration of 2.8 s and a peak amplitude of 16.0 mV. The action potential of the initial segment is not followed by an AHP. The AHP is associated with a decrease in $R_N$, and in most cases can be resolved into an initial, shorter-lasting and usually larger component [fast (FAHP)] followed by a long-lasting component [slow (SAHP)]. An increase in K conductance underlies both components of the AHP as shown by the observations that: (a) both components increase in amplitude with membrane depolarization and decrease with hyperpolarization; (b) both have a null point around $-90$ mV in 3.6 mM extracellular K; (c) for both, the null point shifts in the depolarizing or hyperpolarizing direction when extracellular K concentration is increased or decreased, respectively. However, the K channels giving rise to the two components of the AHP are different, as shown by the observations that: (a) selective depression of the Ca current of the action potential with cobalt or low extracellular Ca concentration attenuates the SAHP but not the FAHP; (b) intracellular Ca chelation with EGTA depresses the SAHP but not the FAHP; and (c) the FAHP reverses in polarity at membrane voltages more negative than $-90$ mV (in 3.6 mM K) and shows an approximately linear relation of amplitude to membrane potential, while the SAHP does not reverse in most cases and thus shows voltage dependence. The dependence of the SAHP on extracellular Ca concentration and its sensitivity to cobalt as well as to intracellular Ca chelation suggest that the SAHP is due to a Ca-activated K conductance. Both AHP components persist when the fast component of the action potential is blocked with TTX. An A current may also participate in the generation of the AHP (44), but this possibility has not been tested.

Dembowsky & colleagues (12) recorded a wide range of AHP durations in vivo (70–4260 ms). Although some of the AHPs were long-lasting, on average the AHP was shorter than in the in vitro recordings. Earlier in vivo studies (7, 18, 30) showed AHPs of even shorter duration. Several factors may be responsible for the shorter duration of the AHP in the in vivo situation. One is the presence of anesthetics, which may interfere with the ionic mechanism of AHP generation (24). Another is the greater amount of synaptic input, which may prevent detection of the low-amplitude, long-lasting tail of the AHP. Still another is the higher probability of impalement damage with resultant shunting of the AHP by inward currents (23, 25). Finally, different concentrations in vivo and in vitro of factors regulating the Ca-activated K conductance [e.g. intracellular Ca (3, 22, 37) or some neurotransmitters (27, 38, 41)] may account for the different duration of the AHP.

During the AHP the SPN is less responsive to intracellular current injection and synaptic excitation (43). The decreased responsiveness seems to be related more to the hyperpolarization itself than to the associated decrease in $R_N$. With repetitive activation, AHPs of successive action potentials summate, resulting in prolonged hyperpolarizations that have peak amplitudes approaching the K equilibrium potential ($E_k$). Summation of successive AHPs may play a role in the progressive increase in interspike interval that characterizes the repetitive firing of SPNs evoked by intracellular injection of long-lasting steps of depolarizing current (42).

## The A Current

Intracellular recordings from SPNs in vitro (42) and in vivo (12) indicate the presence of a transient K current with properties reminiscent of the A current described in other neurons (36). Typically, restoration of the resting membrane potential following a transient hyperpolarization in excess of 10–20 mV induced by intracellular current injection occurs with a time course much slower than predicted from the known time constant of the membrane. This finding suggests that when the SPN membrane is depolarized from a level more negative than the resting potential, an ionic conductance is turned on which then inactivates slowly. The time for complete inactivation is from several hundred milliseconds to more than a second. This transient current increases in low extracellular K, decreases in high extracellular K, has a reversal potential around $-90$ mV, and is suppressed by superfusion with 4-aminopyridine (44). In the firing SPN the membrane potential may be negative enough at the peak of the AHP to remove the inactivation of this transient K current. Thus it may be expected that this transient current will contribute to determining the interspike interval of the repetitively firing SPN, as suggested for the A current of other neurons (6). With regard to silent SPNs, it is not known whether or not at resting potential a significant fraction of these channels is available for activation. If this were the case, this current would be expected to modify the shape of fast excitatory postsynaptic potential (EPSP) and perhaps contribute to the lack of firing of these neurons.

## Afterdepolarization

In some SPNs of the cat the action potential in vivo is followed by an after-depolarization (ADP; 12). This ADP has a duration of 5–12 ms, is abolished by small-amplitude somatic hyperpolarizations or by repetitive soma spike activity, and has been attributed to dendritic propagation of the action potential. This short-duration ADP is reminiscent of ADPs described in other central neurons both in vivo and in vitro, e.g. alpha motoneurons (20, 21, 33) and hippocampal pyramidal cells (39). Such short-duration ADPs have not been observed in SPNs in vitro (42). This may be due either to sampling different from that in the in vivo study or to the loss in the transverse slice, which is 400–500 $\mu$m thick, of a large part of the longitudinal component of the dendritic tree of the SPN, which extends for about 2 mm along the long axis of the cord. In the SPN of the cat in vitro, loading of the neuron with cesium, a K channel blocker, reveals the presence of an ADP of 100–500 ms (46) associated with a decrease in $R_N$. The ADP increases in amplitude with membrane hyperpolarization and is presumably due to an inward Ca current since it is blocked by cobalt or by superfusion with low Ca. In the absence of cesium this inward Ca current is presumably masked by the K current of the AHP. However, its presence in these conditions is suggested by a transient phase of repolarization that appears between the early and late component of the AHP. This transient repolarization gives the afterpotential of some SPNs a triphasic appearance. In these cases cobalt, in addition to eliminating the late component of the AHP, eliminates the transient phase of repolarization and enhances the early component of the AHP (46). A similar ADP was also recorded in the absence of cesium, when Ca in the superfusion medium was replaced by barium, or Na was replaced by tetraethylammonium.

## Synaptic Responses of SPNs

In the slice of the spinal cord of the cat, fast and slow synaptic potentials can be evoked in SPNs by intraspinal stimulation (40). Slow synaptic potentials are more prominent after repetitive stimulation. All synaptic potentials are abolished in low Ca and in TTX. The fast EPSP (duration 40–100 ms) increased in amplitude with membrane hyperpolarization and decreased with depolarization (42). The reversal potential of the fast EPSP, determined in cesium-loaded cells, was $-2.2$ mV (34). Decreasing Na or decreasing K concentration in the extracellular space shifted the reversal potential towards the resting membrane potential. These results suggest that the fast EPSP is caused by an increased conductance of the SPN membrane to these two ions. Increasing intracellular Cl by ionophoresis did not significantly shift the reversal potential of the EPSP.

The fast EPSP is not affected by cholinergic or adrenergic antagonists (34). Glutamate or aspartate depolarized the majority of SPNs in the TTX-treated slice. Glutamate depolarizations were mainly assoicated with $R_N$ decrease, aspartate depolarizations with $R_N$ increase. Thus glutamate is a candidate for a transmitter of the fast EPSP, while aspartate is not. Membrane hyperpolariza-tion enhanced the amplitude of the fast EPSP and of the glutamate depolariza-tion but depressed the aspartate depolarization. The fast EPSP was markedly depressed during the glutamate-induced depolarization or during glutamate superfusion when the membrane potential was maintained at resting level by injection of hyperpolarizing current into the cell. The glutamate antagonist D-glutamylglycine (9) reversibly depressed the fast EPSP, while the glutamate antagonist 2-aminophosphono-valerate, which blocks $N$-methyl-D-aspartate receptors (8), eliminated the aspartate depolarization but did not affect the fast EPSP or the glutamate depolarization (but cf 15). These results suggest that if glutamate is the transmitter of the fast EPSP, it would be acting on receptors of the quisqualate or kainate type but not of the aspartate type.

Slow EPSPs (with a duration of 10–20 s) are characterized by an increase in $R_N$ (47). They decrease in amplitude with membrane hyperpolarization and increase in amplitude with membrane depolarization. The slow EPSP was abolished, without reversal, at membrane voltages close to the presumed value of $E_k$. At constant membrane potential the slow EPSP decreases in amplitude in high [K] and increases in low [K] (34). Changes in intracellular or extracellular Cl concentration did not appreciably alter the slow EPSP. These observations suggest that the slow EPSP is caused by synaptic inactiva-tion of a K conductance of the cell membrane. Depolarizations with character-istics similar to those of the slow EPSP are produced by superfusion with catecholamines and serotonin (40). Some slow EPSPs evoked by intraspinal stimulation are abolished by $\alpha_1$-adrenergic blockers (34).

Fast inhibitory postsynaptic potentials (IPSPs) (duration 50–90 ms) were rarely produced by focal stimulation of the slice. The fast IPSP increased in amplitude with depolarization, decreased with hyperpolarization, and re-versed in polarity at around $-70$ mV (34). It was not affected by cholinergic or adrenergic antagonists. GABA and glycine caused membrane hyperpolarizations with amplitudes that were dependent on the Cl concentration gradient and that had characteristics similar to those of the fast IPSP. In slices of neonatal rat spinal cord spontaneous fast IPSPs and fast IPSPs in SPNs, evoked by dorsal root stimulation, were reversibly blocked by strychnine and not by bicucculine, which suggests that glycine is the mediator of these IPSPs (31). Slow IPSPs (duration 5–10 s) decrease in amplitude with membrane hyperpolarization, are associated with a decrease in neuron input resistance, and are abolished at membrane voltages close to the presumed value of $E_k$ (48). A hyperpolarization with properties similar to those of the slow IPSP is produced in some SPNs by noradrenaline (NA). Both the slow IPSP and the NA-evoked hyperpolarization can be blocked by $\alpha_2$-adrenergic receptor antagonists (34).

Intracellular recording from SPNs in chloralose-anesthetized cats has shown the existence of synaptic potentials that are either spontaneously generated or are evoked by dorsal root or intraspinal stimulation (11). EPSPs with a fast time course (20–40 ms) have been described. IPSPs with a fast time course were infrequently observed and were reversed from hyperpolarizing to depolarizing by intracellular leakage of Cl. Fedorko & colleagues (17) and Dembowsky & colleagues (13) have described a fast IPSP in the cat that is evoked by carotid sinus nerve stimulation and that became depolarizing upon intracellular Cl injection. No recordings of slow excitatory synaptic responses in the SPNs of mammals in vivo are available. A hyperpolarization lasting several hundred milliseconds, always preceded by a fast EPSP and insensitive to intracellular Cl concentration changes, has been described in response to stimulation of the dorsolateral funiculus of the spinal cord or of spinal afferent nerves (11). The mechanism of these longer-lasting hyperpolarizing responses remains to be clarified, but it seems these responses may be analogous to the slow IPSPs observed in vitro.

## Effects of Putative Transmitters on SPN Action Potential and After-Potentials

Some neurotransmitters are known to modify the active properties of nerve cells, i.e. the ionic currents underlying the action potential and afterpotentials of neurons, and indirectly modify neuron responsiveness to input (27, 38). Thus neurotransmitters may influence the activity of postsynaptic neurons by means other than by evoking postsynaptic potentials. In the case of SPNs, only catecholamines have been tested. In the slice of the spinal cord of the cat, superfusion with Krebs solution containing noradrenaline at concentrations of 10–50 $\mu$M reversibly abolished the "shoulder" on the repolarization phase of the action potential and the late component of the AHP which, as discussed above, is due to a Ca-activated K conductance. In addition, NA caused the appearance of a depolarizing afterpotential, which was absent in control conditions, lasting 100–600 ms. The NA-evoked afterdepolarization is voltage-dependent; it is depressed in a nonlinear manner by membrane hyperpolarization. The afterdepolarization was suppressed by cobalt, low [Ca], or by intracellular EGTA injection, as well as by low [Na]. These findings suggest the possibility that the NA-evoked afterdepolarization is due to a Ca-activated Na conductance (45). This afterdepolarization could result in repetitive firing of the neuron in response to a single short intracellular current pulse (41).

## Pacemaker Activity

In the in vitro slice preparation of the upper thoracic spinal cord of the cat, NA at concentrations of 10–50 $\mu$M induced periodic bursts of firing in SPNs (49). The frequency of these bursts was between 0.2 and 1.0 Hz at membrane potentials between $-45$ and $-65$ mV. This rhythm of bursting could be reset by short intracellular current pulses. In the presence of TTX, NA produced a rhythmic oscillation in membrane potential in the same frequency range as the frequency of the bursts. The frequency of oscillation was voltage dependent. Neuronal input resistance decreased at the oscillation peak, and the oscillation was abolished by cobalt or low [Ca].

These findings show that under the influence of a putative transmitter ionic currents are activated in this neuron that result in a behavior of membrane potential typical of pacemaker cells. A similar observation, i.e. the transformation of a nonrhythmic pattern of activity into a rhythmic, endogenous, bursting pattern has been described in neurons of the NTS under the action of thyrotropin releasing hormone (10). Controls of these conductances other than that exerted by NA may exist. Thus the SPN is a conditional pacemaker for which the shift from the nonpacemaker to the pacemaker mode of activity is produced by the presence of the putative transmitter NA. Although experimental evidence shows that the background firing of SPNs in the CNS-intact or spinal preparation is due to synaptic input (11), regular, low-frequency firing of SPNs can be observed in the isolated, deafferented fragment of thoracic cord (28, 35). This firing could be due to pacemaker activity of the type described here. It cannot be excluded that under particular conditions, e.g. increased activity of noradrenergic input, the SPN may develop pacemaker activity even in the CNS-intact preparation. Interestingly, the frequency of this pacemaker activity is within the range of firing frequencies observed in the spinal fragment and, in general, within the range of firing frequencies involved in the maintenance of vasomotor tone (19).

ACKNOWLEDGMENTS

The work by the authors was supported by grants to S. Nishi and M. Yoshimura by the Ministry of Education, Science and Culture of Japan and to

C. Polosa by the Medical Research Council of Canada and the Quebec Heart Foundation.

## Literature Cited

1. Baker, P. F., Meves, H., Ridgway, E. B. 1973. Effects of manganese and other agents on the calcium uptake that follows depolarization of squid axons. *J. Physiol. London* 231:511–26
2. Bezanilla, F., Armstrong, C. M. 1972. Negative conductance caused by entry of sodium and cesium ions into the potassium channels of squid axons. *J. Gen. Physiol.* 60:588–608
3. Brehm, P., Eckert, R. 1978. Calcium entry leads to inactivation of calcium channel in *Paramecium*. *Science* 202:1203–6
4. Brock, L. G., Coombs, J. S., Eccles, J. C. 1953. Intracellular recording from antidromically activated motoneurones. *J. Physiol. London* 122:429–61
5. Cassell, J. F., Clark, A. L., McLachlan, E. M. 1986. Characteristics of phasic and tonic sympathetic ganglion cells of the guinea-pig. *J. Physiol. London* 372:457–83
6. Connor, J. A., Stevens, C. F. 1971. Prediction of repetitive firing behaviour from voltage clamp data on an isolated neurone soma. *J. Physiol. London* 213:31–53
7. Coote, J. H., Westbury, D. R. 1979. Intracellular recordings from sympathetic preganglionic neurons. *Neurosci. Lett.* 15:171–75
8. Davies, J., Francis, A. A., Jones, A. W., Watkins, J. C. 1981. 2-aminophosphonovalerate (2 APV), a potent and selective antagonist of amino acid-induced and synaptic excitation. *Neurosci. Lett.* 21:77–81
9. Davies, J., Watkins, J. C. 1981. Differentiation of kainate and quisqualate receptors in the cat spinal cord by selective antagonism with γ-D- (and L-) glutamylglycine. *Brain Res.* 106:172–77
10. Dekin, M. S., Richerson, G. B., Getting, P. A. 1985. Thyrotropin-releasing hormone induces rhythmic bursting in neurons of the nucleus tractus solitarius. *Science* 229:67–69
11. Dembowsky, K., Czachurski, J., Seller, H. 1985. An intracellular study of the synaptic input to sympathetic preganglionic neurones of the third thoracic segment of the cat. *J. Autonom. Nerv. Syst.* 13:201–44
12. Dembowsky, K., Czachurski, J., Seller, H. 1986. Three types of sympathetic preganglionic neurones with different electrophysiological properties are identified by intracellular recordings in the cat. *Pflüg. Arch.* 406:112–20
13. Dembowsky, K., Czachurski, J., Seller, H. 1986. Baroreceptor induced disfacilitation and postsynaptic inhibition in sympathetic preganglionic neurones of the cat. *Pflüg. Arch.* 406:R24 (Suppl.)
14. Dingledine, R., ed. 1984 *Brain Slices*. New York/London: Plenum. 442 pp.
15. Dun, N. J., Mo, N., Jiang, Z. G. 1986. Excitatory synaptic potentials evoked in rat lateral horn neurons and possible involvement of amino acids. *Fed. Proc.* 45:158
16. Fatt, P., Ginsborg, B. L. 1958. The ionic requirements for the production of action potentials in crustacean muscle fibres. *J. Physiol. London* 142:516–43
17. Fedorko, L., Lioy, F., Terzbski, A. 1985. Synaptic inhibition of sympathetic preganglionic neurones induced by stimulation of the aortic nerve in the cat. *J. Physiol. London* 360:P45
18. Fernandez de Molina, A., Kuno, M., Pel, E. R. 1965. Antidromically evoked responses from sympathetic preganglionic neurones. *J. Physiol. London* 180:321–25
19. Folkow, B. 1952. Impulse frequency in sympathetic vasomotor fibres correlated to the release and elimination of the transmitter. *Acta Physiol. Scand.* 25:49–76
20. Granit, R., Kernell, D., Smith, R. S. 1963. Delayed depolarization and the repetitive response to intracellular stimulation of mammalian motoneurones. *J. Physiol. London* 168:890–910
21. Harada, Y., Takahashi, T. 1983. The calcium component of the action potential in spinal motoneurones of the rat. *J. Physiol. London* 335:89–100
22. Heyer, C. B., Lux, H. D. 1976. Control of the delayed outward potassium currents in bursting pacemaker neurones in the snail, *Helix pomatia*. *J. Physiol. London* 262:349–82
23. Jansen, J. K., Nicholls, J. W. 1973. Conductance changes, an electrogenic pump and the hyperpolarization of leech neurones following impulses. *J. Physiol. London* 229:635–55
24. Kleinhaus, A. L., Pritchard, J. W. 1977. A calcium reversible action of

barbiturates on the leech Retzius cell. *J. Pharmacol. Exp. Ther.* 201:332–39

25. Kuba, K., Morita, K., Nohmi, M. 1983. Origin of calcium ions involved in the generation of a slow afterhyperpolarization in bullfrog sympathetic neurones. *Pflüg. Arch.* 399:194–202

26. Ma, R. C., Dun, N. J. 1985. Vasopressin depolarizes lateral horn cells of the neonatal rat spinal cord in vitro. *Brain Res.* 348:36–43

27. Madison, D. V., Nicoll, R. A. 1982. Noradrenaline blocks accomodation of pyramidal cell discharge in the hippocampus. *Nature* 299:636–38

28. Mannard, A. C., Polosa, C. 1973. Analysis of background firing of single sympathetic preganglionic neurons of cat cervical nerve. *J. Neurophysiol.* 36:398–408

29. Mayer, M. L., Westbrook, G. L. 1983. A voltage-clamp analysis of inward (anomalous) rectification in mouse spinal sensory ganglion neurones. *J. Physiol. London* 340:19–45

30. McLachlan, E. M., Hirst, G. D. 1980. Some properties of preganglionic neurons in upper thoracic spinal cord of the cat. *J. Neurophysiol.* 43:1251–65

31. Mo, N., Dun, N. J. 1987. Is glycine an inhibitory transmitter in rat lateral horn cells? *Brain Res.* 400:139–44

32. Narahashi, T., Moore, J. W., Scott, W. R. 1964. Tetrodotoxin blockage of sodium conductance increase in lobster giant axons. *J. Gen. Physiol.* 47:965–86

33. Nelson, P. G., Burke, R. E. 1967. Delayed depolarization in cat spinal motoneurons. *Exp. Neurol.* 17:16–26

34. Nishi, S., Yoshimura, M., Polosa, C. 1987. Synaptic potentials and putative transmitter actions in sympathetic preganglionic neurons. In *Organization of the Autonomic Nervous System. Central and Peripheral Mechanisms*, ed. J. Ciriello, F. R. Calaresu, L. P. Renaud, C. Polosa, pp. 15–26. New York: Liss

35. Polosa, C. 1968. Spontaneous activity of sympathetic preganglionic neurons. *Can. J. Physiol. Pharmacol.* 46:887–96

36. Rogawski, M. A. 1985. The A-current: How ubiquitous a feature of excitable cells is it? *Trends Neurosci.* 8:214–19

37. Tillotson, D. 1979. Inactivation of Ca conductance dependent on entry of Ca ions in molluscan neurons. *Proc. Natl. Acad. Sci. USA* 76:1497–1500

38. Tokimasa, T. 1984. Muscarinic agonists depress calcium-dependent in bullfrog sympathetic neurons. *J. Autonom. Nerv. Syst.* 10:107–16

39. Wong, R. K. S., Prince, D. A. 1981. Afterpotential generation in hyppocampal pyramidal cells. *J. Neurophysiol.* 45:86–97

40. Yoshimura, M., Nishi, S. 1982. Intracellular recording from lateral horn cells of the spinal cord in vitro. *J. Autonom. Nerv. Syst.* 6:5–11

41. Yoshimura, M., Polosa, C., Nishi, S. 1986. Noradrenaline modifies sympathetic preganglionic neuron spike and afterpotential. *Brain Res.* 362:370–74

42. Yoshimura, M., Polosa, C., Nishi, S. 1986. Electrophysiological properties of sympathetic preganglionic neurons in the cat spinal cord in vitro. *Pflüg. Arch.* 406:91–98

43. Yoshimura, M., Polosa, C., Nishi, S. 1986. Afterhyperpolarization mechanisms in cat sympathetic preganglionic neuron in vitro. *J. Neurophysiol.* 55:1234–46

44. Yoshimura, M., Polosa, C., Nishi, S. 1987. A transient outward rectification in the cat sympathetic preganglionic neuron. *Pflüg. Arch.* 408:207–8

45. Yoshimura, M., Polosa, C., Nishi, S. 1987. Noradrenaline-induced afterdepolarization in cat sympathetic preganglionic neurons in vitro. *J. Neurophysiol.* 57:1314–24

46. Yoshimura, M., Polosa, C., Nishi, S. 1987. Afterdepolarization mechanism in the in vitro, cesium-loaded, sympathetic preganglionic neuron of the cat. *J. Neurophysiol.* 57:1325–37

47. Yoshimura, M., Polosa, C., Nishi, S. 1987. Slow EPSP and the depolarizing action of noradrenaline in sympathetic preganglionic neurons. *Brain Res.* 414:138–42

48. Yoshimura, M., Polosa, C., Nishi, S. 1987. Slow IPSP and the noradrenaline-induced inhibition of the cat sympathetic preganglionic neuron in vitro. *Brain Res.* 419:383–86

49. Yoshimura, M., Polosa, C., Nishi, S. 1987. Noradrenaline induces rhythmic bursting in sympathetic preganglionic neurons. *Brain Res.* 420:147–51

*Ann. Rev. Physiol. 1988. 50:553–64*

# EFFECTS OF PUTATIVE NEUROTRANSMITTERS ON SYMPATHETIC PREGANGLIONIC NEURONS

*Robert B. McCall*

Cardiovascular Diseases Reasearch, The Upjohn Company, Kalamazoo, Michigan 49001

## INTRODUCTION

Sympathetic preganglionic neurons (SPNs) located in the intermediolateral cell column (IML) of the spinal cord represent the final central site for the integration of sympathetic nerve activity emanating from the central nervous system. SPNs and their adjacent antecedent interneurons (26) receive a host of inputs descending from supraspinal sites as well as from visceral and somatic afferent pathways contained within the spinal cord. Tremendous progress has been made over the last several years in identifying the nature of the putative neurotransmitters within these descending projections. The IML has high concentrations of monoamine-, amino acid-, and peptide-containing nerve fibers and terminals (60, 88). However, attempts to assign definitively a functional role of these putative neurotransmitters in modulating SPN discharge have resulted in large bodies of conflicting data. The purpose of this review is to summarize the recent literature on the functional role of putative neurotransmitters in regulating the discharge of SPNs. Limitations of experimental approaches and discrepancies due to conclusions drawn from different techniques are discussed, and potential resolutions to controversies of the functional role of neurotransmitters are offered.

553

0066-4278/88/0315-0553$02.00

## MONOAMINES

A wealth of anatomical evidence demonstrates that the IML receives a particularly dense noradrenergic innervation (15). Noradrenergic terminals are localized in clusters that closely correspond with nuclear regions containing SPNs (43, 86). Autoradiographic studies indicate that $\alpha_2$-adrenergic receptors are highly concentrated over clusters of SPNs in the IML (89). The major noradrenergic input to the IML arises from the A5 cell group; a minor input may come from the A1 cell group (6, 15, 24, 42, 45, 59, 60). Electrical and glutamate stimulation of the A5 area results in increases and decreases in blood pressure, respectively (57, 80). Intraventricular administration of 6-hydroxydopamine abolishes the depressor response to chemical stimulation; however, the pressor response to electrical stimulation remains intact. Since glutamate is thought to activate cell bodies, but not axons, Loewy et al (57, 80) concluded that the pressor response following electrical stimulation was mediated by noncatecholamine fibers that pass through the A5 area. They found that individual A5 neurons project to the IML and the nucleus tractus solitarius and that both these areas contribute to the A5 depressor response (57). Microiontophoretic studies support the theory that a descending noradrenergic pathway to the IML inhibits SPNs. Microiontophoretic application of the catecholamines dopamine, norepinephrine, and epinephrine consistently inhibits the firing rate of SPNs (14, 19, 31, 32, 47). The inhibitory effects of microiontophoretically applied norepinephrine were blocked by $\alpha_2$-adrenergic receptor antagonists (i.e. yohimbine and piperoxane) but not by the $\alpha_1$-receptor antagonist prazosin or by $\beta$-receptor antagonists (31, 47). This indicates that the inhibitory effects of norepinephrine are mediated by $\alpha_2$-adrenergic receptors. Consistent with this view is the observation that microiontophoretic application of the $\alpha_2$-agonist clonidine inhibited SPNs while the $\alpha_1$-agonist phenylephrine had no effect (31).

Although the above data suggest that noradrenergic neurons inhibit SPNs, there is a substantial body of evidence suggesting the opposite. (a) We found that a number of $\alpha_1$-adrenergic receptor antagonist (i.e. prazosin, WB-4101, and ketanserin) inhibit spontaneous sympathetic nerve discharge via an action in the spinal cord (72, 73, 76). Since $\alpha_1$-receptors are thought to mediate excitatory effects of norepinephrine in the central nervous system (1), these data indirectly suggest norepinephrine excites sympathetic neurons in the spinal cord. (b) Administration of the catecholamine precursor L-dopa increases excitability in spinal sympathetic pathways (34). (c) Using a slice preparation, two groups found that superfusion of norepinephrine causes a membrane depolarization in antidromically identified SPNs and results in repetitive cell discharges (63, 81, 103, 104). Pretreating the slices with $\alpha_1$-receptor antagonists but not $\alpha_2$- or $\beta$-receptor antagonists prevented the depolarizing effect of norepinephrine (81).

Thus data exist to support either an excitatory or an inhibitory role of norepinephrine in regulating SPN discharge. An excellent study by Nishi et al (81) may resolve this controversy. They found that SPNs in a slice preparation exhibited a fast excitatory postsynapitic potential (EPSP) [or rarely a fast inhibitory postsynaptic potential (IPSP)] in response to single focal stimulation. Trains of repetitive stimuli produced a slow EPSP, which was occasionally accompanied by a slow IPSP. The slow EPSP was always associated with an increased input resistance, disappeared at levels of anodal hyperpolarization exceeding -80 mV, and was specifically blocked by the $\alpha_1$-receptor antagonist prazosin. Norepinephrine superfusion produced a depolarization that shared the same characteristics of the slow EPSP. The slow IPSP was not normally observed until the slow EPSP was eliminated by prazosin. Following the use of prazosin, norepinephrine produced a hyperpolarization. Both the slow IPSP and the norepinephrine-induced hyperpolarization were accompanied by a decreased input resistance, reversed at $-90$ mV, and abolished by the $\alpha_2$-adrenergic receptor antagonist yohimbine.

From this data we can speculate that noradrenergic neurons can both excite and inhibit SPNs. The inhibitory interaction is mediated by $\alpha_2$-receptors located on or near the soma; the excitatory interaction occurs through $\alpha_1$-receptors located on distal dendrites. Since the recording electrode of large multibarreled pipettes used in microiontophoretic experiments must be near the soma in order to record action potentials, iontophoresis of norepinephrine appears to have only an inhibitory effect. In contrast, norepinephrine reaches the excitatory receptors located on dendritic trees in a superfused slice preparation. The dual action of norepinephrine is supported by a recent study in animals in which the Nucleus of the Tractus Solitarius was lesioned. This study demonstrated that electrical stimulation of the A5 area results in pressor responses that can be prevented by pretreatment with 6-hydroxydopamine (98). A similar dual excitatory-inhibitory role for norepinephrine has been demonstrated in Purkinje cells (99).

On the basis of immunohistochemical studies with antibodies to phenylethanolamine-$N$-methyltransferase (PNMT), the enzyme that converts norepinephrine to epinephrine, Hokfelt et al (38) suggested that the IML receives inputs from epinephrine-containing neurons. Anatomical evidence overwhelmingly indicates that this input arises from C1 epinephrine neurons located in the rostral ventrolateral medulla (45, 84). The importance of the rostral ventrolateral medulla in cardiovascular regulation is reviewed by Calaresu & Yardley (this volume). Briefly, focal electrical or chemical stimulation of the region containing C1 epinephrine neurons, or their descending axons, elicits pressor responses and tachycardia. The magnitude of the pressor response correlates with the placement of the stimulating electrode within the C1 area. Localized bilateral lesions coinciding precisely with the C1 area cause a decrease in blood pressure comparable to levels observed following spinal cord transection. These and similar findings (11, 16, 85, 88) led to the hypothesis that descending epinephrine neurons from the C1 area of the rostral ventrolateral medulla provide a tonic excitatory input to SPNs that is responsible for the maintenance of resting arterial blood pressure. In direct opposition to this hypothesis, however, microiontophoretic application of epinephrine consistently inhibits SPNs (31, 32, 47). We know that the epinephrine-induced inhibition of SPNs is mediated via an $\alpha_2$-adrenergic receptor since the inhibition can be blocked by the $\alpha_2$-antagonists yohimbine and piperoxane (32, 47). Ross et al (85) pointed out that these results must be viewed cautiously since epinephrine released from nerve terminals may act on receptors distant from those acted on by iontophoretic epinephrine (e.g. distal dendrites or antecedent interneurons) (26). Sangdee & Franz (86) found that two selective inhibitors of central epinephrine synthesis (LY 134046 and SKF 64139) gradually, but markedly, enhanced descending intraspinal transmission to SPNs. These data suggest that bulbospinal epinephrine pathways depress rather than enhance the excitability of SPNs.

The most convincing argument that epinephrine-containing C1 neurons mediate a sympathoexcitatory function is the remarkable correlation between the location of rostral ventrolateral pressor sites and the medullospinal C1 epinephrine neurons (16, 85). However, this is only correlative data and should be viewed with caution, particularly in light of recent anatomical data. Loewy et al (36) identified a group of substance P immunoreactive neurons in the immediate vicinity of C1 epinephrine neurons that project to the IML. Jeske & Nelson (45) found that large numbers of non-epinephrine-containing neurons are intermingled with C1 epinephrine neurons and that both groups of neurons project to the IML. The C1 area also contains neurons whose cell bodies are immunoreactive to serotonin (44), acetylcholine (96), met- and leu-enkephalin (22), somatostatin (23), neurotensin (11), neuropeptide Y (9), cholecystokinin (66), vasoactive intestinal peptide (54), and thyrotropin-releasing hormone (21, 46). The fact that several non-epinephrine-containing neurons, some of which project to the IML, are intermingled with epinephrine neurons in the rostral ventrolateral medulla, coupled with the fact that microiontophoretic epinephrine consistently inhibits SPNs, leads to the conclusion that C1 epinephrine neurons have a sympathoinhibitory function rather than a sympathoexcitory function. Clearly, however, further experiments are required to definitively demonstrate the functional importance of these neurons.

The presence of a dense network of 5-HT fibers in the IML was first demonstrated by Dahlstrom and Fuxe (15) by using fluorescence techniques. Receptor autoradiography combined with retrograde labeling of SPNs indicates that 5-HT receptors are more highly concentrated over SPNs than adjacent areas in the IML or the intermediate grey area (89). The 5-HT innervation of the IML arises in the B1, B2, and B3 5-HT cell groups, which corresponds roughly to the nucleus raphe (n.r.) obscurus, n.r. pallidus, and n.r. magnus, respectively (55, 58, 60).

The area of the midline medulla that contains 5-HT neurons projecting to the IML corresponds to the classic medullary depressor region (95). The close association between 5-HT descending neurons and midline sites that elicit vasodepressor responses when electrically stimulated has led to the conclusion that the descending 5-HT pathway inhibits SPNs (8, 12, 28, 40). The finding that stimulation of presumed 5-HT-containing axons in the dorsolateral funiculus of the spinal cord inhibits sympathetic activity (13) supports this hypothesis. In addition, administration of 5-HT precursors produces a dose-dependent depression of spinal sympathetic reflexes (34). Finally, a large amount of pharmacologic data suggests that 5-HT neurons inhibit sympathetic activity (51).

In contrast, microiontophoretically applied 5-HT excites SPNs (14, 19, 67). Coote and co-workers (14, 28) suggested that the contradictory iontophoretic and stimulation data can be explained on the basis that 5-HT is not normally released onto SPNs but onto closely adjacent sympathoinhibitory interneurons. Based on stimulation studies, they concluded that 5-HT inhibits SPNs by activating antecedent inhibitory interneurons. This implies that iontophoretically applied 5-HT (which excites SPNs) has no physiological relevance. Studies performed in our laboratory take exception to this viewpoint. We found that iontophoretic 5-HT consistently excited SPNs and that this effect could be antagonized by the 5-HT antagonists methysergide and metergoline (67, 74). More importantly, iontophoretic 5-HT antagonists decrease the spontaneous discharge rate of SPNs in intact, but not in spinal-transected, animals (67). These observations indicate that medullospinal 5-HT neurons provide a tonic excitatory input to SPNs. The excitatory effects of 5-HT probably result from a direct action on SPNs or an indirect action on excitatory sympathetic interneurons, since inhibitory sympathetic interneurons are not found in the IML (71). Support for a direct excitatory action of 5-HT on SPNs also comes from slice studies that show that super-fused 5-HT depolarizes SPNs, with an associated increase in membrane resistance (65, 81). The depolarizing action of 5-HT persists in the presence of tetrodotoxin or in the absence of external $Ca^{2+}$; this indicates that 5-HT acts directly on SPNs (65).

Recent studies provide an explanation for the conflicting results obtained by stimulation and iontophoretic experiments. (a) Careful search of the midline medulla with stimulating electrodes yields sites that evoke sympathoexcitatory, as well as the expected sympathoinhibitory responses (68). (b) Intravenous or intrathecal administration of 5-HT antagonists block or reverse sympathoexcitatory responses elicited from midline raphe nuclei but not from the rostral ventrolateral medulla. Sympathoinhibitory responses are either unaffected or potentiated by 5-HT antagonists. (c) The 5-HT uptake inhibitor chlorimipramine potentiates the sympathoexcitatory response elicited from the raphe but not from the rostral ventrolateral medulla (68). (*d*) Sympathoinhibitory responses are abolished by gamma amino butyric acid (GABA) antagonists and potentiated by benzodiazepines (75). (*e*) Stimulation of the lateral wings of the B1 and B3 5-HT cell groups elicits a pressor response that is blocked by pretreatment with the 5-HT neurotoxin 5,7-dihydroxytryptamine (41). (*f*) Stimulation of the B3 cell group causes an increase in 5-HT release in the thoracic spinal cord and an associated increase in blood pressure (82). These data indicate the midline medulla is heterogenous in respect to autonomic function with sympathoexcitatory elements mediated by 5-HT and sympathoinhibitory elements mediated in part by GABA (69).

## AMINO ACIDS

Microiontophoretic application of the excitatory amino acids glutamate and aspartate excite most SPNs (2, 27, 67). In a slice preparation, Yoshimura & Nishi (103) found that glutamate-induced depolarizations were associated with both a decreased (84%) and an increased membrane resistance (16%). In contrast, the aspartate-induced depolarizations were always associated with an increased resistance. All responses were unaffected by tetrodotoxin. Focal electrical stimulation evoked a fast EPSP that was quite similar to the ionic mechanisms involved in the glutamate depolarization (81). Furthermore, the fast EPSP was suppressed during glutamate depolarization. These data suggest that the fast EPSP may be mediated by glutamate (81). Intrathecal administration of the excitatory amino acid antagonist kynurenate eliminates spontaneous sympathetic activity and blocks the sympathoexcitatory effect of electrical stimulation of the rostral ventrolateral medulla; these effects could be reversed by intrathecal kainate. This implies that the effects of kynurenate were produced by a specific action on an excitatory amino acid receptor (90). Similarly, we found that intrathecal administration of a second excitatory amino acid antagonist (HA-966) also eliminated sympathetic nerve discharge (SND) and reduced blood pressure to a level observed in spinal-transected animals (unpublished observations). These data suggest that descending medullo-spinal sympathoexcitatory neurons employ an excitatory amino acid as their neurotransmitter. Obviously, this hypothesis requires additional testing with more sophisticated techniques.

Microiontophoresis of the inhibitory amino acids GABA and glycine consistently inhibit SPNs (3). An anatomical correlate to the inhibitory effects of GABA has recently been provided (7). The SPN neuropil contains a dense network of GABA-like immunoreactive processes that surrounds SPNs. At the ultrastructural level, GABA-like terminals make synaptic contacts with SPN soma and dendrites. These GABAergic elements probably provide a tonic inhibitory input to SPNs since intrathecal or iontophoretic application of GABA antagonists increases spontaneous sympathetic activity (3, 30). Furthermore, GABA antagonists block the sympathoinhibitory effect of electrical stimulation of visceral and somatic afferents (100).

Mo & Dun (79) utilized a slice preparation to record spontaneous IPSPs and IPSPs evoked by dorsal root stimulation in SPNs. IPSPs were abolished in a low $Ca^{2+}$ solution, which indicates they were mediated by release of a chemical neurotransmitter. The glycine antagonist strychnine (however; not the GABA antagonist bicuculline) eliminated the IPSPs. Hyperpolarizations elicited by exogenous glycine exhibited electrophysiological and pharmacological charactertistics similar to those of the IPSPs. For example, both IPSPs and glycine-induced hyperpolarizations (a) were associated with increases in membrane conduction, (b) were reduced by membrane hyperpolarization, (c) exhibited similar reversal potentials, and (d) were blocked by strychnine. These data suggest that glycine also plays an important role in regulating the discharges of SPNs. In this regard, glycine has been implicated in a possible recurrent inhibition of SPNs (52).

## NEUROPEPTIDES

A wide variety of neuropeptides are concentrated in the IML. Unfortunately, studies have lagged in determining the functional importance of most neuropeptides in the IML. A notable exception to this is substance P, which is heavily concentrated in the IML (33, 36, 92). Autoradiographic binding studies indicate that the IML contains a dense distribution of high affinity, substance P binding sites that are located on SPNs (35, 91). The origin of the substance P input to the IML remains somewhat controversial. A major source of input appears to be substance P cell bodies in the ventrolateral medulla (36). At least some of these substance P neurons seem to contain epinephrine (62). In addition, substance P is colocalized with 5-HT-containing neurons in medullary raphe nuclei (46). Although these neurons project to the spinal cord, they have not been shown to innervate the IML (36). Finally, a portion of the substance P input to the IML arises from spinal interneurons (17, 18).

Microiontophoretically applied substance P excites SPNs (4, 29). The onset of the excitatory response is delayed (i.e. 30 s) and the increased firing rate of SPNs continues long after the application of substance P is terminated (i.e. 30-320 s). Intrathecal administration of substance P or stable agonist analogs of this peptide increase blood pressure and plasma catecholamine levels (48, 102). Intrathecal administration of substance P antagonists decreases blood pressure to the levels observed in spinal-transected animals (61, 93). Microinjection of kainic acid into the rostral ventrolateral medulla increases blood pressure and is associated with release of immunoreactive substance P from the spinal cord (92). Microinjection of the GABA antagonist bicuculline into the rostral ventrolateral medulla also increases blood pressure; this effect is blocked by intrathecal substance P antagonists (49). These studies led to the hypothesis that substance P neurons arising in the ventral lateral medulla and descending to the IML function as a major tonic excitatory pathway in regulating sympathetic activity (56). This hypothesis hinges on the (as yet unproven) specificity of substance P antagonists at the level of the SPN. Further studies are also required to determine the functional significance of the colocalization of substance P with epinephrine and 5-HT neurons.

In recent years anatomical evidence has accumulated indicating that a pathway exists from the paraventricular nucleus (PVN) of the hypothalamus to the IML (87). Immunohistochemical studies show that spinally projecting neurons from the PVN contain oxytocin and vasopressin and that these two neuropeptides are contained in the IML (39, 50). Investigators in the laboratory of Coote (27) reported that microiontophoresis of arginine vasopressin (AVP) and oxytocin, as well as electrical stimulation of PVN, inhibited SPNs. More recent studies fail to support these observations: Backman & Henry (5) found that microiontophoretic AVP excites SPNs. Ciriello & Calaresu (10) reported that stimulation of the PVN increases sympathetic activity. Ma & Dun (64) found that superfusion of AVP depolarizes SPNs in a slice preparation. Vasopressin 1 antagonists blocked this effect while a vasopressin 2 agonist had little effect. AVP-induced depolarizations were partially reduced by a low Ca/high Mg solution, which suggests that AVP excites SPNs by a direct depolarization and by an indirect effect via the release of an excitatory transmitter. Intrathecal administration of AVP increases blood pressure. Intrathecal administration of a vasopressin 1 antagonist blocked this effect but failed to antagonize the pressor response to electrical stimulation of the PVN (83). Thus vasopressin can excite SPNs, but the pressor response elicited by PVN stimulation is not mediated by a spinal action of this neuropeptide. It is possible that vasopressin released from spinal nerve terminals during PVN stimulation had access to receptors that could not be reached by intrathecally administered antagonists. In any case, these studies suggest the intriguing possibility of an interaction between neuroendocrine and sympathetic regulatory mechanisms.

In addition to substance P, vasopressin, and oxytocin, the IML contains metenkephalin (39, 50, 53), thyrotropin-releasing hormone (TRH) (37), neurophysin (39, 50), somatostatin (39, 50), cholecystokinin (66), corticotropin-releasing factor (78), and neurotensin (50) immunoreactive fibers. At least a portion of the enkephalin and TRH innervation of the IML appears to be colocalized with descending 5-HT neurons located in medullary raphe nuclei (37, 53). Unfortunately, little is known regarding the importance of these neuropeptides in regulating the discharges of SPNs. Intrathecal administration of dynorphin decreases blood pressure, heart rate, and sympathetic activity (101). Enkephalin depresses sympathetic activity in both an intraspinal excitatory pathway and a spinal reflex pathway (25). McKenna & Schramm (77) found that naloxone blocked a portion of the post excitatory depression following SPN discharge, which suggests that the silent period of SPN is modulated in part by an opiate mechanism. These data suggests that enkephalin inhibits sympathetic activity in the IML. Finally, Backman & Henry (4) demonstrated that iontophoretic TRH weakly excited SPNs, a fact suggesting that this neuropeptide may function in sympathoexcitatory processes. Clearly, many additional studies are required to elucidate the role of neuropeptides in the regulation of SPNs.

## SUMMARY

Epinephrine, substance P, and glutamate have all been hypothesized as primary chemical mediators in the descending pathway from the brain stem "vasomotor center" to SPNs. Interestingly, lesions of or antagonists to epinephrine, substance P, glutamate, and 5-HT neurons all abolish sympathetic activity and reduce blood pressure to a level similar to that in a spinal-transected animal. However, it is unlikely that all these substances are primary mediators of sympathetic information carried from the brain stem to the spinal cord. How then do we resolve these findings? A plausible explanation is that monoamines and neuropeptides act in the IML, as in other areas of the central nervous system, as neuromodulators, setting the level of excitability of SPNs rather than relaying sympathetic information over a functionally specific pathway from brain stem sympathetic neurons to the IML. For example, the time course of the norepinephrine-mediated slow EPSPs and IPSPs in SPNs (81) is consistant with a gain-setting function. Likewise, the depolarization of SPNs by 5-HT (65) is similar to the depolarization elicited in myenteric and celiac ganglion cells (20, 97). In these ganglia, 5-HT appears to mediate a slow excitatory potential that enhances incoming fast synaptic potentials. A similar gain-enhancing effect of 5-HT has been demonstrated in facial motoneurons (70). By analogy, epinephrine is likely to act as a neuromodulator in the IML rather than to serve as the primary mediator of sympathetic information descending from the brain stem. Similarly, it is difficult to imagine that an agent with such a long duration of excitatory action as substance P (4) could serve as the primary descending transmitter in a system where moment to moment changes in activity are essential. It is more likely that substance P aids in setting the excitability of SPNs.

Pharmacological antagonism of any of the excitatory neuromodulators (i.e. gain setters) might act to decrease, at least temporarily, the excitability of SPNs to the point where primary sympathetic activity from the brain stem could not excite SPNs. This accounts for the wide variety of pharmacological agents that act to eliminate sympathetic activity and drastically reduce blood pressure. On the basis of the above arguments, the most logical candidate for a transmitter mediating primary excitatory sympathetic information from brain stem "vasomotor centers" would be an excitatory amino acid. Fast EPSPs in SPNs appear to be mediated by glutamate (81) and excitatory amino acid antagonists markedly inhibit sympathetic activity (90). The rapid time course of glutamate effects is consistent with a system in which activity changes from moment to moment. The inhibitory amino acids undoubtedly tonically depress the excitability of SPNs. Needless to say, many studies are required to determine if this picture of neurotransmitter function in the IML is accurate. In addition, the significance of the colocalization of peptides and monoamines in fibers innervating the IML needs to be determined.

## Literature Cited

1. Aghajanian, G. K., Rogawski, M. A. 1983. *Trends in Pharmacol. Sciences* 4:315–17
2. Backman, S. B., Henry, J. L. 1983. *Brain Res.* 277:370–74
3. Backman, S. B., Henry, J. L. 1983. *Brain Res.* 277:365–9
4. Backman, S. B., Henry, J. L. 1983. *Can. J. Physiol. Pharmacol.* 62:248–51
5. Backman, S. B., Henry, J. L. 1984. *Brain Res. Bull.* 13:679–84
6. Blessing, W. W., Goodchild, A. K., Dampney, R. A. L., Chalmers, J. P. 1981. *Brain Res.* 221:35–55
7. Bogan, N., Mennone, A., Cabot, J. 1986. *Neurosci. Abst.* 12:1157
8. Cabot, J. B., Wild, J., Cohen, D. H. 1979 *Science* 203:184–86
9. Chronwall, B. M., DiMaggio, D. A., Massari, V. J., Pickel, V. M., Ruggiero, D. A. et al. 1985. *J. Neurosoci.* 15:1159–81
10. Ciriello, J., Calaresu, F. R. 1980. *Am. J. Physiol.* 239:R137–42
11. Ciriello, J., Caverson, M. M., Polosa, C. 1986. *Brain Res. Rev.* 11:359–91
12. Coote, J. H., Macleod, V. H. 1974. *J. Physiol. (London)* 241:453–75
13. Coote, J. H., Macleod, V. H. 1975. *Pflügers Arch.* 359:335–47
14. Coote, J. H., Macleod, V. H., Fleetwood-Walker, S., Gilbey, M. P. 1981. *Brain Res.* 215:135–45
15. Dahlstrom, A., Fuxe, K. 1965. *Acta Physiol. Scand. Suppl.* 27 64(247):5–36
16. Dampney, R. A. L., Goodchild, A. K., Tan, E. 1985. *J. Auton. Nerv. Syst.* 14: 239–254
17. Davis, B. M., Cabot, J. B. 1984. *J. Neurosci.* 4:2145–59
18. Davis, B. M., Krause, J. E., McKelry, J. F., Cabot, J. B. 1984. *Neuroscience* 13:1311–26
19. DeGroat, W. C., Ryall, R. W. 1967. *Exp. Brain Res.* 3:299–305
20. Dun, N. J., Ma, R. C. 1984. *J. Physiol. (London)* 351:47–60
21. Eskay, R. L., Long, R. T., Palkovits, M. 1983. *Brain Res.* 277: 159–62
22. Finley, J. C., Maderdrut, J. L., Petrusz, P. 1981. *J. Comp. Neurol.* 198:541–65
23. Finley, J. C., Maderdrut, J. L., Roger, L. J., Petrusz, P. 1981. *Neuroscience* 6:2173–92
24. Fleetwood-Walker, S. M., Coote, J. H. 1981. *Brain Res.* 205: 141–55
25. Franz, D. N., Hare, B. D., McCloskey, K. L. 1982. *Science* 215: 1643-45
26. Gebber, G. L., McCall, R. B. 1976. *Am. J. Physiol.* 231:722–33
27. Gilbey, M. P., Coote, J. H., Fleetwood-Walker, S., Peterson, D. F. 1982. *Brain Res.* 251:283–90
28. Gilbey, M. P., Coote, J. H., Macleod, V. H., Peterson, D. F. 1981. *Brain Res.* 226:131–42
29. Gilbey, M. P., McKenna, K. E., Schramm, L. P. 1983. *Neurosci. Lett.* 41:157–59

30. Gordon, F. J. 1985. *Brain Res.* 328:165–69
31. Guyenet, P. G., Cabot, J. B. 1981. *J. Neurosci.* 1:908–17
32. Guyenet, P. G., Stornetta, R. L. 1982. *Brain Res.* 235:271–83
33. Hancock, M. B. 1982. *J. Auton. Nerv. Syst.* 6:263–72
34. Hare, B. D., Neuymayr, R. J., Franz, D. N. 1972. *Nature* 239:336–37
35. Helke, C. J., Charlton, C. G., Wiley, R. G. 1986. *J. Neurosci.* 19:523–33
36. Helke, C. J., Neil, J. J., Massari, V. J., Loewy, A. D. 1982. *Brain Res.* 243:147–52
37. Helke, C. J., Sayson, S. C., Keeler, J. R., Charlton, C. G. 1986. *Brain Res.* 381:1–7
38. Hokfelt, T., Goldstein, M., Fuxe, K., Johansson, O., Verhofstad, A., et al. 1980. *Central Adrenaline Neurons,* pp. 19–47. Oxford: Permagon
39. Holets, V., Elde, R. 1982. *Neuroscience* 7:1155–74
40. Howe, P. R. C. 1985. *J. Auton. Nerv. Syst.* 12:95–115
41. Howe, P. R. C., Kuhn, D. M., Minson, J. B., Stead, B. H., Chalmers, J. P. 1983. *Brain Res.* 270:29–36
42. Hudson, M. E., Fuxe, K., Goldstein, M., Kalia, M. 1986. *Neurosci. Abstr.* 12:535
43. Hwang, B. H., Williams, T. H. 1982. *Brain Res. Bull.* 9:171–77
44. Jacobs, B. L., Gannon, P. J., Azmitia, E. C. 1984. *Brain Res. Bull.* 13:1–31
45. Jeske, I., Nelson, D. O. 1987. *Fed. Abstr.* 46:1243.
46. Johansson, O., Hokfelt, T., Pernow, B., Jeffcoate, S. R., White, N., et al. 1981. *J. Neurosci.* 6:1857–81
47. Kadzielawa, K. 1983. *Neuropharmacology* 22:3–17
48. Keeler, J. R., Charlton, C. G., Helke, C. J. 1985. *J. Pharmacol. Exp. Ther.* 233:755–60
49. Keeler, J. R., Helke, C. J. 1985. *J. Auton. Nerv. Styst.* 13:19–33
50. Krukoff, T. L., Ciriello, J., Calaresu, F. R. 1985. *J. Comp. Neurol.* 240:103–16
51. Kuhn, D. M., Wolf, W. A., Lovenberg, W. 1980. *Hypertension* 2:243–55
52. Lebedev, V. P., Petrov, V. I., Skobelev, V. A. 1980. *Pflügers Arch.* 383:91–92
53. Leger, L., Charnay, Y., Dubois, P. M., Jouvet, M. 1986. *Brain Res.* 362:63–73
54. Leibstein, A. G., Dermietzel, R., Willenberg, I. M., Pauschert, R. 1985. *J. Auton. Nerv. Syst.* 14:299–313.
55. Loewy, A. D. 1981. *Brain Res.* 222:129–33
56. Loewy, A. D. 1987. In *Cardiogenic Re-flexes,* ed. R. Hainsworth, R. J. Linden, P. N. McWilliam, D.A.S.G. Mary, pp 269–85. Oxford: Oxford Univ. Press
57. Loewy, A. D., Marson, L., Parkinson, D., Perry, M. A., Sawyer, W. B. 1986. *Brain Res.* 386:313–24
58. Loewy, A. D., McKellar, S. 1981. *Brain Res.* 211:146-52.
59. Loewy, A. D., McKellar, S., Saper, C. B. 1979. *Brain Res.* 174:309–14
60. Loewy, A. D., Neil, J. J. 1981. *Fed. Proc.* 40:2778–85
61. Loewy, A. D., Sawyer, W. B. 1982. *Brain Res.* 245:379–83
62. Lorenz, R. G., Saper, C. B., Wong, D. L., Ciaranello, R. D., Loewy, A. D. 1985. *Neurosci. Lett.* 55:255–60
63. Ma, R. C., Dun, N. J. 1985. *Neurosci. Lett.* 60:163–68
64. Ma, R. C., Dun, N. J. 1985. *Brain Res.* 348:36–43
65. Ma, R. C., Dun, N. Y. 1986. *Develop. Brain Res.* 24:89–98.
66. Mantyh, P. W., Hunt, S. P. 1984. *Brain Res.* 291:49–54.
67. McCall, R. B. 1983. *Brain Res.* 289:121–27
68. McCall, R. B. 1984. *Brain Res.* 311:131–39
69. McCall, R. B. 1987. *Organization of the Autonomic Nervous System: Central and Peripheral Mechanisms,* pp. 283–93. New York: Liss
70. McCall, R. B., Aghajanian, G. K. 1979. *Brain Res.* 169:11–27
71. McCall, R. B., Gebber, G. L., Barman, S. M. 1977. *Am. J. Physiol.* 232:H657–65
72. McCall, R. B., Harris, L. T. 1987. *J. Pharmacol. Exp. Therap.* 241:736–40
73. McCall, R. B., Humphrey, S. J. 1981. *J. Auton. Nerv. Syst.* 3:9–23
74. McCall, R. B., Humphrey, S. J. 1982. *J. Pharmacol. Exp. Therap.* 222:94–102
75. McCall, R. B., Humphrey, S. J. 1985. *Brain Res.* 339:356–60
76. McCall, R. B., Schuette, M. R. 1984. *J. Pharmacol. Exp. Therap.* 228:704–10
77. McKenna, K. E., Schramm, L. P. 1985. *Brain Res.* 329:233–40
78. Merchenthaler, I., Hynes, M. A., Vigh, S., Shally, A. V., Petrusz, P. 1983. *Brain Res.* 275:373–77
79. Mo, N., Dun, N. J. 1987. *Brain Res.* 400:139–44
80. Neil, J. J., Loewy, A. D. 1982. *Brain Res.* 241:271–78
81. Nishi, S., Yoshimura, M., Polosa, C. 1987. *Organization of the Autonomic Nervous System: Central and Peripheral Mechanisms,* pp. 15–26. New York: Liss
82. Pilowsky, P. M., Kapoor, V., Minson,

J. B., West, M. J., Chalmers, J. P. 1986. *Brain Res.* 366:354–57

83. Porter, J. P., Brody, M. J. 1986. *Am. J. Physiol.* 251:R510–17

84. Ross, C. A., Ruggiero, D. A., Joh, T. H., Park, D. H., Reis, D. J. 1984. *J. Comp Neurol.* 228:168–85

85. Ross, C. A., Ruggiero, D. A., Park, D. H., Joh, T. H., Sved, A. F., et al. 1984. *J. Neurosci.* 4:474–94

86. Sangdee, C., Franz, D. N. 1983. *Neurosci. Lett.* 37:167–73

87. Saper, C. B., Loewy, A. D., Swanson, L. W., Cowan, W. M. 1976. *Brain Res.* 117:305–12

88. Schramm, L. 1986. *Central and peripheral mechanisms of cardiovascular regulation,* pp. 303–52. New York: Plenum

89. Seybold, A. V., Elde, R. P. 1984. *J. Neurosci.* 4:2533–42

90. Sun, M. K., Filtz, T., Guyenet, P. G. 1986. *Neurosci. Abstr.* 12:580

91. Takano, Y., Loewy, A. D. 1984. *Brain Res.* 311:144–47

92. Takano, Y., Martin, J. E., Leeman, S. E., Loewy, A. D. 1984. *Brain Res.* 291:168–72

93. Takano, Y., Sawyer, W. B., Loewy, A. D. 1985. *Brain Res.* 334:105–16.

94. Deleted in proof

95. Wang, S. C., Ranson, S. W. 1939. *J. Comp. Neurol.* 71:437–55

96. Willenberg, I. M., Dermietzel, R., Leibstein, A. G., Effenberger, M. 1985. *J. Auton. Nerv. Syst.* 14:287–98

97. Wood, J. D., Mayer, C. J. 1979. *J. Neurophysiol.* 42:582–93

98. Woodruff, M. L., Baisen, R. H., Whittington, D. L. 1986. *Brain Res.* 379:10–23

99. Woodward, D. J., Moises, H. C., Waterhouse, B. D., Hoffer, B. J., Freedman, R. 1979. *Fed. Proc.* 38:2109–16

100. Wyszogrodski, I. 1972. *Central inhibition in the sympathetic nervous system.* PhD thesis. McGill Univ., Montreal

101. Xie, C. W., Tang, J., Han, J. S. 1986. *Neurosci. Lett.* 65:224–28

102. Yashphal, K., Gauthier, S. G., Henry, J. L. 1985. *Neuroscience* 15:529–36

103. Yoshimura, M., Nishi, S. 1982. *J. Auton. Nerv. Syst.* 6:5–11

104. Yoshimura, M., Polosa, C., Nishi, S. 1986. *Brain Res.* 362:370–74

*Ann. Rev. Physiol. 1988. 50:565–76*
*Copyright © 1988 by Annual Reviews Inc. All rights reserved*

# PERIPHERAL SYMPATHETIC NEURAL ACTIVITY IN CONSCIOUS HUMANS

## B. Gunnar Wallin

Department of Clinical Neurophysiology, Sahlgren Hospital, University of Gothenburg, S-413 45 Gothenburg, Sweden

## Jan Fagius

Department of Neurology, University Hospital, University of Uppsala, S-751 85 Uppsala, Sweden

## Introduction

Hagbarth & Vallbo made the first direct microneurographic recordings of postganglionic sympathetic nerve discharges in man (32). Since then percutaneously inserted microelectrodes have been used extensively for the study of human sympathetic function. Apart from a recent study of sympathetic activity in trigeminal nerve branches (44), the microneurographic exploration of sympathetic mechanisms has been confined to nerves of the extremities. Two different types of sympathetic outflow have been recognized in multifiber recordings: *muscle nerve sympathetic activity* (MSA) and *skin nerve sympathetic activity* (SSA). The former is dominated by vasoconstrictor signals; the latter is a mixture of sudomotor and vasoconstrictor and probably sometimes includes pilomotor and vasodilator impulses. Thus only two subdivisions of the anatomically multifaceted sympathetic nervous system are accessible to study. Despite this limitation, the results have allowed a number of conclusions, not only about peripheral sympathetic function but also about reflex patterns and hence general principles of sympathetic regulation.

## Methodology

Tungsten electrodes with a tip diameter of a few micrometers are used for microneurographic recordings. A similar reference electrode is placed sub-

565

0066-4278/88/0315-0565$02.00

cutaneously 1–2 cm from the active one. Details on recording equipment and procedure are described elsewhere (53). The search for a suitable electrode position may cause minor discomfort, whereas nothing is felt when the electrode is kept in a constant position during recording. Minor paresthesia, arising 1–3 days after the recording and persisting for 5–10 days, is reported by approximately 5–10% of subjects. Permanent nerve damage has not occurred; but to avoid possible hazards to the nerve, the search for an acceptable recording site usually is not extended over 60 min.

Usually multiunit recordings are obtained, but occasionally single units have been studied (33, 34).

The evidence for sympathetic origin of the impulses are as follows: (a) The activity is efferent, as concluded from injection of local anesthetics proximal and distal to the recording electrode (14, 31, 32). (b) The activity is reversibly abolished by the intravenous administration of the ganglion-blocking drug trimetaphan (14, 31). (c) The impulses are conducted at a velocity of about 1 m/s. (14, 25, 32, 34). (d) Changes in the strength of nerve activity are followed by events that indicate changes in sympathetic effector activity, such as changes in blood pressure, vascular resistance, skin electrical resistance, and skin pulse amplitude (14–16, 31).

## Burst Pattern of Sympathetic Activity

Although the temporal patterns of MSA and SSA differ considerably, both types of activity are made up of synchronized discharges separated by more or less complete neural inactivity (silence). A similar grouping of impulses in bursts was observed in the first sympathetic nerve recordings in animals (1) and has been confirmed repeatedly in later studies. The average firing rate in single sympathetic neurons is low (34, 37). Due to the irregularity of discharge, however, the instantaneous firing frequency (the rate calculated from the interval between two succeeding spikes) may reach 35 Hz even at average frequencies of ~1 Hz (34, 36). Therefore, bursts are presumably built up by simultaneous activation of many fibers and brief high-frequency firing in individual fibers.

Although the temporal pattern of MSA changed during temporary baroreceptor deafferentation in man (28), the impulses nevertheless occurred in bursts, and corresponding results have been obtained in animal studies (4). Thus it seems plausible that even at a central level sympathetic neurons share the basic property of discharging in synchronized bursts. This has functional significance since both sympathetic (43) and parasympathetic (3) influences on effector organs as well as sympathetic release of transmitters (40) are produced more effectively by irregular than regular nerve stimulation.

## General Appearance of MSA

Bursts of MSA are locked into the cardiac rhythm (14, 32), usually in sequences interposed by periods without detectable activity. The duration of a burst correlates to that of the corresponding RR interval of the electrocardiogram (ECG). The pulse synchrony of MSA is preserved in cardiac arrythmias (56), and a prolonged RR interval is often followed by a strong burst of MSA, presumably due to the resulting drop in diastolic blood pressure (see below). ECG-triggered averaging of the mean voltage neurogram has shown that there is a reflex latency of ~1.3 s from a heart beat to the corresponding burst of MSA (25). This lag time is independent of heart rate.

The reflex latency correlates with the length of the extremity recorded from, i.e. to the length of the postganglionic fibers (25). This correlation occurs because a large part of the latency is attributable to conduction time in unmyelinated postganglionic fibers, and hence the latency provides an indirect measure of the conduction velocity of the C fiber population recorded from. The average conduction velocity based on such determinations was 0.7 m/s in the median and 1.1 m/s in the peroneal nerve. Similar figures were obtained with determinations of conduction velocity from simultaneous recordings with two electrodes about 10 cm apart in the same nerve (25).

In resting subjects, there is a striking similarity between MSA recorded simultaneously in two extremity nerves, regardless of which muscles the nerves innervate. Most bursts can be identified in both neurograms, and the strength of corresponding bursts varies to a large extent in parallel (48). This observation suggests that sympathetic neurons that innervate skeletal muscle are governed homogenously by the central nervous system and that regional mechanisms are of less importance. However, a recent study disclosed dissociated MSAs in arm and leg nerves during mental stress (2).

The strength of MSA at rest differs considerably between individuals. When measured as burst incidence, the level of activity may vary from less than 10 to more than 90 bursts/100 heart beats (48). The burst incidence tends to increase with age, but this weak correlation contributes only a minor part of the interindividual variation (49). Differences in endurance training do not correlate with the level of MSA (52).

In contrast to the interindividual variability, the burst incidence is stable from one recording to another in the same subject (27, 48). Thus each individual has his characteristic level of MSA at rest, a level that is difficult to predict from other physiological measurements. The reasons for the interindividual differences in MSA are unknown. Short-lasting baroreceptor deafferentation (28) led to similar levels of MSA both in a subject with few and a subject with many bursts under control conditions, thus differences in baroreceptor inhibition may be a more likely source of variability than differences in central drive. At any rate the variability indicates basic interindividual differences in cardiovascular homeostasis.

RELATIONSHIP TO BLOOD PRESSURE    Sequences of bursts of MSA occur during transient reductions of blood pressure, whereas temporary elevations of blood pressure are accompanied by neural silence. This relationship is due to baroreceptor influence on MSA (see below). Detailed analysis of the interplay between MSA and blood pressure suggested that changes in diastolic blood pressure are the major determinant of MSA (49). Moreover, at a given value of diastolic pressure, sympathetic discharges were stronger and more common during the falling phase of a blood pressure change than during the rising phase. The occurrence of bursts often displays a respiratory periodicity (32). This is probably secondary to respiration-induced changes in blood pressure; a blood pressure–independent respiratory rhythm in MSA has not been reported (17).

The mean level of MSA at rest does not correlate with mean blood pressure (49). Subjects with essential hypertension exhibit the same range of burst incidence as normal subjects (63), and the above-mentioned dynamic relationship between MSA and blood pressure is also present in hypertensive patients. Thus MSA appears to be involved in the instantaneous stabilization of blood pressure at a level determined by other mechanisms.

## General Appearance of SSA

SSA is characterized by an irregular burst pattern, the intensity of which varies with environmental temperature and with the emotional state of the patient (16, 31). There is no overt cardiac rhythmicity. The activity is made up of sudomotor and vasoconstrictor impulses (7, 16) and is conducted in fibers with average velocities of 1.3 and 0.8 m/s, respectively (25). Piloerector and vasodilator impulses may also be present in some nerves (7, 11). Simultaneous recordings from two nerves revealed striking similarities of timing and strength of outflow to hands and feet, whereas outflows to the skin of the forearm and the palm of the hand were less coordinated. The differences suggested dominance of sudomotor activity in the nerve to forearm skin and of vasoconstrictor activity in the nerve to glabrous skin (8).

A subject in a relaxing situation with comfortable ambient temperature has virtually no SSA. The thermoregulatory function of SSA is illustrated when the subject is exposed to a warm or cold environment, which causes selective activation of sudomotor or vasoconstrictor activity, respectively (7).

In a comfortably warm subject an inspiratory gasp is followed by a strong reflex burst of SSA that contains both sudomotor and vasoconstrictor impulses (31). Similarly, a sudden arousal stimulus elicits a reflex burst of SSA

(16); in contrast, MSA is not affected by such stimuli (47). General anesthesia leads to suppression of SSA (59).

## Influence from Different Receptor Populations

BARORECEPTORS   MSA is influenced by arterial baroreceptors as well as by intrathoracic low-pressure (volume) receptors. Electrical stimulation of the carotid sinus nerves caused inhibition of MSA with accompanying reduction of muscle vascular resistance (65). However, when changes in transmural carotid pressure were used to alter baroreceptor input, reflex changes of MSA were short-lasting even with maintained stimulation (5, 57). The dynamic character of the response may partly be due to counterregulation from the aortic arch receptors, which are uninfluenced by the stimulus. Following block of baroreceptor input, the normal cardiac rhythmicity of MSA was replaced by a 0.4–0.7 Hz irregular rhythm that was similar to, but not identical with, that of SSA (28). Taken together these observations show that the inhibitory influence from arterial baroreceptors (a) is responsible for the dynamic relationship between MSA and blood pressure and (b) interrupts the outflow of MSA with every systolic blood pressure wave, thereby entraining the bursts in the cardiac rhythm.

At rest a peak of MSA is always followed by cardioacceleration (61); orthostasis and modulation of carotid baroreceptor firing also induce increases in MSA and heart rate (5, 39, 57). The findings suggest that the same baroreceptor events induce changes in MSA and autonomic outflow to the heart which, although coupled to each other, may vary quantitatively. Sometimes there may even be opposite effects on MSA and heart rate, e.g. during breath-holding and diving (24).

When intrathoracic volume receptors are unloaded (without a change in blood pressure), MSA increases significantly for the duration of the stimulus (50). This mechanism probably accounts for most of the increase of MSA that occurs during orthostasis (13). The Valsalva maneuver is associated with a strong increase in MSA that is presumably due to unloading of both arterial and low-pressure baroreceptors (15).

SSA exhibits no overt cardiac rhythmicity and does not change appreciably during carotid sinus nerve stimulation or baroreceptor deafferentation (28, 32, 65). This suggests that baroreceptor influence on SSA is weak. However, with signal averaging during strong sudomotor activation a cardiac-related rhythm was detected (9), the cause of which is uncertain.

CUTANEOUS RECEPTORS   Immersion of the face in water evokes immediate increase of MSA and inhibition of SSA recorded in the peroneal nerve (24). Probably both cold receptors and mechanoreceptors in the face contribute to this response.

Immersion of one hand in ice water for 1–2 min ("cold pressure test") causes an incrementing increase of MSA (21, 54) and immediate activation of SSA (22). Receptor populations responsible for these reactions are unknown, but cold receptors are expected to be involved and nociceptors may be. The possibility that complex central pathways are involved cannot be ruled out: The initial SSA increase may be an arousal response, and the effect on MSA may be a stress effect (2, 13).

Cutaneous thermoreceptors exert a powerful influence on SSA, as illustrated by the sudden inhibition of sudomotor activity seen when cool air is directed against the skin in a warm environment (7), i.e. before there is any change of central core temperature. Painful intraneural electrical stimulation may cause cutaneous reflex vasodilation, but whether this is due to inhibition of vasoconstrictor activity or activation of vasodilator fibers is unknown (11).

CHEMORECEPTORS    Prolonged apnea elicits a strong increase of MSA with simultaneous bradycardia (24) that is probably due to activation of arterial chemoreceptors. Controlled hypoxia in a decompression chamber simulating altitudes up to 6 km above sea level caused an increased outflow of MSA (46). The increase of MSA during simulated diving is strongly reinforced by apnea even when the dive is too short to induce asphyxia (24); the reinforcing mechanism is unknown.

Intramuscular chemoreceptors have been implicated as the cause of the increase of MSA that occurs in both normotensive (41) and hypertensive subjects (60) during isometric muscle contraction. Central command during such contraction has an inhibitory influence, if any, on MSA (41). The finding that rhythmic muscle exercise has much weaker effects on MSA than isometric exercise of similar intensity agrees with these suggestions (55).

## Other Central and Receptor Influences

HYPOGLYCEMIA    Acute hypoglycemia is associated with a protracted increase of MSA (23), whereas SSA displays a dissociated response with activation of the sudomotor and inhibition of the vasoconstrictor system (6). Complex receptor involvement or direct influence on central sympathetic neurons may underlie these responses. By fluid and colloid replacement during hypoglycemia it was recently shown that the MSA response is not secondary to the fall in plasma volume that occurs in hypoglycemia (H. Frandsen, C. Berne, J. Fagius, et al, submitted for publication).

MENTAL STRESS    The pronounced systemic circulatory changes that occur during mental stress (12) have little corresponding effect on MSA. If the stress lasts longer than one minute a significant increase in MSA is observed in the peroneal nerve, but there is no change in MSA in the radial nerve (2).

These results are seemingly paradoxical, since vasodilation has been reported in muscles of the extremities during mental stress (10, 35, 45).

In contrast, SSA is highly sensitive to mental stress. Strong reflex bursts, with both sudomotor and vasoconstrictor components, are regularly elicited by arousing stimuli, and long-lasting strong outflow of SSA constitutes the basis for the "cold sweat" elicited by mental stress (16). Recently, however, mental stress was found to cause cutaneous vasodilation in fingers and toes in subjects with skin temperatures below 25°C and vasoconstriction in those with skin temperatures above 30° (18). The underlying mechanism is unclear, and neither is it known if SSA responses differ at the different temperatures.

## Pharmacological Alterations of Outflow of MSA

β-ADRENOCEPTOR BLOCKADE    When metoprolol was administered intravenously to hypertensive subjects, MSA increased (51). The same effect is regularly observed when propranolol is given intravenously to normal subjects (B. G. Wallin, & G. Sundlöf, unpublished information). With long-term oral treatment of hypertension with metoprolol, the outflow of MSA was reduced to a level lower than that before treatment (67). Whether these effects are of central origin or represent baroreflex adaptation is not known.

SODIUM NITROPRUSSIDE AND PHENYLEPHRINE    These agents act directly on vessels and cause vasodilation, with a fall in blood pressure, and vasoconstriction, with a rise in blood pressure, respectively. Presumably, the pronounced changes in MSA that accompany intravenous infusion of these drugs (strong increase of activity with sodium nitroprusside and reduction of activity with phenylephrine) are reflex effects induced by arterial and low-pressure baroreceptors (D. L. Eckberg, R. F. Rea, O. K. Andersson, et al, submitted for publication).

CLONIDINE    With intravenous injection of the $\alpha$-2 receptor agonist clonidine in hypertensive subjects, blood pressure always fell, but MSA increased in some subjects and decreased in others. This variability may be due to complex interactions between the central and peripheral effects of the drug (58).

ARGININE VASOPRESSIN    Infusion of this vasoconstrictor caused inhibition of MSA with an inconsistent relationship to blood pressure, which indicates that it acts through central mechanisms or sensitization of baroreceptors (30).

## MSA and Plasma Noradrenaline

At rest MSA shows a positive correlation to the antecubital venous plasma concentration of noradrenaline in normotensive (66) and hypertensive subjects (42) and in patients with cardiac failure (38). After a delay of 1–2 min increases of MSA during isometric exercise (60) and the cold pressor test (54) were followed by increases of forearm venous plasma concentration of noradrenaline. When MSA was changed by infusion of vasoactive drugs, there was a linear relationship between steady-state values of MSA and forearm venous plasma noradrenaline concentration (D. L. Eckberg, R. F. Rea, O. K. Andersson, et al, submitted for publication). Since sympathetic outflow is differentiated, the relationship between plasma concentrations of noradrenaline and MSA may seem surprising. Muscle is, however, a large organ responsible for approximately 20% of total noradrenaline spillover (19). In addition, when blood is sampled in the forearm, a disproportionate part of the plasma noradrenaline will derive from muscle, thereby reinforcing the correlation (35).

## Pathophysiological Studies

AUTONOMIC FAILURE    In one individual with acute pandysautonomia (29) and in a few patients with progressive autonomic failure sympathetic activity cannot be detected. In polyneuropathy, which may involve autonomic function, MSA and SSA (when detected) exhibited normal characteristics, including normal conduction velocities in postganglionic fibers (26). However, the frequency of failure to detect sympathetic activity was significantly increased, especially in diabetic polyneuropathy (20). These findings suggest that impulses in postganglionic sympathetic fibers are propagated with normal velocity as long as the fiber conducts and that successive loss of functioning fibers leads to disappearance of detectable activity.

In acute inflammatory polyneuropathy (Guillain-Barré syndrome) a clinical picture suggestive of sympathetic hyperfunction may arise, with acute hypertension and tachycardia. In such patients MSA was abnormally increased, as concluded from the finding of much lower levels of activity at repeated follow-up tests after recovery (27). The abnormality can be explained by damage to baroreceptor afferent fibers during the disease.

Autonomic failure due to spinal cord transection was characterized by (a) almost total absence of spontaneous SSA and MSA; (b) no evidence of baroreflex influence on MSA, and (c) reflex discharges evoked in parallel in MSA and SSA by pressure over the bladder or stimulation of the skin below the level of lesion (47, 62). Increase of intravesical pressure during cystometry induced only a few bursts of MSA, but nevertheless marked elevation of blood pressure occurred. These findings suggest that the excitability in decentralized spinal sympathetic neurons is low and that uninhibited sympathetic outflow is not the basis for episodes of high blood pressure in spinal man.

OTHER DISORDERS OF CIRCULATION    Heart failure is associated with increased levels of MSA and plasma noradrenaline (38), the explanation of which is uncertain. Vasovagal syncope and the rare phenomenon of glossopharyngeal neuralgia with syncope are characterized by sudden total inhibition of MSA with simultaneous bradycardia (64, 68). In patients with the Raynaud phenomenon, SSA was normal, and thus no support was found for the original hypothesis that the phenomenon is caused by increased neural vasoconstrictor drive to finger vessels (22). Migraine has been proposed to be a "generalized vasomotor disorder", but no abnormality has been observed in MSA (21).

COMMENTS    The pathological features described above have been quantitative in nature, with the exception of reflex bursts elicited by certain stimuli in spinal man (47, 62). Qualitative changes of sympathetic outflow, e.g. reflex effects are evoked by stimuli that normally are ineffective, giving rise to abnormal reflex patterns, might exist in pathological conditions. Recently, it was found that qualitative abnormalities may arise after lesions of afferent pathways: During temporary baroreceptor deafferentation arousal stimuli, which normally influences only SSA, also evoked reflex discharges in MSA (28). This observation may represent a principle of sympathetic dysfunction that remains to be elucidated.

ACKNOWLEDGMENTS

The author's work is supported by the Swedish Medical Research Council, grants B87-04x-03546-16C (BGW) and B87-04x-07468-02B (JF).

*Literature Cited*

1. Adrian, E. D., Bronk, D. W., Phillips, G. 1932. Discharges in mammalian sympathetic nerves. *J. Physiol. London* 74:115–33
2. Anderson, E. A., Wallin, B. G., Mark, A. L. 1987. Dissociation of sympathetic nerve activity to arm and leg during mental stress. *Hypertension* 9(Suppl. III):114–119
3. Andersson, P.-O. 1983. *Adrenergic, cholinergic and vipergic neuro-effector control with special reference to high-frequency burst excitation patterns.* PhD thesis. Univ. Lund, Sweden. 133 pp.
4. Barman, S. M., Gebber, G. L. 1980. Sympathetic nerve rhythm of brain stem origin. *Am. J. Physiol.* 239:R42–R47
5. Båth, E., Lindblad, L. E., Wallin, B. G. 1981. Effects of dynamic and static neck suction on muscle nerve sympathetic activity, heart rate and blood pressure. *J. Physiol. London* 311:551–64

6. Berne, C., Fagius, J. 1986. Skin nerve sympathetic activity during insulin-induced hypoglycaemia. *Diabetologia* 29:855–60
7. Bini, G., Hagbarth, K.-E., Hynninen, P., Wallin, B. G. 1980. Thermoregulatory and rhythm-generating mechanisms governing the sudomotor and vasoconstrictor outflow in human cutaneous nerves. *J. Physiol. London* 306:537–52
8. Bini, G., Hagbarth, K.-E., Hynninen, P., Wallin, B. G. 1980. Regional similarities and differences in thermoregulatory vaso- and sudomotor tone. *J. Physiol. London* 306:553–65
9. Bini, G., Hagbarth, K.-E., Wallin, B. G. 1981. Cardiac rhythmicity of skin sympathetic activity recorded from peripheral nerves in man. *J. Autonom. Nerv. Syst.* 4:17–24
10. Blair, D. A., Glover, W. E., Greenfield, A. D. M., Roddie, I. C. 1959.

Excitation of cholinergic vasodilator nerves to human skeletal muscles during emotional stress. *J. Physiol. London* 148:633–47

11. Blumberg, H., Wallin, B. G. 1987. Direct evidence of neurally mediated vasodilatation in hairy skin of the human foot. *J. Physiol. London* 382:105–21

12. Brod, J., Fencl, V., Hejl, Z., Jirka, J. 1959. Circulatory changes underlying blood pressure elevation during acute emotional stress (mental arithmetic) in normotensive and hypertensive subjects. *Clin. Sci.* 18:269–79

13. Burke, D., Sundlöf, G., Wallin, B. G. 1977. Postural effects on muscle nerve sympathetic activity in man. *J. Physiol. London* 272:399–414

14. Delius, W., Hagbarth, K.-E., Hongell, A., Wallin, B. G. 1972. General characteristics of sympathetic activity in human muscle nerves. *Acta Physiol. Scand.* 84:65–81

15. Delius, W., Hagbarth, K.-E., Hongell, A., Wallin, B. G. 1972. Manoeuvres affecting sympathetic outflow in human muscle nerves. *Acta Physiol. Scand.* 84:82–94

16. Delius, W., Hagbarth, K.-E., Hongell, A., Wallin, B. G. 1972. Manoeuvres affecting sympathetic outflow in human skin nerves. *Acta Physiol. Scand.* 84:177–86

17. Eckberg, D. L., Nerhed, C., Wallin, B. G. 1985. Respiratory modulation of muscle sympathetic and vagal cardiac outflow in man. *J. Physiol. London* 365:181–96

18. Elam, M., Wallin, B. G. 1987. Skin blood flow responses to mental stress in man depend on body temperature, *Acta Physiol. Scand.* 129:429–31

19. Esler, M., Jennings, G., Leonard, P., Sacharias, N., Burke, F., et al. 1984. Contribution of individual organs to total noradrenaline release in humans. *Acta Physiol. Scand.* 527:11–16 (Suppl.)

20. Fagius, J. 1982. Microneurographic findings in diabetic polyneuropathy with special reference to sympathetic nerve activity. *Diabetologia* 23:415–20

21. Fagius, J. 1985. Muscle nerve sympathetic activity in migraine. Lack of abnormality. *Cephalalgia* 5:197–203

22. Fagius, J., Blumberg, H. 1985. Sympathetic outflow to the hand in patients with Raynaud's phenomenon. *Cardiovasc. Res.* 19:249–53

23. Fagius, J., Niklasson, F., Berne, C. 1986. Sympathetic outflow in human muscle nerves increases during hypoglycemia. *Diabetes* 35:1124–29

24. Fagius, J., Sundlöf, G. 1986. The div-

ing response in man: Effects on sympathetic activity in muscle and skin nerve fascicles. *J. Physiol. London* 377:429–43

25. Fagius, J., Wallin, B. G. 1980. Sympathetic reflex latencies and conduction velocities in normal man. *J. Neurol. Sci.* 47:433–48

26. Fagius, J., Wallin, B. G. 1980. Sympathetic reflex latencies and conduction velocities in patients with polyneuropathy. *J. Neurol. Sci.* 47:449–61

27. Fagius, J., Wallin, B. G. 1983. Microneurographic evidence of excessive sympathetic outflow in the Guillain-Barré syndrome. *Brain* 106:589–600

28. Fagius, J., Wallin, B. G., Sundlöf, G., Nerhed, C., Englesson, S. 1985. Sympathetic outflow in man after anaesthesia of the glossopharyngeal and vagus nerves. *Brain* 108:423–38

29. Fagius, J., Westerberg, C.-E., Olsson, Y. 1983. Acute pandysautonomia and severe sensory deficit with poor recovery. A clinical, neurophysiological and pathological case study. *J. Neurol. Neurosurg. Psychiatry* 46:725–33

30. Floras, J. S., Aylward, P. E., Leimbach, W. N., Mark, A. L., Abboud, F. M. 1985. Inhibition of sympathetic nerve activity in humans by arginine vasopressin. *Circulation* 72:iii–17 (Abstr.)

31. Hagbarth, K.-E., Hallin, R. G., Hongell, A., Torebjörk, H. E., Wallin, B. G. 1972. General characteristics of sympathetic activity in human skin nerves. *Acta Physiol. Scand.* 84:164–76

32. Hagbarth, K.-E., Vallbo, Å. B. 1968. Pulse and respiratory grouping of sympathetic impulses in human muscle nerves. *Acta Physiol. Scand.* 74:96–108

33. Hallin, R. G., Torebjörk, H. E. 1970. Afferent and efferent C-units recorded from human skin nerves in situ. *Acta Soc. Med. Ups.* 75:277–81

34. Hallin, R. G., Torebjörk, H. E. 1974. Single unit sympathetic activity in human skin nerves during rest and various manoeuvres. *Acta Physiol. Scand.* 92:303–17

35. Hjemdahl, P., Freyschuss, U., Juhlin-Dannfelt, A., Linde, B. 1984. Differentiated sympathetic activation during mental stress evoked by the Stroop test. *Acta Physiol. Scand.* 527:25–29 (Suppl.)

36. Iggo, A., Vogt, M. 1960. Preganglionic sympathetic activity in normal and in reserpine-treated cats. *J. Physiol. London* 150:114–33

37. Jänig, W., Sundlöf, G., Wallin, B. G. 1983. Discharge patterns of sympathetic

neurons supplying skeletal muscle and skin in man and cat. *J. Autonom. Nerv. Syst.* 7:239–56

38. Leimbach, W. N., Wallin, B. G., Victor, R. G., Aylward, P. E., Sundlöf, G., Mark, A. L. 1986. Direct evidence from intraneural recordings for increased central sympathetic outflow in patients with heart failure. *Circulation* 73:913–19

39. Lindblad, L. E., Atterhög, J.-H., Wallin, B. G. 1981. Sympathetic activity in muscle nerves—a factor influencing the postural heart rate increase? *Acta Physiol. Scand.* 111:509–10

40. Lundberg, J. M., Rudehill, A., Sollevi, A., Theodorsson-Norheim, E., Hamberger, B. 1986. Frequency- and reserpine-dependent chemical coding of sympathetic transmission: Differential release of noradrenaline and neuropeptide Y from pig spleen. *Neurosci. Lett.* 63:96–100

41. Mark, A. L., Victor, R. G., Nerhed, C., Wallin, B. G. 1985. Microneurographic studies of the mechanisms of sympathetic nerve response to static exercise in humans. *Circ. Res.* 57:461–69

42. Mörlin, C., Wallin, B. G., Eriksson, B. M. 1983. Muscle sympathetic activity and plasma noradrenaline in normotensive and hypertensive man. *Acta Physiol. Scand.* 119:117–21

43. Nilsson, H., Ljung, B., Sjöblom, N., Wallin, B. G. 1985. The influence of the sympathetic impulse pattern on contractile responses of rat mesenteric arteries and veins. *Acta Physiol. Scand.* 123:303–9

44. Nordin, M., Thomander, L., Wallin, U., Hagbarth, K.-E. 1987. Sympathetic outflow in human trigeminal nerve branches and its relation to facial sudo- and vasomotor responses. *Electroencephalogr. Clin. Neurophysiol.* 66:573

45. Rusch, N. J., Shepherd, J. T., Webb, R. C., Vanhoutte, P. M. 1981. Different behavior of the resistance vessels of the human calf and forearm during contralateral isometric exercise, mental stress, and abnormal respiratory movements. *Circ. Res.* 48:1118–30

46. Saito, M., Mano, T., Iwase, S. 1986. Microneurographic studies of the response in muscle sympathetic activity to acute hypoxia in man. *Proc. Int. Union Physiol. Sci.* 16:222 (Abstr.)

47. Stjernberg, L., Blumberg, H., Wallin, B. G. 1986. Sympathetic activity in man after spinal cord injury. Outflow to muscle below the lesion. *Brain* 109:695–715

48. Sundlöf, G., Wallin, B. G. 1977. The variability of muscle nerve sympathetic activity in resting recumbent man. *J. Physiol. London* 272:383–97

49. Sundlöf, G., Wallin, B. G. 1978. Human muscle nerve sympathetic activity at rest. Relationship to blood pressure and age. *J. Physiol. London* 274:621–37

50. Sundlöf, G., Wallin, B. G. 1978. Effect of lower body negative pressure on human muscle nerve sympathetic activity. *J. Physiol. London* 278:525–32

51. Sundlöf, G., Wallin, B. G., Strömgren, E., Nerhed, C. 1983. Acute effects of metoprolol on muscle sympathetic activity in hypertensive humans. *Hypertension* 5:749–56

52. Svedenhag, J., Wallin, B. G., Sundlöf, G., Henriksson, J. 1984. Skeletal muscle sympathetic activity at rest in trained and untrained subjects. *Acta Physiol. Scand.* 120:499–504

53. Vallbo, Å. B., Hagbarth, K.-E., Torebjörk, H. E., Wallin, B. G. 1979. Somatosensory, proprioceptive, and sympathetic activity in human peripheral nerves. *Physiol. Rev.* 59:919–57

54. Victor, R. G., Leimbach, W. N., Seals, D. R., Wallin, B. G., Mark, A. L. 1987. Effects of the cold pressor test on muscle sympathetic nerve activity: Microneurographic studies in humans. *Hypertension* 9:429–36

55. Victor, R. G., Seals, D. R., Mark, A. L. 1987. Differential control of heart rate and sympathetic nerve activity during dynamic exercise; insight from direct intraneural recordings in humans. *J. Clin. Invest.* 79:508–16

56. Wallin, B. G., Delius, W., Sundlöf, G. 1974. Human muscle nerve sympathetic activity in cardiac arrhythmias. *Scand. J. Clin. Lab. Invest.* 34:293–300

57. Wallin, B. G., Eckberg, D. L. 1982. Sympathetic transients caused by abrupt alterations of carotid baroreceptor activity in humans. *Am. J. Physiol.* 242:H185–90

58. Wallin, B. G., Frisk-Holmberg, M. 1981. The antihypertensive mechanism of clonidine in man: Evidence against a generalized reduction of sympathetic activity. *Hypertension* 3:340–46

59. Wallin, B. G., König, U. 1976. Changes of skin nerve sympathetic activity during induction of general anesthesia with thiopentone in man. *Brain Res.* 103:157–60

60. Wallin, B. G., Mörlin, C., Hjemdahl, P. 1987. Muscle sympathetic activity and venous plasma noradrenaline concentrations during static exercise in normotensive and hypertensive subjects. *Acta Physiol. Scand.* 129:489–97

61. Wallin, B. G., Nerhed, C. 1982. Relationship between spontaneous variations of muscle sympathetic activity

and succeeding changes of blood pressure in man. *J. Autonom. Nerv. Syst.* 6:293–302

62. Wallin, B. G., Stjernberg, L. 1984. Sympathetic activity in man after spinal cord injury. *Brain* 107:183–98

63. Wallin, B. G., Sundlöf, G. 1979. A quantitative study of muscle nerve sympathetic activity in resting normotensive and hypertensive subjects. *Hypertension* 1:67–77

64. Wallin, B. G., Sundlöf, G. 1982. Sympathetic outflow to muscles during vasovagal syncope. *J. Autonom. Nerv. Syst.* 6:287–91

65. Wallin, B. G., Sundlöf, G., Delius, W. 1975. The effect of carotid sinus nerve stimulation on muscle and skin nerve sympathetic activity in man. *Pflüg. Arch.* 358:101–10

66. Wallin, B. G., Sundlöf, G., Eriksson, B.-M., Dominiak, P., Grobecker, H., Lindblad, L. E. 1981. Plasma noradrenaline correlates to sympathetic muscle nerve activity in normotensive man. *Acta Physiol. Scand.* 111:69–73

67. Wallin, B. G., Sundlöf, G., Strömgren, E., Åberg, H. 1984. Sympathetic outflow to muscles during treatment of hypertension with metoprolol. *Hypertension* 6:557–62

68. Wallin, B. G., Westerberg, C.-E., Sundlöf, G. 1984. Syncope induced by glossopharyngeal neuralgia: Sympathetic outflow to muscle. *Neurology* 34:522–24

*Ann. Rev. Physiol. 1988. 50:577–92*

# CARDIOVASCULAR CONTROL IN SPINAL MAN

*Christopher J. Mathias*

Medical Unit, St. Mary's Hospital and Medical School, Norfolk Place, London, W.2. and Institute of Neurology, National Hospital for Nervous Diseases, Queen Square, London, WC1, United Kingdom

*Hans L. Frankel*

National Spinal Injuries Centre, Stoke Mandeville Hospital, Bucks, United Kingdom

## INTRODUCTION

The sympathetic outflow emerges from the thoracic and upper lumbar segments of the spinal cord and in patients with high spinal cord lesions is dissociated from cerebral regulation. This results in disordered cardiovascular control that is influenced by the level and completeness of the lesion, in addition to other factors such as hormones that directly alter cardiovascular function or indirectly influence it by changing renal function or intravascular volume. In this review emphasis is placed on patients with complete cervical spinal cord transection above the sympathetic outflow; they form a human physiological model, in whom the afferent, central, and vagal efferent components of the baroreflex arc are intact, but where the spinal and peripheral sympathetic nervous system is isolated (Figure 1). Other than a section on recently injured tetraplegics in spinal shock, all descriptions refer to chronically injured tetraplegics (synonomous with quadriplegics).

## OBSERVATIONS IN THE BASAL STATE

The basal systolic and diastolic blood pressure in tetraplegics is about 15 mm Hg lower than in normal subjects (1, 2). This is due to reduced sympathetic activity as reflected by low levels of plasma noradrenaline and adrenaline (2),

577

0066-4278/88/0315-0577$02.00

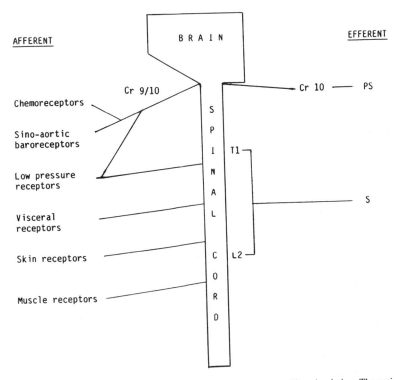

*Figure 1*  Schematic outline of the major autonomic pathways controlling circulation. The major afferent input into the central nervous system is through the glossopharyngeal (Cr, 9) and vagus (Cr, 10) nerves by activation of baroreceptors in the carotid sinus and aortic arch. Chemoreceptors and low pressure receptors also influence the efferent outflow. The latter consists of the cranial parasympathetic (PS) outflow to the heart via the vagus nerves, and the sympathetic outflow from the thoracic and upper lumbar segments of the spinal cord. Activation of visceral, skin, and muscle receptors, in addition to cerebral stimulation, influences the efferent outflow.

and confirmed by direct microneuronographic measurements of peripheral skin and muscle sympathetic activity (3, 4). Heart rate and cardiac output are usually at the lower end of the normal range (5). There is a modest reduction in the basal renal plasma flow of tetraplegics when compared with normal subjects (6). Basal levels of plasma renin activity are often higher than in normal subjects (7, 8).

# RESPONSES TO PHYSIOLOGICAL STIMULATION

## Headup Postural Change

The cardiovascular responses to standing, head-up tilt, and lower body negative suction depend on an intact baroreceptor reflex. During head-up tilt in tetraplegics, there is an immediate fall in both systolic and diastolic blood pressure, which may be quite substantial; there is often some recovery and the blood pressure tends to settle at a lower level (9). On return to the horizontal position, the blood pressure often overshoots before gradually settling back to the previous supine level (Figure 2). The degree of fall is often greater in nonmobile patients, as in the early stages of rehabilitation. The fall is usually reduced by frequent postural change, which activates secondary mechanisms that help sustain blood pressure. This may increase the ability of patients to maintain cerebral perfusion. Cerebral vascular autoregulation may occur at lower pressures than in normal subjects (10).

Hypotension is the result of the inability to activate the sympathetic efferent component of the baroreceptor reflex. Plasma noradrenaline and adrenaline levels do not change during tilt, unlike in normal subjects (7). Occasionally, small changes in plasma noradrenaline are observed; these are likely to result from activation of nonposturally induced spinal sympathetic reflexes through skeletal muscle spasm or urinary bladder contraction. During tilt, the heart rate rises largely because of vagal withdrawal in response to the hypotension. Atropine reduces but may not abolish the elevation in heart rate (9, 11), whereas β-adrenergic blockade with propranolol may reduce the rise, which

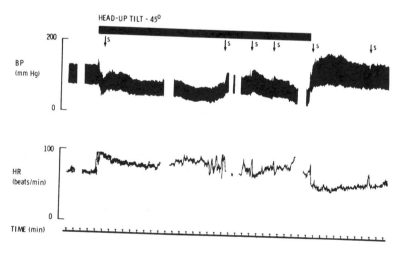

*Figure 2*   Blood pressure (BP) and heart rate (HR) in a tetraplegic patient before, during, and after head-up tilt to 45°. Blood pressure promptly falls with partial recovery, which in this case is linked to skeletal muscle spasms (S), inducing spinal sympathetic activity. Some of the later oscillations are probably due to the rise of renin, measured where there are interruptions in the intra-arterial record. In the later phases, muscle spasms occur more frequently and further elevate blood pressure. On return to the horizontal, blood pressure rises rapidly above the previous basal level and slowly returns to the horizontal. Heart rate tends to move in the opposite direction. There is a transient increase in heart rate during muscle spasms.

suggests an additional role for sympathetic activation (8). The heart rate does not usually exceed 100 beats/min, which indicates that additional sympathetic neural and humoral influences are needed to further raise it, as in patients in shock with a similar level of blood pressure.

During head-up tilt both stroke volume and cardiac output fall substantially (5). Venous return is reduced and venous pooling may cause cyanotic discoloration and, with time, lower limb edema. There is a fall in subcutaneous blood flow with a rise in resistance in the lower limbs that is abolished by local but not proximal nervous blockade, thus favoring a local posturally induced venoarterial reflex (12). Blood flow in lower limb muscle falls with a rise in muscle vascular resistance and in occluded venous pressure, which is suggestive of activation of spinal postural reflexes, although it is difficult to exclude other spinal reflexes that may account for these changes (9, 13).

During head-up tilt, renin levels rise to a greater extent than in normal subjects, probably because of the fall in blood pressure (7, 8). Renin release appears to be independent of sympathetic activation, as it is not influenced either by induction of spinal reflex activity during bladder stimulation (14) or by $\beta$-adrenergic blockade with propranolol (8). There is no evidence of supersensitive responsiveness to infusion of noradrenaline and isoprenaline (14). Renin release is therefore probably dependent on the fall in renal perfusion pressure, with afferent arteriolar dilatation causing stimulation of juxtaglomerular renin-secreting cells.

The subsequent formation of angiotensin-II and the later elevation in plasma aldosterone levels are likely to play a role in the maintenance of blood pressure. The rise in plasma aldosterone is probably the result of direct adrenal stimulation by angiotensin-II, although diminished hepatic clearance may be a contributing factor. These humoral responses, with their subsequent effects on salt and water retention and plasma volume expansion, are likely to explain the beneficial effects of repeated head-up tilt in preventing postural hypotension. Studies with the competitive angiotensin-II antagonist, saralasin, have not further contributed, because of the unmasking of its initial intrinsic angiotensin-II-like myotropic effects, which elevates blood pressure (15). Administration of captopril (which prevents angiotensin-II formation by inhibiting angiotensin-I converting enzyme, in addition to other effects) lowers supine blood pressure and considerably enhances postural hypotension (C. J. Mathias, H. L. Frankel, W. S. Peart, unpublished observations), thus favoring an important secondary role for the renin-angiotensin-aldosterone system during head-up tilt.

During head-up tilt there is a fall in renal plasma flow with a rise in renal vascular resistance (6). This may result from the reduction in blood pressure and cardiac output, although vasoconstriction induced either by spinal reflexes or by humoral mechanisms (including angiotensin-II) may be contributory. The fall in urine volume during tilt may be secondary to these hemodynamic changes. Vasopressin (antidiuretic hormone) levels rise substantially in tetraplegics during head-up tilt and may also play a role by its renal tubular actions (16).

In the majority of tetraplegics, symptoms from postural hypotension mainly occur in the early stages of rehabilitation. The regular use of graded head-up tilt and mobilization often alleviates the symptoms and improves blood pressure control. Drugs such as ephedrine may be of benefit particularly in the early stages. The induction of muscle spasms or urinary bladder stimulation, which often occurs spontaneously during postural change, may be beneficial (17). Biofeedback techniques have been used to elevate blood pressure and three tetraplegics were successfully trained (18). The elevation in blood pressure was achieved by inhibiting vagal tone and raising the heart rate, since these responses were prevented by administration of atropine (Figure 3).

## Stimulation Above the Lesion

Responses induced either by cerebral stimulation (mental arithmetic or a loud noise) or by stimulation of skin in innervated areas above the lesion (ice or pain) do not raise blood pressure as in normal subjects, because of the disruption of descending spinal outflow tracts.

## Stimulation Below the Lesion: "Autonomic Dysreflexia"

In tetraplegics, marked cardiovascular changes may occur during stimulation of localized segments below the lesion (19, 20). Stimuli to the skin, skeletal muscles, or viscera (especially urinary bladder and bowel) result in activity in a number of target organs supplied by sympathetic and sacral parasympathetic nerves—causing the syndrome of autonomic dysreflexia. Constriction of resistance and capacitance vessels below the lesion is widespread, and the blood pressure rises rapidly, sometimes to extremely high levels (Figure 4). Stroke volume and cardiac output are elevated (5). The heart rate may initially rise (suggesting the presence of chronotropic spinal cardiac reflexes), but then falls because of activation of the vagal efferent component of the baroreceptor reflex. In areas above the lesion, such as the face and neck, vasodilatation and sweating may occur through mechanisms that are unclear.

The vasoconstriction and hypertension during autonomic dysreflexia are the result of spinal sympathetic reflexes. Plasma noradrenaline levels rise and are closely related to the elevation in blood pressure (2); adrenaline levels are unchanged, excluding adrenomedullary stimulation. The rise in plasma noradrenaline only marginally exceeds basal levels in normal subjects, which significantly differs from humorally induced hypertension, as in phaeochromocytoma patients. Microneuronographic studies in tetraplegics indicate discrete bursts of sympathetic activity, accompanied by substantial and often

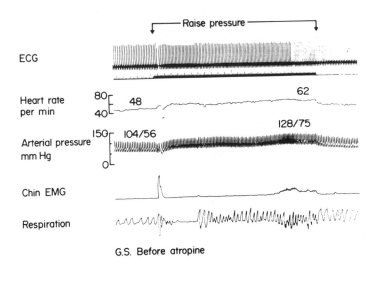

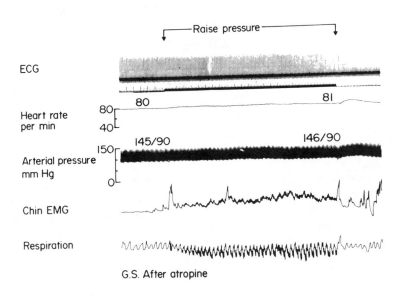

*Figure 3* A voluntary increase in blood pressure in a chronic tetraplegic (with a complete C4/5 lesion) upon request, after a period of biofeedback training. There is a concomitant rise in heart rate. The onset is indicated by movement of the chin on the electromyograph trace (EMG) and by an atrial ectopic beat. In the lower panel blood pressure and heart rate are higher after administration of atropine. The patient cannot now raise his blood pressure, which indicates the role of the vagus. Chin electromyograph changes are more prominent. (From 18.)

sustained cardiovascular responses (3, 4). This response pattern indicates either increased adrenoceptor sensitivity or an inability, because of the lesion, to appropriately influence blood vessels and lower blood pressure. Studies of platelet $\alpha$-adrenoceptor affinity and density in tetraplegics show no difference from platelet studies in normal subjects and thus provide indirect evidence against receptor upregulation, as would be expected in true denervation supersensitivity (21). In tetraplegics the vasoconstriction and hypertension are probably representative of primary cutaneo-, viscero-, and somato-vascular reflexes, which would normally activate supraspinal centers and maintain blood pressure, presumably through descending spinal pathways. Hypertension during stimulation does not occur in patients with lesions below the fifth thoracic segment, probably because adequate baroreflex control of the innervated circulation, which includes the splanchnic bed, can be exerted (Figure 5).

The cardiovascular changes during autonomic dysreflexia can result in considerable morbidity and, at times, death (17). Hypertension may cause a throbbing headache, epileptic seizures or localized neurological deficits, and occasionally intracranial hemorrhage. Management consists of determining and rectifying the precipitating cause. Usually this reflex hypertension originates from stimulation of the bladder (urinary infections and blocked catheters), the large bowel (anal fissures), and skeletal muscle (spasms). A number of pharmacological approaches for the control of hypertension during autonomic dysreflexia provide further evidence of the pathways involved (Table 1).

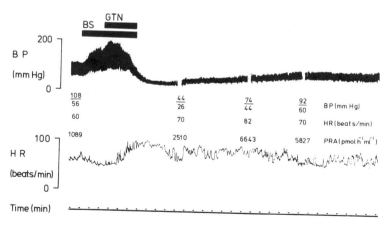

*Figure 4*   Blood pressure (BP) and heart rate (HR) in a tetraplegic in the supine position before, during, and after bladder stimulation (BS) by supra-pubic percussion of the anterior abdominal wall, which induces hypertension. Sublingual glyceryl trinitrate (GTN) (0.5 mg for 3½ min) rapidly reverses the hypertension, elevates the heart rate, and then causes substantial hypotension. Levels of plasma renin activity (PRA) rise as a result of the fall in blood pressure.

## Hypoglycemia

Hypoglycemia is a powerful stimulus that, in normal subjects, increases adrenal secretion. This probably accounts for a number of symptoms accompanying hypoglycemia, such as tremulousness, anxiety, sweating, tachycardia, and elevation of systolic blood pressure. In tetraplegics however, few manifestations accompany hypoglycemia (22). There is a small fall in blood pressure, with a modest rise in heart rate. The latter is probably due to vagal withdrawal in response to the fall in blood pressure. Plasma adrenaline and noradrenaline levels are unchanged. The sympathoadrenal response to hypoglycemia appears dependent not only on stimulation of central receptors, such as in the hypothalamus, but also on the integrity of descending spinal sympathetic pathways. Sedation is the major sign of neuroglycopenia and is readily reversed by glucose. The symptoms of hypoglycemia appear to be largely dependent, therefore, upon centrally induced sympathoadrenal stimulation.

## Food Ingestion

In patients with chronic autonomic failure (who have sympathetic failure and often parasympathetic failure) food ingestion can cause marked and prolonged hypotension (23). The mechanisms responsible probably include the effects of vasodilatatory peptides secreted during food ingestion (such as insulin, neurotensin, and vasoactive intestinal polypeptide), which cause splanchnic vasodilatation without the compensatory changes that maintain blood pressure

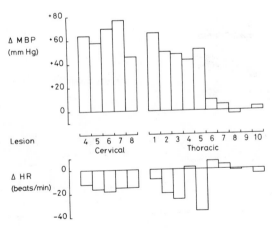

*Figure 5* Changes in mean blood pressure (ΔMBP) and heart rate (ΔHR) in patients with spinal cord lesions at different levels (cervical and thoracic) after bladder stimulation induced by supra-pubic percussion. In the cervical and high thoracic lesions, there is a marked elevation in blood pressure and a fall in heart rate. In patients with lesions below T5 there are minimal changes. (From 37.)

**Table 1**  Some of the drugs used in the management of hypertension that accompanies autonomic dysreflexia

| Site of Action | Drug |
| --- | --- |
| Afferent | Topical lignocaine |
| Spinal cord | Spinal anaesthetics <br> Reserpine <br> Clonidine |
| Sympathetic efferent <br> Ganglia <br> Nerve terminals <br> Alpha adrenoceptors | <br> Hexamethonium <br> Guanethidine <br> Phenoxybenzamine |
| Blood Vessels | Glyceryl trinitrate <br> Nifedipine |

homeostasis in normal subjects. In tetraplegics, however, food ingestion does not lower supine blood pressure, and the reasons for these differences between groups require further investigation.

## Effects of Recumbency

Patients with chronic autonomic failure have nocturnal polyuria and natriuresis, which causes a substantial overnight weight loss, a reduction in extracellular fluid volume, and a lowering of morning blood pressure with a worsening of morning postural hypotension (24). These effects do not appear to result from abnormal circadian rhythms and can be induced by postural changes alone. Recent studies indicate that recumbency itself can induce diuresis and natriuresis in these patients; in tetraplegics, however, diuresis alone occurs without natriuresis (25). The mechanisms for these changes, and the differences between the groups, need further elucidation.

# RESPONSES TO PHARMACOLOGICAL AGENTS

## Response to Pressor Agents

An exaggerated pressor response is observed with a range of vasopressor agents. The response to noradrenaline infusion has been extensively studied (26). There is a 10–20-fold increase in sensitivity over a wide range (Figure 6). In tetraplegics the lesion is preganglionic, spinal cord sympathetic activity can be activated, there is histochemical evidence of integrity of postganglionic nerve terminals (27), and platelet $\alpha$ adrenoceptor numbers are normal, which excludes classical denervation supersensitivity as the explanation. Whether or not the enhanced response is due to the baroreceptor deficit and the inability to influence descending outflow tracts in response to a rise in pressure remains unclear.

Exaggerated pressor responses occur with other adrenoceptor agonists such as phenylephrine and also occur with other drugs such as prostaglandin $F_2\alpha$ and vasopressin (28, 29), thus further excluding specific adrenoceptor changes as the mechanism for the supersensitivity. Enhanced responses also occur to angiotensin-II, despite normal or raised circulating levels of renin and angiotensin-II, and make it unlikely that receptor underoccupancy is responsible for these changes (28).

## Responses to Vasodepressor Agents

Drugs with vasodilator properties may cause a marked reduction in blood pressure because of the lack of baroreflex-induced compensatory sympathetic activity. Isoprenaline lowers blood pressure in tetraplegics to a greater extent than in normal subjects (14, 28), probably because of its vasodilatatory $\beta_2$-adrenoceptor agonist effects. The rise in heart rate results from its direct $\beta_1$-adrenoceptor cardiac effects and reflex vagal withdrawal in response to the fall in blood pressure (28). Glyceryl trinitrate can cause marked hypotension in supine tetraplegics (Figure 4); this can be used advantageously during

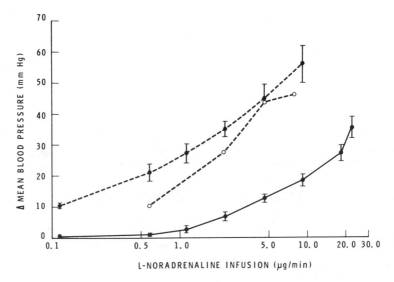

*Figure 6*   Changes ($\Delta$) in average mean blood pressure and heart rate during different dose infusion rates of noradrenaline in 5 chronic tetraplegics (●– – – –●), 3 recently injured tetraplegics (o– – –o), and 10 normal subjects (●———●). The bars indicate SEM ±. There is an enhanced pressor response to noradrenaline in both groups of tetraplegics over the entire dose range studied. (From 26 and 34.)

autonomic dysreflexia. The calcium channel blocker nifedipine is effective when used sublingually acutely, but not when given prophylactically (30).

## Responses to Clonidine

Clonidine is an $\alpha_2$-adrenoceptor agonist that lowers blood pressure in normal and hypertensive man by its cerebral effects, which reduce sympathetic activity. In tetraplegics, clonidine does not change basal blood pressure, thus emphasizing the dependence of its hypotensive effects on a reduction in sympthetic nervous activity (31). Clonidine, however, can reduce hypertension during bladder stimulation, which suggests additional effects either on spinal preganglionic neurons or on peripheral presynaptic $\alpha_2$-adrenoceptors (32). When given intravenously, it initially raises blood pressure because of short lasting peripheral $\alpha$-agonist effects. Clonidine reduces skeletal muscle spasms, as do other imidazolines, some of which have greater spasmolytic than hypotensive effects (33). It is used prophylactically in autonomic dysreflexia (17).

## RECENTLY INJURED TETRAPLEGICS IN "SPINAL SHOCK"

Immediately after cervical cord transection, patients often have hypoexcitability of the isolated cord, resulting in flaccid paralysis, lack of tendon reflexes, and atony of the bladder and bowel. This condition is referred to as spinal shock and is distinct from cardiovascular changes that may accompany this state. In patients without other complications, the diastolic blood pressure is 15–20 mm Hg lower than in normal subjects, because of diminished sympathetic activity, which is reflected in low plasma noradrenaline and adrenaline levels (34). There are some basic differences between cardiovascular control in chronic tetraplegics and recently injured patients in spinal shock. These appear to be predominantly linked to their inability to increase spinal sympathetic activity, although other factors contribute. Two examples are provided below.

## Responses to Stimulation Below the Lesion

Stimuli that raise blood pressure in chronic tetraplegics usually have no effect in patients in spinal shock (34) (Figure 7). The pressor response to noradrenaline is similar to that of chronic tetraplegics (Figure 6), excluding vascular subsensitivity. Isolated spinal cord sympathetic activity appears depressed, along with diminished or absent spinal motor reflex mechanisms. The return of motor reflexes often heralds the onset of both sympathetic and parasympathetic spinal cord reflex activity. The precise reasons for the depression soon after injury are unknown.

### Responses to Tracheal Stimulation

Control of the diaphragm, the major respiratory muscle in tetraplegics, is lost if the lesion is at or above C4/C5. These patients need mechanical respiration and they are prone to severe bradycardia and cardiac arrest during tracheal stimulation (35, 36) (Figure 8). These complications appears to be due to a vago-vagal reflex. Vagal afferents in the trachea are stimulated during suction, causing enhanced vagal efferent activity; this condition is not opposed by sympathetic nerve activity (which is absent even at an isolated spinal level) or by the pulmonary inflation vagal reflex (because of the patient's inability to

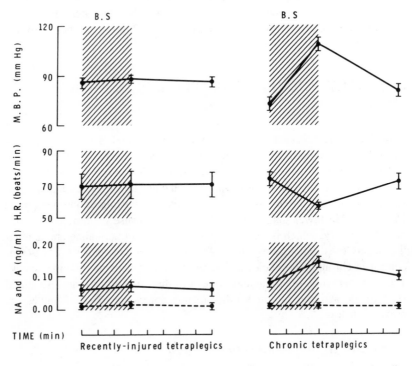

*Figure 7*  Average levels of mean blood pressure (MBP), heart rate (HR), plasma noradrenaline (NA) *(solid line),* and adrenaline (A) *(dotted line)* in recently injured and chronic tetraplegics before, during, and after bladder stimulation (BS). The bars indicate SEM ±. No changes occur in recently injured tetraplegics, unlike the chronic tetraplegics in whom blood pressure and plasma noradrenaline levels rise and heart rate falls. There are no changes in plasma adrenaline levels. (From 34.)

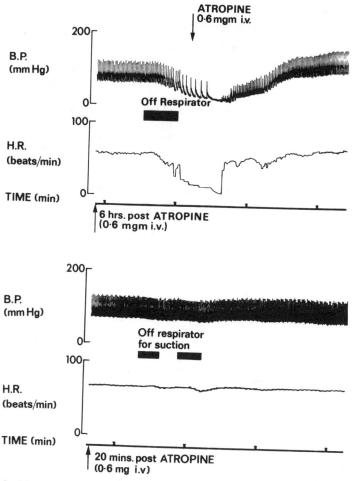

*Figure 8*  Blood pressure (BP) and heart rate (HR) of a recently injured tetraplegic (C4/5 lesion) in spinal shock six hours after the last dose of intravenous atropine. Disconnecting the respirator (as required for aspirating the airways) results in sinus bradycardia and cardiac arrest (which was also observed on an electrocardiograph). This is reversed by reconnection, intravenous atropine, and external cardiac massage. The lower panel shows the effect of disconnection from the respirator and tracheal suction 20 minutes after atropine, which does not lower either heart rate or blood pressure. (From 35 and 36.)

breath spontaneously). Hypoxia, which may be produced by pulmonary infection or emboli, enhances these effects. Atropine prevents the bradycardia, confirming that the efferent arc is in the vagus (Table 2).

Management consists of maintaining normoxia and, if necessary, using regular administration of atropine. Demand cardiac pacemakers and isoprena-

**Table 2** The major mechanisms contributing to bradycardia and cardiac arrest in recently injured tetralegics in spinal shock on respirators

|  | Tracheal suction | Hypoxia |
|---|---|---|
| Normal | Increases sympathetic nervous activity resulting in tachycardia and elevation of blood pressure | Causes bradycardia as a primary response. This is opposed by the pulmonary (inflation) vagal reflex resulting in tachycardia |
| Tetraplegics | Does not increase sympathetic activity; there is no rise in heart rate or blood pressure. Vagal afferent stimulation may lead to an unopposed increase in vagal efferent activity | Causes the primary response, bradycardia, because disconnection from respirator prevents the pulmonary (inflation) vagal reflex |

Increased vagal tone

Bradycardia and cardiac arrest

line have been used, but the latter may cause hypotension and increase the risk of cardiac dysrrhythmias. With the return of isolated spinal cord activity and spontaneous respiration, the risk of bradycardia subsides (36). In chronic tetraplegics, however, a similar problem may arise during endotracheal intubation prior to anesthesia, especially if the vagus is not adequately blocked with atropine (36).

ACKNOWLEDGMENTS

CJM thanks the Wellcome Trust for their support.

*Literature Cited*

1. Frankel, H. L., Michaelis, L. S., Golding, D. R., Beral, V. 1972. The blood pressure in paraplegia—1. *Paraplegia* 10:193–98

2. Mathias, C. J., Christensen, N. J., Corbett, J. L., Frankel, H. L., Spalding, J. M. K. 1976. Plasma catecholamines during paroxysmal neurogenic hypertension in quadriplegic man. *Circ. Res.* 39:204–08

3. Wallin, B. G., Stjernberg, L. 1984. Sympathetic activity in man after spinal cord injury. Outflow to skin below the lesion. *Brain* 107:183–98

4. Stjernberg, L., Blumberg, H., Wallin, B. G. 1986. Sympathetic activity in man after spinal cord injury. Outflow to muscle below the lesion. Brain 109:695–715

5. Corbett, J. L., Debarge, O., Frankel, H. L., Mathias, C. J. 1975. Cardiovascular responses in tetraplegic man to muscle spasm, bladder percussion and head-up tilt. *Clin. Exp. Pharmacol. Physiol.* 1975 (Suppl. 2):189–93

6. Krebs, M., Ragnarrson, K. T., Tuckman, J. 1983. Orthostatic vasomotor response in spinal man. *Paraplegia* 21:72–80
7. Mathias, C. J., Christensen, N. J., Corbett, J. L., Frankel, H. L., Goodwin, T. J., Peart, W. S. 1975. Plasma catecholamines, plasma renin activity and plasma aldosterone in tetraplegic man, horizontal and tilted. *Clin. Sci. Mol. Med.* 49:291–99
8. Mathias, C. J., Christensen, N. J., Frankel, H. L., Peart, W. S. 1980. Renin release during head-up tilt occurs independently of sympathetic nervous activity in tetraplegic man. *Clin. Sci.* 59:251–56
9. Corbett, J. L., Frankel, H. L., Harris, P. J. 1976. Cardiovascular responses to tilting in tetraplegic man. *J. Physiol.* 215:411–31
10. Eidelman, B. H. 1973. *Cerebral blood flow in normal and abnormal man.* D. Phil. Thesis. Univ. Oxford, England
11. Freyschuss, U., Knutsson, E. 1969. Cardiovascular control in man with transverse cervical cord lesions. *Life Sci.* 8:421–24
12. Skagen, K., Jensen, K., Henriksen, O., Knudsen, L. 1982. Sympathetic reflex control of subcutaneous blood flow in tetraplegic man during postural changes. *Clin. Sci.* 62:605–9
13. Andersen, E. B., Boesen, F., Henriksen, O., Sonne, M. 1986. Blood flow in skeletal muscle of tetraplegic man during postural changes. *Clin. Sci.* 70:321–25
14. Mathias, C. J., Frankel, H. L., Davies, I. B., James, V. H. T., Peart, W. S. 1981. Renin and aldosterone release during sympathetic stimulation in tetraplegia. *Clin. Sci.* 60:399–404
15. Mathias, C. J., Unwin, R. J., Pike, F. A., Frankel, H. L., Sever, P. S., Peart, W. S. 1984. The immediate pressor response to saralasin in man; evidence against sympathetic activation and for intrinsic angiotensin-II-like myotropism. *Clin. Sci.* 66:517–24
16. Sved, A. F., McDowell, F. H., Blessing, W. W. 1985. Release of antidiuretic hormone in quadriplegic subjects in response to head-up tilt. *Neurology* 35:78–82
17. Mathias, C. J., Frankel, H. L. 1983. Autonomic failure in tetraplegia. In *Autonomic Failure. A Textbook of Clinical Disorders of the Autonomic Nervous System,* ed. R. Bannister, pp. 453–88. Oxford: Oxford Univ. Press
18. Pickering, T. G., Bruckner, B., Frankel, H. L., Mathias, C. J., Dworkin, B.

R., Miller, N. E. 1977. Mechanisms of learned voluntary control of blood pressure in patients with generalized bodily paralysis. In *Biofeedback and Behaviour, NATO Conf. Ser. III, Human Factors,* ed. J. Beatty, H. Legwie, 2(3):225–34. New York: Plenum
19. Guttmann, L., Whitteridge, D. 1947. Effects of bladder distension on autonomic mechanisms after spinal cord injury. *Brain* 70:361–404
20. Corbett, J. L., Frankel, H. L., Harris, P. J. 1971. Cardiovascular reflex responses to cutaneous and visceral stimuli in spinal man. *J. Physiol.* 215:395–409
21. Davies, I. B., Mathias, C. J., Sudera, D., Sever, P. S. 1982. Agonist regulation of alpha-adrenergic receptor responses in man. *J. Cardiovasc. Pharmacol.* 4:S139–44
22. Mathias, C. J., Frankel, H. L., Turner, R. C., Christensen, N. J. 1979. Physiological responses to insulin hypoglycaemia in spinal man. *Paraplegia* 17:319–26
23. Mathias, C. J., da Costa, D. F., Fosbraey, P., Bannister, R., Christensen, N. J. 1986. Post-cibal hypotension in autonomic failure. In *The Sympathoadrenal System, Alfred Benzon Symposium 23,* ed. N. J. Christensen, O. Henriksen, N. A. Lassen, pp. 402–13. Copenhagen: Munksgaard
24. Mathias, C. J., Fosbraey, P., da Costa, D. F., Thornley, A., Bannister, R. 1986. Desmopressin reduces nocturnal polyuria, reverses overnight weight–loss and improves morning postural hypotension in autonomic failure. *Br. Med. J.* 293:353–54
25. Kooner, J. S., da Costa, D. F., Frankel, H. L., Bannister, R., Peart, W. S., Mathias, C. J. 1987. Recumbency induces hypertension, diuresis and natriuresis in autonomic failure but diuresis alone in tetraplegia. *J. Hypertension* 5(Suppl.):327–29
26. Mathias, C. J., Frankel, H. L., Christensen, N. J., Spalding, J. M. K. 1976. Enhanced pressor response to noradrenaline in patients with cervical spinal cord transection. *Brain* 99:757–70
27. Norberg, K. A., Normell, L. A. 1974. Histochemical demonstration of sympathetic adrenergic denervation in human skin. *Acta Neurol. Scand.* 50:261–71
28. Mathias, C. J. 1976. *Neurological disturbances of the cardiovascular system.* D.Phil. Thesis. Univ. Oxford, England
29. Frankel, H. L., Lightman, S. L., Poole, C. J. M., Williams, T. D. M. 1986. Increased sensitivity to the pressor re-

sponse of AVP in human subjects with high cervical cord transection. *J. Physiol.* 381:P39

30. Lindan, R., Leffler, E. J., Kedia, K. R. 1985. A comparison of the efficacy of an alpha-1-adrenergic blocker and a slow calcium channel blocker in the control of autonomic dysreflexia. *Paraplegia* 23:34–38

31. Reid, J. L., Wing, L. M. H., Mathias, C. J., Frankel, H. L., Neill, E. 1977. The central hypotensive effect of clonidine: studies in tetraplegic subjects. *Clin. Pharmacol. Ther.* 21:375–81

32. Mathias, C. J., Reid, J. L., Wing, L. M. H., Frankel, H. L., Christensen, N. J. 1979. Antihypertensive effects of clonidine in tetraplegic subjects devoid of central sympathetic control. *Clin. Sci.* 57:S425–S428

33. Mathias, C. J., Frankel, H. L., Gardiner, B., Baker, H. 1981. Antispastic

sedative and cardiovascular effects of DS103-282 (tizanidine) in spinal man. In *Proc. 8th Int. Congr. Pharmacol., Tokyo*, p. 774.

34. Mathias, C. J., Christensen, N. J., Frankel, H. L., Spalding, J. M. K. 1979. Cardiovascular control in recently-injured tetraplegics in spinal shock. *Q. J. Med.* 48:273–87

35. Frankel, H. L., Mathias, C. J., Spalding, J. M. K. 1975. Mechanisms of reflex cardiac arrest in tetraplegic patients. *Lancet* 2:1183–85

36. Mathias, C. J. 1976. Bradycardia and cardiac arrest during tracheal suction—mechanisms in tetraplegic patients. *Eur. J. Intensive Care Med.* 2:147–56

37. Mathias, C. J., Frankel, H. L. 1986. The neurological and hormonal control of blood vessels and heart in spinal man. *J. Auton. Nerv. Syst. Suppl.* 457–64

Ann. Rev. Physiol. 1988. 50:593–606

# CENTRAL COORDINATION OF RESPIRATORY AND CARDIOVASCULAR CONTROL IN MAMMALS

*Jack L. Feldman and Howard H. Ellenberger*

Systems Neurobiology Laboratory, Department of Kinesiology, University of California Los Angeles, 405 Hilgard Avenue, Los Angeles, California 90024–1568

Cardiorespiratory homeostasis in mammals requires the regulation of $O_2$, $CO_2$, and pH and is accomplished via central nervous system (CNS) control of two exquisite, constantly active pumping systems. The bidirectional respiratory pump (lung and associated skeletal musculature) moves air in and out of the alveoli, where gas exchange takes place. The unidirectional cardiovascular pump (heart and vasculature) moves $O_2$-enriched blood from the pulmonary circulation to the systemic capillaries, where $O_2$ diffuses into tissue and $CO_2$ moves into blood; the systemic venous blood returns to the heart, then is pumped through the pulmonary circulation for gas exchange. The CNS controls all aspects of the respiratory pump, since skeletal muscle contracts only in response to motoneuronal activity, whereas the CNS controls the cardiovascular pump by modulating the pattern of cardiac and vascular smooth muscle contraction. The CNS also coordinates these pumps and participates in the optimization, adaptation, and adjustment of their performance.

Understanding the CNS role in cardiorespiratory homeostasis requires knowledge of how (*i*) respiratory rhythm and sympathetic and parasympathetic tone are generated; (*ii*) the spatiotemporal patterns of motor outflow are determined; (*iii*) these systems are coordinated, and; (*iv*) responses to changes in behavioral state or afferent signals are mediated. We focus on point (*iii*) and concentrate on brain stem and spinal mechanisms (for discussion of other points see 11, 21, 32, 39, 69).

0066-4278/88/0315-0593$02.00

The subtle organization of the cardiorespiratory control system belies many experimental approaches; in particular it is nonlinear. CNS events underlying responses to isolated stimuli may therefore bear little resemblance to mechanisms in intact mammals. Alterations in function accompanying anesthesia or decerebration further compound the complexities of interpretation. As different protocols are chosen in turn, conflicting or mutually exclusive interpretations can often result, as for example in studies of the cardiorespiratory responses to exercise (26, 39, 114). Care and a healthy skepticism are necessary in interpreting experimental results.

The fundamental organizational precept of cardiorespiratory control is a unitary system. The dualistic concept currently prevails, however, because the physiology and pathophysiology of the lung and of the heart-vasculature are distinct and their end-stage neuromotor control is so different. Yet, afferent, ascending, and descending pathways integrating the efferent control of diverse vegetative functions, including cardiorespiratory control, follow a parallel course in the brain (9, 67, 94, 95); this allows for many sites where coordination of functions can take place (see below; Figure 1). We focus on respiratory related effects on cardiovascular performance. (For information on cardiovascular modulation of respiration, see 21, 49, 69, 93, 104.)

## Respiratory Modulation of Autonomic Outflow

CNS processing of baroreceptor and chemoreceptor sensory information and autonomic outflow controlling cardiovascular function are respiratory modulated. Heart rate is slower during expiration, because of increases in vagal cardioinhibitory activity (respiratory sinus arrhythmia) and sympathetic inhibition; cardiac contractility and A-V conduction velocity (113) are similarly reduced during expiration. Cardioinhibitory reflexes, such as those evoked by chemo- or baro-receptor stimulation (23, 33, 34, 43, 99) or by the diving reflex (44), are attenuated during inspiration. For example, bradycardia produced by chemoreceptor stimulation (22) is markedly attenuated during inspiration (55). In general, respiratory modulation of vagal tone and gating of associated reflexes results from peripheral (mechanical and sensory) and CNS respiratory-related activity: (i) The lowering of intrapleural pressure during inspiration increases venous return; this increases atrial stretch receptor activity and leads to an increase in heart rate (Bainbridge reflex); (ii) inflation-modulated pulmonary mechanoreceptor activity inhibits vagal tone when vagal tone is high (99); and (iii) cardioinhibitory neurons have decreased activity during inspiration and increased activity during (early) expiration (45), even in the absence of peripheral sensory signals.

Sympathetic preganglionic activity (16, 47, 72, 100), especially in control of vascular resistance and the heart (1, 3, 66, 68), can be respiratory modulated and typically is greater during inspiration and lesser during (early)

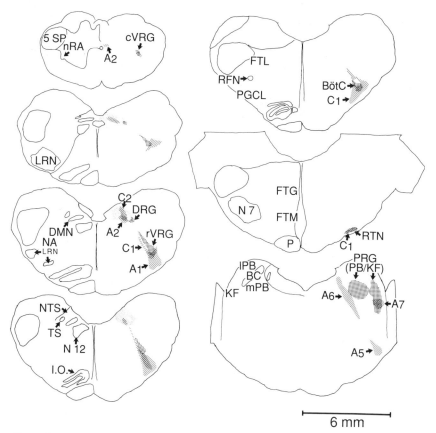

6 mm

*Figure 1*  The proximity of "respiratory" and "cardiovascular" premotor cell groups is high-lighted in a series of transverse sections of the cat brainstem (5). Respiratory cell groups are indicated by large dots, the $A_1$ and $A_2$ cell groups by diagonal lines (///), and the $C_1$ and $C_2$ cell groups by diagonal lines (\\\). The overall termination of cardiorespiratory-related afferent fibers and presumed location of second order neurons in the region of the NTS are indicated en masse by small dots. The catecholamine cell groups shown here may not be equivalent to functionally described cardiovascular groups but may be proximal to or intermingled with them. (See text for explanation and Ref. 5 for detailed neuroanatomy.)

Abbreviations: $A_1$, $A_2$, $A_5$, $A_6$, $A_7$, noradrenergic cell groups; $C_1$, $C_2$, adrenergic cell groups; BötC, Bötzinger Complex; BC, brachium conjunctivum; cVRG, caudal ventral respiratory group; rVRG, rostral ventral respiratory group; DMN, dorsal motor nucleus of the vagus; FTG, gigantocellular tegmental field; FTL, lateral tegmental field; FTM, magnocellular tegmental field; I.O., inferior olive; KF, Kölliker-Fuse nucleus; LRN, lateral reticular nucleus; lPB, lateral parabrachial nucleus; mPB, medial parabrachial nucleus; NTS, nucleus of the solitary tract; NA, nucleus ambiguus; nRA, nucleus retroambigualis; N7, facial nucleus; N 12, hypoglossal nucleus; P, pyramidal tract; PGCL, lateral paragigantocellular reticular nucleus; PRG, pontine respiratory group; RFN, retrofacial nucleus; RTN, retrotrapezoid nucleus; 5 SP, spinal trigeminal nucleus.

expiration; these responses are complementary to the pattern of vagal parasympathetic activity. Pulmonary stretch receptor activity, typically inspiratory modulated, can inhibit sympathetic preganglionic discharge (17, 47). Single preganglionic neurons can exhibit a variety of respiratory-related patterns (46, 97); this heterogeneity might reflect efferent innervation of a multitude of targets in addition to vascular smooth muscle. The phase relationship between sympathetic and respiratory nerve activities can shift (4, 31, 115a), Barman & Gebber (4) have suggested that the phase locking of rhythms is due to entrainment of separate sympathetic and respiratory oscillators. Phase shifts may also be mediated by subtle changes in complex control loops; for example, changes in ventilation alter respiratory-modulated, baroreceptor-mediated control of blood pressure (115a). The inspiratory modulation of sympathetic tone represents an overall increase in activity (89), which emphasizes the importance of the CNS coordination, since respiratory-related activity may contribute to setting control levels for circulatory variables. Respiratory modulation is not necessary, however, for generation of sympathetic tone because tone remains (*i*) in the absence of respiratory modulation (19, 71), (*ii*) during central neural apnea (19, 71), and (*iii*) following midsagittal transections of the medulla that reduce respiratory modulation of sympathetic outflow but do not attenuate vasomotor responses to baro- and chemo-receptor stimuli (18, 53, 70, 101).

The respiratory modulation of CNS control of the heart and vasculature is an important component of cardiovascular performance. The cycle-to-cycle modulation may serve to coordinate heart rate, right and left ventricular stroke volume, contraction timing, and vascular tone, with the direct mechanical influences of respiratory-related thoracic movement on venous return and cardiac performance. For example, respiratory pump–induced changes in preload alter left ventricular stroke volume; the respiratory modulation of autonomic outflow may reduce these fluctuations by precisely timed changes in heart rate and afterload. Modulation of right and left ventricular output with the respiratory cycle may also assure optimal pulmonary blood flow as the lungs expand and contract. In addition, events requiring increases in gas exchange, e.g. exercise, may cause appropriate alterations in cardiovascular variables via increases in respiratory drive and/or by parallel stimulation of both systems. Respiratory modulation may also represent a means to increase transmission of activity at CNS and ganglionic relays without a net increase in average activity (41, 115).

## Role of the CNS

CNS sites that *may* participate in cardiorespiratory control are typically identified by (*i*) neuroanatomical mapping, usually proceeding centrally from the sensory or motor periphery; (*ii*) placement of (small, reversible, or irreversible) lesions that perturb cardiorespiratory performance; (*iii*) (micro) stimulation (electrical or chemical) that perturbs cardiorespiratory perform- ance, or; (*iv*) identification of sites that contain or synthesize molecules related to neuromessengers that have been shown to influence cardiopulmo- nary performance. These techniques give equivocal information concerning the role of any particular site. Nevertheless, based on this data, electrophysio- logical and pharmacological studies of single neurons in candidate regions can be performed.

## Identification of CNS Respiratory and Cardiovascular Neurons

A neuron is a candidate constituent of the CNS cardiorespiratory network if it can influence cardiorespiratory performance. Yet, the actions of individual neurons are rarely consequential and thus force the adoption of more abstract criteria. Neuroanatomical criteria are suggestive, especially at the periphery, since neurons innervating the effector musculature or ganglia are surely involved in control. Similarly, second order CNS neurons that receive car- diorespiratory-related afferent input are likely involved, but their neuroanato- mical identification is tenuous. As we move centrally, respiratory premotor and cardiovascular pre-preganglionic neurons, as well as neurons receiving inputs from second order cardiorespiratory afferent neurons, are also im- plicated. As we proceed even deeper into the CNS, we lose anatomical precision and must rely on correlative physiological and pharmacological criteria.

The basic physiological criterion is the correlation of neuronal (membrane potential or impulse) activity with measures of respiratory, cardiac, or vascu- lar performance. Neurons with rhythmic discharge patterns, phase-correlated with respiratory and/or cardiac rhythm, are compelling choices; so are neurons with tonic discharge patterns related, for example, to blood pressure or $CO_2$. Neurons synthesizing or sensitive to neuromessengers known to influence cardiorespiratory function when applied centrally should also be considered. However, these criteria are neither necessary nor sufficient for functional identification, either singly or in tandem. Although a consensus can sometimes be reached, (preliminary) identification is tentative, fuzzy, and ambiguous, with considerable potential for false classification.

## Anatomical Relationship Between CNS Respiratory and Cardiovascular Neurons

MOTOR OUTFLOW–RESPIRATORY PUMP    Phrenic motoneurons innervating the diaphragm are intermediate in the mid-cervical ($C_4$-$C_6$ in cat and man, $C_3$-$C_5$ in rat) ventral horn. Intercostal motoneurons are ventral in the thoracic ventral horn, and abdominal motoneurons are in the lower thoracic and upper lumbar ventral horns.

HEART AND VASCULATURE   Parasympathetic preganglionic cardioinhibitory neurons are within the dorsal motor nucleus of the vagus and nucleus ambiguus (12, 36, 37, 59, 61, 96); the latter is proximal to cranial respiratory-related motoneurons innervating the larynx, pharynx, and airways and to the inspiratory portion of the ventral respiratory group (see below). Sympathetic preganglionic neurons innervating the heart and vasculature are in the lateral and medial portions of the intermediate gray matter (including the interomediolateral cell column) from the lower cervical to the lower lumbar spinal cord (13).

## Coexistence of Respiratory and Cardiovascular Neurons

When respiratory and cardiovascular premotor control are considered separately, the locations of neurons assigned to each network (biased toward somatic location and presynaptic field distribution), by and large, are distinct (90, 98). The local microcircuitry of each separate neuronal cluster is an important factor in their behavior. However, on a slightly larger scale (Figure 1), the locations of clusters assigned to each control system parallel each other. Their proximity and occasional commingling, with the likely overlapping of their dendritic fields, suggest that shared inputs and local processing, by collaterals or short axon interneurons, underlie cardiorespiratory coordination. Potent local interactions are suggested by the powerful cardiorespiratory effects of microinjection of subpicomole amounts of excitatory amino acid neurotransmitters in these brain stem regions (87, 88, 92).

DESCENDING PATHWAYS AND EFFERENT CONTROL   The basic drive to respiratory and sympathetic neurons originates in the brain stem. Phrenic and intercostal motoneurons receive monosynaptic excitatory inputs from bulbospinal inspiratory neurons in the dorsal and ventral respiratory groups along with oligosynaptic signals relayed by long propriospinal interneurons in the upper cervical spinal cord and by segmental interneurons (39). Sympathetic preganglionic neurons receive excitatory drive mono- or oligo-synaptically from bulbospinal neurons in the rostroventrolateral medulla (106). The respiratory modulation exhibited by spinal sympathetic preganglionics appears to be due to pathways other than those responsible for transmitting respiratory drive to respiratory pump motoneurons (18, 70)

Other descending pathways affecting sympathetic and/or respiratory function originate in the cerebral cortex, amygdala (including the substantia innominata and bed nucleus of the stria terminalis), hypothalamus, the parabrachial region (PB) [especially the Kölliker-Fuse nucleus (K-F)], ventrolateral portions of the caudal pons, raphe pallidus, and obscurus, as well as in the commissural, intermediate, and ventrolateral subnuclei of the nucleus of the solitary tract (NTS) (2, 13, 35, 42, 57, 60, 63, 75–77, 90, 98, 107, 109).

DORSOMEDIAL MEDULLA    General visceral afferent fibers of the ninth and tenth cranial nerves (including those from pulmonary, cardiac, carotid and other vascular mechanoreceptors, and carotid and aortic chemoreceptors) terminate in NTS, which has a complex subnuclear organization with diverse afferent and efferent connections (76). Central axons of pulmonary stretch receptor afferents arborize mainly in the medial subnucleus, but also to a lesser extent in the ventrolateral, lateral (30), and intermediate (62) subnuclei; they synapse onto second order (pump) cells in the medial, dorsolateral, and ventrolateral NTS (15, 24; D. W. Richter, personal communication). Carotid and aortic baroreceptor afferents terminate mainly in the lateral and dorsomedial NTS with some projections to commissural and ventrolateral NTS (28, 29). In contrast, carotid body chemoreceptor afferents terminate most heavily in the dorsomedial, medial, and commissural subnuclei, with sparse lateral innervation (28). In addition to respiratory and cardiovascular afferents separately affecting NTS neurons, some cells receive multimodal inputs (73) and may act as an early stage of integration. The local circuitry for processing of cardiorespiratory signals within NTS is unknown. Second or higher order neurons mainly in medial, commissural, intermediate, and dorsolateral NTS project to portions of the amygdala and hypothalamus, to the parabrachial nuclear region, and to the ventrolateral medulla (8–11, 52, 76, 91, 94, 95, 103, 108, 111). Inspiratory neurons in the ventrolateral region of NTS project to the ventrolateral medulla and are also a source of mono- and oligosynaptic drive to spinal inspiratory neurons [this region of cells is referred to as the dorsal respiratory group (DRG)] (39).

VENTROLATERAL MEDULLA INCLUDING THE VENTRAL SURFACE    Respiratory premotor (bulbospinal) and intrinsic brain stem interneurons form a longitudinal column extending the entire length of the ventrolateral medulla [ventral respiratory group (VRG)] (36, 98, 105). Most caudally, the VRG corresponds to nucleus retroambigualis; vagal motoneurons are medial and dorsomedial at this level. However, VRG cells and vagal, including cardioinhibitory and bronchoconstrictor, motoneurons commingle more rostrally in nucleus ambiguus rostral to obex, although VRG cells tend to span a greater dorsomedial and ventrolateral distance. Vagal motoneurons form two distinct groups in the rostral ventrolateral medulla at the level of the retrofacial nucleus (RFN): a dorsal compact division, and a ventral diffuse (external) division (nucleus ambiguus). Respiratory neurons at this level [Bötzinger Complex (BötC)] are separate from the compact division but commingle with cells of the diffuse division of vagal motoneurons (36). The coexistence of VRG/BötC cells and vagal motoneurons may underlie a functional coupling between these cells or may represent a common site for processing respiratory-related inputs. A more rostral nucleus composed of small, compactly arranged fusiform cells ventral to the medial division of the facial nucleus near the ventral surface projects to the regions of DRG and VRG (38). This group is immediately caudal to the nucleus of the trapezoid body and is called the retrotrapezoid nucleus (RTN). There are no spinal projections from RTN.

Two cell groups implicated in control of sympathetic preganglionic activity, the $A_1$ (noradrenergic) and $C_1$ (adrenergic) catecholamine cell groups (48, 58, 102, 106), also form a continuous column extending the length of the ventrolateral medulla. This column lies parallel to and extends ventral and lateral to the VRG; in fact, some dorsomedial $A_1$ cells commingle with VRG cells, and some $C_1$ cells commingle with rostral VRG and BötC cells (38a). It has been hypothesized that vasomotor tone is mediated by bulbospinal $C_1$ cells exciting sympathetic preganglionics (106). However, a sympathoexcitatory bulbospinal projection of $C_1$ cells mediated by epinephrine (adrenalin) may not be consistent with the inhibitory effect of iontophoresed epinephrine on the activity of sympathetic neurons (50, 51; see also 113a, b). Instead, another transmitter, e.g. substance P or neuropeptide Y that are co-localized in $C_1$ bulbospinal cells (7, 78) may be released at the presynaptic terminals of $C_1$ cells; or noncatecholaminergic transmitters may be released by neurons in or near $C_1$. The most rostral portion of the $C_1$ group extends ventral to the medial division of the facial nucleus. Within this circumscribed location are also found a substance P–containing cell group (38, 80, 83) and the RTN cell group. It is hypothesized that an inhibitory projection from $A_1$ cells modulates the activity of the $C_1$ cells (48). Yet, cells dorsomedial to $A_1$ have instead been implicated as the site of inhibition of cardiovascular-related cells in the rostroventrolateral medulla (25, 112), although the $A_1$ group may be important in the neuroendocrine control of the circulation via connections to the hypothalamus (108). The dorsomedial group overlaps with the VRG and may include respiratory-related cells. That there may be overlap of $A_1$ with VRG, and $C_1$ with rostral VRG, BötC, and RTN is intriguing and has important functional consequences for cardiorespiratory coordination.

Perturbations (cooling, electrical stimulation, low or high pH solutions, or solutions containing glutamate, glycine, acetylcholine, and associated chemicals) applied at the medullary ventral surface affect cardiorespiratory performance. Maps of the most sensitive sites for different perturbations have been drawn (see 39, 83, 84) and suggest some separation of sites affecting predominantly respiratory or cardiovascular function. These ventral surface sites have been proposed as the locale of intracranial chemoreception or integration of various peripheral and CNS inputs (86), especially hypothalamic inputs related to the defense reaction (56, 57). Implicit in these hypotheses is that the observed responses are physiologically relevant; yet perturbations are often gross, unphysiologically potent (for example, use of solutions of pH

7.0 and 7.8 or containing 2 M glutamate), and not focal, and they can affect structures up to 2 mm beneath the ventral surface. Whether responses consistent with a necessary role in cardiorespiratory performance follow appropriately subtle perturbations remains to be demonstrated, although efforts in this regard have not contradicted previous conclusions (79, 84, 85). The neuronal elements and mechanisms underlying the stimulus transductions and, in particular, their location (superficial or deep) are unknown.

PONS    Cells in the PB/K-F region have been implicated in cardiorespiratory control (6, 14, 40, 52, 54, 81, 110). The subnuclear organization and efferent connections of this region in rat have been described (42), although a cardiorespiratory function cannot yet be associated exclusively with any subnuclear group. The K-F nucleus has strong reciprocal connections with the region of the VRG, descending projections to the region of the DRG (38), and a minor premotor projection to the intermediolateral cell column (42, 90) and the phrenic nucleus (98, 105). The medial PB receives some afferent projections from NTS and ventrolateral medulla but has very few descending projections to the medulla; most of its efferent output is to various forebrain nuclei (42). The pathway(s) responsible for mediating effects on respiratory timing from medial PB are unknown.

OTHER STRUCTURES    Suprapontine sites, especially the hypothalamus, amygdala (116), insular cortex (107), and the cerebellum, play major roles in cardiorespiratory control. They are especially important, for example, in mediating cardiorespiratory adjustments associated with change of sleep-wake state (82), arousal (defense reaction) and stress responses, the hypothesized feed-forward component of exercise hyperpnea (27, 35), and integration of orthostatic reflexes.

## General Conclusions

In summary we ask, how is CNS coordination of the separate respiratory and cardiovascular pumps achieved? Koepchen (64, see also 65) postulates three possible mechanisms for coordinated responses to peripheral signals. "First, separate action on both of the control systems; second, an action on one control system which transmits the effect to the other by central connections; third, action on a substrate superposed on both systems." In addition, there are purely central interactions that suggest a unitary organization, with local interactions playing an important role. Whatever the mechanism, these systems are integrated in the brain stem in one or more of the regions described above. Given the nonlinearity of these systems and their state-dependent performance, as during the sleep-wake cycle or exercise, their linkage may be flexible, thus providing a further challenge to our understanding.

## Literature Cited

1. Adrian, E. D., Bronk, D. W., Phillips, G. 1932. Discharges in mammalian sympathetic nerves. *J. Physiol.* 74:115–23
2. Amendt, K., Czachurski, J., Dembowsky, Seller, H. 1979. Bulbospinal projections to the intermediolateral cell column; a neuroanatomical study. *J. Auton. Nerv. Syst.* 1:103–17
3. Bainton, C. R., Richter, D. W., Seller, H., Ballantyne, D., Klein, J. P. 1985. Respiratory modulation of sympathetic activity. *J. Auton. Nerv. Syst.* 12:77–90
4. Barman, S. M., Gebber, G. L. 1976. Basis for synchronization of sympathetic and phrenic nerve discharges. *Am. J. Physiol.* 231:1601–7
5. Berman, A. L. 1968. *The brain stem of the cat*. Madison: Univ. of Wisconsin Press
6. Bertrand, F., Hugelin, A. 1971. Respiratory synchronizing function of nucleus parabrachialis medialis: pneumotaxic mechanisms. *J. Neurophysiol.* 34:189–207
7. Blessing, W. W., Oliver, J. R., Hodgson, A. H., Joh, T. H., Willoughby, J. O. 1987 Neuropeptide Y-like immunoreactive $C_1$ neurons in the rostral ventrolateral medulla of the rabbit project to sympathetic preganglionic neurons in the spinal cord. *J. Auton. Nerv. Syst.* 18:121–29
8. Calaresu, F. R., Cechetto, D. F. 1980. Projections to the hypothalamus from buffer nerves and nucleus tractus solitarius in the cat. *Am. J. Physiol.* 239: R130–36
9. Cechetto, D. F. 1987. Central representation of visceral function. *Fed. Proc.* 46:17–23
10. Cechetto, D. F., Calaresu, F. R. 1983. Parabrachial units responding to stimulation of buffer nerves and forebrain in the rat *Am. J. Physiol.* 245:R811–19
11. Cechetto, D. F., Calaresu, F. R. 1984. Units in the amygdala responding to activation of carotid baro- and chemoreceptors. *Am. J. Physiol.* 246: R832–36
12. Ciriello, J., Calaresu, F. R. 1982. Medullary origin of vagal preganglionic axons to the heart of the cat. *J. Auton. Nerv. Syst.* 5:9–22
13. Ciriello, J., Caverson, M. M., Polosa, C. 1986. Function of the ventrolateral medulla in control of the circulation. *Brain Res. Rev.* 11:359–91
14. Cohen, M. I. 1969. Switching of the respiratory phases and evoked phrenic responses produced by rostral pontine

electrical stimulation. *J. Physiol.* 217: 133–58
15. Cohen, M. I., Feldman, J. L. 1984. Discharge properties of dorsal medullary inspiratory neurons: relation to pulmonary afferent and phrenic efferent discharges. *J. Neurophysiol.* 51:753–76
16. Cohen, M. I., Gootman, P. M. 1970. Periodicity in efferent discharges of splanchnic nerve of the cat. *Am J. Physiol.* 218:1092–1101
17. Cohen, M. I., Gootman, P. M., Feldman, J. L. 1980. Inhibition of sympathetic discharge by lung inflation. In *Arterial Baroreceptors and Hypertension*, ed. P. Sleight, pp. 161–67. Cambridge: Oxford Univ. Press
18. Connelly, C. A., Wurster, R. D. 1985. Spinal pathways mediating respiratory influences on sympathetic nerves. *Am. J. Physiol.* 249:R91–99
19. Connelly, C. A., Wurster, R. D. 1985. Sympathetic rhythms during hyperventilation induced apnea. *Am. J. Physiol.* 249:R424–31
20. Deleted in proof
21. Daly, M. De B. 1986. Interaction between respiration and circulation. In *Handbook of Physiology, Sec. 3: The Respiratory System, Vol. 2: Control of Breathing*, ed. N. S. Cherniack, J. G. Widdicombe, pp. 529–94. Bethesda, Md: Am. Physiol. Soc.
22. Daly, M. De B., Scott, M. J. 1958. The effects of stimulating carotid body chemoreceptors on heart rate in the dog. *J. Physiol.* 144:148–66
23. Davidson, N. S., Goldner, S., McCloskey, D. I. 1976. Respiratory modulation of baroreceptor and chemoreceptor reflexes affecting heart rate and cardiac vagal efferent nerve activity. *J. Physiol.* 259:523–30
24. Davies, R. O., Kubin, L., Pack, A. I. 1986. Pulmonary stretch receptor relay neurones in the cat: location and contralateral medullary projections. *J. Physiol.* 383:571–85
25. Day, T. A., Ro, A., Renaud, L. P. 1983. Depressor area within caudal ventrolateral medulla does not correspond to the $A_1$ catecholamine cell group. *Brain Res.* 279:299–302
26. Dempsey, J. A., Vidruk, E. H., Mastenbrook, S. M. 1980. Pulmonary control systems in exercise. Fed. Proc. 39: 1498–1505
27. Dimarco, A. F., Romaniuk, V. R., von Euler, C., Yamamoto, Y. 1983. Immediate changes in ventilation and respiratory pattern with onset and cessation

of locomotion in the cat. *J. Physiol.* 343:1–16

28. Donoghue, S., Felder, R. B., Jordan, D., Spyer, K. M. 1984. The central projection of carotid baroreceptors and chemoreceptors in the cat: a neurophysiological study. *J. Physiol.* 347:397–409

29. Donoghue, S., Garcia, M., Jordan, D., Spyer, K. M. 1982. Identification and brain-stem projections of aortic baroreceptor afferent neurones in nodose ganglia of cats and rabbits. *J. Physiol.* 322:337–52

30. Donoghue, S., Garcia, M., Jordan, D., Spyer, K. M. 1982. The brainstem projections of pulmonary stretch afferent neurones in cats and rabbits. *J. Physiol.* 322:353–63

31. Dornhorst, A. C., Howard, P., Leathart, G. L. 1952. Respiratory variations in blood pressure. *Circulation* 6:553–58

32. Dorward, P. K., Korner, P. I. 1987. Does the brain "remember" the absolute blood pressure. *News Physiol. Sci.* 2:10–13

33. Eckberg, D. L., Bastow, H. III, Scruby, A. E. 1982. Modulation of human sinus node function by systemic hypoxia. *J. Appl. Physiol.* 52:570–77

34. Eckberg, D. L., Kifle, Y. T., Roberts, V. L. 1980. Phase relationship between normal human respiration and baroreflex responsiveness. *J. Physiol.* 304:489–502

35. Eldridge, F. L., Millhorn, D. E., Kiley, J. P., Waldrop, T. G. 1985. Stimulation by central command of locomotion, respiration and circulation during exercise. *Respir. Physiol.* 59:313–37

36. Ellenberger, H. H., Feldman, J. L. 1987. Anatomical organization of ventral respiratory group (VRG) neurons in the rat. *Fed. Proc.* 46:1420

37. Ellenberger, H. H., Haselton, J. R., Liskowsky, D. R., Schneiderman, N. 1982. Localization of chronotropic cardioinhibitory vagal motor neurons in the medulla of the rabbit. *J. Auton. Nerv. Syst.* 9:513–29

38. Ellenberger, H. H., Smith, J. C., McCrimmon, D. R., Feldman, J. L. 1985. A projection from a discretely localized cell group of the rostral medulla to the ventral respiratory group in the cat. *Soc. Neurosci. Abstr.* 11:1143

38a. Ellenberger, H. H., Zhan, W.-Z., Feldman, J. L. 1987. Anatomical relationship between respiratory and catecholamine neurons in ventrolateral medulla of rat. *Soc. Neurosci. Abstr.* 13:809

39. Feldman, J. L. 1986. Neurophysiology

of breathing in mammals. In *Handbook of Physiology, Sect. 1: The Nervous System, Vol. 4: Intrinsic Regulatory Systems of the Brain,* ed. F. E. Bloom, pp. 463–524. Bethesda, Md: Am. Physiol. Soc.

40. Feldman, J. L., Cohen, M. I., Wolotsky, P. 1976. Powerful inhibition of pontine respiratory neurons by pulmonary afferent activity. *Brain Res.* 104:341–46

41. Feldman, J. L., Grillner, S. 1983. Control of vertebrate respiration and locomotion. *The Physiologist* 26:310–16

42. Fulwiler, C. E., Saper, C. B. 1984. Subnuclear organization of the efferent connection of the parabrachial nucleus in the rat. *Brain Res. Rev.* 7:229–59

43. Gandevia, S. C., McCloskey, D. I., Potter, E. K. 1978. Inhibition of baroreceptor and chemoreceptor reflexes on heart rate during the respiratory cycle. *J. Physiol.* 276:369–81

44. Gandevia, S. C., McCloskey, D. I., Potter, E. K. 1978. Reflex bradycardia occurring in response to diving, nasopharyngeal stimulation and ocular pressure, and its modification by respiration and swallowing. *J. Physiol.* 276:383–94

45. Gilbey, M. P., Jordan, D., Richter, D. W., Spyer, K. M. 1984. Synaptic mechanisms involved in the inspiratory modulation of vagal cardioinhibitory neurones in the cat. *J. Physiol.* 356:65–78

46. Gilbey, M. P., Numao, Y., Spyer, K. M. 1986. Discharge patterns of cervical sympathetic preganglionic neurones related to central respiratory drive in the rat. *J. Physiol.* 378:253–65

47. Gootman, P. M., Feldman, J. L., Cohen, M. I. 1980. Pulmonary afferent influences on respiratory modulation of sympathetic discharge In *Central Interaction Between Respiratory and Cardiovascular Control Systems,* ed. H. P. Koepchen, S. M. Hilton, A. Trzebski, pp. 171–79. New York: Springer-Verlag

48. Granata, A. R., Numao, Y., Kumada, M., Reis, D. J. 1986. A$_1$ noradrenergic neurons tonically inhibit sympathoexcitatory neurons of C$_1$ area in rat brainstem. *Brain Res.* 377:127–46

49. Grunstein, M. M., Derenne, J. P., Milic-Emili, J. 1975. Control of depth and frequency of breathing during baroreceptive stimulation in cats. *J. Appl. Physiol.* 39:395–404

50. Guyenet, P. G., Cabot, J. B. 1981. Inhibition of sympathetic preganglionic neurons by catecholamines and clonidine: mediation by an $\beta$-adrenergic receptor. *J. Neurosci.* 1:908–17

51. Guyenet, P. G., Stornetta, R. L. 1982. Inhibition of sympathetic preganglionic discharges by epinephrine and x-methylepinephrine. *Brain Res.* 235:271–83

52. Hamilton, R. B., Ellenberger, H. H., Liskowsky, D. R., Schneiderman, N. 1981. Parabrachial area as mediator of bradycardia in rabbits. *J. Auton. Nerv. Syst.* 4:261–81

53. Hanna, B. D., Lioy, F., Polosa, C. 1981. Role of carotid and central chemoreception in the $CO_2$ response of sympathetic preganglionic neurons. *J. Auton. Nerv. Syst.* 3:421–35

54. Harper, R. M., Sieck, G. C. 1980. Discharge correlations between neurons in nucleus parabrachialis medialis during sleep-waking states. *Brain Res.* 199:343–58

55. Haymet, B. T., McCloskey, D. I. 1975. Baroreceptor and chemoreceptor influences on heart rate during the respiratory cycle in the dog. *J. Physiol.* 245:699–712

56. Hilton, S. M., Marshall, J. M., Timms, R. V. 1983. Ventral medullary relay neurons in the pathway from the defence areas of the cat and their effect on blood pressure. *J. Physiol.* 345:149–66

57. Hilton, S. M., Smith, P. R. 1984. Ventral medullary neurones excited from the hypothalamic and mid-brain defence areas. *J. Auton. Nerv. Syst.* 11:35–42

58. Hökfelt, T., Martensson, R., Björklund, A., Kleinau, S., Goldstein, M. 1984. Distributional maps of tyrosine-hydroxylase-immunoreactive neurons in the rat brain. In *Handbook of Chemical Neuroanatomy, Vol. 2:Classical Transmitters in the CNS, Pt. 1*, ed. A. Björklund, T. Hökfelt, pp. 277–379. Amsterdam: Elsevier

59. Hopkins, D. A., Armour, J. A. 1979. Cardiac nerves: a comparative study of their medullary cells of origin. *Fed. Proc.* 38:1320

60. Hopkins, D. A. Holstege, G. 1978. Amygdaloid projections to the mesencephalon, pons, and medulla oblongata in the cat. *Exp. Brain Res.* 32:529–47

61. Jordan, D., Khalid, M. E. M., Schneiderman, N., Spyer, K. M. 1982. The location and properties of preganglionic vagal cardiomotor neurons in the rabbit. *Pflügers Arch. Ges. Physiol.* 395:244–50

62. Kalia, M., Richter, D. W. 1985. Morphology of physiologically identified slowly adapting lung stretch receptor afferents stained with intraaxonal horseradish peroxidase in the nucleus of

the tractus solitarius of the cat. I. A light microscopic analysis. *J. Comp. Neurol.* 241:503–20

63. Kapp, B. S., Schwaber, J. S., Driscoll, P. A. 1985. The origin of insular cortex projections to the amygdaloid central nucleus and autonomic regulatory nuclei of the dorsal medulla. *Brain Res.* 360:355–60

64. Koepchen, H. P. 1983. Respiratory and cardiovascular "centres": functional entirety or separate structures. In *Central Neurone Environment*, ed. M. E. Schlafke, H. P. Koepchen, W. R. See, pp. 221–37. Berlin: Springer-Verlag

65. Koepchen, H. P., Klüssendorf, D., Sommer, D. 1981. Neurophysiological background of central neural cardiovascular-respiratory coordination: basic remarks and experimental approach. *J. Auton. Nerv. Syst.* 3:335–68

66. Koepchen, H. P., Seller, H., Polster, J., Langhorst, P. 1968. Über die feinvasomotorik der muskelstrombahn und ihre beziehung zur ateminnervation. *Pflügers Arch.* 302:285–99

67. Koh, E. T., Ricardo, J. A. 1978. Afferents and efferents of the parabrachial region of the cat: evidence for parallel ascending gustatory versus visceroceptive systems arising from the nucleus of the solitary tract. *Anat. Rec.* 190:449

68. Koizumi, K., Seller, H., Kaufman, A., Brooks, C. McC. 1971. Patterns of sympathetic discharge and their relation to baroreceptor and respiratory activities. *Brain Res.* 27:281–93

69. Korner, P. I. 1979. Central nervous control of autonomic cardiovascular function. In *Handbook of Physiology, Sect. 2: The Cardiovascular System, I:*691–769. Bethesda, Md: Am. Physiol. Soc.

70. Kubin, L., Trzebski, A., Lipski, J. 1985. Split medulla preparation in the cat: arterial chemoreceptor reflex and respiratory modulation of renal sympathetic nerve activity. *J. Auton. Nerv. Syst.* 12:211–25

71. Lioy, F., Trzebski, A. 1984. Pressor effects of $CO_2$ in the rat: different thresholds of the central cardiovascular and respiratory response to $CO_2$. *J. Auton. Nerv. Syst.* 10:43–54

72. Lipski, J., Coote, J. H., Trzebski, A. 1977. Temporal patterns of antidromic invasion latencies of sympathetic preganglionic neurons related to central inspiratory activity and pulmonary stretch receptor reflex. *Brain Res.* 133:162–66

73. Lipski, J., McAllen, R. M., Trzebski, A. 1976. Carotid baroreceptor and che-

moreceptor inputs onto single medullary neurones. *Brain Res.* 107:132–36

74. Deleted in proof

75. Loewy, A. D. 1981. Raphe pallidus and raphe obscurus projections to the intermediolateral cell column in the rat. *Brain Res.* 222:129–39

76. Loewy, A. D., Burton, H. 1978. Nuclei of the solitary tract: Efferent projects to the lower brainstem and spinal cord of the cat. *J. Comp. Neurol.* 181:421–50

77. Loewy, A. D., McKeller, S., Saper, C. B. 1979. Direct projections from the A$_5$ catecholamine cell group to the intermediolateral cell column. *Brain Res.* 174:309–14

78. Lorenz, R. G., Saper, C. B., Wong, D. L., Ciaranello, R. D., Loewy, A. R. 1985. Co-localization of substance P- and phenylethanolamine-N-methyltransferase-like immunoreactivity in neurons of ventrolateral medulla that project to the spinal cord: Potential role in control of vasomotor tone. *Neurosci. Lett.* 55:255–60

79. Lovick, T. A., Hilton, S. M. 1985. Vasodilator and vasoconstrictor neurones of the ventrolateral medulla in the cat. *Brain Res.* 331:353–57

80. Lovick, T. A., Hunt, S. P. 1983. Substance P-immunoreactive and serotonin-containing neurones in the ventral brainstem of the cat. *Neurosci. Lett.* 36:223–28

81. Lydic, R., Orem, J. 1979. Respiratory neurons of the pneumotaxic center during sleep and wakefulness. *Neurosci. Lett.* 15:187–92

82. Marks, J. D., Harper, R. D. 1987. Differential inhibition of the diaphragm and posterior cricoarytenoid muscles induced by transient hypertension across sleep states in intact cats. *Exp. Neurol.* 95:730–42

83. Marson, L., Loewy, A. D. 1985. Topographic organization of substance P and monoamine cells in the ventral medulla of the cat. *J. Auton. Nerv. Syst.* 14:271–85

84. McAllen, R. M. 1986. Location of neurones with cardiovascular and respiratory function, at the ventral surface of the cat's medulla. *Neuroscience* 18:43–49

85. McAllen, R. M. 1986. Action and specificity of the ventral medullary vasopressor neurones in the cat. *Neuroscience* 18:51–59

86. McAllen, R. M., Neil, J. J., Loewy, A. D. 1982. Effects of kainic acid applied to the ventral surface of the medulla oblongata on vasomotor tone, the baroreceptor reflex and hypothalamic autonomic responses. *Brain Res.* 238:65–76

87. McCrimmon, D. R., Feldman, J. L., Speck, D. F. 1986. Respiratory motoneuronal activity is altered by picomole injections of glutamate in the cat brainstem. *J. Neurosci.* 6:2384–392

88. McCrimmon, D. R., Feldman, J. L., Speck, D. F., Ellenberger, H. H., Smith, J. C. 1987. Functional heterogeneity of dorsal, ventral and pontine respiratory groups revealed by micropharmacological techniques. In *Neurobiology of the Control of Breathing, 10th Nobel Symposium*, ed. C. von Euler, H. Lagercrantz, pp. 201–08. New York: Raven

89. Millhorn, D. E. 1986. Neural respiratory and circulatory interaction during chemoreceptor stimulation and cooling of the ventral medulla in cats. *J. Physiol.* 370:217–31

90. Miura, M., Onai, T., Takayama, K. 1983. Projections of upper structure to the spinal cardioacceleratory center in cats: an HRP study using a new microinjection method. *J. Auton. Nerv. Syst.* 7:119–39

91. Morest, D. K. 1967. Experimental study of the projections of the nucleus of the tractus solitarius and the area postrema in the cat. *J. Comp. Neurol.* 130:277–300

92. Nelson, D. O., Cohen, H. L., Feldman, J. L., McCrimmon, D. R. 1988. Cardiovascular function is altered by picomole injections of glutamate into rat brainstem. *J. Neurosci.* 8:In press

93. Nishino, T., Honda, Y. 1982. Changes in pattern of breathing following baroreceptor stimulation in cats. *Jpn. J. Physiol.* 32:183–95

94. Norgren, R. 1978. Projections from the nucleus of the solitary tract in the rat. *Neuroscience* 3:207–18

95. Norgren, R., Leonard, C. M. 1973. Ascending central gustatory pathways. *J. Comp. Neurol.* 150:217–38

96. Nosaka, S., Yamamoto, T., Yasunaga, K. 1979. Localization of vagal preganglionic neurons within the rat brainstem. *J. Comp. Neurol.* 186:59–92

97. Numao, Y., Gilbey, M. P. 1986. Effects of aortic nerve stimulation on cervical sympathetic preganglionic neurones in the rat. *Brain Res.* 401:190–94

98. Onai, T., Miura, M. 1986. Projections of supraspinal structures to phrenic motor nucleus in cats studied by a horseradish peroxidase microinjection method. *J. Auton. Nerv. Syst.* 16:61–77

99. Potter, E. K. 1981. Inspiratory inhibition of vagal responses to baroreceptor

and chemoreceptor stimuli in the dog. *J. Physiol.* 316:177–90

100. Preiss, G., Kirchner, F., Polosa, C. 1975. Patterning of sympathetic preganglionic neuron firing by the central respiratory drive. *Brain Res.* 87:363–74

101. Preiss, G., Polosa, C. 1977. The relation between end-tidal $CO_2$ and discharge patterns of sympathetic preganglionic neurons. *Brain Res.* 122:255–67

102. Reiner, P. B., Vincent, S. R. 1986. The distribution of tyrosine hydroxylase, dopamine-$\beta$-hydroxylase, and phenylethanolamine-N-methyltransferase immunoreactive neurons in the feline medulla oblongata. *J. Comp. Neurol.* 248:518–31

103. Ricardo, J. A., Koh, E. T. 1978. Anatomical evidence of direct projections from the nucleus of the solitary tract to the hypothalamus, amygdala, and other forebrain structures in the rat. *Brain Res.* 153:1–26

104. Richter, D. W., Seller, H. 1975. Baroreceptor effects on medullary respiratory neurones of the cat. *Brain Res.* 86:168–71

105. Rikard-Bell, G. C., Bystrzycka, E. K., Nail, B. S. 1984. Brainstem projections to the phrenic nucleus: A HRP study in the cat. *Brain Res. Bull.* 12:469–77

106. Ross, C. A., Ruggiero, D. A., Joh, T. H., Park, D. H., Reis, D. J. 1983. Adrenaline synthesizing neurons in the rostral ventrolateral medulla: a possible role in tonic vasomotor control. *Brain Res.* 273:356–61

107. Ruggiero, D. A., Mraovitch, S., Granata, A., Anwar, M., Reis, D. J. 1987. A role of insular cortex in cardiovascular function. *J. Comp. Neurol.* 257:189–207

108. Sawchenko, P. E., Swanson, L. W. 1982. The organization of noradrenergic pathways from the brainstem to the paraventricular and supraoptic nuclei in the rat. *Brain Res. Rev.* 4:275–325

109. Schwaber, J. S., Kapp, B. S., Higgins, G. 1980. The origin and extent of direct amygdala projections to the region of the dorsal motor nucleus of the vagus and the nucleus of the solitary tract. *Neurosci. Lett.* 20:15–20

110. Sieck, G. C., Harper, R. M. 1980. Discharge of neurons in parabrachial pons related to the cardiac cycle: changes during different sleep-wake states. *Brain Res.* 199:359–79

111. Spyer, K. M. 1972. Baroreceptor sensitive neurones in the anterior hypothalamus of the rat. *J. Physiol.* 224:245–57

112. Sun, M. K., Guyenet, P. G. 1986. Effect of clonidine and $\gamma$-aminobutyric acid on the discharges of medullo-spinal sympathoexcitatory neurons in the rat. *Brain Res.* 368:1–17

113. Warner, M. R., Loeb, J. M. 1987. Beat-by-beat modulation of AV conduction I: Heart rate and respiratory influences. *Am. J. Physiol.* 251:H1126–33

113a. Yoshimura, M., Polosa, C., Nishi, S. 1986. Noradrenaline modifies sympathetic preganglionic neuron spike and after potential. *Brain Res.* 362:370–74

113b. Yoshimura, M., Polosa, C., Nishi, S. 1987. Slow IPSP and the norepinephrine-induced inhibition of the cat sympathetic preganglionic neuron in vitro. *Brain Res.* 419:383–86

114. Wasserman, K., Whipp, B. J., Casiburi, R. 1986. Respiratory control during exercise. See Ref. 21, pp. 595–619

115. Wurster, R. D. 1985. Central nervous system regulation of the heart: an overview. In *Nervous Control of Cardiovascular Function*, ed. W. C. Randall, pp. 307–20. New York: Oxford Univ. Press

115a. Wurster, R. D., Connelly, C. A. 1987. Phase changes of sympathetic activity with respiration before and after pontine lesions. In *Organization of the Autonomic Nervous System: Central and Peripheral Mechanisms*, ed. J. Ciriello, F. R. Calaresu, L. P. Renaud, C. Polosa, pp. 169–78. New York: Liss.

116. Zhang, J-X., Harper, R. M., Ni, H. 1986. Cryogenic blockade of the central nucleus of the amygdala attenuates aversively conditioned blood pressure and respiratory responses. *Brain Res.* 386:136–45

Ann. Rev. Physiol. 1988. 50:607–22

# CENTRAL ORGANIZATION OF SYMPATHETIC CARDIOVASCULAR RESPONSE TO PAIN[1]

## Robert D. Foreman and Robert W. Blair

Department of Physiology and Biophysics, Oklahoma University Health Sciences Center, Oklahoma City, Oklahoma 73104

## INTRODUCTION

During normal and pathological conditions cardiac receptors transmit information about the status of the heart in vagal and sympathetic pathways to the central nervous system. This review presents a summary of the neural mechanisms that underly the processing of nociceptive information arising from the heart. The characteristics and pathways of the cardiac sympathetic afferent fibers are presented. The processing of this information in cells of origin of the spinoreticular tract (SRT) and the spinothalamic tract (STT) and the viscerosomatic convergence of information onto these cells is discussed. These pathways are described because they are involved in the transmission of nociceptive information. A major emphasis will be placed on how the ascending systems respond to noxious stimuli, such as bradykinin or coronary artery occlusion. This overview also describes the termination and functional inputs of the SRT and STT to the medial medulla. The output to the spinal cord, including the motor system, the autonomic system, and descending control of ascending pathways is briefly discussed. Evidence presented in this review provides information about the integration of sympathetic afferent information associated with pain and also provides future directions for research in this area.

---

[1]The abbreviations used in this article are as follows: IML = intermediolateral nucleus; MRF = medial reticular formation; PR = paramedian nucleus; RF = reticular formation; RGC = reticularis gigantocellularis (equivalent to FTG of Berman); RMC = reticularis magnocellularis (equivalent to FTM of Berman); RN = raphe nuclei; RS = reticulospinal; SRT = spinoreticular tract; STT = spinothalamic tract.

607

0066-4278/88/0315-0607$02.00

## SYMPATHETIC AFFERENT FIBERS

Sympathetic sensory fibers of the heart have both A-delta myelinated and unmyelinated afferent nerve fibers (36, 37, 69, 81) that innervate the atria (61, 86, 85, 89) and ventricles (25, 47, 57, 60, 85, 86).

Although innocuous stimuli can activate these sympathetic afferent fibers, the effects of noxious stimulation is summarized. Myocardial ischemia increases impulse activity of sympathetic afferent fibers approximately 10–15 seconds after coronary blood flow is interrupted (25, 57). Myelinated afferent fibers in the ventricle may be excited in association with mechanical events of the heart (19, 60, 88). Unmyelinated fibers more commonly have irregular discharge patterns during the occlusion (57, 88) and are thought to be more chemosensitive than mechanosensitive.

Chemical substances such as potassium, acids, and veratridine can increase the discharge rate of unmyelinated sympathetic fibers from ventricular receptors, but bradykinin is most commonly used (6, 21, 31, 57, 67, 87, 90, 91, 92). Sympathetic afferent fibers increase their discharge rate approximately 10–15 seconds after bradykinin is injected in the heart or applied to the surface. The response could be due to mechanosensitive and/or chemosensitive endings. However, there is disagreement whether both types of receptors are located in the heart. Malliani (58) suggests that unmyelinated sympathetic afferent fibers in the heart are similar to polymodal receptors that are sensitive to mechanical and chemical stimuli (22). They appear to have a degree of mechanosensitivity and are spontaneously active when hemodynamic conditions are normal, but they also markedly increase their activity in response to intracoronary injections of small amounts of bradykinin or to coronary artery occlusion. Malliani (59) hypothesizes that cardiac nociception occurs when a spatially restricted population of polymodal receptors in the heart is strongly excited.

Evidence also exists to suggest that separate mechanosensitive and chemosensitive sympathetic afferent fibers are present (6, 65). Afferent endings could be differentiated according to their discharge pattern when the receptor site was gently stroked with a fine probe or bristle. Impulse activity of chemosensitive units change very little when vascular pressures are increased, but mechanosensitive units are activated more effectively by this stimulus. Bradykinin applied to the surface of the heart activates both mechanosensitive and chemosensitive sympathetic cardiac afferent fibers. However, pretreatment with epicardial application of prostoglandin $E_1$ ($PGE_1$) significantly increases the magnitude and duration of the response of chemosensitive endings to bradykinin, but it does not affect the responsiveness of mechanosensitive endings. Based on this evidence, there appear to be both mechanosensitive and chemosensitive endings in the heart but, in addition, the mechanosensitive afferents may be the polymodal receptors.

# DORSAL ROOT GANGLIA

Neuroanatomical studies show that cell bodies of the afferent fibers originating from the heart and coronary arteries are primarily concentrated in the $T_1$–$T_5$ dorsal root ganglia (52, 69, 92). Clinical studies (55, 94, 95) and experimental animal studies (96) demonstrate that removal of the $T_1$–$T_4$ rami communicantes reduce the symptoms associated with angina pectoris. This further documents the fact that the major concentration of afferent fibers is found between spinal segments $T_1$–$T_5$.

# SPINAL CORD TERMINATIONS

Sympathetic afferent fibers from the cardiopulmonary region terminate primarily in the dorsal horn and intermediate region of the gray matter in the spinal cord (52). Afferent fibers that travel in the inferior cardiac nerve project laterally in small bundles from Lissauer's tract through laminae I along the outer margin of the dorsal horn into lamina V and VII. A weak projection of visceral afferents is also found along the medial edge of the dorsal horn. The regions of the gray matter innervated by these afferent fibers correlate closely with the neurons that participate in nociception and autonomic reflexes.

# CELLS OF ORIGIN OF ASCENDING SPINAL PATHWAYS

Many ascending pathways project to supraspinal regions, but this part of the review focuses on those pathways that have been shown to transmit nociceptive information from sympathetic afferent fibers of the cardiopulmonary region to the caudal brainstem. These ascending pathways are found in anterior lateral white matter and include the SRT and the STT that have collaterals in the caudal brainstem. SRT cells transmit sympathetic afferent information from the cardiopulmonary region to the medial reticular formation of the medulla (14, 15, 38,). This particular area of the reticular formation can be involved in aversive drives and similar pain-related behavior and may provide connections for activating the autonomic nervous system (63).

The STT has been divided into two systems. One system, the medial STT (paleospinothalamic tract), projects directly to the medial and intralaminar nuclei of the thalamus and also has collaterals in the reticular formation (50, 62). The second system, the lateral STT (neospinothalamic tract), which ascends primarily to the ventral posterior lateral region of the thalamus, may mediate the sensory discriminative aspects of pain and may have a few collaterals to the medullary reticular formation (50, 75).

Cells of origin of the SRT and STT have been located by retrograde chromotolysis, antidromic mapping, and retrograde labeling with substances such as horseradish peroxidase (24, 38, 42, 45, 49, 97). These cells are located primarily in laminae I, IV, V, VII, and VIII of the thoracic spinal cord.

## VISCEROSOMATIC CONVERGENCE

A common manifestation of ischemic heart disease is the referral of pain to somatic structures. To explain this symptom, Ruch (78) formulated the theory that ". . . some visceral afferents converge with cutaneous pain afferents to end upon the same neuron at some point in the sensory pathway, that is spinal, thalamic or cortical, and the system of fibers is sufficiently organized topographically to provide the dermatomal reference". Convergence of somatic and visceral afferents onto SRT and STT cells may provide the neural basis for this theory (4, 5, 15, 38). Virtually all of the STT and SRT cells that respond to afferent input receive both visceral and somatic input (4, 15, 38). STT and SRT cells generally are classified according to their responses to somatic manipulation. The classes include (a) low threshold, (b) wide dynamic range (or multireceptive), (c) high threshold (or nociceptive specific), and (d) high threshold inhibitory cells (4, 15, 30, 32, 38, 39, 42, 76, 98). The most common STT cells are wide dynamic range cells; these cells respond with a low discharge rate to hair movement or touching the skin but discharge vigorously when pinch is applied to skin or skin and muscle (4). In contrast, SRT cells most commonly appear to be high threshold; they are not excited by hair movement but increase their discharge rate during a noxious pinch (38, 45).

Somatic receptive fields of lateral STT cells are usually restricted to the left chest and forelimb and do not cross the midline. In contrast, the medial STT cells often have bilateral receptive fields or large unilateral fields (4). The SRT cells can have restrictive somatic fields or fields that extend to multiple areas on the somatic surface (38). However, most somatic receptive fields overlay the heart; these are the same areas in which angina pectoris is commonly experienced in humans.

## SYMPATHETIC AFFERENT INPUT

The A-delta and C fibers of the cardiopulmonary afferent fibers excite STT and SRT cells in the $T_1$–$T_5$ segments (4, 5, 15, 16, 38). Minimum afferent conduction velocity for the A-delta peak is approximately 9 ms$^{-1}$ and approximately 1 ms$^{-1}$ for the C fiber peak (15, 38). About half the population of cells receives only A-delta fiber input and the other half receives both A-delta and C fiber input (4, 15, 38). The significance of these different types of inputs is not understood as yet but may provide important information in formulating hypotheses about cardiac pain and visceral pain in general.

## Coronary Artery Occlusion

Natural stimulation of receptors is important for understanding how cells respond to events occurring in normal and pathological conditions. Myocardial ischemia produced by coronary artery occlusion activates SRT and STT cells and produces varied responses to the ischemic episode (14). Responses of these neurons can be divided into four categories: (a) cell activity increases during ischemia produced by experimental occlusion—this is considered a noxious response, (b) cell activity increases rapidly at the onset or release of occlusion and then adapts during the remainder of occlusion—this is considered a response to innocuous stimuli, (c) cell activity increases at the onset of occlusion, adapts, and then increases again as ischemia develops—the early response is considered to be related to innocuous stimuli and the late response to noxious stimuli, and (d) cell activity does not change during the occlusion. An immediate response of cells to occlusion may be caused by activation of mechanoreceptors located in or near the occluded coronary artery. However, STT and SRT cell activity usually increases approximately 13 s after the onset of occlusion and is associated with ischemic changes of the heart and decreases in blood pressure, left ventricular pressure, and contractility.

STT and SRT neurons were analyzed to determine whether A-delta or A-delta and C fiber input was necessary to excite the cells during an innocuous, i.e. mechanodistortion of the receptors, or noxious stimulus, i.e. an ischemic episode (14). During an ischemic episode cells with only A-delta input are unresponsive, but cells with both the A-delta and C fiber input are more likely to be excited. However, if the responsiveness to both innocuous and noxious stimuli is compared for cells receiving the different classes of afferents, then cells with A-delta and A-delta and C fiber input can respond, but the cells receiving A-delta and C fiber input are most likely to respond to both types of stimuli. These results suggest that C fiber input is necessary for cells to respond during ischemia, but not every cell with C fiber input responds to this stimulus.

## Chemical Effects

SRT and STT cells also have been tested for their responsiveness to intracardiac injections of bradykinin (5, 16, 17). Bradykinin, an endogenous algesic chemical, was chosen because it is found in increased amounts in the effluent of the coronary sinus after coronary artery occlusion (46, 51) and it excites sympathetic afferent fibers (6, 57, 65, 67). Intracardiac injections of bradykinin increase the activity in approximately 75% of the STT cells (5, 16) and 55% of the SRT cells (17). Average latency for the onset of increased cell activity was approximately 15 s; this coincides with the predicted latencies based on single unit recordings of sympathetic afferent fibers. Responses most likely were due to stimulation of cardiac afferent fibers; control injections of bradykinin into either the general systemic circulation or into the heart following a 2% lidocaine injection into the pericardial sac did not activate SRT and STT cells (5, 16, 17). Approximately 60% of the cells with A-delta fiber input respond to bradykinin injections. However, when both A-delta and C fiber input are present, approximately 85% of the cells respond to this noxious stimulus. Baker et al (6) suggest that C fibers might transmit the noxious information. It appears that C fiber input increases the likelihood that a cell will respond to bradykinin, but A-delta fiber input alone also excites a small population of cells. Since C fibers are required to excite STT cells during the ischemic period of coronary artery occlusion, the C fibers appear to play a more important role than the A-delta fibers in the transmission of noxious information from the heart to the spinal cord.

Responses of SRT and STT cells to bradykinin do not rule out other chemicals or mechanisms that might participate in activating these cells. There is evidence that prostaglandins may play an intermediary role in activating and/or enhancing the impulse activity of sympathetic afferent fibers generated by bradykinin (64, 65). This intermediary step may explain the latency of approximately 15 s before cell activity increases with coronary artery occlusion or bradykinin injections. Further studies with other chemicals that are released during coronary artery occlusion may determine the stimulus or stimuli responsible for producing the observed responses of SRT and STT cells to ischemia.

## INPUTS TO MEDIAL MEDULLA

### Terminations of SRT

Anatomical studies have demonstrated that the SRT projects primarily to nucleus reticularis gigantocellularis (RGC, equivalent to FTG in Berman's (8) terminology). There are much less prominent projections to the raphe nuclei (RN) and nucleus reticularis magnocellularis (RMC, equivalent to FTM of Berman) (1, 40). Electrophysiological studies agree well with the anatomical studies; SRT neurons can be antidomically activated mainly from RGC, and some can be activated from the paramedian nucleus (PR) (14, 17, 38, 49, 61). Similar regions of the medulla also receive input from collaterals of STT neurons (14, 17, 38, 50). All these reports agree that the major SRT projection is contralateral, although there is a significant ipsilateral projection as well.

### Cardiovascular Input

As discussed above, SRT neurons convey cardiac input to the medial reticular formation (MRF). Is this information transmitted to reticular neurons? Several recent studies indicate that medial reticular neurons are responsive to stimuli applied to the heart. MRF cells are excited by electrical stimulation of cardiac sympathetic afferents, and about a third of these responsive neurons also respond to bradykinin applied to the epicardium (10, 93). Bradykinin-sensitive neurons are additionally responsive to cardiac ischemia resulting from coronary artery occlusion and to mechanical deformation of the coronary arteries themselves (11). Finally, some neurons are responsive to innocuous mechanical stimuli, such as probing the epicardium, increasing ventricular volume or pressure by aortic occlusion, and generating ventricular fibrillation (12). Thus, noxious and innocuous information arising in the heart is transmitted to MRF neurons by sympathetic afferents.

Although vagal afferents are also excited by cardiac stimuli, MRF neurons apparently do not receive this input. Several investigators indicated that activation of vagal afferents does not influence MRF neurons, although dorsal medullary (eg. dorsal motor nucleus and nucleus of solitary tract) and more lateral reticular (eg. near nucleus ambiguus) neurons do receive vagal input (9, 33, 79). On the other hand, some MRF cells do receive baroreceptor input and are responsive to changes in blood pressure (9, 53, 77).

In summary, cardiovascular input reaches MRF neurons via sympathetic and baroreceptor afferents, but probably not via cardiac vagal afferents.

## Sensory Input

Depending on the study, 75 to 90% of MRF neurons are responsive to somatic stimuli (10, 23, 26, 34, 54, 82, 99). The somatic receptive fields are widespread, often encompassing all four limbs and the trunk. Neurons are responsive to innocuous and noxious stimuli. For example, neurons are responsive to natural and noxious stimulation of the face (23) as well as the rest of the body (10, 26, 54, 99). Injection of bradykinin into the blood supply of muscles also excites MRF neurons (43). Most studies indicate that more neurons respond to nociceptive or intense stimuli than to innocuous stimuli (23, 26, 34, 54, 99). However, other studies (10, 82) suggest that MRF neurons are just as responsive to innocuous stimuli, such as blowing the fur or light tapping of the skin, as they are to noxious pinch. Some of the differences in somatic responses among various studies may be due to different anesthetics or experimental conditions (such as decerebration), as well as stimuli used for testing. Nonetheless, at least 75% of MRF neurons are responsive to somatic stimulation, and many of these are selectively excited by noxious stimuli. The noxious input to MRF cells is likely related to escape or aversive behavior; stimulation of RGC elicits escape behavior (28, 29, 34).

## Other Inputs

The major focus of this review concerns cardiac and somatic input to spinal cord and medulla. However, MRF neurons receive a variety of additional inputs. They are responsive to auditory and visual stimuli (10, 12), to activation of respiratory afferents (9, 53), as well as input from vestibular, cortical, tectal (71–73), and cerebellar (35, 79) pathways. As pointed out by Siegel (83), the proportions of neurons responsive to various stimuli add up to well over 100%. Hence, neurons must be responsive to more than one stimulus. As many as 90% of MRF neurons receive convergent input from multiple sensory sources (10, 12, 53, 80).

## Functional Considerations

A common observation is that MRF neurons adapt rapidly or habituate to repeated applications of the same stimulus. For example, a neuron may cease to respond to repetitive tapping of one part of its somatic field, but would be excited by tapping another area. This observation had led to the suggestion that MRF neurons respond best to novel stimuli (10, 70, 73, 82, 83). This property of MRF neurons would facilitate startle or escape behavior, as well as alerting an animal to a new stimulus.

Another trait of MRF neurons is that apparent inputs can change over time, as can the spontaneous discharge rate (53, 80). Thus a neuron might respond to a flash of light at one time and a few hours later could be unresponsive. An interpretation of this phenomenon is that as the behavioral state of an animal changes over time, the responsiveness of MRF neurons to various stimuli will be altered (53, 80). One of the oldest ascribed functions of the MRF is that of an "ascending reticular activating system," which desynchronizes the EEG and leads to arousal (20). The widespread input from various sensory modalities would seem to facilitate this function of the MRF, as well as providing the animal with information regarding its environment. Since the vast majority of MRF neurons receive multiple sensory inputs, these neurons are unlikely to mediate specific sensory sensations.

Unlike the phasic responses to innocuous stimuli discussed above, MRF neurons respond tonically to noxious somatic or cardiac stimulation. Thus the MRF seems to process noxious information differently from innocuous information. Noxious input may be more "insistent" in gaining an animal's attention and forcing subsequent appropriate behavior to reduce or avoid the noxious stimulus. In addition, the prolonged response to noxious input is probably related to the MRF's role in mediating the motivational-affective (29) component of the pain response.

## OUTPUT TO SPINAL CORD

There are two major descending reticulospinal (RS) pathways from the MRF. The RS motor system is important in the control of movement. A second system modulates ascending sensory information.

## RS Motor System

RS neurons whose cell bodies are in RGC and PR comprise the medullary portion of the RS motor system. The axons course in the ventral half of the lateral funiculus, forming the lateral RS pathway (7, 48, 68, 84). (The pons contributes axons to the medial RS pathway coursing in the ventromedial cord.) The RS pathway is predominantly ipsilateral, and axons terminate in the ventral gray, primarily in laminae VII and VIII (7, 68, 70, 74). Conduction velocity of RS neurons is fast, averaging about 60 ms$^{-1}$ (74). As pointed out above, stimulation of RGC elicits motor responses (28), and RS neurons in RGC and PR can monosynaptically excite axial motor neurons (71).

## Descending Control

Another major RS system causes the descending control of ascending traffic. This pathway is thought to function in analgesia or antinociception as excitation of this pathway inhibits firing of the dorsal horn neurons that transmit nociceptive information, including STT cells (3, 41). Cell bodies mediating this inhibition are located primarily in the midline raphe nuclei and RMC (1, 7, 41). Stimulation in RGC can inhibit or excite STT neurons (44); hence RGC is not a specific region for mediating inhibition of ascending traffic. The axons from the raphe nuclei and RMC course mainly in the dorsolateral funiculus; axons from RMC additionally course in the ventrolateral funiculus. Axons from both regions terminate in the dorsal horn (7).

## Cardiovascular Effects

Stimulating the MRF can elicit depressor or pressor effects, depending on which specific area is stimulated. The mediation of this effect is not due to a direct projection to the intermediolateral nucleus (IML). Anatomical data demonstrate that few neurons in MRF project to IML; neurons in more lateral and ventrolateral regions of the reticular formation do project to IML (2, 56). Consequently, cardiovascular effects from MRF must be mediated by neurons projecting to more lateral regions of medulla or by collaterals from RS neurons mediating motor responses or descending inhibition. Detailed descriptions of medullary sympathetic organization are presented in an article by Calaresu & Yardley (this volume).

## Functional Implications

As discussed previously, the MRF receives converging inputs from a variety of sources. To account for the many functions that these many inputs seem to imply, Siegel (83) proposed that "discharge in most RF cells is primarily related to the excitation of specific muscle groups." The fact that RS motor neurons receive converging inputs supports this hypothesis. Furthermore, RGC is important in modulating motor responses to nociceptive somatic stimuli since escape behavior can be induced by stimulating RGC (28) and RGC neurons are active during aversive or escape behavior (27, 29, 34). RS motor neurons probably mediate these escape behaviors. The auditory and visual information received by RS motor neurons would facilitate appropriate movements related to escape.

Recently, presumed RS motor neurons have been shown to receive noxious cardiac input (13). In response to damage of a visceral organ, overlying musculature contracts (18). People with angina pectoris or myocardial infarction often experience tightness of the chest and pain referred to arm and shoulder. Furthermore, muscles around upper thoracic vertebra can contract during myocardial infarction in humans (66). Activation of RS motor neurons by cardiac ischemia, via pathways discussed above, could mediate contraction of thoracic musculature, thereby contributing to ischemia-induced pain. Hence, RS motor neurons may comprise part of a viscero-somatic supraspinal loop.

MRF (including RS) neurons responsive to innocuous stimulation of the heart are located throughout the RF (12, 13). This innocuous input probably contributes to arousal responses, just as many of the other converging inputs do. Sympathetic activation of the heart, occurring during escape, startle, or fighting behavior, also leads to enhanced sympathetic (and vagal) afferent discharge. This activity would increase the amount of innocuous cardiac information reaching the RF and could facilitate arousal responses, as well as facilitate the motor responses occurring with the enhanced sympathetic outflow. In effect then, innocuous cardiac input to the MRF could not only enhance arousal behavior, but also act in a positive feedback manner to facilitate motor function. Since innocuous cardiac stimuli also influence neurons in RMC, this input could also alter the responsiveness of dorsal horn neurons to additional sensory information; the latter effect might enhance the detection of an event leading to alerting responses.

Finally, these spinal descending pathways could interact. For example, RS motor neurons may send collaterals to influence sympathetic function (70, 83). Thus, RS neurons may have a primary role in modulating spinal motor neurons, but may also have a secondary effect in altering sympathetic activity. A similar argument could be made for MRF neurons modulating ascending traffic. Thus, cardiac input to MRF reticulospinal neurons could evoke complex multifaceted motor and autonomic responses.

## SUMMARY

Figure 1 summarizes the pathways discussed in this review. Noxious and innocuous cardiac and somatic information converge on SRT neurons in the upper thoracic spinal cord; the third thoracic segment ($T_3$) is shown in Fig-

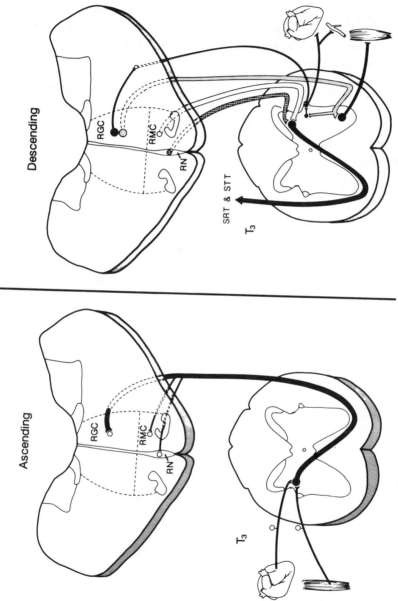

*Figure 1*  Ascending and descending pathways as discussed. See text for description.

ure 1. The SRT pathway and collaterals of the STT convey this information to the MRF (mainly RGC). This input is integrated with other inputs (eg. auditory and visual) by MRF neurons, some of which project to the spinal cord. RS motor neurons (dotted pathway) might mediate motor responses to cardiac pain, as well as motor responses associated with escape or alerting behavior. RS neurons (cross-hatched and clear pathways) can also modulate ascending traffic by altering activity of SRT and STT cells. Finally, RS neurons (dotted pathway) might modify sympathetic function via collaterals to IML or to interneurons, or MRF cells could project to medullary areas possessing neurons (solid pathway) that project directly to IML. The small figurines represent the heart *(top)*, blood vessels *(middle right)* and muscle *(bottom)*.

ACKNOWLEDGMENTS

The authors thank our colleagues D. C. Bolser, M. J. Chandler, S. F. Hobbs and R. Thies for their critique of the manuscript. The authors are grateful to Charlene Clark for her assistance in the preparation of the manuscript and to T. Williams and M. Martindale for their help with the illustration. The authors' studies were supported in part by Public Health Service Grants HL22732, HL29618, HL07430, and a grant from the Oklahoma Affiliate, AHA.

*Literature Cited*

1. Abols, I. A., Basbaum, A. I. 1981. Afferent connections of the rostral medulla of the cat: a neural substrate for midbrain-medullary interactions in the modulation of pain. *J. Comp. Neurol.* 201:285–97
2. Amendt, K., Czachurski, J., Dembowsky, K., Seller, H. 1979. Bulbospinal projections to the intermediolateral cell column; a neuroanatomical study. *J. Auton. Nerv. Syst.* 1:103–17
3. Ammons, W. S., Blair, R. W., Foreman, R. D. 1984. Raphe magnus inhibition of primate $T_1$–$T_4$ spinothalamic cells with cardiopulmonary visceral input. *Pain* 20:247–60
4. Ammons, W. S., Girardot, M.-N., Foreman, R. D. 1985. $T_2$–$T_5$ spinothalamic neurons projecting to medial thalamus with viscerosomatic input. *J. Neurophysiol.* 54:73–89
5. Ammons, W. S., Girardot, M.-N., Foreman, R. D. 1985. Effects of intracardiac bradykinin on $T_2$–$T_5$ spinothalamic cells. *Am. J. Physiol.* 249:R147–52
6. Baker, D. G., Coleridge, H. M., Coleridge, J. C. G., Nerdrum, T. 1980. Search for a cardiac nociceptor; stimulation by bradykinin of sympathetic afferent nerve endings in the heart of cat. *J. Physiol.* 306:519–36
7. Basbaum, A. I., Clanton, C. H., Fields, H. L. 1978. Three bulbospinal pathways from the rostral medulla of the cat: an autoradiographic study of pain modulating systems. *J. Comp. Neurol.* 178:209–224
8. Berman, A. L. 1968. *The Brain Stem of the Cat. A Cytoarchitectonic Atlas with Stereotaxic Coordinates.* Univ. Wisconsin Press, 175 pp.
9. Biscoe, T. J., Sampson, S. R. 1970. Responses of cells in the brain stem of the cat to stimulation of the sinus, glossopharyngeal, aortic and superior laryngeal nerves. *J. Physiol.* 209:359–73
10. Blair, R. W. 1985. Noxious cardiac input onto neurons in medullary reticular formation. *Brain Res.* 326:335–46
11. Blair, R. W. 1986. Cardiac input to feline medullary reticular formation: neuronal responses to CAO. *Am. J. Physiol.* 251:R670–79
12. Blair, R. W. 1986. Cardiac input to

feline medullary reticular formation: neuronal responses to mechanical stimuli. *Am. J. Physiol.* 251:R680–89

13. Blair, R. W. 1987. Responses of feline medial medullary reticulospinal neurons to cardiac input. *J. Neurophysiol.* 58: 1149–67

14. Blair, R. W., Ammons, W. S., Foreman, R. D. 1984. Responses of thoracic spinothalamic and spinoreticular cells to coronary artery occlusion. *J. Neurophysiol.* 51:636–48

15. Blair, R. W., Weber, R. N., Foreman, R. D. 1981. Characteristics of primate spinothalamic tract neurons receiving viscerosomatic convergent inputs in $T_3$–$T_5$ segments. *J. Neurophysiol.* 46:797–811

16. Blair, R. W., Weber, R. N., Foreman, R. D. 1982. Responses of thoracic spinothalamic neurons to intracardiac injection of bradykinin in the monkey. *Circ. Res.* 51:83–94

17. Blair, R. W., Weber, R. N., Foreman, R. D. 1984. Responses of spinoreticular and spinothalamic cells to intracardiac bradykinin. *Am. J. Physiol.* 246:H500–7

18. Blendis, L. M. 1984. Abdominal pain. In: *Textbook of Pain*, ed. P. D. Wall, R. Melzack, pp. 350–58. New York: Churchill. 866 pp.

19. Bosnjak, Z. K., Zuperku, E. J., Coon, R. L., Kampine, J. P. 1979. Acute coronary artery occlusion and cardiac sympathetic afferent nerve activity. *Proc. Soc. Exp. Biol. Med.* 161:142–48

20. Brodal, A. 1958. *The Reticular Formation of the Brain Stem. Anatomical Aspects and Functional Correlations.* Edinburg: Oliver and Boyd. 87 pp.

21. Brown, A. M., Malliani, A. 1971. Spinal sympathetic reflexes initiated by coronary receptors. *J. Physiol.* 212:685–705

22. Burgess, P. R., Perl, E. R. 1973. Cutaneous mechanoreceptors and nociceptors. In *Handbook of Sensory Physiology. Somatosensory System*, ed. A. Iggo, II:29–78. Berlin: Springer-Verlag

23. Burton, H. 1968. Somatic sensory properties of caudal bulbar reticular neurons in the cat (Felis domestica). *Brain Res.* 11:357–72

24. Carstens, E., Trevino, D. L. 1978. Laminar origins of spinothalamic projections in the cat as determined by the retrograde transport of horseradish peroxidase. *J. Comp. Neurol.* 182:151–66

25. Casati, R., Lombardi, F., Malliani, A. 1979. Afferent sympathetic unmyelinated fibres with left ventricular endings in cats. *J. Physiol.* 292:135–48

26. Casey, K. L. 1969. Somatic stimuli, spinal pathways, and size of cutaneous fibers influencing unit activity in the medial medullary reticular formation. *Exp. Neurol.* 25:35–56

27. Casey, K. L. 1971. Responses of bulboreticular units to somatic stimuli eliciting escape behavior in the cat. *Int. J. Neurosci.* 2:15–28

28. Casey, K. L. 1971. Escape elicited by bulboreticular stimulation in the cat. *Int. J. Neurosci.* 2:29–34

29. Casey, K. L., Keene, J. J., Morrow, T. 1974. Bulboreticular and medial thalamic unit activity in relation to aversive behavior and pain. In: *Advances in Neurology*, ed. J. J. Bonica, pp. 197–205. New York: Raven. 850 pp.

30. Chung, J. M., Kenshalo, D. R. Jr., Gerhart, K. D., Willis, W. D. 1979. Excitation of primate spinothalamic neurons by cutaneous C-fiber volleys. *J. Neurophysiol.* 42:1354–69

31. Coleridge, H. M., Coleridge, J. C. G. 1980. Cardiovascular afferents involved in the regulation of peripheral vessels. *Ann. Rev. Physiol.* 42:413–27

32. Craig, A. D., Kniffki, K.-D. 1985. Spinothalamic lumbosacral lamina I cells responsive to skin and muscle stimulation in the cat. *J. Physiol.* 365: 197–221

33. Donoghue, S., Fox, R. E., Kidd, C., Koley, B. W. 1981. The distribution in the cat brain stem of neurones activated by vagal non-myelinated fibres from the heart and lungs. *Q. J. Exp. Physiol.* 66:391–404

34. Eisenhart, S. F. Jr., Morrow, T. J., Casey, K. L. 1983. Sensory and motor properties of bulboreticular and raphe neurons in awake and anesthetized cats. In *Advances in Pain Research and Therapy*, ed. J. J. Bonica, U. Lindblom, A. Iggo, 5:161–68. New York: Raven. 970 pp.

35. Elisevich, K. V., Hrycyshyn, A. W., Flumerfelt, B. A. 1985. Cerebellar, medullary and spinal afferent connections of the paramedian reticular nucleus in the cat. *Brain Res.* 332:267–83

36. Emery, D. G., Foreman, R. D., Coggeshall, R. E. 1976. Fiber analysis of the feline inferior cardiac sympathetic nerve. *J. Comp. Neurol.* 166:457–68

37. Emery, D. G., Foreman, R. D., Coggeshall, R. E. 1978. Categories of axons in the inferior cardiac nerve of the cat. *J. Comp. Neurol.* 177:301–10

38. Foreman, R. D., Blair, R. W., Weber, R. N. 1984. Viscerosomatic convergence onto $T_2$–$T_4$ spinoreticular, spinoreticular-spinothalamic and spinothalamic tract neurons in the cat. *Exp. Neurol.* 85:597–619

39. Fox, R. E., Holloway, J. A., Iggo, A., Mokha, S. S. 1980. Spinothalamic neurones in the cat: some electrophysiological observations. *Brain Res.* 182:186–90

40. Gallagher, D. W., Pert, A. 1978. Afferents to brain stem nuclei (brain stem raphe, nucleus reticularis pontis caudalis and nucleus gigantocellularis) in the rat as demonstrated by microiontophoretically applied horseradish peroxidase. *Brain Res.* 144:257–75

41. Gerhart, K. D., Wilcox, T. K., Chung, J. M., Willis, W. D. 1981. Inhibition of nociceptive and nonnociceptive responses of primate spinothalamic cells by stimulation in medial brain stem. *J. Neurophysiol.* 45:121–36

42. Giesler, G. J., Menétrey, D., Guilbaud, G., Besson, J. M. 1976. Lumbar cord neurons at the origin of the spinothalamic tract in the rat. *Brain Res.* 118:320–24

43. Guilbaud, G., Besson, J. M., Oliveras, J. L., Wyon-Mailland, M. C. 1973. Modifications of the firing rate of bulbar reticular units (nucleus gigantocellularis) after intra-arterial injections of bradykinin into the limbs. *Brain Res.* 63:131–40

44. Haber, L. H., Martin, R. F., Chung, J. M., Willis, W. D. 1980. Inhibition and excitation of primate spinothalamic tract neurons by stimulation in region of nucleus reticularis gigantocellularis. *J. Neurophysiol.* 43:1578–93

45. Haber, L. H., Moore, B. D., Willis, W. D. 1982. Electrophysiological response properties of spinoreticular neurons in the monkey. *J. Comp. Neurol.* 207:75–84

46. Hashimoto, K., Hirose, M., Furukawa, S., Haykawa, H., Kimura, E. 1977. Changes in hemodynamics and bradykinin concentration in coronary sinus blood in experimental coronary artery occlusion. *Jpn. Heart J.* 18:679–89

47. Hess, G. L., Zuperku, E. J., Coon, R. L., Kampine, J. P. 1974. Sympathetic afferent nerve activity of left ventricular origin. *Am. J. Physiol.* 227:543–46

48. Ito, M., Udo, M., Mano, N. 1970. Long inhibitory and excitatory pathways converging onto cat reticular and Deiters' neurons and their relevance to reticulofugal axons. *J. Neurophysiol.* 33:210–26

49. Kevetter, G. A., Haber, L. H., Yezierski, R. P., Chung, J. M., Martin, R. F., Willis, W. D. 1982. Cells of origin of the spinoreticular tract in the monkey. *J. Comp. Neurol.* 207:61–74

50. Kevetter, G. A., Willis, W. D. 1984. Collateralization in the spinothalamic tract: New methodology to support or deny phylogenetic theories. *Brain Res. Rev.* 7:1–14

51. Kimura, E., Hashimoto, K., Furukawa, S., Hayakawa, H. 1973. Changes in bradykinin level in coronary sinus blood after the experimental occlusion of a coronary artery. *Am. Heart J.* 85:635–47

52. Kuo, D. C., Oravitz, J. J., de Groat, W. C. 1984. Tracing of afferent and efferent pathways in the left inferior cardiac nerve of the cat using retrograde and transport of horseradish peroxidase. *Brain Res.* 321:111–18

53. Langhorst, P., Schulz, B., Schulz, G., Lambertz, M. 1983. Reticular formation of the lower brainstem. A common system for cardiorespiratory and somatomotor functions: discharge patterns of neighboring neurons influenced by cardiovascular and respiratory afferents. *J. Auton. Nerv. Syst.* 9:411–32

54. Le Blanc, H. J., Gatipon, G. B. 1974. Medial bulboreticular response to peripherally applied noxious stimuli. *Exp. Neurol.* 42:264–73

55. Lindgren, I., Olivecrona, H. 1947. Surgical treatment of angina pectoris. *J. Neurosurg.* 4:19–39

56. Loewy, A. D. 1981. Descending pathways to sympathetic and parasympathetic preganglionic neurons. *J. Auton. Nerv. Syst.* 3:265–75

57. Lombardi, F., Della Bella, P., Casati, R., Malliani, A. 1981. Effects of intracoronary administration of bradykinin on the impulse activity of afferent sympathetic unmyelinated fibers with left ventricular endings in the cat. *Circ. Res.* 48:69–75

58. Malliani, A. 1982. Cardiovascular sympathetic afferent fibers. *Rev. Physiol. Biochem. Pharmacol.* 94:11–74

59. Malliani, A. 1986. The elusive link between transient myocardial ischemia and pain. *Circulation* 73:201–4

60. Malliani, A., Recordati, G., Schwartz, P. J. 1973. Nervous activity of afferent cardiac sympathetic fibres with atrial and ventricular endings. *J. Physiol.* 229:457–69

61. Maunz, R. A., Pitts, N. G., Peterson, B. W. 1978. Cat spinoreticular neurons: locations, responses and changes in responses during repetitive stimulation. *Brain Res.* 148:365–79

62. Mehler, W. R. 1969. Some neurological species differences—a posteriori. *Ann. NY Acad. Sci.* 167:424–68

63. Melzack, R., Wall, P. D. 1982. *The Challenge of Pain.* New York: Basic Books

64. Needleman, P. 1976. The synthesis and

function of prostaglandins in the heart. *Fed. Proc.* 35:2376–81

65. Nerdrum, T., Baker, D. G., Coleridge, H. M., Coleridge, J. C. G. 1986. Interaction of bradykinin and prostaglandin $E_1$ on cardiac pressor reflex and sympathetic afferents. *Am. J. Physiol.* 250:R815–22

66. Nicholas, A. S., DeBias, D. A., Ehrenfeuchter, W., England, K. M., England, R. W., et al. 1985. A somatic component to myocardial infarction. *Br. Med. J.* 291:13–17

67. Nishi, K., Sakanashi, M., Takenaka, F. 1977. Activation of afferent cardiac sympathetic nerve fibers of the cat by pain producing substances and by noxious heat. *Pfluegers Arch.* 372:53–61

68. Nyberg-Hansen, R. 1965. Sites and mode of termination of reticulo-spinal fibers in the cat. An experimental study with silver impregnation methods. *J. Comp. Neurol.* 124:71–100

69. Oldfield, B. J., McLachlan, E. M. 1978. Localization of sensory neurons traversing the stellate ganglion of the cat. *J. Comp. Neurol.* 182:915–22

70. Peterson, B. W. 1979. Reticulospinal projections to spinal motor nuclei. *Ann. Rev. Physiol.* 41:127–40

71. Peterson, B. W. 1984. The reticulospinal system and its role in the control of movement. In *Brainstem Control of Spinal Cord Function,* ed. C. D. Barnes, pp. 27–86. New York: Academic. 291 pp.

72. Peterson, B. W., Felpel, L. P. 1971. Excitation and inhibition of reticulospinal neurons by vestibular, cortical and cutaneous stimulation. *Brain Res.* 27:373–76

73. Peterson, B. W., Franck, J. I., Pitts, N. G., Daunton, N. G. 1976. Changes in responses of medial pontomedullary reticular neurons during repetitive cutaneous, vestibular, cortical, and tectal stimulation. *J. Neurophysiol.* 39:564–81

74. Peterson, B. W., Maunz, R. A., Pitts, N. G., Mackel, R. G. 1975. Patterns of projection and branching of reticulospinal neurons. *Exp. Brain Res.* 23:333–51

75. Price, D. D., Dubner, R. 1977. Neurons that subserve the sensory-discriminative aspects of pain. *Pain 3* 3:307–38

76. Price, D. D., Hayes, R. L., Ruda, M. A., Dubner, R. 1978. Spatial and temporal transformations of input to spinothalamic tract neurons and their relation to somatic sensations. *J. Neurophysiol.* 41:933–47

77. Przybyla, A. C., Wang, S. C. 1967.

Neurophysiological characteristics of cardiovascular neurons in the medulla oblongata of the cat. *J. Neurophysiol.* 30:645–60

78. Ruch, T. C. 1961. Pathophysiology of pain. In *Neurophysiology,* ed. T. C. Ruch, H. D. Patton, J. W. Woodbury, A. L. Towe, Philadelphia: Saunders

79. Scheibel, M., Scheibel, A., Mollica, A., Moruzzi, G. 1955. Convergence and interaction of afferent impulses on single units of reticular formation. *J. Neurophysiol.* 18:309–31

80. Schulz, B., Lambertz, M., Schulz, G., Langhorst, P. 1983. Reticular formation of the lower brainstem. A common system for cardiorespiratory and somatomotor functions: discharge patterns of neighboring neurons influenced by somatosensory afferents. *J. Auton. Nerv. Syst.* 9:433–49

81. Seagard, J. L., Pederson, H. J., Kostreva, D. R., Van Horn, D. L., Cusik, J. F., Kampine, J. P. 1978. Ultrastructural identification of afferent fibers of cardiac origin in thoracic sympathetic nerves in the dog. *Am. J. Anat.* 153:217–32

82. Segundo, J. P., Takenaka, T., Encabo, H. 1967. Somatic sensory properties of bulbar reticular neurons. *J. Neurophysiol.* 30:1221–38

83. Siegel, J. M. 1979. Behavioral functions of the reticular formation. *Brain Res. Rev.* 1:69–105

84. Tohyama, M., Sakai, K., Salvert, D., Touret, M. 1979. Spinal projections from the lower brain stem in the cat as demonstrated by the horseradish peroxidase technique. I. Origins of the reticulospinal tracts and their funicular trajectories. *Brain Res.* 173:383–403

85. Uchida, Y. 1975. Afferent sympathetic nerve fibers with mechanoreceptors in the right heart. *Am. J. Physiol.* 228:223–30

86. Uchida, Y., Kamisaka, K., Murao, S., Ueda, H. 1974. Mechanosensitivity of afferent cardiac sympathetic nerve fibers. *Am. J. Physiol.* 226:1088–93

87. Uchida, Y., Murao, S. 1974. Potassium-induced excitation of afferent cardiac sympathetic nerve fibers. *Am. J. Physiol.* 226:603–7

88. Uchida, Y., Murao, S. 1974. Excitation of afferent cardiac sympathetic nerve fibers during coronary occlusion. *Am. J. Physiol.* 226:1094–99

89. Uchida, Y., Murao, S. 1974. Afferent sympathetic nerve fibers originating in the left atrial wall. *Am. J. Physiol.* 227:753–58

90. Uchida, Y., Murao, S. 1974. Bradyki-

nin-induced excitation of afferent cardiac sympathetic nerve fibers. *Jpn. Heart J.* 15:84–91

91. Uchida, Y., Murao, S. 1975. Acid-induced excitation of afferent cardiac sympathetic nerve fibers. *Am. J. Physiol.* 228:27–33

92. Vance, W. H., Bowker, R. C. 1983. Spinal origins of cardiac afferents from the region of the left anterior descending artery. *Brain Res.* 258:96–100

93. Weaver, L. C., Meckler, R. L., Fry, H. K., Donoghue, S. 1983. Widespread neural excitation initiated from cardiac spinal afferent nerves. *Am. J. Physiol.* 245:R241–50

94. White, J. C. 1957. Cardiac pain. Anatomic pathways and physiologic mechanisms. *Circulation* 16:644–55

95. White, J. C., Bland, E. F. 1948. The surgical relief of severe angina pectoris. *Medicine* 27:1–42

96. White, J. C., Garrey, W. E., Atkins, J. A. 1933. Cardiac innervation: Experimental and clinical studies. *Arch. Surg.* 26:765–786

97. Willis, W. D., Kenshalo, D. R. Jr., Leonard, R. B. 1979. The cells of origin of the primate spinothalamic tract. *J. Comp. Neurol.* 188:543–74

98. Willis, W. D., Trevino, D. L., Coulter, J. D., Maunz, R. A. 1974. Responses of primate spinothalamic tract neurons to natural stimulation of hindlimb. *J. Neurophysiol.* 37:358–72

99. Wolstencroft, J. H. 1964. Reticulospinal neurones. *J. Physiol.* 174:91–108

# RESPIRATORY PHYSIOLOGY

## *VELOCITY OF $CO_2$ EXCHANGE*

### *Introduction,* Robert E. Forster, II, *Section Editor*

The kinetics of $CO_2$ have been of particular interest to physiologists for 60 years since Henriques (1) pointed out that the velocity at which $HCO_3^-$ dehydrates to form $CO_2$ was not great enough to eliminate metabolic $CO_2$ from blood in the lung capillaries within the approximately one second available. Investigators looked for a catalytic agent, and carbonic anhydrase was discovered almost simultaneously at the Universities of Cambridge and Pennsylvania about 57 years ago. With the passage of time, this enzyme has turned out to be nearly ubiquitous; it is present in many tissues of different species, in cells, subcellular particles, and membranes. While the need for carbonic anhydrase in the original site of discovery is clear, its function in many cells is less obvious. The reviews that follow give the present state of our knowledge of $CO_2$ kinetics and carbonic anhydrase function in a spectrum of tissues.

Klocke reviews the present knowledge of the velocity of $CO_2$ exchange in blood, the original process that attracted physiologists. His discussion includes the reversible catalyzed intracellular and uncatalyzed extracellular reactions of $CO_2$ and $HCO_3^-$, the exchange of $Cl^-$ with $HCO_3^-$, and the effect of the reactions of both $CO_2$ and $O_2$ with hemoglobin. In the second article, Bidani and Crandall discuss the velocity of reversible $CO_2$ reactions in the lung itself and the need to interpret measurements of the velocities of individual steps in blood-gas exchange of blood by means of mathematical models. The kinetics of $CO_2$ diffusion and chemical reactions have long been known to be pivotal in renal function. $[CO_2]$ gradients within the kidney and between kidney cells and blood, and the velocities of the pertinent chemical reactions are next reviewed by Dubose and Bidani.

In the 1930s there was thought to be no carbonic anhydrase in muscle, and we were told to be grateful. More recent investigations show that there are several isozymes in muscle but their function is not clear. This enzyme has also been found in liver, both in cytoplasm and in mitochondria, where it appears to have an important function in several anabolic chains. This represents a new departure because previously carbonic anhydrase was thought to act only as an accelerator of the reversible reactions of $CO_2$ and $HCO_3^-$; however, this is no longer certain. The function of carbonic anhydrase in liver mitochondria is different; it may contribute to a compartmentalization of $CO_2/HCO_3^-$. Gros and Dodgson review these topics in the fourth article.

Maren, in the fifth article, presents a wide perspective on the importance of $HCO_3^-$ and $CO_2$ kinetics in ion transport, particularly $H^+$ and $Na^+$, in a wide variety of tissues and species. For half a century the importance of $CO_2$ to physiologists has been the mechanism and control of its elimination, and the contribution of carbonic anhydrase was to accelerate this. We know today that it has other functions in the cell that may be of equal value and that are not clearly related to the acceleration of the reversible reactions of $CO_2$ and $H_2CO_3$.

*Literature Cited*

1. Henriques, O. M. 1928. Uber die gesch windigkeiten der anhydrierung bzw. der hydratisierung der kohlen saurekomponenten im blute. *Biochem. Z.* 200:1–5

*Ann. Rev. Physiol. 1988. 50:625–37*

# VELOCITY OF CO$_2$ EXCHANGE IN BLOOD

*Robert A. Klocke*

Departments of Medicine and Physiology, State University of New York at Buffalo, 462 Grider Street, Buffalo, New York 14215

## Introduction

The velocity of CO$_2$ exchange in blood is dependent upon a number of interrelated processes, including chemical reactions, diffusion, and convective mixing. Both parallel and serial processes are involved, and alteration of one branch of this complex network (Figure 1) has repercussions throughout the entire system. Hence, there necessarily is no set velocity of CO$_2$ exchange in blood; the rate of carbon dioxide movement is a function of many variables. From an experimental standpoint, it is not possible to investigate all these factors simultaneously. The usual approach is to study the role of a single variable under conditions in which the other parameters are held relatively constant. Extrapolation of these data to physiological circumstances is accomplished using mathematical models of gas exchange. This approach has led to a substantial improvement in our understanding of CO$_2$ exchange (32) compared to that of two decades previously (40). The major drawback of the synthesis of individual processes in computational models is the potential to fail to include a critical, but unknown, process in the theoretical construct.

## Diffusion of CO$_2$

Regardless of the chemical pathway utilized for CO$_2$ transport, transfer of carbon dioxide between body compartments is accomplished by diffusion of molecular CO$_2$. Because of its relatively high solubility, movement of CO$_2$ is assumed to proceed quite rapidly, and this process usually is assumed complete in most models of carbon dioxide exchange (3, 20). Modest reductions ($\sim$60%) of CO$_2$ diffusivity occur in the viscous interior of the red cell (16), but this does not hamper CO$_2$ exchange substantially because in-

625

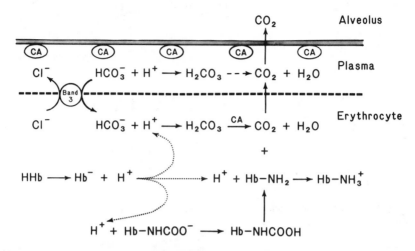

*Figure 1*  Reactions of carbon dioxide in blood. Arrows indicate direction of reactions in the lung. In peripheral tissues, reactions proceed in the opposite direction. Symbols: CA, carbonic anhydrase, either unbound inside the erythrocyte or bound to capillary endothelium; $\rightarrow$, processes that proceed rapidly; $--\rightarrow$, uncatalyzed or slightly catalyzed reaction in plasma; $\cdots\rightarrow$, participation of protons derived from hemoglobin, either from buffering or the Bohr reaction; band 3, transport site for exchange of bicarbonate and chloride ions.

traerythrocytic diffusion distances are on the order of one micrometer (32). In the plasma, diffusion distances are considerably greater, and the possibility exists that diffusion per se may affect the rate of $CO_2$ exchange (vide infra).

Diffusion of $CO_2$ across cell membranes and other tissue barriers is rapid. There are no accurate measurements of erythrocyte permeability to $CO_2$. Forster (12) calculated a $CO_2$ permeability of 0.58 cm $sec^{-1}$ from measurements of ammonia penetration into red cells, and the lipid solubilities and masses of the two compounds. Gutknecht et al (18) measured $CO_2$ permeability in artificial lipid bilayers and obtained a value of 0.35 cm $sec^{-1}$, a value very similar to that calculated by Forster. Although not identical to erythrocyte membranes, lipid bilayers have similar properties, and these are the best experimental data available for membrane permeability to $CO_2$.

These estimates indicate that $CO_2$ penetration of the red cell membrane is rapid and not a limiting factor in the velocity of exchange. The only data challenging this viewpoint are based on measurements of the rate of depletion of isotopic $CO_2$ in erythrocyte suspensions (45). A permeability of 0.0076 cm $sec^{-1}$ was calculated from these observations, a value that would result in definite limitation of $CO_2$ exchange if accurate. This very low estimate of $CO_2$ permeability appears to be the result of unstirred fluid layers known to be present on the surface of erythrocytes even in vigorously stirred suspensions (7). Incomplete penetration of erythrocytes by acetazolamide, a carbonic anhydrase inhibitor used in these experiments, also is likely to have affected the estimate of membrane permeability (13a).

The alveolar capillary membrane is quite permeable to carbon dioxide and probably has little or no effect on the velocity of $CO_2$ transfer from blood (31). Estimates of the diffusing capacity of the pulmonary membrane have been achieved with isotopic $CO_2$ (10, 11, 43). Under physiological circumstances it is unlikely that there is any gradient in $CO_2$ tension across the pulmonary membrane as blood leaves the capillary (10). Enns & Hill (11) have postulated that facilitated diffusion of $CO_2$ through the pulmonary membrane may be achieved by simultaneous movement of bicarbonate ion. They noted that the $CO_2$ membrane diffusing capacity decreased by 39% when carbonic anhydrase in lung tissue was inhibited by acetazolamide. Rapid interconversion of bicarbonate and $CO_2$ under the influence of tissue enzyme would enhance $CO_2$ transfer, since tissue $[HCO_3^-]$ is twenty times greater than tissue $[CO_2]$. This mechanism would also require simultaneous diffusion of hydrogen ion to meet the stoichiometric requirements of the hydration-dehydration reaction of carbon dioxide. Since hydrogen is present in extremely low concentration, its movement would have to be accomplished through diffusion of protons bound to buffers, a mechanism known to operate in the catalysis of some $CO_2$ reactions (44). Whether this potential facilitation of $CO_2$ movement has a physiological role is uncertain since the diffusing capacity of the pulmonary membrane exceeds 1100 ml min$^{-1}$ torr$^{-1}$, a value greater than necessary to maintain $CO_2$ exchange (43).

## Hydration-Dehydration Reaction of CO₂

Bicarbonate ion in plasma and inside the erythrocyte combines with hydrogen ion to form carbonic acid essentially instantaneously. In turn, $H_2CO_3$ dehydrates to $CO_2$ and water (Figure 1), but the natural rate of this reaction is quite slow (32). Catalysis is essential to maintain the normal pattern of $CO_2$ exchange. Bicarbonate ion forms the largest pool for carbon dioxide in blood, and rapid conversion of $HCO_3^-$ to $CO_2$ is necessary to complete the exchange process during the brief duration of capillary transit. The quantity of carbonic anhydrase inside the erythrocyte is substantial—enough to increase the speed of the dehydration reaction 13,000 times (32). This enzyme was thought to be absent from plasma, but in the last decade it has been demonstrated on the intraluminal surface of the capillaries in the lung (8, 9, 30, 35, 42). Vascular carbonic anhydrase also is present in a variety of different tissues (32).

INTRACELLULAR CATALYSIS   When $CO_2$ leaves the red cell in the pulmonary capillary, the equilibrium between bicarbonate and carbon dioxide is disturbed, resulting in production of more $CO_2$ through the hydration-dehydration reaction. The initial rate of $CO_2$ production from bicarbonate is limited by the catalysis of this reaction by carbonic anhydrase (21, 27, 28). After an initial rapid production of $CO_2$ from $HCO_3^-$, lasting 50–100 msec, depletion of intracellular bicarbonate concentration slows the reaction, and $CO_2$ production is no longer proportional to the enzyme concentration. From this point on, the velocity of $CO_2$ production is dependent upon several factors, particularly the rate of bicarbonate movement between plasma and the erythrocyte.

It has been stated that carbonic anhydrase is present in amounts far greater than needed for $CO_2$ exchange (40, 46). In a certain sense this is true. Carbon dioxide exchange can be maintained despite almost complete inhibition of the enzyme (4, 46). However, the pattern of $CO_2$ exchange is altered markedly. Pathways involving dissolved $CO_2$ and carbamino compounds account for a greater fraction of total $CO_2$ exchange, and blood leaves the capillary with chemical reactions in a state of disequilibrium (4).

EXTRACELLULAR CATALYSIS    Carbonic anhydrase has not been demonstrated to be present in plasma. However, recent data from three different laboratories provide strong physiological evidence for the presence of carbonic anhydrase on the luminal surface of the pulmonary capillary (8, 9, 30). The quantity of enzyme present in the pulmonary vasculature is sufficient to catalyze the hydration-dehydration reaction by a factor of 130, about 1/100 of the catalysis present within the erythrocyte (2). Lonnerholm (35) and Ryan et al (42) have published histological evidence that the enzyme is present on the luminal surface of the endothelial cells lining the pulmonary capillaries.

The role of vascular carbonic anhydrase is still uncertain. It could enhance $CO_2$ exchange, but it would not eliminate the need for intracellular enzyme because insufficient buffering capacity is present in plasma to support complete conversion of plasma bicarbonate to molecular $CO_2$ (2). The buffering capacity of intracellular hemoglobin is necessary to supply protons for the dehydration reaction. Furthermore, there is evidence that the plasma of some species may contain inhibitors of carbonic anhydrase that may nullify the effect of the vascular enzyme (19, 39). The influence of vascular carbonic anhydrase on the velocity of $CO_2$ exchange in the lung is discussed extensively in the chapter by Bidani & Crandall (this volume).

## Bicarbonate-Chloride Exchange

Following the rapid initial mobilization of intracellular bicarbonate ion in the hydration-dehydration reaction, further $CO_2$ production in the pulmonary capillary is limited by the replenishment of intracellular bicarbonate ion from the plasma bicarbonate pool (21, 28). The depletion of intracellular $[HCO_3^-]$ slows the dehydration reaction through a mass action effect.

It is now well established that bicarbonate-chloride exchange is mediated through an electrically neutral, obligatory one-for-one exchange of the two anions. The membrane ion carrier, a protein with a molecular mass of 95,000, is known as band 3 protein. There are approximately one million such transport sites per red cell, and this protein comprises more than one quarter of the total protein in the cell membrane (34). The mechanism of anion transport was reviewed in this series a few years ago (26).

At 37°C the bicarbonate-chloride shift proceeds with a half-time of approximately 0.1 sec (6, 29). Although this rate seems sufficiently rapid to allow equilibrium to be reached during capillary transit, this may not always be the case. Wieth & Brahm (51) have calculated that 90% and 99% equilibrium of the bicarbonate-chloride shift is reached in 350–380 msec and 700–760 msec, respectively. This appears to be adequate at rest, but equilibrium will not be reached during exercise, when capillary transit time can be shortened considerably (48). Furthermore, these calculations apply to bicarbonate-chloride exchange. Other processes in series with this reaction, e.g. dehydration of carbonic acid and the release of Bohr protons, will delay the exchange even further. Thus our present understanding of these events leads to the conclusion that blood may leave the pulmonary capillary with bicarbonate-chloride exchange not completed. The influence of the rate of anionic exchange on pulmonary carbon dioxide excretion is described in the chapter by Bidani & Crandall (this volume).

## O$_2$-Dependent Carbon Dioxide Exchange

The exchange of carbon dioxide discussed above is independent of oxygen exchange. This release of CO$_2$ from blood is the result of the reduction of alveolar P$_{CO_2}$ below mixed venous CO$_2$ tension. This stimulates CO$_2$ diffusion out of blood, the dehydration of carbonic acid, bicarbonate conversion, and the bicarbonate-chloride shift. Slightly more than half of normal CO$_2$ exchange occurs as a result of the gradient between P$_{\bar{v}}$CO$_2$ and P$_A$CO$_2$ (20). The remainder is dependent upon concurrent oxygen exchange and is termed oxylabile carbon dioxide exchange. The basis of oxylabile CO$_2$ exchange is the shift in the carbon dioxide dissociation curve accompanying oxygenation (the Haldane effect). At any given P$_{CO_2}$, oxygenated blood has a lower carbon dioxide capacity than reduced blood. The velocity of this change in capacity is dependent upon the individual reaction pathways and the rate of oxygenation.

OXYLABILE CARBAMATE KINETICS    CO$_2$ can bind directly to $\alpha$-amino and $\epsilon$-amino groups on proteins. The combination of CO$_2$ with amino groups produces carbamic acids which dissociate to carbamate ions at body pH (Figure 1).

Change in carbamate concentration between arterial and venous plasma is negligible. Although carbamate formation is dependent upon pH and P$_{CO_2}$, the difference between the arterial and venous values of these variables is so small that there is no plasma carbamate contribution to $CO_2$ exchange (32). However, binding of $CO_2$ to $\alpha$-amino groups of hemoglobin is dependent on the state of oxygenation of the hemoglobin molecule; carbamate formation is much greater when hemoglobin is reduced. As a result, changes in oxylabile carbamate bound to hemoglobin account for 13% of the total quantity of $CO_2$ exchange under normal conditions (32). This is substantially less than earlier estimates of a 29% contribution (40), which were made prior to knowledge of the affect of 2,3-diphosphoglycerate on carbamate formation (32).

The kinetics of $CO_2$ binding to plasma proteins (15) and hemoglobin (13) are rapid and complete within 0.2 sec in the absence of simultaneous oxygenation. The velocity of the oxylabile carbamate reaction appears to be less rapid (28). As seen in Figure 2, following rapid oxygenation of a red cell suspension, release of oxylabile carbamate proceeds with a half-time of 0.12 sec and requires 0.6 sec for completion. Under normal circumstances, oxygenation of blood in the capillary requires approximately 0.3 sec (48), substantially longer than the 0.1 sec necessary in the experiment shown in Figure 2. Accordingly, it is possible that oxygenation and subsequent release of oxylabile carbamate may not be complete during capillary transit.

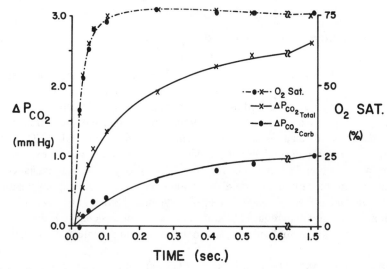

*Figure 2*  Kinetics of the Haldane effect. Deoxygenated erythrocyte suspension was oxygenated (–·–·–·, right-hand scale) with resultant liberation of $CO_2$ (——, left-hand scale). Lower solid curve and filled circles, obtained during carbonic anhydrase inhibition, represent carbamate mobilization. Upper solid curve and X's, obtained without enzyme inhibition, represent total change due to oxylabile bicarbonate and carbamate mobilization. The difference between the two curves is the oxylabile bicarbonate contribution to the Haldane effect [Reproduced with permission from Klocke (28).]

The rate-limiting step in this process (Figure 1) appears to be the break-down of the hemoglobin-carbamic acid (Hb-NHCOOH) to the free $\alpha$-amino group (Hb-NH$_2$) and CO$_2$. The other reactions involving protons are ionic in nature and thus are quite rapid. It is not clear why this oxylabile carbamate reaction (28) is less rapid than carbamate reactions that do not involve oxygenation (13, 15). Possible causes for this discrepancy include the rate of conformational change of hemoglobin associated with oxygenation and differing rates of reaction of carbamate binding and release, but these possibilities are unlikely (32). Another possibility, as discussed below, is that unstirred boundary layers in experiments conducted in vitro may lead to underestimates of the velocity of cellular reactions. Even if carbamate kinetics are not quite complete during capillary transit, this would have little effect on CO$_2$ exchange because the carbamate contributes only one eighth of the total exchange, and slight increments in ventilation can lower alveolar P$_{CO_2}$ to increase CO$_2$ excretion via other pathways.

OXYLABILE BICARBONATE KINETICS    The majority of the Haldane effect is derived from release of Bohr protons and mobilization of bicarbonate ions. With oxygenation of the hemoglobin molecule, Bohr protons are released, thereby shifting the hydration-dehydration reaction in the direction of increased CO$_2$ production (Figure 1). The rate of release of these protons is dependent upon the speed of oxygenation of hemoglobin since the Bohr reaction itself is extremely rapid (14). Subsequent production of CO$_2$ is initially dependent upon the catalysis of dehydration of H$_2$CO$_3$ by carbonic anhydrase (28). Later phases of CO$_2$ production appear to be linked to the rate of replenishment of intracellular bicarbonate ion through bicarbonate-chloride exchange. Hence, oxylabile bicarbonate kinetics are similar to those of bicarbonate mobilization not associated with oxygenation. The only difference is the initial delay, which is required for the oxygenation of hemoglobin with subsequent release of Bohr protons. It is conceivable that this entire series of processes may not reach equilibrium in the capillary (Figure 2). Abnormalities of oxygen exchange may delay or prevent oxygenation, which is a necessary component of the oxylabile exchange. However, even if the full Haldane effect is not realized, slight increases in alveolar ventilation would lower alveolar P$_{CO_2}$ sufficiently to increase oxygen-independent CO$_2$ exchange to compensate for a reduction in the Haldane effect. Clearly, in vivo data are needed to evaluate oxylabile kinetics more thoroughly.

In peripheral tissues these reactions proceed in the opposite direction. With release of oxygen from hemoglobin, protons are bound to the Bohr groups, and the capacity of hemoglobin to bind CO$_2$ as carbamate increases. Presumably the kinetics of these reverse processes occurring in peripheral tissues are the same as in the lung.

## Capillary Transit Time

The time required for blood to traverse the capillary is a major factor in determining whether $CO_2$ reactions reach equilibrium in blood. The lung has perhaps the shortest transit time of all organs, although calculated values of capillary transit time in muscle during extremely heavy work are somewhat less (24). A wide range of pulmonary transit times has been reported. Depending upon the method of measurement, estimates have ranged from 0.1 to 2.0 sec (38). However, the values most commonly accepted are 0.7–0.8 sec at rest and 0.4–0.5 sec during heavy exercise (41, 48). These estimates of transit time are calculated from measurements of the carbon monoxide diffusing capacity obtained at two levels of oxygenation (41).

Recently Wagner and his colleagues (49) have described a new method of measuring pulmonary transit time. A transparent window is placed in the thoracic cage of the dog, and subpleural capillaries are observed in vivo by microscopy. A bolus of fluorescent dye is injected into a pulmonary artery and excited at 440 nm by a light source as it enters the circulation under the thoracic window. The passage of dye through the circulation is recorded on videotape and later replayed for analysis. The time-dependent concentration of the fluorescent dye is recorded from both a precapillary arteriole and its accompanying postcapillary venule (Figure 3). Both curves are referenced to the time of dye injection and the difference between the mean transit times of the two curves yields mean capillary transit time.

The validity of this method is based on the lack of intermediate branches between precapillary arterioles and the capillaries themselves. These 15–20 $\mu$m arterioles give rise to capillaries at right angles without any intervening vessels. The venous architecture is similar. Unfortunately, only the subpleural capillary network, known to be less dense than the capillary bed deeper in the

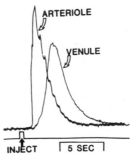

*Figure 3*   Concentration of fluorescent dye as a function of time in a precapillary arteriole and accompanying postcapillary venule. Cardiac pulsations in the arteriolar curves are dampened by passage of blood through the capillary bed and do not appear in the venular curve. The difference between the mean transit times of the curve equals the mean capillary transit time. [Reproduced with permission from Wagner et al (50).]

lung (17), can be visualized with this technique. This could account for the somewhat longer transit times reported with this technique (49). However, comparison of subpleural transit times in the dog with the classical carbon monoxide diffusing capacity technique yielded almost identical average values of 1.75 and 1.85 sec, respectively (5). Wagner et al (50) utilized this technique to demonstrate a vertical gradient of transit times in the canine lung. Transit times averaged 1.6 sec in the lower lung (zone III), 3.1 sec in the mid lung (transition from zone II to zone III), and 12.3 sec in the upper lung (zone II). These values are somewhat greater than those obtained using other means of estimating transit time, but they demonstrate the expected prolongation of transit time in portions of the lung receiving less perfusion. This innovative method offers a promising means of studying the pulmonary capillary bed.

## Validity of In Vitro Data

Current estimates of the velocities of carbon dioxide reactions in blood are based largely upon observations in red cell suspensions and hemoglobin solutions. This necessarily has been the case because of the technical difficulties in measuring kinetic events in vivo. The rapid flow techniques, both stopped flow and continuous flow, have been the major means of studying kinetics of $CO_2$ reactions. Unfortunately, there is increasing evidence that potential artifacts are present in these circumstances (7, 22, 25, 47). Most of this evidence has been obtained with oxygen reactions in blood, but the same factors affect $CO_2$ reactions. Coin & Olson (7) provided strong evidence that a stagnant layer of fluid on the surface of the erythrocyte hinders oxygen diffusion in the stopped flow apparatus during $O_2$ exchange. They demonstrated convincingly that experimentally measured $O_2$ kinetics are limited by mixing in the apparatus and not by physiological events (7, 47). Other laboratories have confirmed these observations (22, 25). The effect of stagnant layers of fluid on cellular kinetics will depend upon the velocity of the process under study. Extremely rapid processes, such as diffusion of $O_2$ and $CO_2$ across cell membranes, certainly are affected to the point where adequate assessment of the kinetics cannot be made. This could be a reason for the discrepancy between carbamate kinetics in solution (13) and in cell suspension (28). The effect of a stagnant layer can be neglected if the process is quite slow, e.g. postcapillary changes in pH (3). Events that occur at intermediate speeds may be accurately monitored under optimal circumstances. Transmembrane movement of substances having permeabilities as great as 0.04 cm $sec^{-1}$ have been measured without any apparent artifact (33). Thus it seems that current estimates of the velocities of bicarbonate-chloride exchange and similar processes are accurate.

Significant intracellular mixing may occur in vivo as a result of deformation of erythrocytes during capillary transit. In a stopped flow apparatus, red cells maintain a discoid shape (37), but in vivo they are deformed in the capillary (36). Zander & Schmid-Schonbein (52) observed an increase in the rate of $O_2$ release from red cell suspensions subjected to shear stress that deformed the cells. It is not clear what role cellular deformity plays in mixing of intracellular contents in vivo. Most models of gas exchange do not include this possibility (3, 20).

The influence of unstirred layers on cellular kinetics in vitro is beyond dispute (7, 22, 25, 47). Boundary layers are present in the stopped flow apparatus, despite the presence of turbulent flow characterized by Reynolds numbers of 5000 and linear velocities of $175 \text{ cm sec}^{-1}$ (33). Almost certainly, stagnant boundary layers must affect gas exchange in vivo, where the intracapillary Reynolds number and linear velocity are only 0.001 and 0.1 cm $\text{sec}^{-1}$, respectively (1). Most models of gas exchange do not address this possibility. Computations indicate that large gradients in $P_{O_2}$ may exist between erythrocytes and plasma under some circumstances (23). Unfortunately, no experimental verification of these gradients has been reported. The technical problems that preclude measurement of kinetics in vivo are immense, but until they are overcome, we are forced into the uncomfortable circumstance of relying upon extrapolations of in vitro measurements.

## Summary

Carbon dioxide exchange involves multiple interrelated processes. Approximately half of $CO_2$ exchange is independent of oxygen exchange and is initiated as soon as blood enters the capillary. The hydration-dehydration reaction initially limits the velocity of $CO_2$ exchange in blood, but shortly thereafter the transmembrane exchange of bicarbonate and chloride ions emerges as the major factor affecting the rate of $CO_2$ movement.

The remainder of $CO_2$ exchange, which is dependent upon prior oxygenation of hemoglobin, is achieved via oxylabile carbamate and oxylabile bicarbonate pathways. The carbamate pathway is of lesser importance. Oxylabile bicarbonate exchange occurs as a result of the liberation of Bohr protons that accompanies oxygenation of hemoglobin. The series of reactions involved in this pathway are similar to those involved in non-oxygen-dependent bicarbonate exchange, except that prior oxygenation of hemoglobin is required. $CO_2$ exchange via both oxylabile pathways may not reach completion during capillary transit, especially if oxygenation is delayed.

The kinetics of $CO_2$ reactions depend critically upon the length of time blood spends in the capillary bed. During $CO_2$ uptake in tissues, capillary transit times are usually somewhat greater than during $CO_2$ unloading in the lung. Therefore, any limitation of $CO_2$ exchange that might occur on a kinetic basis would probably occur in the lung as opposed to peripheral tissues. Exercising muscle may provide a possible exception to this general rule.

Finally, relatively little experimental data have been acquired in vivo. Diffusion and convective mixing in the capillary itself have not been studied extensively. These factors may have a substantial effect on the velocity of $CO_2$ exchange in blood. Further study is needed in this area.

ACKNOWLEDGMENTS

The author appreciates the aid of Mrs. Marsha Barber in the preparation of this review. This work was supported in part by Program Project HL-34323 of the National Heart, Lung and Blood Institute.

*Literature Cited*

1. Aroestry, J., Gross, J. F. 1970. Convection and diffusion in the microcirculation. *Microvasc. Res.* 2:247–67
2. Bidani, A., Crandall, E. D. 1988. Quantitative aspects of capillary $CO_2$ exchange. In *Extra-Pulmonary Manifestations of Respiratory Diseases,* ed. H. K. Chang, M. Paiva. New York: Marcel-Dekker. In press
3. Bidani, A., Crandall, E. D., Forster, R. E. 1978. Analysis of postcapillary pH changes in blood in vivo after gas exchange. *J. Appl. Physiol.* 44:770–81
4. Cain, S. M., Otis, A. B. 1961. Carbon dioxide transport in anesthetized dogs during inhibition of carbonic anhydrase. *J. Appl. Physiol.* 16:1023–28
5. Capen, R. L., Latham, L. P., Wagner, W. W. Jr. 1987. Comparison of direct and indirect measurements of pulmonary capillary transit times. *J. Appl. Physiol.* 62:1150–54
6. Chow, E. I.-H., Crandall, E. D., Forster, R. E. 1976. Kinetics of bicarbonate-chloride exchange across the human red blood cell membrane. *J. Gen. Physiol.* 68:633–52
7. Coin, J. T., Olson, J. S. 1979. The rate of oxygen uptake by human red blood cells. *J. Biol. Chem.* 254:1178–90
8. Crandall, E. D., O'Brasky, J. E. 1978. Direct evidence for participation of rat lung carbonic anhydrase in $CO_2$ reactions. *J. Clin. Invest.* 62:618–22
9. Effros, R. M., Chang, R. S. Y., Silverman, P. 1978. Acceleration of plasma bicarbonate conversion to carbon dioxide by pulmonary carbonic anhydrase. *Science* 199:427–29
10. Effros, R. M., Mason, G., Silverman, P. 1981. Role of perfusion and diffusion in ¹⁴CO₂ exchange in the rabbit lung. *J. Appl. Physiol.* 51:1136–44
11. Enns, T., Hill, E. P. 1983. $CO_2$ diffusing capacity in isolated dog lung lobes

and the role of carbonic anhydrase. *J. Appl. Physiol.* 54:483–90
12. Forster, R. E. 1969. The role of $CO_2$ equilibrium between red cells and plasma. In *$CO_2$: Chemical, Biochemical, and Physiological Aspects,* ed. R. E. Forster, J. T. Edsall, A. B. Otis, F. J. W. Roughton, pp. 275–86. Washington, D.C.: NASA, SP-188
13. Forster, R. E., Constantine, H. P., Craw, M. R., Rotman, H. H., Klocke, R. A. 1968. Reaction of $CO_2$ with human hemoglobin solution. *J. Biol. Chem.* 243:3317–26
13a. Forster, R. E., Dodgson, S. J., Storey, B. T., Lin, L. 1984. Measurement of carbonic anhydrase activity inside cells and subcellular particles. *Ann. NY Acad. Sci.* 429:415–29
14. Gray, R. D. 1970 The kinetics of the alkaline Bohr effect of human hemoglobin. *J. Biol. Chem.* 245:2914–21
15. Gros, G., Forster, R. E., Lin, L. 1976. The carbamate reaction of glycylglycine, plasma, and tissue extracts evaluated by a pH stopped flow apparatus. *J. Biol. Chem.* 251:4398–4407
16. Gros, G., Moll, W. 1971. The diffusion of carbon dioxide in erythrocytes and hemoglobin solutions. *Pflüg. Arch.* 324:249–66
17. Guntheroth, W. G., Luchtel, D. L., Kawabori, I. 1982. Pulmonary microcirculation: Tubules rather than sheet and post. *J. Appl. Physiol.* 53:510–15
18. Gutknecht, J., Bisson, M. A., Tosteson, F. C. 1977. Diffusion of carbon dioxide through lipid bilayer membranes: Effects of carbonic anhydrase, bicarbonate, and unstirred layers. *J. Gen. Physiol.* 69:779–94
19. Hill, E. P. 1986. Inhibition of carbonic anhydrase by plasma of dogs and rabbits. *J. Appl. Physiol.* 60:191–97

20. Hill, E. P., Power, G. G., Longo, L. D. 1973. Mathematical simulation of pulmonary $O_2$ and $CO_2$ exchange. *Am. J. Physiol.* 224:904–17

21. Holland, R. A. B., Forster, R. E. 1975. Effect of temperature on rate of $CO_2$ uptake by human red cell suspensions. *Am. J. Physiol.* 228:1589–96

22. Holland, R. A. B., Shibata, H., Scheid, P., Piiper, J. 1985. Kinetics of oxygen uptake and release by red cells in stopped flow apparatus: Effects of unstirred layer. *Resp. Physiol.* 59:71–91

23. Homer, L. D., Weathersby, P. K., Kiesow, L. A. 1981. Oxygen gradients between red blood cells in the microcirculation. *Microvasc. Res.* 22:308–23

24. Honig, C. R., Odoroff, C. L. 1981. Calculated dispersion of capillary transit times: Significance for oxygen exchange. *Am. J. Physiol.* 240:H199–H208

25. Huxley, V. H., Kutchai, H. 1981. The effect of the red cell membrane and a diffusion boundary layer on the rate of oxygen uptake by human erythrocytes. *J. Physiol.* 316:75–83

26. Jennings, M. L. 1985. Kinetics and mechanism of anion transport in red blood cells. *Ann. Rev. Physiol.* 47:519–33

27. Kernohan, J. C., Roughton, F. J. W. 1968. Thermal studies of the rates of the reactions of carbon dioxide in concentrated haemoglobin solutions and in red blood cells. A. The reactions catalysed by carbonic anhydrase, B. The carbamino reactions of oxygenated and deoxygenated haemoglobin. *J. Physiol. London* 197:345–61

28. Klocke, R. A. 1973. Mechanism and kinetics of the Haldane effect in human erythrocytes. *J. Appl. Physiol.* 35:673–81

29. Klocke, R. A. 1976. Rate of bicarbonate-chloride exchange in human red cells at 37°C. *J. Appl. Physiol.* 40:707–14

30. Klocke, R. A. 1978. Catalysis of $CO_2$ reactions by lung carbonic anhydrase. *J. Appl. Physiol.* 44:882–88

31. Klocke, R. A. 1980. Kinetics of pulmonary gas exchange. In *Pulmonary Gas Exchange. Ventilation, Blood Flow, and Diffusion,* ed. J. B. West, 1:173–218. New York: Academic

32. Klocke, R. A. 1987. Carbon dioxide transport. In *Handbook of Physiology. The Respiratory System,* ed. L. Farhi, S. Marsh Tenney, 4:173–97 Bethesda, MD: Am. Physiol. Soc.

33. Klocke, R. A., Flasterstein, F. 1982. Kinetics of erythrocyte penetration by aliphatic acids. *J. Appl. Physiol.* 53:1138–43

34. Knauf, P. A. 1986. Anion transport in erythrocytes. In *Physiology of Membrane Disorders,* ed. T. E. Andreoli, J. F. Hoffman, D. D. Fanestil, S. G. Schultz, pp. 191–212. New York: Plenum

35. Lonnerholm, G. 1982. Pulmonary carbonic anhydrase in the human, monkey, and rat. *J. Appl. Physiol.* 52:352–56

36. Miyamoto, Y., Moll, W. 1971. Measurements of dimensions and pathway of red cells in rapidly frozen lungs in situ. *Resp. Physiol.* 12:141–56

37. Miyamoto, Y., Moll, W. 1972. The diameter of red blood cells when flowing through a rapid reaction apparatus. *Resp. Physiol.* 16:259–66

38. Piiper, J. 1968. Rates of chloride-bicarbonate exchange between red cells and plasma. In $CO_2$: Chemical, Biochemical, and Physiological Aspects, ed. R. E. Forster, J. T. Edsall, A. B. Otis, F. J. W. Roughton, pp. 267–73. Washington, D.C.: NASA SP-188

39. Rispens, P., Hessels, J., Zwart, A., Zijlstra, W. G. 1985. Inhibition of carbonic anhydrase in dog plasma. *Pflüg. Arch.* 403:344–47

40. Roughton, F. J. W. 1964. Transport of oxygen and carbon dioxide. In *Handbook of Physiology. Respiration,* Sect. 3, ed. W. O. Fenn, H. Rahn, 2:767–825. Washington, D.C.: Am. Physiol. Soc.

41. Roughton, F. J. W., Forster, R. E. 1957. Relative importance of diffusion and chemical reaction rates in determining rate of exchange of gases in the human lung, with special reference to true diffusing capacity of pulmonary membrane and volume of blood in the lung capillaries. *J. Appl. Physiol.* 11:290–302

42. Ryan, U. S., Whitney, P. L., Ryan, J. W. 1982. Localization of carbonic anhydrase on pulmonary artery endothelial cells in culture. *J. Appl. Physiol.* 53:914–19

43. Schuster, K.-D. 1987. Diffusion limitation and limitation by chemical reactions during alveolar-capillary transfer of oxygen-labeled $CO_2$. *Resp. Physiol.* 67:13–22

44. Silverman, D. N., Tu, C. K. 1975. Buffer dependence of carbonic anhydrase catalyzed oxygen-18 exchange at equilibrium. *J. Am. Chem. Soc.* 97:2263–69

45. Silverman, D. N., Tu, C. K., Wynns, G. C. 1976. Depletion of $^{18}O$ from $C^{18}O_2$ in erythrocyte suspensions. The

permeability of the erythrocyte membrane to $CO_2$. *J. Biol. Chem.* 251:4428–35

46. Swenson, E. R., Maren, T. H. 1978. A quantitative analysis of $CO_2$ transport at rest and during maximal exercise. *Resp. Physiol.* 35:129–59

47. Vandegriff, K. D., Olson, J. S. 1984. Morphological and physiological factors affecting oxygen uptake and release by red blood cells. *J. Biol. Chem.* 259:12619–27

48. Wagner, P. D. 1977. Diffusion and chemical reaction in pulmonary gas exchange. *Physiol. Rev.* 57:257–312

49. Wagner, W. W. Jr., Latham, L. P., Gillespie, M. N., Guenther, J. P., Capen,, R. L. 1982. Direct measurement of pulmonary capillary transit times. *Science* 218:379–81

50. Wagner, W. W. Jr., Latham, L. P., Hanson, W. L., Hofmeister, S. E., Capen, R. L. 1986. Vertical gradient of pulmonary capillary transit times. *J. Appl. Physiol.* 61:1270–74

51. Wieth, J. O., Brahm, J. 1980. Kinetics of bicarbonate exchange in human red cells—physiological implications. In *Membrane Transport in Erythrocytes,* ed. U. V. Lassen, H. H. Ussing, J. O. Wieth, pp. 467–82. Copenhagen: Munksgaard

52. Zander, R., Schmid-Schonbein, H. 1972. Influence of intracellular convection on the oxygen release by human erythrocytes. *Pflüg. Arch.* 335:58–73

Ann. Rev. Physiol. 1988. 50:639–52

# VELOCITY OF $CO_2$ EXCHANGES IN THE LUNGS

*Akhil Bidani*

Department of Medicine, University of Texas Medical Branch, Galveston, Texas 77550

*Edward D. Crandall*

Department of Medicine, Cornell University Medical College, New York, New York 10021

## INTRODUCTION

Owing to the high solubility × diffusivity product of $CO_2$ (~20 times that for $O_2$), there had been little concern prior to 1970 regarding the adequacy of contact time between alveolar gas and capillary blood in the pulmonary circulation. This in part led to the use of arterial $P_{CO_2}$ in place of alveolar $P_{CO_2}$ in dead space and other calculations. Indeed, this equality of arterial and alveolar $P_{CO_2}$ has been one of the few unchallenged assumptions in respiratory physiology. Over the last decade, however, there has been significant clarification of the kinetics of $CO_2$ transport and exchange mechanisms relevant to this assumption.

The exchange of $CO_2$ between capillary blood and alveolar gas involves the following chemical and transport events: (*a*) diffusion of molecular $CO_2$ across the red cell and alveolar capillary membranes; (*b*) dehydration of $H_2CO_3$ to $CO_2$ inside the red cell, catalyzed by the large excess of carbonic anhydrase (CA) present in the red cell; (*c*) dehydration of $H_2CO_3$ to $CO_2$ in plasma, which occurs at a rate dependent on the availability of CA activity to plasma; (*d*) exchange of $HCO_3^-$ and $Cl^-$ across the red cell membrane ("chloride shift"); (*e*) release of Bohr protons ($H^+$) from hemoglobin inside the red cell in association with the reversible combination of molecular $O_2$ and deoxygenated hemoglobin; (*f*) consumption of red cell $H^+$ associated with the

0066-4278/88/0315-0639$02.00

dissociation of hemoglobin carbamate molecular $CO_2$; and (g) movement of water across the red cell membrane. Since the rate of uncatalyzed $H_2CO_3$ dehydration is slow ($t_{1/2} \approx$ 5–8 s), Roughton (41, 42) postulated that in the absence of CA activity available to plasma, $CO_2$ reactions might not be completed during pulmonary capillary transit. In vitro confirmation of Roughton's postulate was provided by Crandall & Forster (12, 21) when they showed that the rate of pH equilibration in red cell suspensions was two orders of magnitude slower than the rate of uptake of $CO_2$ ($t_{1/2}$ of 2 and of 0.045 s, respectively). It was further shown (21) that this differential rate was abolished in the presence of extracellular CA. Additional support for the rate-limiting nature of the $H_2CO_3$ dehydration reactions was provided by mathematical analyses of pulmonary capillary gas exchange (5, 12, 21, 30). These calculations suggested that in the absence of availability of CA activity to plasma, blood leaving the pulmonary capillary bed is not in electrochemical equilibrium and that plasma pH rises downstream by ~0.025 with a $t_{1/2}$ of 5–8 s.

Several investigators (3, 9, 29, 40) designed experimental protocols to verify the presence of such slow pH changes in the arterial circulation in anesthetized animals. These experiments have yielded conflicting results. Whereas a smaller than predicted *alkaline* change (pH rise) in blood leaving the lungs was noted by Hill et al (29) and Bidani & Crandall (3), a significant *acidic* change (pH fall) was measured by Rispens et al (40). No significant pH disequilibria were reported by Chakrabarti et al (9). Confounding issues include red cell hemolysis in experimental animals and the recently reported presence of CA inhibitors in the plasma of dogs and rabbits (28, 39). It is now apparent that the issue of pH disequilibria in vivo in man is more complex than previously appreciated.

In the ensuing sections, we review some of the issues and questions that have been clarified over the past decade. These include the roles of lung carbonic anhydrase and of red cell anion transport in $CO_2$ exchange. Next, we briefly discuss the major determinants of capillary $CO_2$ exchange. We close with a summary of the major findings to date and the remaining uncertainties in the velocity of $CO_2$ exchanges in the lungs.

## ROLE OF LUNG CARBONIC ANHYDRASE IN $CO_2$ EXCHANGES

Recognition of the complex interaction of multiple factors in studying the velocity of $CO_2$ exchange in intact animals led to the use of blood-free perfused isolated animal lung preparations (14, 18, 34). In the first phase of these studies, the question examined was a qualitative one: Is lung carbonic anhydrase (17, 37) available to catalyze extracellular $CO_2 \leftrightarrow H_2CO_3$ hydration-dehydration reactions?

Crandall & O'Brasky (14) measured the rate of effluent perfusate pH equilibration in isolated rat lungs using a stopped-flow apparatus. Air-ventilated isolated lungs were perfused with Krebs-Ringer-bicarbonate (KRB) solutions having pH, $P_{CO_2}$, and $P_{O_2}$ similar to those in mixed venous blood. They noted no effluent perfusate pH disequilibrium under control conditions, which indicates that the perfusate $CO_2$ reactions were completed during pulmonary capillary transit. Addition of acetazolamide (ACTZ) to the perfusate yielded an increase in effluent perfusate pH with time ($\triangle pH = 0.05$, $t_{1/2} \approx 3.5$ s) under steady-state conditions, which indicates that lung carbonic anhydrase available to the perfusate can be inhibited by ACTZ. Based on these observations, Crandall & O'Brasky (14) postulated that lung carbonic anhydrase may be bound to the luminal surface of the endothelial cells (as is angiotensin converting enzyme). A similar conclusion was reached independently and simultaneously by Effros et al (18) and Klocke (34) based on their studies of isolated rabbit lungs. Morphological support for such an enzyme location and distribution was provided by Lonnerholm (36) and Ryan & Ryan (43).

Once the question of the availability of lung CA activity to extracellular $CO_2$-$H_2CO_3$ reactions had been answered qualitatively, the next step was to quantify the carbonic anhydrase activity available in situ to the perfusate in the pulmonary vasculature of isolated animal lungs. Bidani et al (7) calculated the velocity of the perfusate $H_2CO_3$ dehydration reaction in isolated rat lungs as a function of inhibitor (ACTZ) concentration by combining an experimental protocol with a theoretical model of capillary $CO_2$ exchange. Isolated, mechanically ventilated rat lungs were perfused at 37°C with phosphate-Ringer-bicarbonate (PRB) solutions containing variable concentrations of acetazolamide (ACTZ = 0.0–0.08 mM), pre-equilibrated with 3, 5, or 10% $CO_2$. Effluent perfusate was withdrawn through a stopped-flow pH electrode apparatus under steady-state conditions to monitor the magnitude of the effluent perfusate pH change ($\triangle pH$). With perfusates containing no ACTZ, no downstream change in pH was noted (i.e. $\triangle pH = 0.0$). With increasing [ACTZ] in the inflowing perfusate, $\triangle pH$ became progressively larger, with a maximum $\triangle pH$ of 0.034 units at [ACTZ] = 0.08 mM.

A theoretical model of capillary gas exchange under the conditions of these experiments (7) was used to calculate values for the initial rate $V$ and catalysis factor $A_o$ (catalyzed/uncatalyzed rate) for the $H_2CO_3$ dehydration reactions in the rat lung capillary bed. Time courses of perfusate pH, $P_{CO_2}$, $P_{O_2}$, and [$HCO_3^-$] changes in effluent perfusate during capillary transit and thereafter were computed. Final estimates of $A_o$, as a function of inhibitor concentrations, were obtained iteratively such that the computed equilibrium effluent perfusate pH, $P_{CO_2}$, and $P_{O_2}$ matched those measured experimentally (Figure 1). The initial velocity $V$ of the $H_2CO_3$ dehydration was determined from the initial rate of change of [$HCO_3^-$] ($d[HCO_3^-]/dt$) as the perfusate enters the pulmonary capillaries. The kinetic parameters characterizing lung CA were determined from the double reciprocal plot ($1/V$ versus $1/[HCO_3^-]$) shown in Figure 2. A noncompetitive pattern of inhibition was observed, and the Michaelis-Menten and inhibition parameters was calculated to be $K_M = 55$ mM, $V_{max} = 25$ mM/s, and $K_I = 1.4 \times 10^{-3}$ mM. Using these values for $V_{max}$ and $K_M$, Bidani et al (7) estimated that for normal physiological conditions in the rat lung, pulmonary vasculature CA is able to catalyze the extracellular hydration-dehydration reactions by a factor of 130–150. The value for $A_o$ of 130–150 can be compared to an estimated intraerythrocyte CA catalysis factor of $\sim 10,000$ (31).

Effros et al (19) have estimated that $1.25 \times 10^{-6}$ mol of receptors for ACTZ are present per liter of extravascular lung water in isolated rabbit lungs. This value for total enzyme concentration and a value of $V_{max}$ of 25 mM/s, as estimated by Bidani et al (7), yield a turnover number (TON) for lung CA of 25,000/s. Comparison of TON, $K_M$, $V_{max}$, and $K_I$ values for pulmonary CA obtained by Bidani et al (7) with those for known CA reported previously (23, 37) suggests that pulmonary vascular CA has human red cell CA B–like activity. This does not imply that lung CA has any structural relationship to human red cell CA B or to bovine CA, especially in view of the marked heterogeneity of CAs in different tissues (45).

In a recent study, Henry et al (27) estimated the carbonic anhydrase activity in homogenized rat lung tissue to be sufficient to catalyze the $CO_2$ hydration-dehydration reactions by a factor of 122. This value of $A_o$ for total CA is surprisingly similar to that calculated by Bidani et al (7) for vascular CA.

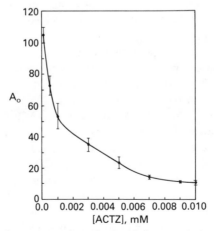

*Figure 1*  Computed pulmonary vascular carbonic anhydrase catalyzing factor $A_o$ for $HCO_3^-$ dehydration reaction versus [acetazolamide]. Each entry represents mean $\pm$SE over all runs at a given [acetazolamide]. Solid line fit to data by eye. (From Ref. 7)

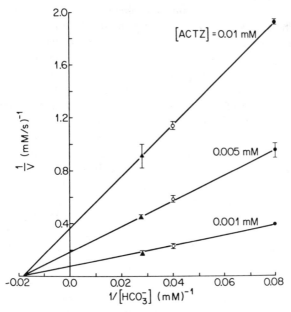

*Figure 2*   Kinetic data on $H_2CO_3$ dehydration in isolated rat lungs. Lineweaver-Burke plot ($1/V$ versus $1/[HCO_3^-]$) at [ACTZ] = 0.001, 0.005, and 0.01 mM. Solid line fit to data by eye. *Filled circles,* 12 mM $HCO_3^-$ in perfusate; *open circles,* 25 mM $HCO_3^-$ in perfusate; *triangles* 35 mM $HCO_3^-$ in perfusate. (From Ref. 7)

Based on the inhibition properties of lung CA measured in their study, Henry et al (27) suggested that pulmonary vascular CA activity might be related to nonspecific adsorption of CA released from hemolysed red cells in vivo. This is less likely in view of the data of Ryan et al (44), which suggest de novo synthesis of CA by pulmonary artery endothelial cells in culture.

Availability of CA activity to plasma in vivo would serve to significantly enhance the rate of $CO_2$ hydration-dehydration reactions in plasma, thereby modifying the kinetics of equilibration between alveolar gas and capillary blood. This is turn would alter the predicted postcapillary pH disequilibrium, as is discussed in further detail below. However, another issue is whether or not lung CA is able to significantly augment the rate of $CO_2$ excretion ($\dot{V}_{CO_2}$). Theoretical calculations by Crandall & Bidani (11) suggest that augmentation of $\dot{V}_{CO_2}$ by extra–red cell CA activity is minimal (<10%). However, Enns & Hill (20) suggest a more significant effect, perhaps due to a mechanism of "facilitated $CO_2$ diffusion" by lung tissue CA. This issue is further complicated by recent data obtained by Heming et al (26), which suggest that the influence of lung CA(s) on pH disequilibria and $\dot{V}_{CO_2}$ may be dissociable.

These latter investigators (26) perfused isolated rat lungs with Krebs-Ringer-bicarbonate solutions containing no inhibitor, a low–molecular weight inhibitor (Prontosil or ACTZ), or a dextran-bound Prontosil (PD) inhibitor of high molecular weight (5 or 100 kilodaltons). Pulmonary $CO_2$ excretion was measured by continuously recording expired $CO_2$ concentrations. The time course of effluent perfusate pH equilibration was measured in a stopped-flow pH electrode apparatus. Prontosil or ACTZ, because of their small size (~250 daltons), are expected to inhibit CA activity everywhere in the lung (both intra- and extravascular activity). The 5-kd PD is expected to be excluded from the intracellular space, whereas the 100-kd PD should be confined to the intravascular space. A maximal effluent perfusate pH rise of 0.046 units and a maximal decrease in $\dot{V}_{CO_2}$ of 26% were obtained with 0.1mM ACTZ or 0.4 mM Prontosil. A 0.1 mM concentration of the 5-kd PD (1000 times its $K_I$ for bovine CA in solution) produced a downstream pH rise of 0.030 but no reduction in $\dot{V}_{CO_2}$. Similarly, the 100-kd PD at 0.2 mM ($1000 \times K_I$) caused a $\triangle pH$ of 0.015 but had no effect on $\dot{V}_{CO_2}$. These data suggest that there is an intravascular CA, presumably associated with endothelial cell membranes, that is accessible to the low and the high molecular weight (5 and 100 kd) CA inhibitors. This CA would be responsible in part for intravascular perfusate $CO_2$-$HCO_3^-$-$H^+$ equilibrium but would play a minimal role in $CO_2$ excretion. Additionally, these data support the idea that an extravascular (possibly intracellular) CA is present that can be inhibited by low molecular weight inhibitors, is primarily responsible for augmented $CO_2$ transfer (perhaps via facilitation of $CO_2$ diffusion), and is in part responsible for extracellular pH equilibration.

The presence of an extravascular, extracellular CA would require a rapid flux of $HCO_3^-$ and $H^+$ across the capillary endothelium so as to allow its participation in intravascular $CO_2$-$HCO_3^-$-$H^+$ reactions. The specific pathway(s) responsible for such rapid ionic movements have not been delineated at present. Conceivably, CA itself could facilitate the translocation of $HCO_3^-$ and $H^+$ through the endothelial cell membranes (16). It is worth noting that, given the absence of luminal CA in skeletal muscle capillaries (22), a similar rapid flux of $HCO_3^-$ and $H^+$ across the capillary endothelium would be required for pH equilibration in that tissue as well.

## ROLE OF RED CELL ANION TRANSPORT IN LUNG $CO_2$ EXCHANGE

Another major determinant of capillary $CO_2$ exchange and transport (besides the effects of intra- and extraerythocyte CA activity, discussed above) involves the kinetics of $HCO_3^-$-$Cl^-$ exchange across the red cell membrane. Since under normal physiological conditions 80% of $\dot{V}_{CO_2}$ is derived from the dehydration of plasma and red cell $HCO_3^-$, the rate of the chloride shift is particularly important. This pathway provides a crucial link between two compartments with different $H^+$ buffering characteristics. Previous estimates of the rate of the chloride shift (10, 33) have been assumed to be sufficiently rapid to not limit the rate of capillary $CO_2$ exchange in vivo.

Over the past decade, significant progress has been made in clarifying the mechanism and kinetics of red cell anion exchange (24, 32, 35). It has been shown that a specialized transport system, involving a major red cell membrane protein (band 3), is involved in the electroneutral translocation of anions into and out of red cells. Furthermore, this pathway follows Michaelis-Menten kinetics and, like other carrier-mediated transport systems, is inhibited by several commonly used pharmacological agents such as salicylate and furosemide (8, 15).

Several investigators (11, 48–50) have suggested that the rate of the chloride shift may indeed be rate limiting under certain conditions in vivo, such as during exercise associated with significantly reduced transit time through the pulmonary capillaries and during inhibition of the anion exchange pathway. Based on measurements of the rate of tracer exchange of chloride and bicarbonate across the red cell membrane (48), Wieth and coworkers (49, 50) calculated that for conditions of normal $CO_2$ transfer (1.9 mmol/liter blood), $t_{0.9}$ and $t_{0.99}$ are 380 ms and 760 ms, respectively. Similar estimates of $t_{0.9}$ and $t_{0.99}$ were obtained under conditions of maximal $CO_2$ transfer (6 mmol/liter blood). Based on these calculations, Wieth and coworkers (49, 50) suggested that the chloride shift may not be completed under conditions of lowered transit time, such as those associated with moderate to heavy exercise.

In order to study the effect of alterations in anion exchange kinetics on overall capillary $CO_2$ transfer, Crandall & Bidani (11) utilized a detailed mathematical model of the chemical and transport events that occur in blood during capillary exchange. As a first approximation, anion exchange in this model was described using phenomenological permeability coefficients ($P_{HCO_3^-}$) and appropriate electrochemical potential gradients. Despite its simplified analysis of anion exchange, the model provides a suitable framework for examining the effects of alterations in $P_{HCO_3^-}$ on $CO_2$ excretion ($\dot{V}_{CO_2}$) and postcapillary pH disequilibria ($\Delta pH_o$).

Computed values for $CO_2$ excretion in the normal human lung ($\dot{V}_{CO_2}$) as a function of the rate of the chloride shift (represented by $P_{HCO_3^-}$) are shown in Figure 3. Results are shown for different rates of the $CO_2$ hydration-dehydration reactions in plasma, using extracellular catalysis factors $A_o$ of 1, 10, and 1000. $A_o = 1$ represents the case in which no CA activity is available to plasma. These calculations suggest that since the "normal" permeability of $10^{-4}$ cm/s lies near the top of a sigmoid curve, any decrement in $P_{HCO_3^-}$

can result in a decrement in $\dot{V}_{CO_2}$. Furthermore, this dependence of $\dot{V}_{CO_2}$ on $P_{HCO_3^-}$ holds for all values of $A_o$. In particular, these calculations suggest that $\dot{V}_{CO_2}$ would decrease by 25% for a reduction in $P_{HCO_3^-}$ from $10^{-4}$ to $10^{-6}$ cm/s. These calculations of $\dot{V}_{CO_2}$, assuming fixed values of the mixed venous blood and alveolar gas parameters, will require modification for in vivo applications since any decrement in $\dot{V}_{CO_2}$ would result in a compensatory increase in ventilatory drive and a reduction in alveolar $P_{CO_2}$ (and perhaps an increase in mixed venous blood $P_{CO_2}$). However, in situations where the cardiopulmonary reserves are limited, such as in patients with chronic obstructive pulmonary disease, the compensatory mechanisms may be minimal and not adequate to maintain $\dot{V}_{CO_2}$ with normal alveolar and mixed venous blood gas values.

In an effort to verify these theoretical predictions, Crandall et al (13) measured $\dot{V}_{CO_2}$ in isolated rat lungs perfused with suspensions of normal red cells or red cells whose membrane $HCO_3^-$-$Cl^-$ exchange rate was inhibited. Isolated rat lungs were ventilated with room air, and inflowing red cell suspension blood gas parameters were similar to those of mixed venous blood in vivo. Rates of $CO_2$ excretion were determined by measuring the fraction of $CO_2$ in mixed expired gas in the steady state. The time course of extracellular pH equilibration in the effluent red cell suspensions was monitored in a downstream stopped-flow pH electrode apparatus. The lungs were perfused at

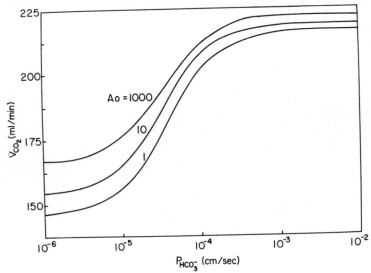

*Figure 3* Computed results of the effects of red cell bicarbonate permeability ($P_{HCO_3^-}$) and extracellular catalysis ($A_o$) of the $CO_2$ hydration-dehydration reactions on the rate of $CO_2$ excretion in the lung ($\dot{V}_{CO_2}$) for normal man at rest. See text for discussion. (From Ref. 11)

37°C with either control red cell suspensions (perfusate A) or suspensions containing DIDS-(4-4'-diisothiocyano-2-2-disulfonic stilbene)-treated red cells in which $HCO_3^- $-$Cl^-$ exchange is 98% inhibited (perfusate B).

In each lung there was little or no change ($\Delta pH_o = 0.0$) in the $pH_o$ of the effluent perfusate after flow was stopped using perfusate A, but a large fall in $pH_o$ ($\Delta pH_o = 0.057$, $t_{1/2} \approx 44$ s) was obtained when perfusate B was used. $\dot{V}_{CO_2}$ averaged 16% lower when the lungs were perfused with perfusate B than when the lungs were perfused with perfusate A. Additionally, when carbonic anhydrase was added to in-flowing perfusate B, no significant change in either $\Delta pH_o$ or $\dot{V}_{CO_2}$ was noted, which supports the contention that in these experiments anion exchange kinetics is clearly the rate-limiting process. Theoretical calculations simulating these experiments showed excellent agreement between the measured and predicted changes in $\dot{V}_{CO_2}$ and $\Delta pH_o$ (13).

These experiments provide confirmation of the hypothesis (11, 49, 50) that inhibition of red cell anion exchange can significantly affect both $CO_2$ excretion ($\dot{V}_{CO_2}$) and postcapillary pH equilibration. Since a number of commonly used drugs, such as salicylate (15), furosemide (8), and anesthetics (38), are known to inhibit the rate of red cell anion exchange, these results imply a potential clinically significant effect on $CO_2$ transfer in vivo by inhibition of red cell $HCO_3^-/Cl^-$ exchange kinetics, especially in patients with limited cardiopulmonary reserve.

## DETERMINANTS OF IN VIVO $CO_2$ EXCHANGE

In vivo kinetics of $CO_2$ exchange are determined by the complex interaction of multiple factors. The most important are those outlined above, including (a) the rate of $CO_2$ hydration-dehydration reactions within plasma and in red cells and (b) the kinetics of red cell anion exchange. Availability of CA activity to plasma results in effluent perfusate pH equilibration in isolated lungs, as described above. However, for the in vivo circumstance in which lungs are perfused with blood (a two-compartment system), the predictions are significantly altered. Figure 4 shows the magnitude of postcapillary plasma pH change in normal man computed using fixed values for mixed venous blood and alveolar gas parameters in our model of capillary gas exchange. $\Delta pH_o$ is shown as a function of $A_o$, the extracellular catalysis factor for different values for $P_{HCO_3^-}$. It can be seen that (with a $P_{HCO_3^-}$ of $10^{-4}$ cm/s) the direction and magnitude of the change in postcapillary plasma pH is markedly dependent on $A_o$. For example, $\Delta pH_o$ is predicted to be 0.025 for $A_o = 1$, but for $A_o > 100$, $\Delta pH_o = 0.01$. The presence of CA inhibitors in plasma (28, 39) would affect $A_o$ and result in a different predicted $\Delta pH_o$. This latter consideration might help reconcile the apparently conflicting results of

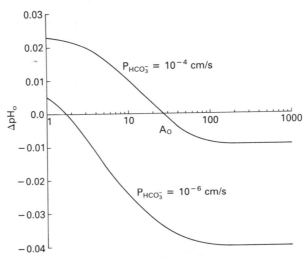

*Figure 4* Computed results of the effects of extracellular catalysis ($A_o$) of the $CO_2$ hydration-dehydration reactions and red blood cell bicarbonate permeability ($P_{HCO_3}$) on the magnitude of the postpulmonary capillary pH change ($\Delta pH_o$) for normal man at rest. See text for discussion.

different investigators for arterial blood pH equilibration kinetics in anesthetized animals (3, 9, 29, 40)

Figure 4 also shows that a decrement in the rate of red cell anion exchange kinetics results in the prediction of a larger acidic pH change, which is in agreement with the findings of Crandall et al (13). For example, for $A_o = 100$ and $P_{HCO_3} = 10^{-6}$ cm/s, the net $\Delta pH_o$ is computed to be $-0.04$. The complete time course of computed postcapillary plasma pH is in fact biphasic (11, 13).

The major influence of alterations in red cell CA activity on both $CO_2$ excretion and postcapillary pH equilibration has been previously described (2, 37). Since there is normally a large excess of red cell CA, significant inhibition of its activity must occur before any physiological alterations become apparent (37). However, in the simultaneous presence of pharmacological agents, such as furosemide, which inhibit red cell anion exchange and CA activity, and acetazolamide, a more potent inhibitor of CA activity, physiological alterations might be manifested at dosages less than those ordinarily considered toxic.

Besides the influence of CA activity (red cell and pulmonary vascular) and red cell anion exchange kinetics on $CO_2$ excretion, there are numerous other secondary factors that may influence $\dot{V}_{CO_2}$ and $\Delta pH_o$. Mathematically, these may be represented by a relationship of the form:

$$\dot{V}_{CO_2} = f(\dot{Q}, P_{vCO_2}, P_{ACO_2}, A_i, A_o, P_{HCO_3^-}, \beta_i, \beta_o, \gamma_c, \gamma_o,$$

$$\dot{V}_{O_2}, Hct, V_c, D_{mCO_2}, pH_v, t_{1/2}^{Bohr} [2,3\text{-DPG}], t_r, T).$$

$\dot{Q}$ represents pulmonary blood flow; $P_{aCO_2}$ is the partial pressure of $CO_2$ in aveolar gas, determined principally by minute ventilation $\dot{V}$ and dead-space fraction $V_d/V_t$; $P_{vCO_2}$ and $pH_v$ represent $P_{CO_2}$ and pH of mixed central venous blood; $V_c$ is the capillary blood volume; $A_i$ and $A_o$ represent catalysis factors for red cell and plasma $CO_2$-$H_2CO_3$ hydration-dehydration reactions, respectively; $P_{HCO_3^-}$ denotes a phenomenological coefficient representing the rate of anion exchange across the red cell membrane; $\beta_i$ and $\beta_o$ are the red cell and plasma buffer capacities; $\gamma_c$ and $\gamma_o$ represent the quantity of $H^+$ consumed and liberated within the red cell per unit carbamate dissociation or oxygen uptake, respectively; $\dot{V}_{O_2}$ represents concomitant $O_2$ uptake; Hct is the hematocrit; $D_{mCO_2}$ is the alveolar capillary membrane diffusing capacity; $t_{1/2}^{Bohr}$ represents the half-time for release of Bohr protons from hemoglobin; [2,3-DPG] is the red cell concentration of 2,3-DPG, which influences both $\dot{V}_{O_2}$ and $\gamma_o$; $t_r$ is the residence time for blood flow in the pulmonary capillaries; and $T$ is the absolute temperature.

Since it is virtually impossible to study the influence of each of the factors listed above in intact animals, the nature and extent of influence of each of these parameters is best delineated in either experiments on isolated lungs or via mathematical analyses and computer simulation. The major influence of ventilation/perfusion inhomogeneities and dead-space fraction ($V_D/V_T$) in setting the alveolar gas tension ($P_{aO_2}$, $P_{aCO_2}$) has been thoroughly discussed previously by West & Wagner (47). Similarly, the influence of pulsatile blood flow ($\dot{Q}$) and pulsatile capillary blood volume ($V_c$) on pulmonary capillary gas exchange has been examined both theoretically (6) and experimentally (25). Alterations in hematocrit affect the amount of red cell surface area available for anion exchange as well as the red cell volume, which in turn affects the size of the high buffer capacity intraerythrocytic pool. The influence of these factors on the velocity of lung $CO_2$ exchange has been examined theoretically by Bidani & Crandall (4). Similarly, the effect of alterations in the membrane diffusing capacity, $D_{mCO_2}$, on $\dot{V}_{O_2}$ and $\dot{V}_{CO_2}$ was studied by Wagner & West (46).

Of the factors listed above, the ones most vulnerable to alteration with pharmacological agents are the plasma and red cell catalysis factors ($A_o$ and $A_i$) and the kinetics of red cell anion exchange. In individuals receiving drugs that affect carbonic anhydrase activity (e.g. ACTZ or furosemide) or that inhibit the rate of red cell anion exchange (e.g. salicylate or furosemide), pH disequilibria can be demonstrated (2, 13) and can lead to impairment of $CO_2$ excretion (11, 13). Much more needs to be learned about the synergistic interactions of these phenomena, since severe deterimental effects on $CO_2$ exchange and acid-base hemostasis have been described in isolated reports (1).

## SUMMARY

As outlined above, investigations over the past decade have provided further insight into the kinetics of many of the component processes that affect the overall velocity of $CO_2$ exchanges in the lungs. The evolution of our understanding of the importance and role of these reactions and transport processes has not been entirely predictable. A variety of investigations into Roughton's original hypothesis (41) regarding the mechanism of pH equilibration in capillary blood resulted in a renewed interest in carbonic anhydrase in the lung and other tissues (45). These latter studies have helped better define the location and kinetic properties of lung CA and its role in the overall velocity of $CO_2$ exchange. Concurrently, a wealth of information has emerged regarding the transport properties of the red cell membrane. This has led to a better understanding of the mechanisms and characteristics of the band 3–mediated pathway for electroneutral anion exchange. Unfortunately, most of the kinetic data for this pathway have been obtained under nonphysiological conditions, making it difficult to utilize them directly in analyses of lung $CO_2$ exchange kinetics. The potential detrimental effect of pharmacological agents in modifying lung CA and red cell CA activity and red cell anion exchange kinetics is among the more important factors to have emerged in the past decade. Ironically, the original question of whether a significant blood pH disequilibrium is present in the arterial circulation in man in vivo remains unresolved. However, the mechanisms underlying these phenomena are now recognized to be more complex than originally appreciated.

*Literature Cited*

1. Anderson, C. J., Kaufman, P. L., Strum, R. J. 1978. Toxicity of combined therapy with carbonic anhydrase inhibitors and aspirin. *Am. J. Ophthalmol.* 85:516–19
2. Bidani, A., Crandall, E. D. 1978. Slow post-capillary changes in blood pH in vivo: Titration with acetazolamide. *J. Appl. Physiol.* 45:565–73
3. Bidani, A., Crandall, E. D. 1978. Slow post-capillary pH changes in anesthetized animals. *J. Appl. Physiol.* 45:674–80
4. Bidani, A., Crandall, E. D. 1982. Analysis of the effect of hematocrit on pulmonary $CO_2$ transfer. *J. Appl. Physiol.* 53:413–18
5. Bidani, A., Crandall, E. D., Forster, R. E. 1978. Analysis of post-capillary pH changes in blood in vivo after gas exchange. *J. Appl. Physiol.* 44:770–81
6. Bidani, A, Flumerfelt, R. W., Crandall, E. D. 1978. Analysis of the effect of pulsatile capillary blood flow and volume on gas exchange. *Resp. Physiol.* 35:27–42
7. Bidani, A., Mathew, S. J., Crandall, E. D. 1983. Pulmonary vascular carbonic anhydrase activity. *J. Appl. Physiol.* 55:75–83
8. Brazy, P, C., Gunn, R. B. 1976. Furosemide inhibition of chloride transport in human red blood cells. *J. Gen. Physiol.* 68:583–99

9. Chakrabarti, M. K., Cobbe, S. M., Loh, L., Poole-Wilson, P. A. 1983. Measurements of pulmonary venous and arterial pH oscillations in dogs using catheter tip pH electrodes. *J. Physiol. London* 336:61–71

10. Chow, E. I., Crandall, E. D., Forster, R. E. 1976. The kinetics of bicarbonate-chloride exchange across the human eyrthrocyte membrane. *J. Gen. Physiol.* 68:633–52

11.. Crandall, E. D., Bidani, A. 1981. Effect of red blood cell $HCO_3^-/Cl^-$ exchange kinetics on lung $CO_2$ transfer: theory. *J. Appl. Physiol.* 50:265–71

12. Crandall, E. D., Forster, R. E. 1973. On some rapid ion exchanges across the red cell membrane. *Am. Chem. Soc. Adv. Chem. Ser.* 118:65–87

13. Crandall, E. D., Mathew, S. J., Fleischer, R. S., Winter, H. I., Bidani, A. 1981. Effects of inhibition of RBC $HCO_3^-/Cl^-$ exchange on $CO_2$ excretion and downstream pH disequilibrium in isolated rat lungs. *J. Clin. Invest.* 68:853–62

14. Crandall, E. D., O'Brasky, J. E. 1978. Direct evidence for participation of rat lung carbonic anhydrase in $CO_2$ reactions. *J. Clin. Invest.* 62:618–22

15. Crandall, E. D., Winter, H. I., Schaefer, J. D., Bidani, A. 1982. Effect of salicylate on $HCO_3^-/Cl^-$ exchange across the human erythrocyte membrane. *J. Membr. Biol.* 65:139–45

16. Diaz, E., Sandblom, J. P., Wistrand, P. J. 1982. Selectivity properties of channels induced by a reconstituted membrane-bound carbonic anhydrase. *Acta Physiol. Scand.* 116:461–63

17. DuBois, A. B. 1968. Significane of carbonic anhydrase in lung tissue. In *$CO_2$: Chemical, Biochemical, and Physiological Aspects,* ed. R. E. Forster, J. T. Edsall, A. B. Otis, F. J. W. Roughton, pp. 257–60. Washington, DC: NASA (NASA SP-188)

18. Effros, R. M., Chang, R. S. Y., Silverman, P. 1978. Acceleration of plasma bicarbonate conversion to carbon dioxide by pulmonary carbonic anhydrase. *Science* 199:427–29

19. Effros, R. M., Shapiro, L., Silverman, P. 1980. Carbonic anhydrase activity of rabbit lungs. *J. Appl. Physiol.* 49:589–600

20. Enns, T., Hill, E. P. 1983. $CO_2$ diffusing capacity in isolated dog lobes and the role of carbonic anhydrase. *J. Appl. Physiol.* 54:483–90

21. Forster, R. E., Crandall, E. D. 1975. Time course of exchanges between red cells and extracellular fluid during $CO_2$ uptake. *J. Appl. Physiol.* 38:710–18

22. Geers, C., Gros, G., Gartner, A. 1985. Extracellular carbonic anhydrase of skeletal muscle associated with the sarcolema. *J. Appl. Physiol.* 59:548–58

23. Gibbons, B. H., Edsall, J. T. 1964. Kinetic studies of human carbonic anhydrase B and C. *J. Biol. Chem.* 239:2539–44

24. Gunn, R. B., Dalmark, M., Tosteson, D. C., Wieth, J. O. 1973. Characteristics of chloride transport in human red cells. *J. Gen. Physiol.* 61:185–206

25. Hauge, A., Nicolaysen, G. 1980. Pulmonary $O_2$ transfer during pulsatile and non-pulsatile perfusion. *Acta Physiol. Scand.* 109:325–32

26. Heming, T. A., Geers, C., Gros, G., Bidani, A., Crandall, E. D. 1986. Effects of dextran bound inhibitors on carbonic anhydrase activity in isolated rat lungs. *J. Appl. Physiol.* 61:1849–56

27. Henry, R. P., Dodgson, S. J., Forster, R. E., Storey, B. T. 1986. Rat carbonic anhydrase: Activity, localization and isozymes. *J. Appl. Physiol.* 60:638–45

28. Hill, E. P. 1986. Inhibition of carbonic anhydrase by plasma of dogs and rabbits. *J. Appl. Physiol.* 60:191–97

29. Hill, E. P., Power, G. G., Gilbert, R. D. 1977. Rate of pH changes in blood plasma in vitro and in vivo. *J. Appl. Physiol.* 42:928–34

30. Hill, E. P., Power, G. G., Longo, L. D. 1973. Mathematical simulation of pulmonary $O_2$ and $CO_2$ exchange. *Am. J. Physiol.* 224:904–17

31. Itada, N., Forster, R. E. 1977. Carbonic anhydrase activity in intact red blood cells measured with $^{18}O$ exchange. *J. Biol. Chem.* 251:3881–90

32. Jennings, M. L. 1985. Kinetics and mechanism of anion transport in red blood cells. *Ann. Rev. Physiol.* 47:519–53

33. Klocke, R. A. 1976. Rate of bicarbonate-chloride exchange in human red cells at 37°C. *J. Appl. Physiol.* 40:707–14

34. Klocke, R. A. 1978. Catalysis of $CO_2$ reactions by lung carbonic anhydrase. *J. Appl. Physiol.* 44:882–88

35. Knauf, P. A. 1986. Anion transport in erythrocytes. In *Physiology of Membrane Disorders,* ed. T. E. Andreoli, J. F. Hoffman, D. D. Fanestil, S. G. Schultz, pp. 191–212. New York: Plenum. 2nd ed.

36. Lonnerholm, G. 1982. Pulmonary carbonic anhydrase in the human, monkey, and rat. *J. Appl. Physiol.* 52:352–56

37. Maren, T. H. 1967. Carbonic anhydrase chemistry, physiology, and inhibition. *Physiol. Rev.* 47:595–781

38. Motais, R., Baroin, A., Motais, A., Baldy, S. 1980. Inhibition of anion and glucose permeabilities by anesthetic in erythrocytes. *Biochem. Biophyhs. Acta* 599:673–88

39. Rispens, P., Hessels, J., Zwart, A., Zijlistra, W. G. 1985. Inhibition of carbonic anhydrase in dog plasma. *Pflüg. Arch.* 403:344–47

40. Rispens, P., Oesburg, B., Zock, J. P., Zijlistra, W. G. 1980. Intra-aortic decrease in plasma pH. *Pflüg. Arch.* 386:97–99

41. Roughton, F. J. W. 1935. Recent work on carbon dioxide transport by the blood. *Physiol. Rev.* 15:241–96

42. Roughton, F. J. W. 1964. Transport of oxygen and carbon dioxide. In *Handbook of Physiology*, Sect. 3. *Respiration*, ed. W. O. Fenn, H. Rahn, 1:767–825. Washington, DC: Am. Physiol. Soc.

43. Ryan, U. S., Ryan, J. W. 1984. Cell biology of the pulmonary endothelium. *Circ. Suppl. III* 70:46–62

44. Ryan, U. S., Whitney, P. L., Ryan, J. W. 1982. Localization of carbonic anhydrase on pulmonary artery endothelial cells in culture. *J. Appl. Physiol.* 3:914–19

45. Tashian, R. E., Hewett-Emmett, D. 1984. *The Biology and Chemistry of the Carbonic Anhydrases*, 429:R13–R14. New York: NY Acad. Sci.

46. Wagner, P. D., West, J. B. 1973. Effects of diffusion impairment on $O_2$ and $CO_2$ time courses in pulmonary capillaries. *J. Appl. Physiol.* 33:62–71

47. West, J. B., Wagner, P. D. 1977. Pulmonary gas exchange. In *Bioengineering Aspects of the Lung*, ed. J. West, pp. 361–457. New York: Dekker

48. Wieth, J. O. 1979. Bicarbonate exchange through the red cell membrane determined with $[^{14}C]HCO_3^-$. *J. Physiol. London,* 294:521–39

49. Wieth, J. O., Anderson, O. S., Brahm, J., Bjerrum, P. J., Borders, C. L. 1982. Chloride-bicarbonate exchange in red blood cells: Physiology of transport and chemical modification of binding sites. *Philos. Trans. R. Soc. London Ser. B* 299:383–99

50. Wieth, J. O., Brahm, J. 1980. Kinetics of bicarbonate exchange in human red cells—physiological implications. In *Membrane Transport in Erythrocytes,* ed. U. V. Lassen, H. H. Ussing, J. O. Wieth, pp. 467–82. Copenhagen: Munksgard

Ann. Rev. Physiol. 1988. 50:653–67

# KINETICS OF CO$_2$ EXCHANGE IN THE KIDNEY

*Thomas D. DuBose, Jr.*

Division of Nephrology, University of Texas Medical Branch, Galveston, Texas 77550

*Akhil Bidani*

Division of Pulmonary Medicine, University of Texas Medical Branch, Galveston, Texas 77550

## INTRODUCTION

Several important issues regarding the kinetics of CO$_2$ exchange in the kidney have been elucidated over the past decade. This review focuses on the factors that generate and maintain the levels of CO$_2$ tension at different points along the nephron and surrounding vasculature. After discussing the historical development of the observation of an elevated renal cortical PCO$_2$, we outline the role of carbonic anhydrase in the kidney. We then review findings employing PCO$_2$ microelectrodes in the kidney in vivo. Finally, we attempt to place these observations into physiologic perspective by evaluating, from a quantitative point of view, possible mechanisms of CO$_2$ generation and maintenance.

The discovery of an elevated CO$_2$ tension in the superficial renal cortex, with respect to systemic arterial blood, was a result of technical advances that emerged from studies investigating the mechanism of urinary acidification. Such studies have employed microelectrodes in vivo to compare the pH of renal tubule fluid in situ and the pH achieved after tubule fluid has been allowed to reach chemical equilibrium at a known PCO$_2$ in vitro (46, 52). If renal carbonic anhydrase is inhibited by drugs such as acetazolamide or benzolamide, or alternatively if tubule fluid is not in physical contact with the

653

0066-4278/88/0315-0653$02.00

enzyme (as occurs in distal segments of the nephron), hydrogen secretion into bicarbonate-containing tubule fluid will generate carbonic acid. Thus, in a hydrogen secretory system, carbonic acid accumulation will result in an in situ pH that is more acidic than the equilibrium (in vitro) pH (acid disequilibrium pH) (20).

Earlier studies investigating the mechanism of renal acidification (46, 52) were criticized because of the assumption that $PCO_2$ was equal in the renal cortex and systemic arterial blood (11). A calculated value for $PCO_2$ in a proximal tubule was later reported, however, that exceeded the systemic arterial blood $PCO_2$ (51). This finding called the disequilibrium pH technique into question, since the acid disequilibrium pH reported previously could have been the result of high $CO_2$ tensions in the proximal tubule if a transepithelial diffusion barrier existed for $CO_2$. Sohtell later measured $PCO_2$ in the proximal tubule with a microelectrode and reported values that exceeded systemic arterial levels by 30 mm Hg (50). Nevertheless, values for $PCO_2$ in the peritubular capillary were at, or below, systemic levels. In sharp contrast to findings of a large $CO_2$ gradient between proximal tubule and peritubular capillary, DuBose et al (27) demonstrated values for $PCO_2$ that were significantly higher than systemic arterial blood (65 vs 37 mm Hg) but equal to one another in the proximal tubule, distal tubule, and stellate vessel, which suggests that $CO_2$ gas was in, or near, diffusion equilibrium throughout the renal cortex. Subsequent studies employed new pH electrode technology that circumvented any assumption regarding $PCO_2$ in vivo and verified the previously reported acid disequilibrium pH (25), indicating that $H^+$ secretion is the major mechanism of bicarbonate reabsorption in both proximal and distal tubules. Moreover, the presence of a disequilibrium pH in the proximal tubule only during inhibition of carbonic anhydrase suggested that tubule fluid in this segment of the nephron was in physical contact with the enzyme (27, 42, 46, 52).

## LOCALIZATION AND FUNCTION OF CARBONIC ANHYDRASE IN THE KIDNEY

Carbonic anhydrase is abundantly distributed in the renal tissue and functions, as in other epithelia, as a catlyst of the hydration-dehydration reaction of $CO_2$. Histochemical studies have demonstrated intense staining for the enzyme in the cytoplasm as well as bound to the membrane portion of the S1 and S2 segments of rat (40), rabbit, and mouse kidney (17, 18). In sharp contrast, proximal straight tubules in rat (40) and rabbit (18) demonstrate a low activity of carbonic anhydrase in both cytoplasm and brush border; no activity has been detected in mouse (18) and human proximal straight tubules (39). Carbonic anhydrase is present in the thin limbs and thick ascending limbs of

Henle in rat and mouse kidney (18, 40). In the rabbit, however, neither cortical nor medullary thick limbs reveal demonstrable activity (17, 18). In general, in all species examined, the intercalated cells of the cortical and medullary collecting tubules stain positively, while the principal cells are only slightly positive or are negative (18). These variations in enzyme distribution agree well with the physiological role of the enzyme in bicarbonate transport in these nephron segments (1). Recent evidence from biochemical and immunocytochemical studies suggests that the enzyme from nephron segments of dog, rat, mouse, and human is similar to human carbonic anhydrase Type II (53, 56). A membrane-bound fraction (Type IV), comprising less than 5% of the total organ carbonic anhydrase, has been reported in human, rat, and dog proximal tubule (29).

Bicarbonate transport in the proximal tubule, mediated by $Na^+/H^+$ exchange, is responsible for 80–90% of total renal bicarbonate reabsorption and is highly dependent on carbonic anhydrase (1). A study in our laboratory (42) investigated the effects of selective inhibition of the membrane-bound form of carbonic anhydrase by infusion of a dextran-bound inhibitor into the proximal tubule lumen. These studies demonstrated clearly that proximal tubule fluid is in functional contact with membrane-bound carbonic anhydrase.

## COMPARISON OF REPORTED VALUES FOR RENAL PCO$_2$

### Superficial Cortex

Five laboratories confirmed independently that the PCO$_2$ in the superficial proximal tubule exceeds the corresponding PCO$_2$ of systemic arterial blood (Table 1). Sohtell reported a PCO$_2$ in the proximal tubule equal to 61 mm Hg, a value that significantly exceeded the CO$_2$ tension in an adjacent stellate vessel (34 mm Hg) (50). The electrode employed in this study was limited, however, both in sensitivity and reliability because it used an antimony pH sensor whose results must be adjusted because of the deleterious effects of variations in ionic composition and temperature, and the presence of other dissolved gases (13).

In contrast to these findings, studies from DuBose et al have consistently demonstrated equal values for PCO$_2$ in the early and late proximal tubule and stellate vessel (65 mm Hg) (22, 26, 27). These studies employed an improved version of the Caflisch-Carter PCO$_2$ microelectrode (12) as developed by Pucacco & Carter (44) that utilizes a glass membrane pH sensor. This electrode has the following characteristics: sensitivity of 57–61 mV/log$_{10}$ PCO$_2$ (near theoretic response), stability of intercept, a tip diameter sufficiently small to allow direct measurement in all accessible segments of the

**Table 1**  Reported Values for Renal $PCO_2$[a]

|  | PCO₂ — Cortex (Control) | | | | |
|---|---|---|---|---|---|
|  | BS | EPCT | LPCT | SV | DCT |
| Sohtell (50) | — | — | 60.6 | 33.7 | — |
| DuBose et al (26, 27) | — | 65.0 | 65.0 | 65.0 | 65.0 |
| Maddox et al (43) | 56.5 | 62.1 | 57.1 | 57.1 | — |
| Bomsztyk & Calalb (10) | — | — | 57.0 | 56.0 | — |

|  | PCO₂ — Medulla (Control) | | | |
|---|---|---|---|---|
|  | LOH | BCD | TCD | VR |
| Graber et al (33) | — | 34.6 | 33.8 | — |
| DuBose et al (24) | 36.3 | 34.5 | 35.2 | 36.2 |

|  | PCO₂ — Medulla (Bicarbonate load) | | |
|---|---|---|---|
|  | BCD | TCD | VR |
| DuBose (19) | 95.0 | 122.0 | 96.0 |
| Graber et al (32) | 80.1 | 83.5 | — |

[a]Values displayed as means (mm Hg). BS = Bowman's space, EPCT = early proximal convoluted tubule, LPCT = late proximal convoluted tubule, SV = stellate vessel, DCT = distal convoluted tubule. LOH = loop of Henle, BCD = base of papillary collected duct, TCD = tip of papillary collecting duct, VR = vasa recta.

rat nephron, and insensitivity to oxygen or nitrogen (27, 44). Furthermore, we attempted to confirm our $PCO_2$ microelectrode data by independently measuring pH and total $CO_2$ content in tubule fluid and vascular structures in the renal cortex (26). For example, our measured value for pH in the stellate vessel (7.27) and for $PCO_2$ (65 mm Hg) resulted in calculated values for total $CO_2$ concentration in complete agreement with values for total $CO_2$ concentration measured by microcalorimetry (28 mM) (26).

Gennari et al (31) have also employed a similar electrode to determine values for $PCO_2$ in the early proximal tubule (52 mm Hg), in the late proximal tubule (49 mm Hg), and in the stellate vessel (48 mm Hg). In a more comprehensive study, Maddox et al (43) determined and compared $PCO_2$ in the superficial proximal convoluted tubule and peritubular segments of the rat renal cortex as well as the renal artery and vein. These findings are compared to the values reported by other laboratories under similar experimental conditions (Table 1). The reported value for $CO_2$ tension in Bowman's space was 17 mm Hg above $PCO_2$ in renal systemic arterial blood, and within the first 2 mm of the proximal tubule $PCO_2$ was shown to increase by approximately 6 mm Hg (43). Moreover, a transepithelial $PCO_2$ gradient of 3.5 mm Hg between early proximal tubule and peritubular capillary was reported. Consistent with findings from our laboratory (21, 23, 24, 26, 27), a transepithelial gradient for PCO$_2$ was not demonstrated between the late proximal convoluted tubule and the efferent arteriole. Similar PCO$_2$ profiles, but slighly lower transepithelial gradients between early proximal tubule and peritubular capillary (1.8 mm Hg) were obtained in plasma-replete rats (43).

PCO$_2$ has also been measured in rabbit superficial renal cortex (34). In this study, in situ PCO$_2$ in proximal convoluted tubules equaled 57 mm Hg, a value significantly higher than systemic arterial PCO$_2$ (36 mm Hg) (34). Moreover, compartive values for PCO$_2$ were reported for liver (64 mm Hg), femoral artery (39 mm Hg), superficial cerebral cortex (42 mm Hg), and femoral nerve (40 mm Hg).

More recently, Bomsztyk & Calalb developed a liquid membrane microelectrode for the simultaneous determination of pH and PCO$_2$ in tissue and body fluids (10). This electrode employed a hydrogen ion–selective liquid membrane for simultaneous determination of pH and PCO$_2$. In these studies they measured a PCO$_2$ of 57 mm Hg in superficial proximal tubule, while the PCO$_2$ in an adjacent peritubular capillary was 56 mm Hg (Table 1). Therefore, this study confirmed values for CO$_2$ tension in superficial proximal convoluted tubule in the range reported by Sohtell (50), DuBose et al ( 27), and Maddox et al (43). Furthermore, since no significant difference for CO$_2$ tension was detected between the proximal tubule and adjacent peritubular capillaries, this study appears to be most compatible with studies from our laboratory (26, 27).

Recent preliminary studies by deMello Aires et al (16) have employed a PCO$_2$ microelectrode using either antimony or an ion exchange resin as a pH sensor that differed from all previous electrodes since the enzyme carbonic anhydrase was added to the reference solution to "facilitate CO$_2$ equilibria." Employing this method to measure PCO$_2$ in the proximal tubule, peritubular capillary, and renal vein they failed to demonstrate an elevated CO$_2$ tension in the renal cortex.

In summary, therefore, the published results of five separate laboratories have demonstrated values for CO$_2$ tension within tubular and vascular structures of the rat and rabbit renal cortex that are elevated significantly above systemic arterial blood PCO$_2$. The findings of DuBose (23–27), Gennari et al (30, 31), Maddox et al (43), Hogg et al (34), and Bomsztyk & Calalb (10) are all compatible with a high, rather than a low, CO$_2$ permeability in the proximal tubule. The permeability of the renal epithelium to CO$_2$, both in vivo and in vitro, has been estimated by several investigators independently. Schwartz et al (49) reported a high CO$_2$ permeability in proximal tubules perfused in vitro equal to $1.7 \times 10^{-2}$ cm s$^{-1}$. Similarly, Lucci et al (41) reported a $CO_2$ permeability in proximal convoluted tubules perfused in vivo by microelectrode techniques equal to $3.9 \times 10^{-3}$ cm s$^{-1}$. These two studies indicate that $CO_2$ is extremely permeable across the proximal tubular epithelium. Moreover, the small but statistically significant $CO_2$ gradient between the early proximal tubule and stellate vessel reported by Maddox & Gennari (30, 43) could also be sustained theoretically, in spite of the high $CO_2$ permeability reported by Lucci et al (41) and Schwartz et al (49).

# DETERMINANTS OF CORTICAL PCO$_2$

In an attempt to explain the finding (Table 1) that the $PCO_2$ along the length of the proximal convoluted tubule and in efferent arteriolar blood is significantly higher than systemic or renal vein $PCO_2$, several hypotheses have been proposed: (a) $CO_2$ is produced in the tubule lumen from the combination of filtered $HCO_3^-$ and secreted $H^+$, (b) the addition of reabsorbed $HCO_3^-$ from the cell into peritubular plasma, in an environment devoid of carbonic anhydrase (CA) activity, results in intravascular disequilibrium for the $H^+$, $HCO_3^-$, $CO_2$ system and (c) $CO_2$ is generated from cell metabolism.

## Effect of Intravascular CO$_2$ Disequilibria on Cortical PCO$_2$

The reaction and transport events that occur in blood during and after the addition of $CO_2$, shown schematically in Figure 1, are complex. Details of these phenomena are provided elsewhere (1, 8, 35, 45, 48). Electrochemical equilibrium for the $CO_2$, $HCO_3^-$, $H^+$ system in plasma and red cells, as well as for $H^+$ across the red cell membrane following addition of molecular $CO_2$, is reestablished principally by three major processes: (a) the rate of the $CO_2/H_2CO_3$ reaction in plasma, (b) the rate of $HCO_3^-/Cl^-$ exchange across the red cell membrane, and (c) the rate of red cell $CO_2$-$H_2CO_3$ reactions. This latter reaction is expected to be the fastest because of the large excess of CA activity in red cells. In the absence of CA activity available to plasma, the $CO_2$-$H_2CO_3$ reactions are rate limiting ($t_{1/2} = 8$ s) and can lead to slow adjustments in downstream blood $PCO_2$ and pH (8).

Based on the above considerations, it has been suggested that, following addition of $CO_2$ to the peritubular capillary, an intravascular disequilibrium for the $H^+$, $HCO_3^-$, $CO_2$ system could occur and lead to a higher $PCO_2$ in the initial segment of the cortical nephron than would exist downstream in the renal vein (26). In an effort to test this hypothesis, we infused CA intravenously and observed a significant decrease in $PCO_2$ in the peritubular capillary ($63.5 \pm 0.9$ to $58.2 \pm 1.2$) (23). However, the measured cortical $PCO_2$ remained significantly higher than the $PCO_2$ of systemic arterial blood. These findings suggest that there was, in fact, a deficiency of CA activity in the renal vasculature resulting in a small disequilibration for the $CO_2$, $HCO_3^-$,

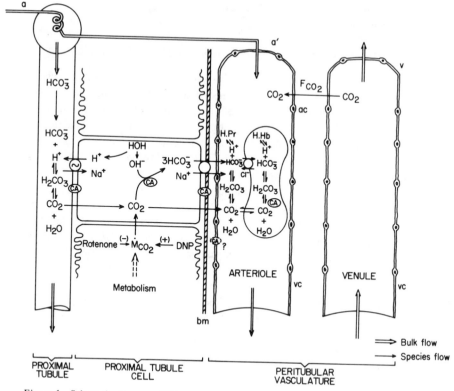

*Figure 1*   Schematic diagram of $CO_2$ generation and maintenance in a representative proximal tubule cell, associated tubule lumen, and peritubular vascular segments. The model incorporates two determinants: (*a*) metabolic $CO_2$ production ($MCO_2$), and (*b*) diffusive flux of molecular $CO_2$ ($FCO_2$) between venous (vc) and arteriolar (ac) capillary segments. a = afferent arteriole; a' = efferent arteriole; ac = preexchange arterial capillary; vc = postexchange venous capillary; v = renal cortical venule. The region between ac and vc in proximity to the associated tubular cell represents the vascular exchange segment. It is assumed that the postexchange vascular segment (vc → v) and the preexchange vascular segment (a' → ac) are in close anatomical and functional proximity so that $CO_2$ diffusion can occur between these segments. Also shown in the figure are the reaction and transport processes occurring in plasma and red cell during $HCO_3^-$ reabsorption. Effect of rotenone and DNP on metabolic $CO_2$ production is denoted by (−) = decrease and (+) = increase, respectively.

$H^+$ system in renal capillaries. This finding is compatible with the histochemical localization of CA in renal tubular cytoplasm and cell membranes but not in glomerular capillaries (17, 39, 40). Effros & Nioko (28), who reported that transport of $^{14}CO_2$ from renal artery to renal vein was observed to be more rapid than transport of $H^{14}CO_3^-$, provide further support for this view. Considered together, these findings suggest that even though a slight intravascular disequilibrium for $CO_2/HCO_3^-/H^+$ may be present, chemical disequilibrium alone is inadequate to explain fully the level of elevated $PCO_2$ in the renal cortex (21, 23).

## Alternative Sources of $CO_2$ Addition to Peritubular Plasma

The finding of an in situ respiratory acidosis in the peritubular capillary (pH = 7.27, $PCO_2$ = 65 mm Hg) (26) suggested that, whatever the mechanism underlying the development of elevated renal cortical $PCO_2$, it must involve addition of molecular $CO_2$ to peritubular plasma. Since luminal production of $CO_2$ is largely consumed within the cell to regenerate $H^+$ and $HCO_3^-$, this source is inadequate as a sole source for $CO_2$ addition to the peritubular vasculature. Alternatively, the $CO_2$ generated by renal metabolic processes has been suggested as another potential source of $CO_2$. However, previous estimates of the amount of $CO_2$ required to raise efferent arterial blood $PCO_2$ from 40 to 65 mm Hg (54) are significantly in excess of the estimated level of renal $CO_2$ production [0.7 mmol $L^{-1}$ renal blood flow (RBF)] (15, 54).

Recognizing the need for a plausible source for $CO_2$ generation, Bidani et al (6, 7, 9) introduced the concept of countercurrent diffusive transfer of $CO_2$ gas between peritubular vascular segments, which could result in trapping of $CO_2$ in the superficial cortex. Such a mechanism is not without precedent since shunting of heat has been reported previously between renal arterial and venous vessels and is assumed to be responsible for the slow clearance of heat from the renal cortex (47). Similarly, the lower renal blood flow obtained using [125]I-iodoantipyrene distribution (14), as compared to that observed with microspheres, suggests that shunt diffusion of [125]I-iodoantipyrene exists in the renal vasculature. The rapid initial transport of $CO_2$ (28), $O_2$ (4, 37, 38), and $H_2$ (3) through the renal circulation also supports the concept of counter-current diffusion of these highly diffusible gases. Moreover, the possibility of vascular-vascular $CO_2$ countercurrent diffusion is particularly attractive, in view of the close anatomical relationship between the renal arterial and venous circulation (36, 55). Thus shunting of highly diffusible gases (like $CO_2$) would be possible in the interlobar, arcuate, and interlobular vessels, and even more prominently between adjacent capillaries of the renal cortex.

# MODEL ANALYSIS OF DETERMINANTS OF CORTICAL $PCO_2$

In an effort to examine the quantitative role played by each of the possible mechanisms for generation and maintenance of elevated renal cortical $PCO_2$—namely (a) luminal $CO_2$ produced during $H^+$ secretion, (b) $CO_2$ production by cell metabolism, and (c) diffusive countercurrent transfer of $CO_2$ between peritubular vascular structures—we developed a mathematical model employing simple steady-state mass balances for $H^+$, $HCO_3^-$, and $CO_2$ in a compartmental description of $HCO_3^-$ reabsorption in the proximal tubule (7). A schematic outline of the above processes is displayed in Figure 1. Both metabolic $CO_2$ production ($\dot{M}CO_2$) and diffusive $CO_2$ transfer ($\dot{F}CO_2$) between venular and arteriolar vascular segments in the vicinity of a representative renal proximal tubular epithelial cell are included in the general formulation. The rate of diffusive transfer of $CO_2$ between postexchange and preexchange vascular segments per unit of renal blood flow is denoted by $\dot{F}CO_2$. Blood within each of the vascular elements is assumed to be composed of well-mixed subcompartments containing plasma (P) and red cells (E). A fixed Donnan ratio of distribution ($r$) for $HCO_3^-$, $Cl^-$, and $H^+$ is assumed across the red cell membrane. Furthermore, it is assumed that blood is in a state of internal electrochemical equilibration at all points and at all times. Significant $CO_2$ diffusion gradients ($> 1$ mm Hg) are assumed to be absent in the vicinity of the pre exchange segment arterial capillary and the post exchange arterial capillary (ac $\rightarrow$ vc), i.e. between tubular lumen, cell, and the adjacent vascular segment. Mathematical expressions are derived (7) on the basis of mass balance considerations that allow one to calculate $PCO_2$ and pH in each of the vascular compartments as well as in the lumen and cell for specified independently varied values for $\dot{M}CO_2$ and $\dot{F}CO_2$.

Values for $PCO_2$ and plasma pH of postexchange capillary blood (vc) corresponding to efferent arteriolar blood (stellate vessel) (7), were computed for a range of values for $\dot{M}CO_2$ (0–3.0 mmol $L^{-1}$ RBF) and $\dot{F}CO_2$ (0–3.0 mmol $L^{-1}$ RBF). The $PCO_2$ in the renal cortex was predicted to be as high as 84 mm Hg when both $\dot{M}CO_2$ and $\dot{F}CO_2$ were high (3.0 mmol $L^{-1}$ RBF) (Figure 2). In the complete absence of any countercurrent diffusive $CO_2$ transfer ($\dot{F}CO_2 = 0.0$), however, the model predicted a $PCO_2$ of only 49 mm Hg for $\dot{M}CO_2 = 0.7$ mmol $L^{-1}$ RBF. Conversely, in the absence of metabolic $CO_2$ production (i.e. $\dot{M}CO_2 = 0.0$), calculated renal cortical $PCO_2$ ranged from only 45 mm Hg at $\dot{F}CO_2 = 0.0$ to as high as 62 mm Hg for $\dot{F}CO_2 = 3.0$ mmol $L^{-1}$ RBF.

## Other Quantitative Analyses

In addition to our efforts to define the quantitative determinants of renal cortical $PCO_2$, Gennari also examined this problem by formulating a mathematical model of the factors affecting peritubular capillary $PCO_2$ (2, 30). Their model, based on a single nephron, consists of steady-state mass balances for the glomerulus, proximal tubule, and peritubular capillaries, as well as the equilibrium relationship for the $CO_2$, $HCO_3^-$, $H^+$ system, blood proteins, and hemoglobin buffering. Unfortunately, blood is treated as a single lumped compartment, without specific separation of plasma and red cell processes and contributions. Despite this limitation, there are several notable features in their formulation. Whereas our calculations were normalized per unit renal

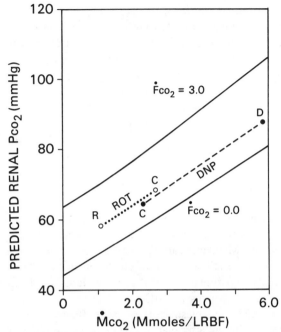

*Figure 2*  Comparison of predicted and experimentally determined values for renal cortical $PCO_2$. The predicted changes in renal cortical $PCO_2$ as a function of change in metabolic $CO_2$ production ($\dot{M}CO_2$) are shown by the solid lines, which correspond to two extremes of diffusive $CO_2$ flux ($\dot{F}CO_2$) (0.0 and 3.0 mmol $L^{-1}$ RBF). The measured values for renal cortical $PCO_2$ during control (C) and after rotenone (R) administration are depicted by open circles. The measured values for renal cortical $PCO_2$ during control (C) and DNP (D) administration are depicted by closed circles (21).

blood flow, their analysis on a single-nephron basis allows specific inclusion of the contribution and role of renal blood flow per se. Additionally, they considered two important factors not included by Bidani et al (7), namely water reabsorption in the peritubular microvasculature and the Bohr effect, which incorporates the consumption of $H^+$ within the red cell associated with $O_2$ uptake (8) in the renal cortex. As a consequence of these latter two processes, these authors (2, 30) predicted a $\Delta PCO_2$ (cortical-arterial) of 5.5 mm Hg compared to 9 mm Hg predicted from our analysis (7). Based on a normal metabolic $CO_2$ production ($\dot{M}CO_2$ = 0.7 mmol $L^{-1}$ RBF), Atherton et al (2) calculated a 60% contribution to baseline $PCO_2$ from cell metabolism and a 40% contribution from the addition of bicarbonate in excess of water to peritubular capillary blood. Other predictions by these investigators included (*a*) an inverse relationship of $PCO_2$ to renal blood flow, (*b*) and a linear relationship between $PCO_2$ and the filtered load of bicarbonate and the fractional reabsorption of bicarbonate in the proximal tubule.

## Relative Roles of Metabolic $CO_2$ Production and Vascular Diffusive $CO_2$ Transfer

In an effort to quantitate the individual contributions of metabolic $CO_2$ production and renal blood flow to the observed elevated renal cortical $PCO_2$, DuBose et al (23) measured renal cortical $PCO_2$ and whole-kidney blood flow following the administration of a series of metabolic and/or transport inhibitors. $PCO_2$ in renal cortical structures changed in parallel with renal blood flow during volume expansion and aortic constriction, a finding in contradistinction to the predictions of Gennari et al (30). Renal $O_2$ consumption decreased significantly with rotenone ($-38.1 \pm 5.6$ to $-13.6 \pm 2.7$ $\mu$mol min$^{-1}$ kg$^{-1}$) as did cortical $PCO_2$ (65 mm Hg to $57.3 \pm 1.3$ mm Hg). Conversely, cortical $PCO_2$ increased dramatically ($87.0 \pm 1.8$ mm Hg) after 2,4-dinitrophenol (DNP) administration and was associated with an increase in $O_2$ consumption ($-35.7 \pm 5.9$ to $-75.9 \pm 6.9$ $\mu$mol min$^{-1}$ kg$^{-1}$). Therefore, we employed our mathematical model to analyze these data and obtained good agreement (Figure 2) between the computed and measured values of cortical $PCO_2$ for each experimental condition (21). While changes in $PCO_2$ could be explained strictly on the basis of the associated changes in renal metabolism with rotenone and DNP, our calculations indicated that a constant nonzero value of $\dot{F}CO_2$ (1.4 mmol L$^{-1}$ RBF) was required to match the calculated and experimental $PCO_2$. Thus, these model calculations, while confirming the predominant role of metabolic $CO_2$ production in the generation and maintenance of an elevated $PCO_2$ in the renal cortex, necessitate the presence of a significant component of diffusive vascular-vascular $CO_2$ transfer.

Quantitative analyses (2, 7) of the determinants of renal cortical $PCO_2$ discussed above have provided useful insights into the generation of renal cortical $PCO_2$. These include the importance of renal metabolism and blood-buffer interactions. Simple mass balance considerations (6, 7) helped generate the hypothesis of countercurrent vascular-vascular $CO_2$ diffusion; however, its quantitative role and the delineation of the actual site of diffusive transfer remain to be clarified. Additionally, a quantitative description of intravascular disequilibrium for $H^+/HCO_3^-/CO_2$ needs to be specifically included in future analyses. Finally, despite the attractiveness and simplicity of a compartmental description, a more realistic and accurate formulation should incorporate a distributed parameter description that allows variation of blood $PCO_2$ and pH along each point of the peritubular vascular pathway, including the region of the medulla. This would allow calculation of renal vein $PCO_2$, as well as that of peritubular structures, as a function of the important determinants included previously (2, 7).

## PCO₂ IN THE INNER MEDULLA AND URINE

During control conditions, in the absence of bicarbonaturia, the $CO_2$ tension of urine is similar to the $PCO_2$ of systemic arterial blood. Furthermore, $PCO_2$ microelectrode studies demonstrated that, within the exposed papilla of the rat, the $PCO_2$ at the bend of the loop of Henle is indistinguishable from the $PCO_2$ of an adjacent vasa recta and is equal to 36 mm Hg (Table 1) (24). Thus, a large centripetal gradient exists for $PCO_2$ from renal cortex (65 mm Hg) to the renal medulla (36 mm Hg) (24) of control rats.

Microcatheterization and micropuncture studies that have measured $PCO_2$ in the medullary collecting tubule during excretion of highly alkaline urine (19, 22, 24, 32, 33) support the view that hydrogen secretion into bicarbonate-containing tubule fluid generates carbonic acid. In the absence of carbonic anhydrase, carbonic acid dehydrates at the uncatalyzed rate to produce $CO_2$, which is then trapped in the collecting system. The precise location at which $CO_2$ tension is elevated is now appreciated more fully. Microcatheterization studies demonstrated that the $PCO_2$ of the medullary collecting tubule is elevated above that of systemic arterial blood during a bicarbonate diuresis (32). Furthermore, the $PCO_2$ increased significantly along the length of the medullary collecting tubule (32, 33). Direct micropuncture of the surgically exposed renal papilla of the mutant Munich-Wistar rat demonstrated that the $PCO_2$ in the papillary collecting tubule was elevated significantly above arterial blood in this condition (19). Furthermore, a significant acid disequilibrium pH was demonstrated at both the base and tip of the papillary collecting duct in conjunction with the elevated $PCO_2$ in situ (19). When carbonic anhydrase was infused, the disequilibrium pH was obliterated completely (19) and $PCO_2$ fell dramatically (19, 32). These findings indicated that delayed dehydration of carbonic acid was an important factor in the generation of the elevated $CO_2$ tension in the collecting tubule during excretion of highly alkaline urine. While the $PCO_2$ in the papillary collecting duct during bicarbonate loading was markedly elevated with respect to systemic arterial blood, this value did not differ from the $PCO_2$ in the adjacent vasa recta. Thus, this observation emphasizes the view that the $CO_2$ was generated within the renal medulla, and that $CO_2$ could be captured within the medullary countercurrent system (19).

The demonstration of an acid disequilibrium pH in the papillary collecting duct, in association with an elevated but equal $CO_2$ tension in the collecting duct and vasa recta (19), suggested that hydrogen ion secretion was the major determinant of carbonic acid formation, and thus, the marked difference between urine and blood PCO$_2$ during excretion of an alkaline urine. Other possible mechanisms that might produce an acid disequilibrium pH have been considered and reviewed in detail recently (5).

Further validation of the urinary PCO$_2$ as a qualitative index of hydrogen ion secretion by the distal nephron has been obtained from in vivo micropuncture studies in which PCO$_2$ was determined in the papillary collecting duct of rats with experimental distal renal tubular acidosis (22). In these studies, PCO$_2$ at the base and tip of the papillary collecting duct was consistently lower after lithium, amiloride, or unilateral ureteral obstruction during bicarbonate loading. Furthermore, the disequilibrium pH, characteristically found in the same segment during a bicarbonate diuresis in control animals, was absent in each of these experimental models of distal renal tubular acidosis (22). Thus, the ability of the papillary collecting tubule to elevate CO$_2$ tension by H$^+$ secretion during an alkaline diuresis is impaired significantly in voltage-dependent and secretory models of distal renal tubular acidosis.

*Literature Cited*

1. Alpern, R. J., Warnock, D. G., Rector, F. C. Jr. 1986. Renal acidification mechanisms. In *The Kidney,* ed. B. Brenner, F. Rector, Jr., pp. 206–49. Philadelphia: Saunders. 3rd ed.
2. Atherton, L. J. Deen, W. M., Maddox, D. A., Gennari, F. J. 1984. Analysis of the factors influencing peritubular PCO$_2$ in the rat. *Am. J. Physiol.* 247(16):F61–72
3. Aukland, K., Bower, B. F., Berliner, R. W. 1964. Measurement of local blood flow with hydrogen gas. *Clin. Res.* 14: 164–87
4. Baumgärtl, H., Leichtweiss, H. P., Lübbers, D. W., Weis, C., Huland, H. 1972. The oxygen supply of the dog kidney: measurement of intrarenal PO$_2$. *Microvasc. Res.* 4:247–57
5. Berliner, R. W. 1985. Carbon dioxide tension of alkaline urine. In *The Kidney: Physiology and Pathophysiolgy,* ed. D. W. Seldin, G. Giebisch, pp. 1527–37. New York: Raven
6. Bidani, A., Crandall, E. D., DuBose, T. D. Jr. 1982. Mechanism for generation and maintenance of elevated renal cortical CO$_2$ tensions. *Physiologist* 25:296 (Abstr.)
7. Bidani, A., Crandall, E. D., DuBose, T. D. Jr. 1984. Analysis of the determinants of renal cortical PCO$_2$. *Am. J. Physiol.* 247(16):F466–74

8. Bidani, A., Crandall, E. D., Forster, R. E. 1978. Analysis of postcapillary pH changes in blood in vivo after gas exchange. *J. Appl. Physiol.* 4:770–81
9. Bidani, A., Lucci, M. S., Crandall, E. D., DuBose, T. D. Jr. 1982. Role of metabolic CO$_2$ production and diffusive gas transfer in generation of elevated renal cortical PCO$_2$. *Am. Soc. Nephrol.* 15:137A (Abstr.)
10. Bomsztyk, K., Calalb, M. B. 1986. A new microelectrode method for simultaneous measurement of pH and PCO$_2$. *Am. J. Physiol.* 251(20):F933–37
11. Brodsky, W. A., Schilb, T. P. 1974. The means of distinguishing between hydrogen secretion and bicarbonate reabsorption: theory and applications to the reptilian bladder and mammalian kidney. *Curr. Top. Membr. Transp.* 5:161–224
12. Caflisch, C. R., Carter, N. W. 1974. A micro PCO$_2$ electrode. *Anal. Biochem.* 60:252–57
13. Caflisch, C. R., Pucacco, L. R., Carter, N. W. 1978. The manufacture and utilization of antimony pH electrodes. *Kidney Int.* 14:12–27
14. Clausen, G., Hope, A., Kirkebo, A., Tyssebotin, I., Aukland, K. 1979. Distribution of blood flow in the dog kidney. Saturation rate for inert diffusible tracers, $^{125}$I-iodoantipyrene and titrated

water, versus uptake of microspheres under control conditions. *Acta Physiol. Scand.* 107:69–81

15. Cohen, J. J., Kamm, D. E. 1981. Renal metabolism: relation to renal function. In *The Kidney*, ed. B. M. Brenner, F. C. Rector, Jr., pp. 144–248. Philadelphia: Saunders

16. deMello Aires, M., Lopes, M. J., Malnic, G. 1986. Comparison of renal cortical and venous $PCO_2$ in the rat. *Proc. Int. Union of Physiol. Sci.* 16:281 (Abstr.). Vancouver, B.C.: IUPS

17. Dobyan, D. C., Bulger, R. E. 1982. Renal carbonic anhydrase. *Am. J. Physiol.* 243(12):F311–24

18. Dobyan, D. C., Magill, L. S., Friedman, P. A., Hebert, S. C., Bulger, R. E. 1982. Carbonic anhydrase histochemistry in rabbit and mouse kidneys. *Anat. Rec.* 204:185–97

19. DuBose, T. D. Jr. 1982. Hydrogen ion secretion by the collecting duct as a determinant of the urine to blood $PCO_2$ gradient in alkaline urine. *J. Clin. Invest.* 69:145–56

20. DuBose, T. D. Jr. 1983. Application of the disequilibrium pH method to investigate the mechanism of urinary acidification. *Am. J. Physiol.* 245(14): F535–44

21. DuBose, T. D. Jr., Bidani, A. 1985. Determinants of $CO_2$ generation and maintenance in the renal cortex: Role of metabolic $CO_2$ production and diffusive $CO_2$ transfer. *Miner. Electrolyte Metab.* 11:223–29

22. DuBose, T. D. Jr., Caflisch, C. R. 1985. Validation of the difference in urine and blood carbon dioxide tension during bicarbonate loading as an index of distal nephron acidification in experimental models of distal renal tubular acidosis. *J. Clin. Invest.* 75:1116–23

23. DuBose, T. D. Jr., Caflisch, C. R., Bidani, A. 1984. Role of metabolic $CO_2$ production in the generation of elevated renal cortical $PCO_2$. *Am. J. Physiol.* 246 (15):F592–99

24. DuBose, T. D. Jr., Lucci, M. S., Hogg, R. J., Pucacco, L. R., Kokko. J. P., et al. 1983. Comparision of acidification parameters in superficial and deep nephrons of the rat. *Am. J. Physiol.* 244(13): F497–503

25. DuBose, T. D. Jr., Pucacco, L. R., Carter, N. W. 1981. Determination of disequilibrium pH in the rat kidney in vivo: evidence for hydrogen secretion. *Am. J. Physiol.* 240(9):F138–46

26. DuBose, T. D. Jr., Pucacco. L. R., Luc-

ci, M. S., Carter, N. W. 1979. Micropuncture determinations of pH, $PCO_2$, and total $CO_2$ concentrations in accessible structures of the rat renal cortex. *J. Clin. Invest.* 64:476–82

27. DuBose, T. D. Jr., Pucacco, L. R., Seldin, D. W., Carter, N. W., Kokko, J. P. 1978. Direct determination of $PCO_2$ in the rat renal cortex. *J. Clin. Invest.* 62:338–48

28. Effros, R. M., Nioka, S. 1983. Deficiency of carbonic anhydrase in the vasculature of rabbit kidneys. *J. Clin. Invest.* 71:1418–30

29. Eveloff, J. E., Swenson, E. R., Maren, T. H. 1979. Carbonic anhydrase activity of brush border and plasma membranes prepared from rat kidney cortex. *Biochem. Pharmacol.* 28:1434–37

30. Gennari, F. J., Maddox, D. A., Atherton, L. J., Deen, W. M. 1984. Determinants of capillary $PCO_2$ in the rat renal cortex. In *$H^+$ Transport in Epithelia*, ed. J. G. Fork, D. G. Warnock, F. C. Rector, Jr. pp. 451–58. New York: Wiley

31. Gennari, F. J., Caflisch, C. R., Johns, C., Maddox, D. A., Cohen, J. J. 1982. $PCO_2$ measurements in surface proximal tubules and peritubular capillaries of the rat kidney. *Am. J. Physiol.* 242(11): F78–85

32. Graber, M. L., Bengele, H. H., Alexander, E. A. 1982. Elevated urinary $PCO_2$ in the rat: An intrarenal event. *Kidney Int.* 21:795–99

33. Graber, M. L., Bengele, H. H., Schwartz, J. H., Alexander, E. A. 1981. pH and $PCO_2$ profiles of the rat inner medullary collecting duct. *Am. J. Physiol.* 241(10):F659–68

34. Hogg, R. J., Pucacco, L. R., Carter, N. W., Laptook, A. R., Kokko, J. P. 1984. In situ $PCO_2$ in the renal cortex, liver, muscle, and brain of the New Zealand white rabbit. *Am. J. Physiol.* 247(16): F491–98

35. Kleinman, J. G., Brown, W. W., Ware, R. A., Schwartz, J. H. 1980. Cell pH and acid transport in renal cortical tissue. *Am. J. Physiol.* 239(8):F440–44

36. Kriz, W., Barrett, P. S. 1976. The renal vasculature: anatomical-functional aspects. In *Kidney and Urinary Tract Physiology, I*, ed. K. Thurau, 2:1–21. Baltimore: University Park

37. Leichtweiss, H., Lübbers, D. W., Weiss, C., Baumgärth, H., Reschke, W. 1969. The oxygen supply of the rat kidney: measurement of intrarenal $PO_2$. *Pfluegers Arch.* 309:328–32

38. Levy, M. N., Sauceda, G. 1959. Diffusion of oxygen from arterial to venous segments of renal capillaries. *Am. J. Physiol.* 196:1336–39

39. Lonnerholm, G. 1973. Histochemical demonstration of carbonic anhydrase activity in the human kidney. *Acta Physiol. Scand.* 88:455–68

40. Lonnerholm, G., Ridderstrale, Y. 1980. Intracellular distribution of carbonic anhydrase in the rat kidney. *Kidney Int.* 17:162–74

41. Lucci, M. S., Pucacco, L. R., Carter, N. W., DuBose, T. D. Jr. 1982. Direct evaluation of the permeability of the rat proximal convoluted tubule to CO$_2$. *Am. J. Physiol.* 242(11):F470–76

42. Lucci, M. S., Tinker, J. P., Weiner, I. M., DuBose, T. D. Jr. 1983. Function of proximal tubule carbonic anhydrase defined by selective inhibition. *Am. J. Physiol.* 245(14):F443–49

43. Maddox, D. A., Atherton, L. J., Deen, W. M., Gennari, F. J. 1984. Proximal HCO$_3^-$ reabsorption and the determinants of tubular and capillary PCO$_2$ in the rat. *Am. J. Physiol.* 247(16):F73–81

44. Pucacco, L. R., Carter, N. W. 1978. An improved PCO$_2$ microelectrode. *Anal. Biochem.* 90:427–34

45. Rector, F. C. Jr. 1983. Sodium, bicarbonate, and chloride absorption by the proximal tubule. *Am. J. Physiol.* 244 (13):F461–71

46. Rector, F. C., Carter, N. W., Seldin, D. W. 1965. The mechanism of bicarbonate reabsorption in the proximal and distal tubule of the kidney. *J. Clin. Invest.* 44:278–90

47. Röed, A., Aukland, K. 1969. Countercurrent exchange of heat in the dog kidney. *Circ. Res.* 25:617–25

48. Schwartz, G. J., Alawqati, Q. 1985. Carbon dioxide causes exocytosis of vesicles containing H$^+$ pumps in isolated perfused proximal and collecting tubules. *J. Clin. Invest.* 75:1638–44

49. Schwartz, G. J., Weinstein, A. M., Stelle, R. E., Stephenson, J. L., Burg, M. B. 1981. Carbon dioxide permeability of rabbit proximal convoluted tubules. *Am. J. Physiol.* 240:F231–44

50. Sohtell, M. 1979. CO$_2$ along the proximal tubules in rat kidney. *Acta Physiol. Scand.* 105:146–55

51. Sohtell, M., Karlmark, B. 1976. In vivo micropuncture PCO$_2$ measurements. *Pfluegers Arch.* 363:179–80

52. Vieira, F. A., Malnic, G. 1968. Hydrogen ion secretion by rat renal cortical tubules as studied by an antimony electrode. *Am. J. Physiol.* 214:710–18

53. Wahlstrand, T., Wistrand, P. J. 1980. Carbonic anhydrase C in human renal medulla. *Uppsala J. Med. Sci.* 85:7–17

54. Warnock, D. G., Rector, F. C. Jr. 1981. Renal acidification mechanisms. In *The Kidney*, ed. B. M. Brenner, F. C. Rector, Jr., pp. 440–94. Philadelphia: Saunders

55. Weinstein, S. W., Szyjewicz, J. 1978. Superficial nephron-tubular vascular relationships in the rat kidney. *Am. J. Physiol.* 234(3):F207–14

56. Wistrand, P. J. 1980. Human renal cyoplasmic carbonic anhydrase. Tissue levels and kinetic properties under near physiological conditions. *Acta Physiol. Scand.* 109:239–48

*Ann. Rev. Physiol. 1988. 50:669–94*

# VELOCITY OF $CO_2$ EXCHANGE IN MUSCLE AND LIVER

*Gerolf Gros*

Zentrum Physiologie, Medizinische Hochschule Hannover, Konstanty-Gutschow-Str. 8, 3000 Hannover 61, West Germany

*Susanna J. Dodgson*

Department of Physiology, University of Pennsylvania, Philadelphia, Pennsylvania 19104

## A. MUSCLE

Until about ten years ago it had been generally believed (82, 108) that carbonic anhydrase is not present in muscle tissue. Although it is acknowledged that exercising skeletal muscle is an organ with one of the highest rates of $CO_2$ production and tissue $P_{CO_2}$, it was questioned whether fast kinetics of the $CO_2$ reactions would be useful for the elimination of $CO_2$. Roughton (108) argued that carbonic anhydrase in such a tissue would be "an enemy to the organism rather than a friend" because it would favour the conversion of $CO_2$, which diffuses quickly and permeates cell membranes easily (41), to $HCO_3^-$, a form of $CO_2$ whose diffusivity is somewhat smaller and whose permeability across the muscle cell membrane is extremely low (131). During the last decade not only have several forms of carbonic anhydrase been found in skeletal muscle, but it is also clear that the presence of carbonic anhydrase is in fact useful for the elimination of $CO_2$ from muscle tissue.

It has been shown by Gros et al (43) that very little carbamate is formed by the muscle proteins. The hydration-dehydration reaction thus appears to be the only reaction of $CO_2$ that is important in muscle. This review will therefore entirely concentrate on the enzyme that determines its velocity, namely carbonic anhydrase.

## The Carbonic Anhydrases Occurring in Skeletal and Cardiac Muscle

It has been shown that at least three types of carbonic anhydrase (CA) are present in striated muscles: (a) a sulfonamide-resistant isozyme, CAIII, which appears in the cytosol of red skeletal muscles (56), (b) a sulfonamide-sensitive cytosolic isozyme that seems to be identical to red cell CAII (117), and (c) a membrane-bound form that is present in the sarcolemma (21, 40) and the sarcoplasmic reticulum (9).

Geers et al (submitted for publication) studied the distribution of these three isozymes among various individual muscles of the rabbit. All muscles were thoroughly perfused to remove the red cells before being excised. In addition, the rabbits' circulating red cells had been labelled with $K^{14}CNO$ before the perfusion began. Thus the presence of residual red cells in the muscles at the end of the perfusion could be quantitated, which allowed them to apply (minor) corrections to the CA activities observed in the perfused muscles. The latter were homogenized and centrifuged at 100,000 g. Using Maren's (81) micromethod, total CA activity and, after addition of $10^{-5}$ M acetazolamide (which inhibits all sulfonamide-sensitive enzymes but does not affect the sulfonamide-resistant isozyme), sulfonamide-resistant carbonic anhydrase (CAIII) activity were determined; by subtraction the activity of the sulfonamide-sensitive enzyme (CAII) was obtained. The membrane-bound CA of the various muscles was studied by first washing the homogenate pellet repeatedly in saline, then extracting the membrane proteins with Triton X-100 and assessing CA activity in the supernatants of the Triton extracts.

Table 1 shows the results obtained in this manner. In heart muscle Geers et al found, in agreement with previous studies (13, 48, 56, 92), no cytosolic CA. However, a high CA activity could be extracted from the membrane fractions. Among the various skeletal muscles, CAII is absent or low in red (i.e. predominantly slow-oxidative) muscles (soleus, vastus intermedius, semimembranosus proprius) and high in white (i.e. fast-glycolytic and fast-oxidative-glycolytic) muscles such as tibialis anterior, extensor digitorum longus and gastrocnemius. In agreement with histochemical results (see below) CAIII shows a reverse pattern: it is high in red and low in white muscles. Heart muscle, which like red skeletal muscle is rich in myoglobin and possesses a high oxidative capacity, constitutes a notable exception to this pattern. Table 1 shows that the membrane-bound Triton-extractable CA is present in all skeletal muscles to a similar degree and is 3–8 times higher in heart muscle. If the Triton-extractable enzyme activity is related to whole muscle tissue, it is apparent that its contribution to overall muscle CA activity is relatively low (15–30 U in the case of cardiac muscle). Geers et al also found that the inhibition constant ($K_I$) of the membrane-bound enzyme of muscle towards acetazolamide is about $8 \cdot 10^{-8}$ M, significantly higher than

**Table 1**  Carbonic anhydrase activities in homogenate supernatant and particulate fraction of various striated rabbit muscles[a]

| Muscle | Sulfonamide-sensitive CA activity in supernatant (U) | Sulfonamide-resistant CA activity in supernatant (U) | CA activity in Triton extract of homogenate pellet (U · ml mg$^{-1}$ protein) |
|---|---|---|---|
| Heart | 0 | 0 | 17.5 |
| Soleus | 0 | 400 | 2.1 |
| Vastus intermedius & semimembranosus proprius | 50 | 360 | 2.5 |
| Tibialis anterior | 390 | 8 | 2.8 |
| Extensor digitorum longus | 250 | 16 | — |
| Gastrocnemius (white) | 290 | — | 4.1 |
| Gastrocnemius intermedius | 170 | — | 3.1 |
| Masseter | — | 0 | 6.7 |

[a]Sulfonamide-resistant activity was determined in the presence of $2 \cdot 10^{-6}$ to $10^{-5}$ M acetazolamide; sulfonamide-sensitive activity was obtained as the difference between total and sulfonamide-resistant activity. 1 U indicates the enzyme concentration necessary to cut the reaction time of CO$_2$ hydration under the conditions of Maren's (81) assay down to one half. Data from C. Geers at al (manuscript submitted).

the $K_I$ for cytosolic CAII. Thus this enzyme, although sulfonamide-sensitive, does not appear to be functionally identical to CAII.

We conclude that three types of carbonic anhydrases, CAII, CAIII and a membrane-bound form, have been demonstrated in striated muscles through biochemical methods.

## Cytoplasmic Carbonic Anhydrase III

The presence of this isozyme in skeletal muscle was not detected until the reports of Holmes (56) and Koester et al (70). It was later shown (11) that this isozyme is identical to the CAIII found in the liver of adult male rats (36, 68, 85, 99). Skeletal muscle CAIII of several species has been shown to have a molecular weight of approximately 30,000, one Zn per molecule, a considerably lower specific hydratase activity than the isozymes CAI and CAII, and $K_I$ values towards sulfonamides that are several orders of magnitude greater than those of CAI and CAII (14, 16, 33, 70, 102, 103). In addition to its activity as a CO$_2$ hydratase, CAIII has been shown to act as an esterase similar to CAI and CAII, and to possess p-nitrophenyl phosphatase activity (69, 94). The amino acid composition of CAIII is known for the horse, ox, pig, rabbit, cat, and man (14, 102, 103, 113, 121, 129). The complete sequence of muscle CAIII for cow and horse has been determined (121, 129).

LOCALIZATION OF CAIII   There is almost general agreement that in human, as well as in rat muscle, CAIII is homogeneously distributed in the cytoplasm of type I (slow-oxidative) fibers and is absent in all other skeletal muscle fiber types. This has been demonstrated by immunocytochemical techniques using antibodies against CAIII in conjunction with standard fiber typing procedures (60, 116, 124, 125) and by the Hansson technique by Riley et al (105). No other species have been studied, but this pattern very likely holds for other mammals as well. This is illustrated for the rabbit in Table 1, which shows that the muscles soleus, semimembranosus proprius, and vastus intermedius, which are almost exclusively composed of type I fibers, have a high activity of CAIII, whereas the muscles tibialis anterior, extensor digitorum longus, and masseter, which have very few or no type I fibers (1, 3, 77), exhibit a very low CAIII activity.

Muscle CAIII activity has been demonstrated in the several mammalian species mentioned above and also in the chicken (120). In the red muscle soleus of the rat, CAIII constitutes about 20% of the soluble proteins (11). In species other than rat, liver CAIII occurs in highly variable levels and is absent in humans (14). Aside from skeletal muscle and liver, all other organs studied (such as lung, heart, brain, kidney, and red cells) contain only trace amounts of CAIII (14, 115).

THE HYDRATASE ACTIVITY OF CAIII   Koester et al (70) showed that the specific hydratase activity of CAIII is low; they reported 3% of the specific activity of CAII and 20% of that of CAI for rabbit CAIII. The corresponding figures for human CAIII are 5% and 30%, respectively (16). Jeffery & Carter (59), comparing the CAIII of different species, observed similar specific hydratase activities for human, baboon, pig, and sheep CAIII (15, 13.4, 13.8, and 22 U mg$^{-1}$, respectively).

The kinetic parameters governing the hydratase activity of CAIII have been estimated for several species; the results are summarized in Table 2. While there is rough agreement between the turnover numbers ($k_{cat}$) obtained by various authors for different species, very large discrepancies between the Michaelis constants for $CO_2$ hydration ($K_M$) are apparent. Accordingly it seems well established that $k_{cat}$ of CAIII is < 1% of that of CAII, but it is unclear whether $K_M$ of CAIII is in the same range as for CAI and CAII or considerably larger. It will be noted that a $K_M$ > 35 mM exceeds the maximal $CO_2$ concentration that occurs in water at 25°C and atmospheric pressure, and its determination is therefore subject to considerable experimental uncertainty. It may also be noted that a CA with a $K_M$ of 40–80 mM would seem ill-adapted to a physiological environment where a $CO_2$ concentration of 1 mM prevails. Further work is required to clarify this property of CAIII.

The molecular cause of the low catalytic efficiency of CAIII as a $CO_2$ hydratase, when compared to CAII, has been discussed by Kararli & Silver-

**Table 2**  Kinetic parameters of carbonic anhydrase III

| Source | Temperature (C°) | $k_{cat}$[a] (s$^{-1}$) | $K_M$[a] (mM) | Author |
|---|---|---|---|---|
| Cat muscle | 1 | 1000 | 40 | Sanyal et al (113) |
|  | 25 | 4200 | 37 | Sanyal et al (113) |
|  | 25 | 2200 | 18 | Kararli & Silverman (65) |
| Pig muscle | 0 | 6000 | 83 | Pullan & Noltmann (134) |
| Rabbit muscle | 0 | 2400 | 95 | Pullan & Noltmann (134) |
| Ox muscle | 25 | 3300 | 9 | Engberg et al (33) |
| Male rat liver | 25 | 2600 | 5 | Sanyal (111a) |

[a]$k_{cat}$, the turnover number of the enzyme, and $K_M$, the Michaelis constant, were estimated from measurements of the rate of CO$_2$ hydration at various initial CO$_2$ concentrations. For comparison, $k_{cat}$ and $K_M$ are 52,000 s$^{-1}$ and 4.4 mM for human CAI, and 860,000 s$^{-1}$ and 12.7 mM for human CAII at 25°C (113).

man (65). They present evidence indicating that in both enzymes the rate-limiting step may be a process not directly involved in the interconversion of CO$_2$ and HCO$_3^-$ (probably a transfer of protons from the Zinc-bound H$_2$O to the solvent water). In CAII this transfer is believed to be facilitated by a "proton shuttle residue", such as His 64, in the neighborhood of the zinc. If such a H$^+$-accepting residue close to the active site is lacking in CAIII, protons would be expected to be transferred directly from Zn to the solvent water with a rate constant similar to that actually observed for CO$_2$ hydration of CAIII. Two other properties that distinguish CAIII from CAII are the independence of $k_{cat}$ from pH (between pH 6 and 8) and from the buffer concentration. Kararli and Silverman (65) suggest that independence from pH is due to an apparent pK of the active site of < 6 (the pK's for CAI and CAII are between 7 and 8), and they propose that independence from buffer concentration may reflect an active site cleft in CAIII that is too narrow to allow access of buffers.

The inhibition by sulfonamides and anions has been studied for the CAIII from several species (Table 3). The most obvious property of all CAIII's is their high resistance towards sulfonamides. It is apparent from Table 3 that the $K_I$'s of all sulfonamides for CAIII are greater by several orders of magnitude than they are for CAII and CAI. There is some ambiguity about the inhibitory mechanism of sulfonamides and anions; whereas Pullan & Noltmann (100) have obtained kinetic evidence for a simultaneous binding of CNO$^-$ and acetazolamide by pig CAIII, Kararli & Silverman (65) have observed competition between $CNO^-$ and chlorzolamide as well as between $N_3^-$ and chlorzolamide. For physiological studies of CAIII it is of interest to note that the most potent CAIII inhibitor among the sulfonamides is chlorzolamide, among the anions, $S^{2-}$ and $CNO^-$. The latter even offers, at least theoretically, the possibility of inhibiting CAIII without affecting CAII activity.

THE ESTERASE ACTIVITY OF CAIII    It was observed by Koester et al (70) that rabbit CAIII is a p-nitrophenyl acetate esterase. CAIII shares this property with CAI and CAII but exhibits a specific activity several orders of magnitude lower than that of isozyme I and II. This property was subsequently confirmed for the CAIII from human, pig, bovine, and chicken muscle (16, 17, 33). It appears that the hydratase and esterase activities of CAIII do not share the same catalytic site. Tu et al (123) have shown that bovine CAIII (a) exhibits a pH profile for the esterase activity different from that of the hydratase, (b) does not lose its esterase activity upon removal of Zn, and (c) maintains its esterase activity at concentrations of $N_3^-$, $CNO^-$, methazolamide, and chlorzolamide that inhibit its hydratase activity. As for the other isozymes, no physiological role for the esterase activity of CAIII is known.

THE PHOSPHATASE ACTIVITY OF CAIII    Koester et al (69) showed that rabbit muscle CAIII is a p-nitrophenyl phosphatase whereas CAI and CAII are

**Table 3**  Inhibition constants for sulfonamides and anions[a]

| Inhibitor | Cat muscle CAIII | Pig muscle CAIII | Ox muscle CAIII | Male rat liver CAIII | Human CAII | Human CAI |
|---|---|---|---|---|---|---|
| Acetazolamide | 306[b] | 44[b] | 90[c] | 100[b] | 0.01[b] | 0.20[b] |
| Methazolamide | 96[b] | — | — | 15[b] | 0.01[b] | 0.01[b] |
| Ethoxzolamide | 54[b] | — | — | 150[b] | 0.002[b] | 0.002[b] |
| Chlorzolamide | 2.0[c]/0.3[b] | — | — | 0.8[b] | 0.0004[b] | 0.001[b] |
| Benzolamide | 3.1[b] | — | — | 4.0[b] | 0.004[b] | 0.002[b] |
| Sulfanilamide | >5,000[b] | — | — | >1,000[b] | 2.0[b] | 50[b] |
| $Na_2S$ | — | — | <0.2[c] | — | — | — |
| $CNO^-$ | 2.9[c]/0.5[b] | 3[b] | 1.4[c] | 0.70[b] | 20[c] | 0.70[c] |
| $CN^-$ | 2.3[b] | — | 14[c] | — | 17[c] | 0.38[c] |
| $N_3^-$ | 20[c]/14[b] | — | 5[c] | — | — | — |
| $I^-$ | 1,100[b] | — | 2,300[c] | 1,000[b] | 26,000[c] | 300[c] |
| $Cl^-$ | 5,900[b] | — | 18,000[c] | 11,000[b] | 200,000[c] | 6,000[c] |

[a] Data for cat muscle CAIII from Sanyal et al (113) and Kararli & Silverman (65), for pig CAIII from Pullan and Noltmann (134), and all other data from Sanyal et al (113). All data in μM.
[b] Temperature: 0°C
[c] Temperature: 25°C

devoid of this activity. They demonstrated the same property for CAIII from cow and pig. Nishita and Deutsch (94) observed a phosphatase activity of equine CAIII (but also found such activity for equine CAI and CAII). There is evidence that CAIII has a catalytic site for phosphatase activity not identical with either the hydratase or the esterase active sites: (a) Phosphate, arsenate, molybdate, and fluoride all inhibit the phosphatase but not the esterase and hydratase activity (69), (b) the phosphatase has a pH optimum < 5.3 and thus a pH profile different from the esterase activity (69), (c) acetazolamide is a much weaker inhibitor of phosphatase than of hydratase activity (69), and (d) modification of one arginine residue of the CAIII molecule results in a complete loss of its phosphatase activity without affecting its hydratase and esterase activities (101). The $K_I$ of the phosphatase activity of CAIII for phosphate, 1.2 mM (69), is at the lower end of the range of phosphate concentrations occurring in the sarcoplasm. Thus, this activity will be markedly reduced as intracellular phosphate rises during contractile activity. It is tempting, therefore, to speculate about a physiological role of the phosphatase activity of CAIII in slow red muscle fibers that is attenuated during muscular work, but no physiological substrate is known.

CAIII DURING DEVELOPMENT    Carter et al (14) studied CAIII levels in muscles of human fetuses and infants. Using an immunological technique, CAIII was just detectable in the 11-week fetus, 10% of the adult level at 15 weeks, 20% at midterm, and about 50% in the muscles of the newborn. Riley et al (105) studied postnatal CAIII activity changes in the soleus of male and female rats. During puberty, day 50–100, they observed a rapid increase in CAIII activity in the soleus by a factor of three; after puberty, activity remained approximately constant up to 400 days.

NEURONAL CONTROL OF CAIII    While rat liver CAIII is low in females and high in males (CAII showing the reverse pattern) and apparently is under the control of growth hormone (15, 61, 62), there is no difference in muscle CAIII levels between males and females (115). That muscle CAIII is controlled by the activity of the innervating nerve has recently been demonstrated by Wistrand et al (130) and by D. Krüger & G. Gros (unpublished results). Wistrand et al used immunofluorescence microscopy to study the effect of denervation on the CAIII levels in the fibers of rat soleus, tibialis anterior, and extensor digitorum longus muscles. After 16 days' denervation, CAIII was markedly increased in all fibers of the three muscles, especially in the type II fibers that normally lack CAIII. Krüger & Gros performed long-term electrical stimulation of the nerve that innervates the extensor digitorum longus (EDL) and the tibialis anterior (TA) of the rabbit and observed the time course and extent of CAIII concentration change in these white muscles that normally have almost no CAIII activity (Table 1). Figure 1 shows the change in

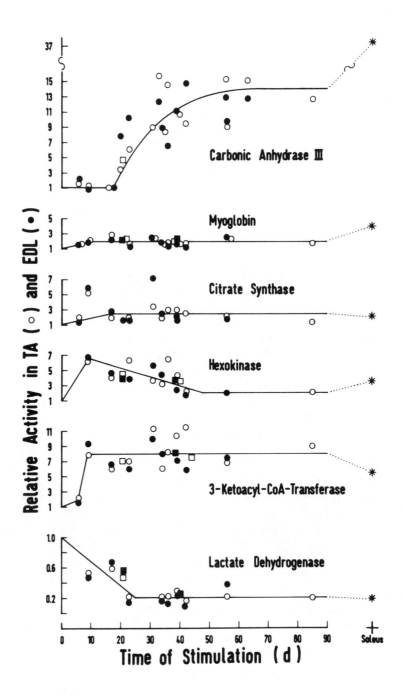

normalized activities (= activity per activity in control muscles) for CAIII and various other enzymes. Several enzymes, e.g. citrate synthase, ketoacyl-CoA-transferase, and myoglobin, begin to rise within a few days, a behavior that is well established (96). It is apparent from Figure 1 that CAIII increases drastically but slower than these other enzymes. During the first three weeks of continuous stimulation there is no increase in CAIII activity, although most other enzymes already reach their new activity plateaus. During the fourth week CAIII then rises to 13-fold of its control level. These differences in time course may indicate that the enzymes of oxidative metabolism and CAIII are switched on by different mechanisms.

PHYSIOLOGICAL ROLE OF CAIII    It is clear from the above that we know nothing about a physiological role of the phosphatase and esterase activities of CAIII. It has also often been questioned whether CAIII plays a role as a CO$_2$ hydratase because of its extremely low specific CA activity (Table 2). Table 1 shows that this is not justified: CAIII accelerates the rate of CO$_2$ hydration in the rabbit soleus by a factor of 400, i.e. it cuts down the half-time of CO$_2$ hydration in slow-oxidative fibers from 10 s to 23 ms (if we assume that this factor holds also for 37°C). This remarkable activity is brought about, in spite of the enzyme's low turnover number, by the high concentration of CAIII in red muscle fibers, for example 0.5 mM in rat soleus (13).

What is the physiological consequence of the CA activity exerted by CAIII? It has previously been shown that in the presence of CA activity and a sufficient concentration of mobile buffers CO$_2$ diffusion is facilitated by simultaneous HCO$_3^-$ and H$^+$ transport (44–47). The known presence of mobile buffers and CAIII would then lead one to expect a facilitation of CO$_2$ diffusion in red skeletal muscle. Indeed, Kawashiro and Scheid (67) showed that CO$_2$ diffusion is facilitated in the partially red abdominal muscle of the rat. Gros et al (42; Gros, Ganghoff & Scheid, unpublished results) have recently shown that this facilitation is due to CAIII. As shown in Figure 2, they demonstrated that (a) facilitated CO$_2$ diffusion in rat abdominal muscle can be suppressed by incubating the muscle in acetazolamide, and (b) the inhibitor concentration necessary to reduce facilitation by 50% (IC$_{50}$) indicates the involvement of the sulfonamide-resistant CAIII. In Figure 2, the

←_____

*Figure 1*   Changes in enzyme activities during chronic stimulation of tibialis anterior (TA) and extensor digitorum (EDL) muscles of the rabbit. The ordinates show relative enzyme acivities in the muscles (activity in stimulated muscle divided by activity in unstimulated control muscles). The abscissa gives the time of electrical stimulation of the peroneal nerve in days; stimulation frequency was 10 Hz, and stimulation was continuous (24 h per day). The stars on the right hand side of the figure indicate for comparison concentrations or activities, respectively, found in unstimulated soleus muscles. Data from D. Krüger & G. Gros (unpublished results).

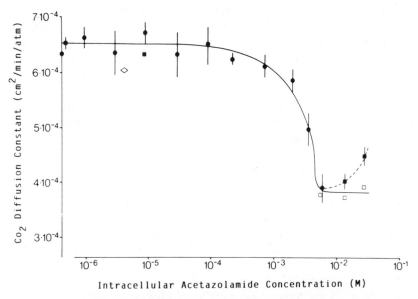

*Figure 2*  The $CO_2$ diffusion constant, $K_{CO_2}$ in rat abdominal muscle as a function of the intracellular concentration of acetazolamide. Temperature 25° C, $P_{CO_2} = 35$ torr on one side of the muscle layer, about 0 torr on the other side. $K_{CO_2}$ was calculated from quasi-steady state measurements of the flux of $^{14}CO_2$ across the abdominal muscle layer. The data points connected by a dashed line represent values that are too high because of facilitated diffusion occurring in the extracellular space due to the buffer action of the very high concentrations of acetazolamide used. The open squares and circle are corrected for this effect on the basis of the slight additional facilitated diffusion observed in layers incubated in similarly high concentrations of a membrane-impermeable buffer. Figure from Gros et al (42; with permission).

$CO_2$ diffusion constant $K_{CO_2}$ in rat abdominal muscle is plotted versus the intracellular concentration of acetazolamide in the muscle. $K_{CO_2}$ was obtained from steady state measurements of the flux of $^{14}CO_2$ across the muscle layer; at room temperature and in the absence of inhibitor, $K_{CO_2}$ averaged $6.5 \cdot 10^{-4}$ $cm^2$ $min^{-1}$ $atm^{-1}$. The intracellular concentrations of acetazolamide were obtained by incubating the muscles in solutions containing $^3H$-acetazolamide and $^{14}C$-inulin.

It is apparent from Figure 2 that $K_{CO_2}$ is unaffected by intracellular acetazolamide concentrations up to $10^{-4}$ M, begins to decrease at concentrations above $10^{-4}$ M, and reaches a minimum of $3.8 \cdot 10^{-4}$ $cm^2$ $min^{-1}$ $atm^{-1}$ at concentrations $> 5 \cdot 10^{-3}$ M. Thus, the presence of active CA increases $K_{CO_2}$ by 70%. The $IC_{50}$ of facilitated $CO_2$ diffusion is seen in Figure 2 to be $3 \cdot 10^{-3}$ M. This is 5 orders of magnitude greater than the $K_I$ of the sulfonamide-sensitive enzyme, but only 10 times the $K_I$ of CAIII (Table 3). A concentration of $10 \cdot K_I$, i.e. a 90% inhibition of the enzyme, can reasonably be expected to be necessary for a 50% reduction of facilitation (42). It was concluded therefore that CAIII is responsible for an enhancement of intracellular CO$_2$ transfer. It appears logical that an enzyme that accelerates the transport of metabolic CO$_2$ out of the muscle cell is present in type I fibers because of their high oxidative capacity, but is absent in type II fibers because of their lower oxidative capacity. It is not clear, however, why cardiac muscle, which also has a high oxidative capacity, does not possess CAIII. The view that muscle CAIII facilitates CO$_2$ transport could be in line with the observation of Swenson (119) that addition of cyanate (at concentrations that inhibit CAIII) to the blood perfusing contracting dog muscle leads to a decrease in CO$_2$ output. This observation could have another explanation as is discussed below.

Barclay (6) studied the isometric force developed by isolated, directly stimulated mouse soleus both in the absence and in the presence of the CA inhibitors acetazolamide and cyanate. He found no effect on isometric tension during exposure of the muscle to $10^{-5}$ M acetazolamide for 25 min. This was not surprising in view of the known poor permeability of acetazolamide in cell membranes. Using CNO$^-$, which is expected to be much more permeable (at a concentration of $10^{-5}$ M in the muscle bath, considered to be sufficient to inhibit CAIII), Barclay observed no change in isometric force at an ambient P$_{CO_2}$ of 35 torr. However, he observed a significant decrease in force at a P$_{CO_2}$ of 70 torr. Barclay concluded that this effect was due to inhibition of CAIII, which would be important in regulating intracellular pH, especially at high P$_{CO_2}$.

Geers & Gros (39), performing similar experiments with rat soleus and EDL and using the inhibitors CNO$^-$ and chlorzolamide, came to a different conclusion. They found that, with incubation times of several hours for chlorzolamide ($5 \cdot 10^{-4}$ M), this inhibitor and CNO$^-$ ($10^{-2}$ M) produced qualitatively the same changes in contractile parameters: a decrease in isometric force and a slowing of relaxation. Because these effects were seen in the CAIII-rich soleus as well as in the almost CAIII-free EDL, it was concluded that some isoenzyme that is present in both muscles (but not CAIII) must be responsible, very likely one of the membrane-bound forms in the sarcoplasmic reticulum or the sarcolemma (see below). Whatever the interpretation of these results, they show that CA inhibition leads to a reduction in force development and thus presumably to a decrease in oxygen consumption, which would explain the observation of Swenson (119). Much further work is required to establish which of the muscle CAs is responsible for these functional effects and what is the role of the acceleration of CO$_2$ diffusion by CAIII in muscle function. It is necessary in these experiments to control not only intracellular pH, ions, and energy-rich phosphates, but also the concentrations at which the inhibitors are actually present within the muscle cell.

## Cytosolic Carbonic Anhydrase II

Table 1 shows that white muscles of the rabbit contain a sulfonamide-sensitive CA in their cytosolic fraction at an activity that accelerates the rate of $CO_2$ hydration 200–400-fold. Siffert & Gros (117), while studying pooled white rabbit muscles, through affinity chromatography, observed that this enzyme is CAII and that CAI is absent from rabbit muscles. That a sulfonamide-sensitive CA other than the sulfonamide-resistant CAIII is present in skeletal muscle has also been shown by several histochemical studies (60, 78, 91, 105). Riley et al (105) found CAII in fast oxidative-glycolytic (FOG) fibers, axons, and capillaries of rat muscles. Jeffery et al (60) found in rat muscles CAI and CAII in the form of intracellular spots and associated with the sarcolemma. With respect to this latter finding it must be asked, however, whether this could be due to cross-reactivity of the antisera used by Jeffery et al with the sarcoplasmic reticulum and the sarcolemmal enzyme (see below). While the results obtained with the Hansson technique by Riley et al (105) suggest the cytoplasm of FOG fibers and capillary endothelia as possible sources of CAII in fast muscles, such a location is not supported by the histochemical results of Jeffery et al (immunocytochemistry) nor those of Dermietzel et al using dansylsulfonamide fluorescence (21). The difficulty in localizing this enzyme may be due to the fact that, although its activity is substantial, its concentration is expected to be low in view of its high specific activity. We have no clue at present of the physiological role of this carbonic anhydrase.

## Extracellular Carbonic Anhydrase—Sarcolemmal Carbonic Anhydrase

The extracellular CA of skeletal muscle was probably first observed—although not recognized—by Zborowska-Sluis et al (132). They found that in blood-free perfused dog hindlimbs the apparent space of distribution for $H^{14}CO_3^-$ is greatly reduced to about the size of the vascular space when acetazolamide is present in the perfusate and is much greater than the vascular space in the absence of the inhibitor. They believed this was due to the presence of an extravascular and intracellular CA that facilitates intracellular $CO_2$ diffusion and thus accelerates the uptake of $^{14}CO_2$ and $H^{14}CO_3^-$ by the tissue. Effros & Weissman (31) made essentially the same observation: they showed that a bolus of $H^{14}CO_3^-$ injected into blood-free perfusate entering the cat hindlimb is washed out from the muscle tissue faster in the presence of acetazolamide in the perfusate than in its absence. Their interpretation, however, differed from that of Zborowska-Sluis et al (132): Effros & Weissman assumed that an intravascular extraerythrocytic CA, bound to the luminal membrane of the capillary endothelial cells, as has been demonstrated for the lung, rapidly converts the injected $H^{14}CO_3^-$ into $^{14}CO_2$, which then can enter the entire intracellular water space of the tissue and cause a delayed washout of $^{14}$C from the hindlimb. O'Brasky & Crandall (95) obtained evidence for this CA in a different way. Using a pH-stop-flow technique they showed that the system H$^+$-HCO$_3^-$-CO$_2$ was near equilibrium in a CA-free perfusate leaving the rabbit hindlimb but that a pH disequilibrium developed when a CA inhibitor was added to the perfusate. Thus, the perfusate had access to a CA while it passed through the hindlimb capillary bed.

Geers et al studied the localization of this enzyme by a functional and a histochemical approach (40). Geers & Gros (38) employed the bolus technique of Effros & Weissman (31) to demonstrate that the CA detected in these experiments is located extracellularly. They showed that (a) The inhibition properties of this enzyme are different from the known cytosolic muscle enzymes CAII and CAIII, (b) the inhibitory potency of different sulfonamides is independent of their membrane permeability, and most importantly, (c) only very short times ($<<$ 1 min) are required for sulfonamides to produce a full effect on $^{14}$C-washout [whereas the uptake, for example of acetazolamide, by muscle cells has a half-time of 30 min (Gros, unpublished observation)]. In a subsequent study Geers et al (40) confirmed the extracellular localization of this enzyme by showing that the full inhibition effect on $^{14}$C-washout can be produced by Prontosil-dextran 5000 (PD 5000), a sulfonamide coupled to dextran of molecular weight 5000, which has access to the entire extracellular but not the intracellular space. In order to study whether this extracellular enzyme is located intravascularly or in the interstitium, Geers et al (40) synthesized a PD 100,000 which is expected to be confined to the vascular bed, and studied the effect of its presence in the perfusate on the washout behavior of $^{14}$C. They found that PD 100,000 does not affect $^{14}$C-washout and concluded from this that the extracellular CA of skeletal muscle is localized in the interstitium.

Since plasma is free of CA, an interstitial CA is expected to be membrane-bound. Dermietzel et al (21) and Geers et al (40) clearly demonstrated using the fluorescent CA inhibitor dansylsulfonamide that a CA is associated with the sarcolemma of rat and rabbit muscles. If the active centers of this enzyme are (at least partly) oriented towards the cell exterior, sarcolemmal CA would functionally be available in the interstitium. A sarcolemmal CA has also been observed with the Hansson technique (78, 104, 105) as well as with immunocytochemical methods (60, 91). Another possible localization of muscle extracellular CA, the luminal membrane of capillary endothelia, has been considered likely by many researchers, has been well documented for the lung (111) and has been consistently observed in skeletal muscle by workers using the Hansson histochemical method (78, 104, 105). But such an endothelial localization (a) is in contrast to the results with PD 100,000 obtained by Geers et al (40), (b) has not been observed in immunocytochemical studies (60, 91), and (c) has also not been detected with the dansylsulfonamide histochemical technique (9, 21, 40). A recent study in our laboratory on isolated sarcolemmal vesicles from rabbit muscle, enriched in $Na^+$-$K^+$-ATPase and cholesterol, confirms the presence of a sarcolemmal CA; a specific activity 10–20 times as great as previously found in sarcoplasmic reticulum was observed (P. Wetzel & G. Gros, unpublished observations).

What is the physiological role of the extracellular-sarcolemmal enzyme? The interstitial activity will result in the (partial) hydration of metabolically produced $CO_2$ right after it has left the cells. The formation of part of the plasma $HCO_3^-$ in the extracellular space (circumventing the red cell) on the basis of the studies of Forster & Crandall (34), Crandall et al (18), Hill et al (55), and Bidani et al (7) is expected to accelerate the $CO_2$ uptake by the blood and increase the amount of $CO_2$ taken up during capillary passage of blood in skeletal muscle. However, direct experimental evidence demonstrating this in resting and exercising skeletal muscle is still lacking. Another interesting, though entirely speculative, question is whether this membrane-bound enzyme could play a role in sarcolemmal ion transport processes.

## Other Sites of Carbonic Anhydrase Localization in Muscle

MITOCHONDRIAL CARBONIC ANHYDRASE    Dodgson et al (29) reported the presence of CA in the mitochondria of guinea pig skeletal muscle, albeit at much lower activity than in liver mitochondria. They found no enzyme activity in heart muscle mitochondria. Bruns et al (9) found little CA activity in a mitochondrial preparation from rabbit skeletal muscle and, on the basis of other enzyme activities, attributed this activity to a slight contamination of their preparation with sarcoplasmic reticulum vesicles.

SARCOPLASMIC RETICULUM CARBONIC ANHYDRASE    Bruns et al (9) showed that preparations of sarcoplasmic reticulum from red as well as white skeletal muscles of the rabbit possess a membrane-bound CA. Its inhibition constant for acetazolamide was similar to that of the enzyme extracted with Triton from muscle homogenate pellet (Table 1) and to that of the membrane-bound CA of the kidney (112), but different from that of human CAI and CAII. Bruns et al confirmed their finding with the dansylsulfonamide histochemical technique, which showed a pattern of intracellular staining in red and white muscles that indicated the structure stained was indeed sarcoplasmic reticulum. Jeffery et al (60) observed a similar staining pattern, although they did not relate it to sarcoplasmic reticulum. The physiological role of this CA is unknown. Bruns et al (9) speculated that it may serve to quickly produce or consume protons that cross the sarcoplasmic reticulum membrane in exchange for $Ca^{2+}$. There is considerable evidence in the literature that protons may act as counterions of $Ca^{2+}$ in the reticulum. The CA activity observed by Bruns et al led to the prediction that $CO_2$ hydration-dehydration has a half-time of 10 ms in the sarcoplasmic reticulum; this appeared sufficiently fast in relation to the kinetics of the $Ca^{2+}$ transients in striated muscle fibers. Geers & Gros (39) pointed out that their observation of a slowed muscle relaxation during CA inhibition could be interpreted in terms of a retardation of $Ca^{2+}$ reuptake into the reticulum caused by limited $H^+$ availability.

The source of the membrane-bound CA in cardiac muscle (Table 1) is not clear at present. The results of Zborowska-Sluis et al (133), however, show that a sarcolemmal-interstitial CA as it occurs in skeletal muscle is not present in cardiac muscle. It appears possible then that this enzyme is associated with heart sarcoplasmic reticulum, an interpretation that is confirmed by preliminary histochemical evidence from our laboratory (R. Dermietzel & G. Gros, unpublished observations) that shows a similar intracellular staining pattern as in skeletal muscle.

CARBONIC ANHYDRASE AT THE NEUROMUSCULAR JUNCTION    Scheid & Siffert (114) compared the effect of CA inhibitors on the isometric force developed by directly and indirectly stimulated frog gastrocnemius. After incubation (2 hr) of the muscles in saline containing the inhibitors, they found that, with indirect stimulation, isometric force had decreased to 50% in $3 \cdot 10^{-9}$ M ethoxzolamide, $10^{-4}$ M acetazolamide, or $10^{-4}$ M methazolamide. In contrast, these same inhibitor concentrations had no effect on the force developed by directly stimulated muscles. Because the inhibitors had no effect on the conduction velocity of the nerve and on the amplitude of the compound nerve action potential, Scheid & Siffert concluded that a CA must be involved somewhere in the process of neuromuscular transmission.

## B. LIVER

In 1935 F. J. W. Roughton reviewed the literature on the enzyme CA (108). Two years had passed since the isolation of this enzyme was reported simultaneously from the Universities of Cambridge and Pennsylvania (87, 118). In this review Roughton discussed studies in which traces of CA activity found in the liver were concluded to be caused by blood contamination. In a review of the CA literature 11 years later, there were still no clues of the existence of CA in the liver (20). Liver CAs remained largely undetected and undiscussed until unique properties of the mitochondrial and cytosolic CAs were discovered within the past ten years. It is noted that CA activity was reported in the liver parenchymal nucleus and microsomes (19, 85); there has been little interest in the enzymes in these organelles and it has not yet been established whether the CA activity is due to lack of purity of the preparation.

## $CO_2$—Producing Enzymes

In the 1935 state-of-the-art review of CA Roughton (108) mentioned work done with Hans Krebs: CA was used as a tool for determining whether the immediate products of urease and yeast decarboxylase were $CO_2$ or $HCO_3^-$. This work was not published in the complete form until 1948. Manometric measurements of evolved $CO_2$ pressure were made in a closed system using small concentrations of substrates and large concentrations of enzyme. $CO_2$ was thus determined to be the product of both these enzymes (76).

Mammalian liver mitochondrial enzymes with $CO_2$ as a product include pyruvate dehydrogenase, which is under strong hormonal control. Pyruvate dehydrogenase has as another product, acetyl CoA, which is an important substrate in several metabolic pathways, including the Krebs cycle. Two other enzymes are isocitrate dehydrogenase and alpha ketoglutarate dehydrogenase; these are also Krebs cycle enzymes. All three enzymes are involved in production of ATP (73).

When glucose is synthesized from lactate by intact hepatocytes prepared from fasted male rats, phosphoenolpyruvate carboxykinase (PEPCK) is the rate-controlling enzyme (106). This enzyme is possibly not the rate-controlling enzyme but is clearly extremely important in gluconeogenesis (71). Cellular localization of PEPCK is species-dependent (2). It is completely mitochondrial in rabbit, 10% only of it is mitochondrial in the rat, and 50% in guinea pig. PEPCK catalyses the reaction of oxaloacetate with guanosine triphosphate (GTP) to form phosphoenolpyruvate, guanosine diphosphate (GDP) and $CO_2$.

## $HCO_3^-$—Utilizing Enzymes

Since the discovery that the carbon in the urea molecule was derived from carbon dioxide (75), it has been known that enzymes fix carbon dioxide. By 1943 it was known that carbon dioxide was fixed during gluconeogenesis in mammalian tissues as well as by autotrophic tissues (72).

There are three types of $HCO_3^-$-requiring enzymes: the biotin-dependent carboxylases, the carbamyl phosphate synthetases, and the phosphoenol carboxylases. All three enzymes also use ATP and produce phosphate (110). Mitochondrial carbon dioxide–fixing enzymes fix it as $HCO_3^-$. In his review (110) Rubio discusses the peculiarity of this since fixation of $CO_2$ would be predicted from the chemistry of the reaction. However, enzymes have clearly evolved to accept as substrate $HCO_3^-$—presumably because at alkaline pH there is such a greater concentration of $HCO_3^-$ than $CO_2$. The Henderson-Hasselbach equation predicts that at equilibrium at any pH over 6.1 (the pK' for the $HCO_3^-$ : $CO_2$ equilibrium) there is more $HCO_3^-$ than $CO_2$; at pH 7.4 about 5% of total $CO_2$ and $HCO_3^-$ is $CO_2$.

The cytosolic biotin-dependent carboxylases include acetyl CoA carboxylase (127), which is involved in fatty acid synthesis. There is a cytosolic carbamyl phosphate synthetase, CPS II, or glutamine CPS (90) which is involved in pyrimidine synthesis.

The mitochondrial carbamyl phosphate synthetase, CPS I or NH$_3$ CPS (79) is the first enzyme in the urea cycle (63, 74, 75). CPS I and the second urea cycle enzyme, ornithine transcarbamylase, (OTC) are mitochondrial. Assay of CPS I activity commonly involves inclusion of excess substrates for OTC so that the rate of synthesis of citrulline is directly related to the activity of CPS I (98):

$$NH_4^+ + 2ATP + HCO_3^- \xrightarrow{\substack{Mg^{2+}, \text{ N-acetyl} \\ \text{glutamate}}} \text{carbamyl phosphate} + 2\ ADP + P_i$$

$$\text{carbamyl phosphate} + \text{ornithine} \longrightarrow \text{citrulline} + P_i \, .$$

The mitochondrial pyruvate carboxylase, a biotin-dependent carboxylase (4) catalyses the conversion of pyruvate to oxaloacetate. Pyruvate carboxylase is possibly the rate controlling enzyme for gluconeogenesis from precursors that enter the gluconeogenic pathway as pyruvate (71):

$$\text{pyruvate} + ATP + HCO_3^- \xrightarrow{\substack{Mg^{2+}, Mn^{2+},\ K^+, \\ \text{acetyl CoA}}} \text{oxaloacetate} + ADP + P_i \, .$$

There are alternative mitochondrial pathways for oxaloacetate production, thus pyruvate carboxylase is not obligatory for gluconeogenesis to proceed.

## Cytosolic Carbonic Anhydrase

In 1940 it was discovered that there were some sulfonamides that were very specific CA inhibitors (80). Since then these inhibitors have been widely used to elucidate the physiological functions of CAs (82, 83). The discovery that there was CA activity in the cytosol of male rat liver cells that was not inhibited by low concentrations of sulfonamides (85) led ultimately to the understanding that the muscle CAIII is the same as the male rat liver cytosolic CA (15, 56).

PROPERTIES    CAIII from male rat liver is unique among the CA isozymes in its resistance towards sulfonamides: 10,000 times greater concentrations of acetazolamide are required for inhibition of its activity than for CAI and CAII (36). It has been suggested that its function in the liver is not primarily the hydration of CO$_2$ since its turnover rate is so much lower than that of CAII.

Originally it was reported that CAIII constituted 8% of the liver cytosolic protein; later radio-immunoassay resulted in an estimation of 1% of total liver cell protein (115). It is known that the rat cytosolic CA isozymes exhibit growth hormone-mediated sexual dimorphism in rat liver, with 30 times as much CAIII in male liver than female liver and, conversely, 3–4 times as much CAII in female liver as in male liver (12, 115).

LOCALIZATION WITHIN THE LIVER    In 1985 a collaboration in Sweden resulted in the discovery that liver CAIII is localized exclusively in the hepatocytes around the central vein (12). These so-called perivenous hepatocytes comprise only 4% of the total. Thus this evidence is suggestive of a most specific function of the cytosolic CAs. They additionally found that the cytosolic CA found in female rats, CAII, is also exclusively perivenous. There is a growing amount of literature on the different metabolic roles of the perivenous compared with the periportal hepatocytes: There is an intercellular glucose cycle with gluconeogenesis occurring in different hepatocytes than does glycolysis (64), urea-synthesizing and glutamine-utilizing enzymes are in hepatocytes other than glutamine-synthesizing enzymes (37) which has been concluded to be responsible for a putative intrahepatic glutamine cycle (50). It was thus intriguing to discover that the rat cytosolic CAs are localized in this manner.

SPECIES DIFFERENCES    Most work with cytosolic CAs has been done with rats (15, 36). It has been reported that there is no cytosolic CA in the guinea pig hepatocyte cytosol (24). More recent experiments with guinea pig have revealed that CA activity of disrupted liver mitochondria is more sensitive to acetazolamide than disrupted hepatocytes (22); thus again the question is open. It is clear that if there are cytosolic CAs in guinea pig these are not as quantitatively important as in the rat. In most species so far examined cytosolic CAs have been found, but the concentration of CAIII is highest in the male rat (N. Carter, personal communication).

## Mitochondrial Carbonic Anhydrase

Until the description of a clean preparation of mitochondria was reported, it was not possible to separate the CA activity of mitochondria from that due to blood as well as hepatocytic cytosolic activity (93). It is for this reason that the first reports of CA activity in mitochondria are extremely cautious as to the origin of this activity. Datta & Shepard (19) presented data which now can clearly be interpreted as definite evidence for CA in mitochondria; their interpretation, however, was that the CA was not associated with any particulate cellular component and that the activity associated with the mitochondria was derived from the cytosol. One year later the data of Karler & Woodbury (66) was not significantly different, but they concluded that the CA activity was bound inextricably to the mitochondrial membrane.

Functional evidence for mitochondrial CA was reported by Elder & Lehninger (32). They observed that rat liver mitochondria respiring in a phosphate-free bicarbonate buffer accumulate $Ca^{2+}$; thus $HCO_3^-$ furnished the coanion to $Ca^{2+}$. Subsequent inclusion of acetazolamide blocked $Ca^{2+}$ uptake. These data were confirmed by Harris (49). A more recent study (5) showed that mitochondrial CA is essential for rapid net uptake of $CO_2$ with $K^+$ or $Ca^{2+}$.

The most widely used CA assay involves timing the evolution of $H^+$ at 4° C after an aliquot of $CO_2$ is added to a CA-containing solution (97). CA contained within a $HCO_3^-$-impermeable membrane cannot be detected (8). It is most probable that the confusion over the existence of CA inside mitochondria was due to the inability to detect activity in intact mitochondria. This problem has been circumvented by the development of a mass spectrometric assay for measurement of CA activity within intact erythrocytes (35, 58, 89). $^{18}O$-labelled $NaHCO_3^-$ is included with aqueous solution in the reaction chamber of the mass spectrometer, the pH is adjusted, and the rate of disappearance of $C^{18}O^{16}O$ is monitored in the presence and absence of CA. It is this technique that has been used to determine CA activity of intact hepatic mitochondria and parenchymal cells (22–30).

LOCALIZATION    Mitochondrial CA is localized entirely in the matrix of guinea pig liver mitochondria (29). Thus in the mitochondria CA is contained within the outer $HCO_3^-$-permeable membrane and the inner $HCO_3^-$-impermeable membrane. Localization of 40 to 60% of CA activity in the inter membrane space was reported after digitonin-treatment of intact rat liver mitochondria (126); these researchers also measured CA activity by a mass spectrometric technique.

Investigation of the possibility that localization of the rat and guinea pig liver enzymes are different led to a series of experiments in which CA activity was measured by a modification of the $H^+$-evolution technique (84). No inter membrane activity was detectable in either intact guinea pig liver mitochondria (26) or intact rat liver mitochondria (23).

PROPERTIES    Mitochondrial carbonic anhydrase (CA V) was first quantitated in guinea pig liver mitochondria (29). It was first suspected to be a unique isozyme when plots of activity against pH at 25° C, 25 mM $NaHCO_3^-$, revealed an 8-fold increase as pH increased from 7.0 to 8.0 (27). CA V was purified by sulfonamide-affinity chromatography (27). Its molecular weight is 29,000; this was determined by SDS-PAGE electrophoresis (30) and confirmed by gel filtration (Dodgson, unpublished data). Its metal ion, determined by atomic absorption spectroscopy, is zinc (Dodgson, unpublished data). It is extremely hydrophobic; this was first observed by its inability to remain in aqueous solution without exceedingly high salt concentration (28, 30). Attempts to determine whether there was a single mitochondrial isozyme by nondenaturing PAGE consistently failed, although the enzymes purified from blood migrated in discreet bands (Dodgson, unpublished data). Conclusive evidence that the enzyme is a unique isozyme was provided by sequencing of the pure enzyme (54); since then, mitochondrial CA has been referred to as CA V.

CA V is sulfonamide-sensitive (22, 24, 29). The $K_M$ determined over the pH range 7.0–8.0 was determined to be 2.2 mM at 25° C (23). There is little temperature effect on CA V activity; $k_{enz}$ (in units of ml s$^{-1}$ mg mitochondrial protein$^{-1}$) determined with disrupted guinea pig mitochondria is 0.12 at 25° C and 0.14 at 37° C and for disrupted rat liver mitochondria 0.06 at 25° C and 0.06 at 37° C (23).

FUNCTION IN UREAGENESIS    It was fifty-one years after the urea cycle was reported that the sulfonamide CA inhibitor acetazolamide was first shown to decrease the production of citrulline by intact guinea pig liver mitochondria (26). The effect of acetazolamide was confirmed in rat liver mitochondria the following year (128). A collaborative study resulted in the finding that at 37° C the inhibition of citrulline synthesis is greater with the more lipophilic sulfonamide, ethoxzolamide, and that much greater quantities of the hydrophilic sulfonamide benzolamide are needed for even slight inhibition (30).

The effect of inhibition by acetazolamide on activity of CPS I is reflected in its inhibition of a product of the final urea cycle enzyme, urea. This has been demonstrated with intact guinea pig hepatocytes (24, 25, 28, 30), intact rat hepatocytes (88, 107), and perfused rat liver (51, 86).

FUNCTION IN GLUCONEOGENESIS    The first reported evidence for sulfonamides interfering with gluconeogenesis appeared in 1963: A study with mice resulted in a strange hypoglycemic effect after sulfonamide administration (109). A subsequent study from the same laboratory showed that mouse liver homogenate pyruvate carboxylase activity was decreased by sulfonamides; they concluded the effect on pyruvate carboxylase was direct since there was thought to be no CA in mitochondria (10). A later study from another laboratory with whole chameleons also led to the conclusion that sulfonamides inhibit gluconeogenesis through their effect on pyruvate carboxylase

(53); these researchers concluded from their knowledge of CA V that the effect was probably due to its inhibition.

Acetazolamide-mediated inhibition of glucose synthesis by intact rat hepatocytes has been reported. In a study with intact guinea pig hepatocytes it was determined that there is a parallel ethoxzolamide-mediated decrease in urea and glucose synthesis when choice of gluconeogenic substrates dictate that the first enzyme is pyruvate carboxylase. When added NH$_3$, ornithine, pyruvate, and lactate are replaced with glutamine, the ethoxzolamide-mediated decrease in urea synthesis is still observed, but glucose synthesis is unaffected (25). These experiments highlight a fundamental difference in the two biosynthetic pathways: Urea synthesis can only proceed through the HCO$_3$$^-$-requiring CPS I; however, glucose synthesis is not dependent on a HCO$_3$$^-$-step, if other substrates are available. Another fundamental difference is that synthesis of each molecule of urea results in complete removal of two molecules of HCO$_3$$^-$ into the blood and ultimately out of the body. Fixation of HCO$_3$$^-$ by pyruvate carboxylase results in its release as CO$_2$ by phosphoenolpyruvate carboxykinase into the mitochondria (in guinea pig) or into the cytosol (in rat). It is not known whether there is a preferred pathway for metabolic CO$_2$ in liver mitochondria from pyruvate dehydrogenase to CPS I; this may well vary with species.

## CO$_2$ Compartmentation

A report from Tomera et al (122) has led to studies from several other laboratories about whether CO$_2$ derived from intramitochondrial sources is fixed preferentially into urea. This report showed that in the perfused rat liver the rates of fixation of $^{14}$C from NaH$^{14}$CO$_3$ added to the perfusate was 3–70 times greater than the net rates of CO$_2$ production. They concluded that calculation of metabolic rates from $^{14}$CO$_2$ production can give substantial underestimates, up to 50%. Hems & Saez (52) used intact rat hepatocytes and concluded from their experiments with $^{14}$C-labelled substrates that metabolic CO$_2$ enters into urea synthesis more readily than it equilibrates with the total CO$_2$ + HCO$_3$$^-$-pool. In a recent study conducted with perfused rat livers Marsolais et al (86) concluded from experiments with acetazolamide that CA V is necessary for rapid equilibration of carbon dioxide across the hepatocyte and mitochondrial membranes.

In a study with intact guinea pig hepatocytes external CO$_2$ was decreased from 25 mM total to zero and urea synthesis was determined as a function of ethoxzolamide concentration (24). The rate of urea synthesis was equally sensitive to ethoxzolamide inhibition but was two-thirds lower with no external CO$_2$. It was thus concluded that urea synthesis can proceed from internally produced carbon dioxide, but at a slower rate than when external carbon dioxide is available.

## Literature Cited

1. Ariano, M. A., Armstrong, R. B., Edgerton, V. R. 1973. Hindlimb muscle fiber population of five mammals. *J. Histochem. Cytochem.* 21:51–55
2. Arinze, I. J., Garber, A. J., Hanson, R. W. 1973. The regulation of gluconeogenesis in mammalian liver. The role of mitochondrial phosphoenol pyruvate carboxykinase. *J. Biol. Chem.* 248:2266–74
3. Armstrong, R. B., Laughlin, M. H. 1983. Blood flows within and among rat muscles as a function of time during high speed treadmill exercise. *J. Physiol.* 344:189–208
4. Attwood, P. V., Keech, D. B. 1983. Pyruvate carboxylase. *Curr. Top. Cell. Regul.* 23:1–55
5. Balboni, E., Lehninger, A. L. 1986. Entry and exit pathways of $CO_2$ in rat liver mitochondria respiring in a bicarbonate buffer system. *J. Biol. Chem.* 261:3563–70
6. Barclay, J. K. 1987. Carbonic anhydrase III inhibition in normocapnic and hypercapnic contracting mouse soleus. *Can. J. Physiol. Pharmacol.* 65:100–4
7. Bidani, A., Crandall, E. D., Forster, R. E. 1978. Analysis of postcapillary pH changes in blood in vivo after gas exchange. *J. Appl. Physiol.* 44:770–81
8. Booth, V. H. 1938. Carbonic anhydrase activity inside corpuscles. Enzyme substrate accessibility factors. *J. Physiol.* 93:117–28
9. Bruns, W., Dermietzel, R., Gros, G. 1986. Carbonic anhydrase in the sarcoplasmic reticulum of rabbit skeletal muscle. *J. Physiol.* 371:351–64
10. Cao, T. P., Rous, S. 1978. Action of acetazolamide on liver pyruvate carboxylase activity, glycogenolysis and gluconeogenesis. *Int. J. Biochem.* 9:603–5
11. Carter, N. D., Hewett-Emmett, D., Jeffrey, S., Tashian, R. E. 1981. Testosterone-induced, sulfonamide-resistant carbonic anhydrase isozyme of rat liver is indistinguishable from skeletal muscle carbonic anhydrase III. *FEBS Lett.* 128:114–18
12. Carter, N. D., Jeffery, S., Legg, R., Wistrand, P., Lönnerholm, G. 1987. Expression of hepatocyte carbonic anhydrase isoenzymes in vitro and in vivo. *Biochem. Soc. Trans.* In press
13. Carter, N., Jeffery, S., Shiels, A. 1982. Immunoassay of carbonic anhydrase III in rat tissues. *FEBS Lett.* 139:265–66
14. Carter, N. D., Jeffery, S., Shiels, A., Edwards, Y., Tipler, T., Hopkinson, D. A. 1979. Characterization of human carbonic anhydrase III from skeletal muscle. *Biochem. Genet.* 17:837–54
15. Carter, N. D., Shiels, A., Jeffery, S., Heath, R., Wilson, C. A., et al. 1984. Hormonal control of carbonic anhydrase III. *Ann. NY Acad. Sci.* 429:287–301
16. Carter, N. D., Shiels, A., Tashian, R. 1978. Carbonic anhydrase III isoenzyme from human and bovine muscle. *Biochem. Soc. Trans.* 6:552–53
17. Chegwidden, W. R., Hewett-Emmett, D., Tashian, R. E. 1984. Active site studies on muscle carbonic anhydrase III. *Ann. NY Acad. Sci.* 429:179–81
18. Crandall, E. D., Bidani, A., Forster, R. E. 1977. Postcapillary changes in blood pH in vivo during carbonic anhydrase inhibition. *J. Appl. Physiol.* 43:582–90
19. Datta, P. K., Shepard, T. H. 1959. Intracellular localization of carbonic anhydrase in rat liver and kidney tissues. *Arch. Biochem. Biophys.* 81:124–29
20. Davenport, H. 1946. Carbonic anhydrase in tissues other than blood. *Physiol. Rev.* 26:560–73
21. Dermietzel, R., Leibstein, A., Siffert, W., Zambglou, N., Gros, G. 1985. A fast screening method for histochemical localization of carbonic anhydrase. Application to kidney, skeletal muscle, and thrombocytes. *J. Histochem. Cytochem.* 33:93–98
22. Dodgson, S. J. 1987. Inhibition of CA V and ureagenesis: a discrepancy examined. *J. Appl. Physiol.* 63:2134–41
23. Dodgson, S. J., Contino, L. C. 1987. Rat kidney mitochondrial carbonic anhydrase. *Arch. Biochem. Biophys.* In press
24. Dodgson, S. J., Forster, R. E. II. 1986. Carbonic anhydrase: inhibition results in decreased urea production by hepatocytes. *J. Appl. Physiol.* 60:646–52
25. Dodgson, S. J., Forster, R. E. II. 1986. Inhibition of CA V decreases glucose synthesis from pyruvate. *Arch. Biochem. Biophys.* 251:198–204
26. Dodgson, S. J., Forster, R. E. II., Schwed, D. A., Storey, B. T. 1983. Contribution of matrix carbonic anhydrase to citrulline synthesis in isolated guinea pig liver mitochondria. *J. Biol. Chem.* 258:7696–701
27. Dodgson, S. J., Forster, R. E. II., Storey, B. T. 1982. Determination of intramitochondrial pH by means of matrix carbonic anhydrase activity measured

with $^{18}$O exchange. *J. Biol. Chem.* 257:1705–11

28. Dodgson, S. J., Forster, R. E. II. Storey, B. T. 1984. The role of carbonic anhydrase in hepatocyte metabolism. *Ann. NY Acad. Sci.* 429:516–24

29. Dodgson, S. J., Forster, R. E. II., Storey, B. T., Mela, L. 1980. Mitochondrial carbonic anhydrase. *Proc. Natl. Acad. Sci. (USA)* 77:5562–66

30. Dodgson, S. J., Meijer, A. J., Tager, J. M., Caro, H. P. L. 1987. CA V and citrulline synthesis, 37° C. *FEBS Proc. Meet.* In press

31. Effros, R. M., Weissman, M. L. 1979. Carbonic anhydrase activity of the cat hind leg. *J. Appl. Physiol.* 47:1090–98

32. Elder, J. A., Lehninger, A. L. 1973. Respiration dependent transport of carbon dioxide into rat liver mitochondria. *Biochemistry* 12:976–82

33. Engberg, P., Millqvist, E., Pohl, G., Lindskog, S. 1985. Purification and some properties of carbonic anhydrase from bovine skeletal muscle. *Arch. Biochem. Biophys.* 241:628–38

34. Forster, R. E., Crandall, E. D. 1975. Time course of exchanges between red cells and extracellular fluid during CO$_2$ uptake. *J. Appl. Physiol.* 38:710–18

35. Forster, R. E. II., Dodgson, S. J., Storey, B. T., Lin, L. 1984. Measurement of carbonic anhydrase activity inside cells and subcellular particles. *Ann. NY Acad. Sci.* 429:415–29

36. Garg, L. C. 1974. Catalytic activity and inhibition of carbonic anhydrase of rat tissues. *Biochem. Pharmacol.* 23:3153–61

37. Gebhardt, R., Mecke, D. 1983. Heterogeneous distribution of glutamine synthetase among rat liver parenchymal cells in situ and in primary culture. *EMBO J.* 2:567–70

38. Geers, C., Gros, G. 1984. Inhibition properties and inhibition kinetics of an extracellular carbonic anhydrase in perfused skeletal muscle. *Respir. Physiol.* 56:269–87

39. Geers, C., Gros, G. 1987. Carbonic anhydrase inhibition affects contraction of directly stimulated rat soleus. *Life Sci.* In press

40. Geers, C., Gros, G., Gärtner, A. 1985. Extracellular carbonic anhydrase of skeletal muscle associated with the sarcolemma. *J. Appl. Physiol.* 59(2):548–58

41. Gros, G., Bartag, I. 1979. Permeability of the red cell membrane for CO$_2$ and O$_2$. *Pflügers Arch.* 382:R21 (Abstr.)

42. Gros, G., Forster, R. E., Dodgson, S. J. 1987. CO$_2$/HCO$_3^-$ equilibria in the body. In *Mechanisms and control of pH homeostasis*, ed. D. Häussinger. London: Academic In press

43. Gros, G., Forster, R. E., Lin, L. 1976. The carbamate reaction of glycylglycine, plasma and tissue extracts—evaluated by a pH stopped flow apparatus. *J. Biol. Chem.* 251:4398–407

44. Gros, G., Gros, H., Lavalette, D., Amand, B., Pochon, F. 1980. Mechanisms of facilitated CO$_2$ diffusion in protein solutions. In *Biophysics and Physiology of Carbon Dioxide*, ed. C. Bauer, G. Gros, H. Bartels, pp. 36–48. Berlin: Springer-Verlag

45. Gros, G., Lavalette, D., Moll, W., Gros, H., Amand, B., Pochon, F. 1984. Evidence for rotational contribution to protein-facilitated proton transport. *Proc. Natl. Acad. Sci. USA* 81:1710–14

46. Gros, G., Moll, W. 1974. Facilitated diffusion of CO$_2$ across albumin solutions. *J. Gen. Physiol.* 64:356–71

47. Gros, G., Moll, W., Hoppe, H., Gros, H. 1976. Proton transport by phosphate diffusion—a mechanism of facilitated CO$_2$ transfer. *J. Gen. Physiol.* 67:773–90

48. Gros, G., Siffert, W., Schmid, A. 1980. Activity and properties of carbonic anhydrase in striated muscle. In *Biophysics and Physiology of Carbon Dioxide*, ed. C. Bauer, G. Gros, H. Bartels, pp. 409–16. Berlin: Springer-Verlag

49. Harris, E. J. 1978. Anion/calcium ion ratios and proton production in some mitochondrial calcium ion uptakes. *Biochem. J.* 176:983–91

50. Häussinger, D., Gerok, W., Sies, H. 1984. Hepatic role in pH regulation: role of the intracellular glutamine cycle. *Trends Biochem. Sci.* 9:300–2

51. Häussinger, D., Sies, H., Gerok, W. 1985. Hepatic urea synthesis and pH regulation. *Eur. J. Biochem.* 152:381–86

52. Hems, R., Saez, G. T. 1983. Equilibration of metabolic CO$_2$ with preformed CO$_2$ and bicarbonate. *FEBS Letts.* 153:438–40

53. Herbert, J. D., Coulson, R. A., Hernandez, T. 1983. Inhibition of pyruvate carboxylation in alligators and chameleons by carbonic anhydrase inhibitors. *Comp. Biochem. Physiol.* 75A:617–53

54. Hewett-Emmett, D., Cook, R. G., Dodgson, S. J. 1986. Carbonic anhydrase from hepatocyte mitochondria of guinea pigs is the products of a novel gene and is not a CA II "splisozyme". *Isozyme Bull.* 19:13

55. Hill, E. P., Power, G. G., Gilbert, R.

D. 1977. Rate of pH changes in blood plasma in vitro and in vivo. *J. Appl. Physiol.* 42:928–34

56. Holmes, R. S. 1977. Purification, molecular properties, and ontogeny of carbonic anhydrase isozymes: evidence for A, B, and C isozymes in avian and mammalian tissues. *Eur. J. Biochem.* 78:511–20

57. Deleted in proof

58. Itada, N., Forster, R. E. II. 1977. Carbonic anhydrase activity in intact red blood cells measured with ${}^{18}O$ exchange. *J. Biol. Chem.* 252:3881–90

59. Jeffery, S., Carter, N. D. 1980. A comparison of carbonic anhydrase III isozymes from human, baboon, pig and sheep muscle. *Comp. Biochem. Physiol.* 66B:439–41

60. Jeffery, S., Carter, N. D., Smith, A. 1986. Immunocytochemical localization of carbonic anhydrase isozymes I, II, and III in rat skeletal muscle. *J. Histochem. Cytochem.* 34:513–16

61. Jeffery, S., Carter, N. D., Wilson, C. 1984. Carbonic anhydrase II isoenzyme in rat liver is under hormonal control. *Biochem. J.* 221:927–29

62. Jeffery, S., Wilson, C. A., Mode, A., Gustafsson, J.-A., Carter, N. A. 1986. Effects of hypophysectomy and growth hormone infusion on rat hepatic carbonic anhydrases. *J. Endocrinol.* 110:123–26

63. Jones, M. E. 1976. Partial reactions of carbamyl-P synthetase: a review and an inquiry into the role of carbamate. In *The Urea Cycle,* ed. S. Grisolia, R., Baguena, F. Mayor, pp. 107–22 New York: Wiley

64. Jungermann, K., Katz, N. 1982. Functional hepatocellular heterogeneity. *Hepatology* 2:385–95

65. Kararli, T., Silverman, D. N. 1985. Inhibition of the hydration of $CO_2$ catalyzed by carbonic anhydrase III from cat muscle. *J. Biol. Chem.* 260:3484–89

66. Karler, R., Woodbury, D. M. 1960. Intracellular distribution of carbonic anhydrase. *Biochem. J.* 75:538–43

67. Kawashiro, T., Scheid, P. 1976. Measurement of Krogh's diffusion constant of $CO_2$ in respiring muscle at various $CO_2$ levels: evidence for facilitated diffusion. *Pflügers Arch.* 362:127–33

68. King, R. W., Garg, L. C., Huckson, J. Maren, T. H. 1974. The isolation and partial characterization of sulfonamide-resistant carbonic anhydrases from the liver of the male rat. *Mol. Pharmacol.* 10:335–43

69. Koester, M. K., Pullan, L. M., Noltmann, E. A. 1981. The p-nitrophenyl phosphatase activity of muscle carbonic

anhydrase. *Arch. Biochem. Biophys.* 211:632–42

70. Koester, M. K., Register, A. M., Noltmann, E. A. 1977. *Biochem. Biophys. Res. Comm.* 76:196–204

71. Kraus-Friedman, N. 1984. Hormonal regulation of hepatic gluconeogenesis. *Physiol. Rev.* 64:170–259

72. Krebs, H. A. 1943. Carbon dioxide assimilation in heterotrophic organisms. *Ann. Rev. Biochem.* 12:529–50

73. Krebs, H. A. 1953. Nobel Prize in Physiology and Medicine. *Nord. Med.* 50:1697–99

74. Krebs, H. A. 1976. The discovery of the ornithine cycle. In *The Urea Cycle,* ed. S. Grisolia, R. Baguena, F. Meyer, pp. 1–12 New York: Wiley

75. Krebs, H. A., Henseleit, K. 1932. Untersuchungen über die Harnstoffbildung im Tierkörper. *Hoppe-Seyler's Z. Physiol. Chem.* 210:33–36

76. Krebs, H. A., Roughton, F. J. W. 1948. Carbonic anhydrase as a tool in studying the mechanism of reactions involving $H_2CO_3$, $CO_2$ or $HCO_3{}^-$. *Biochem. J.* 43:550–95

77. Lobley, G. E., Wilson, A. B., Bruce, A. S. 1977. An estimation of the fibre type composition of eleven skeletal muscles from New Zealand white rabbits between weaning and early maturity. *J. Anat.* 123:501–13

78. Lönnerholm, G. 1980. Carbonic anhydrase in rat liver and rabbit skeletal muscle; further evidence for the specificity of the histochemical cobalt-phosphate method of Hansson. *J. Histochem. Cytochem.* 28:427–33

79. Lusty, C. J. 1978. Carbamoylphosphate synthetase I of rat liver mitochondria. *Eur. J. Biochem.* 85:373–83

80. Mann, T., Keilin, D. 1940. Sulphanilamide as a specific inhibitor of carbonic anhydrase. *Nature* 146:164–65

81. Maren, T. H. 1960. A simplified micromethod for the determination of carbonic anhydrase and its inhibitors. *J. Pharmacol. Exp. Ther.* 130:26–29

82. Maren, T. H. 1967. Carbonic anhydrase: chemistry, physiology and inhibition. *Physiol. Rev.* 47:595–781

83. Maren, T. H. 1984. The general physiology of reactions catalyzed by carbonic anhydrase and their inhibition by sulfonamides. *Ann. NY Acad. Sci.* 429:568–79

84. Maren, T. H., Couto, E. 1979. The nature of anion inhibition of human red cell carbonic anhydrases. *Arch. Biochem. Biophys.* 196:501–10

85. Maren, T. H., Ellison, A. C., Fellner, S. K., Graham, W. B. 1966. A study of

hepatic carbonic anhydrase. *Mol. Pharmacol.* 2:144–57

86. Marsolais, C., Huot, S., David, F., Garneau, M., Brunengraber, H. 1987. Compartmentation of ¹⁴CO₂ in the perfused rat liver. *J. Biol. Chem.* 262: 2604–7

87. Meldrum, N. U., Roughton, F. J. W. 1933. Carbonic anhydrase. Its preparation and properties. *J. Physiol.* 80:113–42

88. Metcalfe, H. K., Monson, J. P., Drew, P. J., Iles, R. A., Carter, N. D., Cohen, R. D. 1985. Inhibition of gluconeogenesis and urea synthesis in isolated rat hepatocyes by acetazolamide. *Biochem. Soc. Trans.* 13:255

89. Mills, C. A., Urey, H. C. 1940. The kinetics of isotopic exchange between carbon dioxide, bicarbonate ion, carbonate and water. *J. Am. Chem. Soc.* 62:1019–26

90. Mori, M., Tatibana, M. 1978. A multienzyme complex of carbamoylphosphate synthase (glutamine): aspartate carbamoyltransferase: dihydroorotase (rat ascites hepatoma cells and rat liver). *Meth. Enzymol.* 51:111–21

91. Moyle, S., Jeffery, S., Carter, N. D. 1984. Localization of human muscle carbonic anhydrase isozymes using immunofluorescence. *J. Histochem. Cytochem.* 32:1262–64

92. Moynihan, J. B. 1977. Carbonic anhydrase activity in mammalian skeletal and cardiac muscle. *Biochem. J.* 168: 567–69

93. Nedergaard, J., Cannon, B. 1979. Overview. Preparation and properties of mitochondria from different sources. *Meth. Enzymol.* 55:3–28

94. Nishita, T., Deutsch, H. F. 1986. Acylation and carbamylation of equine muscle carbonic anhydrase (CA-III) upon reaction with p-nitrophenyl esters and carbamoyl phosphate. *Int. J. Biochem.* 18:319–25

95. O'Brasky, J. E., Crandall, E. D. 1980. Organ and species differences in tissue vascular carbonic anhydrase activity. *J. Appl. Physiol.* 49:211–17

96. Pette, D. 1984. Activity-induced fast to slow transitions in mammalian muscle. *Med. Sci. Sports Exercise* 16:517–28

97. Philpot, F. J., Philpot, J. St. L. 1936. A modified colorimetric estimation of carbonic anhydrase. *Biochem. J.* 30: 2191–92

98. Pierson, D. L. 1980. A rapid colorimetric assay for carbamyl phoshate synthetase I. *J. Biochem. Biophys. Methods* 3:31–37

99. Pihar, O. 1965. Proteins as catalysts of carbon dioxide hydration. *Biochim. Biophys. Acta* 104:608–11

100. Deleted in proof

101. Pullan, L. M., Noltmann, E. A. 1985. Specific arginine modification at the phosphatase site of muscle carbonic anhydrase. *Biochemistry* 24:635–40

102. Pullan, L. M., Noltmann, E. A. 1985. Purification and properties of pig muscle carbonic anhydrase III. *Biochim. Biophys. Acta* 839:147–54

103. Register, A. M., Koester, M. K., Noltmann, E. A. 1978. Discovery of carbonic anhydrase in rabbit skeletal muscle and evidence for its identity with "basic muscle protein". *J. Biol. Chem.* 253: 4143–52

104. Ridderstråle, Y. 1979. Observation on the localization of carbonic anhydrase in muscle. *Acta Physiol. Scand.* 106:239–340

105. Riley, D. A., Ellis, S., Bain, J. 1982. Carbonic anhydrase activity in skeletal muscle fiber types, axons, spindles, and capillaries of rat soleus and extensor digitorum longus muscles. *J. Histochem. Cytochem.* 30:1275–88

106. Rognstad, R. 1979. Rate-limiting steps in metabolic pathways. *J. Biol. Chem.* 254:1875–78

107. Rognstad, R. 1983. CO₂ metabolism in the liver. *Arch. Biochem. Biophys.* 222:442–43

108. Roughton, F. J. W. 1935. Recent work on carbon dioxide transport by the blood. *Physiol. Rev.* 15:241–96

109. Rous, S., Faverger, P. 1963. *Helv. Chim. Acta* 46:2586–91

110. Rubio, V. 1986. Enzymatic HCO₃⁻-fixation: a common mechanism for all enzymes involved *Biosci. Rep.* 4:335–47

111. Ryan, U. S., Whitney, P. L., Ryan, J. W. 1982. Localization of carbonic anhydrase in pulmonary artery endothelial cells in culture. *J. Appl. Physiol.* 53: 914–19

111a. Sanyal, G. 1984. The carbon dioxide hydration activity of the sulfonamide-resistant carbonic anhydrase from the liver of male rat: pH dependence of the steady state kinetics. *Arch. Biochem. Biophys.* 234:576–79

112. Sanyal, G., Pessah, N. I., Maren, T. H. 1981. Kinetics and inhibition of membrane-bound carbonic anhydrase from canine renal cortex. *Biochim. Biophys. Acta* 657:128–37

113. Sanyal, G., Swenson, E. R., Pessah, N. I., Maren, T. H. 1982. The carbon dioxide hydration activity of skeletal mus-

cle carbonic anhydrase. *Mol. Pharmacol.* 22:211–20

114. Scheid, P., Siffert, W. 1985. Effects of inhibiting carbonic anhydrase on isometric contraction of frog skeletal muscle. *J. Physiol.* 361:91–101

115. Shiels, A., Jeffery, S., Wilson, C., Carter, N. 1984. Radioimmunoassay of carbonic anhydrase III in rat tissues. *Biochem. J.* 218:281–84

116. Shima, K., Tashiro, K., Hibi, N., Tsukada, Y., Hirai, H. 1983. Carbonic anhydrase-III immunohistochemical localization in human skeletal muscle. *Acta Neuropathol.* 59:237–39

117. Siffert, W., Gros, G. 1982. Carbonic anhydrase C in white-skeletal-muscle tissue. *Biochem. J.* 205:559–66

118. Stadie, W. C., O'Brien, H. 1933. The catalysis of the hydration of carbon dioxide and dehydration of carbonic acid by an enzyme isolated from red blood cells. *J. Biol. Chem.* 103:521–29

119. Swenson, E. R. 1984. The respiratory aspects of carbonic anhydrase *Ann. NY Acad. Sci.* 429:547–60

120. Tashian, R. E., Hewett-Emmett, D., Goodman, M. 1983. On the evolution and genetics of carbonic anhydrases I, II and III. In *Isozymes: Current Topics in Biological and Medical Research: Molecular Structure and Regulation* 7:79–100. New York: Liss

121. Tashian, R. E., Hewett-Emmett, D., Stroup, S. K., Goodman, M., Yu, Y.-S. L. 1980. Evolution of structure and function in the carbonic anhydrase isozymes in mammals. In *Biophysics and Physiology of Carbon Dioxide,* ed. C. Bauer, G. Gros, H. Bartels, pp. 165–76. Berlin: Springer-Verlag

122. Tomera, J. F., Goetz, P. G., Rand, W. M., Brunengraber, H. 1982. Underestimation of metabolic rates owing to reincorporation of $^{14}CO_2$ in the perfused rat liver. *Biochem. J.* 208:231–37

123. Tu, C., Thomas, H. G., Wynns, G. C., Silverman, D. N. 1986. Hydrolysis of 4-nitrophenyl acetate catalyzed by carbonic anhydrase III from bovine skeletal muscle. *J. Biol. Chem.* 261: 10000–3

124. Väänänen, H. K., Paloniemi, M., Vuori, J. 1985. Purification and localization of human carbonic anhydrase. *Histochemistry* 83:231–35

125. Väänänen, H. K., Takala, T., Morris, D. C. 1986. Immunelectron microscopic localization of carbonic anhydrase III in rat skeletal muscle. *Histochemistry* 86:175–79

126. Vincent, S. H., Silverman, D. N. 1982. Carbonic anhydrase activity in mitochondria from rat liver. *J. Biol. Chem.* 257:6850–55

127. Wakil, S. J., Stoops, J. K., Joshi, Y. C. 1983. *Ann. Rev. Biochem.* 52:537–79

128. Wanders, R. J. A., Van Roermund, C. W. T., Meijer, A. J. 1984. Analysis of the control of citrulline synthesis in isolated rat liver mitochondria. *Eur. J. Biochem.* 142:247–54

129. Wandorff, K. M., Nishita, T., Jabusch, J. R., Deutsch, H. F. 1985. The sequence of equine muscle carbonic anhydrase. *J. Biol. Chem.* 260:6129–32

130. Wistrand, P. J., Carter, N. D., Askmark, H. 1987. Induction of rat muscle carbonic anhydrase by denervation demonstrated with immunofluorescence. *Comp. Biochem. Physiol.* 86A:177–84

131. Woodbury, J. W. 1971. Fluxes of $H^+$ and $HCO_3^-$ across frog skeletal muscle cell membranes. In *Ion Homeostasis in the Brain,* ed. B. K. Siesjö, S. C. Sörensen, pp. 270–89. Copenhagen: Munksgaard

132. Zborowska-Sluis, D. T., L'Abbate, A., Klassen, G. A. 1974. Evidence of carbonic anhydrase activity in skeletal muscle: a role for facilitative carbon dioxide transport. *Resp. Physiol.* 21:341–50

133. Zborowska-Sluis, D. T., L'Abbate, A., Mildenberger, R. R., Klassen, G. A. 1975. The effect of acetazolamide on myocardial carbon dioxide space. *Resp. Physiol.* 23:311–16

REFERENCE ADDED IN PROOF

134. Pullan, L. M., Noltmann, E. A. 1984. Simultaneous and independent versus antagonistic inhibition of muscle carbonic anhydrase (CA III) by acetazolamide and cyanate. *Biochem. Pharmacol.* 33:2641–45

*Ann. Rev. Physiol. 1988. 50:695–717*

# THE KINETICS OF $HCO_3^-$ SYNTHESIS RELATED TO FLUID SECRETION, pH CONTROL, AND $CO_2$ ELIMINATION

*Thomas H. Maren*

Department of Pharmacology and Therapeutics, University of Florida College of Medicine, Gainesville, Florida 32610

## INTRODUCTION

In 1928 Henriques (20) deduced from the rates of $HCO_3^- \rightleftharpoons CO_2$ reactions published by Faurholt (14), that the conversion process was too slow to account for the loss of respiratory $CO_2$ across the lung. Henriques sought for an enzyme in blood to catalyze the process; for reasons I have reviewed elsewhere (32) he concluded that there was none, but that the rapid reaction was mediated by carbaminohemoglobin (20). Meldrum & Roughton, five years later, discovered carbonic anhydrase (CA) in red cells (38). It is now clear that the interconversion of $CO_2 \rightleftharpoons HCO_3^-$ has physiological implications far greater than the carriage and excretion of metabolic $CO_2$ in red cells. This process occurs in other sites, and the reaction is also central to the formation of $H^+$ and $HCO_3^-$ in secretory organs (reviewed in 30).

In the present chapter I consider anew $HCO_3^-$ formation in certain secretory processes, in generation of an alkaline milieu, and in subserving the excretion or removal of $CO_2$ from certain special tissues. Chemically, these are analogous to the interconversion in red cells; the latter is considered by Klocke elsewhere (this volume). An earlier review (34) covers other aspects of $HCO_3^-$ or $CO_3^{2-}$ synthesis, i.e. in shell formation and salivary secretion.

The purpose of this review is to try to coordinate this subject by weaving

695

0066-4278/88/0315-0695$02.00

together those elements that allow for coherent conclusions. In my view this is quite possible and can be stated in a single sentence: $HCO_3^-$ synthesis plays a role in fluid formation as a gegen ion for sodium transport or for chloride exchange, and as a carrier for $CO_2$, and as a pH regulator in metabolism.

Until recently $HCO_3^-$ has been the forgotten ion of physiology and membrane electrobiology. If we use an analogy with $Cl^-$, we find at once that while the distribution $Cl_{in}/Cl_{out} \cong 0.1$, when inserted into the Nernst equation, corresponds to the usual transmembrane potential of $-60$ mV, the distribution for $HCO_3^-$ does not, since $HCO_3^-{}_{in}/HCO_3^-{}_{out} = 10$ mM/25 mM $= 0.4$, yielding $-24$ mV. What is the reason for this, since there is no evidence that $HCO_3^-$ is less permeant than $Cl^-$? Almost certainly this is because $HCO_3^-$ is formed continuously within the cell, raising $HCO_3^-{}_{in}$.

Although the chemical and pharmacological evidence is convincing that $HCO_3^-$ synthesis occurs, there is far less evidence to connect this with transmembrane transport. Even when $HCO_3^-$ transport is discussed, and the effect of CA inhibitors documented, the fact of ion synthesis is rarely mentioned. A brilliant series of experiments initiated by Frömter is given as an introduction, since they demonstrate these important relations (4, 6).

Transmembrane potential difference (P.D.) from cell to peritubular capillaries was measured in rat kidneys in situ, (normally 74 mV) under conditions of changing peritubular $HCO_3^-$ concentration and inhibition of CA. When peritubular (but not luminal ) $HCO_3^-$ was lowered to 3 mM, the P.D. fell about 35 mV. This depolarization is reduced to 15 mV when a CA inhibitor is added to the peritubular perfusate or blood. The drug effect was localized to the enzyme at or in the peritubular membrane (5). Thus, lowering $HCO_3^-{}_{out}$ decreases P.D., but when the formation of $HCO_3^-{}_{in}$ is reduced by CA inhibition, the effect of reducing $HCO_3^-{}_{out}$ is muted, since now both $HCO_3^-{}_{out}$ and $HCO_3^-{}_{in}$ are lowered. The P.D. always favors $HCO_3^-$ exit, even from low intracellular concentration. This type of experiment also was done by reducing pericapillary sodium. This depolarizes the membrane as does reduction of $HCO_3^-$ (45, 67). The circle closes by the finding that acetazolamide inhibits $Na^+$ movement. This shows that $Na^+$ movement is driven by the $HCO_3^-$ gradient (18). A recent short publication reviews the matter and emphasizes that the stoichiometry is 3 $HCO_3^-$:1 $Na^+$ (53) and that $Cl^-$ manipulation has no effect. This evidence suggests a rheogenic $Na^+$-$HCO_3^-$ transport, dependent in part on $HCO_3^-$ synthesis from $CO_2$.

Although the equivalent experiments have not been done with pancreas, choroid plexus, or ciliary processes, partly because of technical problems, it is evident that the data available imply the same synthesis-transport processes as of the Frömter model for renal $HCO_3^-$ reabsorption.

# CHEMISTRY OF $HCO_3^-$ SYNTHESIS

## Uncatalyzed

There are two routes to the formation of $HCO_3^-$ from $CO_2$: hydration and hydroxylation, each with rate constants $k_1$ and $k_2$ given below for 37°C (44):[1]

$$CO_2 + H_2O \xrightarrow{\quad k_1 = 0.11 \text{ sec}^{-1} \quad} H_2CO_3 \rightarrow HCO_3^- + H^+ \qquad 1.$$

$$CO_2 + OH^- \xrightarrow{\quad k_2 = 27{,}000 \text{ M}^{-1} \text{ sec}^{-1} \quad} HCO_3^-. \qquad 2.$$

Reaction 1 is independent of pH, while Reaction 2 obviously is pH dependent. By converting Reaction 2 to pseudo first-order at fixed pH, we may judge the relations between the two reactions. At pH 7, $k_2$ yields 27,000 $M^{-1}$ $sec^{-1}$ × $10^{-7}$ M = 0.0027 $sec^{-1}$, which is small compared to $k_1$. At pH 9, however, the value is 0.27 $sec^{-1}$ and Reaction 2 dominates. This will be used for the physiological model.

I will develop the idea that the driving force in physiological $HCO_3^-$ formation is the $OH^-$ gradient. This makes it unnecessary to invoke a back reaction, since presumably the pH at the site of $HCO_3^-$ formation is considerably higher than the pH in the final fluid.

## Catalyzed

There are multiple CAs, but in secretory cells we are concerned with enzyme II, also known as C. The membrane-bound enzymes, IV, is not completely characterized, and its kinetic properties are akin to II. For II, the hydration turnover number ($k_{cat}$) at 37° is $1.3 \times 10^6$ $sec^{-1}$ and $K_m = 13$ mM (44). We derive the relation between the uncatalyzed rate (or rate constant) and the catalyzed as follows:

$$V_{cat} = (k_{cat} \cdot E \cdot CO_2)/(K_m + CO_2), \qquad 3.$$

where $E$ is the enzyme concentration. Since $K_m > CO_2$ in physiological systems, $CO_2$ may be neglected in the denominator, and

$$V_{cat} = k_{cat}/K_m \cdot E \cdot CO_2 = 10^8 \text{ sec M}^{-1} \cdot E \cdot CO_2. \qquad 4.$$

To obtain a practical "first-order catalytic rate constant" (denoted $k_{pcat}$) we omit the substrate and insert the value of $E$ into Equation 4. Thus if E is $10^{-6}$

---

[1] $k_2$ has not been measured accurately at 37°. The 25° value is 8500 $M^{-1}$ $sec^{-1}$ (51). The ratio of $k_1$ values at 37°/25° is 0.11/.035 (44). Assuming the same for $k_2$, we arrive at 27,000 $M^{-1}$ $sec^{-1}$.

M, $k_{pcat} = 100 \cdot sec^{-1}$ and $V_{cat} = k_{pcat} \cdot CO_2$. For the usual $CO_2$ concentration in tissues (1 mM), $V_{cat} = 100$ mM $sec^{-1}$.

The term $k_{pcat}$ is directly comparable to $k_1$ or $k_2$ (in its pseudo first-order form), the uncatalyzed rate constants. In the above example (in which $E$ is the only variable) the $k_{pcat}$ is about 400 times greater than the uncatalyzed rate constant calculated above for pH 9.[2] The range of $E$ in the cytoplasm of secretory tissues is 0.3 $\mu$M (ciliary processes) to 22 $\mu$M [choroid plexus (30, 60)].

## $HCO_3^-$ SYNTHESIS IN ION AND FLUID MOVEMENT; RATES IN RELATION TO THE CHEMICAL PROCESSES

In this section I will show that $HCO_3^-$ movement is controlled by its synthesis from $CO_2$, and that $H_2O$, $HCO_3^-$ and $Na^+$ move together in pancreatic juice (PJ), aqueous humor (AH), and cerebrospinal fluid (CSF).[3] The alligator kidney, in which $HCO_3^-$ formation subserves $Cl^-$ exchange also, is considered.

The reactions within the cell are conceived as having two parts, the protolysis of water and the hydroxylation of $CO_2$,

$$HOH \rightarrow H^+ + OH^- \qquad\qquad 5.$$

$$CO_2 + OH^- \xrightarrow{k_2} HCO_3^- \qquad\qquad 2.$$

The metabolic path must be similar, if not identical, to that now accepted for the coupling of oxidative metabolism to proton pumps (39). Both constructs demand that the membranes performing these functions be assymetrically disposed in the cell, with vectorial properties, i.e. protons and electrons accumulate on opposite faces acting as cathode and anode. It has been shown that Reactions 2 and 5 above are separable, i.e. one can have acidification (59) or (presumably) alkalinization without $CO_2$. When the numbers shown below are considered, it will be evident that the uncatalyzed formation of $HCO_3^-$ could not have a measurable rate if $[OH^-] = 10^{-7}$ or even $10^{-6}$ M. Yet there is a significant uncatalyzed process, indicated by the residual rates after inhibition of CA. On the other hand, if $[OH^-] = 10^{-4}$, the reaction would be so rapid that an enzyme would not be necessary. Indeed, the effect of an inhibitor would not be apparent since the rate dependent on Reaction 2

---

[2]Since the catalytic rate is maximal at pH 8–9 (24), this comparison appears valid.

[3]There are other instances of $HCO_3^-$ formation not as well studied as the present examples (34). The 1987 Annual Review of Physiology (Vol. 49) has a section on gastrointestinal physiology giving some data on $HCO_3^-$ output in duodenum and colon, and reabsorption in gall bladder. There are also chapters on pancreas and parietal cell pH.

would exceed the physiological rate. Thus, for the purpose of calculation, and so that we are not held up in our thinking by this detail, however important, we use $10^{-5}$ M as the OH$^-$ concentration in the anatomically undefined secretory volume. This yields (see above) $k_2 \cdot$ (OH$^-$) for Equation 2 of 0.27 sec$^{-1}$. The uncatalyzed rate ($V_{unc}$) is for pH 9 and physiological P$_{CO_2}$:

$$V_{unc} = k_2 \text{ (OH}^-) \text{ (CO}_2) = 0.27 \text{ sec}^{-1} \cdot 10^{-3} \text{ M} \cdot 10^{-3} \text{ L.} \qquad 6.$$
$$= 16 \text{ } \mu\text{mole min}^{-1} \text{ for 1 ml of reaction volume.}$$

The reaction volumne, at the present time, must be but an approximation. This will be given, along with its basis, in each physiological example.
The catalytic rate is given by Equation 4, as follows:

$$V_{cat} = 10^8 \text{ sec M}^{-1} \cdot E \cdot 10^{-3} \text{ M} \qquad 7.$$
$$= 60 \times 10^5 \text{ min}^{-1} \cdot E.$$

For a cell reaction volume of 1 ml as used above for $V_{uncat}$, $E$ may be used in units of $10^{-3}$ $\mu$mole ml$^{-1}$. Thus, as in the example in the introduction where $E$ is $10^{-6}$ M or 1 $\mu$mole L$^{-1}$ cell volume,

$$V_{cat} = 6000 \text{ } \mu\text{moles min}^{-1} \text{ per ml or 100 mM sec}^{-1}. \qquad 8.$$

Note that this exceeds $V_{unc}$ by 360-fold. It is shown below that this calculated catalytic rate also greatly exceeds the observed physiological rate. The actual value of $V_{cat}$ is not of great interest since it is so far above the biological rate.

## Pancreas

The overt appearance of HCO$_3^-$ in PJ turned attention early to the role of CO$_2$ and CA (reviewed in 30). A broad and excellent review on HCO$_3^-$ secretion by pancreatic duct cells, emphasizing mechanisms and control, recently appeared (8). The enzyme has been localized in the duct and centroacinar cells, in both cytoplasm and membranes. There was weak cytoplasmic staining in acinar cells (3).

I review two papers which give full data on electrolyte excretion following CA inhibition and alteration in acid-base balance in two species in vivo. The isolated in vitro rabbit pancreas appears less suitable for analysis because of very low secretory rates (26, 27).

Table 1 shows data from dog (42) and pig (41) following secretin in full dose, 2–3 units kg$^{-1}$. When CA is inhibited (Col. 2, Rows 1–2 and 6–7), the rates of HCO$_3$ and fluid output ($V_{inh}$) drop to roughly the same degree in each species (47% in dog and 33% in pig). This illustrates a most important principle: HCO$_3^-$ formation and fluid output are linked. This will recur in all other organs studies.

Is $V_{inh}$ the uncatalyzed rate of $HCO_3^-$ formation, or is some other process involved, i.e. active secretion of $HCO_3^-$? We approach this by calculating the uncatalyzed rate, as in Equation 6 above, which yields that $V_{unc}$ is 16 $\mu$moles min$^{-1}$ for each ml of secretory volume. If the volume of the ductal cells equals the volume they secrete in two minutes (8), their volume per kg body weight is 0.078 ml (dog) and 0.150 ml (pig), from which we calculate $V_{unc} = 1.3$ $\mu$mole min$^{-1}$ for dog and 2.4 $\mu$mol min$^{-1}$ for pig (Col. 4). These are remarkably close to the observed $V_{inh}$ (Col. 2, Rows 1 and 6) in view of the guess at the pH (see above). We tentatively conclude that $HCO_3^-$ formation in pancreas is carried out entirely by the hydroxylation of $CO_2$, uncatalyzed and catalyzed.

The chemically calculated enzyme rate is obtained from Equation 7 after entering the secretory volume (0.078 ml in dog) and the enzyme concentration E. We obtained 0.34 $\mu$mol kg$^{-1}$ for the whole dog pancreas; using the estimate (8) that the secretory cells have but 4% of gland cell mass, we may

**Table 1**    Pancreatic $HCO_3^-$ excretion in dog (42) and pig (41) following secretion

| | Micromoles $HCO_3^-$ min$^{-1}$ per kg body weight | | | |
| | 1[a] | 2[b] | 3[c] | 4[d] |
| | $V_{obs} = V_{total}$ | $V_{inh} = V_{unc}$ | $V_{enz}$ (Col. 1 – Col. 2) | Calc. $V_{unc}$ |
|---|---|---|---|---|
| **Dog** | | | | |
| 1 Normal | 4.3 | 2.1 | 2.2 | 1.3 |
| 2 (Flow, normal $\mu$L min$^{-1} \cdot$ kg$^{-1}$ | 39 | 19 | 20) | |
| 3 HCl | 1.8 | 0.8 | 1.0 | 0.6 |
| 4 NaHCO$_3$ | 5.9 | 3.6 | 2.3 | 2.6 |
| 5 CO$_2$ | 4.6 | 2.7 | 1.9 | 1.3 |
| **Pig** | | | | |
| 6 Normal | 12 | 4 | 8 | 2.4 |
| 7 (Flow, normal $\mu$L min$^{-1} \cdot$ kg$^{-1}$ | 75 | 26 | 49) | |
| 8 HCl | 6 | 3 | 3 | |
| 9 NaHCO$_3$ | 16 | 3 | 13 | |

[a] $V_{obs} = V_{total}$ is the normal rate in vivo.
[b] $V_{inh} = V_{unc}$ is the observed rate in vivo after full carbonic anhydrase inhibition, presumed to represent the uncatalyzed rate of $HCO_3^-$ formation (see text).
[c] $V_{enz}$ = the enzymic rate of $HCO_3^-$ formation in vivo.
[d] Calc. $V_{unc}$ = the uncatalyzed rate calculated from chemical rate constants (see text).

use 8.5 $\mu$mol L$^{-1}$ for $E$. Entering this in Equation 7 along with the cell volume per kg we obtain through Equation 8:

$$V_{cat} = 6000 \; \mu\text{moles min}^{-1} \text{ per ml} \times 8.5 \; \mu\text{mol L}^{-1} \times .078 \text{ ml} \qquad 9.$$
$$= 400 \; \mu\text{moles min}^{-1} \text{ kg}^{-1}.$$

This is 100 times the total in vivo rate and 200 times the observed enzymic rate in the dog (Table 1). These numbers show the "enzyme excess" in the CA system (30) and are supported by inhibition studies as follows. The minimal dose of acetazolamide or methazolamide for complete inhibition is 5–50 mg kg,$^{-1}$ varying with the organ system and enzyme concentration. In pancreas it is 10 mg kg$^{-1}$ (42). Drug concentration in pancreas at this dose is 15 $\mu$M (42); if $E$ is 8.5 $\mu$M, free drug concentration ($I_f$) is 6.5 $\mu$M. The inhibition constant ($K_I$ of acetazolamide is 0.01 $\mu$M, so that fractional inhibition of the enzyme (i) is well over 99% according to Equation 10:

$$\% \text{ inhibition } = \frac{I_f}{K_I + I_f} \times 100 = 99.84, \qquad 10.$$

where $I_f$ is the concentration of free inhibitor. This independent estimate agrees well with the enzyme excess calculated on kinetic grounds.

Table 1 (Col. 1, Rows 3 and 8) shows that metabolic acidosis decreases PJ HCO$_3^-$ output and fluid flow. Rows 4 and 8 show that metabolic alkalosis increases these functions. The same effect is seen in the isolated perfused cat pancreas (1a). These findings are consistent with the idea that the cellular OH$^-$ gradient plays a role in secretion. Specifically, in metabolic acidosis plasma OH$^-$ is decreased by about 2-fold, and in metabolic alkalosis it increased the same degree. P$_{CO_2}$ is nearly unaffected (42). If these changes are reflected in the cell, the calculation through Equation 6 yields the data of Col. 4 for $V_{unc}$. These agree pretty well with the observed $V_{unc}$ shown in Col. 2, so it appears that variations in OH$^-$ affect the uncatalyzed rate, as predicted by Equation 6.

Do variations in OH$^-$ affect $V_{enz}$? Theoretically they should not, since the turnover number of the enzyme is so great compared with observed rates, that small changes in substrate should have no effect. This is the case for metabolic alkalosis, compare in Col. 3, Row 1 with Row 4 and Row 6 with Row 9. However, in acidosis the enzyme rate is lowered (Col. 3, Rows 3 and 8); possibly the HCO$_3^-$ is formed catalytically at usual rate but dissipated by acidotic milieu.[4]

---

[4]The effects of metabolic acidosis and alkalosis on HCO$_3^-$ output in the secretin (or pancreozymin) stimulated in situ dog pancreas were the same as shown in Table 1. Surprisingly, however, HCO$_3^-$ output provoked by dopamine was unresponsive to acid or base infusion (20a).

In respiratory acidosis, data are not substantially different from controls (Table 1, Row 1 and Row 5). This follows from Equation 6 since $OH^-$ and $CO_2$ vary in opposite directions, and $V_{unc}$ should be unchanged. $V_{enz}$ is also unchanged. The same was found in the isolated cat pancreas (1a), but authors interpret this as showing that secretion was independent of blood pH, not realizing that the rise in $P_{CO_2}$ matches the fall in $OH^-$ during respiratory acidosis.

A crucial study supporting the main thesis in this review, that $HCO_3^-$ is formed in the cell by $OH^- + CO_2$, was performed by perfusing the rabbit pancreas in vitro with solutions of various anions. $HCO_3^-$ enhanced PJ and $HCO_3^-$ output, and the effect was reduced by acetazolamide. However, infused acetate (or its homologues with one, three, or four carbon atoms) again enhanced secretion of PJ, but acetazolamide had no effect. The secretion was regarded as originating with basolateral $H^+$ efflux (in exchange for $Na^+$) and thus resulting in apical $OH^-$ formation. The process was not specific for $HCO_3^-$ (57) but extends to the other anions mentioned (and also to sulfamerazine) (47). Since these are not synthesized or involved in the $CO_2 + OH^-$ reaction, CA is not involved.

The major driving force for $HCO_3^-$ secretion is the P.D. at the luminal membrane ($-55$ to $-80$ mV) which allows the ion to move down its electrochemical gradient when the cell concentration is about one tenth of that in the lumen. Notably, secretin (along with theophylline and cyclic AMP) lowers this P.D. (48) and the transepithelial potential (64), which is to be expected if secretin increases cellular $HCO_3^-$.

In summary (Figure 1A): (1.) Pancreatic duct cells are capable of producing high $OH^-$ concentrations destined for secretion, which are then buffered by $CO_2$. The P.D. favors accumulation of $HCO_3^-$ in the lumen. This must be matched by $H^+$ transported to blood. Secretin elicits this process in some species (cat, dog, pig, man) but not in others (rabbit, guinea pig) (8). In some species, cholecystokinin also induces $HCO_3^-$ output. Secretin appears to act via cyclic AMP. The mechanism behind these actions is unknown, but will be of great importance when discovered (8). (2.) Although the normal mechanism involves CA through the reaction $CO_2 + OH^- \rightarrow HCO_3^-$, this is not part of the fundamental process of $H^+$-$OH^-$ separation, since the secretory system works when other anions (cf acetate) are supplied. In this case CA inhibitors have no effect (57). (3.) Fluid movement and $HCO_3^-$ formation are linked (here and below) in a way that has not been explained. Notably, when other anions are substituted for $HCO_3^-$ in perfusates, fluid movement drops, usually by more than 50% (26, 27). (4.) $Na^+$ and $HCO_3^-$ movement are linked in these systems as in others (Figure 1). Are they linked by a secondary active transport process ($Na^+$-$2HCO_3^-$-Cl) (See Ref. 8 for consideration of several models)? Or is there a direct chemical link between $Na^+$ and total $CO_2$, with transported species $NaHCO_3^0$ or $NaCO_3^-$?

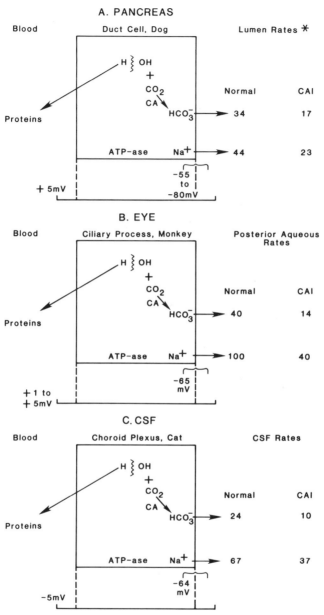

*Figure 1* Rates are $\mu$mol min$^{-1}$ per gram or per ml volume secretory tissue. CA = Carbonic anhydrase; CAI = Complete carbonic anhydrase inhibition in vivo. Catalytic rates are the differences between total observed rates (normal) for HCO$_3$$^-$ and Na$^-$ minus rates during CAI. Note that the rates are surprisingly similar in these three tissues despite widely different concentration of CA (see text). This shows that the enzyme concentration is not the rate-limiting feature of secretion. Cell structure or sites of enzyme activity are not implied. Data are from Tables 1–3, also Table 10 in Ref. 34. Potentials are from Ref. 48 (Pancreas), Refs. 19 and 25 (Eye), and Ref. 12 (CSF).

*Eye*

In the eye there are two (possibly three) tissues that produce $HCO_3^-$ from $CO_2$, catalyzed by CA. The first is the ciliary process, which produces AH. The second is the corneal endothelium, which pumps fluid out of the corneal stroma into the aqueous insuring clarity of the tissue. The third, and quite problematic, is the retina, where CA in Muller cells may have a secretory role.

In this chapter, I consider the the ciliary process since only in this case are there data quantifying $HCO_3^-$ formation, $Na^+$ and fluid movement, and the effect of CA inhibition. I have reviewed the history of this subject elsewhere (35). All vertebrates so far studied have CA in the ciliary process (or folds, in fish). There is good evidence that the secretory mechanism described here is common to all classes of vertebrates.

The posterior chambers of the human, cynomolgus monkey, and rabbit eyes contain about 50 $\mu$L of AH. In the rabbit, and at least in one species of fish, the dogfish *Mustelus canis*, the $HCO_3^-$ concentration is notably higher than in plasma (rabbit 35%, fish 100%). In dog, monkey and (probably) man there is no measurable excess of $HCO_3^-$ in the posterior aqueous; however, the kinetics of $HCO_3^-$ accumulation in dog and monkey show that, as in rabbit, this ion is formed from $CO_2$ and moves with $Na^+$ from plasma to the posterior chamber (35). The underlying chemistry is analagous to that of the pancreas.

Table 2 shows the rate constants and accession rates of $Na^+$, $Cl^-$, and

**Table 2**  The accession rates of ions from plasma to posterior aqueous in the cynomolgus monkey: Effect of carbonic anhydrase inhibition (CAI) (31)[a]

| | | 1<br>Plasma<br><br>(mM) | 2<br>$k_{in}$[b]<br><br>($min^{-1}$) | 3<br>Accession Rate<br>Col. 1 × Col. 2<br>(mM $min^{-1}$) | 4<br>Calc. in<br>New Fluid[c]<br>(mM) |
|---|---|---|---|---|---|
| $Na^+$ | control | 152 | 0.017 | 2.7 | .162 |
| | CA inhibition | | 0.009 | 1.4 | 168 |
| $Cl^-$ | control | 103 | 0.016 | 1.6 | 96[d] |
| | CA inhibition | | 0.012 | 1.2 | 144 |
| $HCO_3^-$ | control | 20 | 0.054 | 1.1 | 66[d] |
| | CA inhibition | | 0.019 | 0.4 | 48 |

[a]50 mg/kg acetazolamide i.v. given 1 hour before injections of isotope.

[b]Rate of isotope delivery to posterior aqueous ÷ counts in plasma.

[c]Column 3 × volume posterior chamber (60 $\mu$L)/aqueous flow (1 $\mu$L $min^{-1}$), for controls. Flow 0.5 $\mu$L $min^{-1}$ during CAI.

[d]Cl and $HCO_3^-$ are 115 and 21 mM, respectively in the measured posterior chámber aqueous.

HCO$_3^-$ from plasma to posterior aqueous of the monkey, as measured by the movement of the isotopes. Note that the calculated HCO$_3^-$ concentration in new fluid is 3.3 times that of plasma, and 37% of the Na$^+$ is accompanied by HCO$_3^-$.[5] Following full CA inhibition, Na$^+$ accession drops 1.3 mM min$^{-1}$; HCO$_3^-$ accession drops 0.7 mM min$^{-1}$. Cl$^-$ movement is but slightly changed. The newly formed fluid has the same Na$^+$ concentration as plasma (Table 2) and indeed is isoosmotic with plasma. Na$^+$, Cl$^-$, and HCO$_3^-$ show one-way passage into AH and CSF; there is no evidence for exchange mechanisms (12).

We may calculate the HCO$_3^-$ transport rates in the light of the uncatalyzed and catalyzed reactions, and the model given in Figure 1B. The total or observed rate is 40 $\mu$moles min$^{-1}$ per g tissue and $V_{inh}$ = 14 $\mu$mole min$^{-1}$ g$^{-1}$. The enzymic rate is thus 26 $\mu$mole min$^{-1}$ g$^{-1}$. This assumes that $V_{inh}$ is also $V_{unc}$; that is, there is no other process for HCO$_3^-$ formation (i.e. active ion transport) at work and which appears as part of $V_{inh}$. As we shall see, this is borne out by calculations to follow.

The calculated rates are derived from Equations 6 and 7. For $V_{unc}$, Equation 6 yields $V_{unc}$ = 16 $\mu$mol min$^{-1}$ per ml secretory volume. Since $V_{unc}$ is remarkably close to that observed for $V_{inh}$ (Figure 1B), we assume that $V_{unc}$ = $V_{inh}$. For $V_{cat}$, we follow Equations 3, 4, and 7 from which we obtain $V_{cat}$ = 6 × 10$^6$ min$^{-1}$ · $E$. The latter concentration in isolated ciliary process is about 0.5 $\mu$mol kg$^{-1}$. Entering this value in Equation 7 and for a cell volume of 1 ml, we get:

$$V_{cat} = 6 \times 10^6 \text{ min}^{-1} \cdot 0.5 \times 10^{-6} \text{ M} \cdot 10^{-3} \text{ L} \qquad 11.$$
$$= 3000 \ \mu\text{moles min}^{-1} \text{ per ml cell volume.}$$

This is about 100 times greater than the observed catalytic rate. The margin is less than usually found in secretory tissues, because of the very small concentration of enzyme present [compare pancreas (above) and choroid plexus (below)]. Still, with 100 times the amount of enzyme needed for normal secretion, it is inevitable that the dose-response curve for inhibition begins at 99% inhibition (no effect) and is complete at 99.9% (36).

The aqueous humor P.D. is slightly lightly negative to plasma (0.75 mV), and full CA inhibition reduces this to 0.5 mV (25). The data may reflect HCO$_3^-$ diffusion potentials, as described below for CSF (2, 11). The P.D. at

---

[5]Table 2 uses the concentration of HCO$_3^-$ in plasma for calculation, although the data and theory hold that the species moving is CO$_2$. In the calculation, 95% of the counts in plasma are considered HCO$_3^-$, and 5% CO$_2$. If CO$_2$ were used for calculation, the rate constant would be 20-fold higher, but the accession rate of total carbon counts in AH (again 95% HCO$_3^-$) would be the same. Table 3 shows the similar relations for CSF.

the apical membrane is $-65$ mV (cell negative, Figure 1B), but, as for pancreas, the effect of CA inhibition on this value has not been studied.

$Na^+$ movement is linked to $HCO_3^-$ synthesis (Table 2, Figure 1B). Since $Na^+$ movement is essentially isotonic, fluid movement is a cardinal result of CA activity. Thus, inhibiition of this enzyme reduces flow. Appropriate drugs have been in use for the treatment of glaucoma for 30 years (35). Although glaucoma is a disease of reduced outflow, the CA inhibitors, by reducing inflow, bring pressure back to normal in most cases of the disease.

## Cerebrospinal Fluid (CSF)

The relations between $CO_2$, CA, and CSF formation have a different history than PJ and AH. In no species is the CSF overtly alkaline, as PJ and AH, although the choroid plexus contains the enzyme and acetazolamide does decrease flow (30). The matter was not understood until it was found that $CO_2$ gas administered to fish greatly increases the concentration of $HCO_3^-$ in CSF and that this effect was reduced by acetazolamide (31). The only explanation appeared to be that CSF $HCO_3^-$ was catalytically synthesized from $CO_2$, just as in PJ and AH. Using labelled $HCO_3^-$, $Cl^-$, and $Na^+$, it was found that bicarbonate access was by far the most rapid; despite the very low ratio of $HCO_3^-/Na^+$ (1/35) in plasma, the accession of $HCO_3^-$ was ¼ that of $Na^+$. Table 3 shows similar experiments in the cat; $HCO_3^-$ accession was about one third of $Na^+$, i.e. 37% of $Na^+$ accession was matched by $HCO_3^-$ and the rest by chloride. $Na^+$ accession was reduced 54% by CA inhibition. The calculated $HCO_3^-$ concentration in newly formed fluid is much higher than in plasma (as in Table 2), even though the chemically measured concentration is the same. The threefold $HCO_3^-$ excess in nascent CSF is reduced markedly by the CA inhibitors.[6]

Using the same treatment to calculate the theoretical rates as done above for PJ and AH, we find for the uncatalyzed rate (Equation 6), $V_{unc} = 11$ $\mu$mol $min^{-1}$ per g tissue. For the catalyzed reaction, using Equation 7, with $E = 22 \times 10^{-6}$ M, we obtain:

$$V_{cat} = 6 \times 10^6 \ min^{-1} \cdot 22 \times 10^{-6} \ M \cdot 10^{-3} \ L = 130,00 \ \mu mol \ min^{-1}. \quad 12.$$

[6]The values of Table 3 (63) have been criticized in a recent review (23) as "not necessarily correct" because outflow of $Na^+$ and $Cl^-$ were not measured. This is not valid criticism, since the $k_{in}$ values are calculated from initial rates. If outflow were a factor, the rates of Table 3 would be an underestimation, and $HCO_3^-$ concentration in new fluid would be even greater than the 62 mM calculated.

We discarded the measured value of 245 mM for nascent $HCO_3^-$ as an artifact of isotope exchange (63). It was never put forward to determine $HCO_3^-$ accession, as claimed in (23). Nascent $HCO_3^-$ is about 62 mM (Table 3).

**Table 3**  The accession rates of ions from plasma to CSF in the cat. Effect of carbonic anhydrase inhibition (CAI) (63)[a]

|  |  | 1<br>Plasma<br><br>(mM) | 2<br>$k_{in}$[b]<br><br>(min⁻¹) | 3<br>Accession Rate<br>Col. 1 × Col. 2<br>(mM min⁻¹) | 4<br>Calc. in<br>New Fluid[c]<br>(mM) | 5<br>Measured<br>CSF conc.<br>(mM) |
|---|---|---|---|---|---|---|
| $Na^+$ | normal | 147 | 0.016 | 2.4 | 164 | 158 |
|  | CAI |  | 0.0076 | 1.1 | 157 |  |
| $Cl^-$ | normal | 115 | 0.013 | 1.5 | 104 | 134 |
|  | CAI |  | 0.0073 | 0.8 | 112 |  |
| $HCO_3^-$ | normal |  |  |  |  |  |
|  | as $CO_2$ | 0.95 | 0.94 | 0.9[d] | 62[d] | 22 |
|  | as $HCO_3^-$ | 20 | 0.044 |  |  |  |
|  | CAI |  |  |  |  |  |
|  | as $CO_2$ | 0.95 | 0.29 | 0.3[d] | 42 |  |
|  | as $HCO_3^-$ | 20 | 0.014 |  |  |  |

[a]Following 50 mg kg⁻¹ acetazolamide or 30 mg kg⁻¹ methazolamide i.v.
[b]Rate of isotope delivery to CSF ÷ counts in plasma.
[c]Col. 3 × fluid turnover time. The latter is given by the ventricular volume (1.4 ml) divided by the rate of CSF flow (0.020 ml min⁻¹) = 70 min. When carbonic anhydrase is inhibited the volume is unchanged and rate of formation is halved, whence fluid turnover time = 140 min. See equation of Table 2.
[d]Calculated from $Na^+$ minus $Cl^-$ entrance (63). The movement of ¹⁴C species was complicated by isotope exchange yielding inaccurate values. See footnote 5.

The calculated and observed rates are compared in Table 4. Note that $V_{unc}$ agrees well with $V_{inh}$, as in the examples given above for PJ and AH. The calculated $V_{cat}$, however, exceeds the observed catalytic rate by about 8000-fold. This ratio is considerably higher than for PJ and AH (see above) since the enzyme concentration in choroid plexus is unusually high, exceeding even kidney and equal to CA II in red cells (30). The result of this, predictably and borne out experimentally, is that the catalytic rate must be reduced nearly 10,000-fold (fractional inhibition = 0.9999) for pharmacological effect. Thus, 30 mg kg⁻¹ methazolamide is required for the CSF effect (60), but only 4 mg kg⁻¹ for AH (66).

Table 4 suggests that all of $HCO_3^-$ entrance can be accounted for by the hydroxylation of $CO_2$, catalyzed and uncatalyzed, but the question remains whether any component of flow lies outside the dependence on this reaction. Recent experiments suggest that the uncatalyzed reaction is susceptible to inhibition, so that the total $CO_2$ contribution can be measured (61, 62). The CSF was perfused with various acids (AlCl₃, GaCl₃, acetic, phosphoric, hydrochloric, at pH 4.7). CSF flow decreased to some 67% of control rates.

**Table 4**  Calculated and observed rates of $HCO_3^-$ formation in CSF of cat

| Calculated[a,b] | | Observed[a,c] | |
|---|---|---|---|
| | | $V_{total}$ = | 24 |
| $V_{unc}$ = | 11 | $V_{inh}$ = | 8 |
| $V_{cat}$ = | 130,000 | $V_{enz}$ = | 16 ($V_{total} - V_{inhib}$) |

[a]$\mu$mol min$^{-1}$ per g choroid plexus
[b]See text.
[c]From Table 3, Col. 3, converting mM min$^{-1}$ to $\mu$mol min$^{-1}$ per g choroid plexus using 1.4 ml as CSF volume, and choroid plexus weight = 50 mg.

We attribute this to reduction of the uncatalyzed reaction to near zero, which would occur if pH were decreased one unit at the secretory site (Equation 2). Since the calculated uncatalyzed rate (using pH 9) agrees with the observed inhibited rate (Table 4), at pH 8 or less the observed uncatalyzed rate should be nearly abolished. CA inhibition causes a 42% decrease in flow, not greatly different from the effect on sodium accession (Table 3). Thus the uncatalyzed reaction contributes 33%, the catalyzed 42%, both dependent on $HCO_3^-$ synthesis: 25% lies outside the $CO_2$ system, probably involving chloride (62).[7]

Thus while normal $HCO_3^-$ accession is but 37% that of $Na^+$ (Table 3, the rest being $Cl^-$), this $Na^+$-$HCO_3^-$ linked moiety controls 75% of flow. This emphasizes the special relation between $HCO_3^-$ synthesis and movement, and fluid flow.

An analysis of the rates of $HCO_3^-$ entrance to CSF under conditions of changing plasma $HCO_3^-$ and $P_{CO_2}$ led to the conclusion that the major factor in $HCO_3^-$ accession is the catalytic conversion of $CO_2 \rightarrow HCO_3^-$ in choroid plexus (33). When CA is inhibited, $HCO_3^-$ rises in choroid cells (21). This reflects an alkaline disequilibrium, i.e. $OH^-$ is elevated when buffering by $CO_2$ is slowed.

The power of choroid plexus CA was shown by injecting $^{11}CO_2$ or $H^{11}CO_3^-$ intravenously in dogs; 80% of the label of either species entered the brain in a single pass (22). This fine experiment demonstrates rapid interconversion of the species in blood and choroid plexus as follows:

---

[7] Our earlier work with $AlCl_3$ and $GaCl_3$ led to the incorrect conclusion that both catalyzed and uncatalyzed reactions were affected by these Lewis acids (61). A more recent study shows that the acids affect only the uncatalyzed reactions (62).

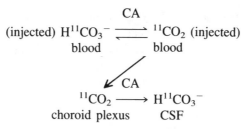

The catalytic power of the enzyme is so great that given the proper buffering and the unlimited source of CO$_2$, the gas can form any amount of HCO$_3^-$ for transport. When the enzyme was inhibited systemically, first pass entry of [11]C from CO$_2$ was reduced to 50% and of [11]C from HCO$_3^-$ to 20%. Even in the uncatalyzed situation, the reaction gives one third the normal rate (Table 3).

The CSF-plasma transepithelial P.D. is dependent on plasma pH: in the dog, at pH 7.4, P.D. = 3–4 mV, CSF positive (2, 11). Acetazolamide increased P.D. about 1 mV (11), the same direction and magnitude reported for CA inhibition in AH (25). pH homeostasis in CSF does not result from the P.D. (2), but from HCO$_3^-$ movement. The critical effect of CA inhibition appears to be to lower the ratio $\Delta$ P.D./$\Delta$ pH (11); this agrees with the role of the enzyme in maintaining a high HCO$_3^-$ gradient from cell to CSF, and that the inhibitor reduces the gradient. The results are consistent with the P.D. in both AH and CSF being a HCO$_3^-$ diffusion potential.

## Alligator Kidney

*Alligator mississippiensis* and related species normally excrete alkaline (pH 7.8) urine with about 60–80 meq L$^{-1}$ of NH$_4^+$ and HCO$_3^-$. Na$^+$ and Cl$^-$ are virtually absent. Clearly an efficient system is at work for formation of both ions. NH$_4^+$ is made by deamination of amino acids, chiefly glycine and alanine. HCO$_3^-$ is made from CO$_2$ + OH$^-$ as described for PJ, AH, and CSF. The kidney excretes some 20% of metabolic CO$_2$ as HCO$_3^-$. When acetazolamide is given, urinary HCO$_3^-$ and pH drop to 5 meq L$^{-1}$ and 7.0 respectively, Cl$^-$ increases 30-fold to about 90 meq L$^{-1}$, and NH$_4^+$ is somewhat increased, due to increased urinary acid. HCO$_3^-$ excretion appears to subserve fluid excretion and Cl$^-$ conservation; this is a clear case of HCO$_3^-$-Cl$^-$ exchange. The alligator physiologists believe that the role of renal CA is mainly to conserve Cl$^-$ (10).

# HCO$_3^-$ and CO$_3^{2-}$ SYNTHESIS TO PROVIDE HIGH pH

## Alkaline Gland of Skate

Males of the genus Raja (or skates) contain small paired sacs on the ventral aspect of the genitourinary system which empty (along with urinary ducts) into the urinary papilla. The glands are highly vascular with simple columnar epithelium and brush border. Depending on the species and size of the fish, the gland contains 1–10 ml of clear fluid. In two species (*Raja ocellata* and *Raja erinacea*) the pH is 9.2 and total $CO_2$ is 212 mM. From the pKs of the proton dissociation of $H_2CO_3$, it may be calculated that this total is divided about equally between $HCO_3^-$. This is the most alkaline fluid recorded for the vertebrate world. The anatomy of the gland and ionic composition of the fluids are given in the original paper (37).

In these two species the gland contains CA, and when fish were treated with methazolamide, the total $CO_2$ concentration was somewhat reduced. This suggests that the catalytic hydroxylation of $CO_2$ forms $CO_3^{2-}$ as well as $HCO_3^-$. Of particular interest was the finding that a third species *Raja stabuliforis*, has alkaline glands of the same type, but the total $CO_2$ concentration is only 100 mM and the pH is less than that in the other 2 species, about 8.7. There is no CA in glands of *R. stabuliforis*. Nature has kindly furnished an example of the uncatalyzed reaction at work, with parallel data for the catalyzed reaction in the other two species (37).

The transcellular P.D. is about 7 mV, lumen negative to serosa, and the apical P.D. is $-41$ mV, cell negative (52). Thus $HCO_3^-$ formed within the cell could diffuse down its electrochemical gradient (to 200 mM in lumen) if cellular concentration were maintained by its synthesis at 40 mM, which is not an impossible value. Chloride secretion accounts for the entire short circuit current, indicating a parallel to $Na^+$-$K^+$ coupled $Cl^-$ transport in the intestine and ascending loop of Henle. The alkalinization process was considered electrically silent—perhaps a close linkage with $Na^+$. Sadly the effect of CA inhibitors on the electrical properties of the system was not studied.

## Rectal Salt Gland of Mosquito Larva

Larva of *Aedes dorsalis* inhabit lakes of extremely alkaline saline environments, with pH to 10.5, $HCO_3^-$ to 250 mM, and $CO_3^{2-}$ to 100 mM. Isolated rectal salt glands of these larva secrete total $CO_2$ at very high rates against a transepithelial potential of $-31$ mV, lumen negative (56).

Using refined microperfusion techniques for net chemical flux measurements and electrical studies of the isolated gland, it was shown that serosal addition of acetazolamide, or $CO_2$ removal, inhibited total $CO_2$ accumulation by about 80% (Figure 2). There was a marked decrease of the transepithelial P.D., with hyperpolarization of the apical membrane (Figure 2), but no effect on the basolateral membrane (54, 55). These and other experiments suggest that $CO_2/HCO_3^-$ enters the cell via a basolateral electroneutral mechanism for $Cl^-$. $HCO_3^-/CO_3^{2-}$ is formed in the cell as shown in Figure 2. Exit to lumen is through an electrogenic $HCO_3^-$ or $H^+$ carrier (54, 55). Although not stressed, it is clear that a key event in $HCO_3^-/CO_3^{2-}$ secretion is their catalytic formation, linked to high apical permeability.

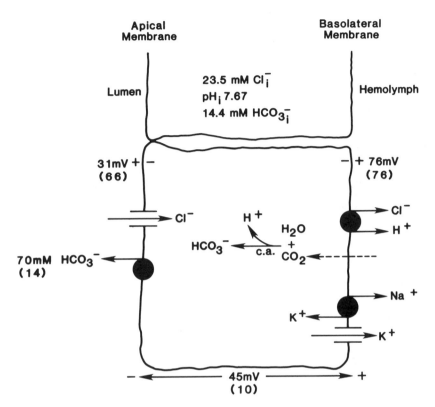

*Figure 2*   Model proposed for HCO$_3^-$ transfer in the rectal gland of mosquito larva (48). Values in parentheses are those following complete carbonic anhydrase inhibition.

## Gastro-Duodenal Alkalinization

Surface mucosal epithelial cells of the amphibian and mammalian gastric fundus and antrum secrete HCO$_3^-$. Duodenal mucosa has the same function. These cells contain CA (28). The purpose appears to be protection of the mucosa against parietal cell acid secretion; indeed when the pH of bulk secretion is 1–2, the surface mucus gel maintains a pH of 7 (15). Addition of $10^{-4}$ M acetazolamide to the luminal side of isolated non-acid secreting fundi of *Rana temporaria* reduced HCO$_3^-$ secretion to 30% of normal. There was no effect on P.D. or resistance (15).

These observations explain an older finding (then appearing paradoxical since CA inhibition reduces acid secretion and has been used to treat ulcers), namely that acetazolamide causes ulcers in dogs, when H$^+$ concentration of the stomach lumen is raised to 30 mM (65). Thus inhibition of alkalinization decreases the ability of the stomach to resist low pH, even though endogenous acid production may be reduced. There is the suggestion that surface mucosal alkalinization is more sensitive to CA inhibition than parietal cell acidification (15); the basis for this may be higher concentration of CA at the latter site. An excellent review is available (16).

## RELATION OF $HCO_3^-$ TO $H^+$ SECRETION

$H^+$ secretion is not considered here, but it is important to mention that it is, chemically, part of the same process as $HCO_3^-$ secretion (Figure 1). In the two chief organs of $H^+$ secretion, kidney and stomach (parietal cell), $HCO_3^-$ is returned to the blood. In kidney, details of this process have been worked out beautifully as described in the introduction (4, 6). In the stomach, the enormous magnitude of $H^+$ secretion is reflected in the "alkaline tide" of the blood, as recognized for many years.

Renal acidification and $HCO_3^-$ reabsorption have been covered in a fine monograph, which points out: (a) Proximal $HCO_3^-$ reabsorption is 80–90% dependent on CA. For these high rates, the uncatalyzed reaction is negligible. (b) Distal $H^+$ secretion is dependent on CA. (c) When the enzyme is inhibited, new high $HCO_3^-$ gradients from lumen to blood are developed distally, since proximal $HCO_3^-$ (but not $H_2O$) reabsorption is greatly reduced. Thus distal $HCO_3^-$ back diffusion becomes dominant, and only about 25% of filtered $HCO_3^-$ appears in the urine (1).

The $CO_2$-CA system in the parietal cell has been neglected recently. I reviewed the large literature on the subject 20 years ago (30) and short texts giving a unified scheme are presently available (49). The particular issue of whether $CO_2$ can be dissociated from $H^+$ secretion has been answered in the affirmative (9, 43), in agreement with our finding in the elasmobranch kidney (59). In the 1987 Annual Review of Physiology a chapter is devoted to the pH of the parietal cell, with some reference to $CO_2$ (see footnote 3).

## $HCO_3^-$ SYNTHESIS SUBSERVING EXCRETION OF $CO_2$ ("FACILITATED DIFFUSION")

In this section, I consider three organs in which neither $H^+$ nor $HCO_3^-$ are excreted. The high concentration of CA and the effect of inhibition were puzzling for many years (30), but now have been clarified.

### Lens

Mammalian, avian and amphibian lenses all have CA, but elasmobranch fish do not (30). This, combined with inhibition studies, provided an unusual opportunity to study function.

Inhibition studies were carried out on rabbit lens in vivo and in vitro, with care taken to use sulfonamides that permeate the lens. There was no effect on fluxes of K$^+$ (as Rb$^+$), Na$^+$, or Cl$^-$. Measured and calculated potentials suggest high K$^+$ permeability in the tissue (19). The effect of the inhibitors appeared solely to increase total CO$_2$ in the lens, from 33 to 66 mmol kg$^{-1}$ (in vivo) and from 28 to 40 mmol kg$^{-2}$ (in vitro). The elasmobranch lens, containing no CA, normally has total CO$_2$ 4 times greater than the surrounding AH, in contrast to the rabbit where the concentration in lens is only about 12% higher (17).

From the metabolic rates and geometry of rabbit lens, it was calculated that, based on CO$_2$ diffusion alone, a gradient of at least 25 mm Hg would be necessary to carry off CO$_2$. Compared to diffusion rates, the uncatalyzed interconversion of HCO$_3^-$ $\rightleftharpoons$ CO$_2$ is negligible. The catalytic rates, however, exceed the CO$_2$ diffusion threefold.

It was concluded that, in this avascular tissue of radius 0.5 cm, CO$_2$ diffusion requires large gradients, as seen in the fish and the inhibited lens. Elimination of CO$_2$ is normally carried out by its interconversion to HCO$_3^-$, as diagramed in Figure 3 (17).

## Rectal Gland of Elasmobranch

This gland is an appendix like structure attached to the intestine of elasmobranch fish. Under the stimulus of volume expansion or saline load (presumably mimicking sea water intake) the gland secretes (in a 2–4 kg fish) some 8–20 ml hr$^{-1}$ of 0.5 M NaCl, which is essentially its concentration in sea water (13).

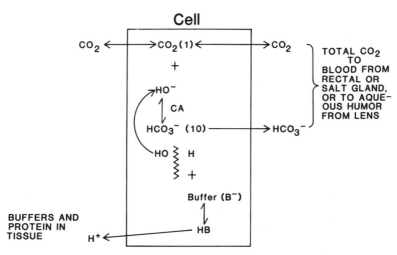

*Figure 3*  Model showing facilitated diffusion of gaseous CO$_2$, produced by the cell and converted to HCO$_3^-$, thus increasing the gradient for diffusion out of elasmobranch rectal gland, avian salt gland, and lens. In parentheses are the equilibrium concentrations (mM) of the CO$_2$ species, presuming pH 7.1 in the cell.

The gland has a high concentration of CA (29), seemingly a mystery since the secretion is neutral. After some conflicting results, it was found that methazolamide, under the right conditions (notably high, well-controlled flow rates) reduced secretion by half. But there was no change in fluid composition; it was still 0.5 M NaCl and slightly acidic. The notable change was a four fold increase in $P_{CO_2}$ and doubling of total $CO_2$ in gland fluid (58). It appeared that as for lens, metabolic $CO_2$ could not be carried off in normal fashion when CA is inhibited. (In the normal secreting gland, $P_{CO_2}$ is not higher than in venous blood.) The gland has adequate vascularization, but when it secretes, $CO_2$ output rises 30-fold (50). In this special situation, catalytic $CO_2 \rightleftharpoons HCO_3^-$ interconversion seems necessary to maintain normal $P_{CO_2}$. The reason that CA inhibition lowers flow is that acidosis is inimical to secretion, as demonstrated by the similar effects of HCl and 5% $CO_2$ (58).

## Avian Salt Gland

The functions of the salt or nasal gland in marine birds (46), like those of the rectal gland in elasmobranchs (7) and the alkaline gland of the skate (37), were discovered at the Mount Desert Island Biological Laboratory about 30 years ago.

As for the rectal gland, the avian gland secretion is turned on by the infusion of saline. Fluid is neutral, hypertonic to the blood and to the sea. The gland contains high concentrations of CA, and is extremely sensitive to inhibition. A full (16 mg $kg^{-1}$) dose of methazolamide cuts the saline stimulated flow (in sea gulls) from about 6 ml $hr^{-1}$ to zero (40). This "complete effect" is unique; for other secretory systems inhibition cuts flow to 20–50% of normal. The effect of methazolamide and high $CO_2$ and HCl is to elicit acidosis, which as stated, is inimical to secretion. Metabolic and respiratory acidosis also reduce secretion (40). Thus it seems reasonable to assume, that as in the elasmobranch rectal gland the stimulated system yielding high $CO_2$ output requires catalytic conversion to $HCO_3^-$.

### Literature Cited

1. Alpern, R. J., Warnock, D. G., Rector, F. C. Jr. 1986. Renal acidification mechanisms. In *The Kidney*, ed. B. M. Brenner, F. C. Rector, Jr., 1:206–49. Philadelphia: Saunders. 3rd ed.
1a. Ammar, E. M., Hutson, D., Scratcherd, T. 1987. Absence of a relationship between arterial pH and pancreatic bicarbonate secretion in the isolated perfused cat pancreas. *J. Physiol. (London)* 388:495–504
2. Bledsoe, S. W., Eng, D. Y., Hornbein, T. F. 1981. Evidence of active regulation of cerebrospinal fluid acid-base balance. *J. Appl. Physiol.* 51:369–75

3. Buanes, T., Grotmol, T., Landsverk, T., Ridderstrale, Y., Raeder, M. G. 1986. Histochemical localization of carbonic anhydrase in the pig's exocrine pancreas. *Acta Physiol. Scand.* 128:437–44
4. Burckhardt, B.-Ch., Cassola, A. C., Frömter, E. 1984. Eletrophysiological analysis of bicarbonate permeation across the peritubular cell membrane of rat kidney proximal tubule. II. Exclusion of $HCO_3^-$-effects on other ion permeabilities and of coupled electroneutral $HCO_3^-$-transport. *Pflüg. Arch.* 401:43–51

5. Burckhardt, B.-Ch., Geers, C., Frömter, E. 1985. Role of membrane-bound carbonic anhydrase in HCO$_3^-$ transport across rat renal proximal tubular cell membranes. *Pflüg. Arch.* 405 (Suppl. 2):R31.

6. Burckhardt, B.-Ch., Sato, K., Frömter, E. 1984. Electrophysiological analysis of bicarbonate permeation across the peritubular cell membrane of rat kidney proximal tubule. I. Basic observations. *Pflüg. Arch.* 401:34–42.

7. Burger, J. W., Hess, W. N. 1960. Function of the rectal gland in the spiny dogfish. *Science* 131:670–71

8. Case, R. M., Argent, B. E. 1986. Bicarbonate secretion by pancreatic duct cells: Mechanisms and control. In *The Exocrine Pancreas: Biology, Pathobiology, and Diseases*, ed. V. L. W. Go, J. D. Gardner, F. P. Brooks, E. Lebenthal, E. P. DiMagno, G. A. Scheele, pp. 213–43. New York: Raven

9. Chacin-Melean, J., Alonso, D., Harris, J. B. 1974. The influence of pH, buffer species and gas composition on acid secretion of frog gastric mucosa. In *Gastric Hydrogen Ion Secretion*, ed. D. K. Kasbekar, G. Sachs, W. S. Rehm 3:237–59. New York: Dekker

10. Coulson, R. A., Hernandez, T. 1983. In *Alligator Metabolism*. New York: Pergaman

11. Davies, D. G., Britton, S. L., Gurtner, G. H., Dutton, R. E., Krasney, J. A. 1984. Effect of carbonic anhydrase inhibition on the DC potential difference between cerebrospinal fluid and blood. *Expl. Neurol.* 86:66–72

12. Davson, H. 1967. *Physiology of the Cerebrospinal Fluid*, pp. 70–79, 124–26. London: Churchill

13. Epstein, F. H., Stoff, J. S., Silva, P. 1983. Mechanism and control of hyperosmotic NaCl-rich secretion by the rectal gland of *Squalus acanthias*. *J. Exp. Biol.* 106:25–41

14. Faurholt, C. 1924. Etudes sur les solutions aqueuses d'anhydride carbonique et d'acide carbonique. *J. Chim. Phys.* 21:400–55

15. Flemström, G. 1977. Active alkalinization by amphibian gastric fundic mucosa in vitro. *Am. J. Physiol.* 233:E1–12

16. Flemström, G. 1987. Gastric and duodenal mucosal bicarbonate secretion. In *Physiology of the Gastrointestinal Tract*, ed. L. K. Johnson 2:1011–30. New York: Raven

17. Friedland, B. R., Maren, T. H. 1981. The relation between carbonic anhydrase activity and ion transport in elasmobranch and rabbit lens. *Exp. Eye Res.* 33:545–61

18. Grassl, S. M., Holohan, P. D., Ross, C. R. 1987. HCO$_3^-$ transport in basolateral membrane vesicles isolated from rat renal cortex. *J. Biol. Chem.* 262:2682–27

19. Green, K., Bountra, C., Georgiou, P., House, C. R. 1985. An electrophysiologic study of rabbit ciliary epithelium. *Invest Ophthalmol. Visual Sci.* 26:371–81

20. Henriques, O. M. 1928. Uber die gesch windigkeiten der anhydrierung bzw. der hydratisierung der kohlen saurekomponenten im blute. *Biochem. Z.* 200:1–5.

20a. Iijima, T., Yamagishi, T., Iwatsuki, K., Chila, S. 1976. Effects of arterial pH and HCO$_3^-$ concentration on HCO$_3^-$ secretion in the isolated blood prefused dog pancreas. *Arch. Int. Pharmacol.* 279:314–23

21. Johansen, C. E. 1984. Differential effects of acetazolamide, benzolamide and systemic acidosis on hydrogen and bicarbonate gradients across the apical and basolateral membranes of the choroid plexus. *J. Pharmacol. Exp. Ther.* 231:502–11

22. Johnson, D. C., Hoop, B., Kazemi, H. 1983. Movement of CO$_2$ and HCO$_3^-$ from blood to brain in dogs. *J. Appl. Physiol.* 54:989–96

23. Kazemi, H., Johnson, D. C. 1986. Regulation of cerebrospinal fluid acid-base balance. *Physiol. Rev.* 66:953–1037

24. Khalifah, R. G. 1971. The carbon dioxide hydration activity of carbonic anhydrase. Stop-flow kinetic studies on the native human isoenzymes B and C. *J. Biol. Chem.* 246:2561–73

25. Kishida, K., Miwa, Y., Iwata, C. 1986. 2-substituted 1,3,4-thiadiazole-5-sulfonamides as carbonic anhydrase inhibitors: Their effects on the transepithelial potential difference of the isolated rabbit ciliary body and on the intraocular pressure of the living rabbit eye. *Exp. Eye Res.* 43:981–95.

26. Kuijpers, G. A. J., Van Nooy, I. G. P., De Pont, J. J. H. H. M., Bonting, S. L. 1984. Anion secretion by the isolated rabbit pancreas. *Biochim. Biophys. Acta* 774:269–76

27. Kuijpers, G. A. J., Van Nooy, I. G. P., De Pont, J. J. H. H. M., Bonting, S. L. 1984. The mechanism of fluid secretion in the rabbit pancreas studied by means of various inhibitors. *Biochim. Biophys. Acta* 778:324–31

28. Lonnerholm, G. 1977. Carbonic anhydrase in the intestinal tract of the guinea pig. *Acta Physiol. Scand.* 99:53–61

29. Maren, T. H. 1962. Ionic composition

of cerebrospinal fluid and aqueous humor of the dogfish, *Squalus acanthias*. II. Carbonic anhydrase activity and inhibition. *Comp. Biochem. Physiol.* 5:201–15

30. Maren, T. H. 1967. Carbonic anhydrase: Chemistry, physiology, and inhibition. *Physiol. Rev.* 47:595–781.

31. Maren, T. H. (with the technical assistance of Kent, B. B., Welliver, R. C. Woodworth, R. B.). 1972. Bicarbonate formation in cerebrospinal fluid: Role in sodium transport and pH regulation. *Am. J. Physiol.* 222:885–99.

32. Maren, T. H. 1979. An historical account of $CO_2$ chemistry and the development of carbonic anhydrase inhibitors. The 1979 Theodore Weicker Memorial Award Oration. *Pharmacologist* 20:303–21.

33. Maren, T. H. 1979. Effect of varying $CO_2$ equilibria on rates of $HCO_3^-$ formation in cerebrospinal fluid. *J. Appl. Physiol.* 41:471–77

34. Maren, T. H. 1984. A general view of $HCO_3^-$ transport processes in relation to the physiology and biochemistry of carbonic anhydrase. In *Secretion: Mechanisms and Control*, ed. R. M. Case, J. M. Lingard, J. A. Young, pp. 47–66. Manchester: Manchester Univ. Press

35. Maren, T. H. 1984. The development of ideas concerning the role of carbonic anhydrase in the secretion of aqueous humor: Relation to the treatment of glaucoma. In *Glaucoma: Applied Pharmacology in Medical Treatment*, ed. S. M. Drance, A. H. Neufeld, pp. 325–55. Orlando, FL: Grune and Stratton

36. Maren, T. H., Haywood, J. R., Chapman, S. K., Zimmerman, T. J. 1977. The pharmacology of methazolamide in relation to the treatment of glaucoma. *Invest. Ophthalmol. Visual Sci.* 16:730–42.

37. Maren, T. H., Rawls, J. A., Burger, J. W., Myers, A. C. 1963. The alkaline (Marshall's) gland of the skate. *Comp. Biochem. Physiol.* 10:1–16.

38. Meldrum, N. U., Roughton, F. J. W. 1933. Carbonic anhydrase: Its preparation and properties. *J. Physiol. (London)* 80:113–42.

39. Mitchell, P. 1985. The correlation of chemical and osmotic forces in biochemistry. *J. Biochem.* 97:1–18

40. Nechay, B. R., Larimer, J. L., Maren, T. H. 1960. Effects of drugs and physiologic alterations on nasal salt excretion in sea gulls. *J. Pharmacol. Exp. Ther.* 130:401–10

41. Raeder, M., Mathisen, O. 1982. Abolished relationship between pancreatic

HCO₃⁻ secretion and arterial pH during carbonic anhydrase inhibition. *Acta Physiol. Scand.* 114:97–102

42. Rawls, J. A., Wistrand, P. J., Maren, T. H. 1963. Effects of acidbase changes and carbonic anhydrase inhibition on pancreatic secretion. *Am. J. Physiol.* 205:651–57

43. Sanders, S. S., Hayne, V. B. Jr., Rehm, W. S. 1973. Normal $H^+$ rates in frog stomach in absence of exogenous $CO_2$ and a note on pH stat method. *Am. J. Physiol.* 225:1311–21

44. Sanyal, G., Maren, T. H. 1981. Thermodynamics of carbonic anhydrase catalysis. A comparison between human isoenzymes B and C. *J. Biol. Chem.* 256:608–12

45. Sasaki, S., Shigai, T., Yoshiyama, N., Takeuchi, J. 1987. Mechanism of bicarbonate exit across basolateral membrane of rabbit proximal straight tubule. *Am. J. Physiol.* 252(21):F11–18

46. Schmidt-Nielsen, K., Jorgensen, G. C., Osaki, H. 1958. Extrarenal salt excretion in birds. *Am. J. Physiol.* 193–101–7

47. Schulz, I., Strover, F., Ullrich, K. J. 1971. Lipid soluble weak organic acid buffers as "substrate" for pancreatic secretion. *Pflüg. Arch.* 323:121–40

48. Schulz, I., Terreros-Aranguren, D. 1982. Sidedness of transport steps involved in pancreatic HCO₃⁻ secretion. In *Electrolyte & Water Transport Across Gastrointestinal Epithelia*, ed. R. M. Case, A. Garner, L. A. Turnberg, J. A. Young, pp. 143–56. New York: Raven

49. Sernka, T., Jacobson, E. 1979. *Gastrointestinal Physiology*. Baltimore, MD: Williams & Wilkins

50. Silva, P., Stoff, J. S., Solomon, R. J., Rosa, R., Stevens, A., et al. 1980. Oxygen cost of chloride transport in perfused rectal gland of *Squalus acanthias*. *J. Membr. Biol.* 53:215–21.

51. Sirs, J. A. 1958. Electrometric stopped flow measurements of rapid reactions in solution. Part II. Glass electrode pH measurements. *Trans. Faraday Soc.* 54:207–12

52. Smith, P. L. 1985. Electrolyte transport by alkaline gland of little skate *Raja erinacea*. *Am. J. Physiol.* 248(17):R346–52

53. Soleimani, M., Grassl, S. M., Aronson, P. S. 1987. Stoichiometry of $Na^+$-HCO₃⁻ cotransport in basolateral membrane vesicles isolated from rabbit renal cortex. *J. Clin. Invest.* 79:1276–80

54. Strange, K., Phillips, J. E. 1984. Mechanisms of $CO_2$ transport in rectal salt gland of *Aedes*. I. Ionic requirements of $CO_2$ secretion. *Am. J. Physiol.* 246(15):R727–34

55. Strange, K., Phillips, J. E. 1985. Cellular mechanism of $HCO_3^-$ and $Cl^-$ transport in insect salt gland. *J. Membr. Biol.* 83:25–37
56. Strange, K., Phillips, J. E., Quamme, G. A. 1982. Active $HCO_3^-$ secretion in the rectal salt gland of a mosquito larva inhabiting $NaHCO_3$-$CO_3$ lakes. *J. Exp. Biol.* 101:171–86.
57. Swanson, C. H., Solomon, A. K. 1975. Micropuncture analysis of the cellular mechanisms of electrolyte secretion by the in vitro rabbit pancreas. *J. Gen. Physiol.* 65:22–45
58. Swenson, E. R., Maren, T. H. 1984. Effects of acidosis and carbonic anhydrase inhibition in the elasmobranch rectal gland. *Am. J. Physiol.* 247(16): F86–92
59. Swenson, E. R., Maren, T. H. 1986. Dissociation of $CO_2$ hydration and renal acid secretion in the dogfish, *Squalus acanthias*. *Am. J. Physiol.* 250(19): F288–93
60. Vogh, B. P. 1980. The relation of choroid plexus carbonic anhydrase activity to cerebrospinal fluid formation: Study of three inhibitors in cat with extrapolation to man. *J. Pharmacol. Exp. Ther.* 213: 321–31.
61. Vogh, B. P., Godman, D. R., Maren, T. H. 1985. Aluminum and gallium arrest formation of cerebrospinal fluid by the mechanism of $OH^-$ depletion. *J. Pharmacol. Exp. Ther.* 233:715–21
62. Vogh, B. P., Godman, D. R., Maren, T. H. 1987. The effect of $AlCl_3$ and other acids on cerebrospinal fluid production: A correction. *J. Pharmacol. Exp. Ther.* 242:35–39
63. Vogh, B. P., Maren, T. H., 1975. Sodium, chloride, and bicarbonate movement from plasma to cerebrospinal fluid in cats. *Am. J. Physiol.* 228:673–83
64. Way, L. W., Diamond, J. M. 1970. The effect of secretin on electrical potential differences in the pancreatic duct. *Biochim. Biophys. Acta* 203:298–307
65. Werther, J., Hollander, F., Altamirano, M. 1965. Effect of acetazolamide on gastric mucosa in canine vivo-vitro preparations. *Am. J. Physiol.* 209:127–33
66. Wistrand, P. J., Rawls, J. A. Jr., Maren, T. H. 1961. Sulfonamide carbonic anhydrase inhibitors and intraocular pressure in rabbits. *Acta Pharmacol. Toxicol.* 5:193–200.
67. Yoshitomi, K., Burckhardt, B.-Ch., Frömter, E. 1985. Rheogenic sodiumbicarbonate cotransport in the peritubular cell membrane of rat renal proximal tubule. *Pflüg. Arch.* 405:360–66

# SUBJECT INDEX

# CONTRIBUTING AUTHORS

## CONTRIBUTING AUTHORS, VOLUMES 46–50

Gros, G., 50:669–94
Gruber, K. A., 46:343–58

**H**

Haddad, G. G., 46:629–43
Haest, C. W. M., 49:221–35
Hansen, J., 48:495–514
Harding, R., 46:645–59
Harris, C., 48:495–514
Havel, R. J., 48:119–34
Heath, J. E., 44:133–43;
  48:595–612
Hedin, L., 50:441–63
Heiligenberg, W., 46:561–83
Henderson-Smart, D. J.,
  46:675–86
Henning, S. J., 47:231–46
Herd, A. H., 46:177–85
Hersey, S., 46:393–402
Hertzberg, E. L., 47:305–18
Heusner, A. A., 49:121–33
Hinkle, P. C., 47:503–18
Hochmuth, R. M., 49:209–19
Holmes, E. W., 47:691–706
Holmsen, H., 47:677–90
Holz, R. W., 48:175–89
Homsher, E., 49:673–90
Hopfer, U., 49:51–67
Housley, P. R., 46:67–81
Houston, D. S., 48:307–20
Howlett, T. A., 48:527–36
Hruby, D. E., 50:323–32
Huckle, W. R., 48:495–514
Hughes, J. P., 47:469–82
Hurley, J. B., 49:793–812
Hutson, J. M., 46:53–65
Huttner, W. B., 50:363–76
Huxley, A., 50:1–16

**I**

Imig, T. J., 46:275–87
Inesi, G., 47:573–602
Inman, R., 49:163–75
Isaksson, O. G. P., 47:483–500
Ishihara, A., 49:163–75
Ito, S., 47:217–30

**J**

Jänne, O. A., 46:107–18
Jacobson, K., 49:163–75
Jacobus, W. E., 47:707–26
Jaffe, L. A., 48:191–200
Jamieson, D., 48:703–20
Jan, L. Y., 50:379–93
Jänig, W., 50:525–39
Jansson, J.-O., 47:483–500
Jennings, M. L., 47:519–34
Jennings, R. B., 47:727–50
Jensen, F. B., 50:161–79
Jensen, R. T., 48:103–17

Johnson, L. R., 47:199–216
Jones, D. P., 48:33–50

**K**

Kaback, H. R., 50:243–56
Kalia, M. P., 49:595–609
Kamagata, S., 46:53–65
Kaplan, J. H., 47:535–44
Karsch, F. J., 49:365–82
Kaunitz, J. D., 46:417–33
Kemnitz, J. W., 47:803–22
Keyes, P. L., 50:465–82
Khan, M. N., 47:383–404
Kick, S. A., 46:599–614
King, R, J., 47:775–88
Kira, Y., 49:533–43
Klocke, R. A., 50:625–37
Kreisberg, J. I., 48:51–71
Kuijpers, G. A. J., 49:87–103

**L**

Lacour, F., 49:383–95
Lakatta, E. G., 49:519–31
LaNoue, K. F., 47:143–72
Larner, J., 47:404–24
LaTorre, R., 46:485–95
Leeman, S. E., 48:537–50
Lefkowitz, R., 44:475–84;
  46:119–30
Lewis, U. J., 46:33–42
Liebman, P. A., 49:765–91
Liedtke, C. M., 49:51–67
Lindemann, B., 46:497–515
Lipkin, M., 47:175–98
Lipton, J. M., 48:613–24
Lown, B., 46:155–76
Luke, R. G., 50:141–58
Lundberg, J. M., 49:557–72

**M**

Machen, T. E., 49:19–33
Mains, R. E., 50:333–44
Mandel, L. J., 47:85–102
Manfredi, J. P., 47:691–706
Marcus, M. L., 49:477–87
Maren, T. H., 50:695–717
Margolius, H. S., 46:309–26
Masterton, R. B., 46:275–87
Mathias, C. J., 50:577–92
Mayo, K. E., 48:431–46
McArdle, C. A., 48:495–514
McCall, R. B., 50:553–64
McDermott, P. J., 49:533–43
Mela-Riker, L. M., 47:645–64
Melchior, D. L., 50:257–71
Mellins, R. B., 46:629–43
Merriam, G. R., 48:569–92
Miller, C., 46:549–58
Miller, V. M., 48:307–20
Moolenaar, W. H., 48:363–76

Morgan, H. E., 49:533–43
Morkin, E., 49:545–54
Moulins, M., 47:29–48

**N**

Navar, L. G., 49:275–93
Needleman, P., 46:327–41
Neher, E., 46:455–72
Nicholson, B. J., 47:263–80
Nishi, S., 50:541–51
Nissley, S. P., 47:425–42
Norris, S. H., 46:393–402

**O**

Owen, W. G., 49:743–64

**P**

Papazian, D. M., 50:379–93
Pappenheimer, J. R., 49:1–15
Paradiso, A. M., 49:19–33
Parker, K. R., 49:765–91
Parsegian, V. A., 48:201–12
Patel, Y. C., 48:551–68
Pearson, J. D., 47:617–28
Perelman, R. H., 47:803–22
Petersen, O. H., 50:65–80
Peterson, C. J., 49:533–43
Philipson, K. D., 47:561–72
Phillips, M. I., 49:413–35
Plotsky, P. M., 48:475–94
Polosa, C., 50:541–51
Porte, D., 49:335–47; 49:383–
  95
Posner, B. I., 47:383–404
Pratt, W. B., 46:67–81
Prosser, C. L., 48:1–6
Pryor, W. A., 48:657–68
Pugh, E. N., 49:715–41
Putney, J. W. Jr., 48:75–88

**Q**

Quinn, S., 50:409–26

**R**

Rakowski, R. F., 50:225–41
Rand, R. P., 48:201–12
Randall, D. C., 46:187–97
Read, D. J. C., 46:675–86
Rechler, M. M., 47:425–42
Rees, L. H., 48:527–36
Reuss, L., 49:35–49
Reuter, H., 46:473–84
Revel, J.-P., 47:263–80
Rhode, W. S., 46:231–46
Richards, J. S., 50:441–63
Rigatto, H., 46:661–74
Riggs, A. F., 50:181–204
Rivier, C. L., 48:475–94

# CHAPTER TITLES, VOLUMES 35–39

CELL BIOLOGICAL APPROACHES TO BRAIN FUNCTION

CNS

COMPARATIVE PHYSIOLOGY